FOURTH CANADIAN EDITION

EXPLORING THE DIVERSITY OF LIFE
BIOLOGY

VOLUME 2

Peter J. Russell

Paul E. Hertz

Beverly McMillan

M. Brock Fenton
Western University

Denis Maxwell
Western University

Tom Haffie
Western University

Bill Milsom
University of British Columbia

Todd Nickle
Mount Royal University

Shona Ellis
University of British Columbia

With contributions by Ivona Mladenovic, Simon Fraser University

NELSON

NELSON

Biology, Fourth Canadian Edition, Volume 2

by Peter J. Russell, Paul E. Hertz, Beverly McMillan, M. Brock Fenton, Denis Maxwell, Tom Haffie, Bill Milsom, Todd Nickle, Shona Ellis

VP, Product Solutions, K–20:
Claudine O'Donnell

Senior Publisher, Digital and Print Content:
Paul Fam

Marketing Manager:
Tia Nguyen

Content Manager:
Toni Chahley

Photo and Permissions Researcher:
Kristiina Paul

Senior Production Project Manager:
Imoinda Romain

Production Service:
MPS Limited

Copy Editor:
Frances Robinson

Proofreader:
MPS Limited

Indexer:
MPS Limited

Design Director:
Ken Phipps

Higher Education Design Project Manager:
Pamela Johnston

Interior Design Modifications:
Ken Cadinouche

Cover Design:
Courtney Hellam

Cover Image:
© Seth Casteel

Art Coordinator:
Suzanne Peden

Managing Designer:
Courtney Hellam

Illustrator(s):
Articulate Graphics, Steve Corrigan, Crowle Art Group, Patrick Gnan, Dave McKay, MPS Limited, Allan Moon, Ann Sanderson, Ralph Voltz

Compositor:
MPS Limited

Library and Archives Canada Cataloguing in Publication

Russell, Peter J., author
Biology : exploring the diversity of life / Peter J. Russell, Paul E. Hertz, Beverly McMillan, M. Brock Fenton, University of Western Ontario, Denis Maxwell, University of Western Ontario, Tom Haffie, University of Western Ontario, Bill Milsom, University of British Columbia, Todd Nickle, Mount Royal University, Shona Ellis, University of British Columbia ; with contributions by Ivona Mladenovic, Simon Fraser University. — Fourth Canadian edition.

Includes index.
Issued also in 1 volume.
ISBN 978-0-17-677081-5 (v. 2 : softcover)

1. Biology—Textbooks.
2. Textbooks. I. Title.

QH308.2.R88 2018b 570 C2017-904624-1

ISBN-13: 978-0-17-677081-5
ISBN-10: 0-17-677081-X

For, and because of,
our generations of students.

About the Canadian Authors

M. B. (Brock) Fenton received his Ph.D. from the University of Toronto in 1969. Since then, he has been a faculty member in biology at Carleton University, then at York University, and then at Western University. In addition to teaching parts of first-year biology, he has also taught vertebrate biology, animal biology, and conservation biology, as well as field courses in the biology and behaviour of bats. He has received awards for his teaching (Carleton University Faculty of Science Teaching Award; Ontario Confederation of University Faculty Associations Teaching Award; and a 3M Teaching Fellowship, Society for Teaching and Learning in Higher Education) in addition to recognition of his work on public awareness of science (Gordin Kaplan Award from the Canadian Federation of Biological Societies; Honorary Life Membership, Science North, Sudbury, Ontario; Canadian Council of University Biology Chairs Distinguished Canadian Biologist Award; The McNeil Medal for the Public Awareness of Science of the Royal Society of Canada; and the Sir Sandford Fleming Medal for public awareness of Science, the Royal Canadian Institute). He also received the C. Hart Merriam Award from the American Society of Mammalogists for excellence in scientific research. Bats and their biology, behaviour, evolution, and echolocation are the topics of his research, which has been funded by the Natural Sciences and Engineering Research Council of Canada (NSERC). In November 2014, Brock was inducted as a Fellow of the Royal Society of Canada.

Denis Maxwell received his Ph.D. from the University of Western Ontario in 1995. His thesis, under the supervision of Norm Hüner, focused on photosynthetic acclimation in green algae. Following his doctorate, he undertook postdoctoral training at the Department of Energy Plant Research Laboratory at Michigan State University, where he studied the function of the mitochondrial alternative oxidase. After taking up a faculty position at the University of New Brunswick in 2000, he moved in 2003 to the Department of Biology at Western University. Denis served as Associate Chair for Undergraduate Education for the Department of Biology from 2009 to 2016. Currently, he is Assistant Dean for the Faculty of Science, with a portfolio that includes Recruitment and First-Year Studies and outreach. He has taught first-year Biology to over 15 000 students, most of the time with Tom Haffie.

Tom Haffie is a graduate of the University of Guelph and the University of Saskatchewan in the area of microbial genetics. Tom has devoted his 33-year career at Western University to teaching large biology classes in lecture, laboratory, and tutorial settings. He led the development of the innovative core laboratory course in the Biology program; he was an early adopter of computer animation in lectures; and, most recently, has overseen a deep blended redesign of introductory biology informed by a students-as-partners approach to development. He is the founding coordinator of the biennial Western Conference on Science Education. He holds a University Students' Council Award for Excellence in Teaching, a UWO Edward G. Pleva Award for Excellence in Teaching, a UWO Fellowship in Teaching Innovation, a Province of Ontario Award for Leadership in Faculty Teaching (LIFT), and a Canadian 3M National Teaching Fellowship for excellence in teaching. Tom is currently a Teaching Fellow for Science at Western University.

Bruce Moffat

Bill Milsom (Ph.D., University of British Columbia) is a professor in the Department of Zoology at the University of British Columbia, where he has taught a variety of courses, including first-year biology, for almost 40 years. His research interests include the evolutionary origins of respiratory processes and the adaptive changes in these processes that allow animals to exploit diverse environments. He examines respiratory and cardiovascular adaptations in vertebrate animals in rest, sleep, exercise, altitude, dormancy, hibernation, diving, and so on. This research contributes to our understanding of the mechanistic basis of biodiversity and the physiological costs of habitat selection. His research has been funded by NSERC, and he has received several academic awards and distinctions, including the Fry Medal of the Canadian Society of Zoologists, the August Krogh Distinguished Lectorship Award of the American Physiological Society, the Bidder Lecture of the Society for Experimental Biology, and the Izaak Walton Killam Award for Excellence in Mentoring. He has served as the President of the Canadian Society of Zoologists and as President of the International Congress of Comparative Physiology and Biochemistry.

Penny Nickle

Todd Nickle received his Ph.D. from Oklahoma State University in 1998, and has been teaching biology at Mount Royal University ever since. He advocates Active Learning: students come to class prepared to *work* with material rather than just hear about it. Student preparation involves reading the text and applying the concepts to online exercises, the results of which inform what the next lecture will be about. Class time focusses on exploring connections between concepts and ideas in biology and how they relate to other disciplines, which inspired him to coauthor a handbook for first-year science students (*Science*[3]). His interest in promoting best teaching practices among educators had him confirm the Alberta Introductory Biology Association as an official Society of Alberta; Todd is currently President. His work put him in the first cohort of Full Professors at Mount Royal University in 2012, garnered the 2015 ACIFA Innovation in Teaching Award, and the Distinguished Faculty Award from MRU in 2016.

Andy Cotton

Shona Ellis (M.Sc., University of British Columbia) is a professor of teaching in the Botany Department and Associate Head of Biology at the University of British Columbia. She developed a keen interest in forests and the ocean growing up on the central coast of British Columbia. As an undergraduate, Professor Ellis pursued her interests in botany and entomology. Her M.Sc. research incorporated tissue culture, phytochemistry, and plant anatomy. As a teaching assistant, she realized a passion for teaching and joined the teaching faculty at the University of British Columbia in 1998. She teaches botany courses that have included nonvascular and vascular plants, economic botany, bryology, and plant systematics, as well as introductory biology. Professor Ellis has taught in a number of settings: large and small lectures, laboratories, and fieldtrips. While she feels the best classroom is outdoors, she integrates online technologies into all her courses; she is an early adopter of online teaching and learning resources. Professor Ellis has received two Killam Teaching Awards and the Charles Edwin Bessey Teaching Award from the Botanical Society of America.

About the U.S. Authors

Peter J. Russell received a B.Sc. in Biology from the University of Sussex, England in 1968 and a Ph.D. in Genetics from Cornell University in 1972. He has been a member of the Biology Faculty of Reed College since 1972, and is currently a Professor of Biology, Emeritus. Peter taught a section of the introductory biology course, a genetics course, and a research literature course on molecular virology. In 1987 he received the Burlington Northern Faculty Achievement Award from Reed College in recognition of his excellence in teaching. Since 1986, he has been the author of a successful genetics textbook: current editions are *iGenetics: A Molecular Approach, iGenetics: A Mendelian Approach,* and *Essential iGenetics.* Peter's research was in the area of molecular genetics, with a specific interest in characterizing the role of host genes in the replication of the RNA genome of a pathogenic plant virus, and the expression of the genes of the virus; yeast was used as the model host. His research has been funded by agencies including the National Institutes of Health, the National Science Foundation, the American Cancer Society, the Department of Defense, the Medical Research Foundation of Oregon, and the Murdoch Foundation. He has published his research results in a variety of journals, including *Genetics, Journal of Bacteriology, Molecular and General Genetics, Nucleic Acids Research, Plasmid,* and *Molecular and Cellular Biology.* Peter has a long history of encouraging faculty research involving undergraduates, including cofounding the biology division of the Council on Undergraduate Research, in Washington, D.C. in 1985. He was Principal Investigator/Program Director of a National Science Foundation Award for the Integration of Research and Education (NSF-AIRE) to Reed College, 1998–2002.

Paul E. Hertz was born and raised in New York City. He received a B.S. in Biology from Stanford University in 1972, an A.M. in Biology from Harvard University in 1973, and a Ph.D. in Biology from Harvard University in 1977. While completing field research for the doctorate, he served on the Biology Faculty of the University of Puerto Rico at Rio Piedras. After spending two years as an Isaac Walton Killam Postdoctoral Fellow at Dalhousie University, Paul accepted a teaching position at Barnard College, where he has taught since 1979. He was named Ann Whitney Olin Professor of Biology in 2000, and he received the Barnard Award for Teaching Excellence in 2007. In addition to serving on numerous college committees, Paul chaired Barnard's Biology Department for eight years and served as Acting Provost and Dean of the Faculty from 2011 to 2012. He is the founding Program Director of the Hughes Science Pipeline Project at Barnard, an undergraduate curriculum and research program that has been funded continuously by the Howard Hughes Medical Institute since 1992. The Pipeline Project includes the Intercollegiate Partnership, a program for local community college students that facilitates their transfer to four-year colleges and universities. He teaches one semester of the introductory sequence for Biology majors and pre-professional students, lecture and laboratory courses in vertebrate zoology and ecology, and a year-long seminar that introduces first-year students to scientific research. Paul is an animal physiological ecologist with a specific research interest in the thermal biology of lizards. He has conducted fieldwork in the West Indies since the mid-1970s, most recently focusing on the lizards of Cuba. His work has been funded by the NSF, and he has published his research in *The American Naturalist, Ecology, Nature, Oecologia,* and *Proceedings of the Royal Society.* In 2010, he and his colleagues at three other universities received funding from NSF for a project designed to detect the effects of global climate warming on the biology of *Anolis* lizards in Puerto Rico.

Beverly McMillan has been a science writer for more than 25 years. She holds undergraduate and graduate degrees from the University of California, Berkeley, and is coauthor of a college text in human biology, now in its 11th edition. She has also written or coauthored numerous trade books on scientific subjects and has worked extensively in educational and commercial publishing, including eight years in editorial management positions in the college divisions of Random House and McGraw-Hill.

Brief Contents

Contents

Preface

Welcome to an exploration of the diversity of life. The main goal of this textbook is to guide you on a journey of discovery about life's diversity across levels ranging from molecules to genes, cells to organs, and species to ecosystems. Along the way, we will explore many questions about the mechanisms underlying diversity as well as the consequences of diversity, for our own species and for others.

An emphasis on the diversity of life …

At first glance, the riot of life that animates the biosphere overwhelms our minds. One way to begin to make sense of this diversity is to divide it into manageable sections on the basis of differences. We also consider features found in all life forms to stress similarities as well as differences. We examine how different organisms solve the common problems of finding nutrients, energy, and mates on the third rock from our Sun. What basic evolutionary principles inform the relationships among life forms regardless of their different body plans, habitats, or life histories? Unlike many other first-year biology texts, this book has chapters integrating basic concepts such as the effects of genetic recombination, light, and domestication across the breadth of life from microbes to mistletoe to moose. As you read this book, you will be referred frequently to other chapters for linked information that expands the ideas further.

Evolution provides a powerful conceptual lens for viewing and understanding the roots and history of the diversity of living things. We will demonstrate how knowledge of evolution helps us appreciate the changes we observe in organisms. Whether the focus is the conversion of free-living prokaryotic organisms into mitochondria and chloroplasts or the steps involved in the domestication of rice, selection for particular traits over time can explain the current condition.

Examining how biological systems work is another theme pervading this text and underlying the idea of diversity. We have intentionally tried to include examples that will tax your imagination, from sea slugs that steal chloroplasts for use as solar panels, to the molecular basis of high altitude adaptations in deer mice, to adaptive radiation of viruses. In each situation, we examine how biologists have explored and assessed the inner workings of organisms, from gene regulation to the challenges of digesting cellulose.

Solving problems is another theme that runs throughout the book. Whether the topic is gene therapy to treat a disease in people, increasing crop production, or reducing the incidence of human obesity, both the problem and the solution lie in biology. We will explore large problems facing planet Earth and the social implications that arise from them.

Emphasizing the big picture …

Many biology textbooks use the first few chapters to review fundamentals of chemistry and biochemistry as well as information on the scientific method. Instead of focusing on this background information, we have used the first chapter, in particular, to immediately engage students by conveying the excitement that is modern biology. We have put important background information in the centre of the book as a distinct reference section entitled *The Chemical and Physical Foundations of Biology*. With their purple borders, these pages are distinct and easy to find, and have become affectionately known as *The Purple Pages*. These pages enable information to be readily identifiable and accessible to students as they move through the textbook rather than being tied to a particular chapter. In this edition, the concepts of atoms, molecules, and macromolecules are connected through the theme of "emergent properties." By considering how the "stuff of life" interrelates as a function of increasing complexity rather than just memorizing the attributes of individual items, students can better grasp *why* biology works the way it does, rather than be awed by how much information we know about it.

We hope that Canadian students will find the subject of biology as it is presented here accessible and engaging because it is presented in familiar contexts. We have highlighted the work of Canadian scientists, used examples of Canadian species, and referred to Canadian regulations and institutions.

Focusing on research to help students engage the living world as scientists …

A primary goal of this book is to evoke and sustain students' curiosity about biology, rather than dulling it with a mountain of disconnected facts. We can help students develop the mental habits of scientists and a fascination with the living world by conveying our passion for biological research. We want to excite students not only with *what biologists know* about the living world but also with *how they know it* and *what they still need to learn*. In doing so, we can encourage some students to accept the challenge and become biologists themselves, posing and answering important new questions through their own innovative research. For students who pursue other careers, we hope that they will leave their introductory—and perhaps only—biology course armed with intellectual skills that will enable them to evaluate future knowledge with a critical eye.

In this book, we introduce students to a biologist's "ways of learning." Research biologists constantly integrate new observations, hypotheses, questions, experiments, and insights with existing knowledge and ideas. To help students engage the world as biologists do, we must not simply introduce them to the current state of knowledge, we must also foster an appreciation of the historical context within which those ideas developed, and identify the future directions that biological research is likely to take.

Because advances in science occur against a background of research, we also give students a feeling for how biologists of the past formulated basic knowledge in the field. By fostering an appreciation of such discoveries, given the information and theories available to scientists in their own time, we can help students understand the successes and limitations of what we consider cutting edge today. This historical perspective also encourages students to view biology as a dynamic intellectual enterprise, not just a collection of facts and generalities to be memorized.

We have endeavoured to make the science of biology come alive by describing how biologists formulate hypotheses and evaluate them using hard-won data; how data sometimes tell only part of a story; and how the results of studies often end up posing more questions than they answer. Our exploration of the Tully Monster in Chapter 27 is a case in point. Since its fossil discovery and description, this mainly soft-bodied animal has been tentatively classified with species in five different groups of animals. Through this example, and throughout Chapter 27, we explore the current recognition that the historical and traditional grouping of animals into protostomes and deuterostomes is more artificial than real.

Although students might prefer simply to learn the "right" answer to a question, they must be encouraged to embrace "the unknown," those gaps in knowledge that create opportunities for further research. An appreciation of what biologists do *not* yet know will draw more students into the field. And by defining *why* scientists do not understand interesting phenomena, we encourage students to think critically about possible solutions and to follow paths dictated by their own curiosity. We hope that this approach will encourage students to make biology a part of their daily lives by having informal discussions and debates about new scientific discoveries.

Presenting the story line of the research process ...

Science is by its nature a progressive enterprise in which answers to questions open new questions for consideration. In preparing this book, we developed several special features to help students broaden their understanding of the material presented and of the research process itself:

- The chapter openers, titled *Why It Matters,* are engaging, short vignettes designed to capture students' imaginations and whet their appetites for the topic that the chapter addresses. In many cases, this feature uses current Canadian examples and tells the story of how a researcher or researchers arrived at a key insight, or how biological research solved a major societal problem, explained a fundamental process, or elucidated a phenomenon. The Why It Matters feature links the insight from the vignette to the contents of the chapter to spark student interest in the topic at hand.

- Three types of specially designed *research figures* provide more detailed information about how biologists formulate specific hypotheses and test them by gathering and interpreting data. *Experimental Research* figures describe specific studies in which researchers used both experimental and control treatments, either in the laboratory or in the field, to test hypotheses or answer research questions by manipulating the system they studied. *Observational Research* figures describe specific studies in which biologists have tested hypotheses by comparing systems under varying natural circumstances. *Research Method* figures provide examples of important techniques, such as light and electron microscopy, the polymerase chain reaction, making a knockout mouse, DNA microarray analysis, plant cell culture, producing monoclonal antibodies, radiometric dating, and cladistic analysis. Each *Research Method* figure leads a student through the purpose of the technique and protocol, and describes how scientists interpret the data it generates.

Integrating effective, high-quality visuals into the narrative ...

Today's students are accustomed to receiving ideas and information visually, making the illustrations and photographs in a textbook and the fully integrated online resources critically important. From the first Canadian edition, our illustration program has provided an exceptionally clear supplement to the narrative in a style that is consistent throughout the book. Graphs and anatomical drawings are annotated with interpretive explanations that lead students, step by step, through the major points they convey.

Over subsequent editions, we have continued to enhance the illustration program, focusing on features that reviewers and users of the book identified as the most useful pedagogical tools. In revising the text, we reevaluated each illustration and photograph, and made appropriate changes to improve their utility as teaching tools.

For this most recent edition, we have made some exciting new additions to our illustration program through the creation of *Chapter Roadmaps* and *Summary Illustrations* for every chapter the book. Chapter Roadmaps appear at the beginning of each chapter and provide a visual overview of the chapter contents. Connections between topics across chapters are emphasized to give students a sense of how the content of each chapter fits within the larger context of the book, and biology as a whole. At the end of each chapter, we have created vivid and engaging

Summary Illustrations that depict the core concepts—and teaching heart—of the chapter. These illustrations provide students with a visual overview of the connections between key concepts, and provide a unique touchstone to review and gauge understanding of the chapter contents.

Organizing chapters around important concepts ...

As authors and university teachers, we understand how easily students can get lost within a chapter. When students request advice about how to read a chapter and learn the material in it, we usually suggest that, after reading each section, they pause and quiz themselves on the material they have just encountered. After completing all the sections in a chapter, they should quiz themselves again, even more rigorously, on the individual sections and, most important, on how the concepts that were developed in the different sections fit together. Accordingly, we have adopted a structure for each chapter to help students review concepts as they learn them.

- The organization within chapters presents material in digestible sections, building on students' knowledge and understanding as they acquire it. Each major section covers one broad topic.
- *Study Break* questions follow every major section. These reading comprehension questions encourage students to pause at the end of a section and review what they have learned before going on to the next topic within the chapter. If a student isn't able to answer a study break question, they can immediately revisit the previous section to solidify their understanding. We feel that this is a better learning tool than directly providing the answers to these questions. If the answer does not come easily, then rereading the material associated with the answer is as important as seeing the answer itself.
- *Self-Test Questions* are found at the end of each chapter. These chapter review questions are organized according to Bloom's taxonomy into three sections: Recall/Understand, Apply/Analyze, and Create/Evaluate. This structure allows students to review the material in a sequence that moves from the basic knowledge of factual material, to more challenging and sophisticated applications of that knowledge, to novel situations. Answers to the Self-Test Questions are found in an appendix at the back of the book.
- *The Chemical and Physical Foundations of Biology,* also known as **The Purple Pages,** keep background information out of the main text, allowing students to focus on the bigger picture.
- *Unit 5: The Diversity of Life,* also known as **The Green Pages,** contains readily identifiable chapters that introduce the tremendous variability among living organisms.

Effectively introducing digital solutions into your classroom—online or in class—is now easier than ever ...

The fourth Canadian edition of *Biology: Exploring the Diversity of Life* represents a fully integrated package of print and media, providing comprehensive learning tools and flexible delivery options. In preparing this edition, we conducted extensive research to determine how instructors prefer to present online learning opportunities. The result of this research is a new MindTap course organized around the instructors' preferred workflow. Instructors can now select just the content they want to assign, chosen from a comprehensive set of learning materials provided with the course for each chapter. Many types of learning activities are assignable and offer students immediate feedback and automated instructor assessment.

Research also indicates that online content is most effective when it enhances conceptual understanding through the use of relevant applications. In this edition, we have developed new assessable online learning activities that provide students the opportunity to explore and practice biology the way scientists practice biology:

- *Interpret the Data* exercises have been enhanced by an additional online exercise to further develop student quantitative analysis and mathematical reasoning skills.
- The *Design an Experiment* feature is delivered online as a guided learning activity that takes the student through the process of designing an experiment.
- *Conceptual Learning Activities* are repeatable in alternate versions to help students learn the material.

The *Instructor Resource Center* provides everything you need for your course in one place. This collection of lecture and class tools is available online for instructors only via **www.nelson.com/instructor.** There you can access and download PowerPoint presentations, images, the Instructor's Manual, the Test Bank, videos, animations, and more.

To maximize the chances of producing a useful text that draws in students (and instructors), we sought the advice of colleagues who teach biology (members of the MindTap Advisory Board). We also asked students (members of the Student Advisory Boards) for their advice and comments. These groups evaluated the effectiveness of important visuals in the textbook, evaluated draft chapters, and provided valuable feedback on the MindTap, but any mistakes are ours.

In summary, we have applied our collective experience as teachers, researchers, and writers to create a readable and understandable foundation for students who may choose to enrol in more advanced biology courses in the future. Where appropriate, we provide straightforward explanations of fundamental concepts from the evolutionary perspective that binds together all the biological sciences. Recognizing that students in an introductory biology course face a potentially daunting quantity of ideas and information, we strive to provide an appropriate balance between factual and conceptual material, taking great care to provide clear explanations of how scientists draw conclusions from empirical data. Our approach helps students understand how we achieved our present knowledge. Clarity of presentation, thoughtful organization, a logical and seamless flow of topics within chapters, and carefully designed illustrations are key to our approach.

We hope that you are as captivated by the biological world as we are, and are drawn from one chapter to another. But don't stop there; use the digital and other resources to broaden your search for understanding, and, most important, observe and enjoy the diversity of life around you.

M. Brock Fenton
Denis Maxwell
Tom Haffie
Bill Milsom
Todd Nickle
Shona Ellis
London, Calgary, and Vancouver
January 2018

New to This Edition

The enhancements we have made in the fourth Canadian edition of *Biology: Exploring the Diversity of Life* reflect our commitment to providing a textbook that introduces students to new developments in biology while fostering active learning and critical thinking.

Our revisions to the new edition were guided by five important principles:

- Reduce the size of the book
- Ensure content is relevant and engaging for students and instructors
- Emphasize connections
- Support concepts with visuals wherever possible
- Extensively revise and rewrite Unit Four: Evolution and Classification

A streamlined textbook ...

In response to feedback from students and instructors across the country, we have made some important changes that have resulted in a briefer edition.

Organizational Changes

By combining and reorganizing information, we have reduced the number of chapters in the book from 52 to 46. The material on protostomes and deuterostomes has been combined into a single super chapter on animals. Using the latest research as our guide, Chapter 27: Animals captures the excitement of how new developments in molecular phylogenetic techniques have resulted in many taxonomic reclassifications as well as changes to phylogenies. This chapter features a unique research box on the Tully Monster as a case in point.

We have also streamlined our coverage of systems and processes in animals by combining reproduction and development to create Chapter 44: Animal Reproduction. The chapters on neural control and neural integration have been combined to create Chapter 45: Control of Animal Processes: Neural Control.

We have also rewritten former Chapter 33: Putting Selection to Work and Chapter 52: Conservation and Evolutionary Physiology into a collection of case studies and placed them on the MindTap for the book.

Streamlined Pedagogy and Prose

Our revisions to the fourth Canadian edition were also informed by a desire to reduce redundancy across the book, including only essential, testable information. As a result, students and instructors will find an efficient use of prose across the new edition, as well as extensive use of cross-references to other chapters, where necessary. The feature boxes "Molecule behind Biology," "People

behind Biology," and "Life on the Edge" have also been moved from the book to the Instructor's Manual, allowing instructors to continue to draw upon these engaging stories and vignettes, without increasing the length of the textbook.

Engaging and relevant content ...

From personal genome reports to cues to recognizing human female ovulation, the new edition is full of engaging examples that reflect everyday biology and its impact on society. In addition to references to Canadian research and researchers throughout the book, our MindTap features profiles of 13 former biology students, and what they have done with their biology degrees in "Where Are They Now?"

Emphasizing connections ...

We recognize that part of the challenge of an introduction to biology course lays in covering a large breadth of knowledge while making meaningful connections across topics, concepts, and the discipline as a whole. In *Biology: Exploring the Diversity of Life*, every chapter begins with a **Chapter Roadmap** that provides students with a visual overview of the chapter contents, while making connections between parts of the chapter and other chapters in the book. Within chapters, students will find cross-references and connections to other chapters where a concept is explored further or from a different perspective. Furthermore, every chapter concludes with a **Summary Illustration,** a two-page spread that synthesizes, integrates, and illustrates connections between important concepts covered in the chapter.

Clear and thoughtful visuals ...

Each of the figures in the new edition delivers a clear and thoughtful message that is tied directly to the discussion it accompanies. The new edition contains over 200 new and 55 revised figures. We have further enhanced this connection through the refinement and integration of research figures. **Experimental Research, Observational Research,** and **Research Methods** are further highlighted in a vivid new design, drawing attention to how biologists formulate and test specific hypotheses by gathering and interpreting data.

Extensively Revised Unit Four: Evolution and Classification

The fundamental concepts of evolution are essential for students to grasp as they explain the diversity of living organisms as well as the commonalities that organisms possess. That said, many first-year students come to university with a poor understanding of evolutionary principles; whether it's the importance of chance mutation as a driver of evolutionary change or that evolution can occur in the absence of natural selection.

With this in mind, we have extensively revised this unit to focus more clearly on conveying the fundamental concepts of evolution, to provide greater clarity on the processes that cause evolutionary change, as well as to make critical connections between evolution and genetics. Chapter 16: Evolution by Natural Selection now includes a section and Research Figure focused on experimental evolution in *E. coli*, as well as a concluding figure that explains the major misconceptions students have concerning evolution and natural selection. Chapter 17: Microevolution: Changes Within Populations has been rewritten to make stronger connections to genetics, which are often not made in the context of evolution, by fully explaining terms such as *allele, gene, gene pool*, and *locus*. This chapter also emphasizes the role of random mutation in evolution and its importance in introducing genetic novelty. Chapter 18: Speciation and Macroevolution has improved flow and clarity, including simpler and more informative figures. Chapter 19: Systematics and Phylogenetics: Revealing the Tree of Life is now its own dedicated chapter. This allows for more clear discussion of the tools and approaches used today to infer evolutionary histories. Great care has been taken to clearly define and present concepts of homology and convergent evolution.

Major revisions to selected chapters are listed below:

Chapter 1: Light and Life

- Streamlined to be more concise

Chapter 2: The Cell: An Overview

- NEW Research Figure about cell fractionalization

Chapter 3: Energy and Enzymes

- More precise description of fundamentals of thermodynamics
- Improved and clarified figures related to exergonic and endergonic reactions

Chapter 4: Cell Membranes and Signalling

- NEW Research Figure: Frye–Edidin Experiment Demonstrating that the Phospholipid Bilayer Is Fluid
- NEW Research Figure: Freeze Fracture

Chapter 5: Cellular Respiration

- Clarified section on chemical basis of cellular respiration to include stronger connections with Chapter 3

Chapter 6: Photosynthesis

- Clarified and improved selected figures

Chapter 7: Cell Cycles

- NEW Why It Matters about algal blooms in Lake Erie
- NEW material on DNA packaging
- NEW figure clarifying replicated versus unreplicated chromosomes

Chapter 8: Genetic Recombination

- Added explicit reference to cytokinesis
- Specified creation of haploid cells

Chapter 9: The Chromosomal Basis of Mendelian Inheritance

- NEW Canadian Why It Matters about the spirit bears of British Columbia
- Enhanced discussion connecting genes/alleles to proteins and protein products, and to the expression of alleles in the phenotype as dominant/recessive

Chapter 10: Genetic Linkage, Sex Linkage, and Other Non-Mendelian Inheritance Mechanisms

- NEW Canadian Why It Matters about disease incidence in Quebec
- NEW figures and examples dealing with translocations, imprinting, and pedigree analysis

Chapter 11: DNA Structure, Replication, and Repair

- NEW Canadian Why It Matters about woolly mammoths in Canada
- Highlighted mechanisms of repair of DNA damage

Chapter 12: Gene Structure, Expression, and Mutation

- NEW Canadian Why It Matters about poisonous mushrooms in British Columbia
- Expanded material on mutations and how they can affect protein function
- NEW discussion about ENCODE versus the junk DNA debate
- Expanded and clarified discussion of mutagenesis

Chapter 13: Regulation of Gene Expression

- NEW Why It Matters featuring epigenetic regulation of honeybee castes

- Updated material on lncRNA
- Updated material on cancer genetics

Chapter 14: DNA Technologies

- NEW section on CRISPR and qPCR
- Clarified and expanded Health Canada position on genetically modified foods
- Added material on knockout mouse protocol

Chapter 15: Genomics

- Fully updated
- NEW section on comparative genomics
- Linked advances in sequencing technologies from Sanger to early next-gen methods to DNA replication outlined in Chapter 11
- Enhanced explanation of principles behind BLAST

Chapter 16: Evolution: The Development of the Theory

- Completely rewritten with a greater focus on fundamental concepts of evolution and less emphasis on historical development
- NEW Why It Matters about antibiotic resistance
- Section and Experimental Research Figure focused on experimental evolution in *E. coli*
- Concluding figure explains the major misconceptions students have with evolution and natural selection

Chapter 17: Microevolution: Changes within Populations

- Completely rewritten with greater clarity on the processes that cause evolutionary change
- Stronger connections with genetics by fully explaining terms such as allele, gene, gene pool, locus
- Emphasis on the role of random mutation, the different types and when they occur, that may drive the introduction of genetic novelty

Chapter 18: Speciation and Macroevolution

- Improved flow and clarity of the writing
- Simpler and more informative figures

Chapter 19: Systematics and Phylogenetics: Revealing the Tree of Life

- In the previous edition, systematics and phylogenetics were grouped with the history of life (geological record) as a single chapter. This made it somewhat disjointed. In this edition, systematics and phylogenetics is its own dedicated chapter. This allows for clearer discussion of the tools and approaches used today to infer evolutionary histories.

- The concepts of homology and convergent evolution are more clearly presented.

Chapter 20: Humans and Evolution

- Unchanged from previous edition

Chapter 21: Defining Life and Its Origins

- In this edition, this chapter includes a section on the fossil record.
- Expanded section discussing possible energy sources for early life
- More in-depth discussion on LUCA

Chapter 22: Viruses, Viroids, and Prions: Infectious Biological Particles

- NEW Canadian example about tracking viral disease
- NEW Research Figure: A New Discovery for Hepatitis C Therapy

Chapter 23: Bacteria and Archaea

- Phylogenetic tree updated to reflect latest research
- NEW Research Figure: Genetic Recombination in Bacteria
- NEW discussion of a recent finding of a group within Archaea (Lokiarchaeota) that has a number of genes in common with eukaryotes

Chapter 24: Protists

- Phylogenetic tree updated to reflect latest research
- Incorporated recent research on Diplonemids that had been previously known from only a single environmental gene from marine planktonic samples
- NEW Research Figure: Isolation and Identification of Marine Diplonemids

Chapter 25: Fungi

- Incorporated information on a recent discovery in lichens related to the third symbiont, a basidiomycete yeast that is part of the symbiosis that influences the morphology of lichen
- Added material on the *Puccinia*–grain interaction
- NEW Research Figure: Hidden Third Partner in Lichen Symbiosis

Chapter 26: Plants

- NEW Research Figure: Exploring a Possible Early Angiosperm Adaptation for Efficient Photosynthesis in Dim Environments
- Extensive revision of key figures for clarity

Chapter 27: Animals

- NEW chapter that combines both protostomes and deuterostomes
- Includes latest research on phylogenetic tree
- NEW Research in Biology box on the Tully Monster

Chapter 28: Conservation of Biodiversity

- NEW Why It Matters featuring the extinction of passenger pigeons
- NEW section on the Anthropocene
- Enhanced discussion of human impact on landscapes
- NEW material on ecosystem services
- NEW discussion of the impact of wolf predation on populations of caribou

Chapter 29: Population Ecology

- NEW Why It Matters about the other malaria
- NEW Research Figure: Evaluating Density-Dependent Interactions between Species
- NEW section on Human Administered Population Control

Chapter 30: Species Interactions and Community Ecology

- NEW Why It Matters about oxpeckers and their hosts
- NEW coverage of blood feeders
- NEW material on venoms, how animals use them and how they work

Chapter 31: Ecosystems

- NEW Why It Matters about cave ecosystems
- Updated discussion of mass mortality
- Enhanced discussion of urban ecosystems

Chapter 32: Animal Behaviour

- NEW Why It Matters about bird migration
- NEW discussion about changing behaviour, featuring moose, salt, and cars
- NEW coverage of echolocation
- NEW material on the evolution of human language

Chapter 33: Organization of the Plant Body

- Incorporation of current research that demonstrates, with the discovery of new transcription factors, that there is an unexpectedly complex regulatory network governing secondary wall development
- NEW Research Figure: Networking the Secondary Cell Wall

Chapter 34: Transport in Plants

- NEW Research Figure: Translocation Pressure

Chapter 35: Reproduction and Development in Flowering Plants

- NEW section explaining the genetics behind the ABC model of floral development
- NEW section showing how plant tissue culture can generate virus-free plants from infected donors

Chapter 36: Plant Nutrition

- Assimilation of nutrients connected with material in *The Purple Pages*

Chapter 37: Plant Signals and Responses to the Environment

- Updated section on Darwin's experiments using light and oat coleoptiles

Chapter 38: Introduction to Animal Organization and Physiology

- NEW Research Figure: Demonstration of the Use of the Bill for Thermoregulation in Birds

Chapter 39: Animal Nutrition

- NEW Research Figure: Association of Bacterial Populations in the Gut Microbiome with Obesity in Humans
- NEW definition of essential nutrients, malnutrition, and undernutrition
- NEW figure illustrating intracellular digestion

Chapter 40: Gas Exchange: The Respiratory System

- NEW Why It Matters, featuring a discussion of adaptations that allow animals to live in oxygen-limited environments (burrows, during diving, at altitude)
- NEW Research Figure: Demonstration of a Molecular Basis for High-Altitude Adaptation in Deer Mice

Chapter 41: Internal Transport: The Circulatory System

- NEW Why It Matters, featuring the effects of animal body size on resting heart rate (but not longevity)
- NEW Research Figure: Demonstration of a Vasodilatory Signalling Molecule

Chapter 42: Regulation of the Internal Environment: Water, Solutes, and Temperature

- NEW Research Figure: ADH-Stimulated Water Reabsorption in the Kidney Collecting Duct

- Added new section on the regulation of mammalian kidney function
- Refined discussion to clarify the difference between osmolality and osmolarity

Chapter 43: Control of Animal Processes: Endocrine Control

- NEW Why It Matters, featuring endocrine control of mating behaviour in elk
- NEW Research Figure: Demonstration That Epinephrine Acts by Binding to a Plasma Membrane Receptor

Chapter 44: Animal Reproduction

- NEW chapter created by combining reproduction and development
- Added sexual reproduction as a route for infection
- Clarified discussion of where organelles were in the sperm
- NEW Research Figure: Vocal Cues of Ovulation in Human Females

Chapter 45: Control of Animal Processes: Neural Control

- NEW chapter created by combining neural control and integration
- Clarified the difference between the spike initiation zone and the axon hillock
- Clarified resting and membrane potential
- NEW Concept Fix addressing passive versus gated channels
- Enhanced discussion of the refractory period and why it is important for nerve conduction
- NEW Research Figure: Demonstration of Chemical Transmission of Nerve Impulses at Synapses

Chapter 46: Muscles, Skeletons, and Body Movements

- NEW Concept Fix addressing the misconceptions about muscles getting smaller as they contract
- More human examples integrated throughout
- NEW Research Figure: The Sliding Filament Model of Muscle Contraction

Welcome to *Biology: Exploring the Diversity of Life,* 4Ce

Biology: Exploring the Diversity of Life and MindTap engage students so they learn not only WHAT scientists know, but HOW they know it and what they still need to learn.

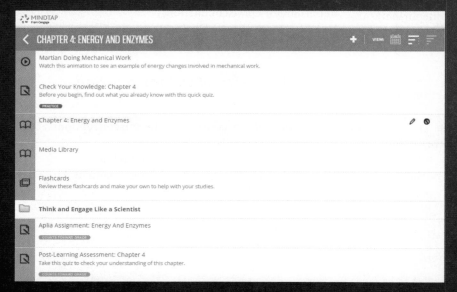

◀ **Engage, Adapt, and Master!** Stay organized and efficient with **MindTap**—a single destination with all the course material and study aids you need to succeed. Built-in apps leverage social media and the latest learning technology to help you succeed. Our customized learning path is designed to help you engage with biological concepts, identify gaps in your knowledge, and master the material!

▼ **Adapt!** Reinforce your knowledge of concepts by working through our Biology MindTap Study Guide, which includes

- animations and videos
- topic maps, learning outcomes, and study strategies
- multimodal quiz questions with instant feedback
- vocabulary flashcards
- chapter summaries

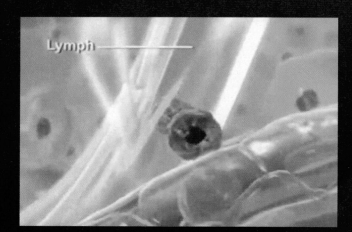

▲ **Engage!** The learning path for each chapter begins with an engaging video designed to pique your interest in the chapter contents. Take the tutorial quiz to assess gaps in your knowledge, and strengthen your knowledge of concepts by reviewing the ebook.

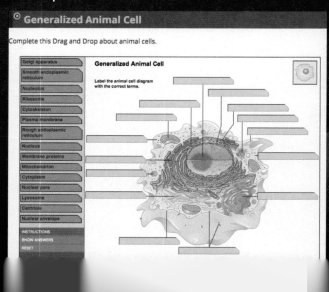

Interpret the Data

Investigators studying protein changes during aging examined enzyme activity in cells extracted from the nematode worm *Caenorhabditis elegans*. The cell extracts were treated to conserve enzyme activity, although the investigators noted that some proteins were broken down by the extraction procedure. The extracts were centrifuged, and seven fractions were collected in sequence to isolate the location of activity by protease enzymes called cathepsins. Examine the activity profiles in the Figure. In which fraction and, hence, in which eukaryotic cellular structure are these enzymes most active?

Figure **Distribution of Enzyme Activity in Fractions from Centrifugation of an Organelle Pellet.**

The fractions are numbered 1 to 7 from the top to the bottom of the centrifuge tube. Fraction 1 contains cytosolic contents and is the supernatant, and fraction 7 contains cellular debris and membrane fragments.

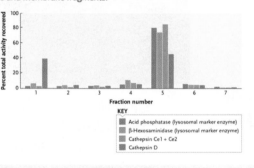

KEY
- Acid phosphatase (lysosomal marker enzyme)
- β-Hexosaminidase (lysosomal marker enzyme)
- Cathepsin Ce1 + Ce2
- Cathepsin D

Determine which strand is which, and complete the blanks to identify them.

The following strand presents the sequence of the _____.

nontemplate DNA
template DNA
mature mRNA

5′ – G* – GCCACC **AUG**GGACCC..**CCAUAG**

The following strand presents the sequence of the _____.

5′ – ...TATAAAA... – GCCACC **ATG**GGACCC..**CCATAG**

The following strand presents the sequence of the encoded polypeptide.

N terminus ——— **Met** AA₂ AA₃ .... AAₙ

The following strand presents the sequence of the _____.

3′ – ...ATATTTT... – CGGTGG **TAC**CCTGGG..**GGTATC**

The blue-colored region is the _____.

Active Learning

Visually stunning features that engage your students in the process of learning because an engaged student is a successful student.

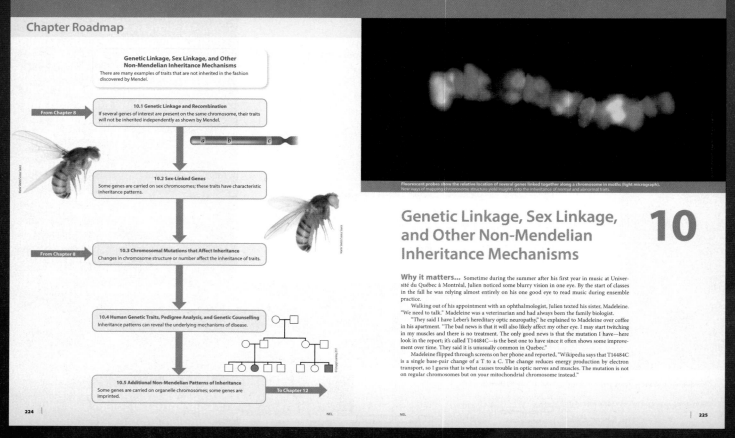

▲ **Chapter Roadmaps** The Chapter Roadmaps provide a visual overview of the major sections in the chapter and show the connections between the topics in the chapter and other chapters in the book.

Why It Matters … Why It Matters draws students in with an engaging vignette that is linked to the concepts discussed in the chapter.

STUDY BREAK QUESTIONS

1. What are the three interrelated systems that contribute to the eukaryotic cell cycle?
2. What is a chromosome composed of?
3. When is a chromosome composed of two chromatids?

▲ **Study Breaks** The Study Breaks fall at the end of each major section and encourage students to pause and review what they have learned before going on to the next topic within the chapter

Concept Fix Icons Concept Fixes draw on the extensive research literature dealing with misconceptions commonly held by biology students. Strategically placed throughout the text, these short segments help students identify—and correct—a wide range of misunderstandings. ▼

◗ CONCEPT FIX   Coming out of high school, many students think that ATP is a product of the respiratory ETC. This is a misconception that we need to fix. The generation of ATP by the ATP synthase complex is linked, or coupled, to electron transport by the proton gradient established across the inner mitochondrial membrane. But electron transport and the chemiosmotic generation of ATP are separate and distinct processes and are not always completely coupled (**Figure 5.17**). For example, it is possible to have high rates of electron transport (and thus high rates of oxygen consumption) and yet no ATP generated by chemiosmosis. This uncoupling of the two processes occurs when mechanisms prevent the formation of a proton-motive force. ⬡

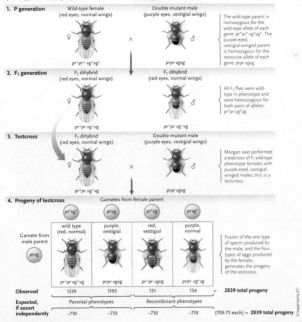

FIGURE 10.2 Experimental Research
Evidence for Gene Linkage
Question: Do the purple-eye and vestigial-wing genes of Drosophila assort independently?
Experiment: Morgan crossed true-breeding, wild-type flies having red eyes and normal wings with purple-eyed, vestigial-winged flies. The F1 dihybrids were all wild type in phenotype. Next he crossed the F1 dihybrid flies with purple-eyed, vestigial-winged flies (this is a testcross) and analyzed the phenotypes of the progeny.
1. P generation
Wild-type female (red eyes, normal wings)
Double mutant male (purple eyes, vestigial wings)
pr⁺pr⁺ vg⁺vg⁺
prpr vgvg
The wild-type parent is homozygous for the wild-type allele of each gene: pr⁺pr⁺ vg⁺vg⁺. The purple-eyed, vestigial-winged parent is homozygous for the recessive allele of each gene: prpr vgvg.
2. F1 generation
F1 dihybrid (red eyes, normal wings)
F1 dihybrid (red eyes, normal wings)
pr⁺pr vg⁺vg
All F1 flies were wild-type in phenotype and were heterozygous for both pairs of alleles: pr⁺pr vg⁺vg.
3. Testcross
F1 dihybrid (red eyes, normal wings)
Double mutant male (purple eyes, vestigial wings)
pr⁺pr vg⁺vg
prpr vgvg
Morgan next performed a testcross of F1 wild-type phenotype females with purple-eyed, vestigial-winged males; this is a testcross.
4. Progeny of testcross
Gametes from female parent
pr⁺vg⁺
prvg
pr⁺vg
prvg⁺
Gamete from male parent
prvg
wild type (red, normal)
purple, vestigial
red, vestigial
purple, normal
pr⁺pr vg⁺vg
prpr vgvg
pr⁺pr vgvg
prpr vg⁺vg
Fusion of the one type of sperm produced by the male, and the four types of eggs produced by the female, generates the progeny of the testcross.
Observed 1339 1195 151 154 = 2839 total progeny
Parental phenotypes
Recombinant phenotypes
Expected, if assort independently ~710 ~710 ~710 ~710 (709.75 each) = 2839 total progeny
Results: 2534 of the testcross progeny flies were parental—wild-type or purple, vestigial—while 305 of the progeny were recombinant—red, vestigial or purple, normal. If the genes assorted independently, the expectation is for a 1:1:1:1 ratio for testcross progeny: approximately 1420 of both parental and recombinant progeny.
Conclusion: The purple-eye and vestigial-wing genes do not assort independently. The simplest alternative is that the two genes are linked on the same chromosome. The small number of flies with recombinant phenotypes is explained by crossing-over.
© Cengage Learning 2017

◄ **Experimental Research Figures** Experimental Research figures describe specific studies in which research used both experimental and control treatments—either in the laboratory or in the field—to test hypotheses or answer research questions by manipulating the system they studied.

Research Method Figures Research Method Figures provide examples of important techniques, lead students through the purpose of the technique and protocol, and describe how scientists interpret the data generated. ▼

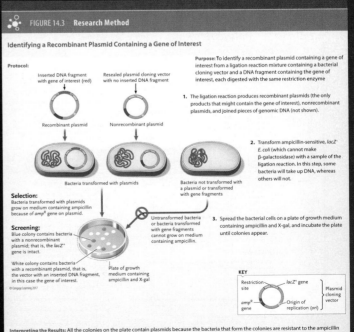

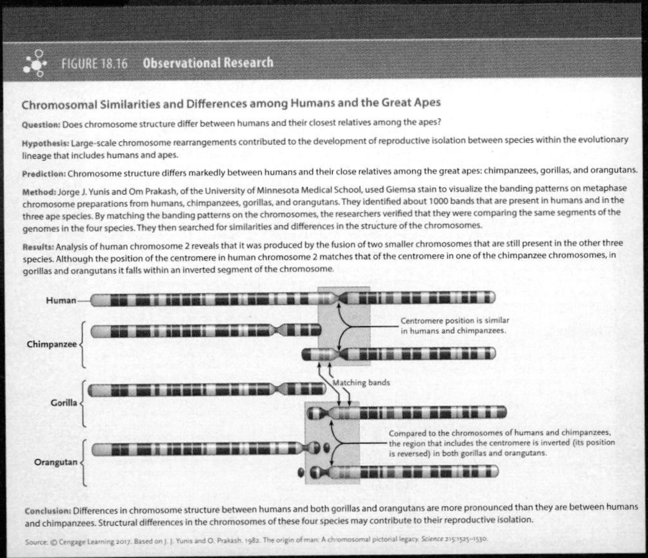

FIGURE 14.3 Research Method
Identifying a Recombinant Plasmid Containing a Gene of Interest
Purpose: To identify a recombinant plasmid containing a gene of interest from a ligation reaction mixture containing a bacterial cloning vector and a DNA fragment containing the gene of interest, each digested with the same restriction enzyme
Protocol:
Inserted DNA fragment with gene of interest (red)
Resealed plasmid cloning vector with no inserted DNA fragment
1. The ligation reaction produces recombinant plasmids (the only products that might contain the gene of interest), nonrecombinant plasmids, and joined pieces of genomic DNA (not shown).
Recombinant plasmid
Nonrecombinant plasmid
2. Transform ampicillin-sensitive, lacZ⁻ E. coli (which cannot make β-galactosidase) with a sample of the ligation reaction. In this step, some bacteria will take up DNA, whereas others will not.
Bacteria transformed with plasmids
Bacteria not transformed with a plasmid or transformed with gene fragments
Selection:
Bacteria transformed with plasmids grow on medium containing ampicillin because of ampᴿ gene on plasmid.
Untransformed bacteria or bacteria transformed with gene fragments cannot grow on medium containing ampicillin.
3. Spread the bacterial cells on a plate of growth medium containing ampicillin and X-gal, and incubate the plate until colonies appear.
Screening:
Blue colony contains bacteria with a nonrecombinant plasmid; that is, the lacZ⁺ gene is intact.
White colony contains bacteria with a recombinant plasmid, that is, the vector with an inserted DNA fragment, in this case the gene of interest.
Plate of growth medium containing ampicillin and X-gal
© Cengage Learning 2017
KEY
Restriction site
lacZ⁺ gene
ampᴿ gene
Origin of replication (ori)
Plasmid cloning vector
Interpreting the Results: All the colonies on the plate contain plasmids because the bacteria that form the colonies are resistant to the ampicillin present in the growth medium. Blue–white screening distinguishes bacterial colonies with nonrecombinant plasmids from those with recombinant plasmids. Bacteria making up blue colonies contain nonrecombinant plasmids. These plasmids have intact lacZ⁺ genes and produce β-galactosidase, which changes X-gal to a blue product. Bacteria that form the white colonies contain recombinant plasmids. Each recombinant plasmid has a DNA fragment (in this example, the gene of interest) inserted into the lacZ⁺ gene, so β-galactosidase cannot be produced. As a result, bacteria with recombinant plasmids cannot convert X-gal to the blue product and the colonies are white. Culturing a white colony produces large quantities of the recombinant plasmid that can be isolated and purified for analysis and/or manipulation of the gene = "gene of interest".

FIGURE 18.16 Observational Research
Chromosomal Similarities and Differences among Humans and the Great Apes
Question: Does chromosome structure differ between humans and their closest relatives among the apes?
Hypothesis: Large-scale chromosome rearrangements contributed to the development of reproductive isolation between species within the evolutionary lineage that includes humans and apes.
Prediction: Chromosome structure differs markedly between humans and their close relatives among the great apes: chimpanzees, gorillas, and orangutans.
Method: Jorge J. Yunis and Om Prakash, of the University of Minnesota Medical School, used Giemsa stain to visualize the banding patterns on metaphase chromosome preparations from humans, chimpanzees, gorillas, and orangutans. They identified about 1000 bands that are present in humans and in the three ape species. By matching the banding patterns on the chromosomes, the researchers verified that they were comparing the same segments of the genomes in the four species. They then searched for similarities and differences in the structure of the chromosomes.
Results: Analysis of human chromosome 2 reveals that it was produced by the fusion of two smaller chromosomes that are still present in the other three species. Although the position of the centromere in human chromosome 2 matches that of the centromere in one of the chimpanzee chromosomes, in gorillas and orangutans it falls within an inverted segment of the chromosome.
Human
Chimpanzee
Gorilla
Orangutan
Centromere position is similar in humans and chimpanzees.
Matching bands
Compared to the chromosomes of humans and chimpanzees, the region that includes the centromere is inverted (its position is reversed) in both gorillas and orangutans.
Conclusion: Differences in chromosome structure between humans and both gorillas and orangutans are more pronounced than they are between humans and chimpanzees. Structural differences in the chromosomes of these four species may contribute to their reproductive isolation.
Source: © Cengage Learning 2017. Based on J. J. Yunis and O. Prakash. 1982. The origin of man: A chromosomal pictorial legacy. Science 215:1525–1530.

▲ **Observational Research Figures** Observational Research Figures describe specific studies in which biologists have tested hypotheses by comparing systems under varying natural circumstances.

Summary Illustrations Vivid, engaging, and carefully developed Summary Illustrations appear at the end of each chapter and help students visualize the main concepts covered in the chapter. ▼

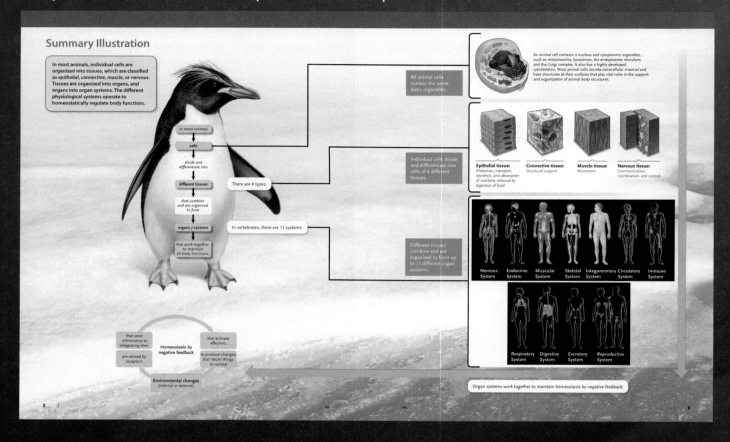

Summary Illustration

In most animals, individual cells are organized into tissues, which are classified as *epithelial, connective, muscle, or nervous.* Tissues are organized into organs, and organs into organ systems. The different physiological systems operate to homeostatically regulate body functions.

In most animals → cells → *divide and differentiate into* → different tissues → *that combine and are organized to form* → organs / systems → *that work together to maintain all body functions.*

There are 4 types:

In vertebrates, there are 11 systems:

that send information to integrating sites → are sensed by receptors → **Homeostasis by negative feedback** → that activate effectors → to produce changes that return things to normal → Environmental changes (internal or external)

All animal cells contain the same basic organelles.

An animal cell contains a nucleus and cytoplasmic organelles, such as mitochondria, lysosomes, the endoplasmic reticulum, and the Golgi complex. It also has a highly developed cytoskeleton. Most animal cells secrete extracellular material and have structures at their surfaces that play vital roles in the support and organization of animal body structures.

Individual cells divide and differentiate into cells of 4 different tissues.

Epithelial tissue: Protection, transport, secretion, and absorption of nutrients released by digestion of food

Connective tissue: Structural support

Muscle tissue: Movement

Nervous tissue: Communication, coordination, and control

Different tissues combine and are organized to form up to 11 different organ systems.

Nervous System Endocrine System Muscular System Skeletal System Integumentary System Circulatory System Immune System

Respiratory System Digestive System Excretory System Reproductive System

Organ systems work together to maintain homeostasis by negative feedback.

2   3

Self-Test Questions These chapter review questions are organized according to Bloom's taxonomy into three sections: Recall/Understand, Apply/Analyze, and Create/Evaluate. This structure allows students to review the material in a sequence that moves from the basic knowledge of factual material, to more challenging and sophisticated applications of that knowledge to novel situations. Answers to the Self-Test Questions are found in an appendix at the back of the book. ▼

SELF-TEST QUESTIONS

Recall/Understand

1. Which of these factors is found in organic molecules that are considered good fuels?
   a. many C—H bonds
   b. many C=C double bonds
   c. an abundance of oxygen
   d. a high molecular weight

2. What is one of the places in a cell where cellular respiration occurs?
   a. in plant mitochondria, but not in animal mitochondria
   b. in plant chloroplasts
   c. in the mitochondria of both animals and plants
   d. in animal mitochondria, but not in plant mitochondria

3. Which of these processes occurs during glycolysis?
   a. oxidation of pyruvate
   b. reduction of glucose
   c. oxidative phosphorylation
   d. substrate-level phosphorylation

4. Which of these processes links glycolysis and the citric acid cycle?
   a. chemiosmosis
   b. formation of G3P
   c. reduction of NAD⁺
   d. pyruvate oxidation

Apply/Analyze

5. The breakdown of fats releases fatty acids. In what form do the carbon molecules enter the respiratory pathway?
   a. as NADH
   b. as acetyl-CoA
   c. a glucose
   d. as pyruvate

6. You are reading this text while breathing in oxygen and breathing out carbon dioxide. Which two processes are the sources of the carbon dioxide?
   a. glycolysis and pyruvate oxidation
   b. glycolysis and oxidative phosphorylation
   c. pyruvate oxidation and the citric acid cycle
   d. the citric acid cycle and oxidative phosphorylation

7. Under conditions of low oxygen, what key role is played by fermentation in overall metabolism?
   a. It regenerates the NAD⁺ required for glycolysis.
   b. It synthesizes additional NADH for the citric acid cycle.
   c. It allows for pyruvate to be oxidized in mitochondria.
   d. By activating oxidative phosphorylation, it allows for the synthesis of extra ATP.

8. Suppose you are a doctor and your patient complains of feeling hot all the time, even on the coldest winter days. The young man perspires constantly and his skin is always flushed. He also eats a lot but is rather thin. You perform some laboratory tests, and find that the patient consumes lots of oxygen in his metabolic pathways. What would you suspect this patient suffers from and why?

Create/Evaluate

9. In cellular respiration, which of the following does the term *uncoupled* refer to specifically?
   a. The two parts of glycolysis are running independently of each other.
   b. Respiratory electron transport is operating, but chemiosmosis is inhibited.
   c. Respiratory electron transport is operating, but proton pumping is inhibited.
   d. Oxidative phosphorylation is occurring, but the proton-motive force remains high.

10. Phosphofructokinase (PFK) is regulated by a number of metabolites. In addition to those mentioned in the text, which one of the following would also make sense?
    a. Pyruvate could function as an activator of PFK.
    b. Glucose could function as an inhibitor of PFK.
    c. ADP could function as an activator of PFK.
    d. Acetyl-CoA could act as an activator of PFK.

11. Which of these statements *best* describes the "paradox of aerobic life"?
    a. Humans are completely protected from the toxic effects of oxygen.
    b. Hydrogen peroxide is formed when a single electron is donated to O₂.
    c. Cytochrome oxidase is a major source of reactive oxygen species.
    d. Strict anaerobes often lack the enzyme(s) superoxide dismutase and/or catalase.

12. Compare direct burning of glucose and cellular respiration with reference to their progression.

13. Distinguish between reduction and oxidation during redox reactions.

14. Explain what happens with hydrogen and its bonding electrons during cellular respiration.

15. Cyanide is a strong toxin that reacts with the final protein in the electron transport chain (ETC). Explain why it can kill a human within a few minutes.

Appendix A: Answers to Self-Test Questions

Chapter 1
1. a 2. a 3. d 4. a 5. c 6. d 7. c 8. a 9. b 10. a 11. c 12. b 13. d
14. Eyes are usually not exposed to full sunlight for a very long period of time, such as the photosynthetic apparatus is. Damage due to exposure of photosystems can be repaired by removing damaged proteins and replacing them with newly synthesized ones, which is not possible in a damaged eye.
15. Melanin protects skin cells because it absorbs ultraviolet light, and it is increasingly synthesized upon exposure to the Sun, which results in the darker shade of her skin.

Chapter 2
1. d 2. c 3. c 4. a 5. a 6. b 7. b 8. a 9. d 10. a 11. d 12. d 13. c
14. ribosomes, rough ER, transport vesicle, Golgi complex, secretory vesicle, plasma membrane
15. Anchoring junctions function to reinforce cell-to-cell connections made by adhesion molecules. Tight junctions seal the spaces between cells. Gap junctions create direct channels for communicating between adjacent cells.

Chapter 3
1. c 2. d 3. b 4. a 5. b 6. c 7. c 8. d 9. c 10. d
11. As they dissolve, the sugar molecules raise their entropy. However, the crystals re-form because the water decreases in its order, changing from compact liquid to disordered vapour.
12. Any substance in ordered state (minimum entropy) will contain molecules with maximum free energy. On the contrary, any substance in disordered state (maximum entropy) will contain molecules with minimum free energy. The relationship is reversed.

Chapter 5
1. a 2. c 3. d 4. d 5. b 6. c 7. a
8. This patient might have defective mitochondria in his cells. This condition is common in a number of diseases. The reason why it was suspected is that, based on his symptoms, probably little ATP is synthesized, in spite of high oxygen consumption, since

13. In an exergonic reaction, reactants contain more free energy than the products; energy is released and the reaction is spontaneous. In an endergonic reaction, reactants contain less free energy than the products; energy is required and the reaction is not spontaneous.
14. At any time in a cell, there must be exergonic reactions happening to provide enough energy for endergonic reactions. In addition, the energy released by exergonic reactions must be higher than the energy needed for endergonic reactions because some energy is always transferred to heat (second law of thermodynamics).

Chapter 4
1. a 2. c 3. b 4. c
5. Some proteins perform transport; others have enzymatic activities; some are a part of signal transduction process; and others are involved in attachment and/or recognition.
6. b 7. c 8. b 9. c 10. c 11. b 12. a 13. d
13. Passive transport occurs down the concentration gradient of the solute, and active transport occurs against the gradient of the transported solute. Active transport therefore requires a protein and energy to perform.
15. They are both a form of passive transport, but facilitated diffusion utilizes proteins to speed up the transport of solute across the membrane.

his cells dissipated a lot of heat (the patient was hot all the time).
9. b 10. c 11. d
12. Direct burning of glucose is an uncontrolled process; cellular respiration occurs in a series of steps and is therefore a form of controlled combustion.
13. Reduction is the acceptance of electrons during a redox reaction. Oxidation is the loss of electrons during a redox reaction.
14. Hydrogen and its electrons move from sugar to oxygen, forming water.
15. The process of oxidative phosphorylation produces the large number of ATP molecules needed for the endergonic reactions in the cell that we are so dependent on. One of the major sequences of proteins embedded in the mitochondrial membrane—called the electron transport chain—can accept electrons rich in energy. As the energized electrons fall from protein to protein in the ETC, they deposit energy that they carry. At the end of the ETC, there must be oxygen ions present to accept these energetically depleted electrons. If these energy-depleted electrons are not carried away by the oxygen ions, ATP production would stop. Cyanide exerts its deadly effects by reacting with the final protein in ETC, blocking oxygen from accepting electrons from this protein.

Chapter 6
1. d 2. c 3. c 4. a 5. c
6. A group of pigment proteins form an antenna complex that surrounds a reaction centre. Light energy absorbed anywhere in the antenna complex is transferred to a special chlorophyll *a* molecule in the reaction centre. The absorbed light is converted to chemical energy when an excited electron from the chlorophyll *a* is transferred to a primary

◄ *The Purple Pages:* The Chemical and Physical Foundations of Biology While many textbooks use the first few chapters to introduce and/or review, we believe that the first chapters should convey the excitement and interest of biology itself. We therefore placed important background information about biology and chemistry in the reference section entitled *The Chemical and Physical Foundations of Biology,* in the centre of the book. With their purple borders, these pages are distinct and easy to find and have become affectionately known as *The Purple Pages.* References to material covered in *The Purple Pages* are set in purple throughout the text.

Secondary Structure

The amino acid chain of a protein, rather than being stretched out in linear form, is folded into arrangements that form the protein's secondary structure. Secondary structure is based on hydrogen bonds between atoms of the backbone. More precisely, the hydrogen bonds form between the hydrogen atom attached to the nitrogen of the backbone and the oxygen attached to one of the carbon atoms of the backbone. Two highly regular secondary structures are the alpha helix and the beta sheet. In the alpha helix, side chains project outward, supporting the tertiary level of structure. Beta sheets have the side chains sticking out from the plane of the sheet alternating to either side, again supporting the overall structure. A third, less regular arrangement, the coil or loop, imparts flexibility to certain regions of the protein. Most proteins have segments of all three arrangements.

The α-Helix

A model of the α-helix (below, left), a coil shape formed when hydrogen bonds form between every N—H group of the backbone and the C=O group of the amino acid four residues earlier. In protein diagrams (below, right), the α-helix is depicted as a cylinder or barrel.

The β-Sheet

A β-sheet is formed by side-by-side alignment of β-strands (picture below shows two strands). The sheet is formed by hydrogen bonds between atoms of each strand. In protein diagrams, the β-strands are depicted as ribbons with arrowheads pointing toward the C-terminal.

Ball-and-stick model of α helix

Cylinder representation of α helix

Amino acid side group

Hydrogen bond

Hydrogen bond

Peptide bond

Hydrogen bond

© Cengage Learning 2017

FIGURE 25.1 **Example of a wood decay fungus: sulfur shelf fungus** (*Polyporus*)

essential components in all ecosystems and Earth's premier decomposers (Figure 25.1).

Despite their profound impact on ecosystems and other life forms, most of us have only a passing acquaintance with fungi, perhaps limited to the mushrooms on our pizza or the invisible but annoying types that cause skin infections, such as athlete's foot. This chapter provides you with an overview of fungal biology. We begin with the features that set fungi apart from all other organisms, and discuss the diversity of fungi existing today before revisiting associations between fungi and other organisms.

25.1 General Characteristics of Fungi

We begin our survey of fungi by examining the features that distinguish fungi from other forms of life, how fungi obtain nutrients, and adaptations for reproduction and growth that enable fungi to spread far and wide through the environment.

Fungi are heterotrophic eukaryotes that obtain carbon by breaking down organic molecules synthesized by other organisms. Although all fungi are heterotrophs, fungi can be divided into two broad groups based on how they obtain carbon. If a fungus obtains carbon from non-living material, it is a **saprotroph**. Fungi that decompose dead plant and animal tissues, for example, are saprotrophs. If a fungus obtains carbon from living organisms, it is a **symbiont**. Symbiosis is the living together of two (or sometimes more) organisms for extended periods; symbiotic relationships range along a continuum from **parasitism**, in which one organism benefits at the expense of the other, to **mutualism**, in which both organisms benefit. Although we often think of fungi as decomposers, fully half of all identified fungi live as symbionts with another organism.

Regardless of their nutrient source, fungi feed by **absorptive nutrition**: they secrete enzymes into their environment, breaking down large molecules into smaller soluble molecules that can then be absorbed into their cells. This mode of nutrition means that fungi cannot be stationary, as they would then deplete all the food in their immediate environment. Instead, fungi have evolved the ability to proliferate quickly through their environment, digesting nutrients as they grow. How can fungi proliferate so quickly? Although some fungi grow as unicellular yeasts, which reproduce asexually by **budding** or binary fission (see Figure 25.13), most are composed of **hyphae** ("web"; singular, *hypha*; **Figure 25.2**), fine filaments that spread through whatever substrate the fungus is growing in—soil, decomposing wood, your skin—forming a network, or **mycelium** (Figure 25.2). Hyphae are essentially tubes of cytoplasm surrounded by cell walls made of chitin, a polysaccharide also found in the exoskeletons of insects and other arthropods.

Hyphae grow only at their tips, but because a single mycelium contains many, many tips, the entire mycelium grows outward very quickly. Together, this **apical growth** and absorptive nutrition account for much of the success of fungi. As the hyphal tips extend, they exert a mechanical force, allowing them to push through their substrate, releasing enzymes and absorbing nutrients as they go. Fungal species differ in the particular digestive enzymes they synthesize, so a substrate that is a suitable food source for one species may be unavailable to another. Although there are exceptions, fungi typically thrive only in moist environments, where they can directly absorb water, dissolved ions, simple sugars, amino acids, and other small molecules. When some of a mycelium's hyphal filaments contact a source of food, growth is channelled in the direction of the food source.

Nutrients are absorbed at the porous tips of hyphae; small atoms and molecules pass readily through these tips, and then transport mechanisms move them through the underlying plasma membrane. Some hyphae have regular cross-walls, or **septa** ("fences" or "walls"; singular, *septum*), that separate a hypha into compartments (**Figure 25.3**), whereas others lack septa and are effectively one large cell. But even septate hyphae should be thought of as interconnected compartments rather than separate cells, as all septa have pores that allow cytoplasm and, in some fungi, even nuclei and other large organelles to flow through the mycelium. By a mechanism called **cytoplasmic streaming** (flow of cytoplasm and organelles around a cell or, in this case, a mycelium), nutrients obtained by one part of a mycelium can be translocated to other non-absorptive regions, such as reproductive structures.

When a fungus releases enzymes into its substrate, it faces competition from bacteria and other organisms for the nutrients that are now available. How can a fungus prevent these competitors from stealing the nutrients that it has just expended energy and resources to obtain? Many fungi produce antibacterial compounds and toxins that inhibit the growth of competing organisms. Many of these compounds are **secondary metabolites**, which are not required for day-to-day survival but are beneficial to the fungus. As we will see, many of these compounds not only are important in the life of a fungus but also benefit organisms associated with the fungus. Many are also of commercial or medical importance to humans; for example, the antibiotic penicillin is a secondary metabolite produced by a species of *Penicillium*.

Fungi reproduce by spores, and this spore production can be amazingly prolific, with some species of fungi producing billions of spores per day (**Figure 25.4**). These spores are microscopic, featherlight, and able to survive in the environment for extended periods after they are released. Reproducing via such spores allows fungi to be opportunists, germinating only when favourable conditions exist and quickly exploiting food sources that occur unpredictably in the environment. Releasing vast numbers of spores, as some fungi do, improves the odds that the spores will germinate and produce a new individual.

Spores can be produced asexually or sexually; some fungi produce both asexual and sexual spores at different stages of their lives. Sexual reproduction in fungi is complex. In all organisms, sexual reproduction involves three stages: the fusion of two haploid cells (**plasmogamy**), bringing together their two nuclei in one common cytoplasm. Cytoplasmic fusion in most organisms is quickly followed by nuclear fusion (**karyogamy**), but in fungi the cells can remain bi-nucleate as the organism grows. Nuclear fusion is often followed by meiosis to produce genetically distinct haploid spores. As we will see, fungi are unique in that plasmogamy and karyogamy can be separated in time for durations ranging from seconds to many years.

a. Multicellular fungus

Fruiting Body

Honey mushroom (*Armillaria ostoyae*)

Mycelium

b. Rhizomorphs

Fungal hyphae

FIGURE 25.2 **Fungal structure: mycelia, hyphae. (a)** Illustration of the mycelium of a mushroom-forming fungus, which consists of branching septate hyphae. *Inset:* Micrograph of fungal hyphae **(b)** Rhizomorph – a cordlike aggregation of hyphae formed by some basidiomycete fungi.

Hyphae

Apical growth

Septum

FIGURE 25.3 **Septa.** In some fungi, septa divide each hypha into separate compartments.

FIGURE 25.4 **Spore production by fungal fruiting bodies.** Some fruiting bodies can release billions of spores per day.

Student and Instructor Resources

Succeed in the course with these dynamic resources!

MindTap

 With relevant assignments that guide students to analyze, apply, and elevate thinking, **MindTap** allows instructors to measure skills and promote better outcomes with ease. Including interactive quizzing, this online tutorial and diagnostic tool identifies each student's unique needs with a pre-test. The learning path then helps students focus on concepts they're having the most difficulty mastering. It refers to the accompanying MindTap Reader eBook and provides a variety of learning activities designed to appeal to diverse ways of learning. After completing the study plan, students take Aplia problem sets and then take a post-test to measure their understanding of the material. Instructors have the ability to customize the learning path, add their own content, and track and monitor student progress by using the instructor Gradebook and Progress app.

Students stay organized and efficient with MindTap, a single destination with all the course material and study aids students need to succeed. Built-in apps leverage social media and the latest learning technology. For example,

- ReadSpeaker will read the text to you.
- Flashcards are prepopulated to provide you with a jump start for review, or you can create your own.
- You can highlight text and make notes in your MindTap Reader. Your notes will flow into Evernote, the electronic notebook app that you can access anywhere when it's time to study for the exam.
- Self-quizzing allows you to assess your understanding.

The **MindTap** resources were developed by Dora Cavallo-Medved of the University of Windsor, Reehan Mirza of Nipissing University, Roy Rea of the University of Northern British Columbia, and Miranda Meents.

Also available in MindTap for Biology are engaging and informative videos that accompany *The Purple Pages*. From matter to polypeptides, author Todd Nickle, of Mount Royal University (pictured), will walk you through these foundational concepts, strengthening your understanding and helping you build a strong base of knowledge and understanding for biology.

Visit www.nelson.com/student to start using MindTap. Enter the Online Access Code from the card included with your textbook. If a code card is *not* provided, you can purchase instant access at NELSONbrain.com.

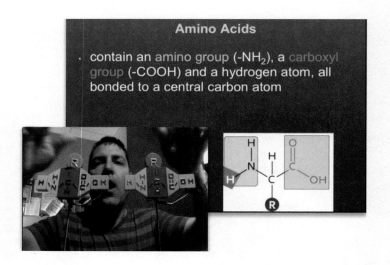

Aplia for Biology

Strengthen your understanding of biology with Aplia™!

Aplia's focused assignments and active learning opportunities help students learn key concepts by randomized, automatically graded questions, exceptional text/art integration, and immediate feedback. Aplia has a full course management system that can be used independently or in conjunction with other course management systems such as Blackboard and WebCT.

This innovative, easy-to-use, interactive technology gives students more practice, with detailed feedback to help students learn with every question!

Aplia's focused assignments and active learning opportunities (including randomized questions, exceptional text/art integration, and immediate feedback) get students involved with biology and help them think like scientists.

Interactive problems and figures help students visualize dynamic biological processes and integrate concepts, art, media, and homework practice.

For more information, visit **www.aplia.com/biology**.

The Aplia course for *Biology: Exploring the Diversity of Life,* Fourth Canadian Edition, was prepared by Anna Rissanen of Memorial University and Todd Nickle of Mount Royal University.

The Nelson Education Teaching Advantage (NETA) program delivers research-based instructor resources that promote student engagement and higher-order thinking to enable the success of Canadian students and educators. To ensure the high quality of these materials, all Nelson ancillaries have been professionally copy-edited.

Be sure to visit Nelson Education's **Inspired Instruction** website at **www.nelson.com/inspired/** to find out more about NETA. Don't miss the testimonials of instructors who have used NETA supplements and have seen student engagement increase!

NETA Test Bank: This resource was written by Ivona Mladenovic of Simon Fraser University. It includes over 2500 multiple-choice questions written according to NETA guidelines for effective construction and development of higher-order questions. The Test Bank was copy-edited by a NETA-trained editor for adherence to NETA best practices. Also included are true/false, essay, short-answer, matching, and completion questions. Test Bank files are available in Microsoft Word format from your Nelson publishing representative.

The **NETA Test Bank** is available in a new, cloud-based platform. **Nelson Testing Powered by Cognero®** is a secure online testing system that allows you to author, edit, and manage test bank content from any place you have Internet access. No special installations or downloads are needed, and the desktop-inspired interface, with its drop-down menus and familiar, intuitive tools, allows you to create and manage tests with ease. You can create multiple test versions in an instant and import or export content into other systems. Tests can be delivered from your learning management system, your classroom, or wherever you want. Nelson Testing Powered by Cognero can be accessed through www.nelson.com/instructor.

NETA PowerPoint: Microsoft PowerPoint® lecture slides for every chapter were created by Jane Young of the University of Northern British Columbia. There is an average of 80 slides per chapter, many featuring key figures, tables, and photographs from *Biology: Exploring the Diversity of Life,* Fourth Canadian Edition. The PowerPoint slides also feature "build slides"—selected illustrations with labels from the book that have been reworked to allow optimal display in PowerPoint. NETA prin-ciples of clear design and engaging content have been incorporated throughout, making it simple for instructors to customize the deck for their courses.

Image Library: This resource consists of digital copies of figures, short tables, and photographs used in the book. Instructors may use these jpegs to customize the NETA PowerPoint slides or create their own PowerPoint presentations.

NETA Instructor's Manual: This resource was written by Tamara Kelly of York University and Tanya Noel of the University of Windsor. It is organized according to the textbook chapters and addresses key educational concerns, such as typical stumbling blocks students face and how to address them. Other features include tips on teaching using cases as well as suggestions on how to present material and use technology and other resources effectively, integrating the other supplements available to both students and instructors. This manual doesn't simply reinvent what's currently in the text, it helps the instructor make the material relevant and engaging to students.

TurningPoint®: Another valuable resource for instructors is **TurningPoint® classroom response software** customized for *Biology: Exploring the Diversity of Life,* Four Canadian Edition, by Jane Young at the University of Northern British Columbia. Now you can author, deliver, show, access, and grade, all in PowerPoint, with no toggling back and forth between screens! JoinIn on TurningPoint is the only classroom response software tool that gives you true PowerPoint integration. With JoinIn, you are no longer tied to your computer. You can walk about your classroom as you lecture, showing slides and collecting and displaying responses with ease. There is simply no easier or more effective way to turn your lecture hall into a personal, fully interactive experience for your students. If you can use PowerPoint, you can use JoinIn on TurningPoint! (Contact your Nelson publishing representative for details.) These contain poll slides and pre- and post-test slides for each chapter in the text.

Acknowledgements

We thank the many people who have worked with us on the production of this text, particularly Paul Fam, Senior Publisher, whose foresight brought the idea to us and whose persistence saw the project through.

We are also grateful to the members of the MindTap Advisory Board and the Student Advisory Boards for the fourth Canadian edition, who provided us with valuable feedback and alternative perspectives (special acknowledgments to these individuals are listed below).

We also thank Richard Walker at the University of Calgary and Ken Davey at York University, who began this journey with us but were unable to continue. We are very grateful to Heather Addy of the University of Calgary for her significant contributions to the first three editions.

We are especially grateful to Toni Chahley, Content Manager, who kept us moving through the chapters at an efficient pace, along with Charu Verma, Project Manager, and Imoinda Romain, Senior Production Project Manager. A very special thanks to Kathy Hamilton, for her guidance and helpful suggestions with the summary illustrations, and we are very grateful to Roy Rea of the University of Northern British Columbia for his critical read of Chapter 27, and his significant contribution to the summary illustrations for Chapters 27–32. We thank Kristiina Paul, our photo researcher, for her hard work with the numerous photos in the book, and Frances Robinson for her careful and thoughtful copy-editing. Finally, we thank Kim Carruthers, Marketing Manager, for making us look good.

Brock Fenton thanks Allan Noon for offering advice about taking pictures; Laura Barclay, Jeremy McNeil, Tony Percival-Smith, C. S. (Rufus) Churcher, and David and Meg Cumming for the use of their images; Karen Campbell for providing a critical read of Putting Selection to Work; and Michael Owen for his outstanding contribution to Chapter 27: Animals.

Tom Haffie would like to acknowledge the cheerful and insightful editorial work of Jennifer Waugh on Chapter 16 and the conscientious research assistance of Dr. Aniruddho Chokroborty-Hoque.

Denis Maxwell would like to thank David Brock for helping fine-tune the coverage of thermodynamics in Chapter 3.

Todd Nickle thanks his family, students, and colleagues for humouring his mad exploits and for their understanding when he doesn't make things easy on himself—or others—as he explores insane and sometimes creative ways to repurpose old ways of doing things.

The authors are all indebted to Ivona Mladenovic of Simon Fraser University for her excellent work on the Self-Test Questions, and Johnston Miller, whose extensive background research anchored our Concept Fixes in the education literature.

It is never easy to be in the family of an academic scientist. We are especially grateful to our families for their sustained support over the course of our careers, particularly during those times when our attentions were fully captivated by bacteria, algae, fungi, parasites, snakes, geese, or bats. Saying "yes" to a textbook project means saying "no" to a variety of other pursuits. We appreciate the patience and understanding of those closest to us that enabled the temporary reallocation of considerable time from other endeavours and relationships.

Many of our colleagues have contributed to our development as teachers and scholars by acting as mentors, collaborators, and, on occasion, "worthy opponents." Like all teachers, we owe particular gratitude to our students. They have gathered with us around the discipline of biology, sharing their potent blend of enthusiasm and curiosity, and leaving us energized and optimistic for the future.

Editorial and Student Advisory Boards

We were very fortunate to have the assistance of some extraordinary students and instructors of biology across Canada who provided us with feedback that helped shape this textbook into what you see before you. As such, we would like to say a very special thank you to the following people:

MindTap Advisory Board

Brett Couch, University of British Columbia
Stewart Daly, Marianopolis College
Jon Houseman, University of Ottawa
William Huddleston, University of Calgary
Ivona Mladenovic, Simon Fraser University
Ken Otter, University of Northern British Columbia
Lisa Prichard, MacEwan University
Roy Rea, University of Northern British Columbia
Frieder Schoeck, McGill University
Marina Silva-Opps, University of Prince Edward Island
Matt Smith, Wilfrid Laurier University
Chris Todd, University of Saskatchewan
Paula Wilson, York University
Ken Wilson, University of Saskatchewan

(Top) Ivona Mladenovic, Ken Wilson, Jon Houseman, Stewart Daly, Frieder Schoeck; (bottom) William Huddleston, Chris Todd, Lisa Prichard

Paula Wilson, York University

Ken Otter, University of Northern British Columbia

Roy Rea, University of Northern British Columbia

Matt Smith, Wilfrid Laurier University

Student Advisory Boards

University of British Columbia

Shown above are members of the University of British Columbia Student Advisory Board. From left to right: Kristina Balce, Amy Dhillon, Humaam Hamado, Ebi Oliya, Laura Fash, Sina Soleimani, Adam Book, Ashley Pinter, Garrett Huwyler, Quinn Stewart, Gavindeep Shinger. Not pictured: Kendrix Kek, Hassan Ali

University of Calgary

Shown above are members of the University of Calgary Student Advisory Board. From left to right: Gina Mannella, Jesse Provick, Amanda Bennett, Leesa Le, Vivian Nguyen

Mount Royal University

Depicted above are members of the Student Advisory Board at Mount Royal University. From left to right, back row: Evan Olar, Moroni Lopez, Taelor Evans, Todd Nickle, Jonathan Roveredo, Darlene Skagen, Andrew Roberts, Surafel Girma, Danielle Schmidt, Laura Villarraga Ulloa. Front row: Kyle Poffenroth, Heaven Berhe Sium, Aderinsoye Ademoye, Ravneet Gill, Meena Kanthimathinathan, Alexandra Presbitero, Anastasia Socolnicova. Not pictured: Ashley Chicote, Cassidy Fleming

Nelson would like to thank some of the current student users of *Biology: Exploring the Diversity of Life,* in particular the students at Western University's Biology 1001A course who shared their feedback via their participation in a student focus group early in the development process.

EVOLUTION, ECOLOGY, AND THE DIVERSITY OF LIFE

aerogondo2/Shutterstock.com

The Lepidoptera (butterflies and moths) are an order of insects that consists of about 150 000 known species, of which about 20 000 are butterflies. Some estimates put the total number of Lepidoptera species at 300 000 to 400 000, with most remaining to be discovered in the tropics.

Divided into three units, Evolution and Classification, The Diversity of Life, and Ecology and Behaviour, the chapters of Volume 2 focus on topics that naturalists have been contemplating for well over 100 years but, unlike today, had very few answers. We start this volume with Unit 4 by providing a thorough introduction to the central unifying theme of biology: evolution. We move from early ideas put forward by Aristotle about the organization of the natural world through to a chapter that focuses on what we currently know about the evolution of our own species. Along the way, we acknowledge the insights that led Charles Darwin and Alfred Wallace to the development of the theory of evolution by natural selection. We discuss how their ideas were profoundly shaped by their travels as well as the work of others. Students often struggle to understand evolution because they carry with them a range of misconceptions about how it actually works. We directly address many of these misconceptions at the end of Chapter 16. You will come to recognize the population as the unit of evolutionary change, and with that we introduce in Chapter 17 microevolution: how single populations change because of changes in how common specific gene variants (alleles) are within the population. This leads then into a critical and important discussion of how evolution links with genetics (covered in Unit 3). It is surprising to realize that Mendel and Darwin were contemporaries of each other and that, while natural selection is based on passing on beneficial traits to offspring, Darwin had no idea of the mechanism of heredity. After this two-chapter introduction to evolution, in Chapter 18 we delve into the concept of a species and the processes that result in the formation of new species. You will quickly find out when reading this chapter that, even in the twenty-first century, an all-encompassing and agreed-upon definition of what a species is remains elusive. Why is that? One of the most basic of all questions in science is addressed in Chapter 19: What is life and how did it originate? The focus here starts with a review of the likely conditions on primordial Earth and the major theories that have been put forward regarding the transition from the non-biological world to one teaming with life, a transition that started about 4 billion years ago. The chapter also includes a detailed section describing the rise of the eukaryotic cell through the process of endosymbiosis, and the critical role played by the fossil record in shaping our understanding of biological history. We close Unit 4 by providing a brief overview of the evolution of humans from early hominids and the unique adaptations that humans possess, such as bipedalism.

Armed with a foundational understanding of evolution and speciation, we delve into Unit 5, where we do something that is not easy: we organize into discrete groups and discuss the huge diversity of life that exists on Earth today. Moving from simple bacteria through to the complexity seen in animals and flowering plants, we survey the product of 4 million years of evolution. Recent analysis suggests that the total number of species on Earth ranges from a low of maybe 4 million to some estimates as high as perhaps 1 trillion different species. While estimates for the number of species inhabiting Earth today vary, researchers agree that perhaps as much as 90% of the total biodiversity that has ever existed on the planet has been lost. Extinction is a major topic of the last chapter of the unit, exploring the need and ways to conserve the current biodiversity. The chapter illustrates the fundamental and deleterious impact that our species has had on global diversity.

As Darwin and Wallace both came to understand, many traits of a particular species are the result of adaptations to the specific environmental conditions in which the species is found. The major themes of Unit 4 (evolution) and Unit 5 (species diversity) are brought together in Unit 6, where the overarching theme is ecology: the distribution and abundance of species and how they interact not only with each other but also with the physical environment. One explanation for the huge diversity of species is that Earth offers a huge range of physical environments for specific populations to become adapted.

As presented in Chapters 30 and 31, organisms interact in a wide range of ways with each other and the physical environment. These interactions put limits on the rate of population growth and its steady-state size (carrying capacity). Competition for resources, a major factor in community dynamics, is discussed as are well-studied predator–prey interactions. This discussion ends with the daunting problem of human population growth and its impact on other species as well as being the cause of rapid dwindling of key natural resources. The human population was 6 billion about the time you were born, but is expected to reach 9 billion by the time you are about 50 years old!

We devote an entire chapter to discussing the ecosystem, a group of organisms interacting with the physical environment. The chapter illustrates the strong interconnectivity among species of the ecosystem and their reliance on one another. As well, we discuss how energy and nutrients (carbon, water, nitrogen) flow through and support ecosystem structures. An understanding of the food chain and its dynamics, including the process of biomagnification of toxins, is also presented.

You will see common themes in the chapters in this volume, including evolution, adaptation, diversification, competition, and resources. The central role of the environment in evolutionary history and ongoing evolution are also made apparent. The vital importance of interactions among organisms is another recurring theme. On more than one occasion we discuss the clear and present danger posed to Earth's biodiversity by unrelenting human population growth.

Chapter Roadmap

Evolution: The Development of the Theory

The theory of Evolution by Natural Selection is the single central concept that permeates all of biology. It took a 20-something Charles Darwin on an expedition to arrive at its basic tenets, which have not changed.

Steve Bower / Shutterstock.com

16.1 The Recognition of Change

To Chapter 5

To Chapter 6

16.2 Natural Selection

Individuals with certain inherited traits are better able to survive and reproduce than individuals without those traits.

16.3 Evolutionary Biology since Darwin

In the 20th century, the molecular basis of evolutionary change became apparent as important connections developed between evolutionary biology and genetics.

16.4 Evolution Is the Core Theory of Modern Biology but Is Plagued by Misconceptions

Evolution by natural selection is one of the unifying themes of biology, yet commonly held misunderstandings have proven hard to fix.

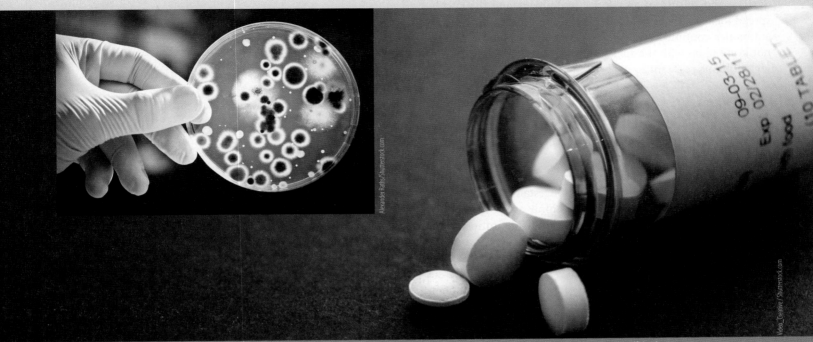

The rate at which new antibiotics are being developed is not keeping up with the speed at which bacteria are becoming antibiotic resistant.

Evolution: The Development of the Theory

16

Why it matters . . . Discovered by Alexander Fleming in 1928, the antibiotic penicillin kills bacteria by inhibiting the function of a crucial enzyme required for cell wall biosynthesis. Penicillin and other antibiotics that became widely available in the 1950s were known as "wonder drugs" for their remarkable ability to stop infections that only a few decades earlier were sometimes fatal.

Today, penicillin is rarely prescribed because it often doesn't work. In fact, whole classes of antibiotics that took years to develop have become essentially useless because many strains of bacteria have become resistant to their action. Over the past decade, Health Canada has seen the incidence of bacterial antibiotic resistance grow to become one of the top health issues in the country. Each year thousands of Canadians become infected with bacteria that are resistant to antibiotics, and many people die from infections that a decade or two ago were easily treated.

What you may not realize is that antibiotic resistance in bacteria is a consequence of evolution by natural selection, which is the focus of this chapter. Antibiotics present bacterial populations with an agent of selection. Within a large population of bacteria, there are a small number of individual cells that are resistant to a particular antibiotic simply because they happen to possess a random mutation that has altered their biochemistry. As a consequence, upon exposure to antibiotic in the environment, while the vast majority of bacterial cells die, the small number of resistant bacteria can continue to grow and divide. As a result, the proportion of drug-resistant bacteria in the population increases over time from one generation to the next.

In October 2014, the Government of Canada released *Antimicrobial Resistance and Use in Canada: A Federal Framework for Action.* The Framework maps out a coordinated, collaborative federal approach to responding to the threat of antibiotic resistance. The incidence of antibiotic resistance has increased over the past few decades as a result of overuse and misuse of antibiotics by humans and their widespread inclusion in animal feed. While the development of new antibiotics continues, the rate of developing new antibiotics is not keeping up with the speed with which bacteria are becoming antibiotic resistant.

16.1 The Recognition of Change

"Nothing in biology makes sense except in the light of evolution" is a quote from the Russian-born evolutionary biologist Theodosius Dobzhansky. This famous phrase succinctly reflects the central role evolution plays in our understanding of life. For this chapter we will define evolution simply as the notion that species change over time. We will refine this definition in the next chapter. Not only does evolution explain the underlying common features that organisms possess, it explains the huge diversity of life on Earth—life exists in so many different forms. An understanding of how evolution operates also helps in our understanding of how species continue to change over time in response to environmental challenges, such as climate change.

16.1a The Early View Is That Life Is Unchanging

The Greek philosopher Aristotle was a keen observer of nature and he examined the form and variety of organisms in their natural habitats. Careful study of the differences and similarities among organisms led Aristotle to create a ladder-like classification of life. In this system, which would later be called the *Scala Naturae* (Scale of Nature), each organism on Earth occupies a specific step on the ladder that leads from the non-living world at the bottom up ever-increasing levels of complexity. Humans are at the very top of the ladder, just below perfection, God **(Figure 16.1)**.

By the fourteenth century, Europeans had merged Aristotle's classification system with the biblical account of creation to arrive at a view of the natural world in which (1) organisms had been specially created by God, (2) species could never change or become extinct, and (3) new species could never arise. At the time, biological research was dominated by natural theology, which provided arguments for the existence of God through the detailed study of nature (God's creation). In the eighteenth century there was no stronger proponent of natural theology than the Swedish botanist Carolus Linnaeus (1707–1778), who undertook the exhaustive goal to classify all organisms. It is Linnaeus that introduced the binomial (two-part) species classification system that is still in place today. In this system, similar-looking organisms are grouped together and organized into broader, more inclusive categories. Interestingly, while Linnaeus noticed similarity among different organisms, he did not ascribe that relationship to anything other than God's design. This discipline of taxonomy that Linnaeus developed is a major topic of Chapter 19.

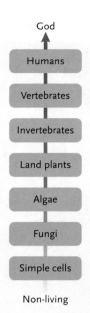

FIGURE 16.1 Scale of nature. This hierarchy was proposed by Aristotle, who believed that every organism had a defined position along a scale that moved from the simplest organisms to the most complex.

16.1b Lamarck Proposed That Acquired Traits Were Inherited

The idea that organisms can never change was challenged in the eighteenth century by the French naturalist Jean Baptiste de Lamarck (1744–1829), who put forward the first comprehensive theory of evolution: species change over time. In it he proposed a so-called "perfecting principle" whereby simple organisms evolved into more complex ones, moving up the Scale of Nature. Microscopic organisms were replaced at the bottom of the ladder by spontaneous generation—an idea, popular at the time, whereby simple forms of life arose from non-living material. Today, Lamarck is most well-known for, *the inheritance of acquired characteristics*. This is the idea that changes that an organism gains during its lifetime are passed on to its offspring. A contemporary example of Lamarckian inheritance would be that the children of the body builder Arnold Schwarzenegger **(Figure 16.2)** would be stronger and more muscular than the children of someone who didn't weight train. Today of course we know that Lamarck was wrong. Although muscles do grow larger through continued use, structural changes acquired during an organism's lifetime are not inherited by the next generation. Within a few years of Lamarck's death, ideas about how organisms could change over time would be forever changed by the research and theories of the young British naturalist Charles Darwin.

16.1c Darwin Proposed the Theory of Evolution by Natural Selection

In 1831, Charles Darwin, who was 22 at the time, was invited to take part in a five-year, around-the-world voyage aboard the naval surveying ship HMS *Beagle*. At the time, Darwin had just dropped out of medical school, determined instead to follow his passion in natural history. The primary purpose of the expedition was to

FIGURE 16.2 **Acquired characteristics are not inherited.** Arnold Schwarzenegger was an accomplished body builder; however, his acquired physique was not inherited by his children.

map the coast of South America (**Figure 16.3**). With no specific role on the ship, Darwin was free during the voyage to spend time ashore collecting specimens of plants, animals, and fossils. He also was a keen observer of the various habitats that plants and animals occupied, and took note of the surrounding geology.

Although Darwin was well educated and very well read, he certainly was not a learned university professor with years of experience in a particular field. Interestingly, many Darwin scholars think this lack of experience may have been to his advantage.

FIGURE 16.3 **Voyage of the HMS *Beagle*.** Its primary mission was to survey South America. Inset: Darwin in 1840

Galápagos Islands

Equator

Because he was young and did not have a prestigious university position to uphold, Darwin felt no pressure to conform to the ideas popular at the time. During the voyage he objectively took notes about what he saw, collecting a vast assortment of specimens as he went and having them shipped back to England. His observations and notes, together with his extensive readings, provided valuable information that shaped his thinking about evolution. Darwin's major insights came from three major areas of study: (1) geology and the fossil record, (2) the geographic distribution of species, and (3) the comparative morphology of species.

EARTH'S GEOLOGY AND THE FOSSIL RECORD During his time on the Beagle, Darwin read Charles Lyell's Principles of Geology, which was published in 1795 and would prove to be a foundational textbook of the science. Lyell championed the idea of the Scottish geologist James Hutton who maintained that the surface of Earth was constantly changing by natural events such as earthquakes, volcanoes, and the erosive action of wind and water operating over very long periods of time. This view went against the dominant idea of the day: the major features of Earth were the result of ancient and supernatural events (e.g., Noah's flood) orchestrated by the hand of God.

In a remarkable coincidence, a changing Earth is something Darwin experienced first-hand when he witnessed one of the most powerful earthquakes in history, the 1835 Concepción earthquake in Chile. Not only did he actually feel the ground shake, he saw the aftermath, including the destruction caused by the earthquake, tsunami waves, and landforms that were uplifted by as much as 10 m.

During his time in Chile, Darwin took the opportunity to climb the Andes Mountains. At a height of about 4000 m, he discovered the fossil shells of marine organisms. Along with experiencing the Concepción earthquake, these fossil findings convinced Darwin that Lyell was right: the geology of Earth is not static, but does change over time. This realization was profound because it set Darwin to thinking that perhaps, like geology, life may also change slowly over time.

Darwin was aware that scientists had begun to uncover fossil animals and plants that, to the surprise of many people, were unlike living species. That the fossil record indicated that some species had become extinct was yet one more piece of evidence that was hard to reconcile with the belief that each organism was specially created by God and that the number of species on Earth is fixed. Darwin collected a huge assortment of fossils during his travels, and while many were unlike any living creature he came across, others did clearly resemble living species. For example, despite an enormous size difference, he observed that living armadillos and fossilized glyptodonts had very similar body armour (**Figure 16.4**). If both species had been created at the same time, and both were found in South America, why didn't glyptodonts still live alongside armadillos? Darwin later wondered whether armadillos might be living descendants of the now-extinct glyptodonts.

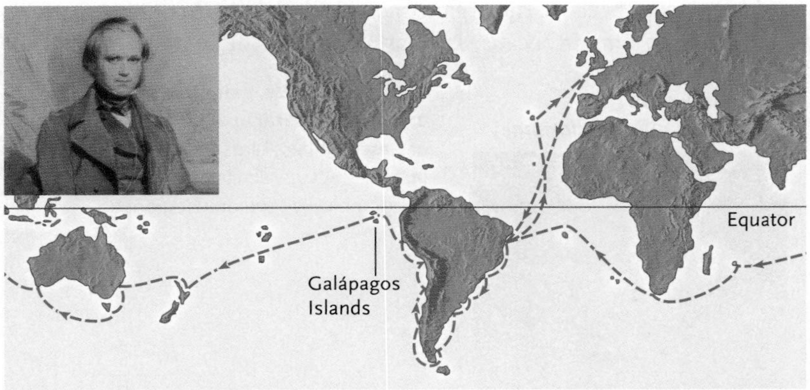

CHAPTER 16 EVOLUTION: THE DEVELOPMENT OF THE THEORY

FIGURE 16.4 **Ancestors and descendants.** Darwin hypothesized that, even though an extinct glyptodont (top) probably weighed 300–400 times as much as a living nine-banded armadillo (*Dasypus novemcinctus*), their obvious resemblance suggests that they are related.

Darwin realized that the geology of Earth changes slowly over time, and that fossils provided evidence that life did as well.

GEOGRAPHIC DISTRIBUTION OF SPECIES As long as naturalists encountered organisms only from Europe and surrounding lands, Aristotle's Scale of Nature was easily followed. But global explorations starting in the fifteenth century provided naturalists with thousands of previously unknown plants and animals. Although some were similar to European species, others were new and very strange.

Studies of the worldwide distribution of plants and animals, now called **biogeography**, raised puzzling questions to many, including Darwin. Was there no limit to the number of species created by God? Where did all these species fit in the Scale of Nature? Why did some species have limited geographical distributions, whereas others were widespread? Why were some species found in Africa or Asia so different from those found in Europe, while others had a similar appearance (**Figure 16.5**)?

One particularly astute observation that Darwin made about oceanic islands is that none that he studied had

terrestrial mammals on them. Later work that he completed after the voyage would confirm that this was a general rule. In contrast, flying mammals (e.g., bats) were found on islands. As well, he noticed that species that were on oceanic islands were clearly most similar to species inhabiting the nearest continent.

Nine hundred kilometres west of South America, on the Galápagos Islands, Darwin found "strange and wonderful creatures," including giant tortoises, lizards, and many species of birds. Darwin noticed that the animals and plants on different islands varied slightly in form. Moreover, many species resembled those on the distant South American mainland. Why did so many different species occupy one small island cluster? Why did these species resemble others from the nearest continent? Darwin hypothesized that the plants and animals of the Galápagos were related to plants and animals on South America but had changed over time.

COMPARATIVE MORPHOLOGY At least from the time of Aristotle, anatomists have noted some remarkable similarities among very diverse creatures. For example, the human arm, the flippers of seals, and the wings of bats differ markedly in size, shape, and function (**Figure 16.6**), yet they share very similar underlying structure. If these limbs were specially created for different means of locomotion, naturalists wondered, why didn't God use entirely different materials and structures for walking, swimming, and flying? Natural theologians countered this argument by stating that the body plans were perfect, and there was no need to invent something new for every species. But an eighteenth century French scientist, George-Louis Leclerc (le Comte de Buffon), was still puzzled by the existence of body parts with no apparent function. For example, he noted that the feet of pigs and some other mammals have two toes that never touch the ground. If each species was anatomically perfect for its particular way of life, Buffon asked, why did useless structures exist? Buffon proposed that some animals must have *changed* since their creation. He suggested that **vestigial structures**, these useless parts he observed, must have functioned in ancestral organisms, although he offered no explanation of how functional structures became vestigial.

To Darwin, the striking similarity seen in the features among different organisms had a far simpler explanation. It was because the organisms are related. A group of organisms look similar because they are decedents of an ancestor they all

**African ostrich
(*Struthio camelus*)**

**South American rhea
(*Rhea americana*)**

**Australian emu
(*Dromaius novaehollandiae*)**

FIGURE 16.5 **Very similar-looking organisms live far apart.** These three species of large flightless birds appear very similar. In fact, they occupy similar habitats in geographically separated regions.

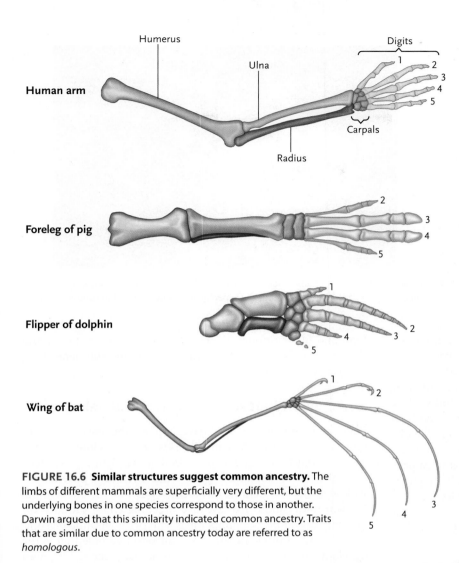

FIGURE 16.6 **Similar structures suggest common ancestry.** The limbs of different mammals are superficially very different, but the underlying bones in one species correspond to those in another. Darwin argued that this similarity indicated common ancestry. Traits that are similar due to common ancestry today are referred to as *homologous*.

shared—a *common ancestor*—and that ancestor possessed those features. The similarity present in a group of organisms because of shared ancestry is called **homology**. We will see in Chapter 19 that one can examine homology at various levels, including through comparing DNA and protein sequences among organisms. To Darwin, the morphological similarity seen among species suggested common ancestry.

STUDY BREAK QUESTIONS

1. How did Aristotle and Lamarck view evolution?
2. How did Darwin's travels to Chile influence his thinking about evolution?
3. Give an example of a homologous trait (that's not in this chapter!).

16.2 Natural Selection

The *Beagle* returned to England in 1836, and Darwin set out reviewing his notes and the vast assortment of specimens he had collected. As well, he presented numerous public lectures and discussed his findings with scholars in various fields. His observations

concerning the fossil record, biogeography, and structural homology indicated to him that all organisms are related by a common ancestor but had changed or evolved over time. Darwin was not the first to propose that organisms changed over time, what set him apart from his predecessors is that he arrived at how evolution occurs, its mechanism. Yet, it would be a remarkable 23 years after returning to England that his theory concerning the mechanism of evolution would become widely known. In 1859, *On the Origin of Species by Means of Natural Selection* was finally published. The first edition sold out in a single day.

16.2a Darwin Was Not Alone in Thinking about Natural Selection

Darwin was not the only one thinking about how species may change over time. The naturalist Alfred Russel Wallace (**Figure 16.7**) had arrived at very similar conclusions to Darwin through eight years of extensive research on the islands of present day Singapore, Malaysia, and Indonesia. Like Darwin, Wallace was a keen observer of nature who kept careful notes and drawings of his observations while collecting a huge number of specimens. Wallace conveyed his ideas on evolution to Darwin in a letter in 1858. Fearing that Wallace may publish his ideas first, Darwin quickly put together *The Origin*, which was published the following year.

FIGURE 16.7 **Alfred Russel Wallace (1823–1913).** Independently of Darwin, Wallace developed a theory of evolution based on natural selection.

CHAPTER 16 EVOLUTION: THE DEVELOPMENT OF THE THEORY |

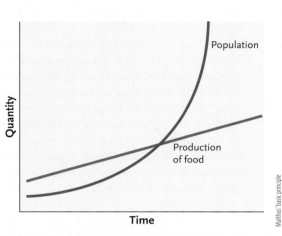

a.

b.

FIGURE 16.8 **Populations have a huge potential to increase over time. (a)** The rate of human population growth increases exponentially, which often exceeds the ability to increase food production. **(b)** In nature, the number of offspring produced far exceeds the capacity of the environment to support all of them. Both situations set up a "struggle for existence."

Many historians suggest that Wallace was, in fact, not upset that Darwin was the first to publish the theory of evolution by natural selection. In fact, Wallace frequently admitted that Darwin's ideas were more thoroughly developed and supported by more examples than his own. Over the years, Darwin and Wallace developed strong respect and admiration for each other and both were bestowed with prestigious honours for their roles in the discovery of natural selection. The fact that, today, Wallace is scarcely remembered is perhaps best explained by the fact that most people connect natural selection, and thus evolution, with the publication of a single book, the one written by Charles Darwin.

16.2b The Writings of Thomas Malthus Influenced Darwin and Wallace

The ideas of both Darwin and Wallace about the mechanism by which species could change over time were profoundly influenced by Thomas Malthus, a late eighteenth century political economist. Both men had read *An Essay on the Principle of Population* (1798) in which Malthus laid out how humanity was destined for disaster. This dire prediction was based on Malthus's own calculations: the human population increases exponentially over time while, at best, gains in agricultural technology lead to only modest (arithmetic) increases in the food supply **(Figure 16.8a)**. Malthus was addressing the decline in living conditions in nineteenth century England and suggested that, unless the government somehow controls the birth rate, increased poverty and starvation were inevitable.

Reading Malthus helped clarify in Darwin's mind how the imbalance between population growth and available food could be applied to plants and animals in nature. For example, Darwin and others had observed that the potential of most species to reproduce is far greater than the actual number of offspring that reach adulthood (Figure 16.8b). That no species seems able to reproduce to their full potential indicates that offspring are under a constant "struggle for existence," according to Darwin. Organisms are in competition with one another for limited

food and other resources. They have to escape predation and they have to survive often unfavourable environments (e.g., temperature extremes, drought).

16.2c So What Actually Is Natural Selection?

Plant and animal breeders have applied the basic facets of inheritance from parents to offspring for thousands of years. By selectively breeding only those individuals with desired characteristics, they enhanced those traits in future generations. Although the mechanism of heredity was not yet understood, Darwin understood that selective breeding could produce for example, bigger beets, plumper pigs, and prize-winning pigeons.

A good example of the power of selective breeding is the development of corn (*maize*). Corn is actually derived from an ancient Mexican grain called *teosinte*. Over thousands of years, farmers selected the teosinte kernels for replanting that were the largest, easiest to eat and most exposed on the cob. The result of this selective breeding is that, today, a typical cob of corn looks nothing like teosinte **(Figure 16.9)**.

FIGURE 16.9 **Which would you prefer to eat?** Through selective breeding, or what Darwin called "artificial selection," farmers in what is now Mexico developed corn (right) from teosinte (left) over thousands of years.

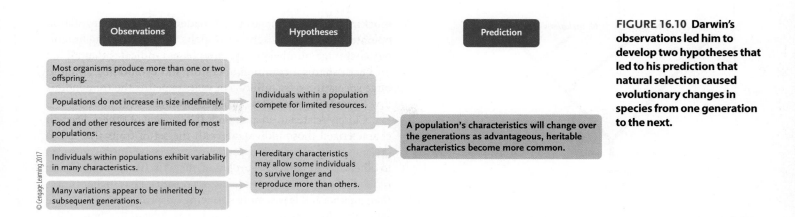

FIGURE 16.10 Darwin's observations led him to develop two hypotheses that led to his prediction that natural selection caused evolutionary changes in species from one generation to the next.

Darwin referred to selective breeding as **artificial selection**, since humans were selecting the characteristics they wanted in the offspring by choosing parents with those traits. Darwin didn't see why a similar process of selection couldn't also work in nature, but the issue was the mechanism: how would it work?

Darwin started to understand that a major aspect of evolutionary change must reside within a **population**—a group of individuals of a species that live together in a specific place. By understanding this, Darwin could see how Lamarck was wrong. Individual organisms don't evolve over their lifetime. But a population could. It is the population that has the capacity to change from one generation to the next.

Darwin thought about two specific attributes of a population: its size and the amount of variation within it. First, Darwin observed that, while organisms have a huge capacity to reproduce, limiting resources constrain the size of a population. From this, Darwin hypothesized that individuals within the population compete for limited resources **(Figure 16.10)**. Second, Darwin observed that individuals within a population are not identical but differ in certain traits (e.g., size, colour, behaviour), and that these traits tend to be inherited. This in turn led to Darwin hypothesizing that organisms with traits that allow them to outcompete others for limiting resources would leave more offspring. For Darwin, this thinking came together into a single idea, **natural selection**: individuals with certain inherited traits are better able to survive and reproduce than individuals without those traits (Figure 16.10). Individuals in the population that lacked such traits would die leaving fewer, if any, offspring. Thus, advantageous traits would become more common in the next generation.

In other words, from generation to generation, the mechanism that is causing a population to change, or evolve, is *nature selecting* for a set of traits that gives an individual an advantage over others in the particular environment that the population inhabits **(Figure 16.11)**. What is remarkable about natural selection is that Darwin had discovered a mechanism for evolutionary change that no one had ever envisioned, much less documented.

16.2d Natural Selection Leads to Adaptation and Increased Fitness

Darwin's insights came from many places, but none seem more significant than his work on the Galápagos Islands. Both Darwin and Wallace were spurred in their thinking through observations on island groups because evolutionary change can often be more easily noticed on islands. Each island in a group is isolated from the others, and conditions on each island can be quite distinct, which leads to differences in the species that inhabit each island. The most famous example of this is what are referred to today as *Darwin's mockingbirds*.

The Galápagos Islands are home to four distinct species of mockingbird (genus *Nesomimus*), which are found on specific islands of the group **(Figure 16.12)**. During his visit to the Galápagos, Darwin collected mockingbirds from different islands, but it wasn't until he got back to England that someone pointed out that the birds from different islands were distinct species. Based on this work, Darwin developed the concept of *descent with modification*. It was clear to Darwin that the underlying similarity of the mockingbirds indicated that birds from all the islands shared a common ancestor (Figure 16.12a) but that, over time, each species had developed distinctly different traits (beak size and shape, coloration). The simplest scenario to explain this is that a popluation of one species of mockingbird came from mainland South America and colonized most of the

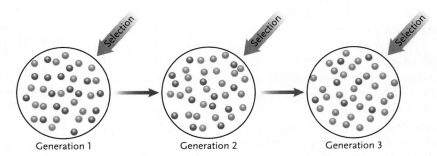

FIGURE 16.11 **Populations change over time.** In this simplistic example, a single population consists of individuals with three different sets of traits (blue, green, orange). Selection pressures (limiting food, resources, predators) favour the growth and reproduction of individuals with a specific set of traits (orange) over the other two. From one generation to the next, the proportion of "orange" individuals in the population increases.

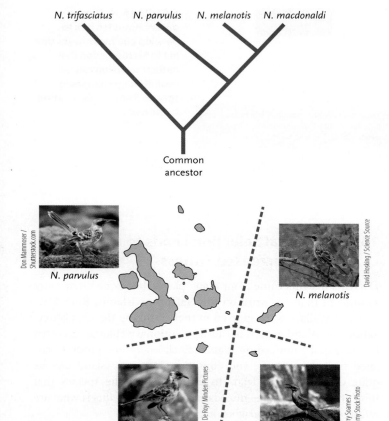

N. trifasciatus   N. parvulus   N. melanotis   N. macdonaldi

Common
ancestor

N. parvulus

N. melanotis

N. trifasciatus

N. macdonaldi

FIGURE 16.12 **The Galápagos mockingbirds are explained by "descent with modification." (a)** The four major mockingbird species (genus *Nesomimus*) are descended from a common ancestor that came from mainland South America thousands of years ago. **(b)** Each of the four species is adapted to the particular environment found on specific islands of the group.

islands at around the same time. Over thousands of years, the populations that developed on different island became less and less alike—their traits diverged. On each island, specific traits would become uniquely modified compared to the traits of birds inhabiting other islands. And all the species become distinct compared to the ancestral mockingbird species from the South American mainland. Darwin's work on mockingbirds would be complemented by even more detailed study of the many species of finches that inhabit the Galápagos Islands.

The evolution of different species of birds on the Galápagos Islands is tied closely to the fact that the islands within the group have different habitats (food sources, microclimate) (Figure 16.12b), which resulted in natural selection favouring a different set of traits on one island compared to another. The inherited aspects of an individual that make it better suited to a particular environment than other individuals are referred to as **adaptation**. From generation to generation, a species becomes better adapted to a specific environment as a consequence of natural selection.

The impact of Darwin's observations on the Galápagos Islands was that he extended his ideas about speciation in

mockingbirds and finches to a broader sense of how evolution operates in all species across the globe. The underlying homology that huge numbers of species possess indicates that all life on Earth shares a common ancestor; and evolution leading to huge speciation over millions of years explains the tremendous diversity of life we witness on Earth today.

Closely related to adaptation is the concept of fitness. Darwin characterized those individuals with the set of traits that led to greater survivorship and reproductive success as "fitter" compared to others. In the context of evolution, the term **fitness** describes an individual's reproductive success—an organism has higher fitness than another if it leaves more surviving offspring. There are three aspects of fitness that are important to understanding how evolution works: (1) *Fitness is a relative concept*. It doesn't matter in absolute terms how many offspring an individual leaves, only that it leaves more than others in the population. (2) *A trait is only valuable if it increases fitness*. We tend to think of traits such as being faster, stronger, bigger as valuable; however, they are only valuable, and thus selected for, if they increase reproductive success. (3) *The traits that increase fitness may change*. If the environment changes (e.g., climate change), those traits that previously increased fitness may not be advantageous any longer.

STUDY BREAK QUESTIONS

1. How did the work of Thomas Malthus influence Darwin's thinking?
2. Explain how corn was developed from teosinte using artificial selection.
3. Define *natural selection*.

16.3   Evolutionary Biology since Darwin

Both Darwin and Wallace laid down the fundamental basis for natural selection and yet, what might surprise you is that neither of them had an understanding of genetics. When *The Origins of Species* came out, Gregor Mendel had just published his work on inheritance in pea plants, and it wasn't until 50 years later, in the early twentieth century, that Thomas Hunt Morgan discerned that genes are carried on chromosomes. His experiments, which are described in Chapter 10, enabled geneticists to forge an important connection between Darwinian evolution and Mendelian genetics that today is referred to as the *modern synthesis* of evolution. At its core, this unification recognized the critical importance that genetic variation within a population plays in evolutionary change.

16.3a   The Source of Variation in a Population Is Random Mutation

Many of the traits possessed by an organism are inherited because they have a genetic basis: they are coded by DNA. It is the variation in DNA sequence that ultimately gives rise to individuals within a population having different inherited traits. While some traits (e.g., wrinkled versus smooth peas) result from variation in the sequence of a single gene, others (e.g., the shape of a finch's beak) are influenced by the variation in sequence of many genes.

Although all organisms within a population have the same set of genes, the DNA sequence of any particular gene in any particular organism may be different due to past **mutation**—a random and heritable change in the DNA sequence. Mutations arise as an inevitable consequence of the imperfect nature of DNA replication as well as from the effects of certain physical, chemical, and biological agents.

First generation

Several generations later

FIGURE 16.13 **A change in selection causes moth evolution.**

You can think of mutation as supplying the raw material for natural selection to work with—the differences in traits among organisms. It is critical to understand, however, that while mutations are the source of variation, they do not determine the path of evolution. Because mutations are undirected, they can occur anywhere in the genome: in essential genes required for life, or in a DNA sequence that has no function. Thus, some mutations are beneficial to an organism because they increase fitness. Other mutations may be harmful and lower fitness, while many others are "neutral," having no effect on fitness. We will discuss the role of mutation in evolution in considerable detail in the next chapter.

16.3b Examples of Natural Selection

Natural selection is referred to as a *theory* of evolution because its basic tenet, *that heritable variation leads to differential survival and reproduction*, has been repeatedly tested and supported using the methodologies of both experimental and observational science (see *The Purple Pages* for a discussion of the scientific method).

Here we present just a few of the hundreds of studies related to natural selection that have been conducted. When reading through each of them, try to identify the key factors driving evolutionary change: What is the genotypic make-up of the starting population? What was the impact of selection on the starting populations? Did the selection change over time and what caused it to change?

MOTH POPULATIONS EVOLVE IN POLLUTED CITIES The peppered moth (*Biston betularia*) shows considerable variation in colour due to differences in genes related to pigmentation: some individuals are lightly coloured (*typica*) and others are very dark, almost black in colour (*carbonaria*). The *carbonaria* variety is darker because of increased production of the pigment

melanin. Interestingly, before the mid-1800s, the lightly coloured *typica* moths were very common, with the sighting of a *carbonaria* individual being rare. However, this scenario rapidly changed with the industrial revolution and increased pollution in the north of England related to the use of coal.

The increased burning of coal resulted in soot being deposited on the bark of usually light coloured trees, turning them dark. As the moths rested on the darkly coloured bark, the lightly coloured *typica* moths became much easier for predatory birds to see compared to the darker *carbonaria* moths. The difference in predation resulted in a huge shift in population structure. In Liverpool, a heavily polluted city at the time, from about 1850 to 1900, the proportion of *carbonaria* moths increased from representing 1% of the population to as high as 95% of the population (**Figure 16.13**).

The change in composition of *Biston* populations is a powerful example of how a change in the environment causes a change in natural selection. The darkened trees and increased predation of the light moths shifted selection to favouring the *carbonaria* variety. After the introduction of stricter pollution policies in the twentieth century, the proportions have since rebounded, with the *typica* variety dominating again.

A recent study has uncovered the genetic basis of the colouring in *Biston* moths. Using DNA sequencing to compare the genomes of the two varieties, researchers have discovered that the pigmentation seen in the *carbonaria* variety is triggered by a transposable element—a piece of DNA that can move from one position to another in the genome (see Chapter 15). In *carbonaria* individuals, the transposable element is inserted into the first intron of a gene called *cortex*, which unexpectedly results in increased expression of the gene. It is not yet fully understood how increased *cortex* expression results in increased melanin production. Additionally, in a remarkable piece of detective work, using sophisticated molecular tools and simulations, the same researchers were also able to estimate that the

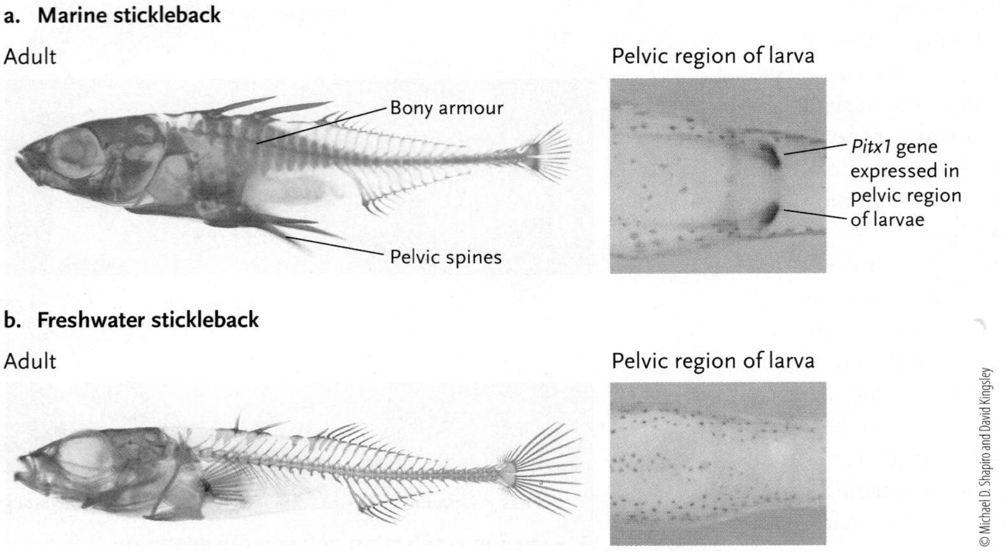

a. Marine stickleback

Adult

Pelvic region of larva

- Bony armour
- Pelvic spines
- *Pitx1* gene expressed in pelvic region of larvae

b. Freshwater stickleback

Adult

Pelvic region of larva

© Michael D. Shapiro and David Kingsley

FIGURE 16.14 Sticklebacks with and without pelvic spines. (a) Marine populations of three-spined sticklebacks (*Gasterosteus aculeatus*) have prominent bony plates along their sides and large spines on their dorsal and pelvic fins. The growth of pelvic spines is induced by the expression of the *Pitx1* gene (the purple crescents in the photo on the right) in the pelvic region during embryonic development. **(b)** Many freshwater populations of the same species lack the bony plates and spines. Pelvic spines do not develop in the freshwater sticklebacks because the *Pitx1* gene is not expressed in the pelvic region. Natural selection has apparently fostered these morphological differences in response to the dominant predators in each environment. The skeletons of these specimens, each about 8 cm long, were dyed bright red.

actual mutational event (insertion of the transposable element into *cortex*) producing the *carbonaria* variety probably occurred between 1810 and 1820. This is consistent with the earliest recorded sighting of the *carbonaria* variety being documented in 1848.

A FISH LOSING ITS ARMOUR INCREASES ITS FITNESS The three-spined stickleback (*Gasterosteus aculeatus*) is a species of small fish found along the coasts of North America, Europe, and Asia. Ancestors of modern sticklebacks lived in the ocean, moving to freshwater streams and lakes only to reproduce. Since the last ice age (11 000 years ago), when retreating glaciers cut off connections between oceans and lakes, two distinct populations of sticklebacks have arisen: sticklebacks that live exclusively in the ocean and those found only in freshwater habitats (lakes and streams).

To defend against a range of saltwater predatory fish, ancestral and present-day oceanic sticklebacks have bony armour along their sides and display prominent spines. In comparison, lake-dwelling sticklebacks have greatly reduced armour and, in many populations, lack spines on their pelvic fins (**Figure 16.14**).

Recent research indicates that, over the thousands of years since the two populations became isolated, the loss of the spines and bony plates from freshwater inhabitants reflects adaptation to the new environment. Not only are there far fewer predator fish in freshwater habitats, but the presence of large spines has been shown to be disadvantageous as they are used by dragonfly larvae to attack juvenile sticklebacks. A way to think about these changes in stickleback armour is that the "force" that is driving selection, the *selection pressure*, changed. In a freshwater habitat, having less armour and smaller spines actually increases fitness. Not only is predation by dragonfly larvae reduced, but the fish no longer have the added metabolic costs associated with building armour and spines. As a result, fish with diminished armour have been shown to grow larger as juveniles, begin breeding sooner, and have higher overwinter survivorship than heavily armoured individuals.

Research has shown that differences in the amount of armour possessed by sticklebacks are an inherited trait. The presence or absence of spines on the pelvic fins of these fishes is governed by the expression of the gene *Pitx1*. In long-spined marine sticklebacks, *Pitx1* is expressed in the embryonic buds from which pelvic fins develop, promoting the development of spines. But *Pitx1* is not expressed in the fin buds of freshwater sticklebacks; hence, pelvic spines do not develop. This loss of *Pitx1* expression has been shown to be due to a mutation to a nearby gene that regulates *Pitx1*.

16.3C EXPERIMENTAL EVOLUTION SUPPORTS NATURAL SELECTION

One of the difficulties with evolutionary biology is that what you are studying (evolution) can occur very slowly. A major factor that determines the actual rate of change within a population is **generation time**, which is the average difference in age between a parent and its offspring (**Figure 16.15**). It is difficult to directly study evolution in humans, for example, because most women don't have children until they are in their 20s. Compare that to the generation time of the fruit fly *Drosophila* (about one week) or a bacterium (less than one hour).

Given that the fundamental processes driving evolutionary change are similar in all organisms, some scientists are using

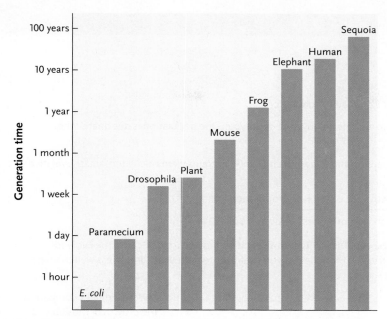

FIGURE 16.15 Generation time of various organisms. The age when an organism produces the next generation varies tremendously among different groups. Organisms with short generation times evolve more rapidly than those with longer generation times.

organisms with short generation times to study evolution as it occurs in real time, an approach that is impossible in most animals and plants. In these studies of *experimental evolution*, one can allow populations to evolve under controlled laboratory conditions and include both adequate controls and replicates, hallmarks of good experimental design (see *The Purple Pages*). The power of this approach is that an evolution experiment can be completed in a matter of months, allowing researchers to directly compare an evolved population with the ancestral population from which is was derived. Even Darwin understood the power of such an approach when he remarked in 1859, "we ought to look exclusively to its lineal ancestors; but this is scarcely ever possible." Using organisms that reproduce rapidly, comparing a population directly with its ancestor is straightforward.

An excellent example that illustrates the power of experimental evolution is a set of experiments that were carried out to look at the ability of the bacterium *Escherichia coli* (*E. coli*) to adapt to different growth temperatures (**Figure 16.16**). The typical laboratory strain of *E. coli* grows fastest at 37°C. This is referred to as its *optimal growth temperature*. But if you grow *E. coli* at a lower temperature, say 32°C for many generations, will the population adapt to that temperature - will 32°C become its optimum growth temperature?

This experiment was performed by taking a single liquid culture of *E.coli* and dividing it into two: one was designated the Ancestral population and the second the Evolved population. The Ancestral population was left to grow under normal laboratory conditions of 37°C, while researchers exposed the Evolved population to a growth temperature of 32°C for 2000 generations.

If the Evolved population had become adapted by being grown at 32°C, it should have a greater fitness than the

Ancestral strain at 32°C. But how do you measure reproductive success (fitness) in bacteria? Bacteria reproduce asexually through binary fission: they divide in two. Given this, a population would have higher fitness if it has a higher growth rate. By combining the Ancestral and Evolved populations into a single flask and exposing the flask to a specific temperature for 24 h, you can measure the growth rate of each. How many more cells of one population are there than the other? As shown in Figure 16.16, from the growth rates you can then measure fitness.

STUDY BREAK QUESTIONS

1. How do mutations arise in a population?
2. In the example of the peppered moth, what is the agent of selection?
3. Why can bacteria adapt to a changing environment faster than humans can?

16.4 Evolution Is the Core Theory of Modern Biology but Is Plagued by Misconceptions

That the theory of evolution by natural selection is so well supported experimentally makes it hard to appreciate the insight and intuition required in the 1800s to formulate a theory that has survived essentially unchanged for 150 years. One of Darwin's contemporaries, the biologist Thomas Huxley, summed up the reaction of many when he quipped that the theory was so obvious, once articulated, that he was surprised he had not thought of it himself.

Disciplines including genetics, molecular biology, developmental biology, systematics, and paleontology have all been profoundly influenced by the findings of evolutionary biology and, in a reciprocal way, these disciplines have provided powerful support for evolutionary biology. As we have seen in this chapter and as will be reinforced in the next four chapters, evolutionary processes explain the natural world without invoking essential life forces, the great chain of being, or a divine guiding hand.

CONCEPT FIX Even though evolution is foundational to the understanding of biology, there is no subject in biology that is more poorly understood by the average person, and plagued by misconception by the average student, as evolution. **Figure 16.17** addresses a number of the most common misconceptions about evolution and natural selection. ⬡

STUDY BREAK QUESTIONS

1. What does it mean when we say mutations are *random*?
2. What role does phenotype play in natural selection?
3. Explain why natural selection will never lead to perfection.

FIGURE 16.16 **Experimental Research**

Adaptation of *E. coli* to a Change in Temperature

Question: Would growing a culture of bacteria for 2000 generations at 32°C lead to adaptation?

Experiment: Two populations of the bacterium *E. coli* were started from a single colony (one genotype). One population is designated the Ancestral strain, the other the Evolved strain.

To determine if the Evolved cells actually adapted to 32°C, the growth rates of the Ancestral and Evolved strains were calculated, and the relative fitness (w) determined as

$$\text{Relative fitness (w)} = \frac{\text{Growth rate of Evolved population}}{\text{Growth rate of Ancestral population}}$$

If w = 1, then no adaptation has occurred, as their growth rates would be equal. If w > 1, then adaptation has occurred because the Evolved population grows faster at that temperature than the Ancestral strain. If w < 1, then the Evolved strain, for some reason, grows less well than the Ancestral strain.

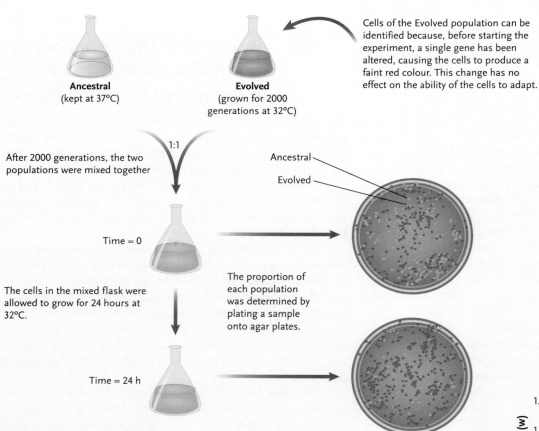

Ancestral
(kept at 37°C)

Evolved
(grown for 2000 generations at 32°C)

Cells of the Evolved population can be identified because, before starting the experiment, a single gene has been altered, causing the cells to produce a faint red colour. This change has no effect on the ability of the cells to adapt.

After 2000 generations, the two populations were mixed together

1:1

Ancestral

Evolved

Time = 0

The cells in the mixed flask were allowed to grow for 24 hours at 32°C.

The proportion of each population was determined by plating a sample onto agar plates.

Time = 24 h

This experiment comparing the growth of the Evolved population (32°C for 2000 generations) with the Ancestral population (maintained at 37°C) was conducted at a range of temperatures, from 20°C to 42°C, with the relative fitness calculated at each temperature.

Results: The data presented below show the Evolved strain did grow better than the Ancestral strain when growth was measured at temperatures between 20°C and 35°C. This results in a relative fitness (w) of greater than 1. However, at temperatures closer to 40°C, the Ancestral strain, which is adapted to 37°C, grew better than the Evolved strain, resulting in the relative fitness (w) being less than 1.

Conclusion: The results indicate that adaptation of the Evolved strain occurred. The data indicate that the relative fitness was greater than 1 at lower growth temperatures, compared to the Ancestral strain. This is what you would predict if evolution had occurred.

Source: Based on data from Albert F. Bennett and Richard E. Lenski, "Evolutionary Adaptation to Temperature II. Thermal Niches of Experimental Lines of Escherichia coli," *Evolution*, Vol. 47, No. 1 (Feb., 1993), pp. 1-12

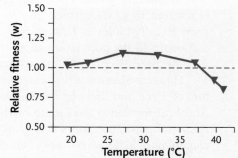

FIGURE 16.17 **Common misconceptions about evolution**

Evolution and natural selection are the same thing.

Natural selection is a major mechanism that causes change (evolution) in a population and one that results in adaptation. But natural selection is not the only process that causes evolution. We will discuss the other mechanisms in Chapter 18.

Evolution occurs slowly.

The rate of evolution is controlled by a number of factors, one of which is generation time. Bacteria and viruses can evolve very quickly.

Selection acts on individuals; therefore, individuals evolve.

Selection does act on individuals that have particular beneficial traits. But the individual cannot change. What changes over time is the makeup of the population.

Natural selection is not directed.

Because natural selection can result in some remarkable adaptations, it is tempting to think of it as a force or guiding hand that will lead to perfection. Natural selection is mindless and mechanistic. It just selects among whatever variations exist within the population.

Because it is driven by mutation, evolution by natural selection is a random process.

It is true that mutations occur randomly in a genome, and thus changes to traits are random. But natural selection is not random. It selects individuals in a population with certain traits. This results in adaption and increased fitness over time.

Favourable traits arise in response to a change in the environment.

Traits that increase the fitness of particular individuals in response to a change in the environment already exist within the population. These came about by random mutation at some time in the past. The change in the environment increases the proportion of individuals with specific traits because they are advantageous.

Selection acts on the genotype because that is what is inherited.

Selection that takes place in the environment is based on the specific phenotype of an organism—its traits, not the underlying genotype.

Humans have stopped evolving.

It is true that because modern humans can modify their environments, we do not face the same threats to reproduction and survival as our ancestors. Humans still evolve; just differently. Recent evolution of human traits that protect against malaria and the development of lactose tolerance are two examples of recent human evolution.

Summary Illustration

First proposed by Charles Darwin, natural selection is a mechanism for how species change over time, or evolve. Within a population, there are individuals with certain inherited traits who are better able to survive and reproduce in a particular environment than those without the traits. These advantageous traits become more common in the next generation. From generation to generation, natural selection causes a population to change, or adapt, which can eventually result in the development of a different species.

A population of finches in South America all have small beaks and they feed on plants that produce small seeds.

The island has limited food resources, and is dominated by plants that produce larger seeds.

The birds with larger beaks are more likely to survive and reproduce because they happen to be better adapted to this new environment.

Birds of the next generation (shown here) will tend to have larger beaks.

- - - GTCATGAA - - -   - - - GTCACGAA - - -

A **random mutation** occurs to a gene involved in beak development. Offspring with this mutation have beaks that are larger than offspring that don't have the mutation.

The population migrates to one of the Galapagos Islands.

The offspring vary in beak size.

After many generations, the birds that migrated to the island in the Galapagos will not only have large beaks but also develop other traits that make them distinct from the original population in South America. They will become a distinctly different species.

SELF-TEST QUESTIONS

Recall/Understand

1. Which of the following did Aristotle propose?
   a. that acquired traits were inherited
   b. that humans are just one of the branches of the evolutionary tree, along with other organisms
   c. that humans are at the top of the evolutionary ladder just below perfection
   d. the existence of God, who created each organism

2. Natural selection acts on _____, with the consequences occurring in _____.
   a. populations; individuals
   b. individuals; the same individuals
   c. individuals; populations
   d. populations; the same populations

3. Which of these statements did Lamarck propose?
   a. There are perfect organisms.
   b. God created organisms.
   c. Species do not change over time.
   d. Acquired characteristics are inheritable.

4. The wings of bats, the forelegs of pigs, and the flippers of dolphins are examples of which of the following?
   a. vestigial structures
   b. homologous structures
   c. acquired characteristics
   d. artificial selection

5. Which of these statements did Darwin mean by "descent with modification"?
   a. that species modifications depend on their ancestors
   b. that species with modifications all have a common ancestor
   c. that species descended from a common ancestor are each adapted, and therefore modified to the particular environment they live in
   d. that species descended from different ancestors have modified characteristics

Apply/Analyze

6. Which of these people was the first strong proponent of natural theology?
   a. Jean Baptiste de Lamarck
   b. Charles Darwin
   c. Carolus Linnaeus
   d. Aristotle

7. Bioinformatics is a field of science that utilizes genetic sequence comparisons. Which of the following is most likely one of its most basic assumptions?
   a. perfection of organisms
   b. artificial selection
   c. Lamarckian hypothesis
   d. descent with modification

8. Which of these factors should you use if you want to hypothesize that an extinct glyptodont is related to a living nine-banded armadillo?
   a. They lived at different times.
   b. They lived at a same time.
   c. Their body size is the same.
   d. They obviously resemble each other.

9. Darwin's theory *excluded* one of the following Lamarckian ideas. Which one?
   a. Organisms change in response to their environments.
   b. Changes that an organism acquires during its lifetime are passed to its offspring.
   c. All species change with time.
   d. Changes are passed from one generation to the next.

Create/Evaluate

10. Many of the characteristics we see in living organisms are adaptations to environments in which their ancestors lived, rather than to the environments in which they live today. Which of these statements best explains the reasoning behind this statement?
    a. Natural selection cannot predict characteristics of future environments.
    b. The ancestors' environments were already perfect and their adaptations were adequate.
    c. Natural selection acts on organisms that live in environments that do not change much.
    d. The environmental conditions of the ancestors are the same as those of the descendants.

11. Compare evolution with natural selection.

12. Explain why evolution by natural selection is a non-random process.

13. Which three observations influenced Darwin to infer that individuals within a population compete for limited resources?

14. Which two observations influenced Darwin to infer that hereditary characteristics may allow some individuals to survive longer and reproduce more than others?

15. Consider the monarch butterfly, which feeds on toxic dandelions. Explain why this is an excellent example of protection conferred by ingested cardenolides.

Chapter Roadmap

Microevolution: Changes within Populations

In this chapter we look at evolution at the scale of the population. We examine the factors that cause a population to change its genetic make-up from one generation to the next; natural selection is just one of the factors.

17.1 Variation in Natural Populations

The phenotypic variation within a population can be influenced by genotype and the environment.

17.2 Population Genetics

How does one actually determine if genetic variation exists within a population and if it changes over time?

17.3 The Agents of Microevolution

From Chapter 9

Four processes can result in a change in allele frequencies from one generation to the next: gene flow, genetic drift, mutation, and natural selection.

17.4 Non-random Mating

One requirement of Hardy–Weinberg equilibrium is that mating with respect to genotype is random, but non-random mating is quite common.

17.5 Maintaining Genetic and Phenotypic Variation

There exist a number of mechanisms that maintain genetic and therefore phenotypic diversity within populations.

Dennis W. Donohue/Shutterstock.com

Humpback whale populations were seriously depleted in the mid-1900s.

Microevolution: Changes within Populations

17

Why it matters... Humpback whales (*Megaptera novaeangliae*) essentially have a global distribution consisting of a number of migrating populations, including the Southern Hemisphere and North Pacific populations. As a result of an international agreement made in 1966 that limited whaling, humpback numbers have rebounded to about 80 000 individuals today. One particularly interesting population of humpbacks that is comprised of about 100 individuals is found localized to the Arabian Sea. While most humpbacks are known to undertake long migrations moving from feeding grounds at northern latitudes to breeding grounds near the equator, the Arabian Sea humpback whales (ASHW) are peculiar in that they do not migrate.

To investigate the population structure of the ASHW compared to the Southern Hemisphere and North Pacific populations, researchers isolated DNA from 67 ASHW and compared it to a similar number of whales from the Southern Hemisphere and North Pacific Populations. Based on DNA sequence differences, researchers were able to conclude that the ASHW was most similar to the population in the Southern Hemisphere, yet different enough that they estimated that the two populations separated about 70 000 years ago. The timing of the divergence seems to coincide with glaciation events that took place at the time.

Using sophisticated molecular analyses based on the DNA sequence data, the researchers were also able to determine that the population of ASHW used to be much larger, but had shrunk due to periodic decreases in food supply and illegal Soviet whaling that was prevalent in the 1960s. These events that cause a sudden drop in population size are called *bottlenecks* and are of concern because, along with decreased numbers, there is also a decrease in the genetic diversity of the population. As we will discuss, small populations that are the result of bottlenecks with low genetic diversity are much more susceptible to disease and have limited ability to survive unfavourable environmental changes.

Because of their large numbers worldwide, humpbacks are classified as "Least Concern" by the International Union for Conservation of Nature (IUCN). But, based on the recent finds on the small population localized to the Arabian Sea, the authors recommend that the status of this particular population should be changed from "Endangered" to "Critically Endangered."

The distinct nature of the ASHW is a result of **microevolution**—change in the genetic makeup of a population from one generation to the next. In this chapter, we will discuss the processes that can drive microevolutionary change. We first examine the extensive variation that exists within natural populations. We then take a detailed look at the most important processes that alter genetic variation within populations, causing microevolutionary change. Finally, we consider how microevolution can fine-tune the functioning of populations within their environments.

17.1 Variation in Natural Populations

In most species, the members of a population look pretty much alike. However, even those that look alike, such as the *Cerion* snails in **Figure 17.1**, are not identical. With a scale and ruler, you could detect differences in their weight, as well as in the length and diameter of their shells. With suitable techniques, you could also document variations in their individual biochemistry, physiology, internal anatomy, and behaviour. All these features are examples of **phenotypic variation**—differences in appearance or function.

17.1a Evolutionary Biologists Describe and Quantify Phenotypic Variation

Both Darwin and Wallace recognized the importance of heritable phenotypic variation within a population as a driver of natural selection. Some forms of a trait lead to greater reproductive success than other forms. Today, microevolutionary studies often begin by assessing the extent of phenotypic variation within populations. Most characters exhibit **quantitative variation**—individuals differ in small, incremental ways. For example, if you weighed everyone in your biology class, you would see that weight varies almost continuously from your lightest to your heaviest classmate. Humans also exhibit quantitative variation in the length of their toes, the number of hairs on their heads, and their height.

We usually display data on quantitative variation in a bar graph or, if the sample is large enough, as a curve (**Figure 17.2**).

a. European garden snails (*Cepaea nemoralis*)

b. Bahaman land snails (*Cerion christophei*)

FIGURE 17.1 Phenotypic variation. (a) Shells of European garden snails from a population in Scotland vary considerably in appearance. **(b)** By contrast, shells of land snails from a population in the Bahamas look very similar.

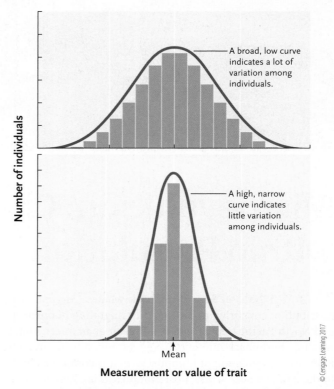

FIGURE 17.2 Quantitative variation. Many traits vary continuously among members of a population, and a bar graph of the data often approximates a bell-shaped curve. The mean defines the average value of the trait in the population, and the width of the curve is proportional to the variability among individuals.

The width of the curve is proportional to the amount of variation among individuals, and the *mean* describes the average value of the character. As you will see shortly, natural selection often changes the mean value of a character or its variability within populations.

Other characters, such as those Mendel studied (see Chapter 9), exhibit **qualitative variation**—they exist in two or more discrete states, and intermediate forms are absent. Snow geese, for example, have *either* blue *or* white feathers (**Figure 17.3**). The existence of discrete variants of a character is called a

FIGURE 17.3 **Qualitative variation.** Individual snow geese (*Chen caerulescens*) are either blue or white. Although both colours are present in many populations, geese tend to associate with others of the same colour.

FIGURE 17.4 **Environmental effects on phenotype.** Soil acidity affects the expression of the gene controlling flower colour in the common garden plant *Hydrangea macrophylla*. When grown in acidic soil, it produces deep blue flowers. In neutral or alkaline soil, its flowers are bright pink.

polymorphism (*poly* = many; *morphos* = form); we describe such traits as *polymorphic*. The *Cepaea nemoralis* snail shells in Figure 17.1a are polymorphic in background colour, number of stripes, and colour of stripes. Biochemical polymorphisms, such as the human A, B, AB, and O blood types, are also common.

We describe phenotypic polymorphisms quantitatively by calculating the *frequency* of each trait. For example, if you counted 123 blue snow geese and 369 white ones in a population of 492 geese, the frequency of the blue phenotype would be 123/492 or 0.25, and the frequency of the white phenotype would be 369/492 or 0.75.

17.1b Phenotypic Variation Can Have Genetic and Environmental Causes

Phenotypic variation within populations may be caused by genetic differences between individuals. But it can also be caused solely by environmental factors that individuals experience, or by an interaction between genetics and the environment. As a result, genetic and phenotypic variations may not be perfectly correlated. Under some circumstances, organisms with different genotypes exhibit the same phenotype. Conversely, organisms with the same genotype sometimes exhibit different phenotypes. For example, the acidity of soil influences flower colour in hydrangeas (**Figure 17.4**).

Knowing whether phenotypic variation is caused by genetic differences, environmental factors, or an interaction of the two is important because only genetically based variation is inherited and thus subject to evolutionary change. Moreover, knowing the causes of phenotypic variation has important practical applications. Suppose, for example, that one field of wheat produced more grain than another. If a difference in the availability of nutrients or water caused the difference in yield, a farmer might choose to fertilize or irrigate

the less productive field. But if the difference in productivity resulted from genetic differences between plants in the two fields, a farmer might plant only the more productive genotype. Because environmental factors can influence the expression of genes, an organism's phenotype is frequently the product of an interaction between its genotype and its environment. In our hypothetical example, the farmer may maximize yield by fertilizing and irrigating the more productive genotype of wheat.

How can we determine whether phenotypic variation is caused by environmental factors or genetic differences? We can test for an environmental cause experimentally by changing one environmental variable and measuring the effects on genetically similar subjects. For example, plants of the same genotype that are grown in full sunlight tend to have smaller leaves and shorter stems than plants grown in the shade. Breeding experiments can demonstrate the genetic basis of phenotypic variation. For example, Mendel inferred the genetic basis of qualitative traits, such as flower colour in peas, by crossing plants with different phenotypes. Breeding experiments are not always practical, however, particularly for organisms with long generation times. Ethical concerns also render these techniques unthinkable for humans. Instead, researchers often study the inheritance of particular traits by analyzing genealogical pedigrees, as discussed in Chapter 10.

STUDY BREAK QUESTIONS

1. If a population of skunks includes some individuals with stripes and others with spots, would you describe the variation as quantitative or qualitative?
2. What factors contribute to phenotypic variation in a population?

17.2 Population Genetics

Most genetics research is focused on the structure of genes, their function, and how they are regulated. As a subdiscipline, **population genetics** is distinct in that it focuses on the genetic variation that exists within a population and how this changes over time as a result of evolution. To predict how certain factors may influence genetic variation, population geneticists first describe the genetic structure of a population. They then create and test hypotheses, formalized in mathematical models, to describe how evolutionary processes may change the genetic structure under specified conditions.

17.2a Evolution Is a Change in Allele Frequencies

One of the misconceptions discussed in the previous chapter is that evolution is driven solely by natural selection. Evolution can in fact be caused by four distinct processes: mutation, genetic drift, gene flow, and natural selection. We will strictly define and discuss each of these processes later in this chapter but, for now, just hold on to the understanding that each of these processes acting alone or in combination has the ability to change the traits in a population over time—each one can drive evolutionary change.

Recall from Chapter 16 that a trait is an inherited characteristic of an individual related to their appearance, abilities, and behaviours. Some traits are simple and are coded by a single gene; others are complex and are the result of many genes.

CONCEPT FIX You may think that the genetic variation that exists in a population is because individuals of the same species have different genes. But that is not exactly right. Rather, the genetic variation is because individuals possess different versions of the same genes. That is, different individuals may carry different **alleles** for one or more genes (**Figure 17.5**). A gene can have several different alleles. In a haploid organism, only one of the possible alleles of a gene exists in a particular individual, but a diploid organism possesses two alleles for each gene. The location of a gene on a chromosome is termed the **locus**. ⬡

In Chapter 16 we defined evolution simply as "species change over time". We can now refine that definition: **evolution** is a change in allele frequencies from one generation to the next. Changing how common a particular allele is within a population (its frequency) changes the genetic makeup of the population. As we will see later in this chapter, mutation, genetic drift, gene flow, and natural selection can each cause evolution because they can each change the frequency of alleles.

The total genetic variability of a population is represented by all the alleles at all the gene loci in all individuals within the population and is referred to as the **gene pool**. As shown in Figure 17.5, the term "gene pool" can also refer only to the frequency of the alleles of one locus within the population.

17.2b Populations Often Contain Substantial Genetic Variation

How much genetic variation actually exists within populations? In the 1960s, evolutionary biologists began to use the molecular technique of gel electrophoresis (see Chapter 14) to to detect the presence and size of various proteins. Scientists were able to detect protein differences between individuals, different populations, and different species. For example, the enzyme hexokinase catalyzes the same reaction in different species, but the primary sequence of the enzyme is not identical in those species. The amino acid sequences among different species are similar, but they aren't identical.

Differences in the amino acid sequence of a protein reflect changes in the gene sequence; and even within individuals of the same species, gene sequences are often different. A difference in the nucleotide sequence of a given gene in different individuals of a species is referred to as a **polymorphism**. This means that the gene occurs in different "forms" in the population. This is the same as saying that the gene has different alleles in the population.

Today, advances in technology have lowered the cost of DNA sequencing, which has allowed scientists to survey genetic

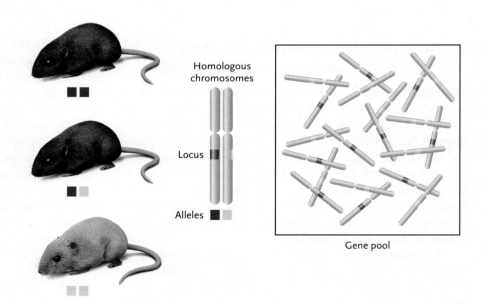

FIGURE 17.5 Alleles, a locus, and a gene pool. Fur colour in this mouse is controlled by a single gene, which is located at its locus on homologous chromosomes. The gene for fur colour has two forms, or alleles (brown and yellow). The brown allele is dominant to yellow since, in the heterozygous form, the mouse is brown. The total of all alleles for fur colour in the population is the gene pool for this particular locus.

variation directly and, as a result, researchers have accumulated an astounding knowledge of the sequences of entire genomes. Research has shown that both protein-coding and non-coding regions of DNA harbour extensive genetic variation. This genetic variation may exist within the two copies of a given gene found in heterozygous individuals, as well as between individuals found within a given population, as well as within different populations and different species. A major facet of research in DNA polymorphisms is the study of single-nucleotide polymorphisms (SNPs, also called "snips"; **Figure 17.6**). These single-nucleotide differences can exist between individuals and have been shown to account for about 90% of the genetic variation found in humans.

Genetic variation, the raw material of evolutionary change, has two potential sources: the production of new alleles and the rearrangement of existing alleles into new combinations. As we will discuss later in this chapter, most new alleles arise from a wide range of processes that result in mutation to DNA. Chapter 8 showed how meiosis is a powerful engine for creating novel arrangements of existing alleles through crossing-over between homologous chromosomes, independent assortment of non-homologous chromosomes, and random fertilizations between genetically different sperm and eggs. For example, an organism might carry the alleles *tS* (read as "small *t*, big *s*") on one chromosome, while on the homologous chromosome there are *Ts*. Recombinant offspring from this cross could have the novel arrangement of *TS* alleles on one of its chromosomes. This shuffling of alleles into new combinations can produce an extraordinary number of novel genotypes in the next generation. By one estimate, more than 10^{600} combinations of alleles are possible in human gametes, yet there are fewer than 10^{10} humans alive today. So, unless you have an identical twin, it is extremely unlikely that another person with your genotype has ever lived or ever will.

17.2c Genetic Structure of Populations

Until the development of the tools of molecular biology, determining the genotype that is responsible for a specific phenotype was often very difficult and thus was a major hindrance to population genetics. As well, not only are some traits the products of many genes, but many traits are strongly influenced by the environment. Because of these compounding factors, early population geneticists chose systems to study where a clearly identifiable heritable trait was controlled by a single gene.

A simple system that has been used to study microevolutionary processes is the diploid plant snapdragon (*Antirrhinum* spp.). Flower colour in snapdragons is controlled by a single gene, referred to as the *flower colour locus, C*. Individuals that are homozygous for the C^R allele ($C^R C^R$) have red flowers; individuals that are homozygous for the C^W allele ($C^W C^W$) have white flowers; heterozygotes ($C^R C^W$) have pink flowers. Because of the three distinct phenotypes, it is straightforward to determine the frequency of each genotype in a population and then calculate the frequency of the two alleles.

Table 17.1 presents data from a population of snapdragons that consists of 1000 individual plants. By examination of the various plant colours within the population, one can determine the frequency of the three genotypes as $C^R C^R = 0.45$, $C^R C^W = 0.5$, and $C^W C^W = 0.05$. Note that the sum of the three genotype frequencies must equal 1.

Now let's calculate the allele frequencies. When a single locus has two alleles, population geneticists denote the frequency of one allele with the letter p and the frequency of the second allele with the letter q. Looking at Table 17.1, you can see that the allele frequency of the C^R allele (p) equals 0.7, while the allele frequency of the C^W (q) allele is 0.3. Like genotype frequencies, the sum of the two allele frequencies must equal 1.

Once we have described the population by determining how common each genotype and allele is (their frequencies), the next question a population geneticist may ask might be, "Is the population evolving?" or "Is there evidence for evolution in the gene controlling flower colour?"

17.2d The Hardy–Weinberg Principle Is a Null Hypothesis That Defines a Population That Is Not Evolving

As discussed in *The Purple Pages*, an important aspect of experimental design is the use of a *control*. While some individuals are subjected to an experimental

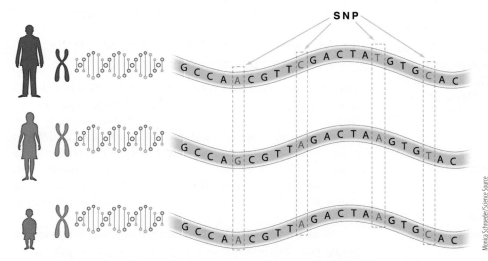

FIGURE 17.6 The genetic variation that exists within a population includes single-nucleotide differences, called *SNPs*, within the same gene

Monica Schroeder/Science Source

Because each diploid individual has two alleles at each gene locus, a sample of 1000 individuals has a total of 2000 alleles at the C locus.

Flower Colour Phenotype	Genotype	Number of Individuals	Genotype Frequency[1]	Total Number of C^R Alleles[2]	Total Number of C^W Alleles[2]
Red	$C^R C^R$	450	450/1000 = 0.45	$2 \times 450 = 900$	$0 \times 450 = 0$
Pink	$C^R C^W$	500	500/1000 = 0.50	$1 \times 500 = 500$	$1 \times 500 = 500$
White	$C^W C^W$	50	50/1000 = 0.05	$0 \times 50 = 0$	$2 \times 50 = 100$
	Total	1000	0.45 + 0.50 + 0.05 = 1.0	1400	600

To calculate allele frequencies, use the total of 1400 + 600 = 2000 alleles in the sample:
p = frequency of C^R allele = 1400/2000 = 0.7.
q = frequency of C^W allele = 600/2000 = 0.3.
$p + q = 0.7 + 0.3 = 1.0$.

[1] Genotype frequency = the number of individuals possessing a particular genotype divided by the total number of individuals in the sample.
[2] Total number of C^R or C^W alleles = the number of C^R or C^W alleles present in one individual with a particular genotype multiplied by the number of individuals with that genotype.

treatment, the control individuals are left alone. The importance of the control is that it tells researchers what they would see if the experimental treatment had no effect. However, in field studies using observational rather than experimental data, there is often no suitable control. In such cases, investigators develop conceptual models, from which they can state a **null hypothesis**. The null hypothesis is a prediction of what researchers would see if that particular factor had no effect.

A null hypothesis related to population genetics that was asked in the early twentieth century was: *What would the genetic makeup of a population be at a particular locus if the population was not evolving?* The mathematical method used to answer this is known as the **Hardy–Weinberg principle**, named after an English mathematician, G. H. Hardy, and a German physician, Wilhelm Weinberg.

The Hardy–Weinberg principle is a mathematical model that specifies the conditions that are necessary so that allele frequencies and genotype frequencies do not change from one generation to the next (**Figure 17.7**). This state is referred to as **genetic equilibrium**. According to the Hardy–Weinberg model, genetic equilibrium is possible only if *all* the following conditions are met:

1. The population is closed to migration from other populations.
2. The population is infinite in size.
3. No mutation is occurring in the population.
4. All genotypes in the population survive and reproduce equally well.
5. Individuals in the population mate randomly with respect to genotype.

STUDY BREAK QUESTIONS

1. Define *allele, locus,* and *gene pool.*
2. Why is the Hardy–Weinberg principle considered a null model of evolution?
3. If the conditions of the Hardy–Weinberg principle are met, when will genotype frequencies stop changing?

17.3 The Agents of Microevolution

A population's allele frequencies will change over time if one or more of the five conditions of the Hardy–Weinberg model are violated. In this section, we discuss the processes that can disrupt Hardy–Weinberg equilibrium and thus cause evolution: gene flow, genetic drift, mutation, and natural selection.

17.3a Gene Flow Introduces New Alleles into Populations

The allele and genotype frequencies of a population can change due to migration into or out of the population. Organisms or their gametes (e.g., the pollen of flowers) sometimes move from one population to another and may introduce novel alleles into a population, shifting its allele and genotype frequencies away from the values predicted by the Hardy–Weinberg model. This phenomenon, called **gene flow**, violates the Hardy–Weinberg requirement that populations must be closed to migration (Condition 1).

Gene flow is seen in some animal species. For example, young male baboons typically move from one local population to another after experiencing aggressive behaviour by older males. Many marine invertebrates disperse long distances as

FIGURE 17.7 **Research Method**

Using the Hardy–Weinberg Principle

To see how the Hardy–Weinberg principle can be applied, we will analyze the snapdragon flower colour locus, using the hypothetical population of 1000 plants described in Table 17.1. This locus includes two alleles: C^R (with its frequency designated as p) and C^W (with its frequency designated as q), and three genotypes: homozygous C^RC^R, heterozygous C^RC^W, and homozygous C^WC^W. Table 17.1 lists the number of plants with each genotype: 450 have red flowers (C^RC^R), 500 have pink flowers (C^RC^W), and 50 have white flowers (C^WC^W). It also shows the calculation of both the genotype frequencies ($C^RC^R = 0.45$, $C^RC^W = 0.50$, and $C^WC^W = 0.05$) and the allele frequencies ($p = 0.7$ and $q = 0.3$) for the population.

1. Allele frequencies in parents and gametes
Let's assume for simplicity that each individual produces only two gametes, and that both gametes contribute to the production of offspring. This assumption is unrealistic, of course, but it meets the Hardy–Weinberg requirement that all individuals in the population contribute equally to the next generation. In each parent, the two alleles segregate and end up in different gametes:

450 C^RC^R individuals produce → 900 C^R gametes

500 C^RC^W individuals produce → 500 C^R gametes + 500 C^W gametes

50 C^WC^W individuals produce → 100 C^W gametes

You can readily see that 1400 of the 2000 total gametes carry the C^R allele and 600 carry the C^W allele. The frequency of C^R gametes is 1400/2000, or 0.7, which is equal to p; the frequency of C^W gametes is 600/2000 or 0.3, which is equal to q. Thus, the allele frequencies in the gametes are exactly the same as the allele frequencies in the parent generation. It could not be otherwise because each gamete carries one allele at each locus.

2. Genotype frequencies in offspring
Now assume that these gametes, both sperm and eggs, encounter each other at random. In other words, individuals reproduce without regard to the genotype of a potential mate. We can visualize the process of random mating in the mating table, shown here.

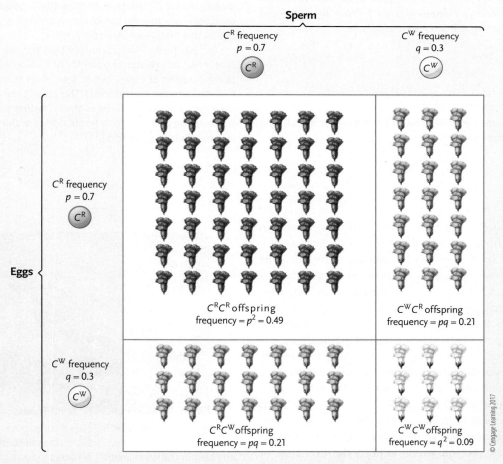

Mating table

(*Continued*)

FIGURE 17.7   Research Method (*Continued*)

We can also describe the consequences of random mating—$(p + q)$ sperm fertilizing $(p + q)$ eggs—with an equation that predicts the genotype frequencies in the offspring generation:

$$(p + q) \times (p + q) = p^2 + 2pq + q^2$$

If the population is at genetic equilibrium for this locus, p^2 is the predicted frequency of the C^RC^R genotype, $2pq$ is the predicted frequency of the C^RC^W genotype, and q^2 is the predicted frequency of the C^WC^W genotype. Using the gamete frequencies determined above, we can calculate the predicted genotype frequencies in the next generation:

$$\text{frequency of } C^RC^R = p^2 = (0.7 \times 0.7) = 0.49$$

$$\text{frequency of } C^RC^W = 2pq = 2(0.7 \times 0.3) = 0.42$$

$$\text{frequency of } C^WC^W = q^2 = (0.3 \times 0.3) = 0.09$$

Notice that the predicted genotype frequencies in the offspring generation have changed from the genotype frequencies in the parent generation: the frequency of heterozygous individuals has decreased, and the frequencies of both types of homozygous individuals have increased. This result occurred because the starting population was *not in equilibrium* at this gene locus. In other words, the distribution of parent genotypes did not conform to the predicted $p^2 + 2pq + q^2$ distribution.

The 2000 gametes in our hypothetical population produced 1000 offspring. Using the genotype frequencies we just calculated, we can predict how many offspring will carry each genotype:

490 red (C^RC^R)

420 pink (C^RC^W)

90 white (C^WC^W)

In a real study, we would examine the offspring to see how well their numbers match these predictions.

3. Allele frequencies in offspring

What about the allele frequencies in the offspring? The Hardy–Weinberg principle predicts that they did not change. Let's calculate them and see. Using the method shown in Table 17.1 and the prime symbol (′) to indicate offspring allele frequencies

$$p' = ([2 \times 490] + 420)/2000 = 1400/2000 = 0.7$$

$$q' = ([2 \times 90] + 420)/2000 = 600/2000 = 0.3$$

You can see from this calculation that the allele frequencies did not change from one generation to the next, even though the alleles were rearranged to produce different proportions of the three genotypes.

4. Genetic equilibrium in future generations

The population is now at genetic equilibrium for the flower colour locus; neither the genotype frequencies nor the allele frequencies will change in succeeding generations as long as the population meets the conditions specified in the Hardy–Weinberg model. To verify this, you can calculate the allele frequencies of the gametes for this offspring generation and predict the genotype frequencies and allele frequencies for a third generation. You could continue calculating until you ran out of either paper or patience, but these frequencies will not change.

Researchers use calculations like these to determine whether an actual population is near its predicted genetic equilibrium for one or more gene loci. When they discover that a population is not at equilibrium, they infer that microevolution is occurring, and they can investigate the factors that might be responsible.

The Hardy–Weinberg principle thus represents the null hypothesis that serves as a reference point for evaluating whether or not a population is evolving at a given locus. If we observe that a population's genotype frequencies do not match the predictions of the null hypothesis, then the population *may be* evolving; further information is needed. If, however, we find that allele frequencies are changing over time, evolution is definitely occurring.

---

larvae carried by ocean currents. Gene flow is common in many plant populations in which dispersal agents, such as pollen-carrying wind or seed-carrying animals, result in gene flow. For example, blue jays foster gene flow among populations of oaks by carrying acorns from nut-bearing trees to their winter caches, which may be as much as a mile away (**Figure 17.8**). Transported acorns that go uneaten may germinate and contribute to the gene pool of a neighbouring oak population.

The importance of gene flow in driving evolutionary change within a population depends on how different the gene pool is between it and other populations and the rate of gene flow into and out of the population. Since the environmental conditions and thus selection experienced by two populations will not be identical, the flow of new alleles into a population may alter its fitness. As you would expect, the exchange of alleles between two populations will decrease the genetic differences between the populations, making them more similar.

FIGURE 17.8 Gene flow. Blue jays (*Cyanocitta cristata*) serve as agents of gene flow for oaks (genus *Quercus*) when the birds carry acorns from one oak population to another. An uneaten acorn may germinate and contribute to the gene pool of the population into which it was carried.

17.3b Genetic Drift Reduces Genetic Variability within Populations

Sometimes allele frequencies in a population change from one generation to the next simply by chance. This phenomenon, known as **genetic drift**, causes allele frequencies to move up and down in unpredictable ways. Genetic drift can have a major impact on allele frequencies, especially in small populations. This then clearly violates the Hardy–Weinberg assumption of infinitely large population size (Condition 2). Drift generally leads to reduced genetic diversity in small populations because rare alleles are often lost. Genetic drift is driven by two circumstances: founder effects and population bottlenecks.

FOUNDER EFFECT When a few individuals colonize a distant locality and start a new population, they carry only a small sample of the parent population's genetic variation. By chance, some alleles may be totally missing from the new population, whereas other alleles that were rare in the original population might be common. This change in the gene pool is called the **founder effect**.

The human medical literature provides some of the best-documented examples of the founder effect. The Old Order Amish, an essentially closed religious community in Lancaster County, Pennsylvania, have an exceptionally high incidence of Ellis–van Creveld syndrome, a genetic disorder caused by a recessive allele. In the homozygous state, the allele produces dwarfism, shortened limbs, and polydactyly (extra fingers). Genetic analysis indicates that, while the incidence of the disease in the general population is about 1 in 60 000, it occurs at a rate of 1 in 200 within the Amish of Lancaster County, with as many as 13% of individuals in the community being heterozygous carriers of the allele.

The high incidence of Ellis–van Creveld syndrome is explained by the founder effect. The Amish community was originally founded by a small group of people from Germany. In fact, the parents of all children with Ellis–van Creveld syndrome can be traced back to a single couple who immigrated to Eastern Pennsylvania in the mid-1700s. The custom of marrying only within the Amish community has led to a much higher incidence of a range of recessive disorders (see "Inbreeding Reduces Heterozygosity," later in this chapter).

POPULATION BOTTLENECKS Factors such as disease, starvation, and hunting may kill a large proportion of the individuals in a population, resulting in what is referred to as a *population bottleneck*. The large reduction in population size is associated with a decrease in the size of the gene pool and therefore the genetic diversity of the population. Alleles that were rare in the original population can be totally lost from the population in the event of a bottleneck (**Figure 17.9**).

In the late nineteenth century, for example, hunters nearly wiped out northern elephant seals (*Mirounga angustirostris*) along the Pacific coast of North America. Since the 1880s, when the species received protected status, the population has rebounded from about 20 individuals to more than 160 000

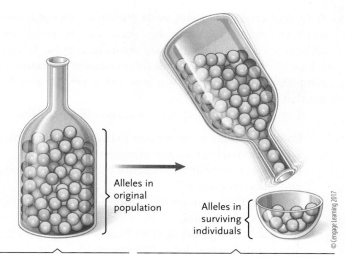

The gene pool of the original population, represented by a bottle filled with colored marbles, includes a locus with three alleles. Two of the alleles, represented by blue and green marbles, occur at high frequency; the third allele, represented by red marbles, occurs at low frequency.

If an environmental event randomly kills a large number of individuals in the population, the drastic reduction in population size is described as a population bottleneck. The process is analogous to shaking only a few of the marbles—the survivors—through the neck of the bottle. As a consequence of chance events associated with population bottlenecks, surviving individuals may not have the same allele frequencies as the original population. Rare alleles are inevitably lost.

© Cengage Learning 2017

FIGURE 17.9 A population bottleneck results in decreased genetic diversity and often the loss of rare alleles

today. Many would view this as a huge success story of conservation. However, things are not as great as they may seem.

Since this large population is derived from a group of perhaps only 20 individuals, what was lost that can never be regained is the genetic diversity in the original large population. That is, there are far fewer alleles at any one locus in the gene pool today than in the original population.

Both the founder effect and population bottlenecks have important implications for conservation biology. Because, in both cases, they result in populations with very few individuals, there is very little genetic variability. The small size of the total gene pool will remain small regardless of how large the population will become. Endangered species can be protected from extinction, but the lack of genetic variability would suggest that the population will always be more susceptible to disease and less able to cope with environmental perturbations such as climate change.

17.3c Mutations Are Random and Create Genetic Novelty

A population can deviate from Hardy–Weinberg equilibrium by the introduction of mutation that can introduce new alleles and therefore change allele frequencies (Condition 3). A **mutation** is a change to the double-strand sequence of DNA. Common factors that cause mutation include radiation (e.g., UV light), which can actually damage individual nucleotides, and some hazardous chemicals that can interfere with

DNA replication. However, most mutations are not caused by some environmental factor, but occur as a result of normal cellular processes. This includes errors in copying DNA during DNA replication as well as the movement of transposable elements (Chapter 15) from one place in the genome to another.

There are five basic types of mutation (**Figure 17.10**):

Point mutation: A single nucleotide (base) is changed. This is also referred to as a *substitution*.
Insertion: One or more nucleotide base pairs are introduced into a DNA sequence.
Deletion: One or more nucleotide base pairs are removed from a DNA sequence.
Inversion: A segment of DNA breaks and is inserted back into its original position in the reverse orientation.
Duplication: DNA is copied twice. The duplication can be part of a gene, a whole gene, or an entire genome.

As mentioned earlier, genetic recombination between homologous chromosomes during meiosis (see Chapter 8) is a source of genetic variation in a population. But recombination is very precise and generally does not result in mutation.

Mutations can occur in the genomes of any cell (e.g., human skin cells). But it is important to realize that, for mutations to alter allele frequencies within a population, the mutation must occur in the DNA of germ-line cells, those that go on to produce gametes (e.g., sperm and egg). As well, mutations can be considered random and spontaneous events. This means that the precise location within a genome that they occur and when they occur cannot be predicted. Mutations are not directed by the selective pressures on a population to occur in specific genes. For example, mutations within a bacterial population exposed to higher than normal temperatures will not be localized to the genes of heat-sensitive enzymes resulting in the enzymes being better able to function at high temperatures.

Mutation does not tend to result in increased fitness. In fact, most mutations either have no effect on fitness (neutral) or they will be harmful (deleterious) to an organism. This can be explained by thinking of the gene that codes for a protein; let's use the example of the enzyme hexokinase again. What are the chances that a single base change (point mutation) to the hexokinase gene will actually improve the function of the enzyme it codes for? The chance is very small compared to the probability that such a change will have either no effect or actually alter the structure of the enzyme in a negative way (e.g., causing the protein to misfold).

Whether they are beneficial, neutral, or deleterious, how common are mutations? Findings by the research group of Daniel Hartl, who is now at Harvard University, have shed light on the actual rate of mutation through work studying a range of organisms, including yeast, a single cell eukaryote. Their findings indicate that there is about a 0.000 000 03% chance of any one base undergoing a point mutation. However, given a population of millions of yeast cells, each with a genome of about 12 million bases, mutations will arise in thousands of individual cells each generation. Research also indicates that duplications and deletions occur at a rate that is about a thousand times more common than point mutations. In humans, measuring the actual rate of mutation has become much easier in recent years as the cost of sequencing whole genomes has become far more reasonable. By sequencing the entire genomes of two siblings and their parents, it has been shown that each child had 70 mutations that were not found in either parent. This may sound like a lot, but it really isn't. The human genome consists of about three billion base pairs.

The importance of mutation to evolution is not that it allows for rapid change to a population; it doesn't. In fact, genetic drift, gene flow, and natural selection can all change allele frequencies faster. Rather, the value of mutation is that it is the only microevolutionary process that gives rise to genetic novelty. Natural selection is usually the most powerful mechanism driving evolutionary change, but selection is only choosing among alleles that already exist in the population. Natural selection does not create, for example, new proteins that have new advantageous functions. These come about when mutation causes DNA sequences

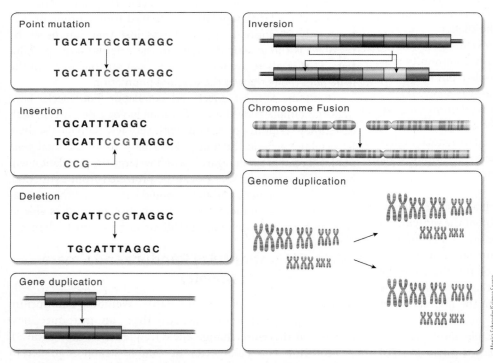

FIGURE 17.10 **There are several different types of mutations.** Each one changes the allele frequency by introducing novel alleles into a population.

Source: Zimmer, Emlen, *Evolution: Making Sense of Life*, Roberts and Company Publishers, 978-1936221363, Figure 5.13

to become rearranged into new combinations that give rise to new functions never seen before. If such a novelty is beneficial, the allele will become more common within the population through natural selection.

17.3d Natural Selection Shapes Genetic Variability by Favouring Some Traits over Others

As we discussed in Chapter 16, the process of natural selection favours some combination of traits over others, resulting in differential survivorship and reproduction. Since all genotypes in the population do not survive and reproduce equally well, natural selection violates Hardy–Weinberg equilibrium and causes allele and genotype frequencies to differ from those predicted by the model (Condition 4).

Biologists measure the effects of natural selection on phenotypic variation by recording changes in the mean and variability of characters over time. Three modes of natural selection have been identified: directional selection, stabilizing selection, and disruptive selection (**Figure 17.11**).

DIRECTIONAL SELECTION Traits undergo **directional selection** when individuals near one end of the phenotypic spectrum have the highest relative fitness. Directional selection shifts a trait away from the existing mean and toward the favoured extreme (see Figure 17.11a). After selection, the trait's mean value is higher or lower than before, and variability in the trait may be reduced.

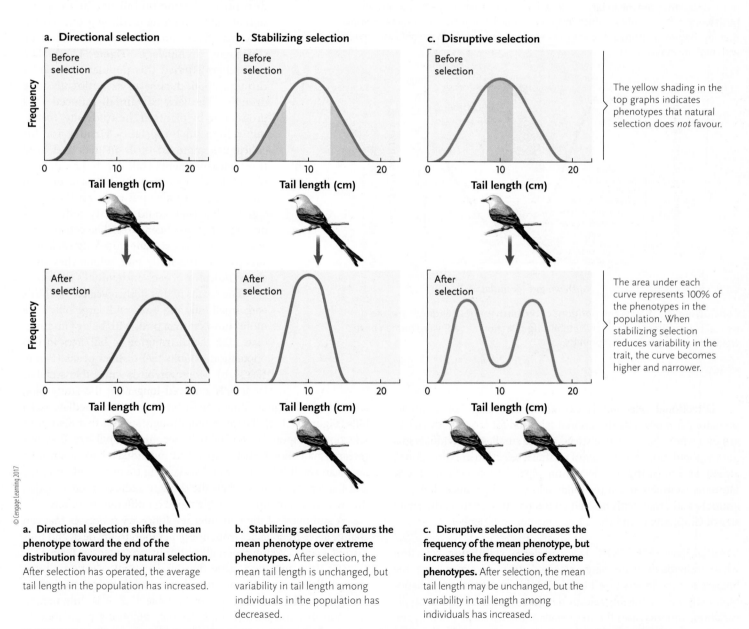

a. Directional selection

b. Stabilizing selection

c. Disruptive selection

The yellow shading in the top graphs indicates phenotypes that natural selection does *not* favour.

The area under each curve represents 100% of the phenotypes in the population. When stabilizing selection reduces variability in the trait, the curve becomes higher and narrower.

a. Directional selection shifts the mean phenotype toward the end of the distribution favoured by natural selection. After selection has operated, the average tail length in the population has increased.

b. Stabilizing selection favours the mean phenotype over extreme phenotypes. After selection, the mean tail length is unchanged, but variability in tail length among individuals in the population has decreased.

c. Disruptive selection decreases the frequency of the mean phenotype, but increases the frequencies of extreme phenotypes. After selection, the mean tail length may be unchanged, but the variability in tail length among individuals has increased.

FIGURE 17.11 Three modes of natural selection. A hypothetic example using tail length of birds as the quantitative trait subject to selection

FIGURE 17.12 **Experimental Research**

Do Humans Experience Stabilizing Selection?

Hypothesis: Human birth weight has been adjusted by natural selection.

Null Hypothesis: Natural selection has not affected human birth weight.

Method: Geneticists Luigi Cavalli-Sforza and Sir Walter Bodmer of Stanford University collected data on the variability in human birth weight—a character exhibiting quantitative variation—and on the mortality rates of babies born at different weights. They then searched for a relationship between birth weight and mortality rate by plotting both data sets on the same graph. A lack of correlation between birth weight and mortality rate would support the null hypothesis.

Results: When birth weight (the bar graph) and mortality rate (the curve) are plotted together, the mean birth weight is seen to be very close to the optimum birth weight (the weight at which mortality is lowest). The two data sets also show that few babies are born at the very low weights and very high weights associated with high mortality.

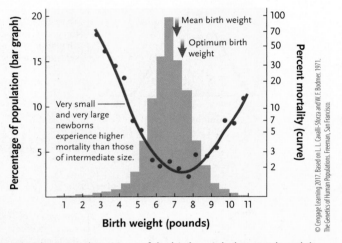

Conclusion: The shapes and positions of the birth weight bar graph and the mortality rate curve suggest that stabilizing selection has adjusted human birth weight to an average of 7–8 pounds.

Directional selection is extremely common. For example, predatory fish promote directional selection for larger body size in guppies when they selectively feed on the smallest individuals in a guppy population. Most cases of artificial selection are directional, aimed at increasing or decreasing specific phenotypic traits. Humans routinely use directional selection to produce domestic animals and crops with desired characteristics, such as the small size of Chihuahuas and the intense heat of chili peppers.

STABILIZING SELECTION Traits undergo **stabilizing selection** when individuals expressing intermediate phenotypes have the highest relative fitness (see Figure 17.11b). By eliminating phenotypic extremes, stabilizing selection reduces genetic and phenotypic variation, and increases the frequency of intermediate phenotypes. Stabilizing selection is probably the most common mode of natural selection, affecting many familiar traits. For example, very small and very large human newborns are less likely to survive than those born at an intermediate weight (**Figure 17.12**).

DISRUPTIVE SELECTION Traits undergo **disruptive selection** when extreme phenotypes have higher relative fitness than intermediate phenotypes (see Figure 17.11c). Thus, alleles producing extreme phenotypes become more common. Under natural conditions, disruptive selection is much less common than directional selection and stabilizing selection.

Andrew P. Hendry, of McGill University, and his colleagues analyzed a likely case of disruptive selection on bill size in a population of the seed-eating medium ground finch (*Geospiza fortis*) on Santa Cruz Island in the Galápagos archipelago (**Figure 17.13**). The researchers studied this population in 2004 through 2006, during an exceptionally long drought. The lack of rainfall reduced seed production by plants at the study site, resulting in high finch mortality. Hendry and his colleagues captured birds in nets and used three measurements (bill depth, length, and width) to characterize the bill size of each individual. They also put rings on the birds' legs so that they could identify individuals during subsequent censuses. The census data allowed them to estimate how long each bird survived on the study plot, which they used as an indicator of each individual's fitness.

The results of this study revealed that birds with small bills and birds with large bills were more common than birds with bills of intermediate size: the distribution of bill sizes in this population exhibits two distinct peaks (Figure 17.13a, b). Moreover, birds with either small or large bills survived longer on the study plot, and thus had higher fitness, than birds with intermediate sized bills (Figure 17.13c). These results strongly suggest that disruptive selection is responsible for the polymorphism in bill size. Previous research had shown that large-billed individuals have a stronger bite than small-billed individuals, allowing them to feed on larger and harder seeds; thus, when the drought reduced food supplies, the two groups of birds probably relied on different resources.

A summary of the four microevolutionary processes that can change allele frequencies from one generation to the next, and thus disrupt Hardy–Weinberg equilibrium, in presented as **Table 17.2**. Genetic drift, mutation, gene flow, and natural selection all can change allele frequencies of a population and thus drive evolutionary change. However, as you see in Table 17.2, it is only natural selection that consistently improves the ability of a population to grow and reproduce in a particular environment, that is, to adapt.

a. Small-billed and large-billed medium ground finches (*Geospiza fortis*) from Santa Cruz island

Dr. Andrew Hendry

b. Distribution of bill sizes for birds marked in 2004

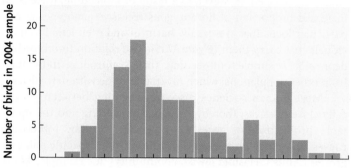

c. Fitness (survival on the study plot, 2004–2006)

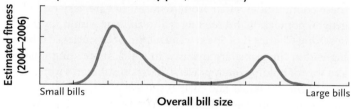

FIGURE 17.13 Disruptive selection. (a) Medium ground finches (*Geospiza fortis*) on Santa Cruz Island have bills of varying sizes. In this bill size polymorphism, birds with small bills or large bills are more common **(b)** and have higher fitness **(c)** than birds with bills of intermediate size. Thus, natural selection reduced the frequency of birds with bills of intermediate size and increased the frequencies of birds with either large bills or small bills.

Republished with permission of Royal Society, from *USA Proc. R. Soc. B*, Andrew P. Hendry, Sarah K. Huber, Luis F De León, Anthony Herrel and Jeffrey Podos, vol. 276(1657), 2009; permission conveyed through Copyright Clearance Center, Inc.

The other evolutionary processes do not always result in a population developing increased fitness in a particular environment over time. As well, it is important to remember that microevolutionary processes do not work in isolation of one another. For example, by itself, a rare beneficial mutation to one individual in a population will do little to change allele frequencies, but they can change appreciably after the population is acted upon by natural selection.

STUDY BREAK QUESTIONS

1. How is the high incidence of rare diseases within small populations explained by the founder effect?
2. Why is it that mutation does not tend to result in increased fitness?
3. Differentiate between directional, stabilizing, and disruptive selection.

TABLE 17.2 | Agents of Microevolutionary Change

Agent	Definition	Effect on Genetic Variation	Effect on Average Fitness
Gene flow	Change in allele frequencies as individuals join a population and reproduce	May introduce genetic variation from another population	Unpredictable effect on fitness; may introduce beneficial or harmful alleles
Genetic drift	Random changes in allele frequencies caused by chance events	Reduces genetic variation, especially in small populations; can eliminate rare alleles	Unpredictable effect on fitness; often harmful because of lost genetic diversity
Natural selection	Differential survivorship or reproduction of individuals with different genotypes	One allele can replace another or allelic variation can be preserved.	Positive effect on fitness through evolution of adaptations
Mutation	Heritable change in DNA	Introduces new genetic variation into population; does not change allele frequencies quickly	Unpredictable effect on fitness; most mutations in protein-coding genes lower fitness

17.4 Non-random Mating

The last requirement of Hardy–Weinberg equilibrium is that individuals select mates at random from the population with respect to their genotypes (Condition 5). However, in many organisms, including some plants and most animals, mating is non-random. Mates are selected because they have a particular phenotype and thus often a particular underlying genotype. Snow geese, for example, usually select mates of their own colour, and a tall woman is more likely to marry a tall man than a short man. As well, in many human societies, cultural and religious traditions influence mate choice.

Non-random mating is a particular case in which Hardy–Weinberg equilibrium is not maintained but, by itself, non-random mating does not result in a change in allele frequencies and thus is not considered a microevolutionary process. (We will revisit this important point.) The two major types of non-random mating are inbreeding and sexual selection.

17.4a Inbreeding Reduces Heterozygosity

A common form of non-random mating is **inbreeding**, which is mating between individuals that are genetically related. Because of this, both parents will share many of the same alleles. Inbreeding is a particular issue in small populations, but is a reproductive strategy that is found in many plant species and invertebrate animals.

To look at what happens to the genotypes in a population as a result of inbreeding, let's consider the most extreme scenario, which also is the simplest to understand: a population in which only individuals of identical genotype mate (**Figure 17.14**). Let's start this example with a population (Generation 0) in which the frequency of allele A is 0.5 (the frequency of a then is also 0.5). The population is in Hardy–Weinberg equilibrium and conforms to the ratio $p^2 + 2pq + q^2$. However, the mating that occurs that gives rise to Generation 1 is not random: AA individuals only mate with AA individuals, Aa individuals only mate with Aa, and aa individuals only mate with other aa individuals. Now, while both AA and aa individuals give rise only to the same genotypes in their offspring, this is not the case for heterozygotes (Aa). $Aa \times Aa$ gives rise to 50% heterozygote offspring and 25% each of AA and aa. In fact, in each successive generation, the proportion of heterozygotes in the population decreases by one half (1/4 going to each of AA and aa genotypes), while the proportion of each homozygous genotype increases by 1/4 (Figure 17.14).

This then is one of the major results of inbreeding: an increase in the proportion of both homozygous genotypes in the population over successive generations, and a decrease in the proportion of individuals that are heterozygous. This results in a deviation from Hardy–Weinberg equilibrium. However, a deviation from equilibrium does not mean that evolution occurred. Inbreeding does not cause evolution because the allele frequencies do not change over time. To appreciate this point, note that the allele frequencies of a population at the zygotic stage are equal to the allele frequencies in the pool of successful gametes from which the zygotes are formed. The pattern of mating simply determines the way in which haploid gametes are "packaged" into diploid zygotes. Inbreeding doesn't change the proportion of alleles in a population, it simply moves them from heterozygous into both homozygous genotypes.

In the majority of species, including humans, inbreeding has negative effects on fitness, a phenomenon known as **inbreeding depression**, which is a decline in the average fitness of inbred individuals in a population. The explanation for this is that deleterious alleles (e.g., they may code for a non-functioning protein) tend to be recessive, and yet they perpetuate in a typical population because they are carried in heterozygotes where they are effectively masked. However, as a result of inbreeding, there is an increased proportion of homozygous recessive genotypes at any particular locus that are usually harmful and even lethal to individuals that carry them (**Figure 17.15**). The solution to inbreeding depression is simple: outbreeding, that is, introduce individuals from other populations, which invariably come with new alleles.

Most human societies discourage mating between genetically close relatives, thereby reducing inbreeding and the inevitable production of recessive homozygotes that inbreeding causes. However, inbreeding is common within specific religious groups (Amish, Hasidic Jewish community), for example, where it is customary to marry within the community. As expected, these communities suffer from diseases that are very rare in the general population. Inbreeding is also an issue within royal families. King Charles II of Spain was a victim of centuries of inbreeding within the Hapsburg dynasty, in which inbreeding was seen as a way of holding on to power. Charles II suffered severe physical and mental issues and died at the age of 39, leaving no heirs and a country in chaos. Research carried out by Gonzao Alvarez, of the University of Santiago in Spain, concluded that Charles II was more inbred than the child of a brother and sister.

17.4b Sexual Selection Often Exaggerates Showy Structures in Males

One type of non-random mating occurs because individuals consider specific aspects of the other sex before deciding to

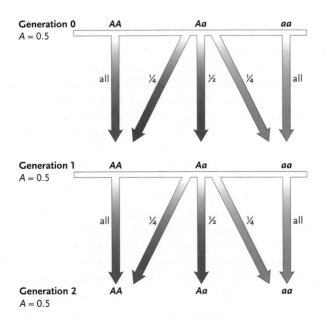

FIGURE 17.14 Effect of inbreeding on genotypes. In the extreme case of inbreeding where the same genotypes mate to give rise to the next generation, the proportion of heterozygotes (Aa) will decline by 50% each generation while the proportion of homozygotes will increase by 25% each. However, from one generation to the next, the allele frequencies do not change.

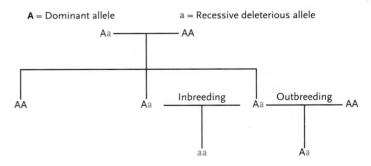

FIGURE 17.15 Inbreeding increases the likelihood of homozygous recessive individuals (*aa*), resulting in the lowering of the overall fitness of the population (inbreeding depression). Outbreeding can counter inbreeding depression by introducing new alleles from other populations.

mate with them. This special case of selection called **sexual selection** favours those individuals with specific traits that enhance their ability to mate with individuals of the other sex. Sexual selection usually acts on the males of a species who often possess a range of ornaments, such as brightly coloured feathers, long tails, or impressive antlers and horns, that often form part of elaborate courtship behaviour.

Sexual selection encompasses two related processes. As the result of *intersexual selection* (i.e., selection based on the interactions between males and females), males produce these otherwise useless ornaments simply because females associate them with health and vigour. In many species, intersexual selection is the likely cause of sexual dimorphism—differences in the size or appearance of males and females. Under *intrasexual selection* (i.e., selection based on the interactions between members of the same sex), males use their large body size, antlers, or tusks to intimidate, injure, or kill rival males.

Like directional selection, sexual selection pushes phenotypes toward one extreme. But the products of sexual selection are sometimes bizarre, such as the ridiculously long tail feathers of male, African widowbirds. How could evolutionary processes favour such elaborate structures, which are costly to produce? Research by Malte Andersson, of the University of Gothenburg, Sweden, suggests that the males' long tail feathers are a product of intersexual selection because females are more strongly attracted to males with long tails than to males with short tails; tail length had no effect on a male's ability to compete with other males for space in the habitat (**Figure 17.16**).

Underlying sexual selection is the reality that females and males do not incur the same costs during reproduction. That is, in almost all sexual species, there is clear sexual asymmetry. Because eggs are more energetically expensive to make than sperm and are limited in number, females are much more heavily invested in successful reproduction than males. Female fitness is closely linked to producing eggs and rearing healthy offspring (e.g., pregnancy, lactation). In contrast, because sperm are energetically very cheap to produce, males can father a huge number of offspring. Male fitness then is limited simply by the number of females an individual male can mate with. This sexual asymmetry means that females need to be far more discriminating than males about who they mate with. They have a limited number of energetically expensive eggs, and identifying a mate that is particularly healthy is important.

STUDY BREAK QUESTIONS

1. Which agents of microevolution tend to increase genetic variation within populations, and which ones tend to decrease it?
2. Which mode of natural selection increases the representation of the average phenotype in a population?
3. In what way is sexual selection like directional selection?

17.5 Maintaining Genetic and Phenotypic Variation

Evolutionary biologists continue to discover extraordinary amounts of genetic and phenotypic variation in most natural populations. How can so much variation persist when, for example, natural selection favours certain alleles over others?

17.5a Diploidy Can Hide Recessive Alleles from the Action of Natural Selection

Recall that most eukaryotes have two copies of each chromosome and thus two copies of each gene—they are diploid. It turns out that diploidy is a valuable mechanism that maintains genetic variability in a population. Although recessive alleles may be harmful, this is only the case when both alleles for a particular gene are recessive. Most often, the recessive allele is present in the heterozygous genotype and thus its potentially harmful effect is masked by the presence of the dominant allele. Since natural selection acts on the phenotype of individuals, heterozygous individuals protect the presence of recessive alleles from being selected out of a population.

In most cases, the masking of recessive alleles in heterozygotes makes it almost impossible to eliminate them completely from a population. Even when very rare, the allele will perpetuate among the heterozygotes in the population (**Table 17.3**). Thus, the diploid state preserves recessive alleles at low frequencies, at least in large populations. In small populations, a combination of natural selection and genetic drift can eliminate harmful recessive alleles.

An important aspect of diploidy is that the maintenance of recessive alleles may have important ecological considerations. Recessive alleles represent genetic diversity and, while under present conditions they may be harmful and lower fitness in the homozygous recessive state, they may prove beneficial to a population if the environmental conditions change.

17.5b Balancing Selection Maintains More Than One Allele

Balancing selection is a type of natural selection in which more than one allele is actively maintained in a population. Natural selection preserves balanced selection when (1) heterozygotes have higher relative fitness, (2) when different alleles are favoured in different environments, and (3) when the rarity of a phenotype provides a selective advantage.

HETEROZYGOTE ADVANTAGE Balanced selection can be maintained by **heterozygote advantage**—when heterozygotes have higher relative fitness than either homozygote. As Darwin first discovered in his experiments on corn, the offspring of crosses between a homozygous dominant individual and a homozygous recessive individual of the same species often exhibit a robustness described as "hybrid vigour." Apparently, being heterozygous at many gene loci provides some advantage,

FIGURE 17.16 **Experimental Research**

Sexual Selection in Action

Question: Is the long tail of the male long-tailed widowbird (*Euplectes progne*) the product of intrasexual selection, intersexual selection, or both?

Experiment: Researchers counted the number of females that associated with individual male widowbirds in the grasslands of Kenya. Researchers shortened the tails of some males by cutting the feathers, lengthened the tails of others by gluing feather extensions to their tails, and left a third group essentially unaltered as a control. One month later, the researchers again counted the number of females associating with each male and compared the results from the three groups.

Results: Males with experimentally lengthened tails attracted more than twice as many mates as males in the control group, and males with experimentally shortened tails attracted fewer. The researchers observed no differences in the ability of altered males and control group males to maintain their display areas.

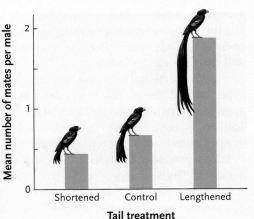

Conclusion: Female widowbirds clearly prefer males with experimentally lengthened tails to those with normal tails or experimentally shortened tails. Tail length had no obvious effect on the interactions between males. Thus, the long tail of male widowbirds is the product of intersexual selection.

---

perhaps by allowing organisms to respond effectively to environmental variation.

The best-documented example of heterozygote advantage with reference to a specific gene locus is the maintenance of the *HbS* (sickle) allele, which codes for a defective form of hemoglobin in humans. As you learned in Chapter 9, hemoglobin is an oxygen-transporting molecule in red blood cells. The hemoglobin produced by the *HbS* allele differs from normal hemoglobin (coded by the *HbA* allele) by just one amino acid. In *HbS/HbS* homozygotes, the faulty hemoglobin forms long, fibrous chains under low oxygen conditions, causing red blood cells to assume a sickle shape (as shown in Figure 9.17). Often, homozygous *HbS/HbS* individuals die of sickle cell anemia before reproducing; yet in tropical and subtropical Africa, *HbS/HbA* heterozygotes make up nearly 25% of many populations.

Why is the harmful allele maintained at such high frequency in some populations? It turns out that sickle cell anemia is common in regions where malarial parasites infect red blood cells in humans (**Figure 17.17**). When heterozygous *HbA/HbS* individuals contract malaria, their infected red blood cells assume the same sickle shape as those of homozygous *HbS/HbS* individuals. The sickled cells lose potassium, killing the parasites, which limits their spread within the infected individual. Heterozygous individuals often survive malaria because the parasites do not multiply quickly inside them, their immune systems can effectively fight the infection, and they retain a large population of uninfected red blood cells. Homozygous *HbA/HbA* individuals are also subject to malarial infection, but because their infected cells do not sickle, the parasites multiply rapidly, causing a severe infection with a high mortality rate.

Therefore, *HbA/HbS* heterozygotes have greater resistance to malaria and are more likely to survive severe malarial infections in areas where the parasite is prevalent. Natural selection preserves the *HbS* allele in these populations because heterozygotes in malaria-prone areas have higher relative fitness than homozygotes for the normal *HbA* allele.

SELECTION IN DIFFERENT ENVIRONMENTS Genetic variability can also be maintained within a population when different alleles are favoured in different places or at different times. For example, the shells of European garden snails range in

TABLE 17.3	Masking of Recessive Alleles in Diploid Organisms

When a recessive allele is common in a population (top of table), most copies of the allele are present in homozygotes. But when the allele is rare (bottom of table), most copies of it exist in heterozygotes. Thus, rare alleles that are completely recessive are protected from the action of natural selection because they are masked by dominant alleles in heterozygous individuals.

Frequency of Allele a	Genotype Frequencies*			% of Allele a Copies in	
	AA	Aa	aa	Aa	aa
0.99	0.0001	0.0198	0.9801	1	99
0.90	0.0100	0.1800	0.8100	10	90
0.75	0.0625	0.3750	0.5625	25	75
0.50	0.2500	0.5000	0.2500	50	50
0.25	0.5625	0.3750	0.0625	75	25
0.10	0.8100	0.1800	0.0100	90	10
0.01	0.9801	0.0198	0.0001	99	1

* Population is assumed to be in genetic equilibrium.

colour from nearly white to pink, yellow, or brown, and may be patterned by one to five stripes of varying colour (look back at Figure 17.1a). This polymorphism, which is relatively stable through time, is controlled by several gene loci. The variability in colour and striping pattern can be partially explained by selection for camouflage in different habitats. Predation by song thrushes (*Turdus ericetorum*) is a major agent of selection for the colour and pattern of these snails in England. Thrushes are visual predators, usually capturing snails that are easy to find. Thus, well-camouflaged snails survive, and the alleles that specify their phenotypes increase in frequency.

FREQUENCY-DEPENDENT SELECTION Sometimes, genetic variability is maintained in a population simply because rare phenotypes—whatever they happen to be—have higher relative fitness than more common phenotypes. The rare phenotype will increase in frequency until it becomes so common that it loses its advantage. Such phenomena are examples of *frequency-dependent* selection because the selective advantage enjoyed by a particular phenotype depends on its frequency in the population.

The agents of evolution cause microevolutionary changes in the gene pools of populations. In the next chapter, we examine how microevolution in different populations can cause their gene pools to diverge. The extent of genetic divergence is sometimes sufficient to cause the populations to evolve into different species.

STUDY BREAK QUESTIONS

1. How does the diploid condition protect harmful recessive alleles from natural selection?
2. What is a balanced polymorphism?
3. Why is the allele that causes sickle cell anemia very rare in human populations that are native to Northern Europe?

a. Distribution of *HbS* allele

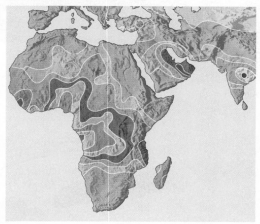

b. Distribution of malarial parasite

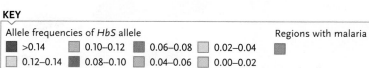

KEY

Allele frequencies of *HbS* allele
- >0.14
- 0.12–0.14
- 0.10–0.12
- 0.08–0.10
- 0.06–0.08
- 0.04–0.06
- 0.02–0.04
- 0.00–0.02

Regions with malaria

© Cengage Learning 2017. Based on L.L. Cavalli-Sforza and W. F. Bodmer. 1971. The Genetics of Human Populations. Freeman, San Francisco.

FIGURE 17.17 Heterozygote advantage. (a) The distribution of the *HbS* allele, which causes sickle cell anemia in homozygotes, roughly matches the distribution **(b)** of the malarial parasite *Plasmodium falciparum* in southern Europe, Africa, the Middle East, and India. Gene flow among human populations has carried the *HbS* allele to some malaria-free regions.

Summary Illustration

Genetic differences among the individuals of a population is due to the existence of different alleles for one or more genes. This genetic variation can change from generation to generation as the frequency of any particular allele within the population changes. Changes in allele frequency from generation to generation is evolution and it often results in changes in the occurrence of particular phenotypes (traits). The study of changing allele frequencies over generations is referred to as *microevolution*, and these changes are driven by four distinct processes: mutation, genetic drift, gene flow, and natural selection.

The Hardy-Weinberg equation can be used to determine whether a population is evolving.

Frequency of heterozygous genotype

$$p^2 + 2pq + q^2 = 1$$

Frequency of homozygous dominant genotype

Frequency of homozygous recessive genotype

For many traits (e.g., fur colour in mice) the proportion of q^2 individuals can be visually determined, and from that you can calculate q. Given that $p + q = 1$, you can calculate the frequency of p. With both p and q you can then use the Hardy–Weinberg formula to determine the frequencies of all three genotypes!

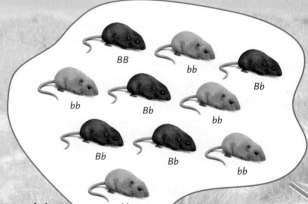

Current population

Frequency of $B = 0.3$
Frequency of $b = 0.7$

Evolution
A change in allele frequency from one generation to the next

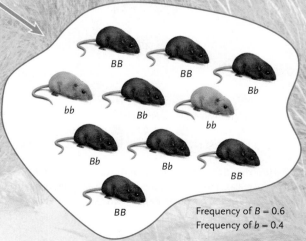

Next generation

Frequency of $B = 0.6$
Frequency of $b = 0.4$

There are four mechanisms that cause a population to evolve.

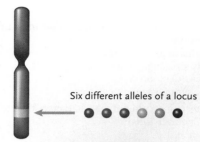

Six different alleles of a locus

	Ancestral Population		Later Population	Result
Hardy-Weinberg equilibrium		Random mating and no gene flow, genetic drift, mutation, or natural selection		Allele frequencies do not change
Gene flow		Individuals with the orange allele enter the population		Orange allele becomes more common
Genetic drift		Chance events cause frequency of certain alleles to change		Purple allele is lost
Mutation		A red allele becomes an orange allele		New allele appears in the population
Natural selection		Environmental factors are unfavourable for red alleles		Red allele becomes less common

Recall/Understand

1. Which of these characteristics is an example of qualitative phenotypic variation?
   a. the lengths of people's toes
   b. the body sizes of pigeons
   c. human ABO blood types
   d. the number of leaves on oak trees

2. What is the term for a phenotypic characteristic that increases the fitness of an individual?
   a. mutation
   b. founder effect
   c. heterozygote advantage
   d. adaptation

3. Which of these statements is the reason why spontaneous mutations have no immediate effect on allele frequencies in a large population?
   a. Mutations are random events, and mutations may be either beneficial or harmful.
   b. Mutations usually occur in males and have little effect on eggs.
   c. Many mutations exert their effects after an organism has stopped reproducing.
   d. Mutations are so rare that mutated alleles are greatly outnumbered by nonmutated alleles.

4. The phenomenon in which chance events cause unpredictable changes in allele frequencies is called _____.
   a. gene flow
   b. genetic drift
   c. inbreeding
   d. stabilizing selection

5. If a storm kills many small sparrows in a population, but only a few medium-sized and large ones, which type of selection is probably operating?
   a. directional
   b. stabilizing
   c. disruptive
   d. artificial

6. Which of these statements is proposed by the neutral mutation hypothesis?
   a. Complex structures in most organisms have not been fostered by natural selection.
   b. Some mutations have a strongly harmful effect.
   c. Most mutations do not alter organism fitness.
   d. Natural selection cannot counteract the action of gene flow.

Apply/Analyze

7. A population of mice is at Hardy–Weinberg equilibrium at a gene locus that controls fur colour. The locus has two alleles, M and m. A genetic analysis of one population reveals that 60% of its gametes carry the M allele. What percentage of mice contains both the M and the m alleles?
   a. 60%
   b. 48%
   c. 36%
   d. 16%

8. The genotype frequencies in a population are 0.60 AA, 0.20 Aa, and 0.20 aa, and the requirements of the Hardy–Weinberg principle apply. Which of the following genotype frequencies will occur in the offspring generation?
   a. 0.70 AA, 0.00 Aa, 0.30 aa
   b. 0.60 AA, 0.20 Aa, 0.20 aa
   c. 0.49 AA, 0.42 Aa, 0.09 aa
   d. 0.36 AA, 0.60 Aa, 0.04 aa

9. Which of these statements describes how directional selection and sexual selection are similar?
   a. They favour the mean genotypes over extreme genotypes.
   b. They favour the mean phenotypes over extreme phenotypes.
   c. They push phenotypes toward one extreme.
   d. They push genotypes toward one extreme.

10. The Old Order Amish, an essentially closed religious community in Lancaster County, Pennsylvania, have an exceptionally high incidence of Ellis–van Creveld syndrome, a genetic disorder caused by a recessive allele. What is this a result of?
    a. Alleles moving into or out of the Amish population.
    b. The affected individuals have the highest relative fitness.
    c. A few Amish individuals initially colonized Lancaster County.
    d. Affected individuals enhanced their ability to mate with individuals of the other sex.

Create/Evaluate

11. The *HbS* (sickle) allele codes for a defective form of hemoglobin in humans. Homozygous *HbS/HbS* individuals often die of sickle cell anemia before reproducing, yet in tropical and subtropical Africa, *HbS/HbA* heterozygotes make up nearly 25% of many populations. The high frequency of the harmful allele in some populations is probably an example of which of the following?
    a. natural selection
    b. the concept of relative fitness
    c. Hardy–Weinberg genetic equilibrium
    d. the founder effect

12. Which of these phenomena explains why the allele for sickle cell hemoglobin is common in some tropical and subtropical areas where the malaria parasite is prevalent?
    a. balanced polymorphism
    b. heterozygote advantage
    c. neutral selection
    d. stabilizing selection

13. Explain what relative fitness refers to.

14. Compare two populations of birds: population A consists of predominantly blue birds, and population B consists of predominantly green birds. Explain what will be the consequences of reciprocal and non-reciprocal gene flow between the two populations.

Chapter Roadmap

Species and Macroevolution

The species is the most studied taxonomic group. But what defines a species, and how do they develop as a result of evolutionary processes?

18.1 What Is a Species?

You would think of all the words in biology that species would be easy to define—it isn't

18.2 Maintaining Reproductive Isolation

Reproductive isolation, key to the biological specie concept, is maintained by a number of distinct mechanisms.

18.3 The Geography of Speciation

Geography has a major impact on the rate of speciation.

18.4 Genetic Mechanisms of Speciation

In many cases, reproductive isolation of species has a simple genetic basis.

Robert L. Kothenbeutel/Shutterstock.com

iStock.com/lightstalker

Birds of paradise. A male Count Raggi's bird of paradise (*Paradisaea raggiana*)

Speciation and Macroevolution

18

Why it matters . . . In 1927, nearly 100 years after Darwin boarded the *Beagle*, a young German naturalist named Ernst Mayr embarked on his own journey to the highlands of New Guinea. He was searching for rare "birds of paradise." These birds were known in Europe only through their ornate and colourful feathers, which were used to decorate ladies' hats. On his trek through the remote Arfak Mountains, Mayr identified 137 bird species (including many birds of paradise) based on differences in their size, plumage, colour, and other external characteristics.

To Mayr's surprise, the native Papuans, who were untrained in the ways of Western science, but who hunted these birds for food and feathers, had their own names for 136 of the 137 species he had identified. The close match between the two lists confirmed Mayr's belief that the *species* is a fundamental level of organization in nature.

Mayr also discovered some remarkable patterns in the geographical distributions of bird species in New Guinea. For example, each mountain range he explored was home to some species that lived nowhere else. Closely related species often lived on different mountaintops, separated by deep valleys of unsuitable habitat. In 1942, Mayr published the book *Systematics and the Origin of Species*, in which he described the role of geography in the evolution of new species; the book quickly became a cornerstone of evolutionary biology.

What mechanisms produce distinct species? As you discovered in the previous chapter, microevolutionary processes alter the pattern and extent of genetic and phenotypic variation within populations. When these processes differ between populations, the populations will diverge genetically, and they may eventually become so different that we recognize them as distinct species. Although Darwin's famous book was titled *On the Origin of Species,* he did not dwell on the question of *how* new species arise, although he clearly saw similar species as having shared inherited characteristics and a common ancestry.

Today, evolutionary biologists view **speciation** (the process of species formation) as a series of events that occur through time. However, using a range of approaches, they study the products of speciation, species that are alive today. Because they can rarely witness the process of speciation from start to finish, scientists make inferences about it by studying organisms in various stages of species formation. In this chapter, we consider four major topics: how biologists define and recognize species; how species maintain their genetic identity; how the geographical distributions of organisms influence speciation; and how different genetic mechanisms produce new species.

18.1 What Is a Species?

Like the hunters of the Arfak Mountains, most of us recognize the different species that we encounter every day. We can distinguish a cat from a dog and sunflowers from roses. The concept of species is based on our perception that Earth's biological diversity is packaged in discrete, recognizable units, and not as a continuum of forms grading into one another. As biologists have learned more about evolutionary processes—and the dazzling biodiversity those processes have produced—they have developed a variety of complementary species concepts.

18.1a The Morphological Species Concept Is a Practical Way to Identify Species

Biologists often describe new species on the basis of visible anatomical characteristics, a process that dates back to Linnaeus' classification of organisms in the eighteenth century (described in Chapter 19). This approach is based on the **morphological species concept**, the idea that all individuals of a species share measurable traits that distinguish them from individuals of other species.

The morphological species concept has many practical applications. For example, researchers use morphological criteria to identify the species of fossilized organisms. And because we can observe the external traits of organisms in nature, field guides to plants and animals list diagnostic (i.e., distinguishing) physical characters that allow us to recognize them (**Figure 18.1**).

Nevertheless, relying exclusively on morphology to identify species can present problems. Some individuals of a single species look very different in size and coloration, for example. Conversely, morphology does not help us distinguish some closely related species that are nearly identical in appearance. Finally, morphological species definitions tell us little about the evolutionary processes that produce new species.

18.1b The Biological Species Concept Is Based on Reproductive Isolation

The **biological species concept** emphasizes the dynamic nature of species. Ernst Mayr defined *biological species* as "groups of … interbreeding natural populations that are reproductively isolated from [do not produce fertile offspring with] other such groups." The concept is based on reproductive criteria and is easy to apply, at least in principle. If the members of two populations interbreed and produce fertile offspring *under natural conditions*, they belong to the same species. Their fertile offspring will go on to produce the next generation of that species. If two populations do not interbreed in nature, or fail to produce fertile offspring when they do, they belong to different species.

The biological species concept defines species in terms of population genetics and evolutionary theory. The first half of Mayr's definition notes the genetic *cohesiveness* of species: populations of the same species experience gene flow, which mixes their genetic material. Thus, we can think of a species as one large gene pool, which may be subdivided into local populations.

The second part of the biological species concept emphasizes the genetic *distinctness* of each species. Because populations of different species are reproductively isolated, they cannot exchange genetic information. In fact, the process of speciation is frequently defined as the evolution of reproductive isolation between populations.

The biological species concept also explains why individuals of a species generally look alike: members of the same gene pool share genetic traits that determine their appearance. Individuals of different species generally do not resemble one another as closely because they share fewer genetic characteristics. In practice, biologists often still use similarities or differences in morphological traits as convenient markers of genetic similarity or reproductive isolation.

However, the biological species concept does not apply to the many forms of life that reproduce asexually, including most bacteria and archaeans; some protists, fungi, and plants; and a few animals. In these species, individuals do not breed, so it is pointless to ask whether members of different populations do. Similarly, we cannot use the biological species concept to study extinct organisms, because we have little or no data on their specific reproductive habits. These species must all be defined using morphological or biochemical criteria. Yet, despite its limitations, the biological species concept currently provides the best evolutionary definition of a sexually reproducing species.

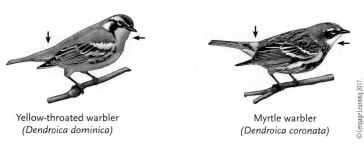

Yellow-throated warbler
(*Dendroica dominica*)

Myrtle warbler
(*Dendroica coronata*)

©Cengage Learning 2017.

FIGURE 18.1 Diagnostic characters. Yellow-throated warblers and myrtle warblers can be distinguished by the colour of feathers on the throat and rump.

18.1c The Phylogenetic Species Concept Focuses on Evolutionary History

Recognizing the limitations of the biological species concept, biologists have developed dozens of other ways to define a species. A widely accepted alternative is the **phylogenetic species concept**. Using both morphological and genetic sequence data, scientists first reconstruct the evolutionary tree for the organisms of interest. They then define a phylogenetic species as a cluster of populations (the tiniest twigs on this part of the Tree of Life) that emerge from the same small branch. Thus, a phylogenetic species comprises populations that share a recent evolutionary history.

One advantage of the phylogenetic species concept is that biologists can apply it to any group of organisms, including species that have long been extinct, as well as living organisms that reproduce asexually. Proponents of this approach also argue that the morphological and genetic distinctions between organisms on different branches of the Tree of Life reflect the absence of gene flow between them, one of the key requirements of the biological species definition. Nevertheless, because detailed evolutionary histories have been described for relatively few groups of organisms, biologists are not yet able to apply the phylogenetic species concept to all forms of life.

18.1d Many Species Exhibit Substantial Geographical Variation

Just as individuals within populations exhibit genotypic and phenotypic variation (see Section 17.1), populations within species also differ both genetically and phenotypically. Neighbouring populations often have shared characteristics because they live in similar environments, exchange individuals, and experience comparable patterns of natural selection. Widely separated populations, by contrast, may live under different conditions and experience different patterns of selection; because gene flow is less likely to occur between distant populations, their gene pools and phenotypes are often somewhat different.

When geographically separated populations of a species exhibit dramatic, easily recognized phenotypic variation, biologists may identify them as different **subspecies (Figure 18.2)**, which are local variants of a species. Individuals from different subspecies usually interbreed where their geographical distributions meet, and their offspring often exhibit intermediate

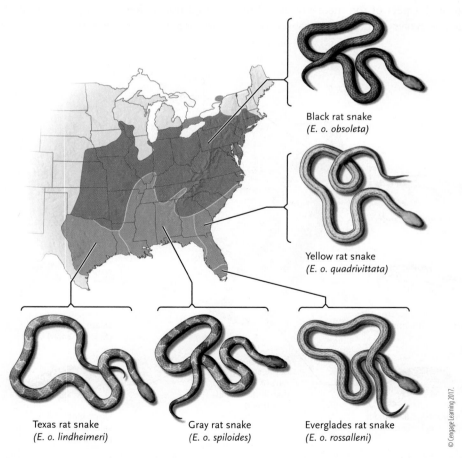

Black rat snake
(*E. o. obsoleta*)

Yellow rat snake
(*E. o. quadrivittata*)

Texas rat snake
(*E. o. lindheimeri*)

Gray rat snake
(*E. o. spiloides*)

Everglades rat snake
(*E. o. rossalleni*)

© Cengage Learning 2017.

FIGURE 18.2 Subspecies. Five subspecies of rat snake (*Elaphe obsoleta*) in eastern North America differ in colour and in the presence or absence of stripes or blotches.

phenotypes. Biologists sometimes use the word "race" as short-hand for the term *subspecies*.

Various patterns of geographical variation, as well as analyses of how the variation may relate to climatic or habitat variation, have provided great insight into the speciation process. Two of the best-studied patterns are *ring species* and *clinal variation*.

RING SPECIES Some plant and animal species have a ring-shaped geographical distribution that surrounds uninhabitable terrain. Adjacent populations of these **ring species** can exchange genetic material directly, but gene flow between distant populations occurs only through the intermediary populations.

The lungless salamander *Ensatina eschscholtzii* an example of a ring species: it is widely distributed in the coastal mountains and the Sierra Nevada of California, but it cannot survive in the hot, dry Central Valley (**Figure 18.3**). Seven subspecies differ in biochemical traits, colour, size, and ecology. Individuals from adjacent subspecies often interbreed where their geographical distributions overlap, and intermediate phenotypes are fairly common. But at the southern end of the Central Valley, adjacent subspecies rarely interbreed. Apparently, they have differentiated to such an extent that they can no longer exchange genetic material directly.

CONCEPT FIX One misconception about speciation is that, although it is a foundational aspect of the theory of evolution by natural selection, it has never actually been observed in nature or in the laboratory. But there are countless examples, including the salamander example above, where populations become so divergent that they can no longer exchange genetic material and thus become distinct species. ⬡

Are the southernmost populations of this salamander subspecies or different species? A biologist who saw *only* the southern populations, which coexist without interbreeding, might define them as separate species; however, they still have the potential to exchange genetic material through the intervening populations that form the ring. Therefore, biologists recognize these populations as belonging to the same species. Most likely, the southern subspecies are in an intermediate stage of species formation.

CLINAL VARIATION When a species is distributed over a large, environmentally diverse area, some traits may exhibit a **cline**, a smooth pattern of variation across a geographical gradient. For example, many birds and mammals in the northern hemisphere show clinal variation in body size (**Figure 18.4**) and the relative length of their appendages. In general, populations living in colder environments have larger bodies and shorter appendages, a pattern that is usually interpreted as a mechanism to conserve body heat (see Chapter 38).

Clinal variation usually results from gene flow between adjacent populations that are each adapting to slightly different conditions. However, if populations at opposite ends of a cline are separated by great distances, they may exchange very little

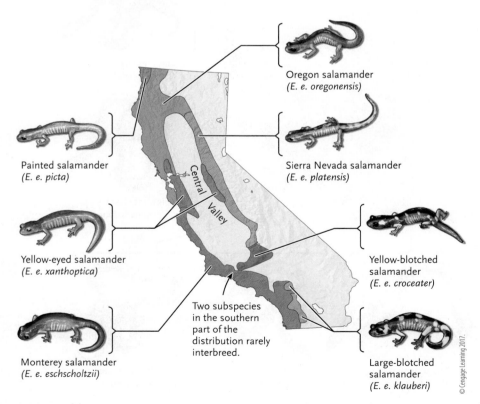

Oregon salamander
(*E. e. oregonensis*)

Painted salamander
(*E. e. picta*)

Sierra Nevada salamander
(*E. e. platensis*)

Central Valley

Yellow-eyed salamander
(*E. e. xanthoptica*)

Yellow-blotched salamander
(*E. e. croceater*)

Monterey salamander
(*E. e. eschscholtzii*)

Two subspecies in the southern part of the distribution rarely interbreed.

Large-blotched salamander
(*E. e. klauberi*)

© Cengage Learning 2017.

FIGURE 18.3 Ring species. Six of the seven subspecies of the salamander *Ensatina eschscholtzii* are distributed in a ring around California's Central Valley. Subspecies often interbreed where their geographical distributions overlap. However, the two subspecies that nearly close the ring in the south (marked with an arrow), the Monterey salamander and the yellow-blotched salamander, rarely interbreed.

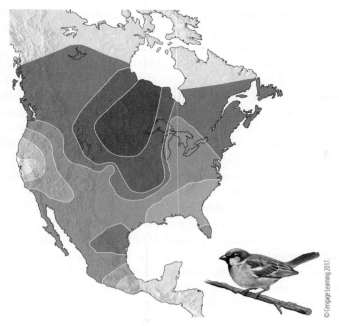

FIGURE 18.4 Clinal variation. House sparrows (*Passer domesticus*) exhibit clinal variation in overall body size, which was summarized from measurements of 16 skeletal features. Darker shading in the map indicates larger size.

genetic material through reproduction. Thus, when a cline extends over a large geographical gradient, distant populations may be genetically and morphologically distinct.

Despite the geographical variation that many species exhibit, even closely related species are genetically and morphologically different from each other. In the next section, we consider the mechanisms that maintain the genetic distinctness of closely related species by preventing their gene pools from mixing.

STUDY BREAK QUESTIONS

1. How do the morphological, biological, and phylogenetic species concepts differ?
2. What is clinal variation?

18.2 Maintaining Reproductive Isolation

The biological species concept uses the criterion of reproductive isolation to define species of sexually reproducing organisms: most individuals produce offspring by mating with another individual of their own species. Indeed, a variety of biological characteristics, collectively described as **reproductive isolating mechanisms**, prevent individuals of different species from mating and producing successful progeny. Thus, by reducing the chance of interspecific (between-species) mating and the production of **hybrid** offspring (i.e., offspring with parents of different species), these isolating mechanisms prevent the gene pools of distinct species from mixing.

Reproductive isolating mechanisms operate at different times during the reproductive process, and biologists categorize them as occurring either before or after an egg is fertilized (summarized in **Table 18.1**): **prezygotic isolating mechanisms** exert their effects before fertilization and the production of a zygote (a fertilized egg); **postzygotic isolating mechanisms** operate after fertilization and zygote formation. These isolating mechanisms are not mutually exclusive, and two or more of them may affect the outcome of a between-species interaction.

18.2a Prezygotic Isolating Mechanisms Prevent the Production of Hybrid Offspring

Biologists have identified five mechanisms that can prevent the production of hybrid offspring. Four of these mechanisms limit the frequency of interspecific matings, whereas one blocks interspecific fertilizations. These five prezygotic mechanisms are *ecological, temporal, behavioural, mechanical,* and *gametic isolation*.

Species living in the same geographical region may experience **ecological isolation** if they live in different habitats. For example, lions and tigers were both common in India until the mid-nineteenth century, when hunters virtually exterminated the Asian lions. However, because lions live in open grasslands and tigers in dense forests, the two species did not encounter one another and did not interbreed. Lion–tiger hybrids are sometimes born in captivity, but they do not occur under natural conditions.

TABLE 18.1	Reproductive Isolating Mechanisms	
Timing Relative to Fertilization	**Mechanism**	**Mode of Action**
Prezygotic ("premating") mechanisms	Ecological isolation	Species live in different habitats.
	Temporal isolation	Species breed at different times.
	Behavioural isolation	Species cannot communicate.
	Mechanical isolation	Species cannot physically mate.
	Gametic isolation	Species have nonmatching receptors on gametes.
Postzygotic ("postmating") mechanisms	Hybrid inviability	Hybrid offspring do not complete development.
	Hybrid sterility	Hybrid offspring cannot produce gametes.
	Hybrid breakdown	Hybrid offspring have reduced survival or fertility.

Species living in the same habitat can experience **temporal isolation** if they mate at different times of day or different times of year. For example, the fruit flies *Drosophila persimilis* and *Drosophila pseudoobscura* overlap extensively in their geographical distributions, but they do not interbreed, in part because *D. persimilis* mates in the morning and *D. pseudoobscura* in the afternoon. Similarly, two species of pine in California are reproductively isolated where their geographical distributions overlap: even though both rely on the wind to carry male gametes (pollen grains) to female gametes (ova) in other cones, *Pinus radiata* releases pollen in February and *Pinus muricata* releases pollen in April.

Many animals rely on specific signals, which may differ dramatically between species, to identify the species of a potential mate. **Behavioural isolation** results when the signals used by one species are not recognized by another. For example, female birds rely on the song, colour, and displays of males to identify members of their own species. Similarly, female fireflies identify males by their flashing patterns (**Figure 18.5**). These behaviours

(collectively called *courtship displays*) are often so complicated that signals sent by one species are like a foreign language that another species simply does not understand.

Mate choice by females and sexual selection (discussed in Chapter 17) generally drive the evolution of mate recognition signals. Females often spend substantial energy in reproduction, and choosing an appropriate mate (i.e., a male of her own species) is critically important for the production of successful young. By contrast, a female that mates with a male from a different species is unlikely to leave any surviving offspring at all. Over time, the number of males with recognizable traits, as well as the number of females able to recognize the traits, increases in the population.

Differences in the structure of reproductive organs or other body parts (**mechanical isolation**) may prevent individuals of different species from interbreeding. In particular, many plants have anatomical features that allow only certain pollinators, usually particular bird or insect species, to collect and distribute pollen. For example, the flowers and nectar of two native

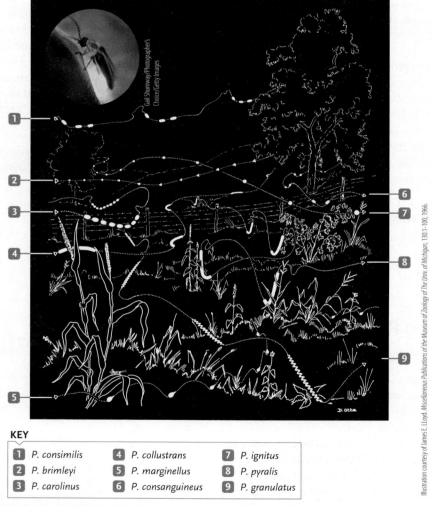

KEY

1	*P. consimilis*	4	*P. collustrans*	7	*P. ignitus*
2	*P. brimleyi*	5	*P. marginellus*	8	*P. pyralis*
3	*P. carolinus*	6	*P. consanguineus*	9	*P. granulatus*

FIGURE 18.5 Behavioural reproductive isolation. Male fireflies use bioluminescent signals to attract potential mates. The different flight paths and flashing patterns of males in nine North American *Photinus* species are represented here. Females respond only to the display given by males of their own species. The inset photo shows *P. pyralis*.

California plants, the purple monkey-flower (*Mimulus lewisii*) and the scarlet monkey-flower (*Mimulus cardinalis*), attract different animal pollinators (**Figure 18.6**). *M. lewisii* is pollinated by bumblebees. It has shallow purple flowers with broad petals that provide a landing platform for the bees. Bright yellow streaks on the petals serve as "nectar guides," directing bumblebees to the short nectar tube and reproductive parts, which are located among the petals. Bees enter the flowers to drink their concentrated nectar, and they pick up and deliver pollen as their legs and bodies brush against the reproductive parts of the flowers. *M. cardinalis*, by contrast, is pollinated by hummingbirds. It has long red flowers with no yellow streaks, and the reproductive parts extend above the petals. The red colour attracts hummingbirds but lies outside the colour range detected by bumblebees. The nectar of *M. cardinalis* is more dilute than that of *M. lewisii* but is produced in much greater quantity, making it easier for hummingbirds to ingest. When a hummingbird visits *M. cardinalis* flowers, it pushes its long bill down the nectar tube and its forehead touches the reproductive parts, picking up and delivering pollen. Recent research has demonstrated that, where the two monkey-flower species grow side by side, animal pollinators restrict their visits to either one species or the other 98% of the time, providing nearly complete reproductive isolation.

Even when individuals of different species mate, **gametic isolation**, an incompatibility between the sperm of one species and the eggs of another may prevent fertilization. Many marine invertebrates release gametes into the environment for external fertilization. The sperm and eggs of each species recognize one another's complementary surface proteins (see Chapter 44), but the surface proteins on the gametes of different species do not match. In animals with internal fertilization, sperm of one species may not survive and function within the reproductive tract of another. Interspecific matings between some *Drosophila* species, for example, induce a reaction in the female's reproductive tract that blocks "foreign" sperm from reaching eggs. Parallel physiological incompatibilities between a pollen tube and a stigma prevent interspecific fertilization in some plants.

18.2b Postzygotic Isolating Mechanisms Reduce the Success of Hybrid Individuals

If prezygotic isolating mechanisms between two closely related species are incomplete or ineffective, sperm from one species sometimes fertilizes an egg of the other species. In such cases, the two species will be reproductively isolated if their offspring (interspecific hybrids) have lower fitness than the offspring of intraspecific (within-species) matings. Three postzygotic isolating mechanisms, *hybrid inviability*, *hybrid sterility*, and *hybrid breakdown*, can reduce the fitness of hybrid individuals.

Many genes govern the complex processes that transform a zygote into a mature organism. Hybrid individuals have two sets of developmental instructions, one from each parent species, which may not interact properly for the successful completion of embryonic development. As a result, hybrid organisms frequently die as embryos or at an early age, a phenomenon called **hybrid inviability**. For example, domestic sheep and goats can mate and fertilize one another's ova, but the hybrid embryos always die before coming to term, presumably because the developmental programs of the two parent species are incompatible.

Although some hybrids between closely related species develop into healthy and vigorous adults, they may not produce functional gametes. This **hybrid sterility** often results when the parent species differ in the number or structure of their chromosomes, which cannot pair properly during meiosis. Such hybrids have zero fitness because they leave no descendants. The most familiar example is a mule, the product of mating between a female horse ($2n = 64$) and a male donkey ($2n = 62$). Zebroids, the offspring of matings between horses and zebras, are also usually sterile hybrids (**Figure 18.7**).

Some first-generation hybrids (F1; see Section 9.1b) are healthy and fully fertile. They can breed with other hybrids and with both parental species. However, the second generation (F2), produced by matings between F1 hybrids, or between F1 hybrids and either

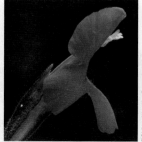

Purple monkey-flower (*Mimulus lewisii*) **Scarlet monkey-flower** (*Mimulus cardinalis*)

FIGURE 18.6 **Mechanical reproductive isolation.** Because of differences in floral structure, two species of monkey-flower attract different animal pollinators. *Mimulus lewisii* attracts bumblebees, and *Mimulus cardinalis* attracts hummingbirds.

FIGURE 18.7 **Interspecific hybrids.** Horses and zebroids (hybrid offspring of horses and zebras) running in a mixed herd. Zebroids are usually sterile.

parental species, may exhibit reduced survival or fertility, a phenomenon known as **hybrid breakdown**. For example, experimental crosses between *Drosophila* species may produce functional hybrids, but the offspring of hybrids experience high rates of chromosomal abnormalities and harmful types of genetic recombination. Thus, reproductive isolation is maintained between the species because there is little long-term mixing of their gene pools.

STUDY BREAK QUESTIONS

1. What is the difference between prezygotic and postzygotic isolating mechanisms?
2. When a male duck of one species performed a courtship display to a female of another species, she interpreted his behaviour as aggressive rather than amorous. What type of reproductive isolating mechanism does this scenario illustrate?

18.3   The Geography of Speciation

As Ernst Mayr recognized, geography has a huge impact on whether gene pools have the opportunity to mix. Biologists define two modes of speciation, based on the geographical relationship of populations as they become reproductively isolated: *allopatric speciation* (*allo* = different; *patria* = homeland) and *sympatric speciation* (*sym* = together).

18.3a   Allopatric Speciation Occurs between Geographically Separated Populations

Allopatric speciation may take place when a physical barrier subdivides a large population or when a small population becomes separated from a species' main geographical distribution. Allopatric speciation occurs in two stages. First, two populations become *geographically* separated, preventing gene flow between them. Then, as the populations experience distinct mutations as well as different patterns of natural selection and genetic drift, they may accumulate genetic differences that isolate them *reproductively*. Allopatric speciation is probably the most common mode of speciation in large animals.

Geographical separation sometimes occurs when a barrier divides a large population into two or more units (**Figure 18.8**). For example, hurricanes may create new channels that divide low coastal islands and the populations inhabiting them. Uplifting mountains or landmasses as well as rivers or advancing glaciers can also produce barriers that subdivide populations. The uplift of the Isthmus of Panama, caused by movements of Earth's crust about 5 million years ago, separated a once-continuous shallow sea into the eastern tropical Pacific Ocean and the western tropical Atlantic Ocean. Populations of marine organisms were subdivided by this event. In the tropical Atlantic Ocean, populations experienced patterns of mutation, natural selection, and genetic drift that were different from those experienced by populations in the tropical Pacific Ocean. As a result, the populations diverged genetically, and pairs of closely related species now live on either side of this divide (**Figure 18.9**).

In other cases, small populations may become isolated at the edge of a species' geographical distribution. Such peripheral populations often differ genetically from the central population because they are adapted to somewhat different environments. Once a small population is isolated, founder effects and small population size may promote genetic drift (see Section 17.3), and natural selection may favour the evolution of distinctive

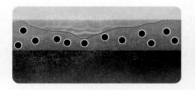 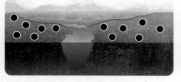  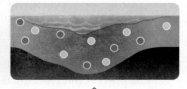

1 At first, a population is distributed over a large geographical area.

2 A geographical change separates the original population, creating a barrier to gene flow.

3 In the absence of gene flow, the separated populations evolve independently and diverge into different species.

4 When another geographical change allows individuals of the two species to come into secondary contact, they do not interbreed.

© Cengage Learning 2017.

FIGURE 18.8   Model of allopatric speciation and secondary contact

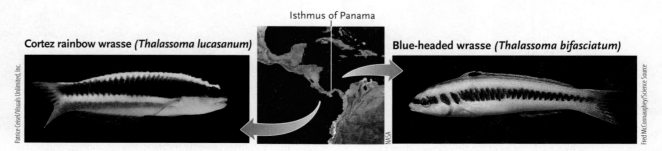

Isthmus of Panama

Cortez rainbow wrasse *(Thalassoma lucasanum)*

Blue-headed wrasse *(Thalassoma bifasciatum)*

Patrice Ceisel/Visuals Unlimited, Inc.

NASA

Fred McConnaughey/Science Source

FIGURE 18.9   Geographical separation. The uplift of the Isthmus of Panama divided an ancestral wrasse population. The Cortez rainbow wrasse now occupies the eastern Pacific Ocean, and the blue-headed wrasse now occupies the western Atlantic Ocean.

traits. If the isolated population experiences limited gene flow from the parent population, these agents of evolution will foster genetic differentiation between them. In time, the accumulated genetic differences may lead to reproductive isolation.

Populations established by colonization of oceanic islands represent extreme examples of this phenomenon. The founder effect makes the populations genetically distinct. And on oceanic archipelagos, such as the Galápagos and Hawaiian Islands, individuals from one island may colonize nearby islands, founding populations that differentiate into distinct species. Each island may experience multiple invasions, and the process may be repeated many times within the archipelago, leading to the evolution of a **species cluster**, a group of closely related species recently descended from a common ancestor (**Figure 18.10**). Sometimes a species cluster can evolve relatively quickly; for example, the nearly 800 species of fruit flies now living on the Hawaiian Islands evolved in less than 5 million years, an average of just over 6000 years per species.

18.3b Secondary Contact Provides a Test of Whether Allopatric Speciation Has Occurred

Allopatric populations may reestablish contact when a geographical barrier is eliminated or breached (see Figure 18.8, step 4). Such **secondary contact** (contact after a period of geographical isolation) provides a test of whether the genes in the populations have diverged enough to make them reproductively isolated. If their gene pools did not differentiate much during geographical separation, the populations will interbreed and merge into one, a phenomenon described as **species fusion**. But if, during their separation, the populations accumulated enough genetic differences to be reproductively isolated on secondary contact, they will be separate species. (The ecological consequences of secondary contact are described in Chapter 30.)

During the early stages of secondary contact, prezygotic reproductive isolation may be weak or incomplete. Some members of each population may mate with individuals from the other, producing viable, fertile offspring in areas called **hybrid zones**. Although some hybrid zones may persist for hundreds or thousands of years, they are generally narrow, and ecological or geographical factors maintain the separation of the gene pools for the majority of individuals in both species.

For example, the breeding ranges of Bullock's oriole (*Icterus bullocki*) and the Baltimore oriole (*Icterus galbula*) overlap in the Midwest of North America (**Figure 18.11**). In 2011, Matthew D. Carling, Lindsay G. Serene, and Irby J. Lovette of Cornell University published a genetic analysis of orioles where the geographical ranges overlap. Their research confirmed that the hybrid zone is narrow (only 325 km wide) and that it encompasses an area where two distinctive environments mix. Bullock's orioles live in the hotter and drier habitats to the west of the hybrid zone; Baltimore orioles occupy the cooler and moister habitats to the east. Researchers hypothesize that, although hybrid individuals may survive and reproduce in the

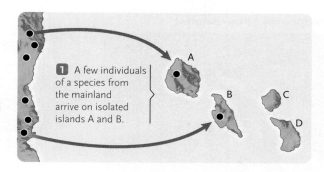

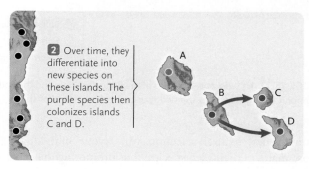

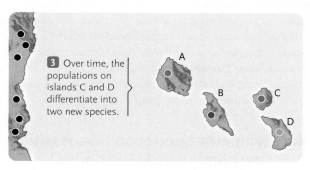

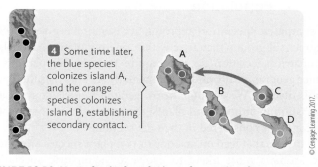

© Cengage Learning 2017.

FIGURE 18.10 Hypothetical evolution of a species cluster on an archipelago. Letters identify four islands in an archipelago; coloured dots represent different species. The ancestor of all the species is represented by black dots on the mainland. At the end of the process, islands A and B are each occupied by two species, and islands C and D are each occupied by one species, all of which evolved on the islands.

mixed habitat where the species' ranges overlap, hybrids may not be well adapted to either the dry habitats to the west or the moist habitats to the east. Thus, if natural selection eliminates hybrids outside the narrow hybrid zone, the two species will remain reproductively isolated.

Postzygotic isolating mechanisms often cause hybrids to have lower fitness than either parent species. Under these

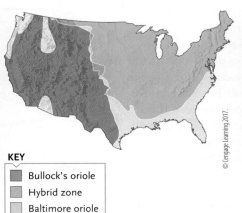

KEY

■ Bullock's oriole
▨ Hybrid zone
▨ Baltimore oriole

FIGURE 18.11 Hybrid zones. Males of the Bullock's oriole and the Baltimore oriole differ in colour and courtship song, but in mixed habitats where their geographical ranges overlap, the two species produce hybrid offspring.

circumstances, natural selection will favour individuals that choose mates of their own species, thus promoting the evolution of prezygotic isolating mechanisms. This phenomenon of the evolution of prezygotic barriers to reproduction after postzygotic barriers already exist is called **reinforcement** because the prezygotic mechanisms *reinforce* those postzygotic barriers. Studies of several *Drosophila* species suggest that reinforcement enhanced the reproductive isolation that had begun to develop while the populations were geographically separated.

18.3c Sympatric Speciation Occurs within One Continuously Distributed Population

In **sympatric speciation**, reproductive isolation evolves between distinct subgroups that arise within one population. Models of sympatric speciation do not require that the populations be either geographically or environmentally separated as their gene pools diverge. We examine below general models of sympatric speciation in animals and plants; the genetic basis of sympatric speciation is considered in the next section.

Insects that feed on just one or two plant species are among the animals most likely to evolve by sympatric speciation. These insects generally carry out most important life cycle activities on or near their "host" plants. Adults mate on the host plant; females lay their eggs on it; and larvae feed on the host plant's tissues, eventually developing into adults, which initiate another round of the life cycle. Host plant choice is genetically determined in many insect species; in others, individuals associate with the host plant species they ate as larvae.

Theoretically, a genetic mutation could suddenly change some insects' choice of host plant. Mutant individuals would shift their life cycle activities to the new host, and then interact primarily with others preferring the same new host, an example of ecological isolation. These individuals would collectively form a separate subpopulation, called a **host race**. Reproductive

isolation could evolve between different host races if the individuals of each host race are more likely to mate with members of their own host race than with members of another. Some biologists criticize this model, however, because it assumes that the genes controlling two traits, the insects' host plant choice and their mating preferences, change simultaneously. Moreover, host plant choice is controlled by multiple gene loci in some insect species, and it is clearly influenced by prior experience in others.

The apple maggot (*Rhagoletis pomonella*) is the most thoroughly studied example of possible sympatric speciation in animals (**Figure 18.12**). This fly's natural host plant in eastern North America is the hawthorn (*Crataegus* species), but at least two host races have appeared in the past 150 years. The larvae of a new host race were first discovered feeding on apples in New York State in the 1860s. In the 1960s, a cherry-feeding host race appeared in Wisconsin.

Genetic analyses have shown that variations at just a few gene loci underlie differences in the feeding preferences of *Rhagoletis* host races. Other genetic differences cause the host races to develop at different rates, and adults of the three races

FIGURE 18.12 Sympatric speciation in animals. Male and female apple maggots (*Rhagoletis pomonella*) court on a hawthorn leaf. The female will later lay her eggs on the fruit, and the offspring will feed, mate, and lay their eggs on hawthorns as well.

mate during different summer months. Nevertheless, individuals show no particular preference for mates of their own host race, at least under simplified laboratory conditions. Thus, although behavioural isolation has not developed between races, ecological and temporal isolation may separate adults in nature. Researchers are still not certain that the different host races are reproductively isolated under natural conditions.

In 2010, Andrew P. Michel, of the University of Notre Dame, and colleagues elsewhere in the United States and Germany published a genomic analysis of the apple- and hawthorn-feeding races of *Rhagoletis*. Their results suggest that, over the past 150 years, the two races have diverged at many loci in their genomes—not just at the loci that influence food choice and developmental rate—and that the divergence has largely been driven by disruptive selection, a diversifying form of natural selection (described in Chapter 17).

Sympatric speciation often occurs in plants through a genetic phenomenon, **polyploidy**, in which an individual has one or more *extra* copies of the entire haploid complement of chromosomes. Polyploidy can lead to speciation because these large-scale genetic changes may prevent polyploid individuals from breeding with individuals of the parent species. Nearly half of all flowering plant species are polyploid, including many important crops and ornamental species. The genetic mechanisms that produce polyploid individuals in plant populations are well understood; we describe them in the next section as part of a broader discussion of the genetics of speciation.

STUDY BREAK QUESTIONS

1. What are the two stages required for allopatric speciation?
2. Why might insects from different host races be unlikely to mate with each other?

18.4 Genetic Mechanisms of Speciation

What genetic changes lead to reproductive isolation between populations? In this section we examine three genetic mechanisms that can lead to reproductive isolation: *genetic divergence* between allopatric populations, *polyploidy* in sympatric populations, and *chromosome alterations* that occur independently of the geographical distributions of populations.

18.4a Genetic Divergence in Allopatric Populations Can Lead to Speciation

In the absence of gene flow, geographically separated populations inevitably accumulate genetic differences through the action of mutation, genetic drift, and natural selection.

How much genetic divergence is necessary for speciation to occur? To understand the genetic basis of speciation in closely related species, researchers first identify the specific causes of reproductive isolation. They then use standard techniques of genetic analysis along with new molecular, genomic, and bioinformatic approaches to analyze the genetic mechanisms that establish reproductive isolation. In cases of postzygotic reproductive isolation, mutations in just a few gene loci can establish reproductive isolation. For example, if two common aquarium fishes, swordtails (*Xiphophorus helleri*) and platys (*Xiphophorus maculatus*), mate, two genes induce the development of lethal tumours in their hybrid offspring. When hybrid sterility is the primary cause of reproductive isolation between *Drosophila* species, at least five gene loci are responsible. About 55 gene loci contribute to postzygotic reproductive isolation between the European fire-bellied toad (*Bombina bombina*) and the yellow-bellied toad (*Bombina variegata*).

In cases of prezygotic reproductive isolation, some mechanisms have a surprisingly simple genetic basis. For example, a single mutation reverses the direction of coiling in the shells of some snails (*Bradybaena* species): some individuals coil in a clockwise spiral and others in a counterclockwise spiral. Snails with shells that coil in opposite directions cannot approach each other closely enough to mate, making reproduction between them mechanically impossible.

Many traits that now function as prezygotic isolating mechanisms may have evolved in response to sexual selection (described in Chapter 17). In sexually dimorphic species, this evolutionary process exaggerates showy structures and courtship behaviours in males, the traits that females use to identify appropriate mates. When two populations encounter one another on secondary contact, these traits may also prevent interspecific mating. For example, many closely related duck species exhibit dramatic variation in the appearance of males, but not females (**Figure 18.13**), an almost certain sign of sexual selection. Yet these species hybridize readily in captivity, producing offspring that are both viable and fertile.

Reproductive isolation and speciation in ducks and other sexually dimorphic birds probably results from geographical isolation and sexual selection on just a few morphological and behavioural characteristics that influence their mating behaviour. Thus, sometimes the evolution of reproductive isolation

Mallard ducks *(Anas platyrhynchos)*   Pintail ducks *(Anas acuta)*

FIGURE 18.13 Sexual selection and prezygotic isolation. In closely related species, such as mallard and pintail ducks, males have much more distinctive coloration than females, a sure sign of sexual selection at work.

may not require much genetic change at all. Indeed, sexual selection appears to increase the rate at which new species arise: bird lineages that are sexually dimorphic generally include more species than do related lineages in which males and females have a similar appearance.

18.4b Polyploidy Is a Common Mechanism of Sympatric Speciation in Plants

Polyploidy is common among plants, and it may be an important factor in the evolution of some fish, amphibian, and reptile species. Polyploid individuals can arise from chromosome duplications within a single species (autopolyploidy) or through hybridization of different species (allopolyploidy).

AUTOPOLYPLOIDY In **autopolyploidy (Figure 18.14a)**, a diploid ($2n$) individual may produce, for example, tetraploid ($4n$) offspring, each of which has four complete chromosome sets. Autopolyploidy often results when gametes, through an error in either mitosis or meiosis, spontaneously receive the same number of chromosomes as a somatic cell. Such gametes are called **unreduced gametes** because their chromosome number has not been reduced compared with that of somatic cells.

Diploid pollen can fertilize the diploid ovules of a self-fertilizing individual, or it may fertilize diploid ovules on another plant with unreduced gametes. The resulting tetraploid offspring can reproduce either by self-pollination or by breeding with other tetraploid individuals. However, a tetraploid plant cannot produce fertile offspring by hybridizing with its diploid

a. Speciation by autopolyploidy in plants
A spontaneous doubling of chromosomes during meiosis produces diploid gametes. If the plant fertilizes itself, a tetraploid zygote will be produced.

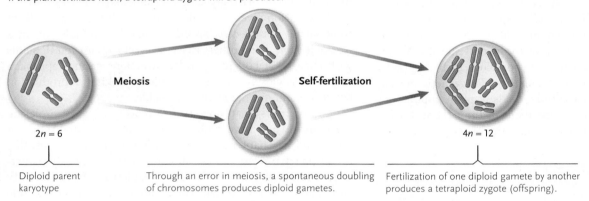

Diploid parent karyotype

Through an error in meiosis, a spontaneous doubling of chromosomes produces diploid gametes.

Fertilization of one diploid gamete by another produces a tetraploid zygote (offspring).

b. Speciation by hybridization and allopolyploidy in plants
A hybrid mating between two species followed by a doubling of chromosomes during mitosis in gametes of the hybrid can instantly create sets of homologous chromosomes. Self-fertilization can then generate polyploid individuals that are reproductively isolated from both parent species.

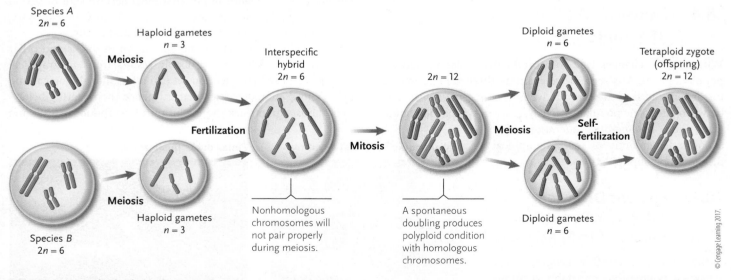

Nonhomologous chromosomes will not pair properly during meiosis.

A spontaneous doubling produces polyploid condition with homologous chromosomes.

© Cengage Learning 2017.

FIGURE 18.14 Polyploidy in plants. (a) Speciation by autopolyploidy in plants can occur by a spontaneous doubling of chromosomes during meiosis, producing diploid gametes. If the plant fertilizes itself, a tetraploid zygote will result. **(b)** Speciation by hybridization and allopolyploidy in plants can occur when two species mate, producing a hybrid. If chromosomes are doubled during mitosis in gametes of the hybrid, sets of homologous chromosomes are created instantly. Self-fertilization can then generate polyploid individuals that are reproductively isolated from both parent species.

parents. The fusion of a diploid gamete with a normal haploid gamete produces a triploid (3n) offspring, which is usually sterile because its odd number of chromosomes cannot segregate properly during meiosis. Thus, the tetraploid is reproductively isolated from the original diploid population. Many species of grasses, shrubs, and ornamental plants, including violets, chrysanthemums, and nasturtiums, are autopolyploids, having anywhere from 4 to 20 complete chromosome sets.

ALLOPOLYPLOIDY In **allopolyploidy** (Figure 18.14b), two closely related species hybridize and subsequently form polyploid offspring. Hybrid offspring are sterile if the two parent species have diverged enough that their chromosomes do not pair properly during meiosis. However, if the hybrid's chromosome number is doubled, the chromosome complement of the gametes is also doubled, producing homologous chromosomes that *can* pair during meiosis. The hybrid can then produce polyploid gametes and, through self-fertilization or fertilization with other doubled hybrids, establish a population of a new polyploid species. Compared with speciation by genetic divergence, speciation by allopolyploidy can be extremely rapid, causing a new species to arise in one generation without geographical isolation.

Even when sterile, polyploids are often robust, growing larger than either parent species. For that reason, both autopolyploids and allopolyploids—including plantains (cooking bananas), coffee, cotton, potatoes, sugarcane, and tobacco—have been important to agriculture. For example, bread wheat (*Triticum aestivum*), a staple food for at least 30% of the worldwide human population, arose through a series of hybridization events. Recent research by members of the International Wheat Genome Sequencing Consortium that was published in the journal *Science* in July 2014 has begun to reveal details of its genetics and ancestry (**Figure 18.15**). The bread wheat genome includes three diploid subgenomes (identified as AA, BB, and DD) that originated in different

ancestors. About 6.5 million years ago, divergence from a wheat-like ancestor produced lineages with subgenomes AA and BB. One million years later, hybridization between descendants of those lineages produced the lineage with subgenome DD. All three subgenomes are diploid, with two sets of seven chromosomes (2n = 14). Then, about 800 000 years ago, a hybridization between two species in lineage AA (*T. monococcum* and *T. urartu*) with one species from lineage BB (a close relative of

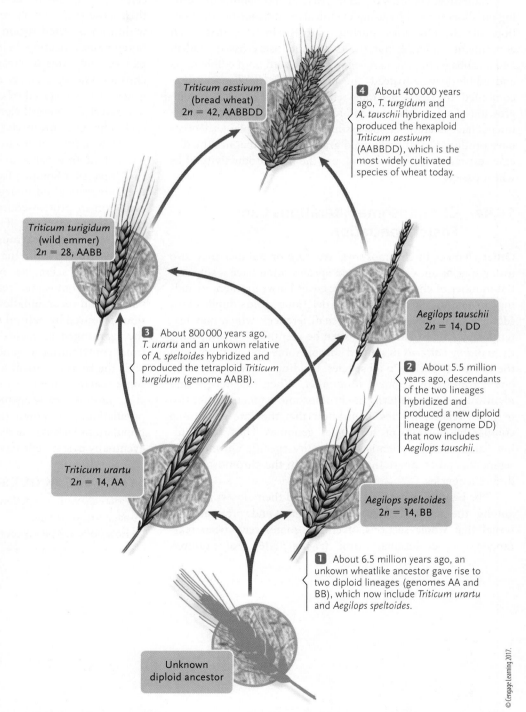

4 About 400 000 years ago, *T. turgidum* and *A. tauschii* hybridized and produced the hexaploid *Triticum aestivum* (AABBDD), which is the most widely cultivated species of wheat today.

3 About 800 000 years ago, *T. urartu* and an unkown relative of *A. speltoides* hybridized and produced the tetraploid *Triticum turgidum* (genome AABB).

2 About 5.5 million years ago, descendants of the two lineages hybridized and produced a new diploid lineage (genome DD) that now includes *Aegilops tauschii*.

1 About 6.5 million years ago, an unkown wheatlike ancestor gave rise to two diploid lineages (genomes AA and BB), which now include *Triticum urartu* and *Aegilops speltoides*.

Triticum aestivum (bread wheat) 2n = 42, AABBDD

Triticum turigidum (wild emmer) 2n = 28, AABB

Aegilops tauschii 2n = 14, DD

Triticum urartu 2n = 14, AA

Aegilops speltoides 2n = 14, BB

Unknown diploid ancestor

© Cengage Learning 2017.

FIGURE 18.15 The evolution of wheat. Researchers believe the evolution of common bread wheat (*Triticum aestivum*) resulted from a series of hybridizations, some of which produced allopolyploid species.

Aegilops speltoides) produced a tetraploid (2n = 28, AABB) wheat, emmer (*Triticum turgidum*), which is still cultivated in the Middle East. About 400 000 years ago, *T. turgidum* hybridized with a diploid species in lineage DD (*A. tauschii*), producing the hexaploid (2n = 42, AABBDD) bread wheat (*T. aestivum*) that is widely grown today. Each of the three ancestors contributed two sets of seven chromosomes to bread wheat, making it a hexaploid with a total of 42 chromosomes.

Plant breeders often try to increase the probability of forming an allopolyploid by using chemicals that foster nondisjunction of chromosomes during mitosis. In the first such experiment, undertaken in the 1920s, scientists crossed a radish and a cabbage, hoping to develop a plant with both edible roots and edible leaves. Instead, the new species, *Raphanobrassica*, combined the least desirable characteristics of each parent, growing a cabbagelike root and radish like leaves. Recent experiments have been more successful. For example, plant scientists have produced an allopolyploid grain, triticale, that has the disease resistance of its rye parent and the high productivity of its wheat parent.

18.4c Chromosome Alterations Can Foster Speciation

Other changes in chromosome structure or number may also foster speciation. Closely related species often have a substantial number of chromosome differences between them, including inversions, translocations, deletions, and duplications (described in Section 10.3). These differences, which may foster postzygotic isolation, can often be identified by comparing the *banding patterns* in stained chromosome preparations from the different species. In all species, banding patterns vary from one chromosome segment to another. When researchers find identical banding patterns in chromosome segments from two or more related species, they know that they are examining comparable portions of the species' genomes. Thus, the banding patterns allow scientists to identify specific chromosome segments and compare their positions in the chromosomes of different species.

The banding patterns of humans and their closest relatives among the apes—chimpanzees, gorillas, and orangutans—reveal that whole sections of chromosomes have been rearranged over evolutionary time (**Figure 18.16**). For example,

humans have a diploid complement of 46 chromosomes, whereas chimpanzees, gorillas, and orangutans have 48 chromosomes. The difference can be traced to the fusion (i.e., the joining together) of two ancestral chromosomes into chromosome 2 of humans; the ancestral chromosomes are separate in the other three species.

Moreover, banding patterns suggest that the position of the centromere in human chromosome 2 closely matches that of a centromere in one of the chimpanzee chromosomes, reflecting their close evolutionary relationship. But this centromere falls within an inverted region of the chromosome in gorillas and orangutans, reflecting their evolutionary divergence from chimpanzees and humans. (Recall from Section 10.3 that an inverted chromosome segment has a reversed orientation, so the order of genes on it is reversed relative to the order in a segment that is not inverted.) Nevertheless, humans and chimps differ from each other in centromeric inversions in six other chromosomes.

How might such chromosome rearrangements promote speciation? In a paper published in 2003, Arcadi Navarro, of the Universitat Pompeu Fabra in Spain, and Nick H. Barton, of the University of Edinburgh in Scotland, compared the rates of evolution in protein-coding genes that lie within rearranged chromosome segments of humans and chimpanzees to those in genes outside the rearranged segments. They discovered that proteins evolved more than twice as quickly in the rearranged chromosome segments. Navarro and Barton reasoned that, because chromosome rearrangements inhibit chromosome pairing and recombination during meiosis, new genetic variations favoured by natural selection would be conserved within the rearranged segments. These variations accumulate over time, contributing to genetic divergence between populations with the rearrangement and those without it. Thus, chromosome rearrangements can be a trigger for speciation: once a chromosome rearrangement becomes established within a population, that population will diverge more rapidly from populations lacking the rearrangement. The genetic divergence eventually causes reproductive isolation.

STUDY BREAK QUESTIONS

1. How can natural selection promote reproductive isolation in allopatric populations?
2. How does polyploidy promote speciation in plants?

FIGURE 18.16 **Observational Research**

Chromosomal Similarities and Differences among Humans and the Great Apes

Question: Does chromosome structure differ between humans and their closest relatives among the apes?

Hypothesis: Large-scale chromosome rearrangements contributed to the development of reproductive isolation between species within the evolutionary lineage that includes humans and apes.

Prediction: Chromosome structure differs markedly between humans and their close relatives among the great apes: chimpanzees, gorillas, and orangutans.

Method: Jorge J. Yunis and Om Prakash, of the University of Minnesota Medical School, used Giemsa stain to visualize the banding patterns on metaphase chromosome preparations from humans, chimpanzees, gorillas, and orangutans. They identified about 1000 bands that are present in humans and in the three ape species. By matching the banding patterns on the chromosomes, the researchers verified that they were comparing the same segments of the genomes in the four species. They then searched for similarities and differences in the structure of the chromosomes.

Results: Analysis of human chromosome 2 reveals that it was produced by the fusion of two smaller chromosomes that are still present in the other three species. Although the position of the centromere in human chromosome 2 matches that of the centromere in one of the chimpanzee chromosomes, in gorillas and orangutans it falls within an inverted segment of the chromosome.

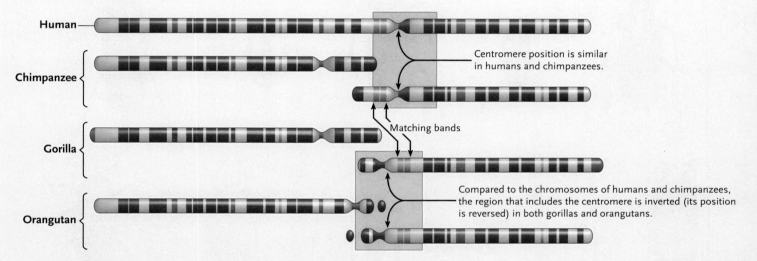

Conclusion: Differences in chromosome structure between humans and both gorillas and orangutans are more pronounced than they are between humans and chimpanzees. Structural differences in the chromosomes of these four species may contribute to their reproductive isolation.

Source: © Cengage Learning 2017. Based on J. J. Yunis and O. Prakash. 1982. The origin of man: A chromosomal pictorial legacy. *Science* 215:1525–1530.

Summary Illustration

When microevolutionary processes differ between populations of a species, the populations will diverge genetically and may eventually be recognized as distinct species. Macroevolution refers to the broader pattern of events that occur, which result in species formation. Studying speciation involves understanding how individual species are defined and recognized, as well as events that influence the process.

Morphological Species
If two organisms look the same, they are the same species.

There are an estimated 350 000 different species of beetles. But what is a species?

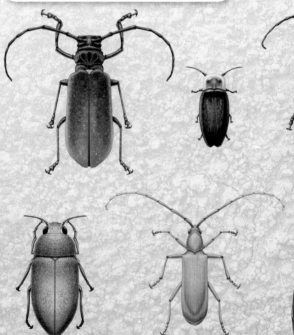

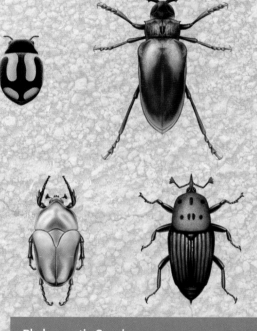

Biological Species
If the members of two populations interbreed and produce fertile offspring, then they belong to the same species.

Phylogenetic Species
Populations that share a recent evolutionary history belong to the same species.

Species can exhibit geographical variation. Populations can differ genetically and phenotypically due to geographical separation.

A	B	C	D	E

Clinal variation across five populations of a species

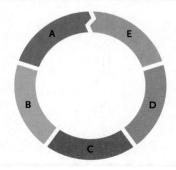

Individual populations may form a ring around a geographic barrier. Populations at the two extremes of the cline, however, are unable to reproduce.

Reproductive isolation prevents individuals of different species from mating and producing viable progeny. This maintains the genetic identity of a species.

Prezygotic isolating mechanisms		Postzygotic isolating mechanisms
Premating	Mating	Fertilization

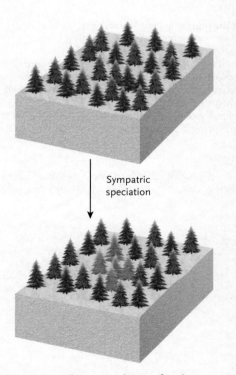

Species 1

Ecological isolation
Species at the same locale occupy different habitats.

Temporal isolation
Species reproduce at different seasons or different times of day.

Behavioural isolation
In animal species, courtship behaviour differs, or individuals respond to different songs, calls, pheromones, or other signals.

Species 2

Mechanical isolation
Genitalia between species are unsuitable for one another.

Gametic isolation
Sperm cannot reach or fertilize the egg.

Hybrid inviability
Fertilization occurs, but the zygote does not survive.

Hybrid sterility
The hybrid survives, but is sterile.

Hybrid breakdown
The hybrid is fertile, but the F₂ hybrid has reduced fitness.

Hybrid offspring

The two modes of speciation are defined based on the geographical relationships of the populations.

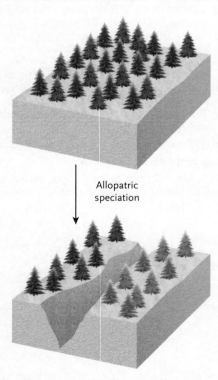

Allopatric speciation

Sympatric speciation

Often slow accumulation of genetic differences due to mutation, genetic drift, and natural selection

Sometimes very rapid genetic isolation, often due to formation of polyploids (e.g., autopolyploidy, allopollyploidy)

SELF-TEST QUESTIONS

Recall/Understand

1. Who is the "father" of the science that identifies, names, and classifies new species?
   a. Charles Darwin
   b. Alfred Wallace
   c. Carolus Linnaeus
   d. Jean Baptiste de Lamarck

2. On what basis does the biological species concept define species?
   a. reproductive characteristics
   b. biochemical characteristics
   c. morphological characteristics
   d. behavioural characteristics

3. Which of the following is a characteristic of prezygotic isolating mechanisms?
   a. They generally prevent zygotes from surviving and reproducing.
   b. They generally prevent individuals of different species from producing zygotes.
   c. They are found only in plants.
   d. They are observed only in organisms that reproduce asexually.

4. In the model of allopatric speciation, which of the following is characteristic of the geographical separation of two populations?
   a. It occurs only after speciation is complete.
   b. It allows gene flow between them.
   c. It reduces the relative fitness of hybrid offspring.
   d. It inhibits gene flow between them.

5. Adjacent populations that produce hybrid offspring with low relative fitness may be undergoing which of the following?
   a. clinal isolation
   b. parapatric speciation
   c. allopatric speciation
   d. sympatric speciation

6. Which of the following could be an example of allopolyploidy?
   a. Chromosome number in the offspring is exactly half that of the parents.
   b. Gametes and somatic cells have the same number of chromosomes.
   c. Chromosome number increases by one in a gamete and in the offspring it produces.
   d. Chromosome number decreases by one in a gamete and in the offspring it produces.

Apply/Analyze

7. The name of the North American beaver is *Castor canadensis*. What does the "*canadensis*" part of its unique name represent?
   a. genus
   b. epithet
   c. domain
   d. family

8. If two species of holly (genus *Ilex*) flower during different months, how might their gene pools be kept separate?
   a. mechanical isolation
   b. ecological isolation
   c. gametic isolation
   d. temporal isolation

9. While attempting to cross a llama with an alpaca for finer wool, an animal breeder found that the hybrid offspring rarely lived more than a few weeks. Which of the following terms best explains this outcome?
   a. prezygotic reproductive isolation
   b. postzygotic reproductive isolation
   c. sympatric speciation
   d. polyploidy

10. Which of the following would apply to evaluating hybrid zones?
    a. the behaviour of the individuals
    b. the morphology of the individuals
    c. the prezygotic isolation mechanisms
    d. the postzygotic isolating mechanisms

Create/Evaluate

11. Suppose that you observe two neighbouring populations of squirrels coexisting in the wild. You consult the literature and you find that these two populations are genetically connected, but that they still do not interbreed. Based on the information that you collected, which of the following are these populations most likely?
    a. hybrid species
    b. same species
    c. ring species
    d. different species

12. Suppose that an original population gets separated by a river flow, and that the individuals came into contact after the river had dried up. Which of the following would most likely indicate that the speciation has occurred?
    a. The individuals in one population look morphologically different from the individuals in another population.
    b. The individuals of the two populations do not interbreed.
    c. The individuals in one population look morphologically the same as individuals in another population.
    d. The individuals of the two populations interbreed successfully.

13. Suggest three limitations of the biological species concept.

14. Compare species and subspecies.

15. A tigon is an offspring of a male tiger and a female lion. Explain why we do not see tigons in the wild.

Chapter Roadmap

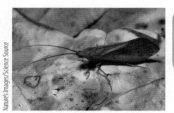

Nature's Images/Science Source

Systematics and Phylogenetics: Revealing the Tree of Life

The diversity of life on Earth is astonishing. In this chapter we discuss the approaches scientists use to organize this diversity: from how organisms are named and classified to the tools and techniques employed to understand evolutionary relationship among species.

19.1 Nomenclature and Classification

Using a system of binomial nomenclature, species are grouped into a taxonomic hierarchy.

19.2 Phylogenetic Trees

Phylogenetic trees attempt to depict the evolutionary history of a group of organisms.

19.3 Sources of Data for Phylogenetic Analyses

Phylogenetic trees are built using a range of data, from morphological characters to molecular sequences.

Millard H. Sharp/Science Source

19.4 Traditional Classification and Paraphyletic Groups

Traditional systematics assesses the amount of phenotypic divergence between lineages as well as the patterns of branching evolution that produced them.

19.5 The Cladistic Revolution

Compared to transitional methods, with cladistics, classifications are based solely on evolutionary relationships.

19.6 Phylogenetic Trees as Research Tools

Phylogenetic trees are very useful tools that facilitate research in many areas of biology.

19.7 Molecular Phylogenetic Analyses

The building of phylogenetic relationships based on sequence data has resolved some evolutionary puzzles that were not easily addressed using other techniques.

Systematics and Phylogenetics: Revealing the Tree of Life

19

Why it matters ... Mention the word "malaria" and people envision old movies about the tropics: explorers wander through the jungle in pith helmets and sleep under mosquito netting; clouds of insects hover nearby, ready to infect them with *Plasmodium*, the protistan parasite that causes this disease. You may be surprised to learn, however, that less than 100 years ago, malaria was also a serious threat in the southeastern United States and much of Western Europe.

Scientists puzzled over the cause of malaria for thousands of years. Hippocrates, a Greek physician who worked in the fifth century BCE, knew that people who lived near malodorous marshes often suffered from fevers and swollen spleens. Indeed, the name *malaria* is derived from the Latin for "bad air." By 1900, scientists had established that mosquitoes, *Plasmodium*'s intermediate hosts, transmit the parasite to humans. Mosquitoes breed in standing water, and anyone living nearby is likely to suffer their bites.

Until the 1920s, scientists thought that the mosquito species *Anopheles maculipennis* carried malaria in Europe. But some areas with huge populations of these insects had little human malaria, whereas other areas had relatively few mosquitoes and a high incidence of the disease.

Then, a French researcher reported variation in the mosquitoes, and Dutch scientists identified two forms of the "species," only one of which seemed to carry malaria. The breakthrough came in 1924, when a retired public health inspector in Italy discovered that individual mosquitoes—all thought to be the same species—produced eggs with one of six distinctive surface patterns (**Figure 19.1**).

a. *Anopheles* mosquito feeding on human blood

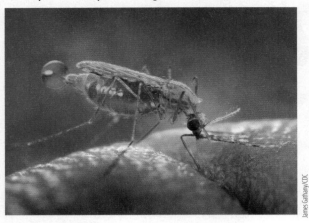

James Gathany/CDC

b. Eggs of six European *Anopheles* mosquito species

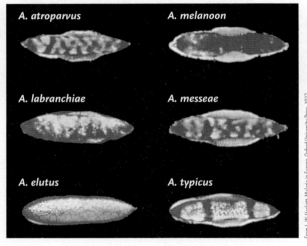

A. atroparvus

A. melanoon

A. labranchiae

A. messeae

A. elutus

A. typicus

From L. W. Hackett, Malaria in Europe, Oxford University Press, 1937.

FIGURE 19.1 **Carriers of malaria. (a)** Like other *Anopheles* mosquitoes, *A. gambiae* frequently take a blood meal from a human host. **(b)** Differences in surface patterns on the eggs of *Anopheles* mosquitoes in Europe helped researchers identify six separate species. The adults of all six species look remarkably alike.

Further research revealed that the name *Anopheles maculipennis* had been applied to six separate mosquito species. Although the adults of these species are almost indistinguishable, their eggs are clearly different. The species are reproductively isolated from each other, and they differ ecologically: some breed in brackish coastal marshes, others in inland freshwater marshes, and still others in slow-moving streams. Only some of these species have a preference for human blood, and researchers eventually determined that only three of them routinely transmit malaria to humans.

These discoveries explained why the geographical distributions of mosquitoes and malaria did not always match. And government agencies could finally fight malaria by eradicating the disease-carrying species. Health workers drained marshes to prevent mosquitoes from breeding. They used insecticides to kill mosquito larvae or introduced fish of the genus *Gambusia*, the mosquitofish, which eats them. These targeted control

programs were very successful in the early and middle decades of the twentieth century.

Today, with the increased mobility of humans, agricultural products, and other goods, some mosquito species—as well as many other organisms—are invading habitats made more hospitable by global climate change (discussed further in Unit 6). Some mosquito species have expanded their geographical ranges substantially: introduced mosquito species have been discovered on all continents except Antarctica. Mosquitoes carry numerous agents of disease, and biologists are now devising new ways to recognize, and eradicate, the species that pose the greatest threats to human welfare.

The historic eradication of malaria in Europe owes a debt to **systematics**, the branch of biology that studies the diversity of life and its evolutionary relationships. Systematic biologists (*systematists* for short) identify, describe, name, and classify organisms, organizing their observations within a framework that reflects the organisms' evolutionary relationships. In this chapter, we briefly describe the traditional approach to classification. We then focus attention on how systematists working today develop hypotheses about the evolutionary relationships of all the branches, twigs, and leaves on the Tree of Life.

19.1 Nomenclature and Classification

The Swedish naturalist Carl von Linné (1707–1778), better known by his Latinized name, Carolus Linnaeus, was the first modern practitioner of **taxonomy**, the science that identifies, names, and classifies new species. A professor at the University of Uppsala, Linnaeus sent ill-prepared students around the world to gather specimens, losing perhaps a third of his followers to the rigors of their expeditions. Although he may not have been a commendable student adviser, Linnaeus developed the basic system of naming and classifying organisms that biologists embraced for two centuries.

19.1a Linnaeus Developed the System of Binomial Nomenclature

Linnaeus invented the system of **binomial nomenclature** in which species are assigned a Latinized two-part name, or **binomial**. The first part of the name identifies a **genus** (plural, *genera*), a group of species with similar characteristics. The second part is the **specific epithet**, or species name. When identifying and naming a new species, Linnaeus used the morphological species concept (described in Section 18.1), assigning the same scientific name to individuals that shared anatomical characteristics.

A combination of the generic name and the specific epithet provides a unique name for every species. For example, *Ursus maritimus* is the polar bear and *Ursus arctos* is the brown bear. By convention, the first letter of a generic name is always capitalized; the specific epithet is never capitalized; and the entire binomial is italicized. In addition, the specific epithet is never used without the full or abbreviated generic name preceding it because the same specific epithet is often given to species in different genera. For instance, *Ursus americanus* is the American black bear, *Homarus americanus* is the Atlantic lobster, and *Bufo americanus* is the American toad. If you were to order just *"americanus"* for dinner, you might be dismayed when your plate arrived—unless you have an adventurous palate!

Nonscientists often use different common names to identify a species. For example, *Bothrops asper*, a poisonous snake native to Central and South America, is called *barba amarilla* (meaning "yellow beard") in some places and *cola blanca* (meaning "white tail") in others; biologists have recorded about 50 local names for this species. Adding to the confusion, the same common name is sometimes used for several different species. Binomials, however, allow people everywhere to discuss organisms unambiguously.

Many binomials are descriptive of the organism or its habitat. *Asparagus horridus*, for example, is a spiny plant. Other species, such as the South American bird *Rhea darwinii*, are named for notable biologists. The naming of newly discovered species follows a formal process of publishing a description of the species in a scientific journal. International commissions meet periodically to settle disputes about scientific names.

19.1b Linnaeus Devised the Taxonomic Hierarchy to Organize Information about Species

Linnaeus described and named thousands of species on the basis of their morphological similarities and differences. Keeping track of so many species was no easy task, so he devised a **classification**, a conceptual filing system that arranges organisms into ever more inclusive categories. Linnaeus' classification, called the **taxonomic hierarchy**, includes a nested series of formal categories (from most inclusive to least): domain, kingdom, phylum, class, order, family, genus, species, and subspecies (**Figure 19.2**). The organisms included within any category of the taxonomic hierarchy compose a **taxon** (plural, *taxa*). Woodpeckers, for example, are a taxon (Picidae) at the family level, and pine trees are a taxon (*Pinus*) at the genus level.

Species that are included in the same taxon at the bottom of the hierarchy (i.e., in the same genus or family) generally share many characteristics. By contrast, species that are included in the same taxon only near the top of the hierarchy (i.e., the same kingdom or phylum) generally share much fewer traits (see Figure 19.2). The hierarchy has been a great convenience for biologists because every taxon is defined by a set of shared characteristics. Thus, when a biologist refers to a

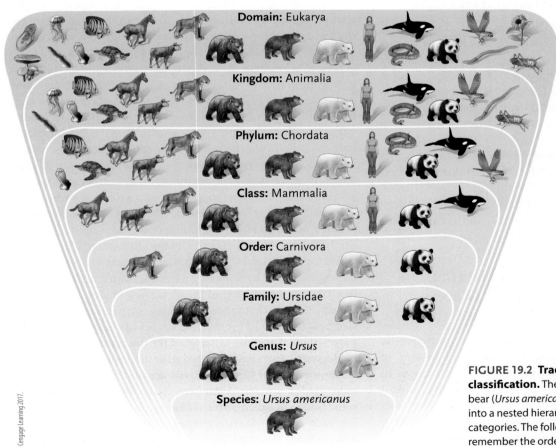

© Cengage Learning 2017.

Domain: Eukarya

Kingdom: Animalia

Phylum: Chordata

Class: Mammalia

Order: Carnivora

Family: Ursidae

Genus: *Ursus*

Species: *Ursus americanus*

FIGURE 19.2 Traditional hierarchical classification. The classification of the American black bear (*Ursus americanus*) illustrates how each species fits into a nested hierarchy of even more inclusive categories. The following sentence can help you remember the order of categories in a classification, from Domain to Species: Diligent Kindly Professors Cannot Often Fail Good Students.

member of the family Picidae, all of his or her colleagues understand that the biologist is talking about a medium-sized bird that uses its stout bill to drill holes in tree trunks.

1. How does the system of binomial nomenclature minimize ambiguity in the naming and identification of species?
2. How does the taxonomic hierarchy help biologists organize information about different species?

19.2 Phylogenetic Trees

As we discussed briefly in Chapter 16, Linnaeus devised the taxonomic hierarchy long before Darwin published his theory of evolution. His goals were to illuminate the details of God's creation and to devise a practical way for naturalists to keep track of their discoveries. But the science of systematics changed in response to Darwin's idea that all organisms in the Tree of Life are descended from a distant common ancestor: systematists began to focus on discovering the evolutionary relationships between groups of organisms.

19.2a Systematists Adapted Linnaeus' Approach to a Darwinian Worldview

The taxonomic hierarchy that Linnaeus defined was easily adapted to Darwin's concept of branching evolution; as we discussed in Chapter 18, ancestral species give rise to descendant species through repeated branching of a lineage. Organisms in the same genus generally share a fairly recent common ancestor, whereas those assigned to the same higher taxonomic category, such as a class or phylum, share a common ancestor that lived in the more distant past.

In the second half of the nineteenth century, systematists began to reconstruct the **phylogeny** (i.e., the evolutionary history) of organisms. Phylogenies are illustrated in **phylogenetic trees**, which are formal hypotheses that identify likely relationships among species and higher taxonomic groups. And like all hypotheses, they are constantly revised as scientists gather new data.

19.2b A Phylogenetic Tree Depicts the Evolutionary History of a Group of Organisms

Contemporary evolutionary biologists construct phylogenetic trees to illustrate the hypothesized evolutionary history of organisms. Researchers tailor the breadth of their analyses to match specific research questions. Thus, some trees might include the evolutionary history of all known organisms; others a small cluster of closely related populations within a species; and still others a group somewhere between those extremes. Regardless of how wide a range of organisms is included, all phylogenetic trees share a specific structure and depict key relationships in similar ways (**Figure 19.3**).

For example, phylogenetic trees are usually drawn along an implicit or explicit timeline. In this book, phylogenetic trees are generally depicted vertically; the most ancient organisms and evolutionary events are at the bottom of the tree (often labelled "long ago"), and the most recent are at the top (often labelled "present"). The common ancestor of all species included in the tree is described as the **root** of the tree. In a few cases in this book, trees are presented with the root on the left, with time passing from left to right.

The tempo of evolution varies within and among lineages. In some cases, evolutionary changes may accumulate slowly in a lineage as the environment shifts over time. This pattern of gradual phyletic change is often described as *anagenesis*. If the changes through time are substantial and the fossil record is incomplete, paleontologists who discover morphologically distinct fossils in different strata may assign them different species names and say that "the ancestral species A evolved into the descendant species B." But the production of such "new" species by anagenesis does not increase biodiversity; rather, it is simply the gradual transformation of one "species" into another as its characteristics shifted over time. Anagenesis is often illustrated by a straight line in a phylogenetic tree.

In other circumstances, an ancestral species undergoes speciation, producing two descendant species, both of which are distinct from their common ancestor. This pattern of evolution is described as *cladogenesis*, a process that *does* increase biodiversity. Cladogenesis is depicted in a phylogenetic tree by a branching pattern, with two descendants arising from their common ancestor. When they first emerge, the two branches may represent new species. But as cladogenesis continues repeatedly through evolutionary time—with branches giving rise to branchlets and branchlets to twigs—each of those new species may become the common ancestor of its own many descendants. Thus, each new species produced by cladogenesis has the potential to become the "root" of its own evolutionary lineage.

When reading a phylogenetic tree, each branching point is called a **node**, and each evolutionary lineage—a node with all the branches, branchlets, and twigs that emerge from it—is called a **clade** (*klados* = branch). You can identify a clade on any phylogenetic tree by following a lineage from a node to the tips of all its twigs at the top of the tree. Some clades, such as Aves (birds), include thousands of species, whereas others, such as *Geospiza* (a genus of ground and cactus finches from the Galápagos Islands), include just a few. Like the taxonomic hierarchy, phylogenetic trees have a nested structure: younger and smaller clades, such as the genus *Geospiza*, are nested within larger and older clades, such as Aves. Two clades that emerge from the same node are called **sister clades** (or *sister taxa*) because they are each other's closest relatives; similarly, two species that emerge from the same node near the very top of the tree are described as **sister species**.

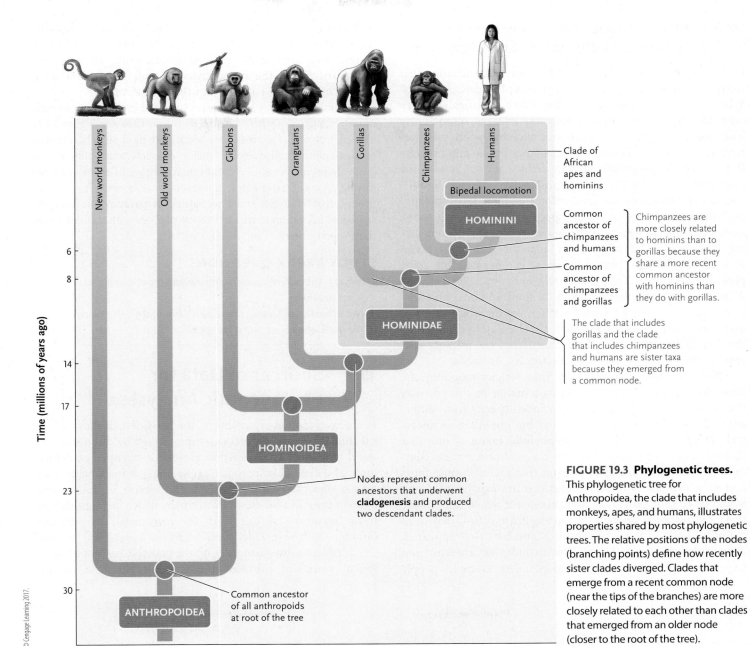

FIGURE 19.3 Phylogenetic trees.
This phylogenetic tree for Anthropoidea, the clade that includes monkeys, apes, and humans, illustrates properties shared by most phylogenetic trees. The relative positions of the nodes (branching points) define how recently sister clades diverged. Clades that emerge from a recent common node (near the tips of the branches) are more closely related to each other than clades that emerged from an older node (closer to the root of the tree).

Labels in figure:
- New world monkeys
- Old world monkeys
- Gibbons
- Orangutans
- Gorillas
- Chimpanzees
- Humans
- Time (millions of years ago)
- Bipedal locomotion
- HOMININI
- HOMINIDAE
- HOMINOIDEA
- ANTHROPOIDEA
- Clade of African apes and hominins
- Common ancestor of chimpanzees and humans
- Common ancestor of chimpanzees and gorillas
- Chimpanzees are more closely related to hominins than to gorillas because they share a more recent common ancestor with hominins than they do with gorillas.
- The clade that includes gorillas and the clade that includes chimpanzees and humans are sister taxa because they emerged from a common node.
- Nodes represent common ancestors that underwent **cladogenesis** and produced two descendant clades.
- Common ancestor of all anthropoids at root of the tree

© Cengage Learning 2017.

Depiction of time: If a phylogenetic tree includes an explicit time axis, the positions of the nodes reveal when on the geological time scale a clade originated; the length of the vertical branch between nodes indexes how long an ancestral group persisted before it diversified. In most phylogenetic trees in this book, the time scale is not precise; often it is not even specified. The sequence of nodes indicates the order in which clades appeared; the lengths of the branches contain no specific information about the time since two clades diverged.

Depiction of relatedness: Horizontal spacing between clades in most of this book's phylogenetic trees does not indicate their degree of difference or their degree of relatedness. However, when the horizontal distance between species or clades is meaningful, how the distances should be interpreted is explained in the horizontal axis label, the figure legend, or the text.

Number of descendants: Most nodes in phylogenetic trees have two branches emerging from them, reflecting the evolution of two descendants from one ancestor. When biologists have not yet discovered the detailed pattern of branching that produced the diversity of clades in the tree, you may see three or more branches emerging from a node or from a horizontal branch. These nodes are currently "unresolved"; future research will allow the portrayal of these evolutionary relationships more precisely.

Relative ages of clades: In most phylogenetic trees in this book, the clades have been arranged from oldest on the left to youngest on the right. But any clade can be rotated around a node without changing the meaning of the phylogenetic tree. When reading a phylogenetic tree, focus on which clades share more recent common ancestors, indicated by the relative positions of the nodes from which they emerge.

Summary: Phylogenetic trees provide hypotheses about the evolutionary histories of the organisms included in the analysis. The common ancestor of sister clades is depicted on the node from which the two clades emerge. An implied or explicit timeline identifies the sequence in which new clades arose from their ancestors. Clades with a common ancestor closer to the top of the tree are more closely related than those with a common ancestor closer to the root of the tree.

19.2c Phylogenetic Trees Allow Biologists to Define Evolutionary Classifications

Evolutionary biologists working today want a classification that mirrors the branching patterns of a group's phylogenetic history. When converting a phylogenetic tree into a classification, they try to identify only **monophyletic taxa** or lineages. A monophyletic taxon comprises one clade, an ancestral species (represented by a node) and *all* of its descendants, but no other species (**Figure 19.4**). Monophyletic taxa are defined at every level of the taxonomic hierarchy. For example, biologists consider the Felidae (the traditional family-level taxon that includes all cat species) to be monophyletic: all cat species living on Earth today, from house cats to tigers, are the descendants—and the only living descendants—of a common ancestor that lived about 25 million years ago. Thus, the Felidae is one small, but complete, branch on the Tree of Life. At a much broader scale, the Animalia is a monophyletic taxon (at the traditional kingdom level) that comprises all animals, which are the descendants of one common ancestor. Even if biologists have not yet identified the very first animal in the fossil record, they can infer its existence at the root of the phylogenetic tree for Animalia.

Biologists have not always defined strictly monophyletic taxa. Because of missing data, or as a matter of convenience, they sometimes named taxa that included species from different clades or taxa that included some, but not all, of an ancestral species' descendants. A **polyphyletic taxon** is one that includes organisms from different clades, but not their common ancestor. For example, a taxon that included only birds and bats, two clades of vertebrates that are capable of flight, would be considered polyphyletic because it would not include their last common ancestor, a four-legged creature that lived many millions of years before birds and bats first appeared. A **paraphyletic taxon** is one that includes an ancestor and some, *but not all*, of its descendants. For example, people

commonly used to define terrestrial dinosaurs and birds as distinct groups. But "terrestrial dinosaurs" was a paraphyletic taxon: birds are the descendants of one group of terrestrial dinosaurs. Thus, the monophyletic taxon Dinosauria must include birds, as well as their nonflying relatives.

Many of the phylogenetic trees included in this book identify monophyletic taxa with labels on their branches (see Figure 19.3). The names of these clades are identified in capital letters in a bronze-coloured plaque; the major characteristics that define large clades are identified in lowercase letters in a tan-coloured plaque. As a convenience, some commonly used names for groups that biologists now recognize as paraphyletic are presented in quotation marks in bronze plaques with dashed rather than solid borders.

STUDY BREAK QUESTIONS

1. What is the difference between a phylogenetic tree and a classification?
2. What are the differences between a monophyletic taxon, a polyphyletic taxon, and a paraphyletic taxon?

19.3 Sources of Data for Phylogenetic Analyses

Linnaeus classified organisms on the basis of their morphological similarities and differences, even though he did not understand how those characteristics arose. For example, he defined birds as a class of oviparous ("egg-laying") animals with feathered bodies, two wings, two feet, and a bony beak. No other animals possess all these characteristics, which distinguish birds from "quadrupeds" (his term for mammals), "amphibians" (among which he included reptiles), fishes, insects, and "worms."

Mendel's subsequent work on the heritable basis of morphological variations provided the scientific rationale for this

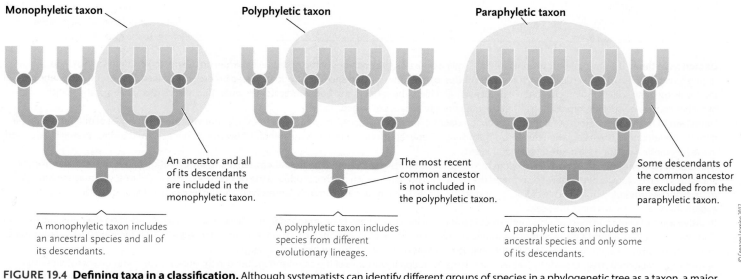

Monophyletic taxon

An ancestor and all of its descendants are included in the monophyletic taxon.

A monophyletic taxon includes an ancestral species and all of its descendants.

Polyphyletic taxon

The most recent common ancestor is not included in the polyphyletic taxon.

A polyphyletic taxon includes species from different evolutionary lineages.

Paraphyletic taxon

Some descendants of the common ancestor are excluded from the paraphyletic taxon.

A paraphyletic taxon includes an ancestral species and only some of its descendants.

© Cengage Learning 2017.

FIGURE 19.4 Defining taxa in a classification. Although systematists can identify different groups of species in a phylogenetic tree as a taxon, a major goal of contemporary systematics is to identify taxa that are monophyletic groups.

endeavour: modern systematists infer that morphological differences serve as indicators of underlying genetic differences between species and lineages. Today, with our much deeper understanding of the genetic basis of variation, systematists undertake phylogenetic analyses using a variety of organismal and molecular characters. Indeed, any heritable trait (i.e., any trait with a genetic basis) that is intrinsic to the organism can be used in a phylogenetic analysis; phenotypic differences caused by environmental variation are excluded. In this section we first consider a general criterion for evaluating characters, and then examine examples of how a few specific types of characters are useful in this effort.

19.3a The Analysis of Homologous Characters Sheds Light on Evolutionary Relationships

A basic premise of phylogenetic analyses is that phenotypic similarities between organisms reflect their underlying genetic similarities. As you may recall from Chapter 16, species that are morphologically similar have often inherited the genetic basis of their resemblance from a common ancestor. Similarity that results from shared ancestry, such as the four limbs of all tetrapod vertebrates, is called **homology**, and biologists frequently describe such traits in two or more species as *homologies* or *homologous characters*. Any trait, from genetic sequences to anatomical structures to mating behaviours, can be described as homologous in two or more species as long as they inherited the trait from their common ancestor.

Even though characters are homologous, they may differ greatly among species, especially if their function has changed over time. For example, the stapes, a bone in the middle ear of tetrapod vertebrates, evolved from, and is therefore homologous to, the hyomandibula, a bone that supported the jaw joint of early fishes. The ancestral function of the bone is retained in some modern fishes, but its structure, position, and function are different in tetrapods (**Figure 19.5**).

Distantly related species living in different biogeographical realms are sometimes very similar in appearance. For example, the overall form of cactuses in the Americas is extraordinarily similar to that of spurges in Africa (**Figure 19.6**). But these lineages arose independently long after those continents had separated; **thus**, cactuses and spurges did not **inherit their** similarities from a shared ancestor. Their overall resemblance is the product of **convergent evolution**, the evolution of similar adaptations in distantly related organisms that occupy similar environments. Phenotypic similarity that evolved independently in different lineages is called **homoplasy**, which is often the product of convergent evolution; biologists describe such similarities as *homoplasies* or *homoplastic characters*. Some biologists use the terms *analogies* or *analogous characters* for homoplastic characters that serve a similar function in different species.

When scientists encounter similar morphological traits, how can they determine whether they are homologous or homoplastic? First, homologous structures are similar in anatomical detail and in their relationship to surrounding structures. For

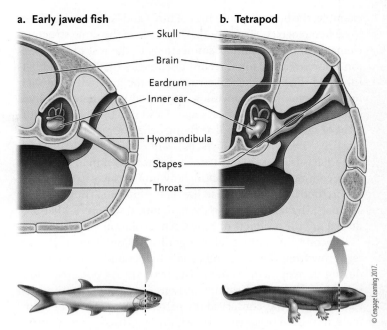

a. **Early jawed fish**   b. **Tetrapod**

Skull · Brain · Eardrum · Inner ear · Hyomandibula · Stapes · Throat

FIGURE 19.5 Homologous bones, different structure, and function. The hyomandibula, which braced the jaw joint against the skull in early jawed fishes **(a)**, is homologous to the stapes, which transmits sound from the eardrum to the inner ear in four-legged vertebrates, exemplified here by an early tetrapod **(b)**. Both large illustrations show a cross-section through the head just behind the jaw joint, as depicted in the small illustrations.

© Cengage Learning 2017.

a. **Cactus (*Echinocereus* species)**

b. **Spurge (*Euphorbia* species)**

Edward S. Ross

FIGURE 19.6 Convergent evolution in plants. (a) North American cactuses (family Cactaceae) are strikingly similar to **(b)** African spurges (family Euphorbiaceae). Convergent evolution adapted both groups to desert environments with thick, water-storing stems, spiny structures that discourage animals from feeding on them, CAM photosynthesis (see Chapter 6), and stomata that open only at night.

example, the bones in the wings of birds and bats are considered to be homologous (**Figure 19.7**). They include the same structural elements and have similar connections to the rest of the skeleton. Moreover, the fossil record documents that birds and bats inherited the basic skeletal structure of the forelimb from their most recent common ancestor, a tetrapod vertebrate that lived more than 300 million years ago. However, the large flat surfaces of their wings, as well as flying behaviour itself, are homoplastic. The wing surfaces are made of different materials—feathers in birds and membranous skin in bats—and their common ancestor, lacking any hint of such structures on its forelimbs, was confined to life on the ground. Thus, for birds and bats, flight and some of the anatomical structures that produce it are the products of convergent evolution.

Second, in multicellular organisms, homologous characters grow from the same embryonic tissues and in similar ways during development. Systematists have always put great stock in embryological indications of homology on the assumption that evolution has conserved the pattern of embryonic development in related organisms. Indeed, recent discoveries in evolutionary developmental biology have revealed that the genetic controls of developmental pathways are very similar across a wide variety of organisms. Genomic techniques are revealing remarkable shared similarities in the underlying genetic and cellular mechanisms that have contributed to the evolution of convergent characters in species that are not closely related.

19.3b Morphological Characters Provide Abundant Clues to Evolutionary Relationships

Morphological structures often provide useful information for phylogenetic analyses. Structural differences between organisms, which often reflect underlying genetic differences, are easy to measure in preserved or living specimens. Moreover, morphological characteristics are often clearly preserved in the fossil record, allowing the comparison of living species with their extinct relatives.

The morphological traits that are useful in phylogenetic analyses vary from group to group. In flowering plants, the details of flower anatomy may reveal common ancestry. Among vertebrates, the presence or absence of scales, feathers, and fur, as well as the structure of the skull and jaws, help scientists to reconstruct the evolutionary history of major groups. Sometimes researchers use obscure characters of unknown function. But differences in the number of scales on the backs of lizards or in the curvature of a vein in the wings of bees may be good indicators of the genetic differentiation that accompanied or followed speciation—even if we do not know *why* these differences evolved.

Sometimes characteristics found only in the earliest stages of an organism's life cycle can provide evidence of evolutionary relationships. For example, analyses of the embryos of vertebrates revealed that they are rather closely related to sea cucumbers, sea stars, and sea urchins and even more closely related to a group of nearly shapeless marine invertebrates called sea squirts or tunicates.

Despite their usefulness, morphological characters alone cannot reveal the details of all evolutionary relationships. For example, some salamander species in North America differ in relatively few morphological features, even when they are genetically, physiologically, and behaviourally distinct. Moreover, researchers cannot easily compare the structures of organisms—such as flatworms and dogs—that share very few morphological traits.

19.3c Behavioral Characters Are Useful When Animal Species Are Not Morphologically Distinct

When external morphology cannot be used to differentiate animal species, systematists often examine their behaviours for clues about their relationships. For example, two species of tree frog (*Hyla versicolor* and *Hyla chrysoscelis*) commonly occur together in forests of the central and eastern United States. Both species have bumpy skin and adhesive pads on their toes that enable them to climb vegetation. They also have grey backs, white bellies, yellowish-orange coloration on their thighs, and large white spots below their eyes. The frogs are so similar that even experts cannot easily tell them apart.

How do we know that these frogs represent two species? During the breeding season, males of each species use a distinctive mating call to attract females (**Figure 19.8**). The difference in calls is a prezygotic, reproductive isolating mechanism that prevents females from mating with males of a different species (see Chapter 18). Prezygotic isolating mechanisms

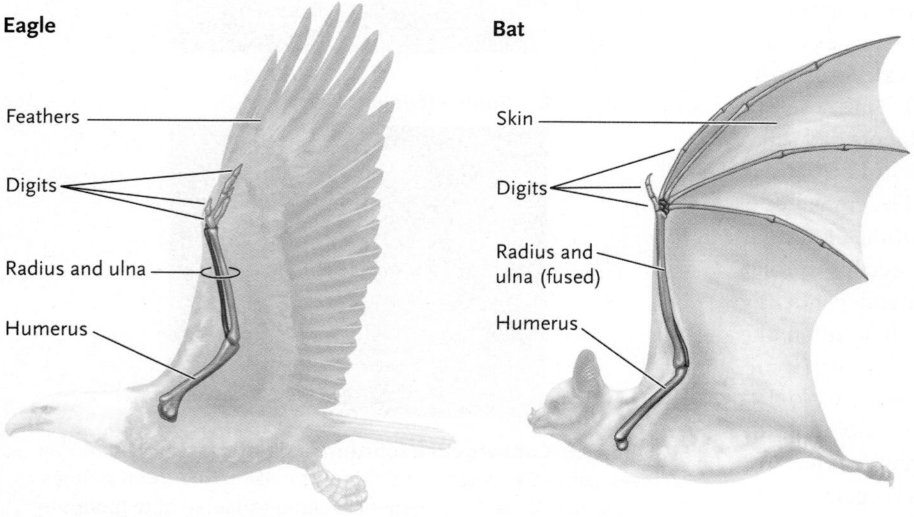

Eagle

Feathers

Digits

Radius and ulna

Humerus

Bat

Skin

Digits

Radius and ulna (fused)

Humerus

© Cengage Learning 2017.

FIGURE 19.7 Assessing homology. The wing skeletons of birds and bats are homologous structures with the same basic elements. However, similarities in the flat wing surfaces are homoplastic because the surfaces are composed of different tissues.

Hyla versicolor

Hyla chrysoscelis

Frequency

Time

Time

© Cengage Learning 2017.

Psyhotic Nature/Shutterstock.com

FIGURE 19.8 Morphologically similar frog species. The frogs *Hyla versicolor* and *Hyla chrysoscelis* are so similar in appearance that one photo can depict both species. Male mating calls, visualized in sound spectrograms for the two species, are very different. The spectrograms, which depict call frequency on the vertical axis and time on the horizontal axis, show that *H. chrysoscelis* has a faster trill rate.

are excellent systematic characters because they are often the traits that animals themselves use to recognize members of their own species. The two frog species also differ in chromosome number—*H. chrysoscelis* is diploid and *H. versicolor* is tetraploid—which is a postzygotic isolating mechanism.

19.3d Molecular Sequences Are Now a Commonly Used Source of Phylogenetic Data

For roughly 200 years, systematists building on Linnaeus' work relied on a variety of organismal traits to analyze evolutionary relationships and classify organisms. Today, most systematists conduct phylogenetic analyses using molecular characters, such as the nucleotide base sequences of DNA and RNA. Because DNA is inherited, shared changes in molecular sequences—insertions, deletions, or substitutions—provide clues to the evolutionary relationships of organisms.

Use of polymerase chain reaction (PCR) technology makes it easy for researchers to produce numerous copies of specific segments of DNA for analysis (see Chapter 14); the technique is so effective that it allows scientists to sequence minute quantities of DNA taken from dried or preserved specimens in museums and even from some fossils. Technological advances have automated the sequencing process, and researchers use analytical software to compare new data to known sequences filed in online data banks. Nuclear DNA is frequently used in phylogenetic

analyses, and the publication of complete genome sequences for an ever-expanding list of organisms allows researchers to undertake broad comparative studies.

Molecular sequences have certain practical advantages over organismal characters. First, they provide abundant data: every base in a nucleic acid can serve as a separate, independent character for analysis. Moreover, because many genes have been conserved by evolution, molecular sequences can be compared between distantly related organisms that share no organismal characteristics. They can also be used to study closely related species with only minor morphological differences.

Molecular characters have certain drawbacks, however. For example, only 4 alternative character states (the 4 nucleotide bases) exist at each position in a DNA or RNA sequence, and only 20 alternative character states (the 20 amino acids) at each position in a protein. (You may want to review *The Purple Pages* on the structures of these molecules.)

Because of the limited number of character states, researchers may find it difficult to assess the homology of a nucleotide base substitution that appears at the same position in the DNA of two or more species. For organismal characters, biologists can determine homology by analyzing the characters' embryonic development, details of their function, or their presence in the fossil record. But molecular characters have no embryonic development; biologists still do not understand the functional significance of many molecular differences they discover; and researchers have only recently improved techniques that allow them to sequence DNA found in fossils. Nevertheless, systematists have devised complex statistical tools that allow them to discern whether molecular similarities are likely to be homologous or homoplastic.

Despite these potential disadvantages, molecular sequences allow researchers to sample the genome directly, and systematists have successfully used sequence data to analyze phylogenetic relationships that organismal characters were unable to resolve. For example, the phylogenetic tree for animals is based on data from several different nucleic acid molecules.

STUDY BREAK QUESTIONS

1. Why do systematists use homologous characters in their phylogenetic analyses?
2. Why are morphological traits often helpful in tracing the long-term evolutionary relationships within a group of organisms?
3. What are three advantages of using molecular characters in phylogenetic analyses?

19.4 Traditional Classification and Paraphyletic Groups

For a century after Darwin published his theory of evolution, systematists followed an approach called **traditional systematics**. Researchers constructed phylogenetic trees and classified organisms by assessing the amount of phenotypic divergence between lineages, as well as the patterns of branching evolution that had produced them. In other words, they focused on the products of anagenesis (i.e., evolutionary change through the accumulation of new or modified characteristics), as well as the products of cladogenesis (i.e., the new species and lineages produced through branching evolution). Thus, their classifications did not always strictly reflect the patterns of branching evolution (**Figure 19.9**).

For example, the fossil record for tetrapod (four-legged) vertebrates reveals that the amphibian and mammalian lineages each diverged early. The remaining lineages, collectively called Reptilia, diverged into the Lepidosauromorpha (including living lizards and snakes) and the Archelosauromorpha (including living turtles, crocodilians, and birds). Thus, although crocodilians, with their scaly skin and sprawling posture, outwardly resemble lizards, evolutionary biologists have long recognized that crocodilians share a more recent common ancestor with birds.

Even though the phylogenetic tree shows six living clades, the traditional classification recognizes only four classes of tetrapod vertebrates: Amphibia, Mammalia, Reptilia, and Aves. These groups are given equal ranking because each represents a distinctive body plan and way of life. However, the traditionally defined taxon Reptilia is clearly paraphyletic because, even though crocodilians share a common ancestor with birds, Reptilia includes the former taxon but not the latter. Traditional systematists justified this definition of Reptilia because it included morphologically similar animals with close evolutionary relationships. Crocodilians were classified with lizards, snakes, and turtles because they share a distant common ancestry and are covered with dry, scaly skin. Traditional systematists also argued that the key innovations initiating the adaptive radiation of birds—a high metabolic rate, wings, and flight—represent such extreme divergence from the ancestral morphology that birds merited recognition as a separate class. As you will learn in Section 19.5, a different approach produces classifications that do not suffer from such inconsistencies.

STUDY BREAK QUESTION

1. Why does a classification produced by traditional systematics sometimes include paraphyletic groups?

19.5 The Cladistic Revolution

In the 1950s and 1960s, some researchers criticized the traditional classifications based on two distinct phenomena, branching evolution and morphological divergence, as inherently unclear. How can we tell *why* two groups are classified in the same higher taxon? They might have shared a recent common ancestor, as did lizards and snakes. Alternatively, they may have retained some ancestral characteristics after being separated on different branches of a phylogenetic tree, as is the case for lizards and crocodilians.

To avoid such confusion, many systematists followed the philosophical and analytical lead of Willi Hennig, a German entomologist (i.e., a scientist who studies insects), who published the influential book *Phylogenetic Systematics* in 1950; its

a. Traditional classification

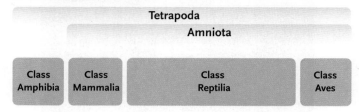

b. Cladistic classification

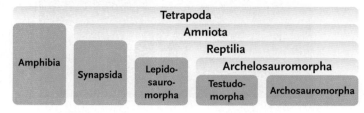

c. Phylogenetic tree

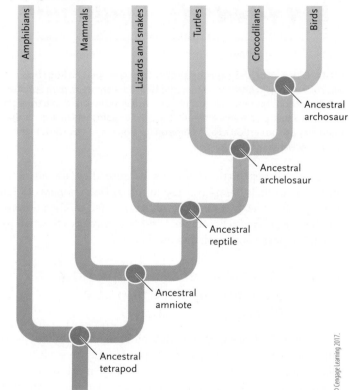

FIGURE 19.9 Phylogenetic trees and classifications for tetrapod vertebrates. (a) The traditional classification and **(b)** the cladistic classifications for tetrapod vertebrates are very different. **(c)** The phylogenetic tree for these animals illustrates why the cladistic classification reflects their evolutionary history better than the traditional classification does.

English translation appeared in 1966. Hennig and his followers argued that classifications should be based solely on evolutionary relationships. This approach, which is called **cladistics**, produces phylogenetic hypotheses and classifications that reflect only the branching pattern of evolution; it ignores morphological divergence altogether.

19.5a Cladistic Analyses Focus on Recently Evolved Character States

Like traditional systematics, cladistics analyzes the evolutionary relationships among organisms by comparing their organismal and, more recently, genetic characteristics. Each **character** can exist in two forms, described as **character states**. Evolutionary processes change characters over time from an original, **ancestral character state** to a newer, **derived character state**. Character states that were present in the ancestors of a clade are considered ancestral; those that are new in descendants are considered derived. For example, ancient fishes, which represent the ancestral vertebrates, had fins, but some of their descendants, the tetrapods, which appeared much later in the fossil record, have limbs. In this example, fins are the ancestral character state, and limbs are the derived character state.

In the jargon of cladistics, a derived character state is called an **apomorphy** (*apo* = away from; *morphe* = form), and a derived character state found in two or more species is called a **synapomorphy** (*syn* = together). The presence of a synapomorphy (i.e., a *shared derived character state*) among species provides a clue that they may be members of the same clade. Once a derived character state becomes established in a species, it is likely to be present in that species' descendants. Thus, unless they are lost or replaced by newer characters over evolutionary time, *synapomorphies can serve as markers for monophyletic lineages.*

Systematists define synapomorphies only when comparing character states among species. Thus, any particular character state is derived *only in relation to* an ancestral character state observed in other organisms, either an older version of the character or its absence. For example, most species of animals lack a vertebral column. However, one animal clade, the vertebrates—including fishes, amphibians, reptiles, birds, and mammals—has that structure. Thus, when systematists compare vertebrates to all other animals, the absence of a vertebral column is the ancestral character state, and the presence of a vertebral column is derived.

How can systematists distinguish between ancestral and derived character states? In other words, how can they determine the direction in which a character has evolved? The fossil record, if it is detailed enough, can provide unambiguous information. For example, biologists are confident that the presence of a vertebral column is a derived character state because fossils of animals that lived before vertebrates lack that structure.

In the absence of evidence from fossils, systematists frequently use a technique called **outgroup comparison** to identify ancestral and derived character states. Using this approach, systematists compare characters in the *ingroup,* the clade under study, to those in an *outgroup*, one or a few species that are related to the clade but are not included within it. Character states observed in the outgroup are considered ancestral, and those observed *only* in the ingroup are considered derived. And because the outgroup and the ingroup are phylogenetically related, outgroup comparison allows researchers to hypothesize the root (i.e., the common ancestor shared by the outgroup and the ingroup) of the phylogenetic tree. Most modern butterflies, for example, have six walking legs, but species in two families have four walking legs and two small, non-walking legs. Which is the ancestral character state, and which is derived? Outgroup comparison with other insects, which are not included in the butterfly clade, demonstrates that most insects have six walking legs as adults; this result suggests that six walking legs is ancestral and four is derived (**Figure 19.10**).

19.5b Cladistics Uses Synapomorphies to Reconstruct Evolutionary History and Classify Organisms

Following the cladistic method, biologists construct phylogenetic trees and classifications by grouping together only those species that *share derived character states*. Ancestral character states, because they are shared by the ingroup and the outgroup, do not help to define the ingroup. For example, mammals are a clade, a monophyletic lineage, because they possess a unique set of synapomorphies: hair, mammary glands, and a reduced number of bones in the lower jaw. The ancestral character states found in mammals, such as a vertebral column and four legs, do not distinguish them from other tetrapod vertebrates. Thus, these shared ancestral character states are not useful in defining the mammal clade.

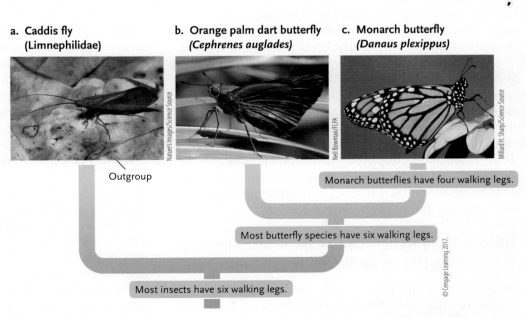

a. **Caddis fly (Limnephilidae)**

b. **Orange palm dart butterfly (*Cephrenes auglades*)**

c. **Monarch butterfly (*Danaus plexippus*)**

Outgroup

Monarch butterflies have four walking legs.

Most butterfly species have six walking legs.

Most insects have six walking legs.

FIGURE 19.10 **Outgroup comparison.** Most adult insects, such as **(a)** the caddis fly and **(b)** the orange palm dart butterfly, have six walking legs. This comparison of butterflies with other insects suggests that the four walking legs of **(c)** the monarch butterfly represents the derived character state.

The results of a cladistic analysis are presented in a phylogenetic tree that illustrates the hypothesized sequence of evolutionary branchings that produced the organisms under study (see Figure 19.9c): a common ancestor is hypothesized at each node, and every branch portrays a strictly monophyletic group. Once a researcher identifies a suitable outgroup and the ancestral and derived character states, a cladistic analysis is straightforward (**Figure 19.11**). The synapomorphies that define each clade are sometimes listed on the branches.

The use of molecular sequence data in phylogenetic analyses relies on the same logic that underlies analyses based on organismal characters, like those considered above: species included within a clade are expected to exhibit more molecular synapomorphies than do species from different clades. The comparison of sequences in the ingroup to those in the outgroup may allow a researcher to define ancestral and derived character states.

The classifications produced by cladistic analysis often differ radically from those of traditional systematics (compare Figure 19.9b with Figure 19.9a). In a cladistics classification, pairs of nested taxa are defined directly from the two-way branching pattern of the phylogenetic tree. Thus, the clade Tetrapoda (the traditional amphibians, reptiles, birds, and mammals) is divided into two taxa: the Amphibia (tetrapods that do not have an amnion, as discussed in Chapter 27) and the Amniota (tetrapods that have an amnion). The Amniota is subdivided into two taxa on the basis of skull morphology and other characteristics: Synapsida (mammals) and Reptilia (turtles, lizards, snakes, crocodilians, and birds). The Reptilia is further divided into the Lepidosauromorpha (lizards and snakes) and the Archelosauromorpha. The latter taxon is divided into Testudomorpha (turtles) and the Archosauromorpha (crocodilians and birds). Thus, a strictly cladistic classification exactly parallels the pattern of branching evolution that produced the organisms included in the classification. These parallels are the essence and strength of the cladistic method.

Most biologists value the evolutionary focus, clear goals, and precise methods of the cladistic approach. In fact, some systematists advocate abandoning the Linnaean hierarchy for classifying and naming organisms. They propose using a strictly phylogenetic system, called **PhyloCode**, that identifies and names clades instead of pigeonholing organisms into traditional taxonomic categories. Although traditional systematics has guided many people's understanding of biological diversity, we use cladistic analyses to describe evolutionary lineages and taxa in Unit 5 (The Diversity of Life).

19.5c Systematists Use Several Techniques to Identify an Optimal Phylogenetic Tree

In practice, most phylogenetic studies are far more complicated than the examples discussed above and in **Figure 19.12**. Researchers may collect data on hundreds of characters in dozens of species. After scoring each character state as ancestral or derived in every species, a systematist uses one or more computer programs to generate a set of alternative phylogenetic trees. The output of these analyses is often substantial: an analysis of 5 species can produce 15 possible phylogenetic trees; an analysis of 50 species can produce 3×10^{76}.

Faced with such an unimaginably large number of alternative hypotheses, how does a systematist decide which phylogenetic tree is the "best" representation of a clade's evolutionary history? This problem is complex, because, when evaluating large data sets, we expect to see some similarities that arise when convergent evolution causes distantly related organisms to evolve similar traits independently; because such traits are not synapomorphies, they are false indicators of relatedness that confound the analysis. We also expect to find some differences between closely related organisms if natural selection or some other microevolutionary process caused a derived character state to be reversed or lost. How can we tell which of the many possible phylogenetic hypotheses is the most likely to represent the evolutionary history of the group? Researchers use several approaches to sort through the alternatives, two of which we describe below.

PARSIMONY APPROACH Many systematists adopt a philosophical concept, the **principle of parsimony**, to identify the optimal phylogenetic tree. This principle states that the simplest plausible explanation of any phenomenon is the best. If we assume that any complex evolutionary change is an unlikely event, then it is extremely unlikely that the same complex change evolved twice in one lineage. Thus, when the principle is applied to phylogenetic analyses, it suggests that the "best" phylogenetic tree is the one that hypothesizes the smallest number of evolutionary changes needed to account for the distribution of character states within a clade; in effect, this approach minimizes the number of homoplasies (i.e., the independent evolution of similar traits) in the tree (Figure 19.12). To apply the principle, computer programs evaluate the number of evolutionary changes hypothesized by each phylogenetic tree they generate, and the researcher identifies the one with the fewest hypothesized changes as the most plausible.

The principle of parsimony also allows researchers to identify homologous characters and infer their ancestral and derived states. Once the most parsimonious phylogenetic tree is identified, a researcher can visualize the distribution of derived character states and pinpoint when each evolved.

STATISTICAL APPROACHES When comparing two genome sequences, each base in a strand of DNA can be treated as a character with four possible states (A, G, T, or C). One could perform a parsimony analysis on molecular sequence data to identify the phylogenetic tree that assumes the fewest mutations. But the application of the parsimony approach to molecular data is complicated by several factors. First, given that there are only four possible character states at each position in a nucleic acid, identical changes in nucleotides often arise independently. Second, segments of DNA that do not code for proteins are less likely than coding regions to be affected by natural

FIGURE 19.11 **Research Method**

Using Cladistics to Construct a Phylogenetic Tree

Purpose: Systematists construct phylogenetic trees to visualize hypothesized evolutionary relationships among organisms. The cladistic method requires a researcher to group together organisms that share derived characters states. The derived character states identified in the tan plaques are the synapomorphies that define each clade.

Protocol:

1. *Select the organisms to study.* To demonstrate the method, we develop a phylogenetic tree for the nine groups of living vertebrates: lampreys, sharks (and their close relatives), bony fishes, amphibians (frogs and salamanders), turtles, lizards (including snakes), crocodilians (including alligators), birds, and mammals. We also include marine animals called lancelets (Chordata, Cephalochordata) as the outgroup. Lancelets are closely related to, but not included within, the vertebrates. The inclusion of an outgroup allows biologists to identify ancestral versus derived character states and root the tree.

2. *Choose the characters on which the phylogenetic tree will be based.* Our simplified example is based on the presence or absence of nine characters: (1) vertebral column, (2) jaws, (3) swim bladder or lungs, (4) paired limbs (with one bone connecting each limb to the body), (5) extraembryonic membranes (such as the amnion), (6) mammary glands, (7) dry, scaly skin somewhere on the body, (8) one opening on each side of the skull in front of the eye, and (9) feathers.

3. *Score the character states in each group.* Because lancelets serve as the outgroup in this analysis, we consider character states observed in lancelets as ancestral; any deviation from the lancelet pattern is considered derived. Because lancelets lack all the characters in our analysis, the presence of each character is the derived condition. We tabulate data on the distribution of ancestral (–) and derived (+) characters in all species included in the analysis.

4. *Construct the phylogenetic tree from information in the table, grouping organisms that share derived character states.* All groups except lancelets have vertebrae. Thus, we group organisms that share this derived character state on the right-hand branch, identifying them as a monophyletic lineage. Lancelets are on their own branch to the left, indicating that they lack vertebrae.

   All the remaining organisms except lampreys have jaws. (Lancelets also lack jaws, but we have already separated them out and do not consider them further.) Place all groups with jaws, a derived character state, on the right-hand branch. Lampreys are separated out to the left, because they lack jaws. Again, the branch on the right represents a monophyletic lineage.

c.

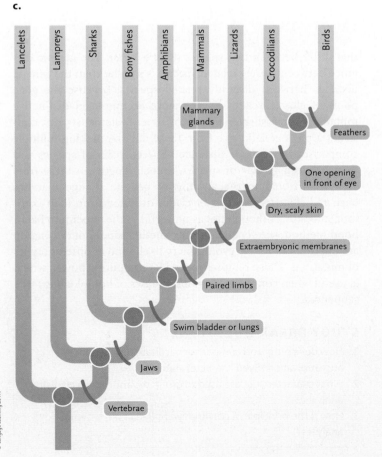

a.

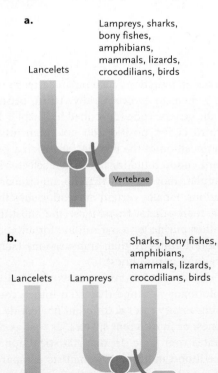

© Cengage Learning 2017.

(Continued)

FIGURE 19.11   **Research Method** (*Continued*)

5. *Construct the rest of the phylogenetic tree using the same step-by-step procedure to separate the remaining groups.* In our completed tree, six groups share a swim bladder or lungs; five share paired limbs; and four have extraembryonic membranes during development. Some groups are distinguished by the unique presence of a derived character state, such as feathers in birds.

Interpreting the Results: Although phylogenetic trees provide information about evolutionary relationships, the common ancestors represented by the branch points are often hypothetical. You can tell from the tree, however, that birds are more closely

	Vertebrae	Jaws	Swim bladder or lungs	Paired limbs	Extraembryonic membranes	Mammary glands	Dry, scaly skin	One opening in front of eye	Feathers
Lancelets	−	−	−	−	−	−	−	−	−
Lampreys	+	−	−	−	−	−	−	−	−
Sharks	+	+	−	−	−	−	−	−	−
Bony fishes	+	+	+	−	−	−	−	−	−
Amphibians	+	+	+	+	−	−	−	−	−
Mammals	+	+	+	+	+	+	−	−	−
Lizards	+	+	+	+	+	−	+	−	−
Crocodilians	+	+	+	+	+	−	+	+	−
Birds	+	+	+	+	+	−	+	+	+

related to lizards than they are to mammals. Follow the branches of the tree from birds and lizards back to their node. Next, trace the branches of birds and mammals to their node. You can see that the bird–mammal node is closer to the root of the tree than the bird–lizard node is. Nodes that are closer to the bottom of the tree indicate a more distant common ancestry than those closer to the top. Note also that this simplified example produces a phylogenetic tree that is easy to interpret because the data set includes no homoplastic similarities and no conflicting evidence. Most phylogenetic analyses include many such complications.

selection. As a result, mutations accumulate faster in noncoding regions, causing them to evolve rapidly. Third, because of the degeneracy of the genetic code (described in Chapter 12), mutations in the third codon position do not often influence the amino acid composition of the protein for which a gene codes. As a result, third codon mutations are often selectively neutral, and they accumulate more rapidly than do mutations in the first or second positions. Finally, certain nucleotide substitutions are more common than others: transitions (the substitution of a purine for another purine, or a pyrimidine for another pyrimidine) occur more frequently than transversions (substitutions between purines and pyrimidines).

To avoid this problem, systematists develop statistical models of evolutionary change that take into account variations in the evolutionary rates at different nucleotide positions, in different genes, or in different species, as well as changes in evolutionary rates over time. In one statistical approach, the **maximum likelihood method**, systematists compare alternative trees with specific models about the rates of evolutionary change in different regions of DNA. The tree that is most likely to have produced the observed distribution of molecular character states is identified as the best hypothesis.

To illustrate how phylogenetic trees are constructed from DNA sequence data, we cite an example using the **genetic distance method**, which calculates the overall proportion of bases

that differ between two species (**Figure 19.13**). The genetic distance between closely related species is smaller than the genetic distance between distantly related species, because the gene pools of closely related species have accumulated distinctive mutations for a shorter period of time. Systematists can construct a phylogenetic tree from these data by making multiple comparisons of genetic distance between pairs of species and then between groups of species; branch lengths in these trees are proportional to the amount of genetic change that has occurred since two species or clades diverged from their common ancestor. Although not as powerful as the maximum likelihood method, the genetic distance method does not depend on assumptions about the evolutionary likelihood of different types of mutations. It also requires much less computing power, which is useful when comparing billions of bases of homologous DNA sequences.

STUDY BREAK QUESTIONS

1. How does outgroup comparison facilitate the identification of ancestral and derived character states?
2. What characteristics are used to group organisms in a cladistic analysis?
3. How is the principle of parsimony applied in phylogenetic analyses?

a. Distribution of character states in six clades of vascular plants

Ferns represent the outgroup: all of its character states are considered ancestral.

Characters (possible states)	Ferns (outgroup)	Gnetophytes	Cycads	Ginkgophytes	Conifers	Angiosperms
Archegonium (present or lost)	Present	Lost	Present	Present	Present	Lost
Double fertilization (absent or present)	Absent	Present	Absent	Absent	Absent	Present
Pollen tube growth (haustorium or tube)	Absent	Tube	Haustorium	Haustorium	Tube	Tube
Sperm flagella (present or lost)	Present	Lost	Present	Present	Lost	Lost
Vessels (absent or present)	Absent	Present	Absent	Absent	Absent	Present

Two alternative phylogenetic trees for the six clades illustrate different hypotheses about their evolutionary relationships. Bars across the branches mark the hypothesized evolution of derived character states in both trees.

b. Phylogenetic tree hypothesizing five evolutionary changes

c. Phylogenetic tree hypothesizing 10 evolutionary changes

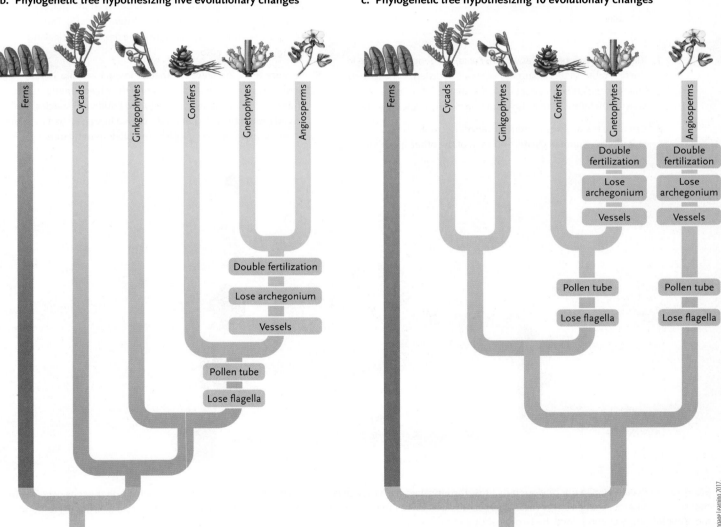

© Cengage Learning 2017.

FIGURE 19.12 The principle of parsimony. (a) Based on this set of 5 characters, **(b)** the phylogenetic tree with 5 hypothesized evolutionary changes is more parsimonious than **(c)** the tree that hypothesizes 10 evolutionary changes. In the absence of additional data, a systematist would accept the more parsimonious tree as the best working hypothesis. (The characters and clades of vascular plants are discussed in detail in Chapter 26.)

FIGURE 19.13   **Research Method**

Using Genetic Distances to Construct a Phylogenetic Tree

Purpose: Systematists use data on genetic distances (the overall differences in DNA sequences) among species to reconstruct their phylogenetic tree.

Protocol:

1. Calculate the genetic distance between each pair of species. The genetic distances between humans and three species of great apes are shown in the first table.

	Chimpanzee	Gorilla	Orangutan
Human	1.37	1.75	3.40
Chimpanzee		1.81	3.44
Gorilla			3.50

2. Identify the pair of species with the smallest genetic distance in the first table; in this example, the smallest distance is between chimpanzee and human (genetic distance = 1.37). These two species therefore form a cluster of two closely related species.

3. Calculate the average genetic distances between the chimpanzee–human cluster and each of the other species in

the analysis, gorilla and orangutan. For example, the genetic distance between the chimpanzee–human cluster and gorilla is the average of the human–gorilla genetic distance and the chimpanzee–gorilla genetic distance [(1.75 + 1.81)/2 = 1.78]. The newly calculated genetic distances are shown in the second table.

	Gorilla	Orangutan
Chimpanzee–human cluster	1.78	3.42
Gorilla		3.50

4. Identify the two groups (individual species or clusters) with the smallest genetic distance in the second table. In this example, the next smallest genetic distance is between the chimpanzee–human cluster and gorilla (genetic distance = 1.78). Thus, chimpanzee–human–gorilla forms the next cluster, leaving orangutan as the outgroup.

5. Because there are only four species in our example, these genetic distance calculations define the phylogenetic tree shown below. If the analysis included additional species, we would repeat the calculation described in steps 2 to 4 as many times as necessary to complete the phylogenetic tree.

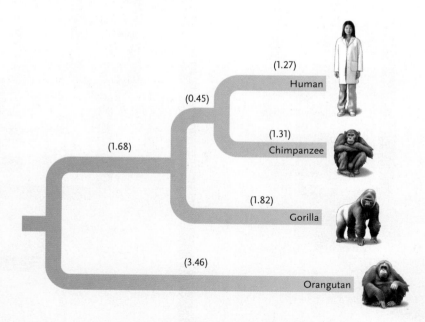

Interpreting the Results: In our phylogenetic tree, the length of each branch is proportional to the amount of genetic change that has occurred in that branch. A longer branch length indicates that the genome of that species has evolved at a correspondingly higher rate (i.e., has undergone more evolutionary change since the two sister branches emerged from their common ancestor).

Source: © Cengage Learning 2017. Based on A. Scally et al. 2012. Insights into hominid evolution from the gorilla genome sequence. *Nature* 483:169–175.

19.6 Phylogenetic Trees as Research Tools

In addition to providing a wealth of information about the patterns of branching evolution across the entire spectrum of living organisms, phylogenetic trees are useful tools that facilitate research in all areas of biology.

19.6a Molecular Clocks Estimate the Time of Evolutionary Divergences

Although many biological molecules have been conserved by evolution, different adaptive changes and neutral mutations accumulate in separate lineages from the moment they first diverge. Because mutations that arise in noncoding regions of DNA do not affect protein structure, they are probably not often eliminated by natural selection. If mutations accumulate in these segments at a reasonably constant rate, differences in their DNA sequences can serve as a **molecular clock**, indexing the time at which two species diverged. Large differences imply divergence in the distant past, whereas small differences suggest a more recent common ancestor.

Because different molecules exhibit individual rates of evolutionary change, every molecule is an independent clock, ticking at its own rate. Researchers study different molecules to track evolutionary divergences that occurred at different times in the past. For example, mitochondrial DNA (mtDNA) evolves relatively quickly; it is useful for dating evolutionary divergences that occurred within the past few million years. Studies of mtDNA have illuminated aspects of the evolutionary history of humans. By contrast, chloroplast DNA (cpDNA) and genes that encode ribosomal RNA evolve much more slowly, providing information about divergences that date back hundreds of millions of years.

To calibrate molecular clocks, researchers examine the degree of genetic difference between species in relation to their time of divergence estimated from the fossil record. Alternatively, the clock can be calibrated biogeographically with independent data on when volcanic islands first emerged from the sea or when landmasses separated.

The reliability of molecular clocks depends on the constancy of evolutionary change in the DNA segment analyzed. Some researchers have noted that even DNA segments that are thought to be selectively neutral may show variable rates of evolution. Many factors can influence the rates at which mutations accumulate, and researchers must be cautious when evaluating divergence times estimated with this technique, especially if there are no independent data to corroborate the estimates.

19.6b Phylogenetic Trees Allow Biologists to Propose and Test Hypotheses

Accurate phylogenetic trees are essential tools for analyses that biologists describe as the "comparative method." With this approach, researchers compare the characteristics of different species to assess the homology of their similarities and infer where on the phylogenetic tree a particular trait appeared. The comparative method is used to study almost any sort of organismal trait, but in this section we will focus on parental care behaviour.

As noted in Figure 19.9b, birds and crocodilians are included within the Archosauria, a clade that also includes nonavian dinosaurs (i.e., extinct terrestrial dinosaurs that are not included within the bird clade), pterosaurs (an extinct group of flying vertebrates, not closely related to bats but with wing surfaces formed by skin), and a number of other groups that became extinct in the early Mesozoic era. Crocodilians and birds share certain anatomical characteristics, such as a four-chambered heart and the one-way flow of air through their lungs. They also share behavioural characteristics, including the production of mating calls (songs in birds and roars in crocodilians), nest-building behaviour, and parental care of their young. Female crocodilians guard their nests and keep them moist with urine. They also excavate the nest as the young hatch, and then carry them to standing water. Young stay with their mother for about a year, feeding on scraps of food that fall from her mouth.

Did similar parental care behaviour evolve independently in birds and crocodilians, or is it truly a synapomorphy? Did most Mesozoic archosaurs care for their young as birds and crocodilians do today? The comparative method seeks answers to these questions by examining the phylogenetic tree for archosaurs (**Figure 19.14**). As you can readily see, crocodilians and birds lie on widely separated branches of the archosaur tree, with pterosaurs and nonavian dinosaurs positioned between them. The most parsimonious inference about the evolution of parental care behaviour is that it evolved once in the common ancestor of crocodilians and birds. If that inference is correct, then nonavian dinosaurs and pterosaurs probably also cared for their young in the nest. Indeed, that prediction was confirmed in 1995, when Mark A. Norell, of George Washington University, and his colleagues discovered a fossil of a nonavian dinosaur (*Oviraptor*) sitting on a nest full of eggs.

STUDY BREAK QUESTIONS

1. What assumption underlies the use of genetic sequence differences between species as a molecular clock?
2. Are birds more closely related to nonavian dinosaurs or to crocodilians?

19.7 Molecular Phylogenetic Analyses

The application of molecular techniques to phylogenetic analyses has allowed systematic biologists to resolve some evolutionary puzzles that could not be addressed with older techniques.

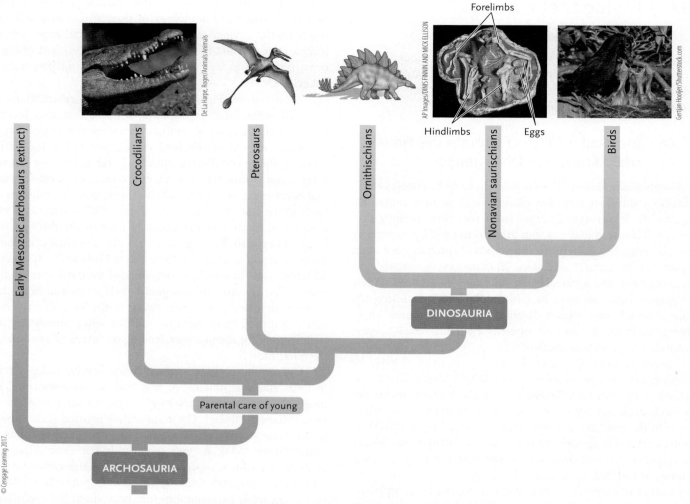

FIGURE 19.14 Phylogenetic trees and the comparative method. By examining the distribution of parental care behaviour on a cladogram of archosaurs, biologists predicted that nonavian dinosaurs probably incubated their eggs and cared for their young. A fossil described in 1995 confirmed that prediction.

In this section we describe how molecular analyses have enabled public health researchers to identify sources of HIV infection in humans and elucidate the relationships among the three domains of the Tree of Life.

19.7a Molecular Phylogenetic Analyses Pinpoint the Origins of Infectious Diseases

Phylogenetic analyses also allow physicians and public health workers to identify the origin of infectious agents and follow their spread through a population. Many pathogenic organisms and viruses mutate as they proliferate, establishing derived character states that are ripe for phylogenetic analysis.

The human immunodeficiency virus (HIV), the agent that causes acquired immunodeficiency syndrome (AIDS) in humans, began to infect large numbers of people in the 1980s. As its devastating effects on humans became apparent, scientists scrambled to discover its origin. Genetic analyses linked it to the lentiviruses, specifically simian immunodeficiency virus (SIV), which infects dozens of monkey species as well as chimpanzees in Africa. Surprisingly, SIV does not cause illness in those animals, perhaps because their populations developed immunity to it after a long period of exposure.

Two distinct strains of HIV infect humans: HIV-1 is common in central Africa, and HIV-2 is common in West Africa. Did these strains evolve within human hosts, or did they exist before the virus was first transmitted to humans? An analysis by Beatrice H. Hahn of the University of Alabama at Birmingham and the Howard Hughes Medical Institute and colleagues at other institutions identified three major clades of SIV. The clade that infects chimpanzees includes HIV-1, and one of the clades that infect monkeys includes HIV-2 (**Figure 19.15**). Thus, the two strains of HIV apparently originated in nonhuman hosts. Scientists suspect that the transmission to humans occurred multiple times when hunters who were butchering bush meat—chimpanzees in central

Africa and sooty mangabey monkeys in West Africa—acquired the virus through cuts on their hands.

In Chapter 21 we will see how DNA sequence data have been used to construct a tree of the entire tree of life. In addition to showing some surprising branching patterns, this tree clearly indicates that all life on Earth today share a common ancestor.

STUDY BREAK QUESTION

1. Did HIV originate in humans, or was the infection acquired from other animals?

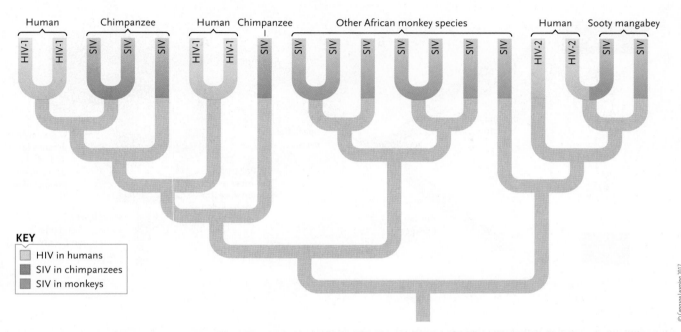

© Cengage Learning 2017.

FIGURE 19.15 Phylogenetic trees and public health. A phylogenetic tree for strains of simian immunodeficiency virus (SIV) and human immunodeficiency virus (HIV) suggests that the virus was transmitted to humans independently from chimpanzees and sooty mangabey monkeys.

Summary Illustration

Systematics is the branch of biology that studies the diversity of life and its evolutionary relationships (i.e., phylogenies). Phylogenetic trees illustrate hypotheses about the likely relationships among species and higher taxonomic groups. These trees can be tailored to include varying breadths of analyses, but all share a common basic structure and depict key relationships in similar ways.

A phylogenetic tree attempts to depict the evolutionary history of a group of organisms.

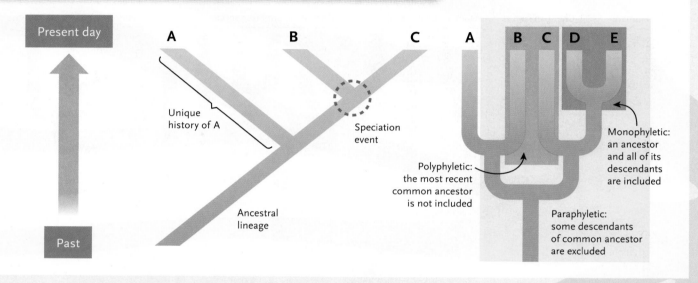

Present day

Past

A   B   C

Unique history of A

Speciation event

Ancestral lineage

A B C D E

Polyphyletic: the most recent common ancestor is not included

Paraphyletic: some descendants of common ancestor are excluded

Monophyletic: an ancestor and all of its descendants are included

An underlying assumption is that taxa that are closely related should look more similar to each other than taxa that are more distantly related.

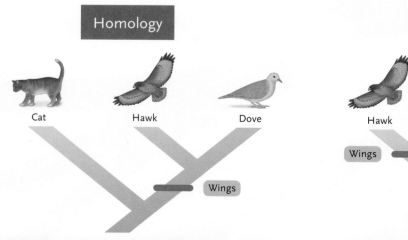

Homology

Cat   Hawk   Dove

Wings

Wings are homologous characters in hawks and doves because both inherited wings from their common winged ancestor.

Homoplasy

Hawk   Bat   Cat

Wings

Wings are homoplasious (or analagous) characters in hawks and bats because they evolved independently (e.g., convergent evolution).

Traditional systematics classification considers both morphological divergence and patterns of branching evolution. Cladistics classification reflects only the branching pattern of evolution.

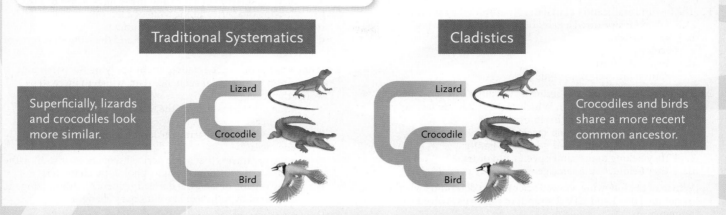

Traditional Systematics

Superficially, lizards and crocodiles look more similar.

Lizard

Crocodile

Bird

Cladistics

Crocodiles and birds share a more recent common ancestor.

Lizard

Crocodile

Bird

Cladistics uses synapomorphies to reconstruct evolutionary histories.

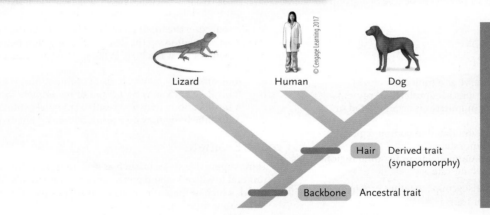

Lizard

Human

Dog

Hair — Derived trait (synapomorphy)

Backbone — Ancestral trait

A synapomorphy is a derived trait that is found in two or more species; one or more synapomorphies are used to define a specific clade. Being derived, synapomorphic traits appear for the first time in the last common ancestor of the clade.

Principle of Parsimony

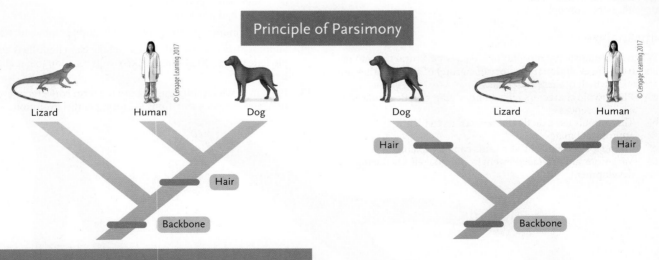

Lizard

Human

Dog

Hair

Backbone

Dog

Lizard

Human

Hair

Hair

Backbone

Compared to the tree at the right, this one is more likely to be correct, as it requires fewer evolutionary changes (principle of parsimony).

SELF-TEST QUESTIONS

Recall/Understand

1. The historic eradication of malaria (transmitted by some mosquitoes) in Europe owed a debt to which of the following?
   b. systematics
   c. ecology
   d. artificial selection
   e. natural life cycle of mosquitoes

2. The name *Ursus maritimus* indicates the polar bear, and the name *Ursus arctos* the brown bear. Which of these statements may you *most* likely conclude from this information?
   a. They belong to the same species and family.
   b. They belong to the same genus and family.
   c. They belong to the same species and order.
   d. They belong to the same genus and species.

3. Which of the following allowed scientists to determine whether or not the HIV-1 and HIV-2 strands of the virus evolved within human hosts?
   a. genetic analysis
   b. phylogenetic tree analyses
   c. molecular phylogenetic analyses
   d. molecular genetic analyses

4. Which of the following portrays a phylogenetic tree of a group of organisms?
   a. its classification
   b. its evolutionary history
   c. its domain
   d. its distribution

5. Which of these conditions can serve as a molecular clock?
   a. sudden differences in mutations accumulated in proteins
   b. constant rate of differences in mutations accumulated in proteins
   c. differences in mutations accumulated in coding regions of DNA at a reasonably constant rate
   d. differences in mutations accumulated in noncoding regions of DNA at a reasonably constant rate

6. In a cladistic analysis, a systematist groups together organisms that share which of these types of traits?
   a. derived homologous
   b. derived homoplasious
   c. ancestral homologous
   d. ancestral homoplasious

Apply/Analyze

7. When systematists use morphological or behavioural traits to reconstruct the evolutionary history of a group of animals, they are assuming which of these statements?
   a. Phenotypic characters reflect underlying genetic similarities and differences.
   b. The animals use exactly the same traits to identify appropriate mates.
   c. The adaptive value of these traits can be explained.
   d. Variations are produced by environmental effects during development.

8. Which of these pairs of structures is a homoplasious pair?
   a. the wing skeleton of a bird and the wing skeleton of a bat
   b. the wing of a bird and the wing of a fly
   c. the eye of a fish and the eye of a human
   d. the wing structures of a pterosaur and the wing structures of a bird

9. If one was to construct a cladogram by applying the parsimony assumption to molecular sequence data, which of these steps would they use?
   a. group organisms sharing the least number of ancestral sequences
   b. group organisms sharing the largest number of ancestral sequences
   c. group organisms that share derived sequences, matching the groups to those defined by morphological characters
   d. group organisms sharing derived sequences, minimizing the number of hypothesized evolutionary changes

10. Suppose you want to convert a phylogenetic tree into a classification. What would you need to identify in order to achieve this?
    a. both monophyletic and paraphyletic taxa or lineages
    b. paraphyletic taxa or lineages only
    c. polyphyletic taxa or lineages only
    d. monophyletic taxa or lineages only

11. While analyzing the fossil record of a birdlike-bodied organism, you insist on examining the details of its skeleton before determining whether it was a bird. What is the significance of your request?
    a. A birdlike body may be a result of mutations.
    b. A birdlike body may be a result of incomplete fossilization.
    c. A birdlike body may be a result of parallel evolution.
    d. A birdlike body may be a result of convergent evolution.

Create/Evaluate

12. Hard supportive systems, such as skeletons, lend themselves to mineral fossilization and appearance of more fossils. With this in mind, which of these observations is suggestive of soft-bodied Ediacarans found in fossils records?
    a. They had cell walls.
    b. They had hidden bones.
    c. They had supportive cuticle.
    d. They had exoskeletons.

13. Compare monophyletic, polyphyletic, and paraphyletic taxa.

14. Suppose that your friend claims that the class Reptilia is a monophyletic taxon. What is most likely your reaction to her claim? Explain.

15. Explain in which situations we use the term convergent evolution, and in which situations the term parallel evolution.

Chapter Roadmap

Humans and Evolution

This chapter provides an account of what is known about the evolution of Homo sapiens. Much of our understanding comes from the fossil record but has more recently been supplemented by molecular tools that have shed new light on the evolutionary history of humans.

©AAAC/Topham/The Image Works

20.1 The Fossil Record of Hominins

Fossil specimens have allowed researchers to develop a map of the evolution of the hominin lineage, starting in Africa between 5 and 10 million years ago.

20.2 Morphology and Bipedalism

An upright posture and bipedal locomotion distinguish hominins from apes.

20.3 Human Features That Do Not Fossilize

We have little knowledge of how early humans behaved, their social networks, or how language developed.

20.4 Dispersal of Early Humans

There exist competing hypotheses about whether modern humans spread out from Africa, or if they were descendants of ancestors that had spread through Europe and Asia.

20.5 Hominins and the Species Concepts

We have evidence that modern humans interbred with Neandertals, so perhaps they were not a distinct species.

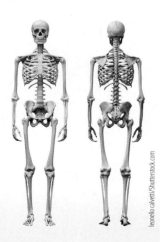

leonello calvetti/Shutterstock.com

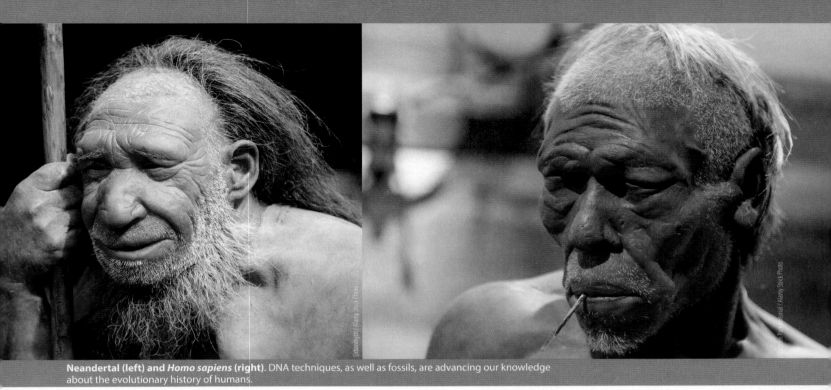
Neandertal (left) and *Homo sapiens* (right). DNA techniques, as well as fossils, are advancing our knowledge about the evolutionary history of humans.

Humans and Evolution

20

Why it matters … From about 500 000 to 30 000 years ago, Neandertals (*Homo neanderthalensis*) roamed much of Europe and eastern and central Asia. Humans (*Homo sapiens*) arrived in the area about 40 000 years ago. Neandertals were shorter, more heavily built, and stronger than humans, and their brains were larger as well. But the Neandertals disappeared about 30 000 years ago, and paleontologists have often wondered why humans won out. Hypotheses include interbreeding between the two species (or subspecies), larger eyes in the Neandertal, and climate change. Only about 2% of the DNA of modern Europeans is Neandertal, so why didn't the two species simply interbreed and blend together? Also, surprisingly, no Neandertal mitochondrial DNA (mtDNA) has shown up in human mtDNA. Since mtDNA is passed only from mother to child, this suggests that, while Neandertal fathers and human mothers might have produced viable offspring, Neandertal mothers and human fathers could not. Was this the only thing that separated *H. sapiens* from *H. neanderthalensis*?

Recently, researchers in Seattle have developed the "Brainscan Atlas," a genetic reference about how the human brain is constructed and how it develops embryonically. Drs. Mohammed Uddin and Stephen Scherer, at Toronto's Hospital for Sick Children, used the Atlas and the Exome Variant Server (a database of all of a human's exomes) to determine which genes were responsible for autism. Uddin and Scherer determined that about 1700 genes were related only to brain development, not to any other function in the body. They then discovered that at least one-third of these 1700 genes had been implicated by other researchers in other brain and cognitive disorders.

Now, back to the Neandertal conundrum: Uddin and Scherer suddenly thought that the 1700 genes could somehow be related to what makes humans uniquely human. People with autism have difficulties with communication and socialization; could these abilities also be what set us apart from Neandertals?

The Cast of Characters: Fossil Hominins

Most of our ancestors' fossils have been found in Africa **(Figure 1)**. Brain size varies with overall body size, so that large individuals (typically males) have more brain size than smaller ones (typically females). Across the species presented here, brain size ranges from the size of chimpanzee brain size (275–500 cm³, *Orrorin tugenensis*) to that of *Homo sapiens* (1000–1900 cm³). Species of *Australopithecus* have brain sizes of about 400–500 cm³; *Homo habilis* about 640 cm³. *Homo erectus* brain size ranges from 930 to 1030 cm³; *Homo neanderthalensis* from 1300 to 1600 cm³.

Orrorin tugenensis: In 2000, researchers found 13 fossils of *O. tugenensis* ("first man" in a local African language), a species that lived in the forests of eastern Africa about 6 mya. The thigh bones and pelvis indicate that it was bipedal.

Ardipithecus ramidus: In 1994, *Ardipithecus ramidus* was described from bone fragments (teeth and jaw fragments) collected in South Africa. These hominids stood 120 cm tall and had apelike teeth. The October 2, 2009, issue of *Science* included 11 papers about *A. ramidus* by an international team of researchers who reported data from 110 specimens. This species lived from about 6 to 4 mya, and many of its features overturned ideas about the evolution of our own species. The structure of its pelvis and feet suggested that it was bipedal. Both males and females had small canine teeth (compared to those of other primates), which imply reduced competition between males, presumably for females in estrus, in turn suggesting concealed ovulation (see Chapter 44). Bipedal locomotion could have enabled the hominins to exploit both land surface and trees in the search for food and shelter. Bipedal animals can carry food and be more effective provisioners. Many features of *A. ramidus* demonstrate that our ancestors showed an earlier than expected departure from a chimpanzee-like existence.

Australopithecus africanus: The first australopith to be described, *Australopithecus africanus*, was discovered by Raymond Dart in 1924. With its relatively small brain, this bipedal species was not immediately recognized as a hominin.

Australopithecus afarensis: Specimens of more than 60 individuals have been found in northern Ethiopia. The sample includes about 40% of a female's skeleton, named "Lucy" (Figure 20.5; apparently the Beatles' song "Lucy in the Sky with Diamonds" was playing on the radio when the skeleton was first uncovered). *A. afarensis* lived 3.5 to 3 mya. This species retained several ancestral characters, including moderately large and pointed canine teeth and a relatively small brain. Males and females were 150 cm and 120 cm tall respectively. Skeletal analyses suggest that Lucy was fully bipedal, a conclusion supported by fossilized footprints preserved in a layer of volcanic ash (Figure 20.1). In 2010, the description of a male specimen of *Australopithecus afarensis* ("big man") provided further evidence of bipedalism, specifically, details of the pelvic girdle and sacrum not preserved in Lucy. Furthermore, a well-preserved scapula (shoulder blade) provided no evidence of suspensory climbing evident in the scapulae of great apes.

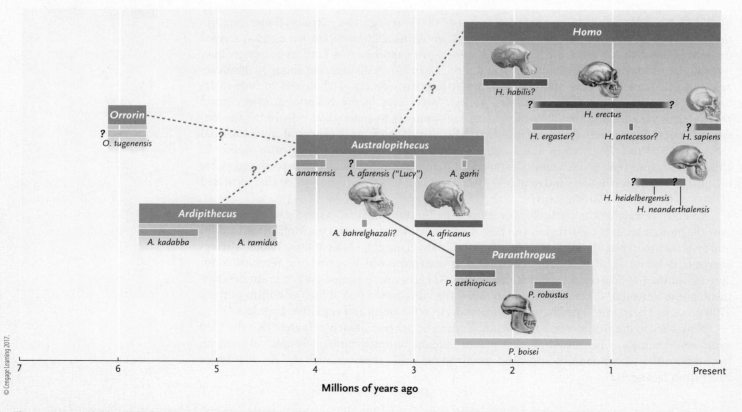

Figure 1 Hominin timeline showing several of the species described in the text. These species lived at the same place and time in eastern and southern Africa. The timeline is shown for each species, and question marks indicate uncertainty about classification and/or ages of fossils. Some skulls are reconstructions from fragments.

Australopithecus anamensis: One of the oldest known species in the genus, *Australopithecus anamensis* lived in eastern Africa around 4 mya. Its teeth had thick enamel, which is typically a derived hominin character. A fossilized thigh bone suggests that it was bipedal.

Australopithecus sediba: In September 2011, the journal *Science* published a series of papers describing the newly discovered *Australopithecus sediba*, an "early" (2 mya) version of Lucy (*A. afarensis*). The fossils, from the Malapa site in South Africa, provided a new perspective on the evolution of humans. The ankles and feet suggest a combination of climbing ability (arboreal life style) and bipedalism that differed from that of Lucy. The pelvis of *A. sediba* shared features, such as the sacral and pubic areas, with those of Lucy and other australopithecines. But in the shape of its ilium, *A. sediba* resembled species of *Homo*. These features in *A. sediba* suggest that giving birth to offspring with large brains had not yet appeared at this stage of australopithecine evolution.

Some of the fossil *A. sediba* had nearly complete wrists and hands, indicating the capacity for strong flexion typically associated with tree climbing. But the long thumb and short fingers of *A. sediba* imply a capacity for precision gripping (see Figure 20.8), suggesting the potential for the use of tools. Construction of a virtual endocast of the skull of *A. sediba* indicates that the frontal lobes of the brain were generally like those of other australopithecines. But the features of the brain suggest its gradual reorganization toward the appearance in species of *Homo*.

This new fossil demonstrates, once again, how such a find can influence our view of evolutionary history. This is not a "missing link" but rather a species whose features reflect the general state of evolutionary development of species in the genus *Australopithecus*. It also presages the transitions that later occur with the emergence of species in the genus *Homo*.

Homo habilis: Pliocene fossils of the earliest *Homo* are fragmentary and widely distributed in space and time. They are thought to have belonged to *Homo habilis* (meaning "handy man"). From 2.3 to 1.7 mya, *H. habilis* occupied the woodlands and savannas of eastern and southern Africa, sharing these habitats with various species of *Paranthropus*. The two genera are easy to distinguish because the brains of *H. habilis* were at least 20% larger, and their **incisors** were larger and **molars** smaller than those of *Paranthropus* spp. They ate hard-shelled nuts and seeds, as well as soft fruits, tubers, leaves, and insects. They may also have hunted small prey or scavenged carcasses left by larger predators.

Researchers have found numerous tools dating to the time of *H. habilis* but are not sure which species made them. Many hominid species of that time probably cracked marrowbones with rocks or scraped flesh from bones with sharp stones. Paleoanthropologist Louis Leakey was the first to discover evidence of tool-*making* at eastern Africa's Olduvai Gorge, which cuts through a great sequence of sedimentary rock layers. The oldest tools at this site are crudely chipped pebbles, probably manufactured by *H. habilis*. However, humans are not the only animals to *use* tools (see Chapter 32).

Homo erectus: Early in the Pleistocene, about 1.8 mya, a new species of humans, *Homo erectus* ("upright man"), appeared in eastern Africa **(Figure 2)**. One nearly complete skeleton suggests that *H. erectus* was taller than its ancestors and had a much larger brain, a thicker skull, and protruding brow ridges. *H. erectus* made fairly sophisticated tools, such as hand axes **(Figure 3)** used to cut food and other materials, to scrape meat from bones, and to dig for roots. *H. erectus* probably ate both plants and animals and may have hunted and scavenged animal prey. Archaeological data point to their use of fire to cook food and to keep warm. Near Lake Turkana in Kenya, fossils identified as *Homo* and dating from 1.55 to 1.45 mya were described in 2007. These suggested that *H. erectus* and *H. habilis* lived together in the same habitats for a considerable time, much as chimps and gorillas do today. Adult male *H. erectus* were much larger than adult females, suggesting a polygynous lifestyle, one male with several females (see Chapter 32).

About 1.5 mya, the pressure of growing populations apparently forced groups of *H. erectus* out of Africa. They dispersed northward from eastern Africa into both northwestern Africa and Eurasia. Some moved eastward through Asia as far as the island of Java. Judging from its geographic distribution, *H. erectus* was successful in many environments. It produced several descendant

Homo erectus

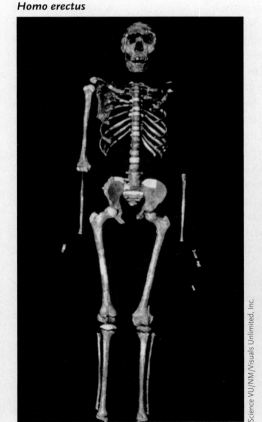

Hand axe

Science VU/NM/Visuals Unlimited, Inc.

©AAAC/Topham/The Image Works

Figure 2 ***Homo erectus*, a nearly complete skeleton from Kenya**

Figure 3 **A hand axe found at a site used by** ***Homo erectus***

CHAPTER 20 HUMANS AND EVOLUTION | **479**

species, of which modern humans (*H. sapiens*, meaning "wise man") are the only survivors. Now-extinct descendants of *H. erectus*, archaic humans, first appeared at least 400 000 years ago. They generally had larger brains, rounder skulls, and smaller molars than *H. erectus*.

Homo floresiensis: *H. floresiensis* was described in 2004 from Flores Island in Indonesia. Although first proposed as a distinct species, its small size was used to support the view that it was just a small individual. In 2013, analyses of various aspects of the morphology of *H. floresiensis* indicated that it was not a dwarf or microcephalic, rather a distinct species most closely related to *H. erectus*.

Homo neanderthalensis: Neandertals lived in Europe and western Asia from 150 000 to 28 000 years ago. They are the best known of the archaic humans and sometimes have been treated as a subspecies of *Homo sapiens*. Compared with modern humans, they had a heavier build, more pronounced brow ridges, and slightly larger brains. Neandertals were culturally and technologically sophisticated. They made complex tools, including wooden spears, stone axes, flint scrapers, and knives. At some sites, they built shelters of stones, branches, and animal hides, and they routinely used fire. They were successful hunters and probably ate nuts, berries, fishes, and bird eggs. Some groups buried their dead, and they may have had rudimentary speech. There is evidence that some were cannibals.

In 1997, two teams of researchers independently analyzed short segments of mtDNA extracted from the fossilized arm bone of a Neandertal. Unlike nuclear DNA, which individuals inherit from both parents, only mothers pass mtDNA to offspring. mtDNA does not undergo genetic recombination (see Chapter 8) and has a high mutation rate, making it useful for phylogenetic analyses. If mutation rates in mtDNA are fairly constant, this molecule can serve as a **molecular clock**. Comparing the Neandertal sequence with mtDNA from 986 living humans revealed three times as many differences between the Neandertals and modern humans as between pairs of modern humans in their sample. These data suggest that Neandertals and modern humans are different species that diverged from a common ancestor 690 000 to 550 000 years ago.

Homo sapiens: Modern humans differ from Neandertals and other archaic humans in having a slighter build, less-protruding brow ridges, and a more prominent chin. The earliest fossils of modern humans found in Africa and Asia are 150 000 years old; those from the Middle East are 100 000 years old. Fossils from about 20 000 years ago are known from Western Europe, the most famous being those of the Cro-Magnon deposits in southern France. The widespread appearance of modern humans roughly coincided with the demise of Neandertals in Western Europe and the Middle East, 40 000 to 28 000 years ago.

Dr. Ajit Varki at the University of California, San Diego, thinks that, despite the physical similarities between humans and Neandertals, they could have been very different in **social behaviour** and in their abilities to communicate. Consequently, children with one *H. sapiens* parent and one *H. neanderthalensis* parent could have been "cognitively sterile," and therefore unable to really communicate with each other. This research was published in 2014.

DNA techniques as well as fossils are advancing our knowledge about the evolutionary history of humans. In this chapter we focus on some of the most important changes in our ancestry. We consider the implications of **bipedalism**, showing that it is much more than walking erect on two legs. We also present some recently discovered fossils and consider how the biological species concept applies to our own species.

20.1 The Fossil Record of Hominins

A combination of genetic and morphological analyses of living and fossil species indicates that, between 10 and 5 mya in Africa, **hominoids** (superfamily Hominoidea, including apes and humans) diverged into several lineages. One lineage, the **hominins** (family Hominidae, subfamily Homininae), includes modern humans and our bipedal ancestors (see Figure 19.3 and "The Cast of Characters: Fossil Hominins"). Where only one species of hominin (*Homo sapiens*) exists today, several species lived in the past.

Most of the hominins that lived in eastern and southern Africa from 6 to 1 mya are currently classified in the genera

Australopithecus (*australo* = southern; *pithecus* = ape) and *Paranthropus* (*para* = beside; *anthropus* = man). With large faces, protruding jaws, and small skulls and brains, these hominins resembled apes. Between 3.7 and 1 mya, several other species of hominins occurred in eastern and southern Africa. These adult males ranged from 40 to 50 kg in mass and from 130 to 150 cm in height; females were smaller. Most of these species had deep jaws and large molars, suggesting a diet of hard food, such as nuts, seeds, and other vegetable products. *Australopithecus africanus*, known only from southern Africa, had small jaws and teeth, suggesting a diet of softer food. The phylogenetic relationships among species in the genera *Australopithecus* and *Paranthropus*, and their exact relationships to later hominids, are not yet fully understood (see Figure 19.3 and "The Cast of Characters: Fossil Hominins"). *Australopithecus* was likely ancestral to humans (various species in the genus *Homo*).

CONCEPT FIX Many people believe that evolutionary biologists say that our species evolved *from* apes. But while the fossil record clearly demonstrates that the evolutionary lineage to which *H. sapiens* belongs includes chimps and gorillas (Figure 19.3), the lineage leading to humans has been distinct from the one leading to gorillas and chimps for over 6 million years. Belonging to an evolutionary lineage does not mean one species in the lineage gives rise to another. Evolutionary biologists are not proposing that humans evolved from apes, but that apes are our closest living relatives (see "Chromosomal Similarities and Differences among the Great Apes" in Chapter 18).

1. What are three adaptations of humans that separate them from chimpanzees?
2. How old are the oldest fossils of humans? Of hominoids?
3. When did the lineage leading to chimps and orangutans diverge from the hominin lineage?

20.2 Morphology and Bipedalism

Upright posture and bipedal locomotion distinguish hominins from apes. Bipedal locomotion meant, largely, that the hands were not used in locomotion, allowing them to become specialized for other activities such as carrying things and using and making tools. Sometimes paleontologists find fossilized hominin footprints, indicating bipedalism **(Figure 20.1)**, but usually the fossil record of mammals such as *Homo sapiens* consists mainly of bones and teeth, the body parts most often fossilized. Bipedalism is obvious from the feet, thighs, pelvis, shoulders, and arms of these fossil and human skeletons **(Figure 20.2)**. When appropriate fossils are available, it may be possible to learn when the skeletal features associated with bipedalism appeared over time.

Bipedalism in hominins involves a suite of anatomical features, not just the pattern of footfall and walking and running behaviour.

20.2a Feet, Legs, and Pelvis

Paleontologists have long inferred bipedalism from the structure of the thigh bones (femora) and pelvis **(Figure 20.3)**. Both ends of the femur, at the hip and knee joints, are larger in the human than in the chimpanzee because more weight is directed through the human joints. Humans have a smaller angle at the hip end of the femur (the ball and socket joint) because of their upright stance. Also, human leg bones (both the upper leg and lower leg) are longer than in chimpanzees; however, chimps have longer foreleg bones than humans have.

More recently, the metatarsals (the long foot bones) provided additional features for recognizing bipedalism in hominins. For example, the fourth metatarsals of *Australopithecus afarensis* were more like those of humans than those of either

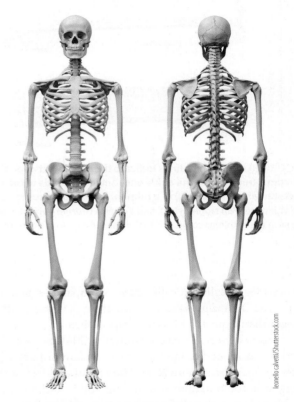

FIGURE 20.2 Human skeleton, front and back views

FIGURE 20.1 Mary Leakey discovered these fossilized footprints of an australopithecine made in soft, damp volcanic ash about 3.7 mya. The footprints appear to have been made by an adult and a youngster.

FIGURE 20.3 A comparison of the thigh bones (femora) of a chimpanzee (bottom) and a human (top)

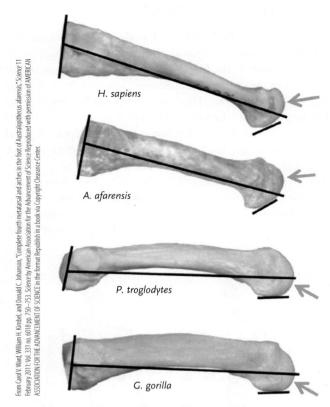

FIGURE 20.4 **The black lines indicate the angles between the proximal (on the left, the ankle end) and distal ends of the fourth metatarsal bone (arrows) of a human, *Australopithecus afarensis*, a chimpanzee (*Pan troglodytes*), and a gorilla (*Gorilla gorilla*).** Note the angle in the hominins compared to the parallel lines in the ape species.

chimps or gorillas **(Figure 20.4)**. Comparable features also appeared in *Ardipithecus ramidus* from 3.4 mya, indicating a longer than expected history of bipedalism.

Australopithecus sediba from the Malapa site in South Africa was an earlier (about 2 mya) version of Lucy (*Australopithecus afarensis*; **Figure 20.5**). The ankles and feet of *A. sediba* suggest a combination of climbing ability (arboreal lifestyle) and bipedalism that differed from that of Lucy. The sacral and pubic areas of the pelvis of *A. sediba* resemble those of Lucy and other australopithecines, but the shape of the ilium of *A. sediba* resembled that of species of *Homo*.

In 2007, S. K. S. Thorpe, R. L. Holder, and R. H. Crompton proposed that bipedalism arose in an arboreal setting. Specifically, they asserted that hand-assisted bipedalism allowed the ancestors of humans and great apes to move on flexible supports (branches) that would otherwise have been too small. Thorpe et al. compared human and orangutan (*Pongo abelii*) locomotion and found that orangutans walking on flexible branches increase knee and hip extension, just as humans do when running on a springy track. In a bipedal gait, humans and orangutans flex the hind limbs in a manner that differs from the gait of gorillas and chimps.

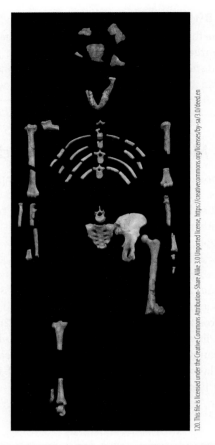

FIGURE 20.5 **The fossil skeleton of *Australopithecus afarensis*, popularly known as "Lucy"**

20.2b Shoulders and Arms

The importance of climbing for australopiths is supported by the appearance of their shoulder blades (scapulae). The angle of the socket (glenoid fossa; **Figure 20.6**) that receives the head of the upper arm bone (humerus) faces cranially (toward the head), as it does in apes that hang from their arms. In humans, the glenoid fossa faces laterally but changes with age. A lateral-facing glenoid fossa also contributes to humans' ability to throw projectiles such as spears or stones at high speeds.

Species in the genus *Homo* have three specializations associated with throwing ability:

1. They have a "long waist" because of an increase in the number of lumbar vertebrae combined with longer

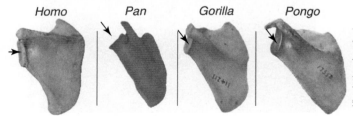

FIGURE 20.6 **A comparison of the shoulder blades (scapulae) of a human, a chimp (*Pan*), a gorilla, and an orangutan (*Pongo*) showing the orientation of the glenoid fossa (arrows)**

individual vertebrae. The long waist allows the movement of hips and thorax (the portion of the body between head and abdomen) to be decoupled, resulting in a large range of motion of the shoulders and the development of torque.

2. Torsion of the humerus (upper arm bone) between the orientation of its head and the axis of the elbow extends the range of motion during rotation.

3. The laterally directed glenoid fossa aligns the moment generated by flexing of a muscle, the pectoral muscles, with the rotation of the torso.

This set of specializations appeared more than 2 mya in *Homo erectus*. It permits elastic storage of energy, which contributes to accurate spear throwing. Effective throwing increased the hunting potential of species in the genus *Homo*.

20.2c Hands

Species in the genus *Homo* have hands that are quite distinct from those of apes. The palms and fingers are short, while the thumbs are long, strong, and mobile **(Figure 20.7)**. This results in our ability to use two different grips **(Figure 20.8)**, a power grip and a precision grip, allowing manipulative skills and a capacity to make precise tools. The proportions of hominin hands also deliver a performance advantage when striking with

FIGURE 20.8 Power grip versus precision grip. Hominins grasp objects in two distinct ways. The power grip **(a)** allows us to grasp an object firmly, whereas the precision grip **(b)** allows us to manipulate objects by fine movements.

a fist. Buttressing of the elements in the hand increases the stiffness of the joint between the second metacarpal (a hand bone) and phalanges (finger bones), enabling hominins to punch with more force. The ability to present our hands palms up (supination) or palms down (pronation) also increases their versatility.

Increasing the force that can be delivered can also be achieved by the leverage associated with attaching a handle or strap (haft) to a projectile point, such as a spear or an arrow. At Kathu Pan in South Africa, hafted tools date from 500 000 years ago. Hafted tools such as spears further enhance the impact of high-velocity throwing, while shorter stabbing blows reflect the importance of the power grip. Other tools found among hominin fossils include stone cutting tools used to take meat off bones and stone axes used for chopping trees. Through time, the tools found show improvement in the technique and the fine motor skills required to make them.

20.2d Pelvis and Birth

Female hominins suffer at least one consequence of being bipedal, namely the shift in the body's centre of mass during pregnancy. A marked posterior concavity of individual lower back (lumbar) vertebrae stabilizes the centre of mass of the upper body over the hips. Bipedal females have a derived curvature of

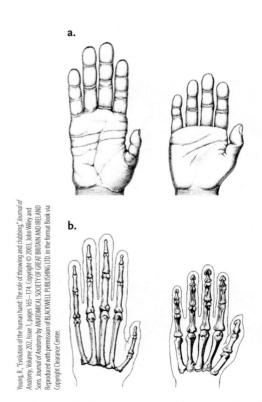

Young, R., "Evolution of the human hand: The role of throwing and clubbing," *Journal of Anatomy*, Volume 202, Issue 1, pages 165–174. Copyright © 2003, John Wiley and Sons. *Journal of Anatomy* by ANATOMICAL SOCIETY OF GREAT BRITAIN AND IRELAND Reproduced with permission of BLACKWELL PUBLISHING LTD. in the format Book via Copyright Clearance Center.

FIGURE 20.7 The chimp's hands (left) are adapted for grasping branches, while human hands (right) are adapted for precision and power grips. The relatively longer thumbs of humans also contribute to our precision grip.

the lumbar area and reinforcement of those vertebrae to compensate for the additional load associated with pregnancy. The anatomy of the pelvis and lower back of *Australopithecus* indicates that these adaptations to bipedalism preceded the evolution of species in the genus *Homo*. Compared to modern humans, the birth canals of Neandertals were not as specialized. The birth process in our species is specialized and may be a relatively recent development.

STUDY BREAK QUESTIONS

1. Name three morphological specializations associated with bipedalism.
2. What effect do these specializations have on hominins, and how do they distinguish hominins from chimps?

20.3 Human Features That Do Not Fossilize

Some features characteristic of humans are unlikely to fossilize, such as behavioural and soft tissue features associated with social organization and language. The structure of jaws and teeth as well as fossilized dung (coprolites) can be used to infer (jaws and teeth) or reveal (coprolites) what fossil animals ate.

Although jaw and tooth structure can suggest the ability to eat hard food, our ancestors may have used tools to break up hard foodstuffs and fire to soften and cook them. Meanwhile, early hominins exploited a range of habitats and thrived on a diversity of food.

Humans show a great capacity for making friends—not genetically related individuals—with whom they have long-term, non-reproductive relationships that involve cooperation and mutual influence. These relationships underlie social networks, a feature of many social species. In humans, social networks may include individuals of other species, such as dogs and cats. Social networks and associated cooperative behaviour are well known from human hunter–gatherer societies, such as the Hadza of Tanzania. One apparently unique feature of human social networks is the common use of some land areas by different groups. This leads to a pattern of movement among groups (dispersal) that enhances social learning and a cumulative culture.

Effective communication among individuals is an essential part of social networks. One aspect is an individual's ability to read and interpret the body language (see Chapter 32) of another. Humans use both body cues and facial expressions to distinguish between intense positive and negative emotions **(Figure 20.9)**.

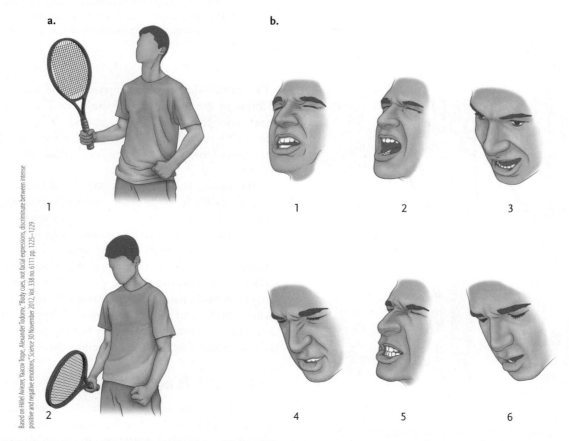

Based on Hillel Aviezer, Yaacov Trope, Alexander Todorov, "Body cues, not facial expressions, discriminate between intense positive and negative emotions," *Science* 30 November 2012, Vol. 338 no. 6111 pp. 1225–1229

FIGURE 20.9 **(a)** Body language in response to winning (1) and losing (2) a point. **(b)** Facial expressions presented as isolated views in response to winning (2, 3, 5) and losing (1, 4, 6) a point

Source: Based on Hillel Aviezer, Yaacov Trope, Alexander Todorov, "Body cues, not facial expressions, discriminate between intense positive and negative emotions," *Science* 30 November 2012, Vol. 338 no. 6111 pp. 1225–1229

Language is a means of communication that involves symbolism and syntax. Although language is sometimes considered a hallmark of *Homo sapiens*, other animals also use a combination of symbolism and syntax in communication. For example, when a vervet monkey (*Chlorocebus pygerythrus*) gives the "eagle" alarm call, its fellows look skyward and move closer to the trunks of trees. When the same monkey gives a "leopard" alarm call, other monkeys in trees look down and those on the ground climb trees.

Language is not unique to *H. sapiens*, and it is not clear when language appeared in human evolution. The *FOXP2* gene is associated with speech and language in *H. sapiens*, and genomic analysis reveals that *H. sapiens* and *Homo neanderthalensis* have similar *FOXP2* genes, implying that Neandertals had language. A trait of many (all?) present-day human languages is a combination of simple categories (to minimize details) and a high level of informativeness to maximize communication efficiency.

STUDY BREAK QUESTIONS

1. How does communication figure in the evolution of humans?
2. What are friends? How do they distinguish humans from other animals?

20.4 Dispersal of Early Humans

There are two main theories about the dispersal of our ancestors from Africa. The **African emergence hypothesis** proposes that early hominin descendants (archaic humans) left Africa and established populations in the Middle East, Asia, and Europe. Some time later, 200 000 to 100 000 years ago, *H. sapiens* arose in Africa and also migrated into Europe and Asia. Perhaps through competition, *H. sapiens* eventually drove archaic humans to extinction. This hypothesis suggests that all modern humans are descended from a fairly recent African ancestor.

The **multiregional hypothesis** suggests that populations of *H. erectus* and archaic humans had spread through much of Europe and Asia by 500 000 years ago, and modern humans (*H. sapiens*) evolved from descendants of these earlier dispersals. Although these geographically separated populations may have experienced some evolutionary differentiation, gene flow between them prevented reproductive isolation and maintained them as a single but variable species, *H. sapiens*.

Paleontological data do not clearly support either hypothesis but, as of 2011, genetic data **(Figure 20.10)** generally supported the African emergence hypothesis. Further work on the Y chromosomes of thousands of men from Africa, Europe, Asia, Australia, and the Americas has confirmed that all modern humans are the descendants of a single migration out of Africa.

A rapid exodus of anatomically modern humans out of Africa may have occurred along the coast of the Indian Ocean. Archaeological material from the United Arab Emirates suggests that early emigrants may have taken advantage of lower sea levels to move along the Arabian coast around 60 000 years ago.

Earlier dispersal is clear from material found at Attirampakkam in India. These fossils indicate that Acheulian humans (probably *Homo erectus*) had occupied this site by about 1.5 mya. Acheulian cultures are typified by large cutting tools with bifaces. Other records indicate that hominins (*Homo floresiensis*) were on Flores Island (Indonesia) by 1 mya. Humans occupied sites on the highlands in New Guinea by about 49 000 years ago. These humans exploited endemic nuts (*Pandanus* spp.) and appeared to have cleared forests to promote growth of their preferred plants. The timing of the arrival of humans in the New World is less well known. Dating of sites at caves in Oregon indicates human occupancy by about 12 000 years ago.

20.4a The Denisovans

Genetic information in the form of DNA recovered from a finger bone of a girl who lived over 50 000 years ago indicates that she had dark skin, brown hair, and brown eyes. The girl's fossilized bone fragments were found in Denisova Cave in Siberia. The name of the cave has been applied to the people, Denisovans, who apparently were a sister group to the Neandertals. Subsequent genomic analysis revealed that the Denisovans lived in Southeast Asia and interbred with the ancestors of today's Melanesians.

Vital components of our immune system (HLA class I) were acquired through the *HLA-B*73* allele inherited from Denisovans in west Asia. Genome analysis also indicates that some *HLA* haplotypes entered modern European and Oceanian human populations from both Neandertals and Denisovans.

STUDY BREAK QUESTIONS

1. What evidence supports the African emergence hypothesis?
2. By when had humans arrived in India? How do we know?

20.5 Hominins and the Species Concepts

The history of hominins clearly demonstrates the challenges inherent in recognizing species and the boundaries between them. This example is particularly illuminating because it involves paleontological, archaeological, and genomic evidence. The genomic analysis shows that the ancestors of modern humans interbred with both Neandertals and Denisovans. If we apply the biological species concept (see Chapter 18), these three groups are not separate species. If we apply the phylogenetic species concept, the distinction is less clear. The morphological evidence from fossils is incomplete and does not necessarily settle the matter.

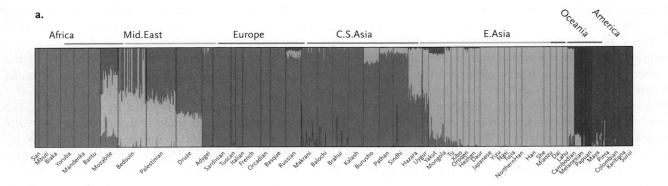

a.

Africa   Mid.East   Europe   C.S.Asia   E.Asia   Oceania   America

San Mbuti Biaka Yoruba Mandenka Bantu Mozabite Bedouin Palestinian Druze Adygei Sardinian Tuscan Italian French Orcadian Basque Russian Makrani Balochi Brahui Kalash Burusho Pathan Sindhi Hazara Uygur Yakut Mongola Tu Xibo Oroqen Hezhen Daur Japanese Yizu Naxi Tujia NorthernHan Han She Miaozu Dai Lahu Cambodian Melanesian Papuan Maya Pima Colombian Karitiana Surui

b.

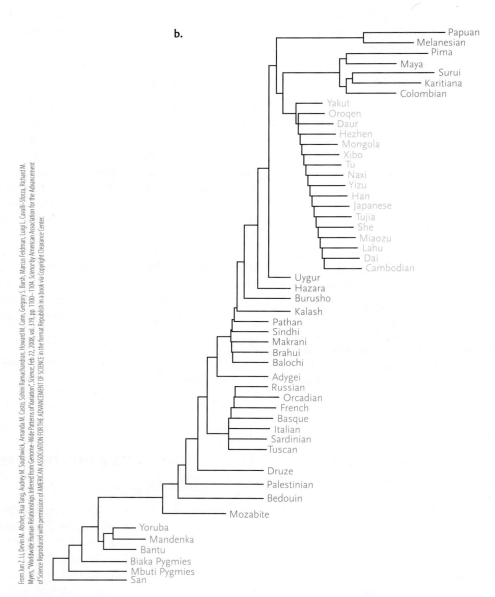

From Jun Z. Li, Devin M. Absher, Hua Tang, Audrey M. Southwick, Amanda M. Casto, Sohini Ramachandran, Howard M. Cann, Gregory S. Barsh, Marcus Feldman, Luigi L. Cavalli-Sforza, Richard M. Myers, "Worldwide Human Relationships Inferred from Genome-Wide Patterns of Variation", Science, Feb 22, 2008, vol. 319, pp. 1100–1104. Science by American Association for the Advancement of Science Reproduced with permission of AMERICAN ASSOCIATION FOR THE ADVANCEMENT OF SCIENCE in the format Republish in a book via Copyright Clearance Center.

FIGURE 20.10 Out of Africa. (a) Genetic data from 650 000 common single-nucleotide polymorphism loci from 928 humans were used to construct an individual ancestry and population dendrogram. **(b)** Maximum likelihood tree of 51 populations shows a single origin in sub-Saharan Africa and a subsequent radiation across Asia to the New World and Polynesia.

In 2013, the description of fossil hominins from Georgia (Dmanisi) changed our view of our ancestors. In 2000, these fossils from 1.7 mya were identified as *Homo georgicus*, but the 2013 presentation of data from five skulls shows the same amount of variation in morphology that we know from living populations of humans and chimpanzees. This discovery suggests a highly variable lineage and obliges us to reconsider which of the named species of *Homo* are valid.

With recent advances in molecular technology, we are learning a great deal more about our evolutionary history. The story continues about what sets humans apart from other animals, whether it is communication abilities, social cooperation, or even an understanding of the future. As we will see later in the book, our animal ancestry is still clear, whether the topic is population ecology (Chapter 29) or animal behaviour (Chapter 32).

STUDY BREAK QUESTIONS

1. What is the impact of the fossils from Dmanisi on our view of species diversity in the genus *Homo*?
2. How do the "species" of hominins fit the biological species concept?

Summary Illustration

The study of human evolution focuses on the time since human and chimpanzee lineages diverged from their common ancestor, approximately 6 million years ago. DNA techniques and fossils of hominins, species most closely related to humans, have provided our current understanding of human evolution. At times, several hominin species coexisted. Eventually, all became extinct except one, *Homo sapiens*.

Bipedalism
- Upright posture and bipedalism distinguish hominins from apes.
- The oldest evidence showing upright walking is about 6 to 7 million years old. However, these species still climbed trees and had ape-like features (e.g., *Orrorin tugenensis* and *Sahelanthropus tchadensis*).

Bipedal locomotion allowed hands to be free to perform more activities, such as carrying things and making and using tools.

Quadrupedalism
Pan troglodytes
(modern chimpanzee)

Bipedalism
Homo sapiens
(modern human)

J. Reader/Science Source

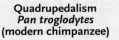

Homo   *Pan*   *Gorilla*   *Pongo*

Shoulder blades show whether the species hangs from its arms (apes) or has the ability to throw projectiles (humans).

From Green and Alemseged, "Australopithecus afarensis Scapular Ontogeny, Function, and the Role of Climbing in Human Evolution," *Science* 26 October 2012: Vol. 338 no. 6106 pp. 514–517. *Science* by American Association for the Advancement of Science Reproduced with permission of AMERICAN ASSOCIATION FOR THE ADVANCEMENT OF SCIENCE in the format Republish in a book via Copyright Clearance Center.

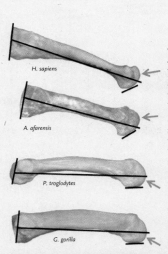

H. sapiens

A. afarensis

P. troglodytes

G. gorilla

Metatarsals can distinguish bipedalism.

From Carol V. Ward, William H. Kimbel, and Donald C. Johanson, "Complete fourth metatarsal and arches in the foot of *Australopithecus afarensis*," *Science* 11 February 2011: Vol. 331 no. 6018 pp. 750–753. *Science* by American Association for the Advancement of Science Reproduced with permission of AMERICAN ASSOCIATION FOR THE ADVANCEMENT OF SCIENCE in the format Republish in a book via Copyright Clearance Center.

Evidence of bipedalism includes fossilized hominin footprints and, more commonly, skeletal features (e.g., bones of feet, hands, thighs, pelvis, shoulders, and arms).

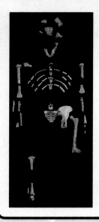

Fossils of more than 60 *Australopithecus afarensis* individuals have been found in northern Ethiopia (including "Lucy," shown here). Males and females were between 120 and 150 cm tall and are thought to have been fully bipedal.

Compared to its ancestors, *Homo erectus* was taller and had a larger brain and a thicker skull. They made sophisticated tools, such as hand axes, and used fire.

Between 150 000 and 30 000 years ago, Neandertals, with shorter, heavier builds than humans, lived in Europe and Asia.

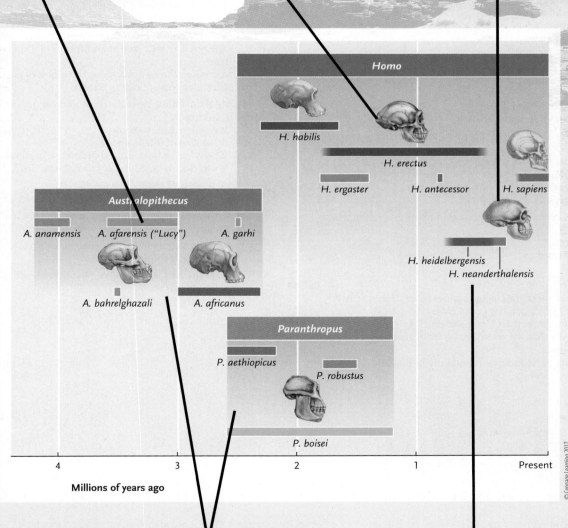

Homo

H. habilis

H. erectus

H. ergaster   H. antecessor   H. sapiens

Australopithecus

A. anamensis   A. afarensis ("Lucy")   A. garhi

A. bahrelghazali   A. africanus

H. heidelbergensis

H. neanderthalensis

Paranthropus

P. aethiopicus

P. robustus

P. boisei

4   3   2   1   Present

Millions of years ago

Most of the hominins that lived in eastern and southern Africa from 1 to 6 mya are classified in the genera *Australopithecus* and *Paranthropus*. They resembled apes, with large faces, protruding jaws, and small skulls and brains.

Species in the genus Homo have hands quite distinct from apes, giving them the ability to use grips that allow manipulative skills and the crafting of precise tools.

Recall/Understand

1. Which of these statements can be applied to Neandertals (*Homo neanderthalensis*)?
   a. They did not occur in the same places and times as *Homo sapiens*.
   b. They did not interbreed with *Homo sapiens*.
   c. They were not behaviourally distinct from *Homo sapiens*.
   d. They were extinct by 20 000 years ago.

2. Which of these factors applies to the family Hominidae?
   a. excludes gorillas and chimps
   b. first appear in the fossil record about 1 mya
   c. includes species in the genera *Homo, Australopithecus,* and *Paranthropus*
   d. includes only species in the genus *Homo*

3. In hominids, bipedalism involves specializations of which of these structures?
   a. feet and legs
   b. knees and ankles
   c. ankles and pelvis
   d. pelvis and legs

4. Which of these structures in humans are specializations for throwing?
   a. feet and hands
   b. hands and arms
   c. feet, shoulders, and arms
   d. waist, shoulders, and arms

5. Which one of these statements refers to the ability to make friends?
   a. It occurs in social organisms.
   b. It is unique to humans.
   c. It depends upon individual recognition.
   d. It occurs only in some people.

6. A variety of evidence indicates that humans evolved in which place?
   a. Africa
   b. South America
   c. Europe
   d. Australia

7. Which one of these statements applies to the Denisovans?
   a. another species in the genus *Homo*
   b. a species larger than *Homo sapiens*
   c. originally discovered in Siberia from genetic analysis of one finger bone
   d. a variety of Neandertal found only in England

8. Which of the following species of fossil hominin is the oldest?
   a. *Homo neanderthalensis*
   b. *Homo sapiens*
   c. *Ardipithecus ramidus*
   d. *Australopithecus sediba*

9. When did hominins move out of Africa?
   a. 3 million years ago
   b. 2 million years ago
   c. 1.5 million years ago
   d. 100 thousand years ago

Apply/Analyze

10. Which of these statements describes genetic similarity among humans, chimps, gorillas, and orangutans?
    a. They all belong to the same species.
    b. They share a relatively recent common ancestor.
    c. They are evidence of creation.
    d. They can interbreed and produce fertile offspring.

11. Which of the following statements is a misconception?
    a. Genus *Homo* evolved from Genus *Australopithecus*.
    b. The phylogenetic tree of hominin evolution is a very bushy tree.
    c. *Australopithecus africanus* is the oldest of australopiths.
    d. Chimpanzees are our ancestors.

12. Which of the following is the most likely significance of tool usage by hominins?
    a. It requires a larger brain.
    b. It is a sign of intelligence.
    c. It proves that hominin evolution is a ladder in progress.
    d. It was documented in very early hominins.

Create/Evaluate

13. Suggest three reasons that might be significant in evolving of bipedalism.

14. Evaluate the statement that bipedalism evolved to free the hands in order to carry things.

15. Compare the African emergence hypothesis with the multiregional hypothesis.

Chapter Roadmap

Defining Life and Its Origins

Earth is 4.6 billion years old and there is evidence that life may have developed within the first 600 million years. In this chapter we discuss what the conditions were like on early Earth that led to the development of life as well as the major events that occurred after. You will realize that there are two fundamental questions of biology that remain hard to answer: what is life actually, and how did life evolve?

21.1 What Is Life?
All forms of life possess seven key characteristics.

21.2 The Chemical Origins of Life
Experiments have shown that the major biological molecules can be synthesized in the laboratory.

21.3 From Macromolecules to Life
Having the molecules required for life is one thing, but how life actually got started remains largely a mystery.

From Chapter 6

21.4 Evidence of the Earliest Life
The earliest forms of life were almost certainly heterotrophic prokaryotic cells; we just don't know for sure.

Many molecules move across membranes by diffusion: from high to low concentration.

From Chapter 2

21.5 Eukaryotes and the Rise of Multicellularity
The development of oxygenic photosynthesis followed by aerobic respiration was critical to the development of the eukaryotic cell.

21.6 The Fossil Record
The study of fossils has provided a wealth of information about the evolution of life, but the fossil record is incomplete.

21.7 The Tree of Life
The three domains of life have the same evolutionary origin and have shared genetic information.

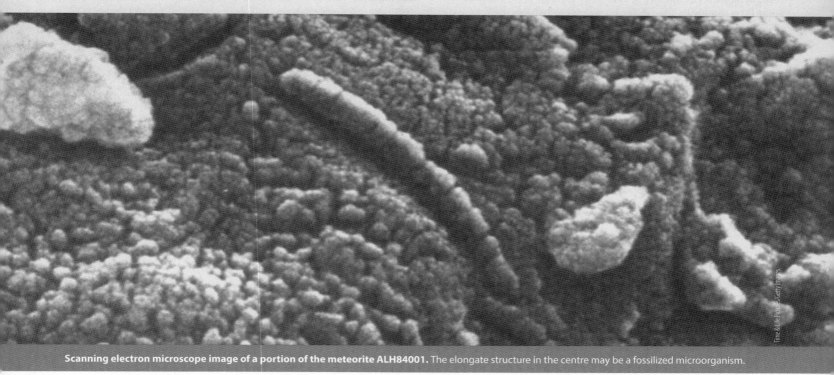

Scanning electron microscope image of a portion of the meteorite ALH84001. The elongate structure in the centre may be a fossilized microorganism.

Defining Life and Its Origins

21

Why it matters . . . In 1984, a group of scientists in the Antarctic discovered a 1.9 kg meteorite that they catalogued as ALH84001. Initial studies of the meteorite showed that it was about 4.5 billion years old, which is about the same age as the solar system. Its chemical composition indicated that it had originated from Mars and had impacted Earth approximately 13 000 years ago. The meteorite garnered headlines around the world in 1996 when an article was published in the prestigious journal *Science* with evidence that ALH84001 contained distinct evidence that life had at one time existed on Mars.

Chemical analysis showed that, when on Mars, ALH84001 had at one time been fractured and subsequently infiltrated by liquid water. Using scanning electron microscopy, the coauthors of the article observed very small, elliptical, ropelike, and tubular structures in the fractured surfaces of ALH84001 that look very similar to fossilized prokaryotic cells. Furthermore, the scientists found microscopic mineral "globules" that bear strong resemblance to mineral alterations caused by primitive cells on Earth.

The analysis of meteorites for microfossils continues and remains controversial. In 2011, an article published in the *Journal of Cosmology* provided additional evidence of bacteria-like fossils within meteorites. Using sophisticated electron microscopy techniques and chemical analysis on three freshly fractured carbonaceous meteorites, data are presented in the article that show the presence of filaments that are strikingly similar in shape to cyanobacteria, a dominant form of photosynthetic bacteria on Earth. The difficulty of unequivocally assigning these structures as remnants of ancient life will continue to make the conclusions of such analyses controversial.

In this chapter, we explore some of the most basic of biological questions: What is life and how did life evolve? After introducing the fundamental characteristics that all organisms share, we work through a discussion of the origins of life. Starting with how biologically important molecules could have been synthesized in the absence of life, we move through hypotheses regarding how the very first cells may have developed, and consider how the molecules that are central to information transfer (DNA, RNA, protein) may have evolved. A central question to evolution of life that we discuss is about what gave rise to eukaryotic organisms. The importance and limitations of the fossil record in addressing questions about the evolution of life are considered. The chapter closes with a discussion of how the molecular tool of DNA sequencing has been used to compare organisms and has allowed scientists to develop a comprehensive tree of life.

21.1   What Is Life?

All life is composed of cells—the fundamental unit of all life. But what is life? How can we define it? Picture a frog sitting on a rock, slowly shifting its head to follow the movements of insects flying nearby (**Figure 21.1**). You know instinctively that the frog is alive and the rock is not. But if you examine both at the atomic level, you will find that the difference between them is lost. The types of elements and atoms found in living things are also found in non-living forms of matter. As well, living cells obey the same fundamental laws of physics and chemistry as the **abiotic** (non-living) world. For example, the biochemical reactions that take place within living cells, although remarkable, are only modifications of chemical reactions that occur outside cells.

21.1a   Seven Characteristics Shared by All Life Forms

Although life seems relatively easy to recognize, it is not easy to define using a single sentence, or even two. Life is defined most effectively by a list of attributes that all forms of life possess. As detailed in **Figure 21.2**, all life displays order, harnesses and utilizes energy, reproduces, responds to stimuli, exhibits homeostasis, grows and develops, and evolves.

There are a small number of biological systems that straddle the line between the **biotic** and the abiotic worlds. The best

FIGURE 21.1   Red-eyed tree frog on a rock

example of this is a virus (**Figure 21.3**). Viruses are very small infectious agents that you will learn more about in Chapter 22. They display many of the properties of life, including the ability to reproduce and evolve over time. However, the characteristics of life that a virus has are based on its ability to infect cells. For example, although viruses contain nucleic acids (DNA and RNA), they lack the cellular machinery and metabolism to use that genetic information to synthesize their own proteins. To make proteins, they have to infect living cells and essentially hijack their translational machinery and metabolism to reproduce. You can find other entities that display some, but not all of life's properties that are not alive. Computer programs, for example, have as many characteristics of life as do viruses. For this reason, most scientists do not consider viruses to be alive.

21.1b   The Characteristics of Life Are Emergent

Each of the characteristics of life depicted in Figure 21.2 reflects a remarkable complexity resulting from a hierarchy of interactions that begins with atoms and progresses through molecules to macromolecules and cells. Depending upon the organism, this hierarchy may continue upward in complexity and include organelles, tissues, and organs. The seven properties of life shown in Figure 21.2 are a result of emergent properties because they come about, or emerge, from many simpler interactions that, in themselves, do not have the properties found at the higher levels. For example, the ability to harness and utilize energy is not a property of molecules or proteins or biological membranes in isolation; rather, the ability emerges from the interactions of all three of these as part of a metabolic process. In this way, not only is the structural or functional complexity of living systems more than the sum of the parts, but it is fundamentally different.

A classic example that illustrates the concept of emergence is a type of termite nest called a *cathedral* (**Figure 21.4**). These elegantly complex structures, most common in Australia, can grow to over 3 m tall and are the product of the activities of thousands of termites. Remarkably, there is no master plan that is followed or "queen" that gives instructions. Termites build up the mound cell by cell, based on local conditions, totally unaware of the overall structure that emerges.

STUDY BREAK QUESTIONS

1. List the seven fundamental characteristics common to all life.
2. What does it mean that life displays emergent properties?

21.2   The Chemical Origins of Life

You may recall, as discussed in Chapter 2, that one of the tenets of the cell theory states that cells arise only from the growth and division of preexisting cells. This tenet has probably been true

a. Display order: All forms of life, including this flower, are arranged in a highly ordered manner, with the cell being the fundamental unit that exhibits all properties of life.

b. Harness and utilize energy: Like this hummingbird, all forms of life acquire energy from the environment and use it to maintain their highly ordered state.

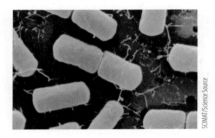

c. Reproduce: All organisms have the ability to make more of their own kind. Here, some of the bacteria have just divided into two daughter cells.

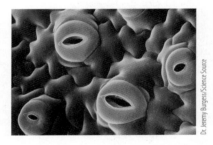

d. Respond to stimuli: Organisms can make adjustments to their structure, function, and behaviour in response to changes to the external environment. A plant can adjust the size of the pores (stomata) on the surface of its leaves to regulate gas exchange.

e. Exhibit homeostasis: Organisms are able to regulate their internal environment such that conditions remain relatively constant. Sweating is one way in which the human body attempts to remove heat and thereby maintain a constant temperature.

f. Grow and develop: All organisms increase their size by increasing the size and/or number of cells. Many organisms also change over time.

g. Evolve: Populations of living organisms change over the course of generations to become better adapted to their environment. The snowy owl illustrates this perfectly.

FIGURE 21.2 The seven characteristics of life

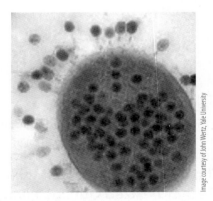

FIGURE 21.3 Bacteriophage infecting a bacterium. Notice the bacteriophages on the cell surface as well as inside the bacterium. A bacteriophage is a type of virus, and most scientists do not consider viruses to be alive.

for hundreds of millions of years, yet there must have been a time when this was not the case. There must have been a time when no cells existed, when there was no life. It is thought that, over the course of hundreds of millions of years, cells with the characteristics of life arose out of a mixture of molecules that existed on primordial Earth. In this section we discuss the formation of the solar system and present hypotheses for how biologically important molecules could have been synthesized on early Earth in the absence of life.

21.2a Earth Is 4.6 Billion Years Old

Earth was formed approximately 4.6 billion years ago. To give us some sense of just how long 4.6 billion years is, as well as the relative timing of some major events in the history of life on Earth, **Figure 21.5** condenses the entire history of Earth into a unit of time that we are more familiar with: one year. With 4.6 billion years condensed into a single year, each day represents an interval of 12.6 million years!

FIGURE 21.4 **A termite cathedral.** The sophisticated structure of a termite nest emerges from the simple work of thousands of individual termites. In a similar way, the complex properties of life emerge from much simpler molecular interactions.

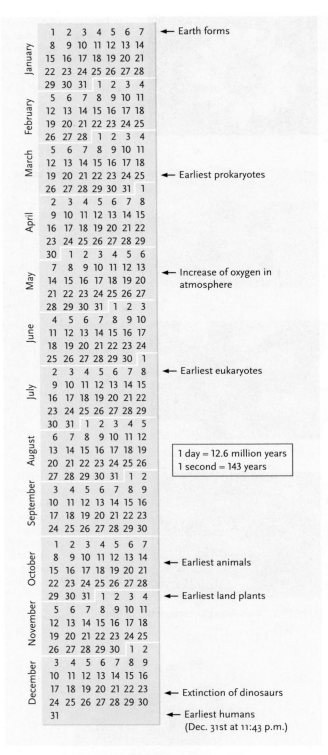

| January | 1 2 3 4 5 6 7 | ← Earth forms |

FIGURE 21.5 **The history of Earth condensed into one year**

Using our condensed version of the history of Earth, we set the date of the formation of Earth as January 1 at 12:00 a.m. We will discuss this in detail later, but based on chemical evidence, life may have started as early as 4.0 billion years ago. This translates to mid-March in our one-year calendar. The first clear fossil evidence of prokaryotic cells occurs in late March, or about 3.5 billion years ago. Fossil evidence of eukaryotes has been dated to about 2 billion years ago, which is not until early July using our one-year analogy. Perhaps surprisingly, animals do not make an appearance until mid-October (about 525 million years ago), and land plants until the following month. The extinction of dinosaurs, which was completed by about 65 million years ago, does not occur until late December. What about humans? We may think humans, *Homo sapiens,* have been around a long time, but relative to other forms of life, the roughly 150 thousand years that modern humans have existed is a very short period of time—a blip on our time scale. Using our year analogy, modern humans have existed only since December 31, more precisely, since December 31 at 11:43 p.m.!

21.2b Biologically Important Molecules Can Be Synthesized Outside Living Cells

All forms of life are composed of four classes of essential macromolecules: nucleic acids, proteins, lipids, and polysaccharides (see *The Purple Pages* for an overview of these molecules).

These molecules are constantly being synthesized within cells by various biochemical pathways and metabolic processes. But if these molecules are an absolute requirement for life, then simple forms of these molecules must have been produced early on in the absence of life, in what is referred to as *abiotic synthesis*. There are three major hypotheses proposed to explain how these macromolecules were produced by abiotic processes: reducing atmosphere, deep-sea vents, and extraterrestrial origins.

HYPOTHESIS 1: REDUCING ATMOSPHERE The early atmosphere of about 4 billion years ago was vastly different from the one today. The primordial atmosphere probably contained an abundance of water vapour from the evaporation of water at the surface, as well as large quantities of hydrogen (H_2), carbon dioxide (CO_2), ammonia (NH_3), and methane (CH_4). There was an almost complete absence of oxygen (O_2). In the 1920s, two scientists, Aleksandr Oparin and John Haldane, independently proposed that organic molecules, essential to the formation of life, could have formed in the atmosphere of primordial Earth. A critical aspect of what is known as the *Oparin–Haldane hypothesis* is that the early atmosphere was a *reducing atmosphere* because of the presence of large concentrations of molecules such as hydrogen, methane, and ammonia. These molecules contain an abundance of electrons and hydrogen, and they would have entered into reactions with one another that would have yielded larger and more complex organic molecules.

In comparison to the proposed reducing atmosphere of primordial Earth, today's atmosphere is classified as an *oxidizing atmosphere*. The presence of high levels of oxygen prevents complex, electron-rich molecules from being formed because oxygen is a particularly strong oxidizing molecule and would itself accept the electrons from organic molecules and be reduced to water. Apart from allowing for the buildup of electron-rich molecules, the lack of oxygen in the primordial atmosphere also meant that there was no ozone (O_3) layer, which only developed after oxygen levels in the atmosphere began to increase. Both Oparin and Haldane hypothesized that, without the ozone layer, energetic ultraviolet light was able to reach the lower atmosphere and, along with abundant lightning, provided the energy needed to drive the formation of biologically important molecules.

Experimental evidence in support of the Oparin–Haldane hypothesis came in 1953 when Stanley Miller, a graduate student of Harold Urey's at the University of Chicago, created a laboratory simulation of the reducing atmosphere believed to have existed on early Earth. Miller placed components of a reducing atmosphere—hydrogen, methane, ammonia, and water vapour—in a closed apparatus and exposed the gases to an energy source in the form of continuously sparking electrodes **(Figure 21.6)**. Water vapour was added to the "atmosphere" in one part of the apparatus and subsequently condensed back into water by cooling in another part. After running the experiment for one week, Miller found a large assortment of organic compounds, including urea; amino acids; and lactic, formic, and acetic acids after condensing the atmosphere into a liquid. In fact, as much as 15% of the carbon that was originally in the methane at the start of the experiment ended up in molecules that are common in living organisms.

Other chemicals have been tested in the Miller–Urey apparatus, including hydrogen cyanide (HCN) and formaldehyde (CH_2O), which are considered to have been among the substances formed in the primitive atmosphere. When cyanide and formaldehyde were added to the simulated primitive atmosphere in Miller's apparatus, all the building blocks of complex biological molecules were produced: amino acids; fatty acids; the **purine** and **pyrimidine** components of nucleic acids; sugars such as glyceraldehyde, ribose, glucose, and fructose; and phospholipids, which form the lipid bilayers of biological membranes.

Over the years since the Miller–Urey experiment was first conducted, considerable debate has developed in the scientific community over whether the atmosphere of primitive Earth contained enough methane and ammonia to be considered reducing. Some geologists have suggested that, based on the analysis of volcanic activity, primitive Earth was probably somewhat less reactive—neither reducing nor oxidizing—with molecules including nitrogen gases (N_2), carbon monoxide (CO), and carbon dioxide (CO_2) the most dominant. Even with this composition, scientists have been able to successfully synthesize the same crucial building blocks of life in the laboratory. Regardless of the actual composition of the atmosphere on

~**4.5 billion years ago**

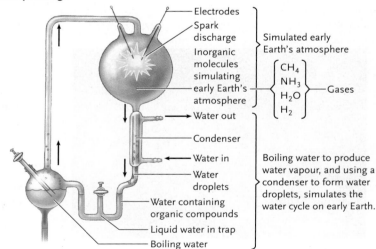

FIGURE 21.6 The Miller–Urey experiment. Using this apparatus, Stanley Miller, a graduate student, demonstrated that organic molecules can be synthesized under conditions simulating primordial Earth.

primordial Earth, the significance of the Miller–Urey experiment cannot be overstated. It was the first experiment to demonstrate the abiotic formation of molecules critical to life, such as amino acids, nucleotides, and simple sugars, and it showed that they could be produced relatively easily. At the time, this remarkable finding laid the groundwork for further research into the origins of life.

HYPOTHESIS 2: DEEP-SEA VENTS Apart from originating in the atmosphere, an alternative hypothesis maintains that the complex organic molecules necessary for life could have originated on the ocean floor at the site of deep-sea (hydrothermal) vents. These cracks are found around the globe near sites of volcanic or tectonic activity and release superheated, nutrient-rich water at temperatures in excess of 300°C, as well as reduced molecules, including methane, ammonia, and hydrogen sulfide (H_2S; **Figure 21.7**). Today, the areas around these vents support a remarkable diversity of life. Many of these life forms are of tremendous scientific interest because of their ability to thrive in an environment that is characterized by extreme pressure and the total absence of light.

HYPOTHESIS 3: EXTRATERRESTRIAL ORIGINS It is entirely possible that the key organic molecules required for life to begin came from space. Each year more than 500 meteorites impact Earth, many of which belong to the class called *carbonaceous chondrites*, which are particularly rich in organic molecules. One of the most famous is the Murchison meteorite that landed in Murchison, Victoria, Australia, in 1969 **(Figure 21.8)**. Analysis of the Murchison meteorite showed that it contains an assortment of biologically important molecules, including a range of amino acids such as glycine, glutamic acid, and alanine, as well as purines and pyrimidines. Even if our life did not arise from extraterrestrial sources, the presence of these molecules is evidence that abiotic production of life's chemicals is possible.

FIGURE 21.8 The Murchison meteorite. Many meteorites have been shown to contain a range of biologically important molecules, including a number of amino acids.

21.2c Life Requires the Synthesis of Polymers

Primordial Earth contained very little oxygen and, because of this, complex organic molecules could have existed for much longer than would be possible in today's oxygen-rich world. Even if they did accumulate on early Earth, molecules such as amino acids and nucleotides are **monomers**, which are simpler and easier to synthesize than the key chemical components of life, such as nucleic acids and proteins, which are polymers (macromolecules formed from the bonding together of individual monomers). Nucleic acids are polymers of nucleotides, proteins are polymers of amino acids, and polysaccharides (starch, cellulose) are polymers of simple sugars. Polymers are synthesized by dehydration synthesis, which is discussed in *The Purple Pages*.

Today, the synthesis of proteins and nucleic acids requires protein-based catalysts called *enzymes*, and results in macromolecules that often consist of hundreds to many thousands of monomers linked together. So how do you make the polymers that are required for life without sophisticated enzymes? The basis of a working hypothesis to address this question must be built from the supposition that the very earliest forms of life must have been very simple, far simpler than a modern bacterium, for example. Scientists hypothesize that a polymer that consists of even 10–50 monomers may have been of sufficient length to impart a specific function (like a protein) or store sufficient information (like a nucleic acid) to make their formation advantageous to an organism. It is, however, doubtful that polymerization could have occurred in the aqueous environment of early Earth, as it would be very rare for monomers to interact precisely enough with one another to polymerize. It is more likely that solid surfaces, especially clays, could have provided the type of environment necessary for polymerization to occur **(Figure 21.9)**. Clays consist of very

FIGURE 21.7 Deep-sea vent. Researchers from the Woods Hole Oceanographic Institute watch from inside the submersible Alvin as a "black smoker" chimney erupts from a seafloor vent. The regions surrounding these vents have been found to be teeming with a diversity of life.

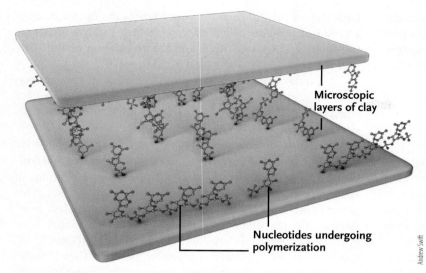

Microscopic
layers of clay

Nucleotides undergoing
polymerization

Andrew Swift

FIGURE 21.9 Clay surfaces catalyze polymerization. The charged, microscopic, layered structure of clay allows for the formation of relatively short polymers of proteins and nucleic acids.

thin layers of minerals separated by layers of water only a few nanometres thick. The layered structure of clay is also charged, allowing for molecular adhesion forces to bring monomers together in precise orientations that could more readily lead to polymer formation. Clays can also store the potential energy that may have been used for energy-requiring polymerization reactions. This *clay hypothesis* is supported by laboratory experiments that demonstrate that the formation of short nucleic acid chains and polypeptides can be synthesized on a clay surface.

STUDY BREAK QUESTIONS

1. For understanding the origins of life, what was the significance of the Miller–Urey experiment?
2. What is the difference between a reducing atmosphere and an oxidizing atmosphere?

21.3 From Macromolecules to Life

In the previous section, we discussed how processes present on early Earth could have generated macromolecules crucial to the development of life. However, if we are to develop a comprehensive model for the origin of life, we need to explain the evolution of three key attributes of a modern cell: (1) a membrane-defined compartment, the cell; (2) a system to store genetic information and use it to guide the synthesis of specific proteins; and (3) energy-transforming pathways to bring in energy from the surroundings and harness it to sustain life. In this section, we discuss possible scenarios for the

evolution of these key attributes and consider a number of hypotheses, some of which are supported by laboratory experiments.

21.3a Lipid Spheres May Have Led to the Development of Cells

A critical step along the path to life is the formation of a membrane-defined compartment. Such a compartment would allow for primitive metabolic reactions to take place in an environment that is distinctly different than the external surroundings; the concentration of key molecules could be higher, and greater complexity could be maintained in a closed space. **Protobiont** is the term given to a group of abiotically produced organic molecules that are surrounded by a membrane or membranelike structure. Laboratory experiments have shown that protobionts could have formed spontaneously (i.e., without any input of energy), given the conditions on primordial Earth. An early type of protobiont could have been similar to a liposome, which is a lipid vesicle in which the lipid molecules form a bilayer very similar to a cell membrane **(Figure 21.10)**. Liposomes can easily be made in the laboratory and are **selectively permeable**, allowing only some molecules to move in and out. As well, liposomes can swell and contract depending on the osmotic conditions of their environment.

Recent research from the laboratory of Jack Szostak at Harvard University has shown that the presence of clay not only catalyzes the polymerization of nucleic acids but also accelerates the formation of lipid vesicles. As well, clay particles often become encapsulated in these vesicles, which would provide catalytically active surfaces within membrane vesicles upon which key reactions could take place. Researchers continue to

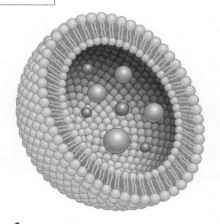

a.

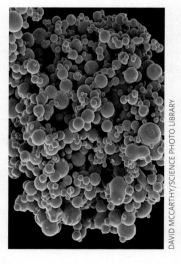

b.

DAVID MCCARTHY/SCIENCE PHOTO LIBRARY

FIGURE 21.10 Liposome. (a) An artist's rendition of a liposome, which is composed of a lipid bilayer. Liposomes can assemble spontaneously under simulated primordial conditions. **(b)** SEM image of lipid vesicles assembled from phospholipids in the laboratory

experiment with producing different types of protobionts in the laboratory as a step toward understanding the origins of the first living cell. Present-day thinking is that a lipid membrane system must have evolved simultaneously with a genetic information system (see below).

21.3b RNA Can Carry Information and Catalyze Reactions

As discussed in earlier chapters, DNA is the molecule that provides every cell with the genetic instructions necessary to function. Recall as well that the information in DNA is copied into RNA, which directs protein synthesis on ribosomes. Even the simplest prokaryotic cell contains thousands of proteins, each coded by a unique DNA sequence, a gene. The flow of information from DNA to RNA to protein is common to all forms of life and is referred to as the *central dogma* (**Figure 21.11**).

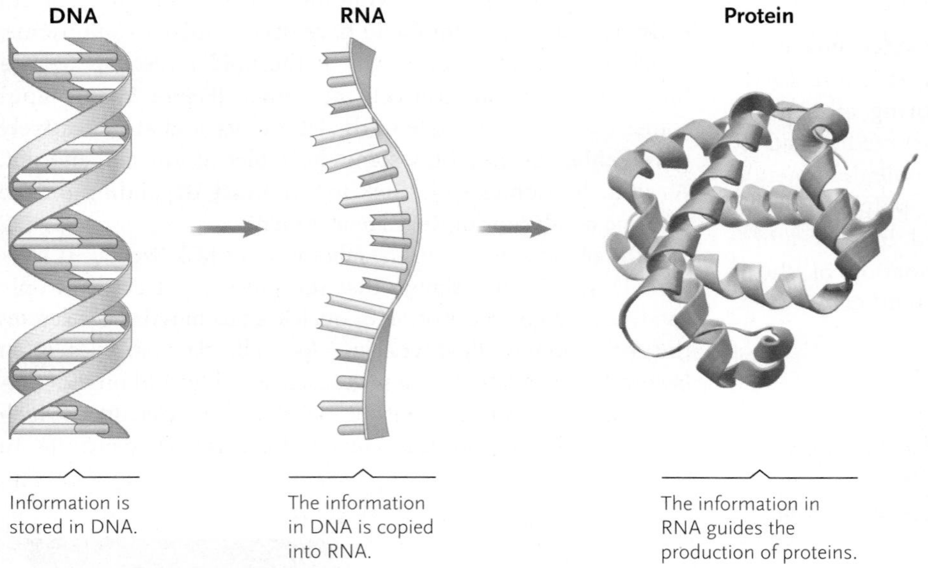

Each step of the information flow requires the involvement of a group of proteins called *enzymes*, which catalyze the transcription of DNA into RNA and the translation of the RNA into protein.

A fundamental question about the flow of information from DNA to RNA to protein is: How did such a system evolve when the final products, proteins, are required to catalyze each step (e.g., transcription, translation) of the process? A breakthrough in our understanding of how such a system may have evolved came in the early 1980s when Thomas Cech and Sydney Altman, working independently, discovered a group of RNA molecules that could themselves act as catalysts. This group of RNA catalysts, called **ribozymes**, can catalyze reactions on the precursor RNA molecules that lead to their own synthesis, as well as on unrelated RNA molecules (**Figure 21.12**). Ribozymes have catalytic properties because these single-stranded molecules can fold into very specific shapes based on intramolecular hydrogen bonding or base pairing. The fact that specificity in folding imparts specificity in function is very common to proteins, especially enzymes, where precise three-dimensional shape is critical for reacting with substrate molecules. Protein folding is discussed in more detail in *The Purple Pages*.

The discovery of ribozymes revolutionized thinking about the origin of life. Instead of the contemporary system that requires all three molecules—DNA, RNA, and protein—early life may have existed in an "RNA world," where a single type of molecule, RNA, could serve as a carrier of information (due to its nucleotide sequence) and a structural/functional molecule similar to a protein (due to its ability to form unique three-dimensional shapes). Before the discovery of ribozymes, enzymes were the only known biological catalysts. For their remarkable discovery, Sydney Altman and Thomas Cech shared the Nobel Prize in Chemistry in 1989.

DNA   **RNA**   **Protein**

Information is stored in DNA.

The information in DNA is copied into RNA.

The information in RNA guides the production of proteins.

FIGURE 21.11 The central dogma. Information in DNA is used to synthesize proteins through an RNA intermediate. How did such a system evolve when the product, proteins, is required in modern-day cells to catalyze each step?

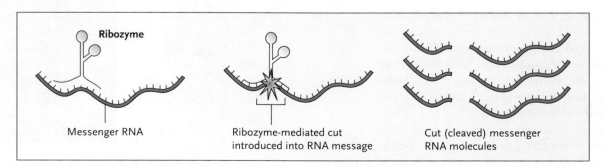

Ribozyme

Messenger RNA

Ribozyme-mediated cut introduced into RNA message

Cut (cleaved) messenger RNA molecules

FIGURE 21.12 Ribozyme. An example of a ribozyme binding to an RNA molecule and catalyzing its breakage. Within a modern-day cell, such reactions may help control gene expression by altering the abundance of functional messenger RNA (mRNA) molecules.

21.3c RNA Is Replaced by DNA for Information Storage and Proteins for Catalysis

If life developed in an RNA world, where RNA served as both an information carrier and a catalyst, why is it that, in all contemporary organisms, genetic information is stored in DNA, and why do enzymes (proteins) catalyze the vast majority of biological reactions? The simple answer is that they do the respective jobs of information storage (DNA) and catalysis (protein) far better than RNA does by itself; thus, the evolution of these molecules would have given organisms that had them a distinct advantage over others that relied solely on RNA.

A possible scenario for the development of today's system of information transfer is shown in **Figure 21.13**. The first cells may have contained only RNA, which was self-replicating and could catalyze a small number of reactions critical for survival. It is hypothesized that a small population of RNA molecules then evolved that could catalyze the formation of very short proteins before the development of ribosomes. Recall that, in contemporary organisms, the ribosome is required for protein synthesis. It is interesting to note that the ribosome, which plays a key role as an intermediate between RNA and protein, is composed of about two-thirds RNA and one-third protein. In fact, it is the RNA component of the ribosome, and not the protein, that actually catalyzes the incorporation of amino acids onto a growing peptide chain. So the ribosome can be considered a type of ribozyme.

Cells that evolved the ability to use the information present in RNA to direct the synthesis of even small proteins would be at a tremendous advantage because proteins are far more versatile than RNA molecules for three reasons. First, the catalytic power of most enzymes is much greater than that of a ribozyme. A typical enzyme can catalyze the same reaction using a pool of substrate molecules many thousands of times a second. By comparison, the rate of catalysis of most ribozymes is one-tenth to one-hundredth that of enzymes. Second, while the number of ribozymes is very small, a typical cell synthesizes a huge array of different proteins. Twenty different kinds of amino acids, in different arrangements, can be incorporated into a protein, whereas an RNA molecule is composed of different combinations of only four nucleotides. Third, amino acids can interact chemically with each other in bonding arrangements not possible between nucleotides. For these reasons, proteins are the dominant structural and functional molecule of a modern cell.

Continuing with the possible scenario shown in Figure 21.13, the evolution of DNA would have followed that of proteins. Compared with RNA, molecules of DNA are more structurally complex. Not only is DNA double stranded, but it also contains the sugar deoxyribose, which is more difficult to synthesize than the ribose found in molecules of RNA. A possible sequence begins with DNA nucleotides being produced by random removal of an oxygen atom from the ribose subunits of RNA nucleotides. At some point, the DNA nucleotides paired with the RNA informational molecules and were assembled into complementary copies of the RNA sequences. Some modern-day viruses carry out this RNA-to-DNA reaction using the enzyme reverse transcriptase (see Chapter 22). Once the DNA copies were made, selection may have favoured DNA, as it is a much better way to store information than RNA, for three main reasons:

- Each strand of DNA is chemically more stable, and less likely to degrade, than a strand of RNA.
- The base uracil found in RNA is not found in DNA; it has been replaced by thymine. This may be because the conversion of cytosine to uracil is a common mutation in DNA. By utilizing thymine in DNA, any uracil is easily recognized as a damaged cytosine that needs to be repaired.
- DNA is double stranded, so in the case of a mutation to one of the strands, the information contained on the complementary strand can be used to correctly repair the damaged strand.

The stability of DNA is illustrated by the fact that intact DNA can be successfully extracted from tissues that are many thousands of years old. The well-known novel and the movie *Jurassic Park* are based on this demonstrated ability. By comparison, RNA needs to be isolated quickly, even from freshly isolated cells, using a strict protocol to prevent its degradation.

21.3d The Evolution of Biological Energy Sources

Life has an absolute requirement for energy. As open systems, all forms of life are constantly bringing in energy and using it to maintain their organized structure and to drive biosynthetic reactions (see Section 3.1). Thus, harnessing energy in the environment was an absolute requirement for the earliest of life

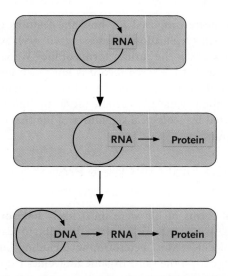

FIGURE 21.13 Possible scenario for the evolution of the flow of information from DNA to RNA to protein

forms. Today, life on Earth derives almost all its energy from photons coming from the Sun, but photosynthesis is not thought to have evolved until hundreds of millions of years after the first forms of life. Instead, the earliest living things are most likely to have evolved in places where energy was released through geochemical activity.

Some geochemical activity persists on Earth today, giving us the opportunity to study environmental conditions that may be similar to those in which life first evolved, but geochemical activity was even more abundant at the time life originated. One very promising candidate for the site of life's origin are alkaline hydrothermal vents. These are sources of free energy because the chemical reactions that take place within them cause the water they release to be chemically distinct from the surrounding ocean water. The vent water is rich in H_2 and CH_4 and has very low concentrations of free H^+, whereas ocean water has higher concentrations of H^+, CO_2, and bicarbonate (HCO_3^-). At the time life originated on Earth, the oceans were much richer in CO_2 than they are today. By reacting with water, CO_2 produces H^+ and HCO_3^-, so that all three of these molecules would have been even more concentrated in ancient ocean water than they are in oceans today.

Chemical reactions that take place where the vent water encounters ocean water cause calcium carbonate to precipitate out of the water, forming chimneys made of calcium carbonate that are honeycombed with microscopic pores that the water percolates through (see chapter-opening photo). Within these porous chimneys, the two different chemical environments of the vent water and the ocean water encounter each other. Because a fresh supply of alkaline water is constantly released from the vent, the interface between vent water and ocean water is constantly out of equilibrium. We discussed in Chapter 3 that free energy is at a minimum when any system reaches equilibrium, so the non-equilibrium conditions produced by the alkaline vents represent a continually renewing source of energy.

One very intriguing source of energy in the vent environment is the H^+ concentration gradient between the ocean water and vent water, because this is still a prime energy source for living things today. Although some ATP is made in living things today directly by substrate-level phosphorylation (see Section 5.3), during glycolysis, for example, most ATP molecules are produced by ATP synthase enzymes using energy released from the diffusion of H^+ down a concentration gradient (see Section 5.5). Scientists studying the alkaline vent environment have hypothesized that the importance of H^+ gradients as sources of energy for all living things may be a relic of the release of energy stored in H^+ gradients in calcium carbonate chimneys.

A second source of energy in the vent environment is the difference in electron affinity between the reduced H_2 and CH_4 in the vent water and the more oxidized CO_2 in the ocean water. In Chapter 5, you learned how energy is released as electrons are transferred between reduced molecules such as NADH and the oxidized carrier complexes of the mitochondrial electron transfer system. This is just one example of the many electron transfer systems that release energy in a wide variety of living things today. The interface between the reduced H_2 and CH_4 in vent water and oxidized CO_2 in ocean water would have provided a perfect opportunity for the evolution of energy-releasing electron transfer reactions in the earliest cells (protobionts). The fact that electron transfer systems are such common and indispensable mechanisms for releasing energy in living things today may be a relic of the evolution of life in an alkaline vent chemical environment. Some of the microscopic compartments in alkaline vent chimneys are only micrometres in diameter, in other words, about the size of a cell. These structures provide a promising model of how protocells could have evolved to make use of the non-equilibrium chemical conditions of alkaline vents. According to one hypothesis, molecular replicators may have taken up residence in microscopic compartments in the porous chimneys, and lipid membranes may have formed on the inner surfaces of the chamber walls of these compartments and across the porous openings (Figure 21.14). By growing within chimneys, protocells would have been ideally placed to take advantage of the enduring H^+ concentration gradients and oxidation–reduction differences between the vent water and surrounding ocean water. The energy provided by these gradients could have supported the synthesis of organic molecules and the maintenance of molecular organization in protocells.

STUDY BREAK QUESTIONS

1. What are ribozymes, and what is their significance in our understanding of the origins of life?
2. In what ways is DNA better than RNA for storing genetic information?
3. Describe how H+ gradients could be generated in alkaline hydrothermal vents.

21.4   Evidence of the Earliest Life

Given hypotheses proposed for how the features of life may have developed (replication, harnessing energy), what do we actually know about the earliest forms of life? We will see later in this chapter that the fossil record is not much help in shedding light on the earliest forms of life. Instead, scientists rely on hypotheses about what the earliest life forms must have been like, supported by geological signatures of life that early organisms left behind.

21.4a   The First Cells Were Probably Anaerobic Heterotrophs

The earliest forms of life were most likely **heterotrophs** (see Chapter 6), which are organisms that obtain carbon from organic molecules. Most heterotrophs, including humans, also obtain energy from the same organic molecules (food). Central to most forms of heterotrophy are the respiratory pathways of glycolysis and fermentation. These pathways are found in

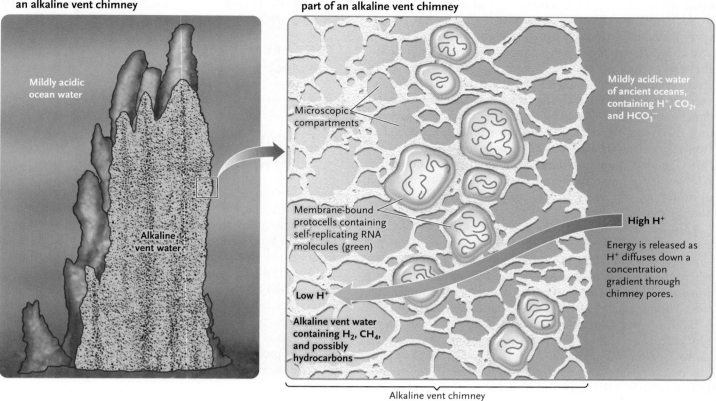

a. Cross-sectional view through an alkaline vent chimney

Mildly acidic ocean water

Alkaline vent water

b. Magnified cross section through part of an alkaline vent chimney

Microscopic compartments

Membrane-bound protocells containing self-replicating RNA molecules (green)

Low H⁺

Alkaline vent water containing H_2, CH_4, and possibly hydrocarbons

Mildly acidic water of ancient oceans, containing H^+, CO_2, and HCO_3^-

High H⁺

Energy is released as H^+ diffuses down a concentration gradient through chimney pores.

Alkaline vent chimney

© Cengage Learning 2017.

FIGURE 21.14 A hypothesis for the origin of cells in alkaline vent chimneys. (a) A cross-sectional view through an alkaline vent chimney. Within the porous material of the chimney, warm (30°C–90°C) alkaline water issuing from the vent mixes with cooler and mildly acidic ocean water. **(b)** A magnified cross-sectional view through a part of the chimney. Membrane-bound protocells containing populations of self-replicating RNA molecules are shown, which are hypothesized to have formed within the microcompartments of the porous chimneys.

virtually all forms of life and are relatively simple, the energy present in organic molecules being used directly to synthesize ATP. There is no requirement for membrane bound complexes, which is necessary for electron transport chains, and there is no requirement for O_2, which was found in only trace amounts in the early atmosphere. Thus, the earliest forms of life were most certainly anaerobic.

Compared to heterotrophs, **autotrophs** obtain carbon from the environment in an inorganic form, most often carbon dioxide. Plants and other photosynthetic organisms are the dominant autotrophs today and are classified as photoautotrophs because they use light as an energy source. As discussed in Chapter 6, the products of the light reactions, ATP and NADPH, are used to synthesize organic molecules from CO_2.

21.4b Oxygenic Photosynthesis Led to a Rise in Oxygen in the Atmosphere

Starting about 2.5 billion years ago, oxygen (O_2) levels in the atmosphere began increasing. Evidence for this comes from dating a type of sedimentary rock called *banded iron* **(Figure 21.15)**.

Geologists believe that these distinctive striped rocks were formed in the sediments of lakes and oceans when dissolved oxygen reacted with the iron in the water, forming a red-coloured precipitate, iron oxide (rust), which ended up being incorporated into the resulting sedimentary rock formations (see Figure 21.15).

© Commonwealth of Australia

FIGURE 21.15 Banded iron. The rust layers in banded iron formations provide evidence for the rise of atmospheric oxygen.

CHAPTER 21 DEFINING LIFE AND ITS ORIGINS |

An obvious question to ask is: where did the oxygen come from? There is clear evidence—which we will discuss in Section 21.6—that the oxygen had a biological source, specifically derived from a group of photosynthetic prokaryotic cells called *cyanobacteria*. Compared to other photosynthesizers at the time that used hydrogen sulfide or Fe_2^+ as an electron donor, cyanobacteria had the remarkable ability to extract electrons from a molecule that was much more abundant: water (**Figure 21.16**). The oxidation of water releases not only electrons, which can be used for photosynthetic electron transport, but also molecular oxygen (O_2). Over time, this O_2 started to accumulate in the atmosphere. Because it releases oxygen, photosynthesis that relies on the oxidation of water as the source of electrons is termed *oxygenic photosynthesis*.

Unlike organisms that use hydrogen sulfide or Fe_2^+ as a source of electrons, the ability to oxidize water meant that cyanobacteria could thrive almost anywhere on the planet where there was sunlight. After all, when was the last time you crossed campus and stepped in a puddle of hydrogen sulfide? The huge ecological advantage that came with being able to oxidize water resulted in an explosion of growth of photosynthetic bacteria (cyanobacteria). Astonishingly, although it evolved perhaps as early as 2.5 billion years ago, oxygenic photosynthesis remains the dominant form of photosynthesis and is used by all plants and algae, as well as present-day cyanobacteria.

The oxygen that accumulated in the atmosphere was simply a by-product of oxygenic photosynthesis. But it led to the next remarkable development in the evolution of early life: aerobic respiration. As discussed in Chapter 5, compared to anaerobic respiration, the pathway of oxidative phosphorylation that required O_2 for electron transport results in a huge increase in the amount of ATP that can be generated from the breakdown of food molecules (e.g., glucose). The huge advantage to be gained in energy production led to the evolution of prokaryotic cells that could undergo aerobic respiration. This in turn set the stage for the next huge step: the evolution of the eukaryotic cell.

STUDY BREAK QUESTION

1. Compared to anoxygenic photosynthesis, what is the ecological advantage of oxygenic photosynthesis to an organism?

21.5 Eukaryotes and the Rise of Multicellularity

There is general agreement that the first cells had a prokaryotic cell structure and were morphologically and functionally simple. Present-day eukaryotic cells are, in comparison, vastly more complex in both structure and function. There are two major characteristics that distinguish eukaryotic cells from prokaryotic cells: (1) the separation of DNA and cytoplasm by a nuclear envelope, and (2) the presence in the cytoplasm of membrane-bound organelles with specialized functions: mitochondria, chloroplasts, the endoplasmic reticulum (ER), and the Golgi complex, among others. In this section, we discuss how eukaryotes most probably evolved from associations of prokaryotic cells, and we end with a discussion of the rise of multicellular eukaryotes.

21.5a The Theory of Endosymbiosis Suggests That Mitochondria and Chloroplasts Evolved from Ingested Prokaryotic Cells

One feature that is found in virtually all eukaryotic cells is energy-transforming organelles: mitochondria and chloroplasts. A wealth of evidence indicates that mitochondria and chloroplasts are actually descended from free-living prokaryotic cells (**Figure 21.17**): mitochondria are descended from aerobic bacteria, and chloroplasts are descended from cyanobacteria. The established model of **endosymbiosis** states that the prokaryotic ancestors of modern mitochondria and chloroplasts were engulfed by larger prokaryotic cells, forming a mutually advantageous relationship called a **symbiosis**. Slowly, over time, the **host** cell and the endosymbionts became inseparable parts of the same single-celled organism.

If the theory of endosymbiosis is correct and both mitochondria and chloroplasts are indeed descendants of bacteria, then these organelles should share some clear structural and biochemical features with the forms of life that they evolved from. Six lines of evidence suggest that both chloroplasts and mitochondria have distinctly prokaryotic characteristics that are not found in other eukaryotic organelles:

1. **Morphology.** The shape and size of both mitochondria and chloroplasts are similar to those of prokaryotic cells.
2. **Reproduction.** A cell cannot synthesize a mitochondrion or a chloroplast. Just like free-living prokaryotic cells,

a.

b. $2H_2O + \text{light energy} \longrightarrow 4H^+ + 4e^- + O_2$

FIGURE 21.16 Cyanobacteria. (a) Micrograph of a filamentous cyanobacterium of the genus *Nostoc*. **(b)** Ancient cyanobacteria, like modern photosynthetic organisms, were able to use water as an electron donor for photosynthesis. A consequence was the formation of oxygen (O_2), which accumulated in the atmosphere.

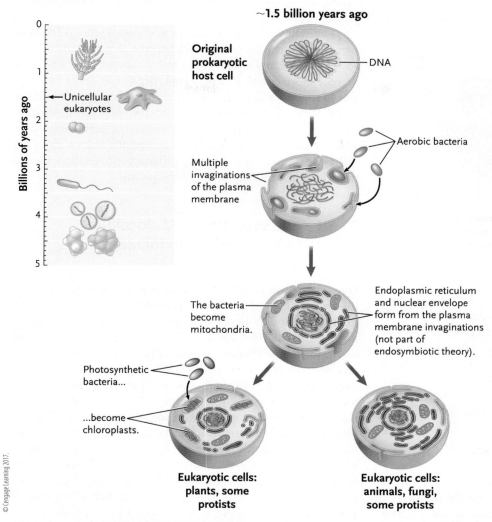

~1.5 billion years ago

Original prokaryotic host cell — DNA

Aerobic bacteria

Multiple invaginations of the plasma membrane

The bacteria become mitochondria.

Endoplasmic reticulum and nuclear envelope form from the plasma membrane invaginations (not part of endosymbiotic theory).

Photosynthetic bacteria...

...become chloroplasts.

Eukaryotic cells: plants, some protists

Eukaryotic cells: animals, fungi, some protists

© Cengage Learning 2017.

FIGURE 21.17 The theory of endosymbiosis. The mitochondrion is thought to have originated from an aerobic prokaryote that lived as an endosymbiont within an anaerobic prokaryote. The chloroplast is thought to have originated from a photosynthetic prokaryote that became an endosymbiont within an aerobic cell that had mitochondria.

tional machinery. They contain ribosomes and tRNAs that are necessary to translate organelle mRNAs into proteins.

5. **Electron transport.** Similar to free-living prokaryotic cells, both mitochondria and chloroplasts have electron transport chains and the enzyme ATP synthase, which together are used to generate chemical energy. The electron transport chains of bacteria and archaea are found associated with the plasma membrane.

6. **Sequence analysis.** Sequencing of the genes that encode the RNA component of the ribosome (ribosomal RNA or rRNA) firmly establishes that these organelles belong on the bacterial branch of the tree of life (we will discuss this later in the chapter). The sequence of chloroplast rRNA most closely matches that of cyanobacteria, and the sequence of mitochondrial rRNA is most similar to that of heterotrophic bacteria.

Whereas virtually all eukaryotic cells contain mitochondria, only plants and algae contain both mitochondria and chloroplasts. This fact suggests that endosymbiosis occurred in stages (see Figure 21.17), with the event leading to the evolution of mitochondria occurring first. Once eukaryotic cells with the ability for aerobic respiration developed, some became photosynthetic after taking up cyanobacteria, evolving into the plants and algae of today.

where daughter cells arise by cell division, new mitochondria and chloroplasts are derived from the division of preexisting organelles. Both chloroplasts and mitochondria divide by binary fission, which is how prokaryotic cells divide (see Chapter 23).

3. **Genetic information.** If the ancestors of mitochondria and chloroplasts were free-living cells, then these organelles should contain their own DNA. Both mitochondria and chloroplasts contain their own DNA, which contain both protein-coding and non-coding genes (see Chapter 12) that are essential for organelle function. As with prokaryotic cells, the DNA molecule in most mitochondria and chloroplasts is circular, while the DNA molecules in the nucleus are linear.

4. **Transcription and translation.** Both chloroplasts and mitochondria contain a complete transcription and transla-

21.5b The Endomembrane System May Be Derived from the Plasma Membrane

As detailed in Chapter 2, in addition to energy-transforming organelles (mitochondria and chloroplasts), eukaryotic cells are characterized by an endomembrane system: a collection of internal membranes that divide the cell into structural and functional regions. These include the nuclear envelope, the ER, and the Golgi complex. As we have just seen, there is very strong evidence in support of the endosymbiotic origin of chloroplasts and mitochondria; however, the origin of the endomembrane system remains less clear. The most widely held hypothesis is that it is derived from the infolding of the plasma

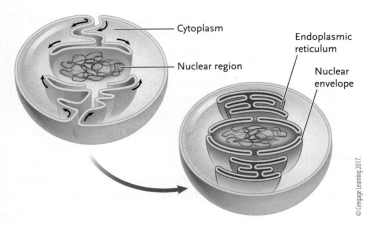

Cytoplasm

Nuclear region

Endoplasmic reticulum

Nuclear envelope

© Cengage Learning 2017.

FIGURE 21.18 A hypothetical route for the formation of the nuclear envelope and ER through segments of the plasma membrane that were brought into the cytoplasm by endocytosis

membrane **(Figure 21.18)**. Researchers hypothesize that, in cell lines leading from prokaryotic cells to eukaryotes, pockets of the plasma membrane may have extended inward and surrounded the nuclear region. Some of these membranes fused around the DNA, forming the nuclear envelope, which defines the nucleus. The remaining membranes formed vesicles in the cytoplasm that gave rise to the ER and the Golgi complex.

21.5c Solving an Energy Crisis May Have Led to Eukaryotes

Bacteria and archaea outnumber eukaryotes on the planet by a huge margin. Compared to eukaryotes, archaea and bacteria show remarkable biochemical flexibility, being able to use an assortment of molecules as sources of energy and carbon and thrive in harsh environments uninhabitable to eukaryotes. That said, prokaryotic cells are simple: they lack the complexity of eukaryotes, which evolved into a tremendous diversity of forms, including plants, fungi, and animals. Within each of these groups are cells with remarkable specialization in form and function (e.g., cells of the flower of a plant, muscle and brain cells of animals). Contrast this to archaea and bacteria, which have remained remarkably simple even though they evolved as early as 4 billion years ago.

The reason that bacteria and archaea have remained very simple is that increased complexity requires increased energy, and while eukaryotic cells can generate huge amounts of it, prokaryotic cells cannot. Mitochondria, like their aerobic progenitor bacteria, undergo aerobic respiration, which generates much greater amounts of ATP from the breakdown of organic molecules than pathways of anaerobic metabolism (see Chapter 5). As well, while a typical aerobic bacterium relies on its plasma membrane for many functions, including nutrient and waste transport and energy production, a typical eukaryotic cell contains hundreds of mitochondria, each

having a huge internal membrane surface area dedicated to generating ATP.

The ability of early eukaryotes to generate more ATP led to remarkable changes. Cells could become larger, as now there was enough energy to support a greater volume. And cells could become more complex. This complexity comes about by being able to support a larger genome that codes for a greater number of proteins. By overcoming an energy production barrier, eukaryotes could support a wider variety of genes that led to what we know today to be eukaryotic-specific traits such as the **cell cycle,** sexual reproduction, phagocytosis, endomembrane trafficking, the nucleus, and multicellularity.

21.5d The Evolution of Multicellular Eukaryotes Led to Increased Specialization

One of the most profound transitions in the history of life was the evolution of multicellular eukaryotes. Clear evidence of multicellularity, in the form of species of algae, appears in the fossil record starting about 1.2 billion years ago. The actual events that led to the development of multicellularity are a mystery but it is easy to envision how it may have occurred. Perhaps a group of individual cells of a particular species came together to form a colony, or a single cell divided and the resulting two cells did not separate. In the simplest of multicellular organisms, all cells are structurally and functionally autonomous (independent). This gave way to a key trait of more advanced multicellular organisms: division of labour. Over time, cells became structurally and functionally distinct. For example, some cells may have specialized in harvesting energy, whereas others developed a role related to the motility of the organism. In a multicellular system, the cells cooperate with one another for the benefit of the entire organism. Over evolutionary time, this specialization of cell function led to the development of the specialized tissues and organs that are so clearly evident in larger eukaryotes.

Like the earliest forms of life, there is little, if any, evidence in the fossil record of the earliest multicellular organisms. How they arose and developed is still an area of intense research. It is thought, however, that multicellularity arose more than once, most probably independently along each of the lineages leading to fungi, plants, and animals. A very useful model for the study of multicellularity is found in a group of green algae called the *volvocine*. All the members of this group are evolutionarily closely related and span the full range of size and complexity, from the unicellular *Chlamydomonas* through various colonial genera to the multicellular *Volvox* **(Figure 21.19)**. Unlike a true multicellular organism, a cell colony is a group of cells that are all of one type; there is no specialization in cell structure or function. *Volvox* consists of a sphere of two to three thousand small, flagellated *Chlamydomonas*-like cells that provide the individual *Volvox* with the ability to move. In addition, within the sphere lie

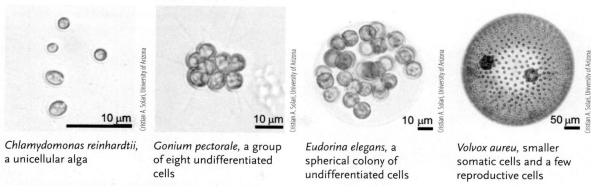

Chlamydomonas reinhardtii, a unicellular alga

Gonium pectorale, a group of eight undifferentiated cells

Eudorina elegans, a spherical colony of undifferentiated cells

Volvox aureu, smaller somatic cells and a few reproductive cells

FIGURE 21.19 Differences in degree of multicellularity among volvocine algae

about 16 large nonmotile cells that serve a specialized role in reproduction.

21.6 The Fossil Record

Testing hypotheses related to how the first forms of life could have developed on early Earth is a robust area of research involving scientists with expertise in Chemistry, Earth Science, and Biology. However, we can only speculate at what the first forms of life really were like because we have no direct evidence of their existence. This section provides an overview of what we actually do know about the history of life on Earth as reflected by the remains of organisms that have been preserved in the fossil record.

21.6a The Fossil Record Is Invaluable but Incomplete

The fossil record provides the only direct evidence about what life was like millions of years ago. Fossilized skeletons, shells, stems, leaves, and flowers tell us about the size and appearance of ancient animals and plants. The fossil record also has allowed scientists to see how species have changed over time as it chronicles the proliferation and extinction of evolutionary lineages, and it provides data on the geographical distribution of extinct species. As discussed in Chapter 16, Darwin's ability to compare fossil specimens with living relatives was very influential in his development of the notion of natural selection.

Obviously the fossil record is an invaluable resource to understand the past, but it is important to note that it represents only a small fraction of the organisms that once lived on Earth, and thus it vastly underrepresents the diversity of life. The fossil record only really represents a record of the most successful of organisms; those that were very abundant, had wide distributions, and possessed hard parts that could be fossilized (see below). Soft-bodied organisms with small geographic distributions that lived in environments where erosion was a dominant process are underrepresented in the fossil record, if they are in it at all.

21.6b Fossils Form When Organisms Are Buried by Sediments or Preserved in Oxygen-Poor Environments

Most fossils form in sedimentary rocks. Rain and runoff constantly erode the land, carrying fine particles of rock and soil downstream to a swamp, a lake, or the sea. Particles settle to the bottom as sediments, forming successive layers, called *strata*, over millions of years **(Figure 21.20)**. The weight of newer sediments compresses the older layers beneath them into a solid matrix: sand into sandstone and silt, or mud into shale. Fossils form within the layers when the remains of organisms are buried in the accumulating sediments. Because sedimentation superimposes new layers over old ones, the lowest strata in a sedimentary rock formation are usually the oldest, and the highest layers are the newest.

The process of fossilization is a race against time because the soft remains of organisms are quickly consumed by scavengers or decomposed by microorganisms. Thus, fossils usually preserve the details of hard structures, such as the bones, teeth, and shells of animals and the wood, leaves, and pollen of plants. During fossilization, dissolved minerals replace some parts molecule by molecule, leaving a fossil made of stone **(Figure 21.21a)**; other fossils form as moulds, casts, or impressions in material that is later transformed into solid rock (Figure 21.21b).

In some environments, the near absence of oxygen prevents decomposition, and even soft-bodied organisms are preserved. Some plants, insects, and tiny lizards and frogs are embedded in amber, the fossilized resin of coniferous trees (Figure 21.21c). Other organisms are preserved in glacial ice, deeply frozen soil, coal, tar pits, or the highly acidic water of peat bogs (Figure 21.21d). Sometimes organisms are so well preserved that researchers can examine their internal anatomy, cell structure, food in their digestive tracts, and even their DNA sequences.

a. Sedimentation

Highest strata contain the most recent fossils.

© Cengage Learning 2017.

Lowest strata contain the oldest fossils.

b. Geological strata in the Painted Desert, Arizona

Nick Greaves/Alamy Stock Photo

FIGURE 21.20 Sedimentation and geological strata. (a) Sedimentation deposits successive layers at the bottom of a lake or sea. **(b)** Over millions of years, the upper layers compress those below them into rock. When the rocks are later exposed by uplifting or erosion, the different layers are evident as geological strata.

a. Petrified wood (Araucariaceae)

Newman Mark/Prisma/AGE Fotostock

b. *Sphenopteris*

David Lyons/AGE Fotostock

c. Mosquitoes in amber

tobkatrina/Shutterstock.com

d. Mammoth (*Mammonteus*) in permafrost

Novosti/Topham/The Image Works

FIGURE 21.21 Fossils. (a) Petrified wood in Arizona formed when minerals replaced the wood of dead trees, molecule by molecule. These forests lived during the late Triassic period, about 225 million years ago. **(b)** The remains of a fern (*Sphenopteris*) from the Carboniferous period, 300 million years ago, were preserved in coal. **(c)** These 10-million-year-old mosquitoes were trapped in the oozing resin of a coniferous tree and are now encased in amber. **(d)** A frozen baby mammoth that lived about 40 000 years ago was discovered embedded in Siberian permafrost in 1977.

21.6c The Earliest Fossils

The earliest indirect evidence of life, which predates any actual fossil evidence, comes from research looking at the carbon composition of ancient rocks. Early photosynthetic organisms would have had the ability to take CO_2 from the atmosphere and use it to synthesize various organic molecules (see Chapter 6 for

details). During this process, organisms would have preferentially incorporated the carbon-12 isotope (^{12}C) over other isotopes such as carbon-13 (^{13}C) (see *The Purple Pages* for a discussion of isotopes). Researchers have discovered sedimentary rocks originating from the ocean floor that contain deposits that have lower levels of the ^{13}C isotope than expected. The most likely explanation is that the deposits are actually the remains of carbon molecules of ancient microbes. These sediments have been dated to approximately 3.9 billion years ago. If correct, this would push the origins of life to perhaps as early as 4 billion years ago, approximately 600 million years after Earth was formed.

The earliest conclusive evidence of life is found in the fossilized remains of structures called *stromatolites*, the oldest being formed about 3.5 billion years ago. A **stromatolite** is a type of layered rock that is formed when microorganisms bind particles of sediment together, forming thin sheets **(Figure 21.22)**. Modern stromatolites are found in habitats characterized by warm shallow water and are most common in Australia. Modern-day stromatolites are formed by the action of a specific group of photosynthetic bacteria called *cyanobacteria*. Because they were able to undertake oxygenic photosynthesis, cyanobacteria (see Figure 21.16) were not the earliest forms of life but rather must have been preceded by much simpler organisms.

a.

Bill Bachmann/Science Source

b.

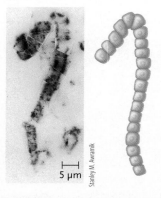

Stanley M. Awramik

|— 5 µm

FIGURE 21.22 Early fossil evidence of life. (a) Stromatolites exposed at low tide in Western Australia's Shark Bay. These mounds, which consist of mineral deposits made by photosynthetic cyanobacteria, are about 2000 years old; they are highly similar in structure to fossil stromatolites that formed more than 3 billion years ago. **(b)** Structures that are believed to be a strand of fossil prokaryote cells in a rock sample that is 3.5 billion years old.

21.6d Scientists Assign Relative and Absolute Dates to Geological Strata and the Fossils They Contain

The sediments found in any one place form recognizable strata (layers) that differ in colour, mineral composition, particle size, and thickness (see Figure 21.20b). If they have not been disturbed, the strata are arranged in the order in which they formed, with the youngest layers on top.

Geologists of the early nineteenth century deduced that the fossils discovered in a particular sedimentary stratum, no matter where on Earth it is found, represent organisms that lived and died at roughly the same time in the past. Because each stratum formed at a specific time, the sequence of fossils in the lowest (oldest) to the highest (newest) strata reveals their *relative ages*. Geologists originally used the sequence of strata and their distinctive fossil assemblages to establish the geological time scale **(Table 21.1)**.

Although the geological time scale provides a relative dating system for sedimentary strata, it does not tell us how old the rocks and fossils actually are. But many rocks contain unstable radioisotopes, which, from the moment they form, begin to break down into other, more stable elements. The breakdown proceeds at a steady rate that is unaffected by chemical reactions or environmental conditions such as temperature or pressure. Using a technique called **radiometric dating**, scientists can estimate the age of a rock by noting how much of an unstable "parent" isotope has decayed to another form. By measuring the relative amounts of the parent radioisotope and its breakdown products and comparing this ratio with the isotope's **half-life** (the time it takes for half a given amount of radioisotope to decay), researchers can estimate the *absolute age* of the rock **(Figure 21.23)**. Table 21.1 presents these age estimates along with the major geological and evolutionary events of each period.

STUDY BREAK QUESTIONS

1. What biological materials are the most likely to fossilize?
2. Why does the fossil record provide an incomplete portrait of life in the past?
3. What sorts of information can paleobiologists discern from the fossil record?

21.7   The Tree of Life

At the time of Darwin, scientists had a hard time explaining the huge diversity of life that biologists were discovering; it was varied and many organisms did not seem to have obvious connections with others. With the use of modern DNA sequencing technology, it is now remarkably easy to build a single tree of life. The most surprising feature of this tree is that it has a single starting point. DNA can be shown to

TABLE 21.1 | The Geological Time Scale and Major Evolutionary Events

Eon	Era	Period	Epoch	Millions of Years Ago	Major Evolutionary Events	Mass Extinctions
Phanerozoic	Cenozoic	Quaternary	Holocene	0.01	Origin of modern humans; major glaciations	
			Pleistocene	2.6	Origin of bipedal human ancestors	
			Pliocene	5.3		
		Neogene	Miocene	23.0	Angiosperms and mammals further diversify and dominate terrestrial habitats	
			Oligocene	33.9	Primates diversify; origin of apes	
		Paleogene	Eocene	55.8	Angiosperms and insects diversify; modern orders of mammals differentiate	
			Paleocene	65.5	Grasslands and deciduous woodlands spread; modern birds, mammals, snakes, pollinating insects diversify; continents approach current positions	RIP Cretaceous
	Mesozoic	Cretaceous		145.5	First angiosperms; insects, marine invertebrates, fishes, dinosaurs diversify; asteroid impact causes mass extinction at end of period, eliminating most dinosaurs and many other groups	
		Jurassic		201.6	Gymnosperms abundant in terrestrial habitats; modern fishes diversify; dinosaurs diversify and dominate terrestrial habitats; frogs, salamanders, lizards, birds, and placental mammals appear; continents continue to separate	RIP Triassic
		Triassic		251.0	Predatory fishes and reptiles dominate oceans; gymnosperms dominate terrestrial habitats; diversification of dinosaurs; early mammals; Pangaea starts to break up; mass extinction at end of period	RIP Permian
	Paleozoic	Permian		299.0	Insects and amniotes abundant and diverse in swamp forests; some amniotes colonize oceans; fishes colonize freshwater habitats; continents coalesce into Pangaea, causing glaciation and decline in sea level; huge volcanic eruptions cause mass extinction at end of period, eliminating 85% of species worldwide	
		Carboniferous		359.0	Vascular plants form large swamp forests; first flying insects; amphibians diversify; first amniotes appear	RIP Devonian
		Devonian		416.0	Terrestrial vascular plants diversify; fungi, invertebrates, tetrapod vertebrates colonize land; first insects and seed plants; major glaciation at end of period; mass extinction, mostly of marine life	
		Silurian		444.0	Jawless fishes diversify; first jawed fishes, first terrestrial arthropods and vascular plants	RIP Ordovician
		Ordovician		488.0	Major radiations of marine invertebrates and jawless fishes; first terrestrial plants, fungi, and animals; major glaciation at end of period causes mass extinction of marine life	RIP Cambrian
		Cambrian		542.0	Appearance of modern animal phyla, including vertebrates (Cambrian explosion); simple marine communities; mass extinctions eliminate many groups at end of period	
Proterozoic				2500	High concentration of oxygen in atmosphere; origin of eukaryotic cells; evolution and diversification of protists; fungi, soft-bodied animals	
Archean				3850	Origin of life; evolution of prokaryotes, including anaerobic and photosynthetic bacteria; oxygen starts to accumulate in atmosphere; origin of aerobic respiration	
Hadean				4600	Formation of Earth, including crust, atmosphere, and oceans	

© Cengage Learning 2017.

FIGURE 21.23   **Research Method**

Radiometric Dating

Knowing the number of half-lives that have passed allows you to estimate the age of the sample.

Purpose: Radiometric dating allows researchers to estimate the absolute age of a rock sample or fossil.

Protocol:

1. Knowing the approximate age of a rock or fossil, select a radioisotope that has an appropriate half-life. Because different radioisotopes have half-lives ranging from seconds to billions of years, it is usually possible to choose one that brackets the estimated age of the sample under study. For example, if you think that your fossil is more than 10 million years old, you might use uranium-235. The half-life of ^{235}U, which decays into the lead isotope ^{207}Pb, is about 700 million years. Or if you think that your fossil is less than 70 000 years old, you might select carbon-14. The half-life of 14C, which decays into the nitrogen isotope ^{14}N, is 5730 years.

Radioisotopes Commonly Used in Radiometric Dating			
Radioisotope (Unstable)	More Stable Breakdown Product	Half-Life (Years)	Useful Range (Years)
Samarium-147 ⟶	Neodymium-143	106 billion	>100 million
Rubidium-87 ⟶	Strontium-87	48 billion	>10 million
Thorium-232 ⟶	Lead-208	14 billion	>10 million
Uranium-238 ⟶	Lead-206	4.5 billion	>10 million
Uranium-235 ⟶	Lead-207	700 million	>10 million
Potassium-40 ⟶	Argon-40	1.25 billion	>100000
Carbon-14 ⟶	Nitrogen-14	5730	<70000

© Cengage Learning 2017

2. Prepare a sample of the material and measure the quantities of the parent radioisotope and its more stable breakdown product.

Interpreting the Results: Compare the relative quantities of the parent radioisotope and its breakdown product (or some other stable isotope) to determine what percentage of the original parent radioisotope remains in the sample. Then use a graph of radioactive decay for that isotope to determine how many half-lives have passed since the sample formed.

Theory of radiometric dating

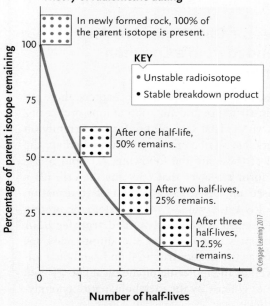

In newly formed rock, 100% of the parent isotope is present.

KEY
- Unstable radioisotope
- Stable breakdown product

After one half-life, 50% remains.

After two half-lives, 25% remains.

After three half-lives, 12.5% remains.

© Cengage Learning 2017

Radiometric dating of a fossilized mollusk

Photodisc/Getty Images

A living mollusk absorbed trace amounts of ^{14}C, a rare radioisotope of carbon, and large amounts of ^{12}C, which is the more stable and common isotope of carbon.

Photodisc/Getty Images

When the mollusk died, it was buried in silt and fossilized. From the moment of its death, the ratio of ^{14}C to ^{12}C began to decline through radioactive decay. Because the half-life of ^{14}C is 5,730 years, half of the original ^{14}C was eliminated from the fossil in 5,730 years and half of what remained was eliminated in another 5,730 years.

Photodisc/Getty Images

After the fossil was discovered, a scientist determined that its ^{14}C to ^{12}C ratio was one-eighth (12.5%) of the ^{14}C to ^{12}C ratio in living organisms. Thus, radioactive decay had proceeded for three half-lives—about 17,000 years—since the mollusk's death.

connect lineages as diverse as prokaryotes and peacocks, or hummingbirds and humans.

21.7a Analyses of Gene Sequences Have Revealed the Branching Pattern of the Entire Tree of Life

The ultimate in phylogenetic analysis is to produce a tree that shows the evolutionary relationship among all living organisms. The first efforts to create the "tree of life" were based on morphological analyses: differences in what organisms look like. In the 1960s and early 1970s, biologists organized living systems into five kingdoms based largely on morphological differences. All organisms with prokaryotic morphology were grouped into the kingdom Monera. Eukaryotic organisms were divided into four kingdoms: Fungi, Plantae, Animalia, and "Protista." The kingdom Protista was always recognized as a polyphyletic "grab bag" of unicellular organisms (discussed further in Chapter 24).

As we discussed in Chapter 19, relying on morphological characteristics to build phylogenetic trees can lead to problems, since two organisms may look superficially similar but have very different evolutionary histories. For example, trying to resolve the branches of the tree that contains organisms with prokaryotic cell structure proved very difficult. This was simply because there was a lack of significant structural variability for analysis. As well, it wasn't clear how closely or distantly some of these prokaryotic groups were related to eukaryotes.

By the 1970s, evolutionary biologists realized that using differences in the sequence of particular genes or proteins would provide a far more powerful approach to building the Tree of Life than relying on what organisms looked like. Given our understanding of evolution and how differences in sequence arise, if you compare the sequence of a specific gene among different organisms, those with fewer differences can be assumed to be more closely related than species where the sequence of the gene is more different. The problem then became what sequence to compare. Ideally you want to choose a single gene, but which one? Here are the important criteria:

1. Because you want to build a tree that contains representatives from all major groups of life, the gene must be universal: it must be present in all forms of life.

2. You want the gene sequence to be strongly conserved. Although it is essential that there is variation in the sequence, too much variation will make it hard to compare the sequences between two distantly related organisms. Genes critical for the survival of the cell are ideal for this purpose.

3. You want the gene to be fairly long, because the longer the gene sequence, in essence, the more information it contains. In fact, longer genes are statistically harder to match, and therefore consistencies in their sequence are more convincing than shorter sequences that may have similarities for reasons other than a common history.

Using these criteria, Carl R. Woese, a microbiologist at the University of Illinois at Urbana-Champaign, realized that the gene that codes for the RNA molecule that makes up the small subunit of the ribosome (rRNA) was an ideal candidate. Ribosomes, the organelles that that translate messenger RNA molecules into proteins (see Section 12.4), are found in all forms of life and are remarkably similar in their structure. Recall as well that ribosomes contain both protein and RNA as components of their structure.

Starting in 1977, the phylogenetic tree that Carl Woese and his colleagues built based on rRNA sequences completely changed how scientists saw the tree of life **(Figure 21.24)**. Instead of the old five kingdoms, the rRNA data clearly delineated only three primary lineages of organisms, which we refer to as domains: Bacteria, Archaea, and Eukarya. **Table 21.2** lists the major molecular and cellular distinctions of these three domains. According to this hypothesis, the domains Bacteria and Archaea consist of prokaryotic organisms, and only Eukarya consists of eukaryotes. The domain Bacteria includes well-known microorganisms. Archaea includes microorganisms that live in physiologically harsh environments, such as hot springs and very salty habitats, as well as less extreme environments. The domain Eukarya includes the familiar animals, plants, and fungi as well as the many lineages formerly included among the "Protista," which is not a monophyletic group. As the tree in Figure 21.24 suggests, Archaea and Eukarya are more closely related to each other than either is to Bacteria. The next unit of this book is devoted to detailed analyses of the biology and evolutionary relationships between and within these three domains.

21.7b All Present-Day Organisms Are Descended from a Common Ancestor, LUCA

As will be discussed in detail in subsequent chapters, there are clear distinctions in structure and function among archaeans, bacteria, and eukaryotes. That said, all life forms currently on Earth share a remarkable set of common attributes. Perhaps the most fundamental of these are the following: (1) lipid molecules assemble to form a bilayer that contains the cell; (2) a genetic system based on DNA; (3) a system of information transfer: DNA to RNA to protein; (4) a system of protein assembly using messenger RNA (mRNA) and **transfer RNA** (tRNA) using ribosomes to polymerize the amino acids; (5) reliance on proteins as the major structural and catalytic molecule; (6) use of ATP as the molecule of chemical energy; and (7) the breakdown of glucose by the metabolic pathway of glycolysis to generate ATP.

The fact that these seven attributes are shared by all life on Earth suggests that all present-day organisms are descended from a common ancestor (Figure 21.24) that had all these attributes. We call the original life form from which all archaea, bacteria, and eukaryotes are descended LUCA, which stands for "Last Universal Common Ancestor" (see Figure 21.24).

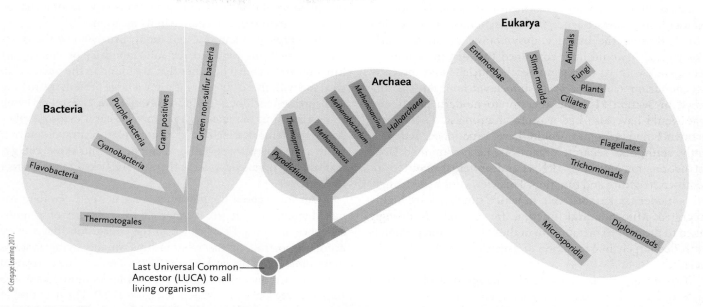

FIGURE 21.24 The three domains in the Tree of Life. Carl R. Woese's analysis of rRNA sequences suggests that all living organisms can be classified into one of three domains: Bacteria, Archaea, or Eukarya.

TABLE 21.2	Some Differences among the Three Domains		
Character	Bacteria	Archaea	Eukarya
Chromosome structure	Circular	Circular	Linear
DNA location	Nucleoid	Nucleoid	Nucleus
Chromosome segregation	Binary fission	Binary fission	Meiosis/mitosis
Introns in genes	Rare	Common	Common
Operons	Present	Present	Absent
Initiator tRNA	Formylmethionine	Methionine	Methionine
Ribosomes	70S	70S	80S
Membrane-enclosed organelles	Absent	Absent	Present
Membrane lipids	Ester-linked	Ether-linked	Ester-linked
Peptidoglycan in cell wall	Present	Absent	Absent
Methanogenesis	Absent	Present	Absent
Temperature tolerance	Up to 90°C	Up to 120°C	Up to 70°C

Recent sequence analysis of certain proteins that have representatives in all three domains of life has given strong quantitative support to the common-ancestry hypothesis.

CONCEPT FIX You may think that LUCA was the earliest and only form of life to exist on early Earth, but that is probably not the case. LUCA was the ancestor to all life that currently exists but that is not to say that life evolved only once. It is quite possible that life arose many times on early Earth, each form perhaps having some of the seven attributes listed above. The similarities across all domains of life present today indicate, however, that only one of these primitive life forms has descendants that survive today. ⬡

21.7c Horizontal Gene Transfer

Our discussion of phylogenetic analysis has emphasized the importance of direct descent: the transmission of traits from ancestors to descendants through the inheritance of DNA. But as scientists analyze the complete genome sequences of an ever-growing list of organisms, they are discovering that the three domains in the Tree of Life have not had entirely independent evolutionary histories. Although inheritance from one generation to the next, what we can refer to as **vertical gene transfer**, has produced the clades of organisms we recognize today, the movement of genetic material between unrelated organisms, what is referred to as **horizontal gene transfer**, has also been important. Horizontal gene transfer, which is common in bacteria, can occur between different species, introducing genes from one species into another. As well, gene transfer can occur through viral infection.

Horizontal gene transfer between the major divisions of life was also a consequence of endosymbiosis (see Section 21.5). Following the initial endosymbiosis event, the early eukaryotic cell would have contained two distinct compartments, each with its own genome: the nucleus and the early mitochondrion (called a *proto-mitochondrion*). As we discussed in Section 21.5, the ancestor to modern plants and algae would have also had a proto-chloroplast. These compartments and genomes would have functioned independently, acting like separate organisms. Each contained DNA instructions for molecules (RNAs and proteins) required for their own structure and function. This view contrasts strongly with a modern eukaryotic cell, in which functions are highly integrated. Mitochondrial function, for example, is strongly linked to the overall metabolism of the cell. This integration is controlled largely by regulation of gene expression within the nucleus.

Two major processes led to this integration of function between the various compartments: First, some of the genes that were within the proto-mitochondrion or proto-chloroplast were lost. Most of these genes would have been redundant as the nucleus would already have genes that encode proteins with the same function. Second, many of the genes within the proto-mitochondrion and proto-chloroplast were relocated to the nucleus through horizontal gene transfer. It is understood that gene transfer to the nucleus was evolutionarily advantageous as it would have centralized genetic information and its control in one place, the nucleus. It's important to realize that the outcome of this horizontal gene transfer was not a change in gene function, only a change in its location.

In a typical eukaryotic cell today, over 90% of the thousands of proteins required for mitochondrial or chloroplast function are encoded by genes that are found in the nucleus. To go along with this change of location, a large protein trafficking and sorting machinery had to evolve (**Figure 21.25**). Following transcription in the nucleus and translation on cytosolic ribosomes, proteins destined for the chloroplast or mitochondrion need to be correctly sorted and imported into these energy-transducing organelles, where they are trafficked to the correct location.

Our ideas about the movement of genes between the various domains of life are supported by a wealth of genome sequence analysis. This has led to the conclusion that a more accurate portrait of the relationships among living systems looks more like a network (**Figure 21.26**). Thus, a true portrait of the relationships among living systems looks more like a web than the tree Darwin envisioned (**Figure 21.27**). The next unit of this book is devoted to detailed analyses of the biology and evolutionary relationships between and within the three domains: Bacteria, Archaea, and Eukarya.

STUDY BREAK QUESTIONS

1. What is the evidence in support of endosymbiosis?
2. What are the key traits of a multicellular organism?

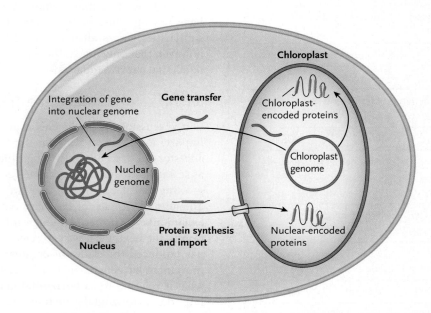

FIGURE 21.25 Horizontal gene transfer. Over evolutionary time, some protein-coding genes that were once part of the chloroplast or mitochondrial genome have been relocated to the nuclear genome. Following transcription of these genes, translation occurs in the cytosol before protein import into the organelle (mitochondrion or chloroplast).

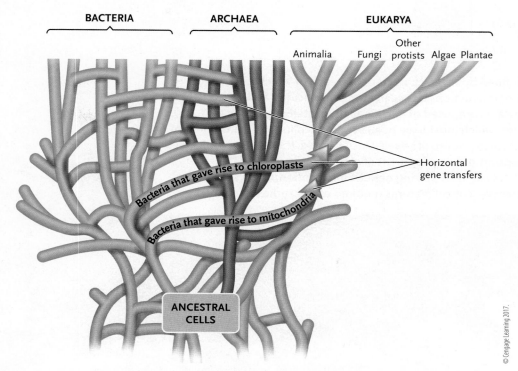

FIGURE 21.26 **Horizontal gene transfer between the three major trunks of the Tree of Life.** Horizontal gene transfer was an important process in producing present-day clades. As shown in this stylized phylogenetic tree, molecular analyses suggest that mitochondria evolved from an aerobic bacterium that was engulfed by an anaerobic archaean, transforming it into a eukaryotic cell. Over time, many genes on the mitochondrial chromosome were transferred to nuclear chromosomes, an example of horizontal gene transfer. Later in the history of life, photosynthetic bacteria were engulfed by eukaryotic cells; the engulfed bacteria evolved into chloroplasts, which are responsible for photosynthesis in algae and plants.

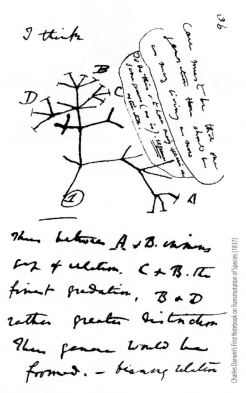

FIGURE 21.27 **Darwin's Evolutionary Tree.** This entry from his notebook on the "transmutation of species" demonstrates that Charles Darwin first thought about the branching pattern of evolution in 1837, more than 20 years before he published *On the Origin of Species*.

Summary Illustration

Life is often defined by seven characteristics, each of which is the result of a hierarchy of interactions between atoms, molecules, and processes. All forms of life are composed of nucleic acids, proteins, lipids, and polysaccharides, which must have been synthesized in the environment of the primordial Earth prior to life itself. Once formed, these macromolecules would then support the development of a membrane-defined compartment, a system for storing genetic information, and a system for harnessing energy—critical features required of the earliest life forms.

What Is Life?

Responds to stimuli

Displays order

Grows and develops

Reproduces

Exhibits homeostasis

Populations evolve

Requires energy

Scenario Leading to Modern Cells

The presence of certain polymeric macromolecules (e.g., nucleic acids, proteins, and lipids) was crucial for the development of life.

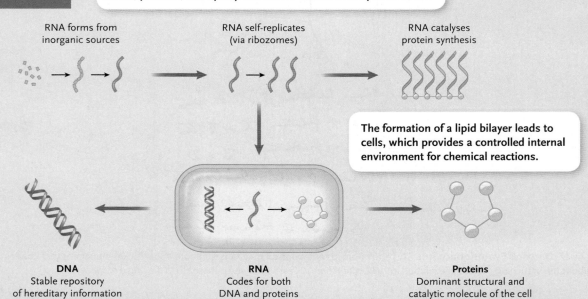

RNA forms from inorganic sources

RNA self-replicates (via ribozomes)

RNA catalyses protein synthesis

The formation of a lipid bilayer leads to cells, which provides a controlled internal environment for chemical reactions.

DNA
Stable repository of hereditary information

RNA
Codes for both DNA and proteins

Proteins
Dominant structural and catalytic molecule of the cell

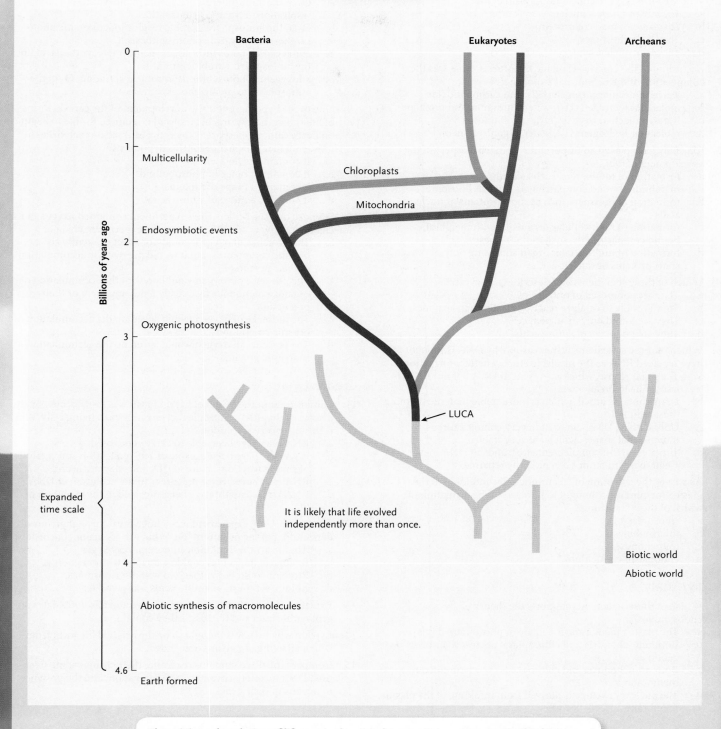

The Tree of Life

Bacteria   Eukaryotes   Archeans

Billions of years ago

0

1 — Multicellularity

Chloroplasts

Mitochondria

Endosymbiotic events

2

Oxygenic photosynthesis

3

← LUCA

Expanded time scale

It is likely that life evolved independently more than once.

Biotic world

Abiotic world

4

Abiotic synthesis of macromolecules

4.6 — Earth formed

The origin and evolution of life required certain key events to occur over Earth's history. The earliest forms of life were most likely anaerobic heterotrophs. The development of oxygenic photosynthesis in certain groups of prokaryotic cells led to oxygen accumulating in the atmosphere. In turn, this led to the evolution of aerobic respiration, which allowed for increased production of ATP. Increased energy production is a prerequisite for the evolution of the eukaryotic cell, greater cell complexity, and multicellularity.

SELF-TEST QUESTIONS

Recall/Understand

1. Why are viruses NOT considered a form of life?
   a. They do not have a nucleus.
   b. They are not made of protein.
   c. They lack ribosomes.
   d. They lack nucleic acid.

2. According to the Oparin–Haldane hypothesis, what was the composition of the primordial atmosphere?
   a. water, molecular nitrogen (N2), and carbon dioxide
   b. molecular hydrogen (H_2), water, ammonia, and methane
   c. water, molecular oxygen (O_2), and ammonia
   d. molecular hydrogen (H_2), water, argon, and neon

3. Clay may have played an important role in what aspect of the development of life?
   a. formation of monomers, such as amino acids, and membrane-bound compartments, such as liposomes
   b. formation of polymers such as short proteins or nucleic acids
   c. formation of multicellular organisms with membrane-bound compartments, such as liposomes
   d. formation of multicellular organisms using polymers such as short proteins or nucleic acids

4. Which of these statements *best* describes ribozymes?
   a. They are composed of only RNA.
   b. They are able to catalyze reactions faster than enzymes.
   c. They are found only in ancient cells.
   d. They are polymers of amino acids.

5. Which of these statements is the reason why DNA is thought to have replaced RNA as the means to store genetic information?
   a. The sugar ribose, which is present in DNA but not RNA, is less prone to breakdown.
   b. DNA contains uracil, which is more stable than the thymine present in RNA.
   c. Unlike RNA, DNA can exist in very complex three-dimensional shapes, which are very stable.
   d. The presence of complementary strands in DNA means that single-base mutations can be easily repaired.

6. As part of the evolution of eukaryotic cells, infolding of the plasma membrane is thought to have led to the formation of which of these structures?
   a. ribosomes
   b. microtubules
   c. mitochondria
   d. endoplasmic reticulum

Apply/Analyze

7. Which of these statements supports the theory of endosymbiosis?
   a. The plasma membrane is a made of phospholipid bilayer.
   b. Both mitochondria and chloroplasts possess their own genomes.
   c. Both mitochondria and chloroplasts are surrounded by a membrane.
   d. The nuclear envelope is derived from infolding of the plasma membrane.

8. Which of these lists of events is in the correct order by first appearance?
   a. O_2 in the atmosphere, anoxygenic photosynthesis, aerobic respiration, oxygenic photosynthesis
   b. O_2 in the atmosphere, aerobic respiration, oxygenic photosynthesis, anoxygenic photosynthesis
   c. anoxygenic photosynthesis, oxygenic photosynthesis, O_2 in the atmosphere, aerobic respiration
   d. anoxygenic photosynthesis, aerobic respiration, O_2 in the atmosphere, oxygenic photosynthesis

9. One of the hypotheses for the development of the earliest forms of life is that the key organic molecules required for life to begin on Earth came from space. Why is the Murchison meteorite the most convincing evidence for this hypothesis?
   a. It contains nucleic acids.
   b. It contains a range of phospholipids.
   c. It contains a range of proteins.
   d. It contains a range of amino acids.

10. Suppose that the Miller–Urey experiment contained oxygen in its chamber. How would the results of the experiment change?
    a. The presence of oxygen would not affect the synthesis of organic compounds, but it would prevent the accumulation of their precursors.
    b. The presence of oxygen would prevent the accumulation of organic compounds by quickly oxidizing them or their precursors.
    c. The presence of oxygen would speed up the accumulation of organic compounds.
    d. The presence of oxygen would speed up the accumulation of inorganic precursors.

Create/Evaluate

11. Thinking about the origin of life on Earth was transformed by the discovery that RNA molecules act as catalysts in living cells. Why is this discovery revolutionary?
    a. RNA may have been able to carry genes on it.
    b. RNA may have been capable of self-replication and catalysis of simple reactions, before DNA and enzymes arose.
    c. RNA may have been a precursor in the evolution of DNA.
    d. RNA viruses might have been involved in the evolution of life.

12. The Miller–Urey experiment was a huge breakthrough in our understanding of the origins of life. What was its major conclusion?
    a. Abiotic synthesis of molecules requires oxygen (O_2).
    b. Biological molecules could be formed without energy.
    c. Proteins could be synthesized without ribosomes.
    d. Abiotic synthesis of amino acids was possible.

13. Explain how scientists determine relative and absolutes dates of geological strata and the fossils they contain.

14. Explain why LUCA is thought to be the original life form from which all living organisms descended.

15. Compare the three domains regarding their chromosome structure, DNA location, chromosome segregation, and the presence of introns in their genes.

Chapter Roadmap

Viruses, Viroids, and Prions: Infectious Biological Particles

Viruses, viroids, and prions, non-cellular, elegant in their simplicity, highjack the machinery of cells of both prokaryotes and eukaryotes.

22.1 What Is a Virus? Characteristics of Viruses

Viruses are non-living infective agents consisting of a nucleic acid genome enclosed in a protein coat. Recognition proteins that enable the virus to attach to host cells extend from the surface of infectious viruses.

From Chapter 5

From Chapter 7

From Chapter 10

From Chapter 12

From Chapter 21

22.2 Viruses Infect Bacterial, Animal, and Plant Cells by Similar Pathways

Viruses reproduce by entering a host cell and directing the cellular machinery to make new particles of the same kind.

Courtesy of S. Ferreira, copyright-free

22.3 Treating and Preventing Viral Infections

These agents do not respond to antibiotics and other treatment methods. Research efforts have focused on development of vaccines and on preventing infection by viruses that cause serious or fatal diseases.

22.4 Viruses May Have Evolved from Fragments of Cellular DNA or RNA

Viruses may have evolved after cells and descended from nucleic acid fragments that "escaped" from a cell.

22.5 Viroids and Prions Are Infective Agents Even Simpler in Structure than Viruses

Viroids, which infect crop plants, consist of only a very small, single-stranded, RNA molecule. Prions, which cause brain diseases in some animals, are infectious proteins with no associated nucleic acid.

To Chapter 26

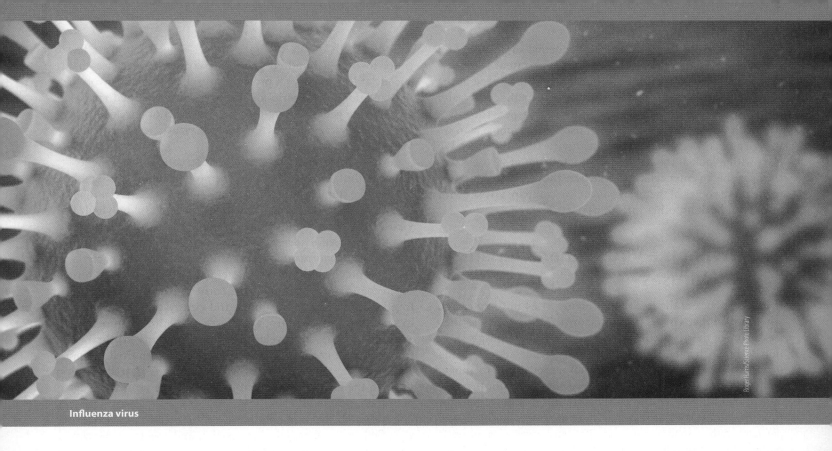

Influenza virus

Viruses, Viroids, and Prions: Infectious Biological Particles

22

Why it matters . . . Imagine yourself sitting in a crowded airplane bound from London, United Kingdom, to Vancouver. The person sitting beside you has a runny nose; is sneezing, coughing, and sucking on lozenges; and appears to have a fever. Recognizing that your seatmate is exhibiting many of the symptoms of influenza, a respiratory illness caused by the influenza virus shown in the micrograph above, you worry that the virus will spread to you through your seatmate's coughing and sneezing.

At any given time, 5%–15% of the global population of people exhibit the symptoms of influenza, and each year about 500 000 people die from influenza A. Recent research has shown that new strains of influenza A arise each year from just a few initial sources in East and Southeast Asia and then spread around the world. As influenza viruses travel through populations around the world, they evolve, changing so much that the vaccines we developed in previous years are no longer effective, and new vaccines must be developed.

Understanding the global pattern of influenza migration will help the World Health Organization to develop effective vaccines. Knowing which strains cause the initial outbreak in Asia allows scientists to formulate vaccines to target these strains, offering people in other regions some protection from the illness.

Why was the 1918 Spanish flu pandemic so deadly? And why do we need to develop new flu vaccines so often? We investigate these questions later in this chapter. We also look at the beneficial roles played by viruses—not all are pathogenic—and investigate ways in which we may be able to harness the infective abilities of viruses for our own uses. For example, can we use viruses as vectors for gene therapy to fight diseases? We start with a look at the defining characteristics of viruses: how they are able to enter cells and take over the cell's machinery to make more copies of themselves. And we compare viruses with viroids and prions, other infectious particles.

22.1   What Is a Virus? Characteristics of Viruses

If you look back at the tree of life (Figure 21.24 in Chapter 21), you'll notice that viruses are not shown. That is because they lack many of the properties of life shared by all organisms (Section 21.1a in Chapter 21), and so are not considered to be living organisms. For example, viruses cannot reproduce on their own and they lack a metabolic system to provide energy for their life cycles; instead, they depend on the host cells that they infect for these functions. For this reason, viruses are infectious biological particles rather than organisms. The structure of a virus is reduced to the minimum necessary to transmit its genome from one host cell to another. A virus is simply one or more nucleic acid molecules surrounded by a protein coat, or **capsid (Figure 22.1a, b)**. Some capsids might be enclosed within a membrane, or **envelope**, derived from their host cell's membrane (Figure 22.1c). So a virus, while able to evolve, is not a cell: it does not have cytoplasm enclosed by a plasma membrane, as do all known living organisms.

The nucleic acid genome of a virus may be either DNA or RNA and can be composed of either a single strand or a double strand of RNA or DNA. Viral genomes range from just a few genes to over a hundred genes; all viruses have genes that encode at least their coat proteins, as well as proteins involved in regulation of transcription. Genomes of **enveloped viruses** also include genes required for the synthesis of envelope proteins. Some viral genomes also include virus-specific enzymes for nucleic acid replication.

Most viruses take one of two basic structural forms, helical or polyhedral. In **helical viruses** the protein subunits assemble in a rodlike spiral around the genome (Figure 22.1a). A number of viruses that infect plant cells are helical. In **polyhedral viruses**, the coat proteins form triangular units that fit together like the parts of a soccer ball (Figure 22.1b). The polyhedral viruses include forms that infect animals, plants, and bacteria. In some polyhedral viruses, protein spikes that provide host cell recognition extend from the corners, where the facets fit together. Both helical and polyhedral viruses can be enveloped in a membrane derived from the host's membrane (Figure 22.1c and **Figure 22.2**). In enveloped viruses, proteins synthesized from the viral genome in the host cell are transported to and embedded in the membrane before the virus particle buds through the host cell. These proteins allow the virus to recognize and bind to host cells.

Although they are not considered to be alive, viruses are classified into orders, families, genera, and species using several criteria, including virus size and structure, genome structure (RNA or DNA, single stranded or double stranded), and how their nucleic acid is replicated. More than 4000 species of viruses have been classified into more than 80 families. The family names end in -*viridae* (**Table 22.1**) and may refer either to the geographic region where the virus was first discovered or to the structure of the virus. For example, Coronaviridae, the family to which the influenza virus and SARS (Severe Acute Respiratory Disorder) belong, is named for the "crown" of protein spikes on the capsid, as shown in the photomicrograph at

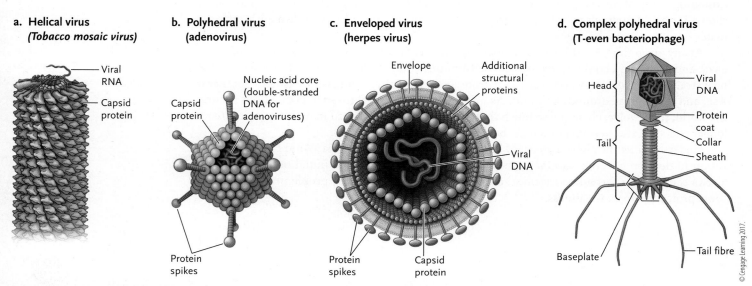

a. Helical virus *(Tobacco mosaic virus)*

Viral RNA
Capsid protein

b. Polyhedral virus (adenovirus)

Nucleic acid core (double-stranded DNA for adenoviruses)
Capsid protein
Protein spikes

c. Enveloped virus (herpes virus)

Envelope
Additional structural proteins
Viral DNA
Protein spikes
Capsid protein

d. Complex polyhedral virus (T-even bacteriophage)

Head
Tail
Viral DNA
Protein coat
Collar
Sheath
Baseplate
Tail fibre

© Cengage Learning 2017.

FIGURE 22.1 Viral structure. All viruses consist of nucleic acid surrounded by a protein coat, but they can have a very wide range of sizes and shapes.

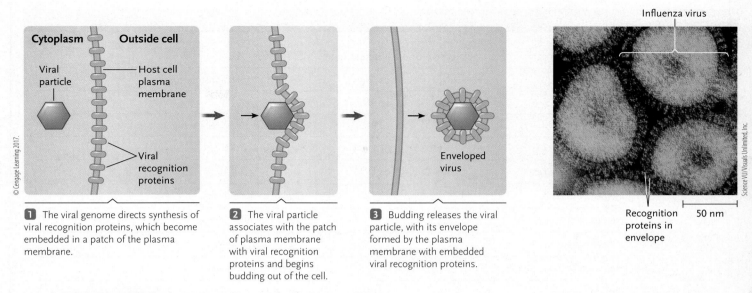

① The viral genome directs synthesis of viral recognition proteins, which become embedded in a patch of the plasma membrane.

② The viral particle associates with the patch of plasma membrane with viral recognition proteins and begins budding out of the cell.

③ Budding releases the viral particle, with its envelope formed by the plasma membrane with embedded viral recognition proteins.

FIGURE 22.2 How enveloped viruses acquire their envelope

the start of this chapter (*corona* = crown). Like some bacteria, some viruses are named for the disease they cause; these names can be one or two words, for example, herpesvirus or Ebola virus. Each type of virus is made up of many strains, which are differentiated by their virulence.

As is the case for our look at prokaryotic organisms in the next chapter, we will just scratch the surface of viral diversity in this chapter. For example, there are millions of viruses in every millilitre of ocean water, most of which have not been identified. As we learn more about viruses, the classification system will change.

Every living organism is likely permanently infected by one or more kinds of viruses. Usually, a virus infects only a single species or a few closely related species. A virus may even infect only one organ system or a single tissue or cell type in its host. However, some viruses are able to infect unrelated species, either naturally or after mutating.

Of the roughly 80 viral families described to date, 21 include viruses that cause human diseases. Viruses also cause diseases of wild and domestic animals. Plant viruses cause annual losses of millions of tonnes of crops, especially cereals, potatoes, sugar beets, and sugar cane. (**Table 22.1** lists some important families of viruses that infect animals.) The effects of viruses on the organisms they infect range from undetectable to merely bothersome to seriously debilitating or lethal. For instance, some viral infections of humans, such as those causing cold sores or the common cold, are usually little more than a nuisance to healthy adults. Others cause some of the most severe and deadly human diseases, including AIDS, encephalitis, and Ebola hemorrhagic fever.

However, not all viruses are pathogens. Many viruses actually benefit their hosts; for example, infection by certain non-pathogenic viruses protects human hosts against pathogenic viruses. The "protective" viruses interfere with replication or other functions of the pathogenic viruses. Some viruses also act to defend their host cells. For example, one of the primary reasons that bacteria do not completely overrun this planet is that they are destroyed in incredibly huge numbers by viruses known as **bacteriophages**, or **phages** for short (*phagein* = to eat) (Figure 22.1d). Viruses also provide a natural means to control some insect pests, such as spruce budworm.

Viruses are vital components of ecosystems and may be the dominant entity in some ecosystems, such as the oceans. We don't yet fully understand their roles in these ecosystems, but it is clear that they affect nutrient cycling through their effects on prokaryotic organisms. For example, in certain regions of the ocean, a few genera of cyanobacteria dominate the marine phytoplankton, making major contributions to global photosynthesis. Bacteriophages infect these cyanobacteria, causing high levels of mortality, thus influencing cyanobacterial population dynamics as well as the release of nutrients from bacterial cells. But these viruses also help keep photosynthesis going in their cyanobacterial hosts, as recently discovered by Nicholas Mann and colleagues at the University of Warwick. As you read in Chapter 6, one of the proteins that make up photosystem II is very susceptible to light-induced damage and so is constantly being replaced by newly synthesized molecules. As long as the cell can make new protein quickly enough to keep up with damage, photosynthesis can continue, but if the rate of damage to photosystem II exceeds the repair rate, the rate of photosynthesis will drop. When these bacteriophages infect cyanobacteria, they shut down their host's protein synthesis. Without continued synthesis of the photosystem protein, photosynthesis should slow down following infection; but it doesn't. How is the photosynthetic rate maintained? Mann and his colleagues found that the virus's genome includes genes for this protein; expression of these viral proteins enables the repair rate to keep up with

TABLE 22.1 | Major Animal Viruses

Viral Families	Viral Genera	Envelope	Nucleic Acid	Diseases
Adenoviridae	Adenovirus	No	ds DNA	Respiratory infections, tumours
Coronaviridae	*Betacoronavirus*	Yes	ss RNA	SARS
Flaviviridae	*Flavivirus*	Yes	ss RNA	Yellow fever, West Nile, dengue, hepatitis C, Zika
Hepadnaviridae	Hepadnavirus	Yes	ds DNA	Hepatitis B
	Human herpesvirus	Yes	ds DNA	
	Herpes simplex I			Oral herpes, cold sores
	Herpes simplex II			Genital herpes
	Varicella-zoster virus			Chickenpox, shingles
	Herpesvirus 4 (Epstein–Barr virus)			Infectious mononucleosis
Orthomyxoviridae	Orthomyxovirus	Yes	ss RNA	Influenza
Papillomaviridae	Papillomavirus	No	ds DNA	Human papillomavirus (genital warts)
Papovaviridae	Papovavirus	No	ds DNA	Benign and malignant warts
Paramyxoviridae	Paramyxovirus	Yes	ss RNA	Measles, mumps, pneumonia
Picornaviridae	Picornavirus	No	ss RNA	
	Enterovirus			Polio, hemorrhagic eye disease, gastroenteritis
	Rhinovirus			Common cold
	Hepatitis A virus			Hepatitis A
	Aphthovirus			Foot-and-mouth disease in livestock
Poxviridae	Poxvirus	Yes	ds DNA	Smallpox, cowpox
Retroviridae	Retrovirus	Yes	ss RNA	
	HTLV I, II			T-cell leukemia
	HIV			AIDS
Rhabdoviridae	Rhabdovirus	Yes	ss RNA	Rabies, other animal diseases

ds = double-stranded; HTLV = human T-lymphotropic virus; ss = single-stranded

light-induced damage, allowing the cell to photosynthesize. Although the virus is doing this for "selfish" reasons (i.e., to ensure that its host has sufficient resources for the virus to complete its life cycle), the outcome of this association is that much of the carbon fixed on Earth may be facilitated by virus-controlled photosynthesis.

STUDY BREAK QUESTIONS

1. What is a virus?
2. List three features of viruses that distinguish them from living organisms.

22.2 Viruses Infect Bacterial, Animal, and Plant Cells by Similar Pathways

Viral particles move by random molecular motions until they contact the surface of a host cell. For infection to occur, the virus or the viral genome must then enter the cell. Inside the cell, the viral genes are expressed, leading to replication of the viral genome and assembly of progeny viruses. The new viral particles, or **virions** as the extracellular form of a virus is known, are then released from the host cell, a process that often ruptures the host cell, killing it.

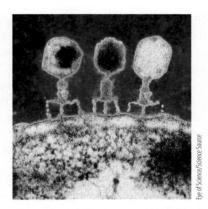

FIGURE 22.3 **Bacteriophages injecting their DNA into *E. coli***

22.2a Bacteriophages: Viruses That Infect Bacteria

We have learned a great deal about the infective cycles of viruses, as well as the genetics of both viruses and bacteria, from studies of the bacteriophages infecting *Escherichia coli* (*E. coli*). Some of these are **virulent bacteriophages**, which kill their host cells during each cycle of infection, whereas others are **temperate bacteriophages**. Temperate bacteriophages enter an inactive phase while inside the host cell and can be passed on to several generations of daughter cells before becoming active and killing their host.

VIRULENT BACTERIOPHAGES Among the virulent bacteriophages infecting *E. coli*, the **T-even bacteriophages** T2, T4, and T6 have been the most valuable in genetic studies. The coats of these phages are divided into a *head* and a *tail* (Figure 22.1d). A double-stranded linear molecule of DNA is packed into the head. The tail, assembled from several different proteins, has **recognition proteins** at its tip that can bind to the surface of the host cell. Once the tail is attached, it functions as a sort of syringe that injects the DNA genome into the cell **(Figure 22.3)**.

Infection begins when a T-even phage collides randomly with the surface of an *E. coli* cell and the tail attaches to the host cell wall (**Figure 22.4**, step 1). An enzyme present in the viral coat, *lysozyme*, then digests a hole in the cell wall, through which the tail injects the DNA of the phage (step 2). The proteins of the viral coat remain outside. Throughout its life cycle within the bacterial cell, the phage uses host cell machinery to express its genes. One of the proteins produced early in the infection is an enzyme that breaks down the bacterial chromosome. The phage gene for a DNA polymerase that replicates the phage's DNA is also expressed early on. Eventually, 100–200 new viral DNA molecules are synthesized (step 3). Later in the infection, the host cell machinery transcribes the phage genes for the viral coat proteins (step 4). As the head and tail proteins assemble, the replicated viral DNA is packed into the heads (step 5).

FIGURE 22.4 **The infective cycle of a T-even bacteriophage, an example of a virulent phage**

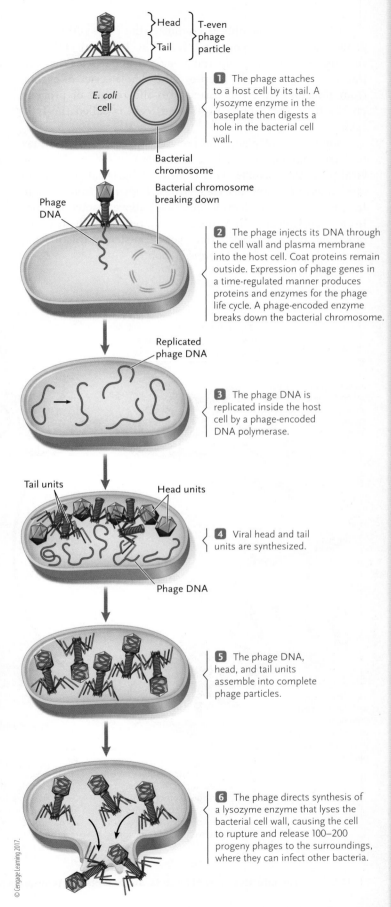

Head ⎱ T-even
Tail ⎰ phage particle

E. coli cell

1 The phage attaches to a host cell by its tail. A lysozyme enzyme in the baseplate then digests a hole in the bacterial cell wall.

Bacterial chromosome

Phage DNA

Bacterial chromosome breaking down

2 The phage injects its DNA through the cell wall and plasma membrane into the host cell. Coat proteins remain outside. Expression of phage genes in a time-regulated manner produces proteins and enzymes for the phage life cycle. A phage-encoded enzyme breaks down the bacterial chromosome.

Replicated phage DNA

3 The phage DNA is replicated inside the host cell by a phage-encoded DNA polymerase.

Tail units · Head units

Phage DNA

4 Viral head and tail units are synthesized.

5 The phage DNA, head, and tail units assemble into complete phage particles.

6 The phage directs synthesis of a lysozyme enzyme that lyses the bacterial cell wall, causing the cell to rupture and release 100–200 progeny phages to the surroundings, where they can infect other bacteria.

When viral assembly is complete, the cell synthesizes a phage-encoded lysozyme that lyses the bacterial cell wall, causing the cell to rupture and release viral particles that can infect other *E. coli* cells (step 6). This whole series of events, from infection of a cell through to the release of progeny phages from the ruptured (or **lysed**) cell, is called the **lytic cycle**.

Some virulent phages (although not T-even phages) may package fragments of the host cell's DNA in the heads as the viral particles assemble. This transfer of bacterial genes from one bacterium to another via a virus is known as *transduction*. In the type of transduction described above, bacterial genes from essentially any DNA fragment can be randomly incorporated into phage particles; thus, gene transfer by this mechanism is termed *generalized transduction*.

A SCIENTIST'S FAVOURITE TEMPERATE *E. COLI* BACTERIOPHAGE, LAMBDA
The infective cycle of the bacteriophage lambda (λ), an *E. coli* phage used extensively in research, is typical of temperate phages. Phage lambda infects *E. coli* in much the same way as the T-even phages. The phage injects its double-stranded, linear DNA chromosome into the bacterium (**Figure 22.5**, step 1). Once inside, the linear chromosome forms a circle and then follows one of two paths. Sophisticated molecular switches govern which path is followed at the time of infection.

One path is the lytic cycle, which is like the lytic cycles of virulent phages. The lytic cycle (Figure 22.5, left side) starts with steps 1 and 2 (infection) and then goes directly to steps 7 through 9 (production and release of progeny virus) and back to step 1. A second and more common path is the **lysogenic**

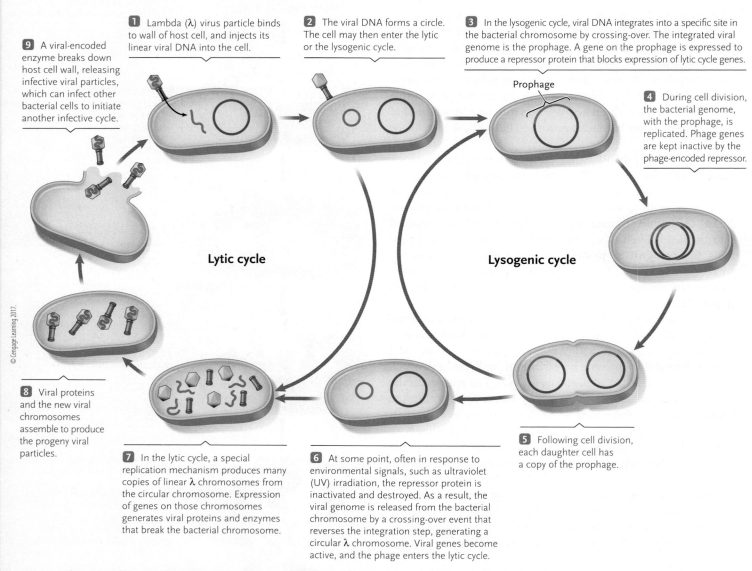

9 A viral-encoded enzyme breaks down host cell wall, releasing infective viral particles, which can infect other bacterial cells to initiate another infective cycle.

1 Lambda (λ) virus particle binds to wall of host cell, and injects its linear viral DNA into the cell.

2 The viral DNA forms a circle. The cell may then enter the lytic or the lysogenic cycle.

3 In the lysogenic cycle, viral DNA integrates into a specific site in the bacterial chromosome by crossing-over. The integrated viral genome is the prophage. A gene on the prophage is expressed to produce a repressor protein that blocks expression of lytic cycle genes.

Prophage

4 During cell division, the bacterial genome, with the prophage, is replicated. Phage genes are kept inactive by the phage-encoded repressor.

Lytic cycle

Lysogenic cycle

8 Viral proteins and the new viral chromosomes assemble to produce the progeny viral particles.

7 In the lytic cycle, a special replication mechanism produces many copies of linear λ chromosomes from the circular chromosome. Expression of genes on those chromosomes generates viral proteins and enzymes that break the bacterial chromosome.

6 At some point, often in response to environmental signals, such as ultraviolet (UV) irradiation, the repressor protein is inactivated and destroyed. As a result, the viral genome is released from the bacterial chromosome by a crossing-over event that reverses the integration step, generating a circular λ chromosome. Viral genes become active, and the phage enters the lytic cycle.

5 Following cell division, each daughter cell has a copy of the prophage.

© Cengage Learning 2017.

FIGURE 22.5 **The infective cycle of lambda, an example of a temperate phage, which can go through the lytic cycle or the lysogenic cycle**

cycle (Figure 22.5, right side). This cycle begins when the viral chromosome integrates into the host cell's DNA by recombination (Figure 22.5, steps 1 through 3). The DNA of a temperate phage typically inserts at one or possibly a few specific sites in the bacterial chromosome through the action of a phage-encoded enzyme that recognizes certain sequences in the host DNA. Once integrated, the lambda genes are mostly inactive, so no structural components of the phage are made. While inserted in the host cell DNA, the virus is known as a **prophage** (*pro* = before). When the host cell DNA replicates, so does the integrated viral DNA, which is passed on to daughter cells along with the host cell DNA (Figure 22.5, steps 4 and 5).

What triggers the integrated prophage to become active (step 6)? Certain environmental signals, such as nutrient availability and ultraviolet irradiation, stimulate this change, causing the prophage to enter the lytic cycle (Figure 22.5, steps 6 through 9). Genes that were inactive in the prophage are now transcribed. Among the first viral proteins synthesized are enzymes that excise the lambda chromosome from the host chromosome. The result is a circular lambda chromosome that replicates itself and directs the production of linear viral DNA and coat proteins. This active stage culminates in the lysis of the host cell and the release of infective viral particles.

The excision of the prophage from its host's DNA is not always precise, resulting in the inclusion of one or more host cell genes with the viral DNA. These genes are replicated with the viral DNA and packed into the coats, and may be carried to

a new host cell in the next cycle of infection. Clearly, only genes that are adjacent to the integration site(s) of a temperate phage can be cut out with the viral DNA, can be included in phage particles during the lytic stage, and can undergo transduction. Accordingly, this mechanism of gene transfer is termed **specialized transduction**.

22.2b Animal Viruses

Viruses infe[...] [...] similar to that for bacterial cel[...] and the genome enter a host [...]val of the coat to release the [...] entry; the envelope does n[...]

Viruse[...]liovirus, bind by their recog[...]mbrane and are then taken [...]he virus coat and genome of some enveloped [...] erpesvirus, HIV, and the virus causing rabies, enter the host cell by fusion of their envelope with the host cell plasma membrane. Other enveloped viruses, such as influenza virus, enter host cells by endocytosis.

Once inside the host cell, the genome directs the synthesis of additional viral particles by basically the same pathways as bacterial viruses. Some animal viruses replicate themselves in very complex ways; one example is HIV, the virus that causes AIDS **(Figure 22.6)**. HIV, a retrovirus, contains two copies of

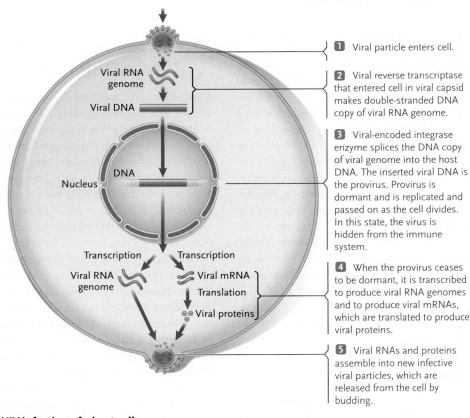

1. Viral particle enters cell.

2. Viral reverse transcriptase that entered cell in viral capsid makes double-stranded DNA copy of viral RNA genome.

3. Viral-encoded integrase enzyme splices the DNA copy of viral genome into the host DNA. The inserted viral DNA is the provirus. Provirus is dormant and is replicated and passed on as the cell divides. In this state, the virus is hidden from the immune system.

4. When the provirus ceases to be dormant, it is transcribed to produce viral RNA genomes and to produce viral mRNAs, which are translated to produce viral proteins.

5. Viral RNAs and proteins assemble into new infective viral particles, which are released from the cell by budding.

© Cengage Learning 2017.

FIGURE 22.6 The steps in HIV infection of a host cell

single-stranded RNA. It also carries several molecules of an enzyme, reverse transcriptase, in its capsid. Replication of retroviruses is unusual: the virus's genome enters the host cell along with reverse transcriptase, which generates a complementary strand of DNA from viral RNA. A second strand of DNA is then synthesized using the first strand as a template. The resulting double-stranded DNA integrates into the host cell's DNA as a provirus (comparable to the prophage previously described). This DNA is transcribed by the host cell into mRNA, which is translated to produce viral proteins, including capsid proteins and reverse transcriptase molecules. New virus particles are released from the cell to infect other cells or to be passed to new hosts. In some cases, newly completed viruses rupture the host cell's plasma membrane, typically killing the cell.

The vast majority of animal virus infections are asymptomatic because causing disease is of no benefit to the virus. However, a number of pathogenic viruses cause diseases in a variety of ways. Some viruses (e.g., herpesvirus) cause cell death when progeny viruses are released from the cell. This can lead to massive cell death, destroying vital tissues such as nervous tissue or white or red blood cells, or causing lesions in skin and mucous membranes. Other viruses release cellular molecules when infected cells break down, which can induce fever and inflammation (e.g., influenza virus). Yet other viruses alter gene function when they insert into the host cell DNA, leading to cancer and other abnormalities.

Some animal viruses enter a **latent phase**, similar to the lysogenic cycle for bacteriophages, in which the virus remains in the cell in an inactive form. The herpesviruses that cause oral and genital ulcers in humans remain in a latent phase in the cytoplasm of some body cells for the life of the individual. At times, particularly during periods of stress, the virus becomes active in some cells, directing viral replication and causing ulcers to form as cells break down during viral release.

Understanding the life cycle and genetic sequence of a virus is important in combatting and tracking the spread of viral diseases. For example, SARS (Severe Acute Respiratory Syndrome) became the first pandemic in the twenty-first century of a previously unknown cause. A woman from Canada contracted the virus in 2003 while travelling in China. She fell ill upon her arrival to Toronto, where she died. This was the first of two outbreaks in the Toronto area. Approximately 400 people subsequently became ill and 44 people died; 25 000 Torontonians were placed in quarantine. Later the same year, using samples from infected patients from Toronto, scientists at the Michael Smith Laboratories at the University of British Columbia mapped its genetic sequence. Using the genetic sequence data, the origin of the virus was shown to be bats, in which infection is asymptomatic.

22.2c Plant Viruses

Plant viruses may be rodlike or polyhedral. Although most include RNA as their nucleic acid, some contain DNA. None of the known plant viruses have envelopes. They enter cells through mechanical injuries to leaves and stems; they can also be transmitted from one plant to another during pollination or via herbivorous animals such as leafhoppers, aphids, and nematodes. Plant viruses can also be transmitted from one generation to the next in seeds. Once inside a cell, plant viruses replicate via the same processes as animal viruses. However, within plants, virus particles can pass from infected to healthy cells through plasmodesmata, the openings in cell walls that interconnect the cytoplasm of plant cells, and through the vascular system.

Plant viruses are generally named and classified by the type of plant they infect and their most visible effects. *Tomato bushy stunt virus*, for example, causes dwarfing and overgrowth of leaves and stems of tomato plants; and *tobacco mosaic virus* causes a mosaic-like pattern of spots on the leaves of tobacco plants. Most species of crop plants can be infected by at least one destructive virus.

The tobacco mosaic virus was the first virus to be isolated, disassembled, and reassembled in a test tube (Figure 22.1a).

STUDY BREAK QUESTIONS

1. What is the difference between a virulent phage and a temperate phage?
2. What are the two types of transduction? How do they differ from each other?
3. How do plant viruses differ from animal viruses?

22.3 Treating and Preventing Viral Infections

Viral infections are typically difficult to treat because viruses are, for much of the infection, "hidden" inside host cells and use host cell machinery to replicate. Thus, there often are no obvious viral products to be targeted by drugs. Viral infections are unaffected by antibiotics and other treatment methods used for bacterial infections. As a result, many viral infections are allowed to run their course, with treatment limited to relieving the symptoms while the natural immune defences of the patient attack the virus. Some viruses, however, cause serious and sometimes deadly symptoms on infection; for these, the focus has often been on prevention through vaccine development (e.g., measles, polio). Viruses that use their own polymerases (e.g., RNA viruses such as influenza) provide more obvious targets, so researchers have spent considerable effort developing antiviral drugs to treat them. Many of these drugs fight the virus directly by targeting a stage of the viral life cycle; for example, the drug Sofosbuvir targets RNA polymerase, which is essential for viral RNA replication (**Figure 22.7**).

The influenza virus illustrates the difficulties inherent in controlling or preventing viral diseases. As mentioned at the start of the chapter, the influenza type A virus causes flu

FIGURE 22.7 **Experimental Research**

A New Discovery for Hepatitis C Therapy

Question: Which form of β-D-20-deoxy-20-R-fluoro-20-β-C-methyl nucleoside (group of compounds shown to be effective inhibitors of the hepatitis C nonstructural protein 5B (NS5B)) should be developed into a therapy for hepatitis C virus (HCV)?

Experiment: β-D-20-deoxy-20-R-fluoro-20-β-C-methyl nucleoside compounds were identified and purified by NMR (nuclear magnetic resonance), MS (mass spectrometry), high performance liquid chromatography (HPLC), crystallization, and X-ray. Assays for anti-viral activity as well as cell and mitochondrial toxicity were performed on a subset of original compounds. Testing for chemical stability was done with simulated intestinal and gastric fluids as well as human liver and plasma. Animal testing was performed on rats, dogs, and monkeys.

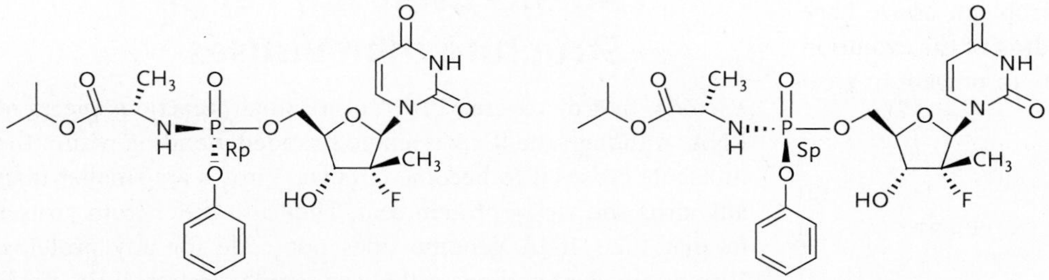

50 (PSI-7976) **51** (PSI-7977)

Structures of diastereomers 50 and 51

Results: A phosphate derivative of the β-D-20-deoxy-20-R-fluoro-20-β-C-methyluridine nucleoside (51) showed significant antiviral activity in the livers of rats, dogs, and monkeys when administered *in vivo* and was stable in a human environment. An X-ray structure determined the stereochemistry of diastereomer 51, which was selected as a clinical development candidate.

Conclusions: The identification of a new drug therapy was a major breakthrough in the treatment of hepatitis C. It is estimated that 170 million people worldwide are infected with the virus, with approximately 80% having chronic hepatitis C, which in many cases leads to cirrhosis (scarification of the liver) and/or carcinoma (cancer in epithelial cells). Standard treatments until this time were regular injections with interferon (protease inhibitor) and oral ribavirin. The severe side effects and long treatment duration made this therapy unsatisfactory. Current therapies target NS5B, which is an RNA polymerase and essential for viral RNA replication. This research led to the development of the first anti-hepatitis C medication (Sofosbuvir; named after the principle investigator Michael J. Sofia) that targeted binding proteins and has very few side effects, high efficacy, and shorter drug administration time.

Source: Michael J. Sofia, et al. 2010. Discovery of a β-D-20-Deoxy-20-r-fluoro-20-β-C-methyluridine Nucleotide Prodrug (PSI-7977) for the Treatment of Hepatitis C Virus. J. Med. Chem. 53, 7202–7218

epidemics that sweep over the world each year. Why does a new vaccine have to be developed each year? One reason for the success of this virus is that its genome consists of eight separate pieces of RNA. When two different influenza viruses infect the same individual, these RNA pieces can assemble in random combinations derived from either parent virus. The new combinations can change the protein coat of the virus, making it unrecognizable to antibodies developed against either parent virus. Being "invisible" to these antibodies means that new virus strains can infect people who have already had the flu caused by a different strain, or who had flu shots effective against only the parent strains of the virus. Random mutations in the RNA genome of the virus add to the variations in the coat proteins that make previously formed antibodies ineffective.

In the 1918 Spanish flu pandemic, the influenza virus killed many of its hosts. Why was this strain so virulent? Researchers have learned that the 1918 influenza virus had mutations in the polymerase genes that replicated the viral genome in host cells, likely making this strain capable of replicating more efficiently.

Other viruses that infect humans are also considered to have evolved from a virus that previously infected other animals. HIV is one of these. Until the second half of the twentieth century, infections of this virus were apparently restricted almost entirely to chimpanzees and gorillas in Africa. Now the virus infects nearly 36 million people worldwide, with the greatest concentration of infected individuals in sub-Saharan Africa.

As illustrated by this example, our efforts to control or eliminate human diseases caused by viral pathogens are complicated when dealing with viruses that have broad host specificity and can infect other animals besides humans. Because other animals can harbour these viruses, we can never successfully eradicate the diseases they cause. For example, the influenza virus can infect birds, swine, and other animals in addition to humans.

Also, as human encroachment on wildlife habitats increases, we create the potential for the evolution of new human viruses, as strains that infect other animals mutate to infect humans. These factors, together with increasing global travel and trade, create the potential for a new human pathogenic virus to readily become a global problem, as we have experienced with HIV. A better understanding of the evolution and life cycles of viruses is crucial if we are to prevent or treat emerging viral diseases.

STUDY BREAK QUESTION

Why can a viral infection be more difficult to treat than a bacterial infection?

22.4 Viruses May Have Evolved from Fragments of Cellular DNA or RNA

Where did viruses come from? Several different hypotheses have been proposed to explain the origin of viruses. Some biologists have suggested that, because viruses can duplicate only by infecting a host cell, they probably evolved after cells appeared. They may represent "escaped" fragments of DNA molecules that once formed part of the genetic material of living cells or an RNA copy of such a fragment. The fragments first became surrounded by a protective layer of protein with recognition functions, and then these fragments escaped from their parent cells. As viruses evolved, the information encoded in the core of the virus became reduced to a set of directions for producing more viral particles of the same kind.

More recent hypotheses suggest that viruses are very ancient, with virus-like particles predating the first cells. The first viruses originated from the "primordial gene pool," the pool of RNA that is thought to have been the first genetic material.

Regardless of when viruses originated, they do not share a common evolutionary origin. Thus, unlike cellular life, there is no common ancestor for all viruses and we cannot draw a phylogenetic tree for all viruses. However, viruses have played an important role in the evolution of cellular life because of their ability to integrate their genes into their hosts and to acquire genes from their hosts, as described above. In this way, viruses can be a source of new cellular genetic material, providing new enzymes and other proteins to a cell. Viruses may also have played a more direct role in the evolution of eukaryotic cells: some biologists have suggested that the nucleus originated from a large, double-stranded DNA virus that infected prokaryotic cells, resulting in the first eukaryotic cell.

STUDY BREAK QUESTION

1. Why do some biologists think viruses must have originated after cells evolved, rather than predating cells?

22.5 Viroids and Prions Are Infective Agents Even Simpler in Structure than Viruses

Viroids, first discovered in 1971, are small infectious pieces of RNA. Although the RNA is single stranded, bonding within the molecule causes it to become circular. Viroids are smaller than any virus and lack a protein coat. They also differ from viruses in that their RNA genome does not code for any proteins. Viroids are plant pathogens that can rapidly destroy entire fields of citrus, potatoes, tomatoes, coconut palms, and other crop plants. How do viroids cause such devastating diseases without synthesizing any proteins?

The manner in which viroids cause disease remains unknown. In fact, researchers believe that there is more than one mechanism. Recent research indicates that the viroid may cause disease when its RNA interacts with molecules in the cell. For example, it may disrupt normal RNA processing of the host cell: if the viroid's RNA sequence is complementary to the mRNA of the host cell, it can bind to the host's mRNA, thus preventing normal protein synthesis and causing disease.

Like viruses and viroids, **prions** are small infectious particles, but they are not based on nucleic acids; instead, they are infectious protein molecules (the term "prion" is a loose acronym for *pro*teinaceous *in*fectious particle). Prions cause spongiform encephalopathies (SEs), degenerative diseases of the nervous system in mammals characterized by loss of motor control and erratic behaviour. The brains of affected animals are full of spongy holes (**Figure 22.8**; hence the "spongiform" designation) and deposits of proteinaceous material. Under the microscope, aggregates of misfolded proteins, called *amyloid fibres*, are seen in brain tissues; the accumulation of these proteins is the likely cause of the brain damage. SEs progress slowly, meaning animals may be sick for a long time before their symptoms become obvious, but death is inevitable.

One SE disease is *scrapie*, a brain disease that causes sheep to rub against fences, rocks, or trees until they scrape off most of their wool. In cattle, a similar disease is bovine spongiform encephalopathy (BSE), also known as "mad cow disease." Humans also have SE diseases, such as *kuru*, found among cannibals in New Guinea who became infected by eating raw human brain during ritual feasts following the death of an individual. *Creutzfeldt–Jakob disease (CJD)* is a very rare SE

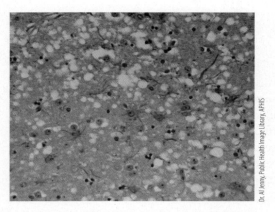

FIGURE 22.8 Bovine spongiform encephalopathy (BSE). The light-coloured patches in this thin section from a brain damaged by BSE are areas where tissue has been destroyed.

disease that affects about one person in a million per year, globally. The symptoms of CJD include rapid mental deterioration, loss of vision and speech, and paralysis; autopsies show spongy holes and deposits in brain tissue similar to those of cattle with BSE. We don't know how CJD is transmitted naturally, but we know it can be transmitted inadvertently, for example, with corneal transplants.

Spongiform encephalopathy diseases hit the headlines worldwide in the late 1980s when farmers in the United Kingdom reported a new disease, later determined to be BSE, spreading among their cattle. It is estimated that over 900 000 cattle in the United Kingdom were affected, many of which entered the human food chain before they developed symptoms. Where did BSE come from? The source was determined to be meat and bone meal fed to the cows; this meal came from the carcasses of sheep and cattle. The practice of feeding animal meal to cattle had been followed for years, but a money-saving change in processing in the early 1980s (a reduction in how long rendered material was held at high temperature) allowed the infectious agent—maybe from scrapie-infected sheep—to survive in the meat and bone meal. Worse was to come when it became evident that BSE had spread to humans who had eaten contaminated beef. This new human disease, known as *variant CJD*, is linked to eating meat products from cattle with BSE. Between 1996, when variant CJD was first described, and 2007, there were 208 cases from 11 countries, with the vast majority of these in the United Kingdom. A 12-year study of human tissue samples removed during appendix operations in the United Kingdom suggests that about 1 in

every 2000 people in the United Kingdom is a carrier for variant CJD. Will these people actually develop the disease? Evidence from studies of kuru suggests that it may take more than 50 years for prion diseases to develop, so there is some concern that a spike in variant CJD cases is still to come.

Concern about variant CJD explains why the discovery of even one steer with BSE can wreak havoc on a country's beef exports, as happened in Canada when an infected cow was found in Alberta in 2003. The United States closed its border to all beef from Canada within a day, followed shortly by border closings of 40 other countries. Loss of these markets caused serious economic hardship for Canadian ranchers and farmers.

What is the cause of BSE and other SE diseases, and how does this causative agent spread? Stanley Prusiner was awarded a Nobel Prize for demonstrating that infectious proteins cause these diseases. Prions are the only known infectious agents that do not include a nucleic acid molecule, and their discovery changed some fundamental views of biology.

CONCEPT FIX Did you know that our brains have prions? These are called *normal prions* and there is an indication that they are important for maintaining myelin around nerve cells. Mice lacking normal prion proteins have subtle impairments in memory and cognition. Perhaps the inability of the misfolded prion proteins to carry out their normal functions results in dementia and the other symptoms of BSE. ⬡

Our current understanding of prion infection is that prion proteins are able to survive passage through the stomach of an animal consuming them; they then enter that animal's bloodstream and proceed to the brain, where they somehow interact with normal prion proteins, causing these proteins to change shape to become abnormal and infectious. Prion proteins and the normal precursor proteins share the same amino acid sequences but differ in how they are folded. Prions are somehow able to impose their folding on normal proteins, thus "infecting" the normal proteins. As the infection spreads, neural functioning is impaired and protein fibrils accumulate, producing aggregations of fibrils that trigger apoptosis of infected cells, leading to the SE characteristic of these diseases.

In this chapter, we focused on the simplest biological entities: viruses, viroids, and prions, which possess only some of the properties of life.

STUDY BREAK QUESTION

1. How do viroids and prions differ from viruses? How do they differ from each other?

Summary Illustration

Viruses, viroids, and prions are non-cellular, infectious biological particles. Although viruses have a wide range of shapes and sizes, all consist of one or more nucleic acid molecules surrounded by a protein coat. Some are also surrounded by a membranous envelope. Viruses can infect bacterial, animal, and plant cells, and rely on these hosts for reproduction and essential metabolic processes. Viroids are plant pathogens that consist solely of small pieces of circular RNA. Prions are protein molecules that cause degenerative diseases of mammalian nervous systems.

Viruses

Tobacco mosaic virus (ssRNA)

Enterobacteria phage T4 (dsDNA)

Hepatitis B (dsDNA)

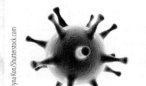

Influenza (flu) (ssRNA)

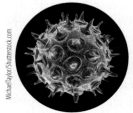

Chickenpox shingles (dsDNA)

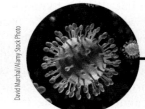

Hepatitis C (ssRNA)

Viroids

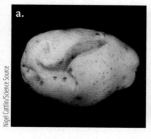
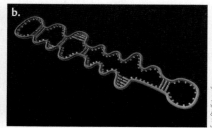

Potato spindle tuber disease. (a) Infected potato. (b) Illustration of viroid

Viroids are plant pathogens.

Prions

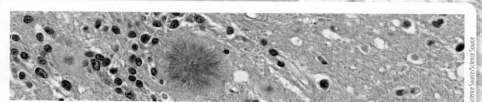

Human brain tissue showing an amyloid plaque from a person with a case of variant Creutzfeldt-Jakob disease (vCJD), a fatal human neurodegenerative condition caused by protein particles called *prions*. It is contracted by eating beef from cows that have bovine spongiform encephalopathy (BSE), also known as "mad cow disease."

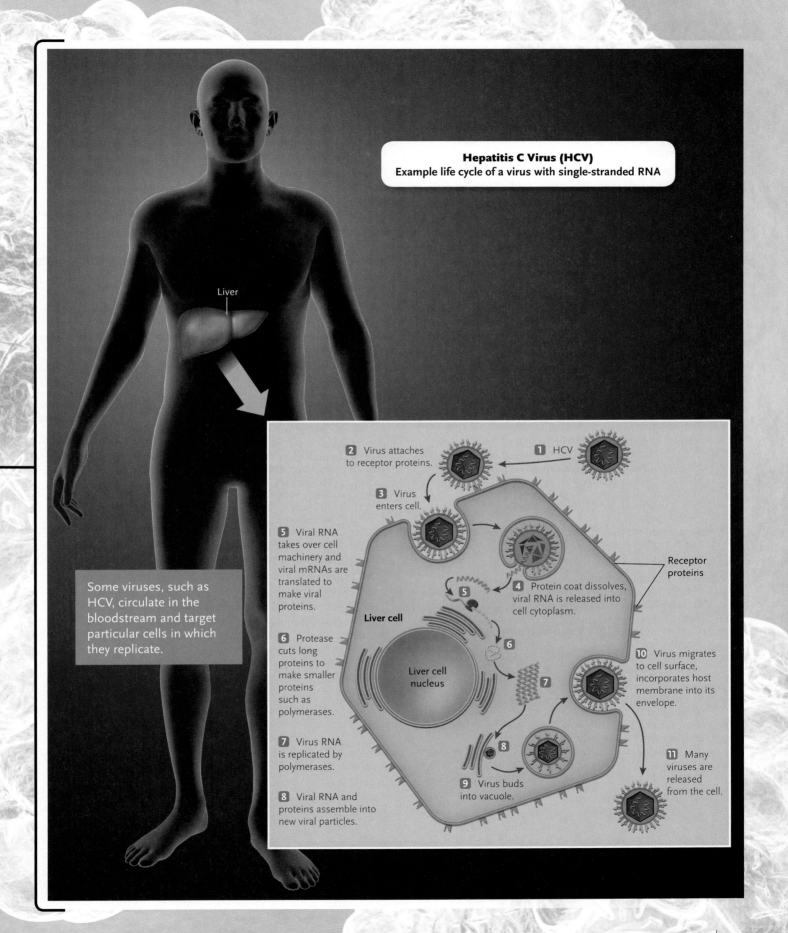

Hepatitis C Virus (HCV)
Example life cycle of a virus with single-stranded RNA

Liver

Some viruses, such as HCV, circulate in the bloodstream and target particular cells in which they replicate.

2 Virus attaches to receptor proteins.

1 HCV

3 Virus enters cell.

5 Viral RNA takes over cell machinery and viral mRNAs are translated to make viral proteins.

4 Protein coat dissolves, viral RNA is released into cell cytoplasm.

Receptor proteins

Liver cell

6 Protease cuts long proteins to make smaller proteins such as polymerases.

Liver cell nucleus

10 Virus migrates to cell surface, incorporates host membrane into its envelope.

7 Virus RNA is replicated by polymerases.

8 Viral RNA and proteins assemble into new viral particles.

9 Virus buds into vacuole.

11 Many viruses are released from the cell.

SELF-TEST QUESTIONS

Recall/Understand

1. Which of these statements best defines a virus?
   a. a naked fragment of nucleic acid
   b. a disease-causing group of proteins
   c. an entity composed of proteins and nucleic acids
   d. an entity composed of proteins, nucleic acids, and ribosomes

2. Viruses form a capsid around their nucleic acid core. What is this capsid composed of?
   a. protein
   b. lipoprotein
   c. glycoprotein
   d. polysaccharides

3. Which of the following is synthesized by reverse transcriptase?
   a. RNA from DNA
   b. DNA from RNA
   c. proteins from DNA
   d. proteins from RNA

4. Which of these statements best describes viroids?
   a. the smallest type of virus
   b. small infectious pieces of DNA
   c. small infectious pieces of RNA
   d. infectious pieces of DNA wrapped in a protein coat

5. Which of these statements best describes temperate phages?
   a. They cannot lyse host cells.
   b. They turn their host cell into a prophage.
   c. They integrate their DNA into the host cell's chromosomes.
   d. They break down the host cell's chromosomes when their DNA enters the cell.

6. Which one of these characteristics applies to prions?
   a. They can be transmitted only from animals to humans.
   b. The diseases they cause progress very rapidly.
   c. They have an amino acid sequence different from the normal protein.
   d. They reproduce by misfolding normal proteins.

Apply/Analyze

7. Which of these statements applies to viral envelopes?
   a. They contain glycoproteins of viral origin.
   b. They are located between the virus's capsid and its nucleic acid.
   c. They are composed of a lipid bilayer derived from the viral membrane.
   d. They are composed of peptidoglycan, the same material as bacterial cell walls.

8. What happens when a bacteriophage enters the lysogenic stage?
   a. The bacteriophage enters the host cell and kills it immediately.
   b. The bacteriophage enters the host cell, picks up host DNA, and leaves the cell unharmed.
   c. The bacteriophage merges with the host cell's plasma membrane, forming an envelope, and then exits the cell.
   d. The bacteriophage's DNA integrates into the host cell's genome.

9. Which of these characteristics applies to both animal viruses and bacterial viruses?
   a. They commonly have envelopes.
   b. Only their nucleic acid enters the host cell.
   c. They have a capsid divided into a head and a tail.
   d. They bind to specific receptors on the host cell.

10. Which of the following characteristics distinguishes plant viruses from animal viruses?
    a. Plant viruses are easily curable.
    b. Plant viruses are covered by a membrane envelope.
    c. Plant viruses lack the ability to actively infect a host cell.
    d. Plant viruses lack the ability to replicate their RNA genome.

Create/Evaluate

11. Suppose that your friend has chickenpox. Which of the following you might conclude?
    a. She was infected with *Flavivirus* during her recent trip to Africa.
    b. She was infected with *Flavivirus*, which she contacted after being in contact with livestock.
    c. She was infected with varicella-zoster virus, and her immune system will prevent the onset of shingles later in her life.
    d. She was infected with varicella-zoster virus, which might later in her lifetime also give her shingles.

12. You recently travelled to a tropical island and, upon your return, you start feeling fatigued, nauseated, and have a loss of appetite. You feel some abdominal pain on your right side beneath your lower ribs and you notice your stool is clay-coloured. Which of the following is the most likely reason for your condition?
    a. You contracted hepatitis B, caused by a virus from Papovaviridae viral family.
    b. You contracted hepatitis B, caused by a virus from Picornaviridae viral family.
    c. You contracted hepatitis A, caused by a virus from Picornaviridae viral family.
    d. You contracted hepatitis A, caused by a virus from Papovaviridae viral family.

13. Explain why it is typically difficult to treat and prevent viral infections.

14. Describe the cycle of a virulent phage.

15. Compare the lytic cycle with the lysogenic cycle.

Chapter Roadmap

Bacteria and Archaea

Prokaryotes look simple; they are unicellular and lack nuclei, mitochondria, and any other membrane-bound organelle. Yet, they can be found in almost every habitat, including those so inhospitable that no eukaryote could survive.

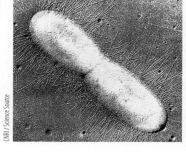

CNRI / Science Source

From Chapter 2

From Chapter 4

From Chapter 5

From Chapter 12

23.1 The Full Extent of the Diversity of Bacteria and Archaea Is Unknown
Prokaryotes cannot be cultured easily, and habitats are difficult to access.

Hans Reichenbach, Gesellschaft für Biotechnologische Forschung, Braunschweig, Germany

23.2 Prokaryotic Structure and Function
Archaea and bacteria show great diversity in their modes of obtaining energy and carbon. They share two modes with eukaryotic organisms (chemoheterotrophy and photoautotrophy), but two other modes are unique to prokaryotic organisms: chemoautotrophs obtain energy by oxidizing inorganic substrates and use carbon dioxide as their carbon source, and photoheterotrophs use light as a source of energy and obtain their carbon from organic molecules.

23.3 The Domain Bacteria
Bacteria are divided into more than a dozen evolutionary branches, including Gram-negative proteobacteria, Gram-negative green bacteria, cyanobacteria, Gram-positive bacteria, spirochetes, and chlamydias.

To Chapter 25

To Chapter 26

23.4 The Domain Archaea
Archaea include the Euryarchaeota (methanogens, extreme halophiles, and some extreme thermophiles); the Crenarchaeota (most of the extreme thermophiles, but also some psychrophiles and mesophiles); and the Korarchaeota (known only from DNA samples).

The bacterium *Salmonella* serotype *Typhi*

Bacteria and Archaea

23

Why it matters . . . Who are you? What makes you "you"? Would you feel less like "you" if you knew that most of the cells in your body weren't human cells at all? The bacterial cells on and in our bodies outnumber our cells by 10 to 1. And given that, as Princeton University scientist Bonnie Bassler points out, the average person has about 30 000 human genes but more than 3 million bacterial genes, we are, at most, 1% human! But these bacteria aren't alien invaders; many of them are crucial for making us unique individuals. There are about a hundred trillion bacteria of hundreds (or thousands) of different species lining your large intestine. When you were born, your gut was sterile, but immediately after birth, your intestines started to be colonized; the exact composition of these "pioneers" depends on where you were born and whether you were breastfed, among other factors. The early colonists were essential for the normal development of your gut as an infant. And throughout your life, your gut bacteria have continued to help you in many ways: they help digest your food, synthesize vitamin K, and produce antimicrobial factors to protect you from pathogens. Recent research has revealed that the diversity of your gut bacteria plays a role in your odds of developing metabolic diseases and becoming obese, and may even be involved in your mental health.

◗ CONCEPT FIX The idea that all bacteria cause disease is a major misconception; nothing could be farther from the truth. In addition to the benefits discussed above, most known bacteria and members of the other group of prokaryotic organisms, archaea, play a crucial role in ecosystems, recycling nutrients and breaking down compounds that no other organisms can. Others carry out reactions important in food production, in industry (e.g., production of pharmaceutical products), and in **bioremediation** of polluted sites. ⬡

In this chapter, we first look at the structure and function of prokaryotic organisms, emphasizing the features that differentiate them from other organisms, and conclude with a look at the diversity of these fascinating organisms.

23.1 The Full Extent of the Diversity of Bacteria and Archaea Is Unknown

While reading this chapter, keep in mind that everything we know so far about bacteria and archaea is based on a tiny fraction of the total number of species. We have isolated and identified only about 6000 species, which may be as low as 1% of the total number. We know almost nothing about the prokaryotic organisms of entire habitats, such as the oceans, which make up 70% of Earth's surface. Why have we identified so few, and why are we not even sure how many prokaryotic organisms there might be? In the past, we identified and classified bacteria and archaea based on external features (e.g., cell wall structure) and physiological differences, which meant that we had to be able to grow the organisms in culture. We have learned a great deal about the biology of some bacteria and archaea, but have been unable to learn much about the majority of prokaryotic organisms, since they cannot be grown in culture (e.g., those that require extreme physicochemical conditions). Recently, molecular techniques have been developed that allow us to isolate and clone DNA from an environment and then analyze gene sequences; this means that we can now identify and characterize bacteria and archaea without having to culture them. This approach, known as **metagenomics**, enables us to investigate the diversity of prokaryotic organisms in a wide range of environments. However, our understanding of the full extent of microbial diversity faces other challenges, such as the fact that many environments (e.g., the deep ocean and Earth's crust) are remote and thus very difficult and/or costly to sample.

23.1a Prokaryotic Organisms Make Up Two of the Three Domains of Life

Two of the three domains of living organisms, **Archaea** and **Bacteria**, consist of prokaryotic organisms (the third domain, **Eukarya**, includes all eukaryotes). Bacteria are the prokaryotic organisms most familiar to us, including those responsible for diseases of humans and other animals, as well as those that we rely on for production of cheese, yogurt, chocolate, and other foods. Archaea are not as well known, as they were discovered only about 40 years ago. As you will see in this chapter, archaea share some cellular features with eukaryotes and some with bacteria but have still other features that are unique. Many of the archaea live under very extreme conditions that no other organisms, including bacteria, can survive.

23.2 Prokaryotic Structure and Function

We begin our survey by examining prokaryotic cellular structures, modes of reproduction, and how prokaryotes obtain energy and nutrients.

In general, prokaryotic organisms are the smallest cells in the world that lack a distinct nucleus and other organelles (**Figure 23.1**). Few species are more than 1 to 2 μm long (although the longest is 600 μm long, which is larger than some eukaryotes!); 500–1000 such cells would fit side by side across the dot on this letter "i." Despite the small size of bacteria and archaea, they dominate life on Earth; current estimates of total prokaryotic diversity are in the billions of species, and their total collective mass, their **biomass**, on Earth exceeds that of animals and may be greater than that of all plant life. Prokaryotic organisms colonize every niche on Earth that supports life, and even occur deep in Earth's crust. They also colonize other organisms; for example, huge numbers of bacteria inhabit the surfaces and cavities of a healthy human body, including the skin, mouth and nasal passages, and large intestine. As mentioned in *Why It Matters*, collectively, the bacteria in and on your body outnumber all the other cells in your body. It is not surprising that the diversity of bacteria and archaea should be so much greater than that of eukaryotes because, for about 3 billion years, they were the only forms of life on Earth and so had time to diversify and expand into every habitat on Earth before the first eukaryotes appeared on the scene (see Chapter 2).

23.2a Prokaryotic Cells Appear Simple in Structure Compared with Eukaryotic Cells

Three cell shapes are common among prokaryotes: spiral, spherical (or **coccoid**; *coccus* = berry), and cylindrical (known as **rods**). However, some archaea have square cells (**Figure 23.2**).

At first glance, a typical prokaryotic cell seems much simpler than a eukaryotic cell (**Figure 23.3**): images taken with standard electron microscopy typically reveal little more than a cell wall and plasma membrane surrounding cytoplasm that has DNA concentrated in one region and ribosomes scattered throughout. The chromosome is not contained in a membrane-

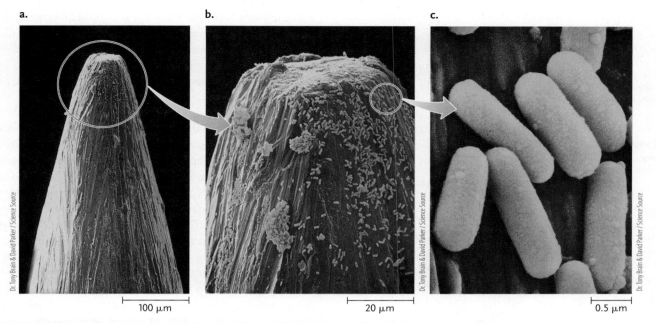

a.

b.

c.

100 μm   20 μm   0.5 μm

Dr. Tony Brain & David Parker / Science Source

FIGURE 23.1 *Bacillus* **bacteria on the point of a pin.** Cells magnified **(a)** 70 times, **(b)** 350 times, and **(c)** 14 000 times.

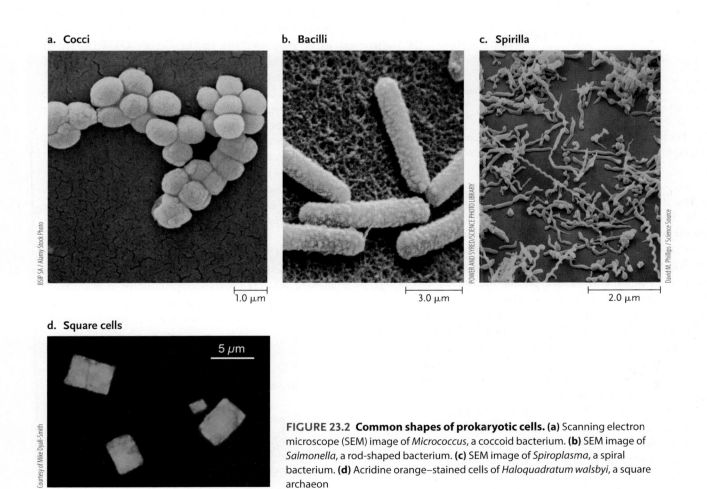

a. Cocci

b. Bacilli

c. Spirilla

1.0 μm   3.0 μm   2.0 μm

BSIP SA / Alamy Stock Photo

POWER AND SYRED/SCIENCE PHOTO LIBRARY

David M. Phillips / Science Source

d. Square cells

5 μm

Courtesy of Mike Dyall-Smith

FIGURE 23.2 Common shapes of prokaryotic cells. (a) Scanning electron microscope (SEM) image of *Micrococcus*, a coccoid bacterium. **(b)** SEM image of *Salmonella*, a rod-shaped bacterium. **(c)** SEM image of *Spiroplasma*, a spiral bacterium. **(d)** Acridine orange–stained cells of *Haloquadratum walsbyi*, a square archaeon

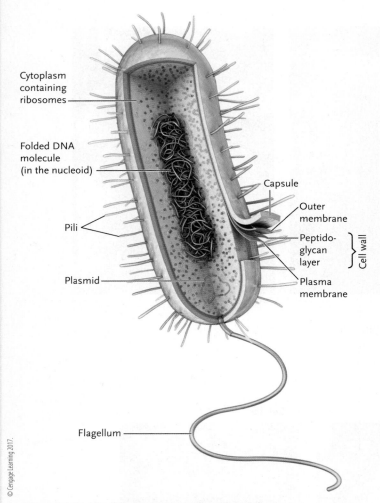

Cytoplasm containing ribosomes

Folded DNA molecule (in the nucleoid)

Pili

Plasmid

Flagellum

Capsule

Outer membrane

Peptido-glycan layer

Cell wall

Plasma membrane

© Cengage Learning 2017.

FIGURE 23.3 The structure of a bacterial cell. The high concentration of ribosomes gives the cytoplasm a granular appearance.

compartment, a proton-motive force could be generated across the membrane, generating ATP. Van Niftrik and her colleagues found that the membrane around this compartment does contain ATP synthase, supporting the above hypothesis. Thus, it appears that some prokaryotic cells have organelles with specialized functions.

INTERNAL STRUCTURES The genome of most prokaryotic cells consists of a single, circular DNA molecule, although some, such as the causative agent of Lyme disease (*Borrelia burgdorferi*), have a linear chromosome. Many prokaryotic cells also contain small circles of DNA called **plasmids (Figure 23.4)**, which generally contain genes for nonessential but beneficial functions such as antibiotic resistance. Plasmids replicate independently of the cell's chromosome and can be transferred from one bacterium to another, resulting in genetic recombination **(Figure 23.5)**. This makes it possible for genes for antibiotic resistance to be readily shared among prokaryotic cells, even among cells of different species. This *horizontal gene transfer* allows antibiotic resistance and other traits to spread very quickly. Horizontal gene transfer also occurs when bacterial cells take up DNA from their environment (e.g., from other cells that have lysed) or when viruses transfer DNA from one bacterium to another (see Chapter 22). Evidence indicates that a virus transferred toxin-encoding genes from *Shigella dysenteriae* (which causes bloody diarrhea) to *E. coli*, resulting in the deadly O157:H7 strain responsible for serious illness or even death in people eating beef and other food contaminated with this bacterium.

Like eukaryotic cells, prokaryotic cells contain ribosomes. Bacterial ribosomes are smaller than eukaryotic ribosomes but carry out protein synthesis by essentially the same mechanisms as those of eukaryotes (see Chapter 12). Archaeal ribosomes resemble those of bacteria in size but differ in structure; protein synthesis in Archaea is a combination of bacterial and eukaryotic processes, with some unique archaeal features. As a result, antibiotics that stop bacterial infections by targeting ribosome activity do not interfere with archaeal protein synthesis.

PROKARYOTIC CELL WALLS Most prokaryotic cells have a cell wall that lies outside their plasma membrane and protects the cell from lysing if subjected to hypotonic conditions or exposed to membrane-disrupting compounds such as detergents. The primary component of bacterial cell walls is **peptidoglycan**,

bound nucleus but is packed into an area of the cell called the **nucleoid**. Prokaryotic cells have no membranous cytoplasmic organelles equivalent to the endoplasmic reticulum (ER) or Golgi complex of eukaryotic cells (see Chapter 2). With few exceptions, the reactions carried out by organelles in eukaryotes are distributed between the plasma membrane and the cytoplasm of prokaryotic cells; this means that macromolecules such as proteins are very concentrated in the cytoplasm of these cells, making the cytoplasm quite viscous. This evident simplicity of prokaryotic cells led people to regard these cells as featureless and disorganized. New microscopic techniques reveal that prokaryotic cells do have a cytoskeleton, not homologous to that of a eukaryote but serving some of the same functions. In fact, recent research carried out by Laura van Niftrik, of the Netherlands, and her colleagues has identified a prokaryotic organelle! Certain bacteria that obtain energy by oxidizing ammonia have an internal, membrane-bound compartment where ammonia oxidation occurs. It was hypothesized that, as ammonia oxidation proceeds inside this

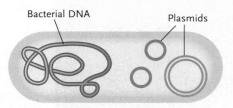

Bacterial DNA

Plasmids

FIGURE 23.4 Plasmids inside a prokaryotic cell

FIGURE 23.5 **Experimental Research**

Genetic Recombination in Bacteria

Question: Does genetic recombination occur in bacteria?

Experiment: To answer the question, Lederberg and Tatum used two mutant strains of *E. coli*: Mutant strain 1's genotype was *bio⁻ met⁻ leu⁺ thr⁺ thi⁺*, where the "1" means a normal allele and the "2" means a mutant allele. This strain required biotin and methionine to grow. Mutant strain 2's genotype was *bio⁺ met⁺ leu⁻ thr⁻ thi⁻*; it required leucine, threonine, and thiamine to grow.

Lederberg and Tatum plated about 100 million cells of a mixture of the two mutant strains on minimal medium, which lacked any of the nutrients the strains needed for growth. As controls, they also plated large numbers of the two mutant strains individually on minimal medium.

Results: No colonies grew on the control plates, meaning that the mutant alleles in the strains had not mutated back to normal alleles. However, for the mixture of mutant strain 1 and mutant strain 2, several hundred colonies grew on the minimal medium.

Conclusion: To grow on minimal medium, the bacteria must have been able to make biotin, methionine, leucine, threonine, and thiamine; meaning that they had the genotype *bio⁺ met⁺ leu⁺ thr⁺ thi⁺*. Lederberg and Tatum concluded that the colonies on the plate must have resulted from genetic recombination between mutant strains 1 and 2.

© Cengage Learning 2017. Based on J. Lederberg and E. Tatum. 1946. Gene recombination in *Escherichia coli*. *Nature* 158:558.

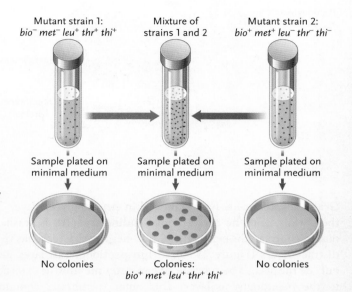

a polymer of sugars and amino acids that forms linear chains. Peptide cross-linkages between the chains give the cell wall great strength and rigidity. The antibiotic penicillin prevents the formation of these cross-linkages, resulting in a weak cell wall that is easily ruptured, killing the cell **(Figure 23.6)**.

Bacteria can be divided into two broad groups, Gram-positive and Gram-negative cells, based on their reaction to the **Gram stain procedure** traditionally used as the first step in identifying an unknown bacterium. Cells are first stained with crystal violet and then treated with iodine, which forms a complex with crystal violet. The cells are then rinsed with ethanol and counterstained with safranin. Some cells retain the crystal violet–iodine complex and thus appear purple when viewed under the microscope; these are termed Gram-positive cells. In other bacteria, ethanol washes the crystal violet–iodine complex out of the cells, which are colourless until counterstained with safranin; these Gram-negative cells appear pink under the microscope. The differential response to staining is related to differences in cell wall structure: **Gram-positive** bacteria have cell walls composed almost entirely of a single, relatively thick layer of peptidoglycan **(Figure 23.7a)**. This thick peptidoglycan layer retains the crystal violet–iodine complex inside the cell.

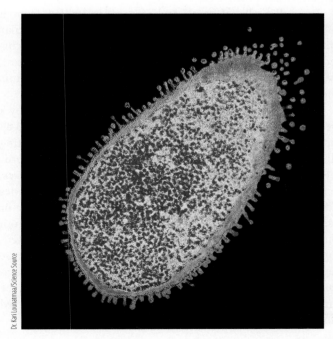

Dr. Kari Lounatmaa/Science Source

FIGURE 23.6 Image showing degradation of the cell wall following antibiotic treatment. The cell will eventually lyse, killing the bacterium.

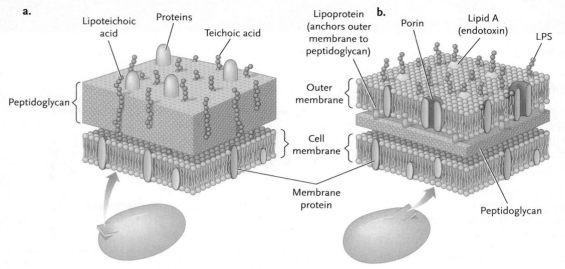

a.

Lipoteichoic acid

Proteins

Teichoic acid

Peptidoglycan

Cell membrane

b.

Lipoprotein (anchors outer membrane to peptidoglycan)

Porin

Lipid A (endotoxin)

LPS

Outer membrane

Membrane protein

Peptidoglycan

FIGURE 23.7 Cell wall structure in Gram-positive and Gram-negative bacteria. (a) The thick cell wall in Gram-positive bacteria. (b) The thin cell wall of Gram-negative bacteria has a thin peptidoglycan layer and outer membrane with lipopolysaccharides (LPSs). The uppermost part of LPS is the O antigen, a carbohydrate chain that elicits an antibody response in vertebrates exposed to Gram-negative bacteria such as *E. coli* O157:H7. More information on the toxic effects of lipid A, which embeds LPSs in the outer membrane, is provided in Section 23.2e.

Gram-negative cells have only a thin peptidoglycan layer in their walls, and the crystal violet–iodine complex is washed out. In contrast, the cell wall of Gram-negative bacteria has two distinct layers (Figure 23.7b): a thin peptidoglycan layer just outside the plasma membrane and an **outer membrane** external to the peptidoglycan layer. This outer membrane contains **lipopolysaccharides (LPSs)** and thus is very different from the plasma membrane. The outer membrane protects Gram-negative bacteria from potentially harmful substances in the environment; for example, it inhibits entry of penicillin. Therefore, Gram-negative cells are less sensitive to penicillin than are Gram-positive cells.

The cell walls of some archaea are assembled from a molecule related to peptidoglycan but with different molecular components and bonding structure. Others have walls assembled from proteins or polysaccharides instead of peptidoglycan. Archaea have a variable response to the Gram stain, so this procedure is not useful in identifying archaea.

The cell wall of many prokaryotic cells is surrounded by a layer of polysaccharides known as a **capsule (Figure 23.8)**. Capsules are "sticky" and play important roles in protecting cells in different environments. Cells with capsules are protected to some extent from desiccation, extreme temperatures, bacterial viruses, and harmful molecules such as antibiotics and antibodies. In many pathogenic bacteria, the presence or absence of the protective capsule differentiates infective from non-infective forms. For example, normal *Streptococcus pneumoniae* bacteria are capsulated and virulent, causing severe pneumonia in humans and other mammals. Mutant *S. pneumoniae* without capsules are nonvirulent and can easily be eliminated by the body's immune system when they are injected into mice or other animals.

FLAGELLA AND PILI Many prokaryotic cells can move actively through liquids and even through films of liquid on a surface, most commonly via **flagella** (singular, *flagellum* = whip) extending from the cell wall (see Figure 23.3). As outlined in

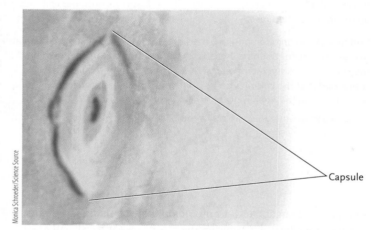

Capsule

Monica Schroeder/Science Source

FIGURE 23.8 Capsules surrounding the cell wall of *Rhizobium*, a Gram-negative soil bacterium

Chapter 2, prokaryotic flagella are very different from eukaryotic flagella in both structure and pattern of movement. Prokaryotic flagella are made of rigid helical proteins, some of which act as a motor rotating the flagellum much like the propeller of a boat. Archaeal flagella are superficially similar to bacterial flagella and carry out the same function, but the two types of flagella contain different components, develop differently, and are coded for by different genes.

Some prokaryotic cells have rigid shafts of protein called **pili** (singular, *pilus* = hair) extending from their cell walls **(Figure 23.9a)**, which enable them to adhere to or move along a surface. One type, called a *sex pilus*, not only allows bacterial cells to adhere to each other but also acts as a conduit for the transfer of plasmids from one cell to another (Figure 23.9b). Other types of pili enable bacteria to bind to animal cells. The bacterium that causes gonorrhea (*Neisseria gonorrhoeae*) uses pili to adhere to cells of the throat, eye, urogenital tract, or rectum in humans. In 2005, it was discovered that the pili of

growth as one cell becomes two, two become four, and so on. Some prokaryotic cells can double their population size in only 20 minutes, and will even begin a second round of cell division before the first round is complete. Thus, one cell, given ideal conditions, can produce millions of cells in only a few hours.

These short generation times, combined with the small genomes (roughly one-thousandth the size of the genome of an average eukaryote), mean that prokaryotic organisms have higher mutation rates than do eukaryotic organisms. This translates to roughly 1000 times as many mutations per gene, per unit time, per individual as for eukaryotes. Genetic variability in prokaryotic populations, the basis for their diversity, derives largely from mutation and to a lesser degree from horizontal gene transfer (see Chapter 8). Further, the typically much larger populations of prokaryotic organisms compared with eukaryotes contribute to the much greater genetic variability in bacteria and archaea. In short, prokaryotic organisms have an enormous capacity to adapt, which is one reason for their evolutionary success.

As we have seen, the success of bacteria is beneficial to humans in many ways but can also be detrimental to us when dealing with successful pathogenic bacteria. In the next section, we investigate how some bacteria cause disease and how they are able to resist treatment with antibiotics.

23.2e Pathogenic Bacteria Cause Diseases by Different Mechanisms

Some bacteria produce **exotoxins**, toxic proteins that leak from or are secreted from the bacterium. For example, botulism food poisoning is caused by the exotoxin of the Gram-positive bacterium *Clostridium botulinum*, which grows in poorly preserved foods **(Figure 23.12)**. The botulism exotoxin, botulin, is one of the most poisonous substances known: just a few nanograms can cause severe illness. What makes botulin so toxic? It produces muscle paralysis that can be fatal if the muscles that control breathing are affected. Interestingly, botulin is used under the brand name Botox for the cosmetic removal of wrinkles and in the treatment of migraine headaches and some other medical conditions. Exotoxins produced by certain strains of *Streptococcus pyogenes* have "superantigen properties" (i.e., overactivation of the immune system) that cause necrotizing fasciitis ("flesh-eating disease"). In 1994, Lucien Bouchard, who was then premier of Quebec, lost a leg to this disease.

Other bacteria cause disease through **endotoxins**. Endotoxins are the lipid A portion of the LPS molecule of the

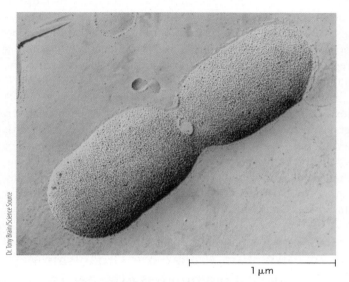

Dr. Tony Brain/Science Source

|—————— 1 μm ——————|

FIGURE 23.11 *E. coli* **cell dividing by binary fission.** Note that a septum is forming between the two daughter cells.

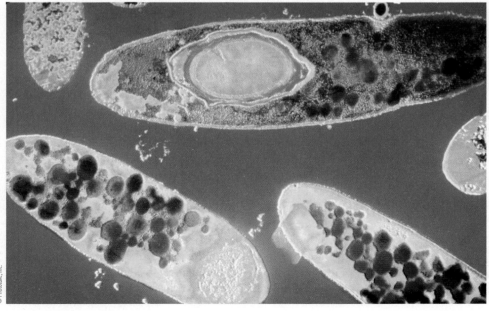

© Photatake, Inc.

FIGURE 23.12 The bacterium *Clostridium butyricum*, one of the *Clostridium* species that produces the toxin botulin (colourized TEM). The large stained structure in the cells is a spore (a survival structure).

outer membrane of all Gram-negative bacteria, such as *E. coli*, *Salmonella*, and *Shigella*. When a Gram-negative cell lyses, the LPSs of the outer membrane are released; exposure to a specific component of this layer, known as *lipid A*, causes endotoxic shock. When Gram-negative bacteria enter the bloodstream, endotoxin overstimulates the host's immune system, triggering inflammation and an often lethal immune response. Endotoxins have different effects, depending on the bacterial species and the site of infection.

23.2f Pathogenic Bacteria Commonly Develop Resistance to Antibiotics

An **antibiotic** is a natural or synthetic substance that kills or inhibits the growth of bacteria and other microorganisms. Prokaryotic organisms and fungi produce these substances naturally as defensive molecules, and we have also developed ways to synthesize several types of antibiotics. Different types of antibiotics have different modes of action: for example, streptomycins, produced by soil bacteria, block protein synthesis in their targets, whereas penicillins, produced by fungi, target the peptide cross-linkages in peptidoglycan, as described above.

How are bacteria able to block the actions of antibiotics? There are various mechanisms by which bacteria resist antibiotics **(Figure 23.13)**. For example, some bacteria are able to pump antibiotics out of the cell using membrane-bound pumps. They can also produce molecules that bind to the antibiotic or enzymes that break down the antibiotic, rendering it ineffective against its target. Alternatively, a simple mutation can result in a change in the structure of the antibiotic's target, so that the antibiotic cannot bind to it. Finally, bacteria can develop new enzymes or pathways that are not inhibited by the antibiotic.

Bacteria can develop resistance through mutations, but they can also acquire resistance via horizontal gene transfer (e.g., plasmid transfer). Taking antibiotics routinely in mild doses or failing to complete a prescribed dosage may contribute to the spread of resistance by selecting strains that can survive in the presence of the drug; there is, however, current research that puts this widely held belief into question. Antibacterial agents that may promote resistance are commonly included in such commercial products as soaps, detergents, and deodorants. Resistance is a form of evolutionary adaptation: antibiotics alter the bacterium's environment, conferring a reproductive advantage on those strains best adapted to the altered conditions.

The development of resistant strains has made tuberculosis, cholera, typhoid (photo at beginning of chapter) fever, gonorrhea, and other bacterial diseases difficult to treat with antibiotics. For example, as recently as 1988, drug-resistant strains of *Streptococcus pneumoniae*, which causes pneumonia, meningitis, and middle-ear infections, were practically unknown. Now, resistant strains of *S. pneumoniae* are common and increasingly difficult to treat.

23.2g In Nature, Prokaryotic Organisms May Live in Communities Attached to a Surface

Often, researchers grow bacteria and archaea as individuals in pure cultures. We have learned a lot about prokaryotic organisms from these pure cultures but, in nature, prokaryotic organisms rarely exist as individuals or as pure cultures. Instead, bacteria and archaea live in communities where they interact in a variety of ways. One important type of community is known as a **biofilm**, which consists of a complex aggregation of microorganisms attached to a surface and surrounded by a film of polymers **(Figure 23.14)**. Life in a biofilm offers several benefits: organisms can adhere to hospitable surfaces, they can live on the products of other cells, conditions within the biofilm promote gene transfer between species, and the biofilm protects cells from harmful environmental conditions. Biofilms form on any surface with sufficient water and nutrients. For example, you're probably familiar with how slippery rocks in a stream can be when you try to step from one to the next; the slipperiness is due to biofilms on the rocks. Dental plaque is also a biofilm; if this biofilm spreads below the gum line, it causes inflammation of the gums (gingivitis). Regular removal of plaque by brushing, flossing, and dental checkups helps prevent gingivitis.

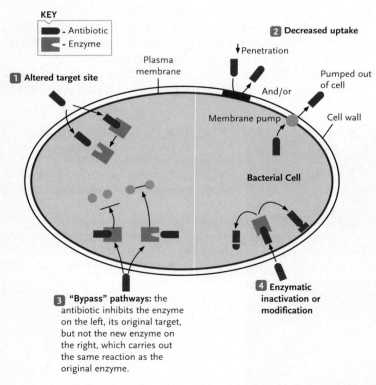

KEY
- Antibiotic
- Enzyme

1 Altered target site

Plasma membrane

2 Decreased uptake

↓Penetration

And/or

Pumped out of cell

Membrane pump

Cell wall

Bacterial Cell

3 "Bypass" pathways: the antibiotic inhibits the enzyme on the left, its original target, but not the new enzyme on the right, which carries out the same reaction as the original enzyme.

4 Enzymatic inactivation or modification

FIGURE 23.13 Four major mechanisms of antibiotic resistance. See the text for further explanation of each mechanism.

Biofilms have practical consequences for humans, both beneficial and detrimental. On the beneficial side, for example, are the health effects each of us gains from the bacteria that live in biofilms in our gastrointestinal tracts. We also make use of biofilms in commercial applications: biofilms on solid supports are used in sewage treatment plants to process organic matter before the water is discharged, and they can be effective in bioremediating toxic organic molecules contaminating ground-water. But biofilms can also be harmful to human health. Biofilms adhere to many kinds of surgical equipment and supplies, including catheters, pacemakers, and artificial joints. Even if the bacteria colonizing these devices are not pathogenic, their presence is obviously not desirable given that these devices should be sterile. Given their nature, the presence of any Gram-negative bacteria is a concern. As well, many heterotrophic bacteria will become opportunistic pathogens, given the right conditions. Biofilm infections are difficult to treat because

bacteria in a biofilm are up to 1000 times as resistant to antibiotics as are the same bacteria in liquid cultures. For example, outbreaks of the disease caused by *E. coli* O157:H7 have been caused by biofilms that are very difficult to wash off spinach, lettuce, and other produce.

How does a biofilm form? Imagine a surface, such as a rock in a stream, over which water is flowing **(Figure 23.15)**. Due to the nutrients in the water, the surface rapidly becomes coated with polymeric organic molecules, such as polysaccharides or glycoproteins. Once the surface is conditioned with organic molecules, free cells attach in a reversible manner in a matter of seconds (see Figure 23.15, step 1). If the cells remain attached, the association may become irreversible (step 2), at which point the cells grow and divide on the surface (step 3). Next, the physiology of the cells changes and they begin to secrete *extracellular polymeric substances* (EPSs), slimy, gluelike substances similar to the molecules found in bacterial capsules. EPS extends between cells in the mixture, forming a matrix that binds cells to each other and anchors the complex to the surface, thereby establishing the biofilm (step 4). The slime layer entraps a variety of materials such as dead cells and insoluble minerals. The physiological change accompanying the formation of a biofilm results from marked changes in a prokaryotic organism's gene expression pattern—in effect, the prokaryotic cells in a biofilm become very different organisms. Over time, other organisms are attracted to and join the biofilm; depending on the environment, these may include other bacterial species, algae, fungi, or protozoa producing diverse microbial communities. Prokaryotic organisms in a biofilm communicate with each other via **quorum sensing**; in fact, this communication is part of biofilm formation: it allows cells to start secreting EPS when a high enough cell density is reached.

Much remains to be learned about how organisms form and interact within a biofilm, and how changes in gene expression during the transition are regulated.

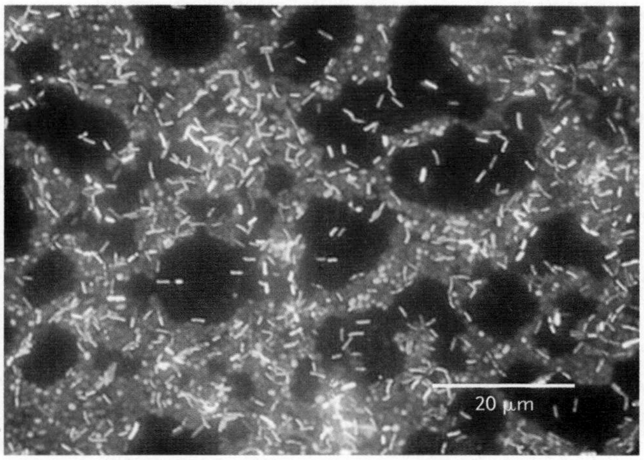

Emerg Infect Dis © 2002 Centers for Disease Control and Prevention (CDC)

FIGURE 23.14 Biofilm grown on a stainless steel surface

20 µm

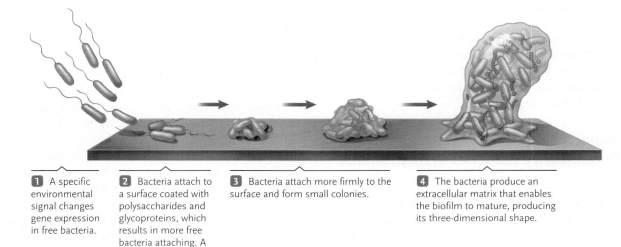

1 A specific environmental signal changes gene expression in free bacteria.

2 Bacteria attach to a surface coated with polysaccharides and glycoproteins, which results in more free bacteria attaching. A monolayer forms.

3 Bacteria attach more firmly to the surface and form small colonies.

4 The bacteria produce an extracellular matrix that enables the biofilm to mature, producing its three-dimensional shape.

© Cengage Learning 2017.

FIGURE 23.15 Steps in the formation of a biofilm

In the next two sections, we describe the major groups of prokaryotic organisms.

STUDY BREAK QUESTIONS

1. What features differentiate a prokaryotic cell from a eukaryotic cell? What features do both kinds of cells have?
2. How does the presence of a capsule affect the ability of the human body to mount an immune response to those bacteria?
3. How is a pilus similar to a flagellum? How is it different?
4. How does the amount of peptidoglycan in a bacterial cell wall relate to its Gram-stain reaction?
5. What is the difference between a chemoheterotroph and a photoautotroph?
6. What is the difference between an obligate anaerobe and a facultative anaerobe?
7. What is the difference between nitrogen fixation and nitrification? Why are nitrogen-fixing prokaryotic organisms important?
8. What is binary fission?
9. What is the difference between an endotoxin and an exotoxin? Explain how they differ with respect to how they cause disease.
10. Explain four mechanisms by which bacteria protect themselves from antibiotics.
11. What is a biofilm? Give an example of a biofilm that is beneficial to humans and another that is harmful. What advantages do prokaryotic cells in a biofilm gain?
12. What is quorum sensing?

23.3 The Domain Bacteria

As for other organisms, classification of bacteria and archaeans has been revolutionized by molecular techniques that allow researchers to compare nucleic acid and protein sequences as tests of evolutionary relatedness. Ribosomal RNA (rRNA) sequences have been most widely used in the evolutionary studies of prokaryotic organisms. Researchers have identified several evolutionary branches within each prokaryotic domain (**Figure 23.16**), but these classifications will likely change in the future when full genomic sequences can be compared. We discuss the major groups of the domain Bacteria, which is much better characterized than the domain Archaea, in this section, and those of the domain Archaea in the next section.

23.3a Molecular Studies Reveal Numerous Evolutionary Branches in the Domain Bacteria

Bacteria as a domain is much better characterized than Archaea; sequencing studies reveal that bacteria have several distinct and separate evolutionary branches. We restrict our discussion to five particularly important groups: proteobacteria, cyanobacteria, Gram-positive bacteria, spirochetes, and chlamydias (see Figure 23.16).

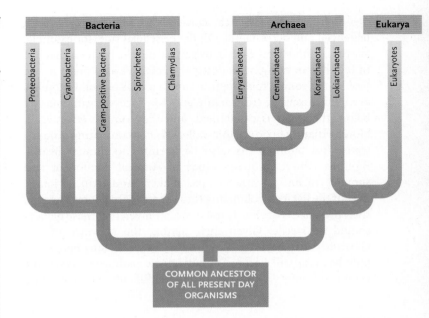

FIGURE 23.16 An abbreviated phylogenetic tree of Bacteria and Archaea

PROTEOBACTERIA: THE PURPLE BACTERIA AND THEIR RELATIVES This highly diverse group of Gram-negative bacteria likely evolved from a purple photosynthetic ancestor. Their purple colour comes from their photosynthetic pigment, a type of chlorophyll distinct from that of plants. Many present-day species are either photoautotrophs (the purple sulfur bacteria) or photoheterotrophs (the purple non-sulfur bacteria); both groups carry out a type of photosynthesis that does not use water as an electron donor and does not release oxygen as a by-product.

Other present-day proteobacteria are **chemoheterotrophs** that are thought to have evolved as an evolutionary branch following the loss of photosynthetic capabilities in an early proteobacterium. The evolutionary ancestors of mitochondria are considered likely to have been ancient non-photosynthetic proteobacteria.

Among the chemoheterotrophs classified with the proteobacteria are *E. coli*; plant pathogenic bacteria; and bacteria that cause human diseases such as bubonic plague, gonorrhea, various forms of gastroenteritis and dysentery, as well as *Helicobacter pylori*, a cause of gastric ulcers. The proteobacteria also include both free-living and symbiotic nitrogen-fixing bacteria.

Myxobacteria are an unusual group of non-photosynthetic proteobacteria that form colonies held together by the slime they produce. Enzymes secreted by the colonies digest "prey"—other bacteria, primarily—that become stuck in the slime. When environmental conditions become unfavourable, as when soil nutrients or water are depleted, myxobacteria form a fruiting body, a differentiated multicellular stage large enough to be visible to the naked eye (**Figure 23.17**). The fruiting body contains clusters of spores that are dispersed to form new

FIGURE 23.17 **The fruiting body of *Chondromyces crocatus*, a myxobacterium.** Cells of this species collect together to form the fruiting body.

100 μm

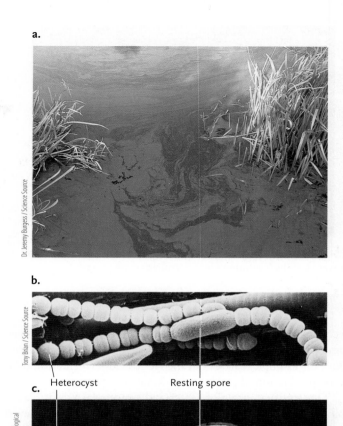

a.

b.

Heterocyst   Resting spore

c.

6 μm

FIGURE 23.18 **Cyanobacteria. (a)** A population of cyanobacteria covering the surface of a pond. **(b)** and **(c)** Chains of cyanobacterial cells. Some cells in the chains form spores. The heterocyst is a specialized cell that fixes nitrogen.

colonies when the fruiting body bursts. Quorum sensing is involved in spore formation.

CYANOBACTERIA These Gram-negative photoautotrophs are blue-green in colour **(Figure 23.18)** and carry out photosynthesis by the same pathways and using the same chlorophyll as eukaryotic algae and plants. Like plants and algae, they release oxygen as a by-product of photosynthesis.

The direct ancestors of present-day cyanobacteria were the first organisms to use the water-splitting reactions of photosynthesis. As such, they were critical to the accumulation of oxygen in the atmosphere, which allowed the evolutionary development of aerobic organisms. Chloroplasts probably evolved from early cyanobacteria that were incorporated into the cytoplasm of primitive eukaryotes, which eventually gave rise to the algae and higher plants, as discussed in Chapter 26. In addition to releasing oxygen, present-day cyanobacteria help fix nitrogen into organic compounds in aquatic habitats and act as symbiotic partners with fungi in lichens (see Chapter 25).

GRAM-POSITIVE BACTERIA This large group contains many species that live primarily as chemoheterotrophs. Some cause human diseases, including *Bacillus anthracis*, the causal agent of anthrax; *Staphylococcus*, which causes some forms of food poisoning, toxic shock syndrome, pneumonia, and meningitis; and *Streptococcus* **(Figure 23.19)**, which causes strep throat,

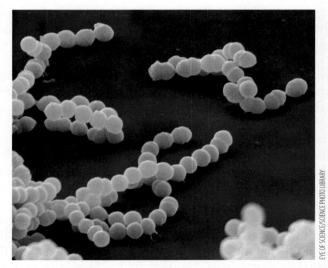

FIGURE 23.19 ***Streptococcus* bacteria forming the long chains of cells typical of many species in this genus**

CHAPTER 23   BACTERIA AND ARCHAEA

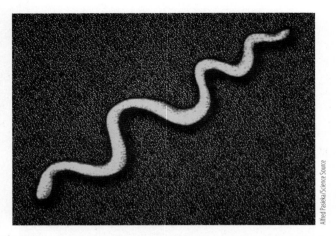

FIGURE 23.20 *Treponema pallidum*, a spirochete bacterium that causes syphilis (scanning electron microscope image)

necrotizing fasciitis, and some forms of pneumonia. However, some Gram-positive bacteria are beneficial to humans: *Lactobacillus*, for example, carries out the lactic acid fermentation used in the production of pickles, sauerkraut, and yogurt.

One unusual group of bacteria, the mycoplasmas, is placed among the Gram-positive bacteria by molecular studies even though they show a Gram-negative staining reaction. This staining reaction results because they are naked cells that secondarily lost their cell walls in evolution. Some mycoplasmas, with diameters from 0.1 to 0.2 μm, are the smallest known cells.

SPIROCHETES These organisms have helically spiralled flagella embedded in their cytoplasm, causing the cells to move in a twisting, corkscrew pattern **(Figure 23.20)**. Their corkscrew movements enable them to move in viscous environments such as mud and sewage, where they are common. Some spirochetes are harmless inhabitants of the human mouth; another species, *Treponema pallidum*, is the cause of syphilis. Termites have symbiotic spirochetes in their intestines that enable them to digest cellulose.

CHLAMYDIAS These bacteria are unusual because, although they are Gram-negative and have cell walls with an outer membrane, they lack peptidoglycan. All the known chlamydias are intracellular parasites that cause various diseases in animals. One bacterium of this group, *Chlamydia trachomatis*, is responsible for one of the most common sexually transmitted infections of the urinary and reproductive tracts of humans and also causes trachoma, an infection of the cornea that is the leading cause of blindness in humans.

In this section, you have seen that bacteria thrive in nearly every habitat on Earth. However, some members of the second prokaryotic domain, the Archaea, the subject of the next section, live in habitats that are too forbidding even for bacteria.

STUDY BREAK QUESTIONS

1. What methodologies have been used to classify prokaryotic organisms?
2. What were the likely characteristics of the evolutionary ancestor of present-day proteobacteria?
3. How does photosynthesis in photosynthetic proteobacteria differ from photosynthesis in cyanobacteria?

23.4 The Domain Archaea

The first Archaea were isolated from extreme environments, such as hot springs, hydrothermal vents on the ocean floor, and salt lakes **(Figure 23.21)**. For that reason, these prokaryotes were called *extremophiles* (organisms that live in extreme environments). Subsequently, archaea have also been found living in less extreme environments.

Archaea share some cellular features with eukaryotes and some with bacteria, and have other features that are unique **(Table 23.2)**.

a.

b.

FIGURE 23.21 **Typically extreme archaeal habitats. (a)** Highly saline water in Great Salt Lake, Utah, coloured red–purple by archaeans. **(b)** Hot, sulfur-rich water in Emerald Pool, Yellowstone National Park, brightly coloured by the oxidative activity of archaea, which convert H2S to elemental sulfur

TABLE 23.2	Characteristics of the Bacteria, Archaea, and Eukarya		
Characteristic	Bacteria	Archaea*	Eukarya
DNA arrangement	Single; circular in most, but some linear and/or multiple	Single, circular	Multiple linear molecules
Chromosomal proteins	Prokaryotic histonelike proteins	Five eukaryotic histones	Five eukaryotic histones
Genes arranged in operons	Yes	Yes	No
Nuclear envelope	No	No	Yes
Mitochondria	No	No	Yes
Chloroplasts	No	No	Yes
Peptidoglycan in cell wall	Present	Absent; some have pseudopeptidoglycan	Absent
Membrane lipids	Unbranched; linked by ester linkages	Branched; linked by ether linkage; may have polar heads at both ends	Unbranched; linked by ester linkages
RNA polymerase	Limited variations	Multiple types	Multiple types
Ribosomal proteins	Prokaryotic	Some prokaryotic, some eukaryotic	Eukaryotic
First amino acid placed in proteins	Formylmethionine	Methionine	Methionine
Aminoacyl–tRNA synthetases	Prokaryotic	Eukaryotic	Eukaryotic
Cell division proteins	Prokaryotic	Prokaryotic	Eukaryotic
Proteins of energy metabolism	Prokaryotic	Prokaryotic	Eukaryotic

* Given that very few Archaea have been identified or cultured, the information in this table is based on an extremely small data set.

23.4a Unique Characteristics of Archaea

Among their unique characteristics are certain features of their plasma membranes and cell walls. The lipid molecules in archaeal plasma membranes are unlike those in the plasma membranes of the majority of bacteria: there is a different linkage between glycerol and the hydrophobic tails, and the tails are isoprenes rather than fatty acids (see Chapter 4). Also, some lipids have polar head groups at both ends. Why would such seemingly minor differences be significant? These unique lipids are more resistant to disruption, making the plasma membranes better suited to extreme environments. Similarly, the unique cell walls of archaea are more resistant to extremes than those of bacteria; some archaea can even survive being boiled in strong detergents!

Many archaea are chemoautotrophs, whereas others are chemoheterotrophs. Interestingly, no known member of the Archaea has been shown to be pathogenic.

23.4b Molecular Studies Reveal Three Evolutionary Branches in the Archaea

The phylogeny of Archaea is poorly developed relative to Bacteria and in quite a state of flux because a tremendous number of archaea have not been cultured, meaning that we have only metagenomic data for most of these organisms. Based on differences in rRNA sequence data, the domain Archaea is divided into three groups (see Figure 23.16). Two major groups, the **Euryarchaeota** and the **Crenarchaeota,** contain archaea that have been cultured in the laboratory. The third and fourth groups, the **Korarchaeota** and **Lokiarchaeota**, have been recognized solely on the basis of DNA taken from environmental samples.

EURYARCHAEOTA These organisms are found in various extreme environments. They include methanogens, extreme halophiles, and some extreme thermophiles, as described below.

Methanogens (methane generators) live in low-oxygen environments **(Figure 23.22)** and represent about one-half of all known species of Archaea. Methanogens are obligate anaerobes that live in the anoxic (oxygen-lacking) sediments of swamps, lakes, marshes, and sewage works, as well as in more moderate environments, such as the rumen of cattle and sheep, the large intestine of dogs and humans, and the hindgut of insects such as termites and cockroaches. Methanogens generate energy by converting various substrates such as carbon dioxide and hydrogen gas or acetate into methane gas, which is released into the atmosphere.

Halophiles are salt-loving organisms. Extreme halophilic Archaea live in highly saline environments such as the Dead Sea and on foods preserved by salting. They require a minimum NaCl concentration of about 1.5 M (about 9% solution) to

FIGURE 23.22 A colony of the methanogenic archaeon *Methanosarcina*, which lives in the sulfurous, waterlogged soils of marshes and swamps

survive and can live in a fully saturated solution (5.5 M, or 32%). Most are aerobic chemoheterotrophs, which obtain energy from sugars, alcohols, and amino acids using pathways similar to those of bacteria. Many extreme halophiles use light as a secondary energy source, supplementing the oxidations that are their primary source of energy.

Extreme thermophiles live in extremely hot environments such as hot springs and ocean floor hydrothermal vents. Their optimal temperature range for growth is 70°C to 95°C, close to the boiling point of water. By comparison, no eukaryotic organism is known to live at a temperature higher than 60°C. Thermophilic archaea are important commercially. For example, they are very important in biotechnological applications as sources of enzymes that function under extreme physicochemical conditions (e.g., high temperature, high salinity).

Some extreme thermophiles are members of the Euryarchaeota, but most belong to the **Crenarchaeota**, the next group that we discuss.

CRENARCHAEOTA This group includes most of the extreme thermophiles, which have a higher optimal temperature range than those belonging to the Euryarchaeota. For example, the most thermophilic member of this group, *Pyrobolus*, dies below 90°C, grows optimally at 106°C, and can survive an hour of autoclaving at 121°C! (Autoclaving is a process using sustained high-pressured steam to sterilize items.) *Pyrobolus* lives in ocean floor hydrothermal vents, where the pressure creates water temperatures greater than the boiling point of water on Earth's surface.

Also in this group are **psychrophiles** ("cold loving"), organisms that grow optimally in cold temperatures in the range from –10°C to –20°C. These organisms are found mostly in the Antarctic and Arctic oceans, which are frozen most of the year, and in the intense cold at ocean depths.

Mesophilic members of the Crenarchaeota make up a large part of plankton found in cool marine waters, where they are food sources for other marine organisms.

KORARCHAEOTA This group has been recognized solely on the basis of DNA samples obtained from marine and terrestrial hydrothermal environments. To date, no members of this group have been isolated and cultivated in the lab, and nothing is known about their physiology. Molecular data indicate that they are the oldest archaeal lineage.

LOKIARCHAEOTA A research team in Sweden has made a very exciting discovery while sampling deep marine sediments near hydrothermal vents along the Arctic Mid-Ocean Ridge. Spang's research group identified archaean DNA that shares a number of genes with eukarya (lineage that includes all nucleated organisms) that had previously been thought to be unique to eukarya. It was called *Lokiarchaeota* based on the name of the vent field from which it was discovered, Loki's Castle. The strong support for Lokiarchaeota and Eukarya being sister groups has phylogenetic and taxonomic implications. Lokiarchaeota is clearly archaean, so in Figure 23.16 the archaea grouping is paraphyletic. To resolve this, the three-domain system will need to be modified into either a two-domain or a four-domain system. There is anticipation that a more immediate ancestor to the eukaryotes will soon be discovered.

In this chapter, we have focused on bacteria and archaea, whose metabolic diversity and environmental range and ecological importance belie their structural simplicity. In the next five chapters, we investigate more structurally complex organisms: the eukaryotic protists, fungi, plants, and animals.

STUDY BREAK QUESTIONS

1. What distinguishes members of the domain Archaea from members of the domains Bacteria and Eukarya?
2. How does a methanogen obtain energy? In which group or groups of Archaea are methanogens found?
3. Where do extreme halophilic Archaea live? How do they obtain energy? In which group or groups of Archaea are the extreme halophiles found?
4. What are extreme thermophiles and psychrophiles?

Summary Illustration

Bacteria and Archaea represent two of the three domains of living organisms. These prokaryotic organisms lack a nucleus and membrane-bound organelles. Common structural features include a genome that consists of a single, circular DNA molecule; ribosomes; a cell wall; flagella; and pilli. Although structurally simple, prokaryotes have the greatest metabolic diversity of all organisms.

Prokaryote Structure

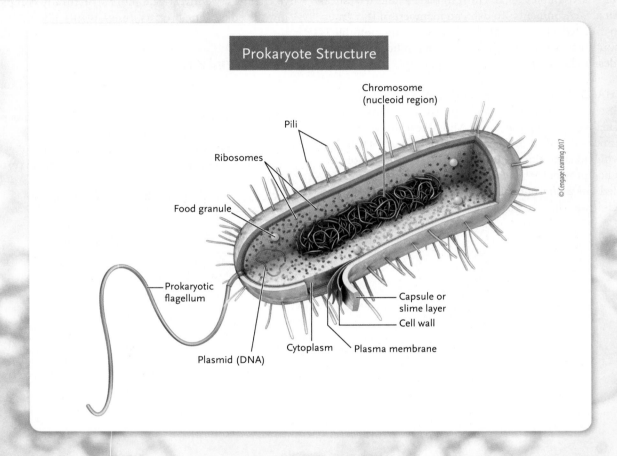

Chromosome (nucleoid region)

Pili

Ribosomes

Food granule

Prokaryotic flagellum

Plasmid (DNA)

Cytoplasm

Plasma membrane

Capsule or slime layer

Cell wall

© Cengage Learning 2017

Prokaryote Shapes

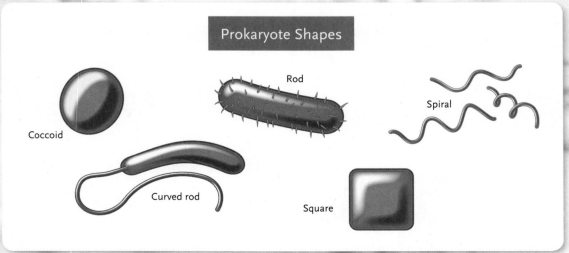

Coccoid

Rod

Spiral

Curved rod

Square

There are four modes of nutrition, based on sources of energy and carbon. Energy transformation can occur aerobically, anaerobically, or by fermentation.

Chemoheterotrophs obtain carbon from organic molecules and energy from oxidizing organic molecules.

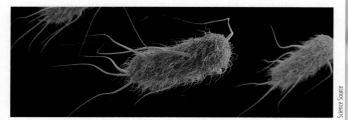

Science Source

Escherichia coli is common in the lower intestine of humans.

Photoautotrophs obtain carbon from carbon dioxide and energy from light.

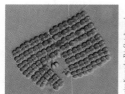

Janina Kownacka. This file is licensed under the Creative Commons Attribution-NoDerivs 3.0 Unported license, https://creativecommons.org/licenses/by-nd/3.0/

Merismopedia elegans, a cyanobacterium, forms rectangular colonies in a mucilaginous matrix.

Chemoautotrophs obtain carbon from carbon dioxide and energy from oxidizing inorganic molecules.

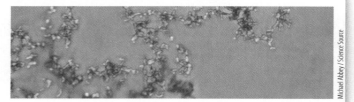

Michael Abbey / Science Source

Thiobacillus thioparus, a sulphur-oxidizing bacterium, breaks down stone.

Photoheterotrophs obtain carbon from organic molecules and energy from light.

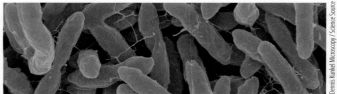

Dennis Kunkel Microscopy / Science Source

Roseobacters make up about 25% of bacterial biomass in coastal marine waters.

Nitrogen fixation is an important way prokaryotes contribute to the nitrogen cycle. They are the only organisms that convert atmospheric nitrogen into a usable form. Symbioses with plants and other organisms develop around this ability.

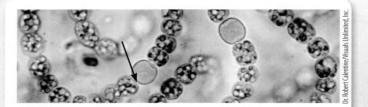

Dr. Robert Calentine/Visuals Unlimited, Inc.

Nostoc, a filamentous cyanobacterium, has cells called *heterocysts* (indicated with arrow) in which nitrogen is fixed.

ChWeiss / Shutterstock.com

Azolla is a fern that houses *Nostoc* in cavities in its leaves and, in turn, receives fixed nitrogen from the cyanobacterium.

Prokaryotes—Two Groups

Bacteria

Bacteria sit at the bottom of food webs as they are important decomposers and nitrogen fixers. They also live in the gut of many organisms, including humans, to break down food. Bacteria are the sources of a number of antibiotics as well as flavouring (the sour in sourdough, the tang in yogurt).

Archaea

Archaea differ from bacteria in cell membrane and cell wall composition. Many archaea are extremophiles, living where other organisms cannot (low oxygen, high salinity, extreme temperatures).

SELF-TEST QUESTIONS

Recall/Understand

1. Which of the following structures is found in prokaryotic cells?
   a. cellulosic cell walls
   b. ribosomes
   c. mitochondria
   d. nuclear membrane

2. Which of these statements best describes Archaea?
   a. Their cell walls contain peptidoglycan.
   b. Most are pathogens.
   c. Many are extremophiles.
   d. They have no traits in common with eukaryotic cells.

3. Which of these statements applies to plasmids?
   a. They are pieces of RNA taken up from the environment by prokaryotic cells.
   b. They are small circular pieces of RNA outside a cell's chromosomes.
   c. They are small circular pieces of non-chromosomal DNA.
   d. They are pieces of DNA taken up from the environment by prokaryotic cells.

4. Which of these processes converts ammonium (NH_4^+) to nitrate (NO_3)?
   a. nitrogen fixation
   b. ammonification
   c. nitrification
   d. denitrification

5. Which of these groups of bacteria are oxygen-producing photoautotrophs?
   a. spirochetes
   b. cyanobacteria
   c. proteobacteria
   d. green bacteria

6. Which statement refers to chlamydias?
   a. They lack peptidoglycan and are Gram-positive.
   b. They lack peptidoglycan and are Gram-negative.
   c. They are not pathogenic and have an outer membrane in the cell wall.
   d. They are pathogenic and lack an outer membrane in the cell wall.

Apply/Analyze

7. You have isolated an unknown bacterium that produces a toxin. You are trying to determine if it is an endotoxin or an exotoxin. Which of the following features would be associated with the toxin if it were an endotoxin?
   a. It would be secreted from the cell.
   b. It would be a part of the cell wall.
   c. It would be a part of the plasma membrane.
   d. It would be produced by an archaeon.

8. A bacterium that oxidizes nitrite as its only energy source was found deep in a cave. How would you classify this bacterium based on its carbon and energy source?
   a. as a chemolithotroph
   b. as a chemoheterotroph
   c. as a photoautotroph
   d. as a photoheterotroph

9. Which of these lists shows the order of steps by which prokaryotic cells form a biofilm?
   a. cells grow and divide; the cells' physiology changes; cells attach to a surface that is covered in organic polymers; cells secrete extracellular polymers that "glue" the cells to the surface and to each other
   b. the cells' physiology changes; cells grow and divide; cells secrete extracellular polymers that "glue" the cells to the surface and to each other; cells attach to a surface that is covered in organic polymers
   c. cells secrete extracellular polymers that "glue" the cells to the surface and to each other; cells attach to a surface that is covered in organic polymers; cells grow and divide; the cells' physiology changes
   d. cells attach to a surface that is covered in organic polymers; cells grow and divide; the cells' physiology changes; cells secrete extracellular polymers that "glue" the cells to the surface and to each other

Create/Evaluate

10. You are growing a facultative anaerobic archaeon in culture under two conditions: one culture is in anaerobic conditions, and the other is in aerobic conditions. How would you expect the growth of the cells to compare between the two cultures?
    a. Growth would be greater in the culture in aerobic conditions.
    b. Growth would be greater in the culture in anaerobic conditions.
    c. Growth would be great in both conditions.
    d. Growth would be negligible in both conditions.

11. Suppose that you found an unknown microorganism and you want to determine if it is a bacterium or an archaeon. Which of these features would help you conclude that it is an archaeon?
    a. the absence of peptidoglycan in the cell wall and the presence of branched membrane lipids
    b. the presence of peptidoglycan in the cell wall and the absence of branched membrane lipids
    c. the presence of circular DNA and the presence of a nuclear envelope
    d. the presence of linear DNA and the absence of a nuclear envelope

12. Suppose that you want to have a Botox treatment. What is the link between the Botox treatment and bacteria?
    a. Botox is a mixture of cyanobacteria, which can capture light and produce lots of oxygen, which is good for our skin.
    b. Botox is the brand name for botulin, an exotoxin produced by a bacterium that causes botulism.
    c. Botox is made of endotoxin, which is produced by a Gram-negative bacterium and causes food poisoning.
    d. Botox is made of cultured bacteria that have been dried and turned into a powder that is used for treatment.

13. Distinguish between different prokaryotes based on their relationship with oxygen.

14. Contrast Gram-positive and Gram-negative bacteria.

15. Contrast the habitats of different extremophiles.

Chapter Roadmap

Protists

Protists live in a number of different habitats, including aquatic and terrestrial, as well as within other eukaryotes.

From Chapter 2

24.1 The Vast Majority of Eukaryotes Are Protists

Most eukaryotes are protists, with the exception of land plants, animals, and fungi.

From Chapter 5

From Chapter 6

24.2 Characteristics of Protists

Protists have a diversity of morphologies: they can be single-celled, colonial, or multicellular organisms.

From Chapter 12

From Chapter 21

24.3 Protists' Diversity Is Reflected in Their Metabolism, Reproduction, Structure, and Habitat

Protists have a range of life styles: autotrophs, heterotrophs, mixotrophs, saprotrophs, mutualistic symbionts, and parasites. This diversity is reflected in their structure, reproduction, and habitat.

From Chapter 21

24.4 The Eukaryotic Supergroups and Their Key Protist Lineages

In this chapter we classify the eukaryotes into five supergroups, most of which are exclusively protists: Excavata, Chromalveolata, Rhizaria, Unikonta (includes fungi and animals), and Plantae (includes land plants).

To Chapter 25

To Chapter 26

To Chapter 27

24.5 Some Protist Lineages Arose from Primary Endosymbiosis and Others from Secondary Endosymbiosis

Chloroplasts arose via endosymbiosis events: 1. primary endosymbiosis: a eukaryotic cell engulfed a cyanobacterium; 2. secondary endosymbiosis: a non-photosynthetic eukaryote engulfed a photosynthetic eukaryote.

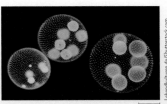

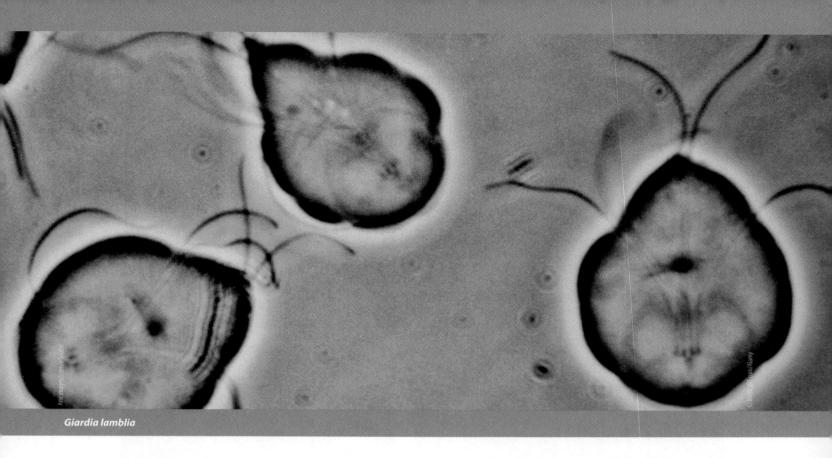

Giardia lamblia

Protists

24

Why it matters . . . You are on a backpacking trip in your favourite wilderness area on a hot and sunny day. You pause to take a drink of water from your water bottle but discover it is almost empty. You are very thirsty, so you refill your bottle from a nearby stream. The water is clear and cold and looks clean, and, besides, you're out in the middle of nowhere, so it must be safe to drink, right? You continue on the hike and feel fine. But a few days after you get home, you don't feel so great: you have abdominal pain, cramps, and diarrhea. Your doctor says that you have giardiasis, or "beaver fever," caused by *Giardia lamblia*, the most common intestinal parasite in North America (it is very prevalent in water bodies formed by beaver dams). What is *Giardia*, and how does it make you sick?

Giardia is a single-celled eukaryote that can exist in two forms: a dormant cyst and a motile feeding stage. When you drank from that seemingly clean stream, you ingested some cysts. The cysts can survive for months, so it is important to boil or filter water when you are out hiking or camping. In your small intestine, the cysts released the motile feeding stage, **trophozoites** (*troph* = food; *zoon* = animal), shown in the photographs above. Using their multiple flagella, the trophozoites, with their numerous flagella were able to swim about in your intestinal space and attach themselves to the epithelial cells of your intestine. Infection with *Giardia* can become chronic, causing inflammation and reduction of the absorptive capacity of the gut. Why doesn't your immune system detect the presence of *Giardia* and get rid of the parasite? *Giardia* can alter the proteins on its surface that your immune system relies on to recognize an invader, so it escapes recognition; thus, *Giardia* infections can be persistent or recur.

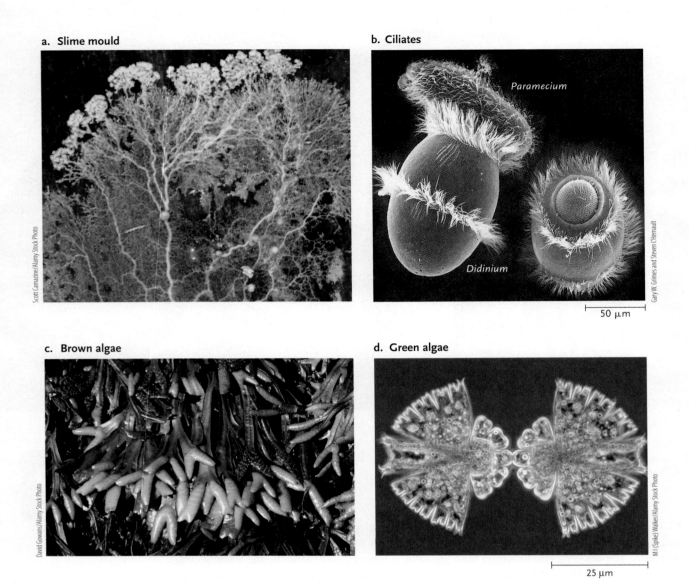

a. Slime mould

b. Ciliates

Paramecium

Didinium

50 μm

c. Brown algae

d. Green algae

25 μm

FIGURE 24.1 A sampling of protist diversity. (a) *Physarum*, a plasmodial slime mould. **(b)** *Didinium*, a ciliate, consuming another ciliate, *Paramecium*. **(c)** *Fucus gardneri* (common rockweed), a brown alga growing in rocky intertidal zones. **(d)** *Micrasterias*, a single-celled green alga, here shown dividing in two

Giardia is a **protist** (Greek; *protistos* = the very first). Protists are a very heterogeneous collection of about 200 000 eukaryotes. Most are unicellular and microscopic, but some are large, multicellular organisms. Like their most ancient ancestors, almost all these eukaryotic species are aquatic. **Figure 24.1** shows a number of protists, illustrating their great diversity.

24.1 The Vast Majority of Eukaryotes Are Protists

The diversity among protists makes it very difficult to define what a protist is. The simplest definition, and the one that we will use in this book, is that a protist is any eukaryotic organism that is not an animal, a land plant, or a fungus. Earlier classifications grouped all these "other" eukaryotes together in one kingdom, Protista. This oversimplified classification reflected our earlier understanding of eukaryote biology, which traditionally has been based almost entirely on the study of animals, land plants, and fungi. But these groups are only three branches of the very large and diverse tree of living eukaryotes (**Figure 24.2**). This evolutionary tree is based on molecular data, which are considered the most informative data for determining evolutionary relationships. The tree shows that eukaryotic organisms are divided into approximately five "supergroups," a taxonomic level above that of Kingdom. As you can see by looking at Figure 24.2, the vast majority of eukaryotes are not land plants, animals, or fungi but protists. The tree shown here represents our current understanding of the relationships among eukaryotic organisms, which is actively changing as

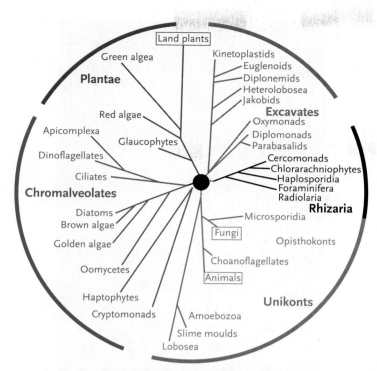

FIGURE 24.2 Major lineages of protists within the supergroups of eukaryotic organisms. The current evolutionary tree for eukaryotes divides these organisms among approximately five supergroups: Excavata, Unikonta (including animals and fungi), Plantae (including land plants and their algal relatives), Chromalveolata, and Rhizaria. Selected lineages of protists in each supergroup are discussed in this chapter. Branch lengths are arbitrary.

Source: Eugene V Koonin, 2010 and direct communication with Patrick Keeling (UBC)

researchers continue to investigate the evolutionary history of eukaryotes. The actual number of supergroups is still being debated, with some researchers dividing eukaryotes into additional supergroups to those shown in Figure 24.2. You may notice that the "root" of the tree—the last eukaryote common ancestor (LECA)—is not identified. The identity of this ancestral group is a major mystery that researchers are actively working to unravel.

The first eukaryotes likely evolved about 1.5–2 billion years ago (bya) ago. While we don't fully understand how they evolved, we know that endosymbiosis played an important role in the process. Eukaryotes contain mitochondria (although some have very reduced versions of this organelle) and many also contain chloroplasts. As outlined in Chapter 2, mitochondria and chloroplasts are the descendants of free-living prokaryotes that, over evolutionary time, became organelles. All mitochondria are thought to have arisen from a single endosymbiotic event, but the history of chloroplasts is more complex. We will return to the evolution of chloroplasts at the end of this chapter, once you have had a chance to become familiar with the various groups of protists.

In this chapter, we will start with an overview of features of protists and then focus on key protist lineages in each of the

eukaryotic supergroups. In this way, you will gain an understanding of how diverse protists are morphologically, functionally, and ecologically. As you read about the various groups of protists, think about how they differ from animals and plants, and how learning about these "other" eukaryotes changes your understanding of eukaryote biology. Protists are sometimes called the "rule-breakers" of the eukaryotic world: many of the general rules, or "facts," that we think we know about eukaryotic organisms are revealed as not being generally true at all once protists are considered, forcing us to rethink what is "typical" or "normal" in eukaryote biology.

STUDY BREAK QUESTION

1. By what process did eukaryotes such as protists acquire mitochondria and chloroplasts?

24.2 Characteristics of Protists

Because protists are eukaryotes, the boundary between them and prokaryotic organisms is clear and obvious. Unlike bacteria and archaea, protists have a membrane-bound nucleus with multiple linear chromosomes. In addition to cytoplasmic organelles, including mitochondria and chloroplasts (in some species), protists have microtubules and microfilaments, which provide motility and cytoskeletal support. As well, they share characteristics of transcription and translation with other eukaryotes.

The phylogenetic relationship between protists and other eukaryotes is more complex (Figure 24.2). Over evolutionary time, the eukaryotic family tree branched out in many directions. Almost all eukaryotic lineages are protists with the exception of three groups: animals, land plants, and fungi, which arose from protist ancestors. Although some protists have features that resemble those of the fungi, plants, or animals, several characteristics are distinctive. In contrast to fungi, most protists are motile or have motile stages in their life cycles, and their cell walls are made of cellulose, not chitin.

How do photosynthesizing protists differ from plants? Unlike plants, many photoautotrophic protists can also live as heterotrophs, and some regularly combine both modes of nutrition. Protists do not retain developing embryos in parental tissue, as plants do, nor do they have highly differentiated structures equivalent to roots, stems, and leaves. Photosynthetic protists are often referred to as *algae*; these protists are generally aquatic and often unicellular and microscopic (although many are multicellular). However, the different groups of algae are not closely related to each other (Figure 24.2), so the term *algae* does not indicate any sort of relatedness among organisms referred to by that term.

How do protists differ from animals? Unlike protists, all animals are multicellular and have features such as an internal digestive tract and complex developmental stages. Protists also lack features that characterize many animals, including nerve cells; highly differentiated structures such as limbs and a heart; and collagen, an extracellular support protein.

STUDY BREAK QUESTION

1. What features distinguish protists from prokaryotic organisms? What features distinguish them from fungi, plants, and animals?

24.3 Protists' Diversity Is Reflected in Their Metabolism, Reproduction, Structure, and Habitat

As you might expect from looking at Figure 24.2, protists are highly diverse in habitat, structure, metabolism, and reproduction.

24.3a Habitat

Protists live in aqueous habitats, including aquatic or moist terrestrial locations, such as oceans, freshwater lakes, ponds, streams, and moist soils, and within host organisms. In bodies of water, small photosynthetic protists collectively make up the **phytoplankton** (*phytos* = plant; *planktos* = drifting), the organisms that capture the energy of sunlight in nearly all aquatic habitats. These phototrophs provide organic substances and oxygen for heterotrophic bacteria, other protists, and the small crustaceans and animal larvae that are the primary constituents of **zooplankton** (*zoe* = life, usually meaning animal life). Although protists are not animals, biologists often include them among the zooplankton. Phytoplankton and larger multicellular protists forming seaweeds collectively account for about half the Earth's total organic matter produced by photosynthesis.

In the moist soils of terrestrial environments, protists play important roles among the detritus feeders that recycle matter from organic back to inorganic form. In their roles in phytoplankton, in zooplankton, and as detritus feeders, protists are enormously important in world ecosystems.

Protists that live in host organisms are **parasites**, obtaining nutrients from the host. Indeed, many of the parasites that have significant effects on human health are protists, causing diseases such as malaria, sleeping sickness, and amoebic dysentery.

24.3b Structure

Most protists are single cells, while others live as **colonies** (**Figure 24.3**) in which individual cells show little or no differentiation and are potentially independent. Within colonies, individuals use cell signalling to cooperate on tasks such as feeding and movement. Some protists are large multicellular organisms; for example, the giant kelp of coastal waters can rival forest trees in size.

FIGURE 24.3 **Colonial protist (*Dinobryon*)**

Many single-celled and colonial protists have complex intracellular structures, some found nowhere else among living organisms (**Figure 24.4**). These unique structures reflect key aspects of the habitats in which protists live. For example, consider a single-celled protist living in a freshwater pond. Its cytoplasm is hypertonic to the water surrounding it, meaning that water flows into the cell by osmosis. How can the protist stop itself from bursting? A specialized cytoplasmic organelle, the **contractile vacuole**, gradually fills with fluid. When this vacuole reaches its maximum size, it moves to the plasma membrane and forcibly contracts, expelling the fluid to the outside through a pore in the membrane.

The cells of some protists are supported by an external cell wall or by an internal or external shell built up from organic or mineral matter; in some, the shell takes on highly elaborate forms. Instead of a cell wall, other protists have a **pellicle**, a layer of supportive protein fibres located inside the cell just under the plasma membrane, providing strength and flexibility (**Figure 24.5**).

At some time during their lives, almost all protists move. Some move by amoeboid motion, in which the cell extends one or more lobes of cytoplasm called **pseudopodia** (*false feet*; see **Figure 24.6**); the rest of the cytoplasm and the nucleus then flow into the pseudopodium, completing the movement. Other protists move by the beating of flagella or cilia. In some protists,

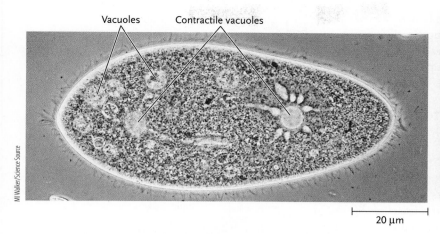

Vacuoles   Contractile vacuoles

20 μm

MI Walker/Science Source

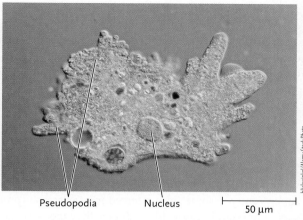

Pseudopodia   Nucleus

50 μm

blickwinkel/Alamy Stock Photo

FIGURE 24.6 *Amoeba proteus* **of the Amoebozoa is perhaps the most familiar protist of all.**

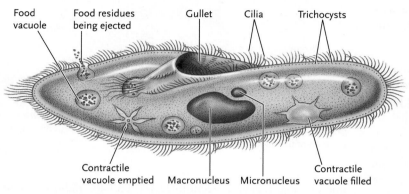

Food vacuole   Food residues being ejected   Gullet   Cilia   Trichocysts

Contractile vacuole emptied   Macronucleus   Micronucleus   Contractile vacuole filled

© Cengage Learning 2017. Based on V. & J. Pearse and M. & R. Buchsbaum, Living Invertebrates, The Boxwood Press, 1987.

FIGURE 24.4 **A ciliate,** *Paramecium,* **showing the cytoplasmic structures typical of many protists**

Source: Redrawn from V. & J. Pearse and M. & R. Buchsbaum, *Living Invertebrates.* The Boxwood Press, 1987.

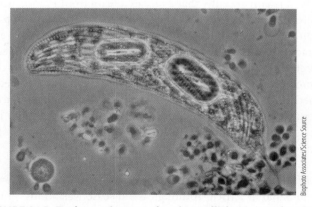

Biophoto Associates/Science Source

FIGURE 24.5 *Euglena spirogyra,* **showing pellicle (strips of protein fibres)**

cilia are arranged in complex patterns, with an equally complex network of microtubules and other cytoskeletal fibres supporting the cilia under the plasma membrane.

Many protists can exist in more than one form, for example, as a motile form and as a nonmotile cyst that can survive unfavourable conditions. This morphological variability allows the species to live in different habitats at different stages in its life.

24.3c Metabolism

Almost all protists are aerobic organisms that live either as heterotrophs—obtaining carbon from organic molecules produced by other organisms—or as photoautotrophs—producing organic molecules for themselves by photosynthesis (see Chapter 6). Some heterotrophic protists obtain organic molecules by engulfing part or all of other organisms (*phagocytosis*) and digesting them internally. Others absorb small organic molecules from their environment by diffusion. Some protists can live as either heterotrophs or autotrophs.

24.3d Reproduction

Reproduction may be asexual, by mitosis, or sexual through meiotic cell division and formation of gametes. In protists that reproduce by both mitosis and meiosis, the two modes of cell division are often combined into a **life cycle** that is highly distinctive among the different protist groups. We do not yet have a complete understanding of the reproductive biology of many protists.

STUDY BREAK QUESTION

1. Define each of the following terms in your own words, and indicate the role that each plays in the life of a protist: *pellicle, pseudopodia, contractile vacuole.*

24.4 The Eukaryotic Supergroups and Their Key Protist Lineages

In this section, we look at the biological features of the major protist lineages in each eukaryote supergroup shown in Figure 24.2. Our focus is the ecological or economic importance of each lineage, the habitats in which you would find these organisms, and key features that differentiate the group from other protists. As you read through the information on each lineage, think about how the structural features of that group relate to its habitat and lifestyle.

24.4a Excavata Are Unicellular, Flagellated Protists, Many of Which Lack Mitochondria

This supergroup takes its name from the hollow (excavated) ventral feeding groove found in most members. Protists of this supergroup are sometimes referred to as *protozoa* (*proto* = first; *zoon* = animal) because, like animals, they ingest their food and move by themselves. We will consider five lineages of Excavates: euglenids, diplonemids, kinetoplastids, diplomonads, and parabasalids.

EUGLENIDS You have probably seen an example of one genus of euglenids, *Euglena*, in your earlier biology classes (**Figure 24.7**), as they are often used to illustrate how some protists have plant-like features (photosynthesis) combined with features that we consider animal-like (movement). Euglenids are important primary producers in freshwater ponds, streams, and lakes, and even some marine habitats. Most are autotrophs that carry out photosynthesis using the same photosynthetic pigments and mechanisms as plants. If light is not available, many of the photosynthetic euglenids can also live as heterotrophs by absorbing organic molecules through the plasma membrane or by engulfing small particles. Organisms that can act as autotrophs and heterotrophs are called **mixotrophs**. Other euglenids lack chloroplasts and live entirely as heterotrophs.

The name *Euglena* roughly translates as "eyeball organism," a reference to the large *eyespot* that is an obvious feature of photosynthetic euglenids (Figure 24.7). The eyespot contains pigment granules in association with a light-sensitive structure and is part of a sensory mechanism that stimulates cells to swim toward moderately bright light or away from intensely bright light so that the organism finds optimal conditions for photosynthetic activity. In addition to an eyespot, euglenids contain numerous organelles, including a contractile vacuole.

Rather than an external cell wall, euglenids have a spirally grooved pellicle formed from strips of transparent protein-rich material underneath the membrane (Figure 24.5). In some euglenids, the strips are arranged in a spiral pattern, allowing the cell to change its shape in a wriggling sort of motion (known as *euglenoid movement*) that allows the cell to change direction. Euglenids can also swim by whiplike movements of flagella that extend from one end of the cell. Most have two flagella: one rudimentary and short, the other long.

DIPLONEMIDS Diplonemids are flagellated unicells that have recently been touted the "most prolific predator known." University of British Columbia's Patrick Keeling, evolutionary

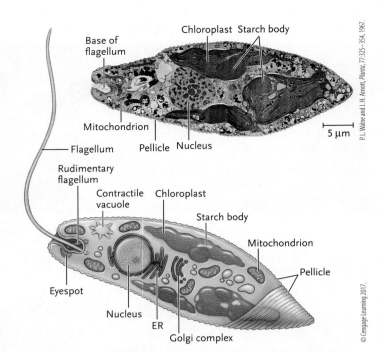

FIGURE 24.7 Body plan and an electron micrograph of *Euglena gracilis*. The plane of section in the electron micrograph has cut off all but the base of the flagellum.

microbiologist, gave a recent interview on CBC radio where he told the fascinating story about how this group of organisms, while likely the most abundant and diverse marine planktonic lineage, have not been given much attention. Their existence was known, but they were considered an evolutionary peculiarity. It is only recently that a research team from France, using different tools, discovered DNA sequences of this group in ocean samples. Dr. Keeling's research group wanted to find and characterize the actual organism. Members of the research team collected samples in the north Pacific Ocean. They not only discovered 10 different species of diplonemids, but they also determined that one of the species is the most abundant marine heterotrophic eukaryote. The abundance of this predator has broad ecological implications as it has a central position in the ocean food web (**Figure 24.8**).

KINETOPLASTIDS Sleeping sickness is a fatal disease endemic to sub-Saharan Africa. Although the disease was almost eradicated about 40 years ago, it has been making a comeback due to wars, the subsequent refugee movement, and damage to health-care systems. Sleeping sickness is caused by various subspecies of *Trypanosoma brucei* (**Figure 24.9**) that are transmitted from one host to another by bites of the tsetse fly. Early symptoms include fever, headaches, rashes, and anemia. Untreated, the disease damages the central nervous system, leading to a sleeplike coma and eventual death. The disease has proved difficult to control because the same trypanosomes infect wild mammals, providing an inexhaustible reservoir for the parasite. Other trypanosomes, also transmitted by insects, cause Chagas disease in

FIGURE 24.8   **Observational Research**

Isolation and Identification of Marine Diplonemids, Potentially the Most Abundant Marine Organism

Hypothesis: Diplonemids, previously known from only a single environmental gene from marine planktonic samples, are predacious unicellular flagellates.

Prediction: Diplonemids play a significant role in the marine ecosystem due to their abundance and diversity; they have been touted as the most prolific predator known.

Method: Samples were taken at different locations in the Pacific Ocean at varying depths. Heterotrophic marine protists were manually isolated, examined microscopically, photographed, and the SSU rRNA (small subunit ribosomal RNA) sequenced.

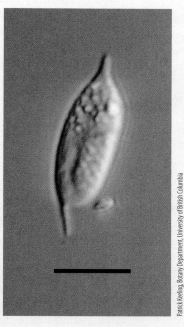

Patrick Keeling, Botany Department, University of British Columbia

Results: Ninety-two colourless flagellates were isolated. Sequence data helped to identify 40 cells, of which 25% were diplonemids; this supports the claim that they are abundant planktonic eukaryotes. Diplonemids are colourless, oblong to elliptical in shape, approximately 20 μm in length, and have two subapical flagella (below or near the tip).

Conclusions: Prior to this research, marine diplonemids were identified through surveys of only a single gene. During this study, 10 representatives were documented, including one of the single-most common heterotrophic marine eukaryotes, which is potentially the principle consumer of other microscopic protists, including primary producers (i.e., algae). They therefore have a central position in the marine food chain, and as such would have a significant role in the oceans' responses to global climate change.

parasites that lack mitochondria and move by means of flagella. Because they lack mitochondria, these organisms are limited to producing ATP via glycolysis (see Chapter 5). Originally, the lack of mitochondria in many Excavata led biologists to consider this group as the most ancient line of protists; however, it now appears that the ancestor of this group did have mitochondria. The nuclei of Excavata that lack mitochondria contain genes derived from mitochondria, and they also have organelles that likely evolved from mitochondria. These Excavata may have lost their mitochondria as an adaptation to the parasitic way of life, in which oxygen is in short supply.

Diplomonad means *double cell*, and these organisms do look like two cells together (see the figure at the beginning of the chapter), with their two apparently identical, functional nuclei and multiple flagella arranged symmetrically around the cell's longitudinal axis. The best-known diplomonad is *Giardia lamblia*, profiled at the beginning of this chapter. Some are free living, but many live in animal intestines; some diplomonads do not cause harm to the host, whereas others, like *Giardia*, live as parasites.

Parabasalids include the sexually transmitted disease trichomoniasis is caused by *Trichomonas vaginalis* (**Figure 24.10a**). The infection is usually symptomless in men, but in women, *T. vaginalis* can cause severe inflammation and irritation of the vagina and vulva. If untreated, trichomoniasis can cause infection of the uterus and fallopian tubes that can result in infertility. Luckily, drugs can easily cure the infection.

Central and South America and leishmaniasis in many tropical countries. Humans with Chagas disease have an enlarged liver and spleen and may experience severe brain and heart damage; leishmaniasis causes skin sores and ulcers, as well as liver and spleen damage.

Like trypanosomes, other kinetoplastids are heterotrophs that live as animal parasites. Kinetoplastid cells are characterized by a single mitochondrion that contains a large DNA-protein deposit called a *kinetoplast* (Figure 24.9). Most kinetoplastids also have a leading and a trailing flagellum, which are used for movement. In some cases, the trailing flagellum is attached to the side of the cell, forming an undulating membrane that allows the organism to glide along or attach to surfaces.

DIPLOMONADS AND PARABASALIDS Like many Excavata, diplomonads and parabasalids are single-celled animal

Parabasalids take their names from cytoplasmic structures associated with the nucleus, *parabasal bodies*; some biologists consider these structures to be the Golgi apparatus of these cells. Parabasalids are also characterized by a sort of fin called an **undulating membrane**, formed by a flagellum buried in a fold of the cytoplasm, in addition to freely beating flagella. The buried flagellum allows parabasalids to move through thick viscous fluids, such as those lining human reproductive tracts.

Other parabasalids (e.g., *Trichonympha*; Figure 24.10b) are symbionts that live in the guts of termites and other wood-eating insects, digesting the cellulose in the wood for their hosts. As if this endosymbiotic relationship were not complex enough, biologists recently discovered that the protists themselves cannot produce the enzymes necessary to break down cellulose but instead rely on bacterial symbionts to do it.

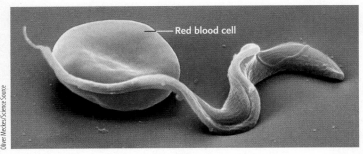

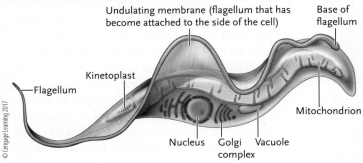

FIGURE 24.9 *Trypanosoma brucei*, the parasitic kinetoplastid that causes African sleeping sickness

24.4b Chromalveolates Have Complex Cytoplasmic Structures and Move via Flagella or Cilia

This group is named for the small, membrane-bound vesicles called *alveoli* (*alvus* = belly) in a layer just under the plasma membrane. The chromalveolates supergroup includes two motile, free-living lineages as well as a motile parasitic group. We will take a closer look at some representative lineages over the next few pages.

CILIATES This group of protists has helped us understand key aspects of eukaryotic cells, such as the existence of telomeres at the ends of eukaryotic chromosomes and the function of telomerase. These protists are examples of model organisms—organisms that are easily manipulated and easily raised in the lab and for which we have abundant data, for example, genome sequences (see *The Purple Pages*). Several protists are ideal model organisms because, even though they are single celled, the complexity of their structures and functions is comparable to that of humans and other animals. One ciliate, *Tetrahymena* (**Figure 24.11**), was the organism in which telomeres and telomerase were discovered; it was also the cell in which the first motor protein was identified, cell cycle control mechanisms were first described, and ribozymes were discovered. The involvement of ciliates with scientific research dates back several centuries: they were among the first organisms observed in the seventeenth century by the pioneering microscopist Anton van Leeuwenhoek.

The ciliates are a large group, with nearly 10 000 known species of primarily single-celled but highly complex heterotrophic organisms that swim by means of cilia (see Figures 24.4 and 24.11). Any sample of pond water or bottom mud contains a wealth of these creatures. Some ciliates live individually, whereas others are colonial. Certain ciliates are animal parasites; others live and reproduce in their hosts as mutually beneficial symbionts. A compartment of the stomach of cattle and other grazing animals contains large numbers of symbiotic ciliates that digest the cellulose in their hosts' plant diet. The host animals then digest the excess ciliates.

Ciliates have many highly developed organelles, including a mouthlike gullet lined with cilia, structures that exude toxins and other defensive materials from the cell surface, contractile vacuoles, and a complex system of food vacuoles. A pellicle reinforces the cell's shape. A complex cytoskeleton anchors the

a. *Trichomonas vaginalis*

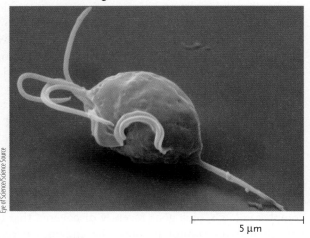

5 μm

b. *Trichonympha*

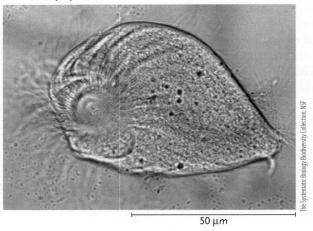

50 μm

FIGURE 24.10 **Examples of parabasalids (Excavata). (a)** A parabasalid, *Trichomonas vaginalis*, that causes a sexually transmitted disease, trichomoniasis. **(b)** *Trichonympha*, a parabasalid that lives in the guts of termites

a. Ciliate

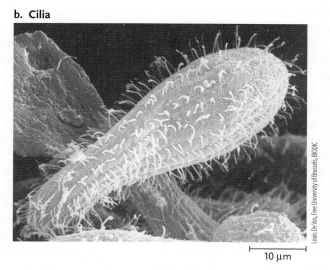

10 μm

Jacek Gaertig, University of Georgia, Athens

b. Cilia

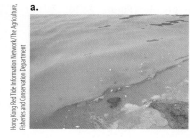

10 μm

Louis De Vos, Free University of Brussels, BIODIC

FIGURE 24.11 *Tetrahymena*, **a ciliate. (a)** Stained with fluorescent dye to show cilia and microtubules. **(b)** SEM image showing cilia

cilia just below the pellicle and coordinates the ciliary beating. The cilia can stop and reverse their beating in synchrony, allowing ciliates to stop, back up, and turn if they encounter negative stimuli.

Ciliates are the only eukaryotes that have two types of nuclei in each cell: one or more small nuclei called *micronuclei* and a single larger *macronucleus* (see Figure 24.4). A **micronucleus** is a diploid nucleus that contains a complete complement of genes. It functions primarily in cellular reproduction, which may be asexual or sexual. The number of micronuclei present depends on the species. The **macronucleus** develops from a micronucleus but loses all genes except those required for basic functions (e.g., feeding, metabolism) of the cell and for synthesis of ribosomal RNA. The macronucleus contains numerous copies of these genes, allowing it to synthesize large quantities of proteins and rRNA.

Ciliates abound in freshwater and marine habitats, where they feed voraciously on bacteria, algae, and each other. *Paramecium* and *Tetrahymena* are typical of the group (see Figures 24.4 and 24.11). Their rows of cilia drive them through their watery habitat, rotating the cell on its long axis while it moves forward or back and turns. The cilia also sweep water laden with prey and food particles into the gullet, where food vacuoles form. The ciliate digests food in the vacuoles and eliminates indigestible material through an anal pore. Contractile vacuoles with elaborate, raylike extensions remove excess water from the cytoplasm and expel it to the outside. When under attack or otherwise stressed, *Paramecium* discharges many dartlike protein threads from surface organelles called **trichocysts**.

DINOFLAGELLATES In spring and summer, the coastal waters of Canada sometimes turn reddish in colour **(Figure 24.12a)**. These **red tides** are caused by a population explosion, or *bloom*, of certain dinoflagellates that make up a large proportion of marine phytoplankton. These protists typically have a shell formed from cellulose plates (Figure 24.12b). The beating of flagella, which fit into grooves in the plates, makes dinoflagellates spin like a top (*dinos* = spinning) as they swim.

Red tides are caused by conditions such as increased nutrient runoff into coastal waters (particularly from farms and industrial areas), warm ocean surface temperatures, and calm water. Red tides occur in the waters of many other

a.

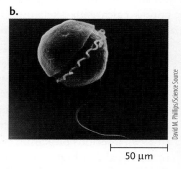

Hong Kong Red Tide Information Network/The Agriculture, Fisheries and Conservation Department

b.

50 μm

David M. Phillips/Science Source

FIGURE 24.12 (a) Red tide caused by dinoflagellate bloom. **(b)** *Karenia brevis*, a toxin-producing dinoflagellate

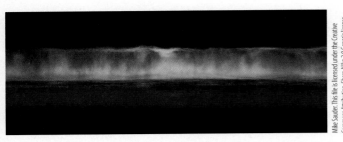

FIGURE 24.13 Bioluminescent dinoflagellates (*Lingulodinium polyedrum*) lighting a breaking wave at midnight

FIGURE 24.14 Bleached elkhorn coral (*Acropora palmata*)

countries besides Canada and are more common in warmer waters. Some red tide dinoflagellates produce a toxin that interferes with nerve function in animals that ingest them.

More than 4500 dinoflagellate species are known, and most, like those that cause red tides, are single-celled organisms in marine phytoplankton. Their abundance in phytoplankton makes dinoflagellates a major primary producer of ocean ecosystems. You can sometimes see their abundance because some are **bioluminescent**; that is, they glow or release a flash of light, particularly when disturbed. Dinoflagellate luminescence can make the sea glow in the wake of a boat at night and coat nocturnal surfers and swimmers with a ghostly light (**Figure 24.13**). Why do these organisms emit light? One explanation is that this burst of light would be likely to scare off predators. The production of light is caused by the enzyme *luciferase* and its substrate *luciferin* in forms similar to the system that produces light in fireflies.

Dinoflagellates live as heterotrophs or autotrophs; many can carry out both modes of nutrition. Some dinoflagellates live as symbionts in the tissues of other marine organisms, such as jellyfish, sea anemones, corals, and molluscs, and give these organisms their distinctive colours. Dinoflagellates in coral use the coral's carbon dioxide and nitrogenous waste while supplying 90% of the coral's carbon. The vast numbers of dinoflagellates living as photosynthetic symbionts in tropical coral reefs allow the reefs to reach massive sizes; without dinoflagellates, many coral species would die. When stressed, corals eject their endosymbionts, a phenomenon known as *coral bleaching* because the absence of the pigmented dinoflagellates allows the coral's calcareous skeleton to be visible (**Figure 24.14**). What causes the coral to become stressed? Increased water temperatures appear to be the main cause, although exposure to contaminants such as oil can also cause bleaching. If the stress causing the bleaching is transient, the coral usually regains its endosymbionts, but if the stress persists, the coral will die. The severity and spatial extent of coral bleaching has been increasing over the past few decades such that it is now a global problem. In 1998, a serious bleaching event destroyed 16% of the world's reefs. Localized high ocean temperatures in the Caribbean in 2005 resulted in more than 80% of corals bleaching, with more than 40% of these being killed.

APICOMPLEXANS **Apicomplexans** are nonmotile parasites of animals. They take their name from the *apical complex*—a group of organelles at one end of a cell—which helps the cell attach to and invade host cells. Apicomplexans absorb nutrients through their plasma membranes (rather than by engulfing food particles) and lack food vacuoles. One genus, *Plasmodium*, is responsible for malaria, one of the most widespread and debilitating human diseases. About 500 million people are infected with malaria in tropical regions, including Africa, India, Southeast Asia, the Middle East, Oceania, and Central and South America. In 2012, malaria killed an estimated 627 000 people, about half as many as were killed by AIDS that year. It is particularly deadly for children younger than six years. In many countries where malaria is common, people are often infected repeatedly, with new infections occurring alongside preexisting infections.

Plasmodium is transmitted by 60 different species of mosquitoes, all members of the genus *Anopheles*. Infective cells develop inside the female mosquito, which transfers the cells to human or bird hosts (**Figure 24.15**). The infecting parasites multiply in their hosts, initially in liver cells and then in red blood cells. Their growth causes red blood cells to rupture in regular cycles every 48 or 72 hours, depending on the *Plasmodium* species. The ruptured red blood cells clog vessels and release the parasite's metabolic wastes, causing cycles of chills and fever.

The victim's immune system is ineffective because, during most of the infective cycle, the parasite is inside body cells and thus "hidden" from antibodies. Furthermore, like *Giardia*, *Plasmodium* regularly changes its surface molecules, continuously producing new forms that are not recognized by antibodies developed against a previous form. In this way, the parasite keeps one step ahead of the immune system, often making malarial infections essentially permanent. For a time, malaria was controlled in many countries by insecticides such as DDT. However, the mosquitoes developed resistance to the insecticides and have returned in even greater numbers than before the spraying began.

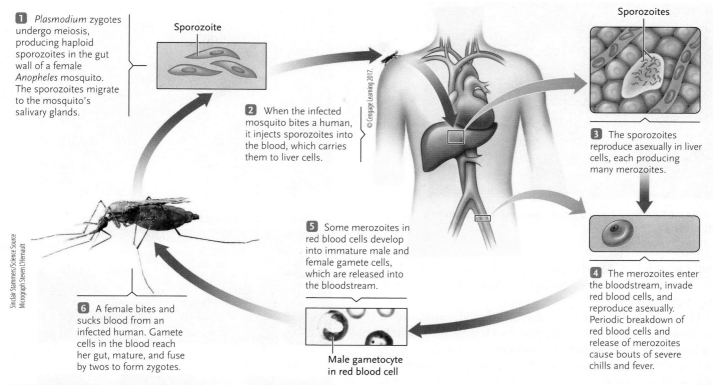

1. *Plasmodium* zygotes undergo meiosis, producing haploid sporozoites in the gut wall of a female *Anopheles* mosquito. The sporozoites migrate to the mosquito's salivary glands.

Sporozoite

2. When the infected mosquito bites a human, it injects sporozoites into the blood, which carries them to liver cells.

© Cengage Learning 2017.

Sporozoites

3. The sporozoites reproduce asexually in liver cells, each producing many merozoites.

4. The merozoites enter the bloodstream, invade red blood cells, and reproduce asexually. Periodic breakdown of red blood cells and release of merozoites cause bouts of severe chills and fever.

5. Some merozoites in red blood cells develop into immature male and female gamete cells, which are released into the bloodstream.

6. A female bites and sucks blood from an infected human. Gamete cells in the blood reach her gut, mature, and fuse by twos to form zygotes.

Sinclair Stammers/Science Source
Micrograph Steven L'Hernault

Male gametocyte in red blood cell

FIGURE 24.15 Life cycle of a *Plasmodium* species that causes malaria

In addition to the asexual reproduction described above for *Plasmodium*, apicomplexans also reproduce sexually, forming gametes that fuse and then form cysts. As in *Giardia*, when a host organism ingests the cysts, they divide to produce infective cells. Many apicomplexans use more than one host species for different stages of their life cycle. For example, another organism in this group, *Toxoplasma*, has the sexual phase of its life cycle in cats and the asexual phases in humans, cattle, pigs, and other animals. Feces of infected cats contain cysts; humans ingesting or inhaling the cysts develop toxoplasmosis, a disease that is usually mild in adults but can cause severe brain damage or even death to a fetus. Because of the danger of toxoplasmosis, pregnant women should avoid emptying litter boxes or otherwise cleaning up after a cat.

The groups of chromalveolates discussed below all share a distinctive arrangement of flagella at some stage of their life cycles. As indicated in Figure 24.16, motile cells in these organisms have two different flagella: one smooth and a second covered with bristles, giving it a "hairy" appearance (**Figure 24.16**). In many of these chromalveolates, the flagella occur only on reproductive cells such as eggs and sperm. This group of chromalveolates includes the oomycetes (water moulds), diatoms, golden algae, and brown algae. Recall that algae is a general term for photosynthetic protists, but the different groups of algae are not closely related to each other, so the term does not imply a phylogenetic grouping.

OOMYCETES: WATER MOULDS AND DOWNY MILDEWS In Ireland, the summer of 1846 started off warm and sunny. This was a welcome change, as the previous summer had been cool and damp, causing the potato crop to fail. But then the weather turned wet and cold again, and within one week at the end of July, the entire potato crop was destroyed: the leaves rotted and the tubers turned to black, putrid mush (**Figure 24.17**). Worse was to come: the unseasonably cool and damp growing seasons persisted until 1860, causing the potato crops to fail year after year. These crop failures were catastrophic because potatoes were virtually the only food source for most people. Altogether,

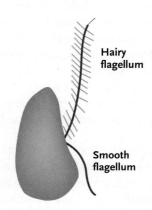

Hairy flagellum

Smooth flagellum

FIGURE 24.16 Stramenopile protist, with "smooth" and "hairy" flagella

FIGURE 24.17 **Blight caused by *Phytophthora infestans* in a potato crop**

a. Water mould

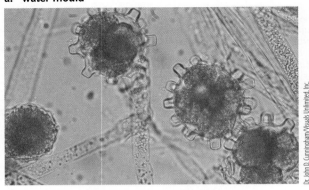

b. Water mould infecting fish

c. Downy mildew

FIGURE 24.18 **Oomycetes. (a)** The water mould *Saprolegnia parasitica*. **(b)** S. parasitica growing as cottony white fibres on the tail of an aquarium fish. **(c)** Downy mildew, *Plasmopara viticola*, growing on grapes. At times, it has nearly destroyed vineyards in Europe and North America.

about one-third of the Irish population died or emigrated (to Canada and the United States, among other countries) due to the potato famines.

In 1861, the organism that caused the blight was identified as a water mould, *Phytophthora infestans*. Originally thought to be a fungus, *P. infestans* produces infective cells that are easily dispersed by wind and water. The blight caused by this organism has recently re-emerged as a serious disease in potato-growing regions of Canada and the United States due to the migration of new strains from Mexico that are resistant to existing pesticides.

Oomycetes (**Figure 24.18a**) are commonly known as *water moulds*, but they are not fungi at all; however, they do share some features with fungi. Like fungi, oomycetes grow as microscopic, nonmotile filaments called **hyphae** (singular, *hypha*), forming a network called a **mycelium** (Figure 24.18b). Also like fungi, they are heterotrophs, which secrete enzymes that digest the complex molecules of surrounding organic matter or living tissue into simpler molecules that are small enough to be absorbed into their cells. Other features, however, set the Oomycota apart from the fungi; chief among them are differences in nucleotide sequence, which clearly indicate close evolutionary relationships to other heterokonts rather than to the fungi.

The water moulds live almost exclusively in freshwater lakes and streams or moist terrestrial habitats, where they are key decomposers. Dead animal or plant material immersed in water commonly becomes coated with cottony water moulds. Other water moulds, such as the mould growing on the fish shown in Figure 24.18b, parasitize living aquatic animals. The downy mildews are parasites of land plants (Figure 24.18c). Oomycetes may reproduce asexually or sexually.

DIATOMS The organisms shown in **Figure 24.19** may not look like living organisms at all but instead like artwork or jewels. These are **diatoms**, single-celled organisms with a glassy silica shell, which is intricately formed and beautiful in many species. The two halves of the shell fit together like the top and bottom of a Petri dish or box of chocolates. Substances move in and out

of the cell through elaborately patterned perforations in the shell. Diatom shells are common in fossil deposits. In fact, more diatoms are known as fossils than as living species: some 35 000 extinct species have been described compared with 7000 living species. For about 180 million years, diatom shells have been accumulating into thick layers of sediment at the bottom of lakes and seas.

In fact, you probably use diatoms—or their remnants—a couple times a day when you brush your teeth. Many toothpastes contain a mild abrasive to assist in removing plaque, a bacterial biofilm that forms on your teeth. This abrasive is commonly made from grinding the fossilized shells of diatoms into a fine powder, called *diatomaceous earth*. In addition to toothpaste, diatomaceous earth is used in filters, as an insulating material, and as a pesticide. Diatomaceous earth kills crawling insects and insect larvae by abrading their exoskeleton, causing

FIGURE 24.19 Diatoms. Depending on the species, the shells are either radially or bilaterally symmetrical, as seen in this sample.

Jan Hinsch/Science Source

poison, causes amnesic shellfish poisoning when ingested by humans; the poisoning can be fatal.

Asexual reproduction in diatoms occurs by mitosis followed by a form of cytoplasmic division in which each daughter cell receives either the top or the bottom half of the parent shell. The daughter cell then secretes the missing half, which becomes the smaller, inside shell of the box. The daughter cell receiving the larger top half grows to the same size as the parent shell, but the cell receiving the smaller bottom half is limited to the size of this shell. As asexual divisions continue, the cells receiving bottom halves become progressively smaller. When a minimum size is reached, sexual reproduction is triggered. The cells produce flagellated gametes, which fuse to form a zygote. The zygote grows to normal size before secreting a completely new shell with full-sized top and bottom halves.

Although flagella are present only in gametes, many diatoms move by an unusual mechanism in which a secretion released through grooves in the shell propels them in a gliding motion.

them to dehydrate and die. Insects also die when they eat the powder, but larger animals, including humans, are unaffected by it.

Diatoms are photoautotrophs that carry out photosynthesis by pathways similar to those of plants. They are among the primary photosynthetic organisms in marine plankton and are also abundant in freshwater habitats as both phytoplankton and bottom-dwelling species. Although most diatoms are free living, some are symbionts inside other marine protists. One diatom, *Pseudonitzschia*, produces a toxic amino acid that can accumulate in shellfish. The amino acid, which acts as a nerve

GOLDEN ALGAE Nearly all golden algae are autotrophs and carry out photosynthesis using pathways similar to those of plants. Their colour is due to a brownish carotenoid pigment, fucoxanthin, which masks the green colour of the chlorophylls **(Figure 24.20a)**. However, most of these organisms can also live as heterotrophs if there is insufficient light for photosynthesis. They switch to feeding on dissolved organic molecules or preying on bacteria and diatoms. Golden algae are important in

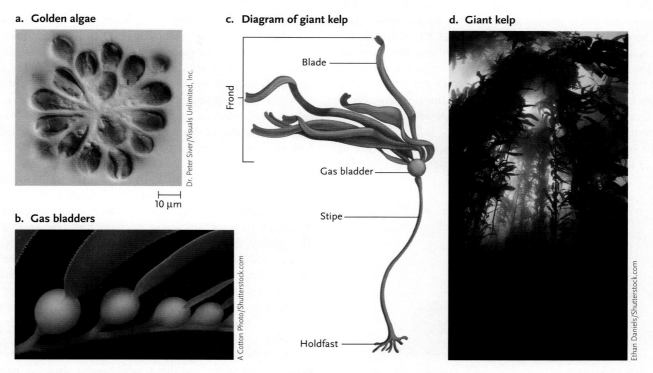

FIGURE 24.20 Golden and brown algae. (a) A microscopic swimming colony of *Synura*. Each cell bears two flagella, which are not visible in this light micrograph. **(b)** Gas bladders connect kelp's stipes ("stems") to its blades ("leaves"). **(c)** The fronds of giant kelp are borne on stalks known as *stipes*, which are anchored to the substrate by holdfasts. **(d)** A forest of *Macrocystis pyrifera* (giant kelp)

freshwater habitats and in *nanoplankton*, a community of marine phytoplankton composed of huge numbers of extremely small cells. During the spring and fall, blooms of golden algae are responsible for the fishy taste of many cities' drinking water.

Most golden algae are colonial forms (see Figures 24.3 and 24.20a) in which each cell of the colony bears a pair of flagella. The golden algae have glassy shells, but in the form of plates or scales rather than in the Petri dish form of the diatoms.

BROWN ALGAE If you were asked where in Canada you'd find forests of giant trees, you'd likely think of the **temperate rainforests** in British Columbia. But there are also vast underwater forests in the waters off the British Columbia coast, formed not by trees but by a type of brown algae known as *kelp* (*Macrocystis integrifolia*), which can grow to lengths of 30 m. A related species, giant kelp (*M. pyrifera*) (Figure 24.20b–d), can grow up to 60 m long. Kelps are the largest and most complex of all protists. Their tissues are differentiated into leaflike *blades*, stalklike *stipes*, and rootlike *holdfasts* that anchor them to the bottom. Hollow gas-filled bladders give buoyancy to the stipes and blades and help keep them upright and oriented toward the sunlit upper layers of water (Figure 24.20b). The stipes of some kelps contain tubelike vessels, similar to the vascular elements of plants, which rapidly distribute the products of photosynthesis throughout the body of the alga. Kelps have an astonishingly fast growth rate: giant kelp can grow up to 30 cm per day!

Just as for terrestrial forests, kelp forests provide food and habitat for many marine organisms. Herds of sea otters (*Enhydra lutris*), for example, tend to live in and near kelp forests. When sea otters sleep at sea, they wrap kelp around themselves to keep from drifting away (**Figure 24.21**). Although the forest is an important habitat for the sea otters, the otters, in turn, are critical for the survival of these forests. Sea otters are one of the few predators of sea urchins, which graze on the kelp and can cause deforestation if their populations get very large. Predation by sea otters keeps sea urchin populations in control, preventing destruction of kelp forests.

All brown algae are photoautotrophs, but not all are as large as kelps. Nearly all of the 1500 known species inhabit

temperate or cool coastal marine waters. Like golden algae, brown algae contain fucoxanthin, which gives them their characteristic colour. Their cell walls contain cellulose and a mucilaginous polysaccharide, alginic acid. This alginic acid, called **algin** when extracted, is an essentially tasteless substance used to thicken such diverse products as ice cream, salad dressing, jellybeans, cosmetics, and floor polish. Brown algae are also harvested as food crops and fertilizer.

Life cycles among the brown algae are typically complex and in many species consist of alternating haploid and diploid generations (**Figure 24.22**). The large structures that we recognize as kelps and other brown seaweeds are diploid **sporophytes**, so called because they give rise to haploid spores by meiosis. The spores, which are flagellated swimming cells, germinate and divide by mitosis to form an independent, haploid **gametophyte** generation. The gametophytes produce haploid gametes (egg and sperm). Most brown algal gametophytes are multicellular structures only a few centimetres in diameter. Cells in the gametophyte, produced by mitosis, differentiate to form nonmotile eggs or flagellated, swimming sperm cells. The sperm cells have the two different types of flagella characteristic of heterokont protists. Fusion of egg and sperm produces a diploid zygote that grows by mitotic divisions into the sporophyte generation. This complex life cycle is very similar to that of land plants (see Chapter 26).

24.4c Rhizaria Are Eukaryotes with Filamentous Pseudopods

Amoeba (*amoibe* = change) is a descriptive term for a single-celled protist that moves by means of pseudopodia, as described earlier in this chapter (see Figure 24.6). Several major groups of protists contain amoebas, which are similar in form but are not all closely related. Amoebas in the Rhizaria produce stiff, filamentous pseudopodia, and many produce hard outer shells, called *tests*. We consider here two heterotrophic groups of amoebas, the Radiolaria and the Foraminifera, and a third, photosynthesizing group, the Chlorarachniophyta.

RADIOLARIA Radiolarians (*radiolus* = small sunbeam) are marine organisms characterized by a glassy internal skeleton and **axopods**, slender raylike strands of cytoplasm supported internally by long bundles of microtubules (**Figure 24.23a, b**). This glassy skeleton is heavy—when radiolarians die, their skeletons sink to the ocean floor—so how do radiolarians keep afloat? The axopods provide buoyancy, as do the numerous vacuoles and lipid droplets in the cytoplasm. Axopods are also involved in feeding: prey stick to the axopods and are then engulfed, brought into the cell, and digested in food vacuoles.

Radiolarian skeletons that accumulate on the ocean floor become part of the sediment, which, over time, hardens into sedimentary rock. The presence of radiolarians in such rocks is very useful to the oil industry as indicators of oil-bearing strata.

FIGURE 24.21 A sea otter (*Enhydra lutris*) wrapped in kelp

worldswildlifewonders/Shutterstock.com

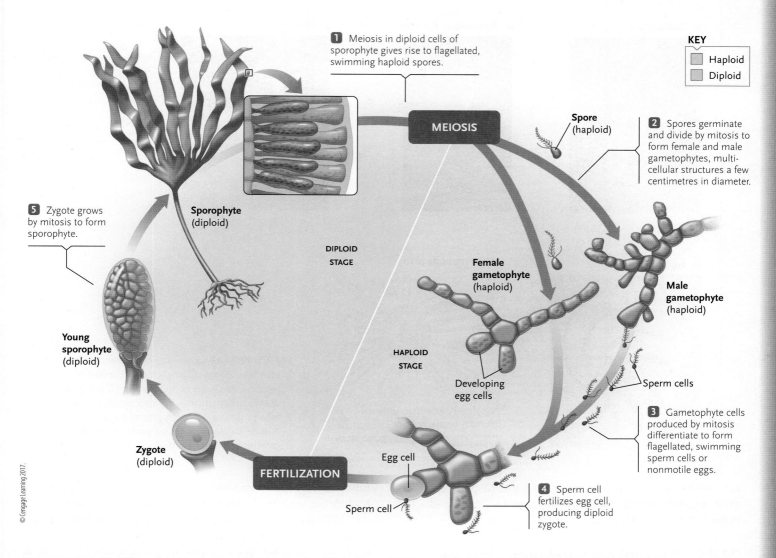

FIGURE 24.22 The life cycle of the brown alga *Laminaria,* which alternates between a diploid sporophyte stage and a haploid gametophyte stage

FORAMINIFERA: FORAMS These organisms take their name from the perforations in their shells (*foramen* = little hole), through which extend long slender strands of cytoplasm supported internally by a network of needlelike spines. Their shells consist of organic matter reinforced by calcium carbonate (Figure 24.23c–e). Most foram shells are chambered spiral structures that, although microscopic, resemble those of molluscs.

Like radiolarians, forams live in marine environments. Some species are planktonic, but they are most abundant on sandy bottoms and attached to rocks along the coasts. Forams feed in a manner similar to that of radiolarians: they engulf prey that adhere to the strands and conduct them through the holes in the shell into the central cytoplasm, where they are digested in food vacuoles. Some forams have algal symbionts that carry out photosynthesis, allowing them to live as both heterotrophs and autotrophs.

Marine sediments are typically packed with the shells of dead forams. The sediments may be hundreds of feet thick: the White Cliffs of Dover in England are composed primarily of the shells of ancient forams. Most of the world's deposits of limestone and marble contain foram shells; the great pyramids of ancient Egypt are built from blocks cut from fossil foram deposits. Because distinct species lived during different geologic periods, they are widely used to establish the age of sedimentary rocks containing their shells. As they do with radiolarian species, oil prospectors use forams as indicators of hydrocarbon deposits because layers of forams often overlie oil.

CHLORARACHNIOPHYTA Chlorarachniophytes are an obscure group of amoebas that contain chloroplasts. They are studied by biologists investigating the origin and evolution of chloroplasts as they acquired their chloroplasts by secondary endosymbiosis (discussed later in this chapter). Interestingly, they are both

a. Radiolarian

Perennou Nuridsany/Science Source

10 μm

b. Radiolarian skeleton

Eye of Science/Science Source

c. Living foram

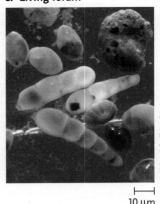

Jerry McCormick-Ray/Science Source

10 μm

d. Foram shells

Eric V. Grave/Science Source

e. Foram body plan

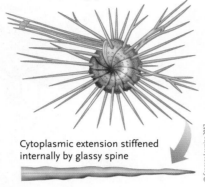

Cytoplasmic extension stiffened internally by glassy spine

© Cengage Learning 2017.

FIGURE 24.23 **(a)** A living radiolarian. **(b)** The internal skeletons of a radiolarian. Bundles of microtubules support the cytoplasmic extensions of the radiolarian. **(c)** A living foram **(d)** Empty foram shells. **(e)** The body plan of a foram. Needlelike glassy spines support the cytoplasmic extensions of the forams.

autotrophic and heterotrophic; in addition to photosynthesis, they engulf food with the many filamentous pseudopodia that extend from the cell surface.

24.4d The Unikont Supergroup Includes Slime Moulds and Most Amoebas

The unikonts include most of the amoebas other than those in Rhizaria, as well as the cellular and plasmodial slime moulds. All members of this group use pseudopods for locomotion and feeding for all or part of their life cycles.

AMOEBAS Amoebas of the unikonts are single-celled organisms that are abundant in marine and freshwater environments and soil. All amoebas are microscopic, although some species can grow to 5 mm in size and so are visible with the naked eye. Some amoebas are parasitic, such as the 45 species that infect the human digestive tract. One of these parasites, *Entamoeba histolytica*, causes amoebic dysentery. Cysts of this amoeba contaminate water supplies and soil in regions with inadequate sewage treatment. When ingested, a cyst breaks open to release an amoeba that feeds and divides rapidly in the digestive tract. Enzymes released by the amoebas destroy cells lining the intestine, producing the ulcerations, painful cramps, and debilitating diarrhea characteristic of the disease. Amoebic dysentery afflicts millions of people worldwide; in less-developed countries, it is a leading cause of death among infants and small children.

Most amoebas, however, are heterotrophs that feed on bacteria, other protists, and bits of organic matter. Unlike the stiff, supported pseudopodia of Rhizaria, pseudopods of amoebas extend and retract at any point on their body surface and are unsupported by any internal cellular organization; amoebas are thus "shape-shifters." How can an amoeba capture a fast-moving organism? As an amoeba moves, its cytoplasm doesn't just move but also changes state, from a more liquid state to a more solid state and back again, allowing the amoeba to send out pseudopodia in different directions very quickly. These fast-moving pseudopods can capture even fast-swimming prey such as ciliates (**Figure 24.24**).

Amoebas reproduce only asexually, via binary fission. In unfavourable environmental conditions, some amoebas can form a cyst, essentially by rolling up and secreting a protective membrane. They survive as cysts until favourable conditions return.

SLIME MOULDS After a very wet spring in 1973, residents of Dallas, Texas, were alarmed to see large, yellow blobs that resembled scrambled eggs *crawling* on their lawns. People thought it was an alien invasion. Luckily, a local biologist was able to prevent mass panic by identifying the blobs as slime

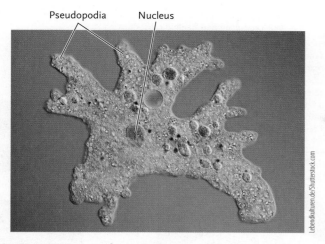

Pseudopodia   Nucleus

FIGURE 24.24 An amoeba capturing prey with pseudopods

moulds, unusual heterotrophic protists. Slime moulds exist for part of their lives as individuals that move by amoeboid motion, but then come together in a coordinated mass—essentially, a large amoeba—that ultimately differentiates into stalked structures called **fruiting bodies**, in which spores are formed.

There are two major evolutionary lineages of slime moulds: the **cellular slime moulds** and the **plasmodial slime moulds**, which differ in cellular organization. Both types of slime moulds have been of great interest to scientists because of their ability to differentiate into fruiting bodies with stalks and spore-bearing structures. This differentiation is much simpler than the complex developmental pathways of other eukaryotes, providing a unique opportunity to study cell differentiation at its most fundamental level. Slime moulds also respond to stimuli in their environment, moving away from bright light and toward food. We have learned a great deal about eukaryotic signalling pathways, cell differentiation, and cell movement from studies of slime moulds.

Slime moulds live on moist, rotting plant material such as decaying leaves and bark. The cells engulf particles of dead organic matter, along with bacteria, yeasts, and other microorganisms, and digest them internally. They can be a range of colours: brown, yellow, green, red, and even violet or blue.

These organisms exist primarily as individual cells, either separately or as a coordinated mass. Among the 150 or so species of cellular slime moulds, *Dictyostelium discoideum* is the best known. Its life cycle begins when a haploid spore lands in a suitably moist environment containing decaying organic matter (**Figure 24.25**). The spore germinates into an amoeboid cell that grows and divides mitotically into separate haploid cells as long as the food source lasts. When the food supply dwindles, some of the cells release a **chemical signal** in pulses; in response, the amoebas move together and form a sausage-shaped mass that crawls in coordinated fashion like a slug. Some "slugs," although not much more than a millimetre in length, contain more than 100 thousand individual cells. At some point, the "slug" stops moving and differentiates into a

stalked fruiting body, with some cells becoming spores, whereas others form the stalk. The cells that form the stalk die in the process, essentially sacrificing themselves so that a stalk can form. Why is formation of a stalk crucial? Raising the spore-forming cells higher up in the air increases the likelihood that spores will be carried away by air currents and dispersed farther away from the parent. Because the cells forming the slug and fruiting body are all products of mitosis, this is asexual reproduction.

Cellular slime moulds also reproduce sexually: two haploid cells fuse to form a diploid zygote (also shown in Figure 24.25) that enters a dormant stage. Eventually, the zygote undergoes meiosis, producing four haploid cells that may multiply inside the spore by mitosis. When conditions are favourable, the spore wall breaks down, releasing the cells. These cells grow and divide into separate amoeboid cells.

Plasmodial slime moulds exist primarily as a multinucleate **plasmodium**, in which individual nuclei are suspended in a common cytoplasm surrounded by a single plasma membrane. (This is not to be confused with *Plasmodium*, the genus of apicomplexans that causes malaria.) There are 888 known species of plasmodial slime moulds. The plasmodium (**Figure 24.26a**) flows and feeds by phagocytosis like a single huge amoeba—a single cell that contains thousands to millions or even billions of diploid nuclei surrounded by a single plasma membrane. The plasmodium, which may range in size from a few centimetres to more than a metre in diameter, typically moves in thick, branching strands connected by thin sheets. The movements occur by cytoplasmic streaming, driven by actin microfilaments and myosin. These plasmodia are what the people in Dallas thought were aliens invading; after a period of heavy rain, plasmodia will sometimes crawl out of the woods to appear on lawns or the mulch of flowerbeds.

At some point, often in response to unfavourable environmental conditions, fruiting bodies form on the plasmodium. At the tips of the fruiting bodies, nuclei become enclosed in separate cells. These cells undergo meiosis, forming haploid, resistant spores that are released from the fruiting bodies and carried by water or wind. If they reach a favourable environment, the spores germinate to form gametes that fuse to form a diploid zygote. The zygote nucleus then divides repeatedly without an accompanying division of the cytoplasm, forming many diploid nuclei suspended in the common cytoplasm of a new plasmodium.

Plasmodial slime moulds are particularly useful in research because they become large enough to provide ample material for biochemical and molecular analyses. Actin and myosin extracted from *Physarum polycephalum*, for example, have been used in studies of actin-based motility. A further advantage of plasmodial slime moulds is that the many nuclei of a plasmodium usually replicate and pass through synchronous mitosis, making them useful in research that tracks the changes that take place in the cell cycle. More recently, slime moulds have been used in robotics research.

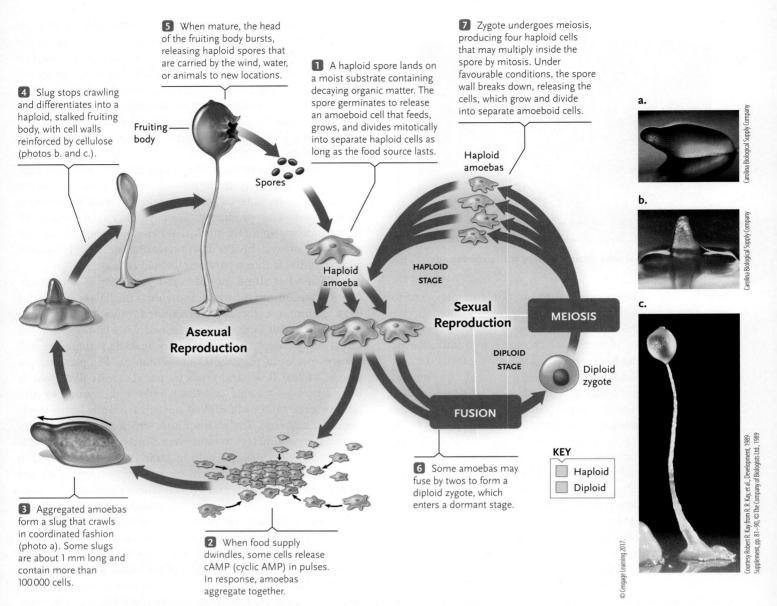

4 Slug stops crawling and differentiates into a haploid, stalked fruiting body, with cell walls reinforced by cellulose (photos b. and c.).

5 When mature, the head of the fruiting body bursts, releasing haploid spores that are carried by the wind, water, or animals to new locations.

1 A haploid spore lands on a moist substrate containing decaying organic matter. The spore germinates to release an amoeboid cell that feeds, grows, and divides mitotically into separate haploid cells as long as the food source lasts.

7 Zygote undergoes meiosis, producing four haploid cells that may multiply inside the spore by mitosis. Under favourable conditions, the spore wall breaks down, releasing the cells, which grow and divide into separate amoeboid cells.

Fruiting body

Spores

Haploid amoeba

Haploid amoebas

HAPLOID STAGE

Asexual Reproduction

Sexual Reproduction

MEIOSIS

DIPLOID STAGE

Diploid zygote

FUSION

KEY

Haploid
Diploid

6 Some amoebas may fuse by twos to form a diploid zygote, which enters a dormant stage.

3 Aggregated amoebas form a slug that crawls in coordinated fashion (photo a). Some slugs are about 1 mm long and contain more than 100 000 cells.

2 When food supply dwindles, some cells release cAMP (cyclic AMP) in pulses. In response, amoebas aggregate together.

a.
b.
c.

FIGURE 24.25 **Life cycle of the cellular slime mould *Dictyostelium discoideum*.** The light micrographs show **(a)** a migrating slug, **(b)** an early stage in fruiting body formation, and **(c)** a mature fruiting body.

CHOANOFLAGELLATES Also included in the unikonts are the choanoflagellates. Opisthokonta (*opistho* = posterior; *kontos* = flagellum) are named for the single posterior flagellum found at some stage in the life cycle of these organisms. This diverse group includes the choanoflagellates, protists thought to be the ancestors of fungi and animals.

Choanoflagellata (*choanos* = collar) are named for the collar surrounding the flagellum that the protist uses to feed and, in some species, to swim (**Figure 24.27**). The collar resembles an upside-down lampshade and is made up of small finger-like projections (microvilli) of the plasma membrane. As the flagellum moves water through the collar, these projections engulf bacteria and particles of organic matter in the water.

About 150 species of choanoflagellates live in either marine or freshwater habitats. Some species are mobile, with the flagellum pushing the cells along (in the same way that animal sperm are propelled by their flagella), but most choanoflagellates are *sessile* (attached by a stalk to a surface). A number of species are colonial with a cluster of cells on a single stalk; these colonial species are of great interest to biologists studying the evolution of multicellularity in animals.

Why are choanoflagellates thought to be the ancestor of animals? Both molecular and morphological data indicate that a choanoflagellate type of protist gave rise to animals; for example, there are many morphological similarities between choanoflagellates and the collar cells (choanocytes) of sponges

FIGURE 24.26 Slime moulds. (a) Plasmodia of slime moulds. **(b)** Fruiting bodies of slime moulds

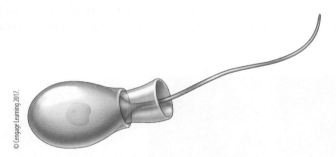

FIGURE 24.27 A choanoflagellate

Filamentous red alga

FIGURE 24.28 Red algae. *Antithamnion plumula,* showing the filamentous and branched body form most common among red algae

as well as the cells that act as excretory organisms in flatworms and rotifers (see Chapter 27). Comparisons of nucleic acid sequences done to date also support the hypothesis that choanoflagellates are the closest living relatives to animals. Molecular data also indicate that a choanoflagellate-like organism was also likely the ancestor of the fungi (see Chapter 25).

24.4e Plantae Include the Red and Green Algae and Land Plants

The Plantae supergroup consists of the red and green algae, which are protists, and the land plants. These three groups of photoautotrophs share a common evolutionary origin. Here we describe the two types of algae; we discuss land plants and how they evolved from green algae in Chapter 26.

RHODOPHYTA: RED ALGAE Nearly all the 7000 known species of red algae, which are also known as the *Rhodophyta (rhodon =* rose), are small marine seaweeds (**Figure 24.28**). Approximately 5% are found in freshwater lakes and streams or in soils. If you have had sushi, then you have eaten red algae: *Porphyra* is harvested for use as the *nori* wrapped around fish and rice.

Rhodophyte cell walls contain cellulose and mucilaginous pectins that give red algae a slippery texture. These pectins are

widely used in industry and science. Extracted **agar** is used as a culture medium in the laboratory and as a setting agent for jellies and desserts. **Carrageenan** is used to thicken and stabilize paints, dairy products such as ice cream, and many other emulsions.

Some species secrete calcium carbonate into their cell walls; these coralline algae are important in building coral reefs; in some places, they play a bigger role in reef building than do corals.

Red algae are typically multicellular organisms, with diverse morphologies, although many have plantlike bodies composed of stalks bearing leaflike blades. Although most are free-living autotrophs, some are parasites that attach to other algae or plants.

Although most red algae are reddish in colour, some are greenish purple or black. The colour differences are produced by accessory pigments, *phycobilins,* that mask the green colour of their chlorophylls. Phycobilins absorb the shorter wavelengths of light (green and blue-green light) that penetrate to the ocean depths, allowing red algae to grow at deeper levels than any other algae. Some red algae live at depths up to 260 m if the water is clear enough to transmit light to these levels.

Red algae have complex reproductive cycles involving alternation between diploid sporophytes and haploid gametophytes. No flagellated cells occur in the red algae; instead, gametes are released into the water to be brought together by random collisions in currents.

CHLOROPHYTA: GREEN ALGAE The green algae, or Chlorophyta (*chloros* = green), carry out photosynthesis using the same pigments as plants, whereas other photosynthetic protists contain pigment combinations that are very different from those of land plants. This shared pigment composition is one line of evidence that one lineage of green algae was the ancestor of land plants. With at least 16 thousand species, green algae show more diversity than any other algal group. They also have very diverse morphologies, including single-celled, colonial, and multicellular species (**Figure 24.29**; see also Figure 24.1d). Multicellular forms have a range of morphologies, including filamentous, tubular, and leaflike forms. Most green algae are microscopic, but some range upward to the size of small seaweeds.

Most green algae live in freshwater aquatic habitats, but some are marine, others live on rocks, soil surfaces, or tree bark, or even in snow. Other organisms rely on green algae to photosynthesize for them by forming symbiotic relationships. For example, most lichens are symbioses between green algae and fungi (see Chapter 25), and many animals contain green algal chloroplasts, or entire green algae, as symbionts in their cells.

Life cycles among the green algae are as diverse as their body forms. Many can reproduce either sexually or asexually, and some alternate between haploid and diploid generations. Gametes in different species may be undifferentiated flagellated cells or differentiated as a flagellated sperm cell and a nonmotile egg cell. Most common is a life cycle with a multicellular haploid phase and a single-celled diploid phase (**Figure 24.30**).

Among all the algae, the green algae are the most closely related to land plants, based on molecular, biochemical, and morphological data. Evidence of this close relationship includes

a. Single-celled green alga

c. Multicellular green alga

1 cm

b. Colonial green alga

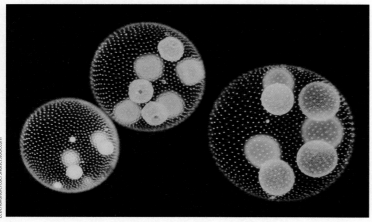

200 μm

FIGURE 24.29 Green algae. (a) A single-celled green alga, *Acetabularia*, which grows in marine environments. Each individual in the cluster is a large single cell with a rootlike base, a stalk, and a cap. **(b)** A colonial green alga, *Volvox*. Each green dot in the spherical wall of the colony is a potentially independent, flagellated cell. Daughter colonies can be seen within the parent colony.
(c) A multicellular green alga, *Ulva*, common to shallow seas around the world

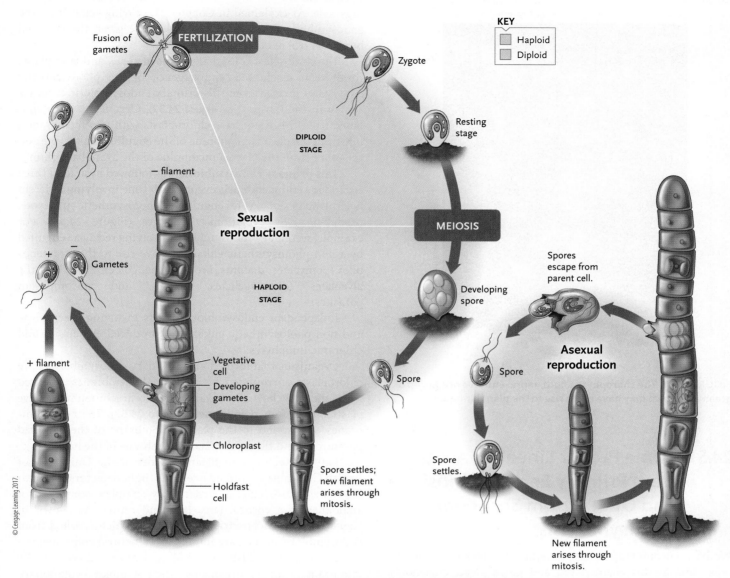

FIGURE 24.30 **The life cycle of the green alga *Ulothrix*, in which the haploid stage is multicellular and the diploid stage is a single cell, the zygote.** + and − are morphologically identical mating types ("sexes") of the alga.

not only the shared photosynthetic pigments, but also the use of starch as storage reserve and the same cell wall composition.

Which green alga might have been the ancestor of modern land plants? The evidence points to a group known as the **charophytes** as being most similar to the algal ancestors of land plants. This does not mean that modern-day charophytes are the ancestors of land plants but rather that the two groups have a common ancestor. Charophytes, including *Chara* (**Figure 24.31**), *Spirogyra*, *Nitella*, and *Coleochaete*, live in freshwater ponds and lakes. Their ribosomal RNA and chloroplast DNA sequences are more closely related to plant sequences than those of any other green alga. We discuss the

evolution of land plants from an algal ancestor more thoroughly in Chapter 26.

STUDY BREAK QUESTIONS

1. For each of these protist groups, indicate the cell structure that characterizes the group: apicomplexans, dinoflagellates, euglenoids, radiolarians.
2. Which eukaryotic supergroups contain amoeboid forms?
3. What is the major difference between cellular slime moulds and plasmodial slime moulds?

Reproductive structures

Dr. John Clayton, National Institute of Water and Atmospheric Research, New Zealand

FIGURE 24.31 The charophyte *Chara*, representative of a group of green algae that may have given rise to the plant kingdom

24.5 Some Protist Lineages Arose from Primary Endosymbiosis and Others from Secondary Endosymbiosis

We have encountered chloroplasts in a number of eukaryotic organisms in this chapter: red and green algae, euglenoids, dinoflagellates, stramenopiles, chlorarachniophytes, and land plants. How did these chloroplasts evolve? Unlike the endosymbiotic event that gave rise to mitochondria, endosymbiosis involving photoautotrophs happened more than once, resulting in the formation of a wide range of photosynthetic eukaryotes.

About 1 bya, the first chloroplasts evolved from free-living photosynthetic prokaryotic organisms (cyanobacteria) ingested by eukaryote cells that had already acquired mitochondria (see Chapter 21). In some cells, the cyanobacterium was not digested but instead formed a symbiotic relationship with the engulfing host cell: it became an endosymbiont, an independent organism living inside another organism. Over evolutionary time, the prokaryotic organism lost genes no longer required for independent existence and transferred most of its genes to the host's nuclear genome. In this process, the endosymbiont became an organelle. As explained in Chapter 21, moving genes from the endosymbiont to the nucleus would have given the host cell better control of cell functioning.

The chloroplasts of red algae, green algae, and land plants result from evolutionary divergence of the photosynthetic eukaryotes formed from this primary endosymbiotic event (as shown in the top part of **Figure 24.32**). Organisms that originated from this event have chloroplasts with two membranes, one from the plasma membrane of the engulfing eukaryote and the other from the plasma membrane of the cyanobacterium.

This **primary endosymbiosis** was followed by at least three **secondary endosymbiosis** events, each time involving different heterotrophic eukaryotes engulfing a photosynthetic eukaryote, producing new evolutionary lineages (Figure 24.32). For example, secondary endosymbiosis involving red algae engulfed by a non-photosynthetic eukaryote gave rise to the stramenopiles (oomycetes, diatoms, brown algae, golden algae) and the alveolates (dinoflagellates, ciliates, and apicomplexan parasites).

Independent endosymbiotic events involving green algae and non-photosynthetic eukaryotes produced euglenoids and chlorarachniophytes.

Organisms that formed via secondary endosymbiosis have chloroplasts surrounded by additional membranes acquired from the new host. For example, chlorarachniophytes have plastids with four membranes (Figure 24.32). The new membranes correspond to the plasma membrane of the engulfed phototroph and the food vacuole membrane of the host.

Patrick Keeling and Brian Leander at the University of British Columbia examined ocelloids (light detectors) of dinoflagellates. An ocellus is structurally complex, composed of analogues to a cornea, lens, iris, and retina. As shown in **Figure 24.33**, mitochondria and plastids, which resulted from endosymbiotic events, are important structural components.

In sum, the protists are a highly diverse and ecologically important group of organisms. Their complex evolutionary relationships, which have long been a subject of contention, are now being revised as new information is discovered, including more complete genome sequences. A deeper understanding of protists is also contributing to a better understanding of their recent descendants, the fungi, plants, and animals. We turn to these descendants in the next four chapters, beginning with the fungi.

STUDY BREAK QUESTION

1. In primary endosymbiosis, a non-photosynthetic eukaryotic cell engulfed a photosynthetic cyanobacterium. How many membranes surround the chloroplast that evolved?

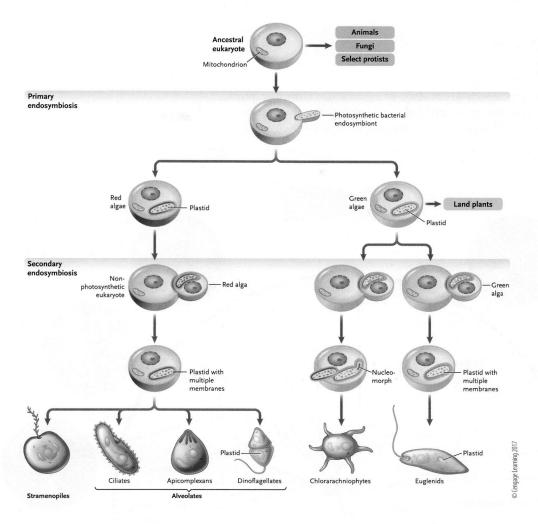

FIGURE 24.32 The origin and distribution of plastids among the eukaryotes by primary and secondary endosymbiosis

© Cengage Learning 2017

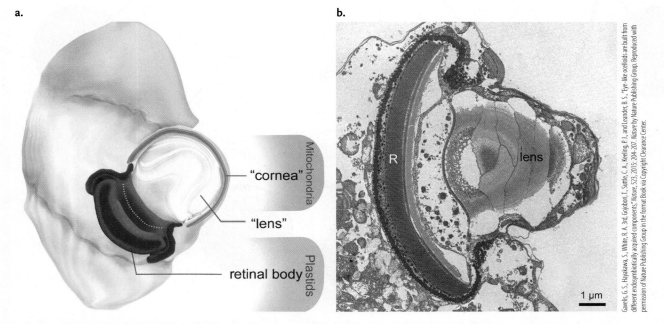

Gavelis, G. S., Hayakawa, S., White, R. A. 3rd, Gojobori, T., Suttle, C. A., Keeling, P. J., and Leander, B. S., "Eye-like ocelloids are built from different endosymbiotically acquired components," *Nature, 523, 2015; 204–207. Nature* by Nature Publishing Group. Reproduced with permission of Nature Publishing Group in the format Book via Copyright Clearance Center.

FIGURE 24.33 Organelles in the ocelloid. (a) Illustration of *Nematodinium* showing the basic components of the ocelloid with their putative organellar origins. **(b)** Transmission electron micrograph of the ocelloid of *Erythropsidinium*; lens and retinal body (R)

Summary Illustration

Protists live in aquatic or moist terrestrial habitats, or as parasites within animals. They may be single-celled, colonial, or multicellular organisms, and they range in size from microscopic to some of Earth's largest organisms.

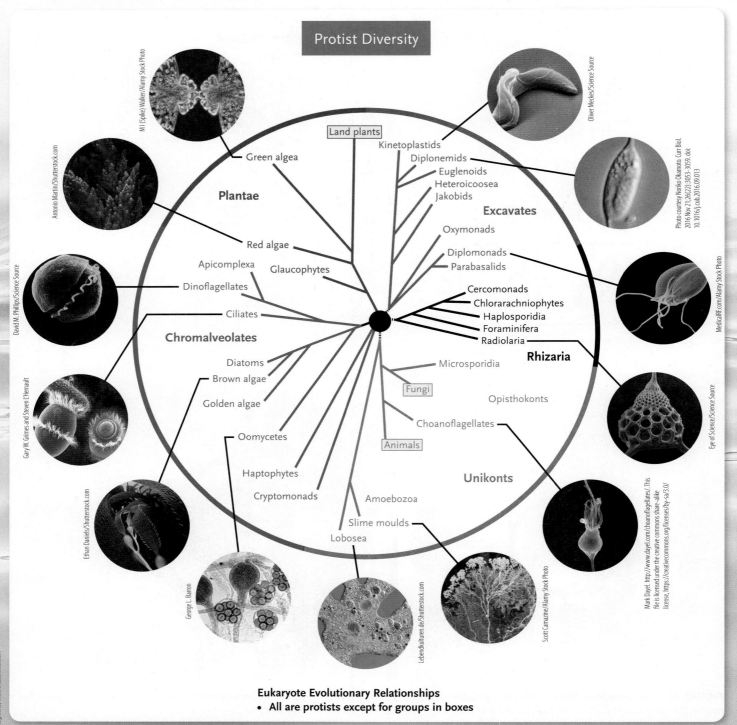

Protist Diversity

Eukaryote Evolutionary Relationships
- All are protists except for groups in boxes

Protist Lifestyles

Modes of obtaining energy and carbon

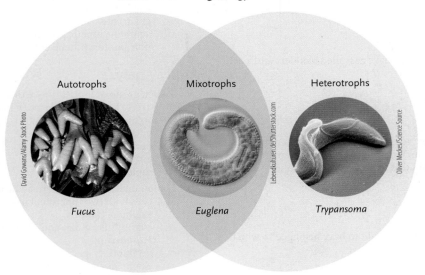

Autotrophs

David Gowans/Alamy Stock Photo

Fucus

Mixotrophs

Lebendkulturen.de/Shutterstock.com

Euglena

Heterotrophs

Oliver Meckes/Science Source

Trypansoma

SYMBIOSES

Mutualistic example:
Some organisms rely on green algae (or cyanobacteria) to photosynthesize for them by forming symbiotic relationships. For example, lichens are a symbiosis between green algae and fungi. It is a mutualistic association because both organisms benefit.

Parasitic example:
Trichonympha vaginalis infects the genitals of both men and women. The unicellular organism is sexually transmitted and obtains nutrients from its host directly through its cell membrane as well as by phagocytosis. It is a parasitic association because it has a negative impact on its host.

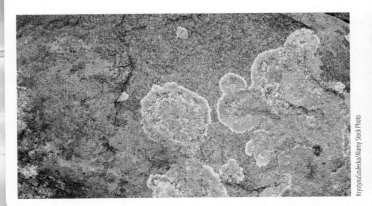

KrystynaSzulecka/Alamy Stock Photo

Eye of Science/Science Source

ENDOSYMBIOSES
An endosymbiotic event gave rise to mitochondria, whereas endosymbiosis involving photoautotrophs occurred more than once, resulting in the formation of a wide range of photosynthetic eukaryotes.

SELF-TEST QUESTIONS

Recall/Understand

1. Which of the following groups is the greatest contributor to protist fossil deposits?
   a. oomycetes
   b. brown algae
   c. golden algae
   d. diatoms

2. Which of the following groups have gas-filled bladders and a cell wall composed of alginic acid?
   a. oomycetes
   b. brown algae
   c. golden algae
   d. diatoms

3. *Plasmodium* is transmitted to humans by the bite of a mosquito (*Anopheles*). Its life cycle includes infective spores, gametes, and cysts. To which group does this infective protist belong?
   a. oomycetes
   b. euglenoids
   c. dinoflagellates
   d. apicomplexans

4. The ancestor of land plants is thought to have belonged to which group of protists?
   a. red algae
   b. diatoms
   c. green algae
   d. golden algae

5. In oil exploration, the presence of shells is an indicator of oil-rich rock layers. To which group of protists would these shells belong?
   a. diatoms
   b. foraminiferans
   c. golden algae
   d. red algae

6. Which supergroup are animals thought to have evolved from?
   a. Excavata
   b. Rhizaria
   c. Unikonta
   d. Chromalveolata

7. Which of these statements describes cellular slime moulds?
   a. They are autotrophs.
   b. They move using cilia.
   c. They reproduce only asexually.
   d. They form a fruiting body that produces spores.

8. The double membrane observed in algal chloroplasts is thought to involve the combining of which two organisms?
   a. two ancestral, photosynthetic, prokaryotic organisms
   b. two ancestral, non-photosynthetic, prokaryotic organisms
   c. a non-photosynthetic eukaryote with a photosynthetic eukaryote
   d. a photosynthetic prokaryotic organism with a non-photosynthetic eukaryote

Apply/Analyze

9. Which group of protists move through viscous fluids using both freely beating flagella and a flagellum buried in a fold of cytoplasm, and cause a sexually transmitted disease in humans?
   a. ciliates
   b. parabasalids
   c. euglenoids
   d. diplomonads

10. Diplomonads are characterized by which of these features?
    a. cells with two functional nuclei and multiple flagella; for example, *Giardia*
    b. a mouthlike gullet and a hairlike surface; for example, *Paramecium*
    c. nonmotility, parasitism, and sporelike infective stages; for example, *Toxoplasma*
    d. large protein deposits, movement by two flagella that are part of an undulating membrane; for example, *Trypanosoma*

Create/Evaluate

11. Contrast protists and animals.
12. Contrast photosynthetic protists and plants.
13. Explain how protist diversity is reflected in their metabolism.
14. Explain why protist diversity is reflected in their habitat.
15. Contrast the different modes of reproduction in protists.

Chapter Roadmap

Fungi

From nutrient recyclers to important symbionts to disease vectors to food, fungi have many important roles in our world.

25.1 General Characteristics of Fungi

Morphology ranges from single-celled yeasts to multicellular filaments (mycelium). The mycelium grows within its nutrition source. The cell walls are made of chitin.

apiguide/Shutterstock.com

From Chapter 5

From Chapter 6

25.2 Evolution and Diversity of Fungi

Fungi evolved over 700 million years ago from a protistan ancestor that is more closely related to the ancestors of animals than to plants. Today we recognize five phyla: Chytridiomycota (causes chytridiomycosis in frogs), Zygomycota (fruit moulds), Glomeromycota (mycorrhizae), Ascomycota (cup fungi), Basidiomycota (mushrooms, puffballs).

To Chapter 26

To Chapter 27

To Chapter 31

To Chapter 36

Martin Fowler/Shutterstock.com

25.3 Fungal Lifestyles

All fungi are heterotrophs, and they obtain carbon by degrading dead organic matter (as saprotrophs) or from living hosts (as symbionts). The plethora of lifestyles makes fungi very important players in all ecosystems.

To Chapter 31

To Chapter 36

POWER AND SYRED/SCIENCE PHOTO LIBRARY

INTERFOTO/Alamy Stock Photo

The mushroom-forming fungus *Inocybe fastigiata*, a forest-dwelling species that commonly lives in close association with conifers and hardwood trees

Fungi

25

Why it matters . . . What do ringworm, beer, and penicillin have in common? Fungus! Ringworm is not a worm at all, but a dermatophyte (skin fungus) closely related to the fungus that causes athlete's foot. Beer and other alcoholic beverages rely on the fermenting action of fungi for their alcohol content and fizz. They are also ingredients in foods, such as flavourful cheeses and leavened breads. Some moulds, such as *Penicillium*, provide humans with life-saving antibiotics, such as penicillin. While fungi can be beneficial, many species cause disease in humans, other animals, and plants; some even produce carcinogenic toxins. As you know from previous chapters, species such as the yeast used to make beer, *Saccharomyces cerevisiae*, and the mould *Neurospora crassa* have long been pivotal model organisms in studies of DNA structure and function and in the development of genetic engineering methods.

In addition to human uses, fungi play many other roles on Earth. Evidence suggests that fungi were present on land at least 760 mya and possibly much earlier. Their presence on land was likely crucial for the successful colonization of land by plants that relied on symbiotic associations with the fungi to obtain nutrients from the nutrient-poor soils of early land environments. Over the course of the intervening millennia, evolution equipped fungi with a remarkable ability to break down a wide range of compounds from both living and dead organisms. This makes them

FIGURE 25.1 **Example of a wood decay fungus: sulfur shelf fungus (*Polyporus*)**

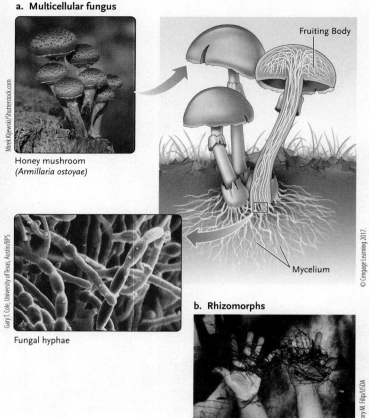

a. **Multicellular fungus**

Honey mushroom
(*Armillaria ostoyae*)

Fungal hyphae

Fruiting Body

Mycelium

b. **Rhizomorphs**

FIGURE 25.2 **Fungal structure: mycelia, hyphae. (a)** Illustration of themycelium of a mushroom-forming fungus, which consists of branching septate hyphae. *Inset:* Micrograph of fungal hyphae **(b)** Rhizomorph – a cordlike aggregation of hyphae formed by some basidiomycete fungi.

essential components in all ecosystems and Earth's premier decomposers **(Figure 25.1)**.

Despite their profound impact on ecosystems and other life forms, most of us have only a passing acquaintance with fungi, perhaps limited to the mushrooms on our pizza or the invisible but annoying types that cause skin infections, such as athlete's foot. This chapter provides you with an overview of fungal biology. We begin with the features that set fungi apart from all other organisms, and discuss the diversity of fungi existing today before revisiting associations between fungi and other organisms.

25.1 General Characteristics of Fungi

We begin our survey of fungi by examining the features that distinguish fungi from other forms of life, how fungi obtain nutrients, and adaptations for reproduction and growth that enable fungi to spread far and wide through the environment.

Fungi are heterotrophic eukaryotes that obtain carbon by breaking down organic molecules synthesized by other organisms. Although all fungi are heterotrophs, fungi can be divided into two broad groups based on how they obtain carbon. If a fungus obtains carbon from non-living material, it is a **saprotroph**. Fungi that decompose dead plant and animal tissues, for example, are saprotrophs. If a fungus obtains carbon from living organisms, it is a **symbiont**. Symbiosis is the living together of two (or sometimes more) organisms for extended periods; symbiotic relationships range along a continuum from **parasitism**, in which one organism benefits at the expense of the other, to **mutualism**, in which both organisms benefit. Although we often think of fungi as decomposers, fully half of all identified fungi live as symbionts with another organism.

Regardless of their nutrient source, fungi feed by **absorptive nutrition**: they secrete enzymes into their environment, breaking down large molecules into smaller soluble molecules that can then be absorbed into their cells. This mode of nutrition means that fungi cannot be stationary, as they would then deplete all the food in their immediate environment. Instead, fungi have evolved the ability to proliferate quickly through their environment, digesting nutrients as they grow. How can fungi proliferate so quickly? Although some fungi grow as unicellular yeasts, which reproduce asexually by **budding** or binary fission (see Figure 25.13), most are composed of **hyphae** ("web"; singular, *hypha*; **Figure 25.2**), fine filaments that spread through whatever substrate the fungus is growing in—soil, decomposing wood, your skin—forming a network, or **mycelium** (Figure 25.2). Hyphae are essentially tubes of cytoplasm surrounded by cell walls made of chitin, a polysaccharide also found in the exoskeletons of insects and other arthropods.

Hyphae grow only at their tips, but because a single mycelium contains many, many tips, the entire mycelium grows outward very quickly. Together, this **apical growth** and absorptive nutrition account for much of the success of fungi. As the hyphal tips extend, they exert a mechanical force, allowing them to push through their substrate, releasing enzymes and absorbing nutrients as they go. Fungal species differ in the particular digestive enzymes they synthesize, so a substrate that is a suitable food source for one species may be unavailable to another. Although there are exceptions, fungi typically thrive only in moist environments, where they can directly absorb water, dissolved ions, simple sugars, amino acids, and other small molecules. When some of a mycelium's hyphal filaments contact a source of food, growth is channelled in the direction of the food source.

Nutrients are absorbed at the porous tips of hyphae; small atoms and molecules pass readily through these tips, and then transport mechanisms move them through the underlying plasma membrane. Some hyphae have regular cross-walls, or **septa** ("fences" or "walls"; singular, *septum*), that separate a hypha into compartments **(Figure 25.3)**, whereas others lack septa and are effectively one large cell. But even septate hyphae should be thought of as interconnected compartments rather than separate cells, as all septa have pores that allow cytoplasm and, in some fungi, even nuclei and other large organelles to flow through the mycelium. By a mechanism called **cytoplasmic streaming** (flow of cytoplasm and organelles around a cell or, in this case, a mycelium), nutrients obtained by one part of a mycelium can be translocated to other non-absorptive regions, such as reproductive structures.

When a fungus releases enzymes into its substrate, it faces competition from bacteria and other organisms for the nutrients that are now available. How can a fungus prevent these competitors from stealing the nutrients that it has just expended energy and resources to obtain? Many fungi produce antibacterial compounds and toxins that inhibit the growth of competing organisms. Many of these compounds are **secondary metabolites**, which are not required for day-to-day survival but are beneficial to the fungus. As we will see, many of these compounds not only are important in the life of a fungus but also benefit organisms associated with the fungus. Many are also of commercial or medical importance to humans; for example, the antibiotic penicillin is a secondary metabolite produced by a species of *Penicillium*.

Fungi reproduce by spores, and this spore production can be amazingly prolific, with some species of fungi producing billions of spores per day **(Figure 25.4)**. These spores are microscopic, featherlight, and able to survive in the environment for extended periods after they are released. Reproducing via such spores allows fungi to be opportunists, germinating only when favourable conditions exist and quickly exploiting food sources that occur unpredictably in the environment. Releasing vast numbers of spores, as some fungi do, improves the odds that the spores will germinate and produce a new individual.

Spores can be produced asexually or sexually; some fungi produce both asexual and sexual spores at different stages of their lives. Sexual reproduction in fungi is complex. In all organisms, sexual reproduction involves three stages: the fusion of two haploid cells (**plasmogamy**), bringing together their two nuclei in one common cytoplasm. Cytoplasmic fusion in most organisms is quickly followed by nuclear fusion (**karyogamy**), but in fungi the cells can remain bi-nucleate as the organism grows. Nuclear fusion is often followed by meiosis to produce genetically distinct haploid spores. As we will see, fungi are unique in that plasmogamy and karyogamy can be separated in time for durations ranging from seconds to many years.

FIGURE 25.4 **Spore production by fungal fruiting bodies.** Some fruiting bodies can release billions of spores per day.

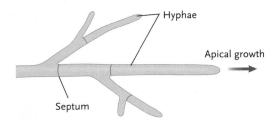

FIGURE 25.3 **Septa.** In some fungi, septa divide each hypha into separate compartments.

25.2 Evolution and Diversity of Fungi

25.2a Fungi Were Present on Earth by at Least 760 Million Years Ago

For many years, fungi were classified as plants because the earliest classification schemes had only two kingdoms, plants and animals. Fungi, like plants, have cell walls and do not move, so they were grouped with plants. As biologists learned more about the distinctive characteristics of fungi, however, it became clear that fungi should be treated as a separate kingdom.

CONCEPT FIX The idea that fungi are most closely related to plants has persisted, but this is a misconception! The discovery of chitin in fungal cells and recent comparisons of DNA and RNA sequences all indicate that fungi and animals are more closely related to each other than they are to other eukaryotes. The close biochemical relationship between fungi and animals may explain why fungal infections are typically so resistant to treatment and why it has proved rather difficult to develop drugs that kill fungi without damaging their human or other animal hosts. ⬡

Analysis of the sequences of several genes suggests that the lineages leading to animals and fungi likely diverged between 760 mya and 1 billion years ago (bya). What were the first fungi like? We do not know for certain; phylogenetic studies indicate that fungi first arose from a single-celled, flagellated protist. In Chapter 24 you were introduced to the choanoflagellates. Single-celled choanoflagellates evidently gave rise to the lineage of animals. These are closely related to nucleariids (single-celled amoebas), belonging to a different line of protists. This suggests that multicellular forms of animals and fungi evolved independently.

Although traces of what may be fossil fungi exist in rock formations nearly 1 billion years old, the oldest fossils that we can confidently assign to the modern **kingdom Fungi** appear in rock strata laid down in the late Proterozoic (900–570 mya).

25.2b Once They Appeared, Fungi Radiated into Several Major Lineages

Most likely, the first fungi were aquatic. When other kinds of organisms began to colonize land, they may well have brought fungi along with them. For example, researchers have discovered what appear to be mycorrhizae—symbiotic associations of a fungus and a plant—in fossils of some of the earliest-known land plants.

Over time, fungi diverged into the strikingly diverse lineages that we consider in the rest of this section (**Table 25.1**). Today, there are approximately 100 000 described species of fungi, with at least 1.6 million more that have not yet been described.

As the lineages diversified, different adaptations associated with reproduction arose. For example, structures in which sexual spores are formed and mechanisms by which spores are dispersed became larger and more elaborate over evolutionary time. Traditionally, therefore, biologists have classified fungi primarily by the distinctive structures produced in sexual reproduction. These features are still useful indicators of the phylogenetic standing of a fungus, but the powerful tools of molecular analysis are bringing many revisions to our understanding of the evolutionary journey of fungi.

The evolutionary origins and lineages of fungi have been obscure ever since biologists began puzzling over the

TABLE 25.1	Summary of Fungal Phyla		
Phylum	Body Type	Key Feature	
Chytridiomycota (chytrids)	One to several cells	Motile spores propelled by flagella; usually asexual	
Zygomycota (zygomycetes)	Hyphal	Sexual stage in which a resistant zygospore forms for later germination	
Glomeromycota (glomeromycetes)	Hyphal	Hyphae associated with plant roots, forming arbuscular mycorrhizae	
Ascomycota (ascomycetes)	Hyphal	Sexual spores produced in sacs called *asci*	
Basidiomycota (basidiomycetes)	Hyphal	Sexual spores (basidiospores) form in basidia of a prominent fruiting body (basidiocarp).	
Cryptomycota (proposed)	Single cell	Sporelike parasites	

© Cengage Learning 2017.

characteristics of this group. With the advent of molecular techniques for research, these topics have become extremely active and exciting areas of biological research that may shed light on fundamental events in the evolution of all eukaryotes. Currently, we recognize five phyla of fungi, known formally as the Chytridiomycota, Zygomycota, Glomeromycota, Ascomycota, and Basidiomycota **(Figure 25.5).** However, we know now that two of these phyla, the Chytridiomycota and the Zygomycota, are not monophyletic (i.e., they are taxa that do not contain only one ancestor and all of its descendants). The earliest diverging branch of fungi indicated in Figure 25.5 is the Cryptomycota, included here at the phylum level (Figure 25.5). It is a clade encompassing groups of single-celled fungi. The classification scheme presented in Figure 25.5 will soon change to reflect this new information. Why do classifications of organisms change so often? Bear in mind that classification schemes such as those presented here are hypotheses that explain our best understanding of evolutionary relationships among organisms at any one time; like any other hypotheses, classification schemes are open to revision as we find out more about the organisms. Molecular data also suggest that some other eukaryotic organisms currently classified elsewhere may actually be fungi; we haven't included those organisms in this chapter but instead will focus on the groups of fungi that are best understood. Even though fungal classification will change greatly over the next few years, we summarize the major phyla recognized today as a way of illustrating the diversity of this group of organisms.

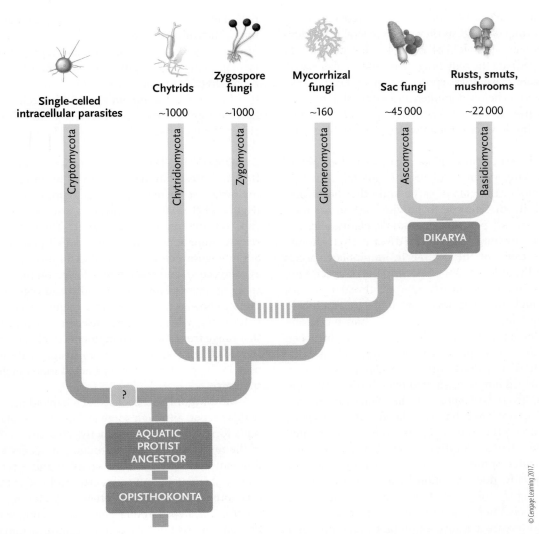

FIGURE 25.5 A phylogeny of fungi. This scheme represents a widely accepted view of the general relationships between major groups of fungi, but it may well be revised as new molecular findings provide more information. The dashed lines indicate that two groups, the chytrids and the zygomycetes, are probably paraphyletic—they include subgroups that are not all descended from a single ancestor. Based on genomic studies, some mycologists place microsporidia and certain fungi formerly classified as chytrids in a new, basal phylum, the Cryptomycota. The question mark indicates ongoing debate about whether the clade meets the technical definition of a phylum.

a. Chytridiomycosis in a frog

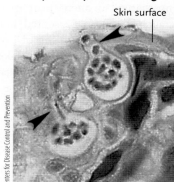

Skin surface

b. Harlequin frog

FIGURE 25.6 **Chytrids. (a)** Chytridiomycosis, a fungal infection, shown here in the skin of a frog. The two arrows point to flask-shaped, spore-producing cells of the parasitic chytrid *Batrachochytrium dendrobatidis*, which has devastated populations of harlequin frogs **(b)**.

PHYLUM CHYTRIDIOMYCOTA The Chytridiomycota are likely the most ancient group of fungi, as they retain several traits characteristic of an aquatic lifestyle. For example, chytrids (as they are commonly called) are the only fungi that produce flagellated, motile spores **(Figure 25.6a)**; these spores use chemotaxis (movement in response to a chemical gradient) to locate suitable substrates. Chytrids live in soil or freshwater habitats, wherever there is at least a film of water through which their motile spores can swim.

Most chytrids are saprotrophs, organisms that obtain nutrients by breaking down dead organic matter, although some are symbionts in the guts of cattle and other herbivores where they break down cellulose to provide carbon for their hosts, and still others are parasites of animals, plants, algae, or other fungi. These tiny fungi also cause a disease, chytridiomycosis, that is one cause of the decline in amphibian species worldwide. Globally, at least 43% of all amphibian species are declining in population, and nearly 33% are threatened with extinction. Although many factors contribute to amphibian decline, including habitat loss, fragmentation, and increasing levels of environmental pollutants, chytridiomycosis has been linked to the decline of amphibian populations in Australia, New Zealand, Central and South America, and parts of Europe. This disease has wiped out an estimated two-thirds of the species of harlequin frogs (*Atelopus*) in the American tropics (Figure 25.6b). The epidemic has correlated with the rising average temperature in the frogs' habitats, an increase credited to global climate change. Studies show that the warmer environment provides optimal growing temperatures for the chytrid pathogen. How does infection by a chytrid kill these animals? The fungus colonizes the skin of amphibians (Figure 25.6b), which interferes with the electrolyte balance and functioning of organs because amphibians take up water and exchange gases through their skins.

Most chytrids are unicellular, although some live as chains of cells and have rhizoids (branching filamentous extensions) that anchor the fungus to its substrate and that may also absorb nutrients from the substrate (Figure 25.6a). The vegetative stage of most chytrids is haploid; asexual reproduction involves the formation of a **sporangium**, in which motile spores are formed. A few chytrids reproduce sexually via male and female gametes that fuse to form a diploid zygote. This cell may form a mycelium that gives rise to sporangia, or it may directly give rise to either asexual or sexual spores.

ZYGOMYCOTA This group of fungi includes the moulds on fruit and bread familiar to many of us and takes its name from the structure formed in sexual reproduction, the **zygospore (Figure 25.7)**. Many zygomycetes are saprotrophs that live in soil, feeding on organic matter. Their metabolic activities release mineral nutrients in forms that plant roots can take up. Some zygomycetes are parasites of insects (and even other zygomycetes), and some wreak havoc on human food supplies, spoiling stored grains, bread, fruits, and vegetables **(Figure 25.8)**. Others, however, have become major players in commercial enterprises, where they are used in manufacturing products that range from industrial pigments to pharmaceuticals such as steroids (e.g., anti-inflammatory drugs). Zygomycetes are also used in the production of fermented foods such as tempeh and soy sauce.

Most zygomycetes consist of a haploid mycelium that lacks regular septa, although some groups have septa, and in others, septa form to wall off reproductive structures and aging regions of the mycelium. Sexual reproduction occurs when mycelia of different **mating types** (known as + and − types, rather than male and female) produce specialized hyphae that grow toward each other and form sex organs (**gametangia**) at their tips (Figure 25.7, steps 1 and 2). How do gametangia find each other? Pheromones secreted by each mycelium stimulate the development of sexual structures in the complementary strain and cause gametangia to grow toward each other. The gametangia fuse, forming a thick-walled structure, a **zygosporangium**

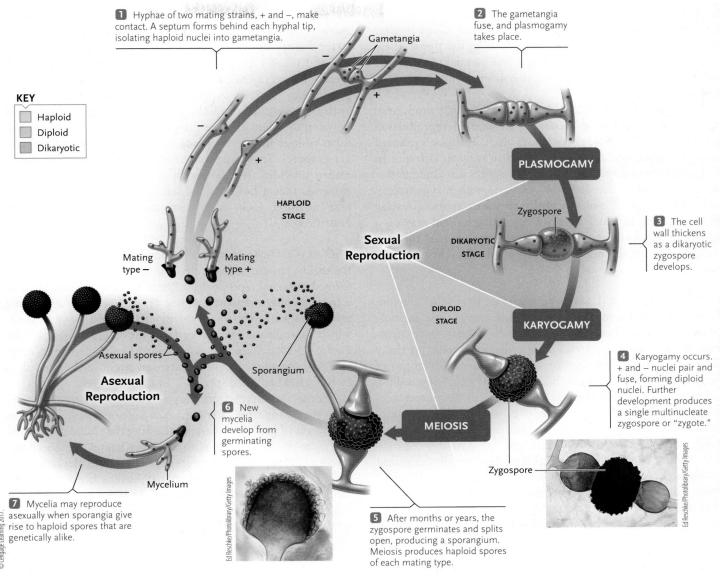

1 Hyphae of two mating strains, + and −, make contact. A septum forms behind each hyphal tip, isolating haploid nuclei into gametangia.

2 The gametangia fuse, and plasmogamy takes place.

Gametangia

KEY

	Haploid
	Diploid
	Dikaryotic

HAPLOID STAGE

Sexual Reproduction

PLASMOGAMY

Zygospore

DIKARYOTIC STAGE

3 The cell wall thickens as a dikaryotic zygospore develops.

Mating type −

Mating type +

DIPLOID STAGE

KARYOGAMY

Asexual spores

Sporangium

Asexual Reproduction

4 Karyogamy occurs. + and − nuclei pair and fuse, forming diploid nuclei. Further development produces a single multinucleate zygospore or "zygote."

MEIOSIS

6 New mycelia develop from germinating spores.

Zygospore

Mycelium

Ed Reschke/Photolibrary/Getty Images

7 Mycelia may reproduce asexually when sporangia give rise to haploid spores that are genetically alike.

© Cengage Learning 2017.

Ed Reschke/Photolibrary/Getty Images

5 After months or years, the zygospore germinates and splits open, producing a sporangium. Meiosis produces haploid spores of each mating type.

FIGURE 25.7 Life cycle of the bread mould *Rhizopus stolonifer*, a zygomycete. Asexual reproduction is common, but different mating types (+ and −) also reproduce sexually. In both cases, haploid spores are formed and give rise to new mycelia.

humbak/Shutterstock.com

FIGURE 25.8 Zygomycete fungus growing on strawberries

(Figure 25.7, step 3), which can remain dormant for months or years, allowing the zygomycete to survive unfavourable environmental conditions. Eventually, meiosis occurs in the zygosporangium, forming a meiosporangium that will produce haploid spores by meiosis. (Figure 25.7, step 5). Note that meiosis does not always produce gametes! We often tend to characterize meiosis as the formation of gametes, probably because we are so familiar with how sexual reproduction occurs in humans and other animals. But in many organisms, such as fungi and plants, meiosis results in the formation of haploid spores.

Like other fungi, however, zygomycetes also reproduce asexually, as shown in steps 6 and 7 of Figure 25.7. When a haploid spore lands on a favourable substrate, it germinates and gives rise to a branching mycelium. Some of the hyphae grow upward, and saclike sporangia form at the tips of these aerial hyphae. Inside the sporangia, the asexual cycle comes full circle as new haploid spores arise through mitosis and are released.

The black bread mould *Rhizopus stolonifer* may produce so many charcoal-coloured sporangia in asexual reproduction **(Figure 25.9a)** that mouldy bread looks black. The spores released are lightweight, dry, and readily wafted away by air currents. In fact, winds have dispersed *R. stolonifer* spores just about everywhere on Earth, including the Arctic. Another zygomycete, *Pilobolus* (Figure 25.9b), forcefully spews its sporangia away from the dung in which it grows. A grazing animal may eat a sporangium on a blade of grass; the spores then pass through the animal's gut unharmed and begin the life cycle again in a new dung pile.

GLOMEROMYCOTA Until recently, fungi in the phylum Glomeromycota were classified as zygomycetes based on morphological similarities such as the lack of regular septa. However, these fungi are quite dissimilar to zygomycetes in many ways (e.g., sexual reproduction is unknown in this group of fungi, with spores usually forming asexually simply by walling off a section of a hypha **(Figure 25.10b)**, causing many researchers to question the inclusion of these fungi in the phylum Zygomycota. Recent evidence from molecular studies resulted in these fungi being placed in their own phylum.

The 160 known members of this phylum are all specialized to form **mycorrhizae**, or symbiotic associations with plant roots. These fungi have a tremendous ecological importance, as they collectively make up roughly half the fungi in soil and form mycorrhizal associations with many land plants, including most major crop species such as wheat and maize. Mycelia of these fungi colonize the roots of host plants and also proliferate in the soil around the plants. Inside the roots, hyphae penetrate cell walls and branch repeatedly to form **arbuscules** ("little trees"; Figure 25.10). The branches of each arbuscule are enfolded by the cell's plasma membrane, forming an interface with a large surface area through which nutrients are exchanged between the plant and the fungus. Some glomeromycetes also form vesicles inside roots, which store nutrients and can also act as spores. The fungus obtains sugars from the plant and in return provides the plant with a steady supply of dissolved minerals that it has obtained from the surrounding soil. We take a closer look at mycorrhizae in Chapter 36 (Plant Nutrition).

ASCOMYCOTA The phylum Ascomycota takes its name from the saclike structures (**asci**; singular, *ascus*) in which spores are formed in sexual reproduction. These asci are often enclosed in a fruiting body (**ascocarp; Figure 25.11a, b, c**). However, some ascomycetes are yeasts or filamentous fungi with a yeast stage, which reproduce asexually by budding or binary fission (see Figure 25.13). Ascomycetes are much more numerous than chytrids, zygomycetes, or glomeromycetes, with more than 30 thousand identified species.

Some ascomycetes are very useful to humans. One species, the orange bread mould *Neurospora crassa*, has been important in genetic research, including the elucidation of the one gene–one enzyme hypothesis (see Chapter 12). *Saccharomyces cerevisiae*, which produces the ethanol in alcoholic beverages and the carbon dioxide that leavens bread, is also a model organism used in genetic research. By one estimate, it has been the subject of more genetic experiments than any other eukaryotic microorganism. This multifaceted phylum

a. Sporangia of Rhizopus nigricans

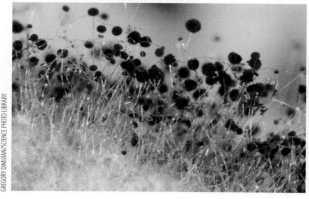

b. Sporangia (dark sacs) of *Pilobolus*

500 μm

FIGURE 25.9 Two of the numerous strategies for spore dispersal by zygomycetes. (a) The sporangia of *Rhizopus stolonifer*, shown here on a slice of bread, release powdery spores that are easily dispersed by air currents. **(b)** In *Pilobolus*, the spores are contained in a sporangium (the dark sac) at the end of a stalked structure. When incoming rays of sunlight strike a light-sensitive portion of the stalk, turgor pressure (pressure against a cell wall due to the movement of water into the cell) inside a vacuole in the swollen portion becomes so great that the entire sporangium may be ejected outward as far as 2 m—a remarkable feat given that the stalk is only 5 to 10 mm tall.

a. Arbuscules and Vesicle in roots colonized by arbuscular mycorrhizal fungus

b. Arbuscules inside root

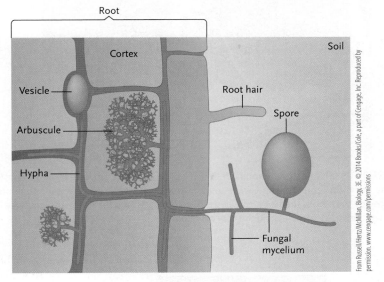

FIGURE 25.10 Glomeromycete fungus forming a mycorrhiza. (a) Root cells of leek growing in association with the glomeromycete fungus *Glomus versiforme* (longitudinal section). **(b)** Arbuscules and vesicle that have formed as fungal hyphae branch after entering the root.

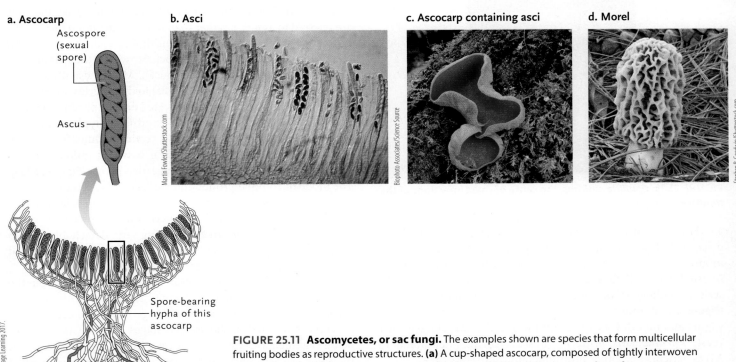

FIGURE 25.11 Ascomycetes, or sac fungi. The examples shown are species that form multicellular fruiting bodies as reproductive structures. **(a)** A cup-shaped ascocarp, composed of tightly interwoven hyphae. The spore-producing asci occur inside the cup. **(b)** Asci on the inner surface of an ascocarp. **(c)** Scarlet cup fungus (*Sarcoscypha*). **(d)** A true morel (*Morchella esculenta*), a prized edible fungus

also includes gourmet delicacies such as truffles (*Tuber melanosporum*) and the succulent morel *Morchella esculenta* (Figure 25.11d).

Many ascomycetes are saprotrophs, playing a key role in the breakdown of cellulose and other polymers. Ascomycetes are also common in symbiotic associations, forming mycorrhizae and lichens (see Section 25.3). A few ascomycetes prey on various agricultural insect pests—some are even carnivores that trap their prey in nooses **(Figure 25.12a)**—and thus have potential for use as biological pesticides.

a. A trapping ascomycete

George L. Barron

b. Stump of pine tree infected with blue-stain fungus

U.S. Forest Service

FIGURE 25.12 **(a)** Nematode-trapping fungus. Hyphae of this ascomycete (*Arthrobotrys*) form nooselike rings. When a prey organism enters the loop, rapid changes in ion concentration draw water into the loop by osmosis. The increased turgor pressure causes the noose to tighten, trapping its prey. Enzymes produced by the fungus then break down the nematode's tissues. **(b)** Stump of a pine tree infected with blue-stain fungus. The fungus grows into the tree's water-conducting tissue, blocking the flow of water.

Yeast cells

BSIP/Contributor/UIG via Getty Images

FIGURE 25.13 *Candida albicans,* **the cause of yeast infections of the mouth and vagina**

However, other ascomycetes are devastating plant pathogens, including the blue-stain fungi that are associated with mountain pine beetles and contribute to the death of beetle-infested trees (Figure 25.12b). Several ascomycetes can be serious pathogens of humans. The yeast *Candida albicans* **(Figure 25.13)** infects mucous membranes, especially of the vagina and mouth (causing a condition called *thrush*). Another yeast, *Pneumocystis jirovecii*, causes virulent pneumonia in AIDS patients and other immunocompromised people.

Claviceps purpurea, a parasite on rye and other grains, causes ergotism, a disease marked by vomiting, hallucinations, convulsions, and, in severe cases, gangrene and even death. It has even been suggested that this fungus was the cause of the Salem witch hunts of seventeenth century New England. Other ascomycetes cause nuisance infections, such as athlete's foot and ringworm.

Most ascomycetes grow as haploid mycelia with regular septa; large pores in the septa allow organelles, including nuclei, to move with cytoplasm through the mycelium. Sexual reproduction generally involves fusion of hyphae from mycelia of $+$ and $-$ mating types **(Figure 25.14)**. The cytoplasms of the two hyphae fuse, but fusion of the nuclei is delayed, resulting in the formation of **dikaryotic hyphae** that contain two separate nuclei and thus are referred to as $n + n$ rather than n or $2n$. Sacs (asci) form at the tips of these dikaryotic hyphae; inside the asci, the two nuclei fuse, forming a diploid zygote nucleus, which then undergoes meiosis to produce four haploid nuclei. Mitosis usually follows, resulting in the formation of eight haploid spores (**ascospores**).

Unlike zygomycetes, ascomycetes do not produce asexual spores in sporangia. Instead, modified hyphae produce numerous asexual spores called **conidia** ("dust"; singular, *conidium*), such as those seen when powdery mildew attacks grasses, roses, and other common garden plants **(Figure 25.15a)**. The mode of conidial production varies from species to species, with some ascomycetes producing chains of conidia, whereas in others, the conidia are produced on a hypha in a series of "bubbles," rather like a string of detachable beads (Figure 25.15b). Either way, conidia are formed and released much more quickly than zygomycete spores.

Asexual reproductive structures look very different from the sexual stages and are often not formed at the same time or under the same conditions as the sexual stage of the life cycle. These differences resulted in the asexual stages of many ascomycetes being classified as separate organisms from the sexual stages of the same species. Since fungal classification traditionally relied on features produced in sexual reproduction, these asexual stages could not be placed in any of the phyla; instead, researchers grouped them together in an artificial group called the *Deuteromycota* (also known as *Fungi Imperfecti*, or the "imperfect fungi"—imperfect meaning that a sexual stage is absent). Well-known examples of fungi once classified as deuteromycetes are *Penicillium* and *Aspergillus*. Certain species of *Penicillium*

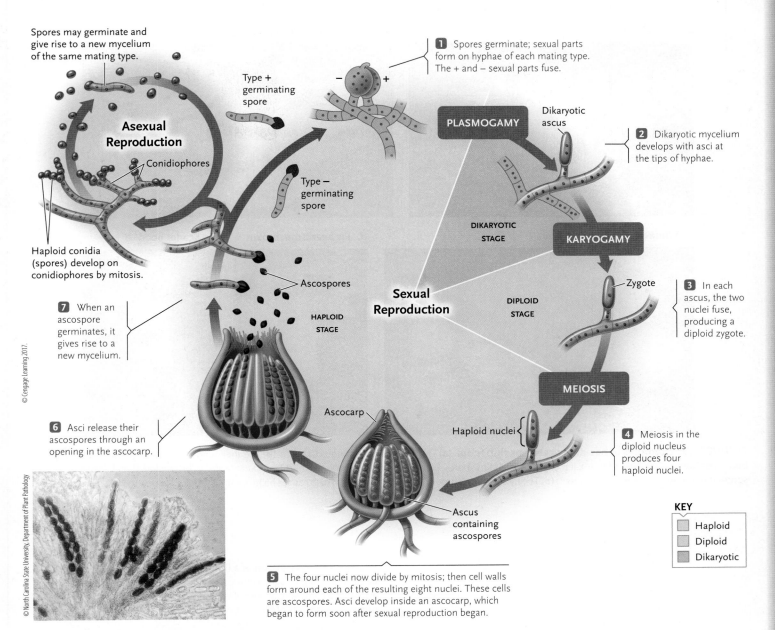

FIGURE 25.14 Life cycle of the ascomycete *Neurospora crassa*

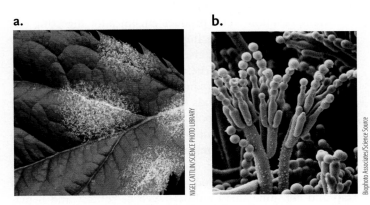

FIGURE 25.15 **(a)** Powdery mildew on leaves. **(b)** Conidia of *Penicillium*. Note the rows of conidia (asexual spores) atop the elongate cells that produce them.

(Figure 25.15b) are the source of the penicillin family of antibiotics, whereas others produce the aroma and distinctive flavours of Camembert and Roquefort cheeses. Strains of *Aspergillus* grow in damp grain or peanuts. Their metabolic wastes, known as *aflatoxins*, can cause cancer in humans who eat the poisoned food over an extended period. With the development of molecular sequencing techniques, many fungi that were classified as deuteromycetes can now be reassigned to the appropriate phylum; most are ascomycetes, but some are basidiomycetes, which also produce conidia in asexual reproduction.

BASIDIOMYCOTA The 24 000 or so species of fungi in the phylum Basidiomycota include the mushroom-forming species, bracket fungi, stinkhorns, smuts, rusts, and puffballs **(Figure 25.16)**. The common name for this group is club fungi

a. Coral fungus

b. Shelf fungus

c. White-egg bird's nest fungus

d. Fly agaric mushroom

e. Scarlet hood

FIGURE 25.16 Examples of basidiomycetes, or club fungi. (a) The light red coral fungus *Ramaria*. **(b)** The shelf fungus *Polyporus*. **(c)** The white-egg bird's nest fungus *Crucibulum laeve*. Each tiny "egg" contains spores. Raindrops splashing into the "nest" can cause "eggs" to be ejected, thereby spreading spores into the surrounding environment. **(d)** The fly agaric mushroom *Amanita muscaria*, which causes hallucinations. **(e)** The scarlet hood *Hygrophorus*

FIGURE 25.17 A portion of a lignin molecule. Unlike most other biopolymers, lignin is not composed of regularly repeating monomers, but instead is a complex polymer of various phenylpropanoid units joined together by a range of diverse bonds, making it very difficult to degrade.

due to the club-shaped cells (**basidia**; singular, *basidium*) on which sexual spores are produced.

Many basidiomycetes produce enzymes for digesting cellulose and lignin, and are important decomposers of woody plant debris. Very few organisms can degrade lignin due to its very complex, irregular structure **(Figure 25.17)**. The ability to degrade lignin also enables some basidiomycetes to break down complex organic compounds such as DDT, PCBs, and other persistent environmental pollutants that are structurally similar to lignin. Bioremediation of contaminated sites by these fungi is a very active research area.

A surprising number of basidiomycetes, including the prized edible oyster mushrooms (*Pleurotus ostreatus*), can also trap and consume small animals such as rotifers and nematodes by secreting paralyzing toxins or gluey substances that immobilize the prey, in a manner similar to that shown earlier for ascomycetes (Figure 25.12). As is the case for insectivorous plants, such as the pitcher plants (*Sarracenia purpurea*) discussed in Chapters 19 and 31, this adaptation gives the fungus access to a rich source of molecular nitrogen, an essential nutrient that is often scarce in terrestrial habitats. For example, the wood that is the substrate for many basidiomycetes is high in carbon but low in nitrogen; many wood-decay fungi have been found to be carnivorous, obtaining supplemental nitrogen from various invertebrates.

Some basidiomycetes form mycorrhizae with the roots of forest trees, as discussed in Chapter 36 (Plant Nutrition). Recent research has shown that these mycorrhizae can be drawn into associations with achlorophyllous plants (plants that lack chlorophyll and so cannot carry out photosynthesis), which thus obtain nutrients from the trees via shared mycorrhizal fungi. Other basidiomycetes, the rusts and smuts, are parasites that cause serious diseases in wheat, rice, and other plants. Still others produce millions of dollars' worth of the common edible button mushroom (*Agaricus bisporus*) sold in grocery stores. *Amanita muscaria* (Figure 25.16d) has been used in the religious rituals of ancient societies in Central America, Russia, and India. Other species of this genus, including the death cap mushroom *Amanita phalloides*, produce deadly toxins. The *A. phalloides* toxin, called α-amanitin, halts gene transcription, and hence protein synthesis, by inhibiting the activity of RNA polymerase. Within 8–24 hours of ingesting as little as 5 mg of the mushroom, vomiting and diarrhea begin. Later, kidney and liver cells start to degenerate; without intensive medical care, death can follow within a few days. You can read more about the effect of amanitin on gene expression in Chapter 12.

Most basidiomycetes are mycelial, although some grow as yeasts. The mycelium of many basidiomycetes contains two different, separate nuclei as a result of fusion between two different haploid mycelia and is thus a dikaryon (**Figure 25.18**). A dikaryotic mycelium is formed following fusion of the two

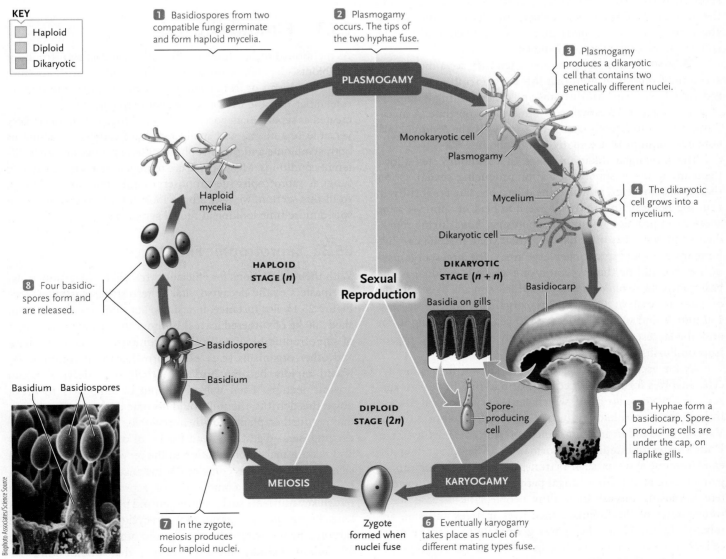

FIGURE 25.18 **Generalized life cycle of the basidiomycete *Agaricus bisporus*, a species known commonly as the *button mushroom*.** During the dikaryotic stage, cells contain two genetically different nuclei, shown here in different colours. Inset: Micrograph showing basidia and basidiospores

haploid mycelia when both types of nuclei divide and migrate through the mycelium such that each hyphal compartment contains two dissimilar nuclei.

Basidiomycete fungi can grow for most of their lives as dikaryon mycelia, a major departure from an ascomycete's short-lived dikaryotic stage. After an extensive mycelium develops, favourable environmental conditions trigger the formation of fruiting bodies (**basidiocarps**) in which basidia develop. A basidiocarp consists of tight clusters of hyphae; the feeding mycelium is buried in the substrate. The shelflike bracket fungi visible on trees are basidiocarps, as are the structures we call mushrooms and toadstools. Each mushroom is a short-lived reproductive body consisting of a stalk and a cap; basidia develop on "gills," the sheets of tissue on the underside of the cap. Inside each basidium, the two nuclei fuse; meiosis follows, resulting in the formation of four haploid **basidiospores** on the outside of the basidium (Figure 25.18). Why does the fungus expend energy and resources on such elaborate spore-dispersal structures? A layer of still air occurs just above the ground (and any other surface); by elevating the basidia above this layer, the fungus increases the likelihood that its spores will be carried away by the wind.

CONCEPT FIX People often assume when they see a mushroom sprouting from the ground that this fungal fruiting body is an individual. Not true! Mushrooms and other fruiting bodies are produced by mycelia growing through their substrate. A mycelium, not a mushroom or fruiting body, is the "individual." One mycelium produces many fruiting bodies.

The prolonged dikaryon stage in basidiomycetes allows them many more opportunities for producing sexual spores than in ascomycetes, in which the dikaryon state is short lived. Fruiting bodies can produce huge numbers of spores—some species can produce 100 million spores *per hour* during reproductive periods, day after day! Basidiomycete mycelia can live for many years and spread over large areas. The largest organism on Earth could be the mycelium of a single individual of the basidiomycete *Armillaria ostoyae*, which spreads over 8.9 km^2 of land in eastern Oregon. This organism weighs at least 150 tonnes and is likely at least 2400 years old, making it not only the largest but also one of the heaviest and oldest organisms on Earth.

As for ascomycetes, asexual reproduction in basidiomycetes involves formation of conidia or budding in yeast forms such as *Cryptococcus gattii*, which causes cryptococcal disease in humans. A virulent strain of *C. gattii*, first reported from Vancouver Island in 1999, has since spread to the northwestern United States and California. Normally, only people with weakened immune systems, such as transplant recipients and cancer patients, are at risk from fungal pathogens, but *C. gattii* is different, causing disease in healthy people. The disease starts when spores of the fungus, which lives in trees and soil, are inhaled. In the lungs, the spores germinate to produce yeast cells that proliferate by budding in the warm, moist lung environment; the yeast cells then spread to the central nervous system via the bloodstream. The disease is characterized by a severe cough, fever, and, if the nervous system is affected, seizures and other neurological symptoms.

STUDY BREAK QUESTIONS

1. What evidence is there that fungi are more closely related to animals than to plants?
2. Name the five phyla of the kingdom Fungi, and describe the reproductive adaptations that distinguish them.
3. What are the two main differences between asexual spores produced by zygomycetes and asexual spores produced by ascomycetes?
4. Fungi reproduce sexually or asexually but, for many species, the life cycle includes an unusual stage not seen in other organisms. What is this genetic condition, and what is its role in the life cycle?

25.3 Fungal Lifestyles

As mentioned earlier, fungi can be categorized as saprotrophs or symbionts, depending on whether they obtain nutrients from living organisms or from dead organic matter. It is important to remember that the categories of *saprotroph* and *symbiont* were created as separate categories to classify fungi, but fungi are very versatile organisms, and many fungi are capable of acting as both symbionts and saprotrophs at different times or under different conditions. Most people are more familiar with the role of fungi as saprotrophs (decomposers) rather than as symbionts, so in this section, we take a brief look at saprotrophy and then spend more time looking at fungal symbioses.

25.3a Saprotrophic Fungi

With their adaptations for efficient extracellular digestion, fungi are masters of the decay so vital to terrestrial ecosystems (see Figure 25.1). For instance, in a single autumn, one elm tree can shed 200 kg of withered leaves! Without the metabolic activities of saprotrophic fungi and other decomposers such as bacteria and other organisms (e.g., earthworms), natural communities would rapidly become buried in their own **detritus** (dead organic matter). Even worse, without decomposers to break down this detritus, the soil would become depleted of nutrients, making further plant growth impossible. As fungi (and other decomposers) digest the dead tissues of other organisms, they also make a major contribution to the recycling of the chemical elements those tissues contain. For instance, over time, the degradation of organic compounds by saprotrophic fungi helps return key nutrients such as nitrogen and phosphorus to ecosystems. But the prime example of this recycling virtuosity involves carbon. The respiring cells of fungi and other decomposers give off carbon dioxide, liberating carbon that would otherwise remain locked in the tissues of dead organisms. Each year, this activity recycles a vast amount of carbon to plants, the primary producers of nearly all ecosystems on Earth.

However, there is a downside to the impressive enzymatic abilities of saprotrophic fungi; for example, when they decompose materials that are part of our houses, they can cause major economic and health problems. Fungi growing on wood and drywall following flooding or water damage to a building **(Figure 25.19a)** not only weaken the structural integrity of the building but also can be health hazards. The airborne spores of these fungi act as allergens, and some can also cause more serious health problems; for example, some fungi can colonize and grow in sinus cavities. Another example is dry rot, which causes millions of dollars in damage to buildings in Europe, Asia, and Australia (Figure 25.19b). Dry rot is notorious not only because it causes widespread and costly damage but also because the responsible fungus, *Serpula lacrymans*, seems to have the mysterious ability to break down dry wood completely, which should not be possible—as described above, wood decay usually happens once wood becomes wet. Does this fungus really have the amazing ability to break down dry wood? In fact, this fungus is as dependent on water for growth as any other, but it can form specialized mycelial cords, which very efficiently transport water and nutrients over long distances through concrete, bricks, and other unfavourable substrates until the fungus at last finds wood. Then the mycelial cords release water into the substrate, allowing the fungus to spread through the wood and begin the process of decay.

25.3b Symbiotic Fungi

Symbiotic associations range from mutualism, in which both partners benefit, to parasitism, in which one partner benefits at the expense of the other. Many fungal parasites are pathogens, parasites that cause disease symptoms in their hosts. We discussed several examples of fungal diseases in humans and other animals earlier in this chapter as well as very important, mutually beneficial symbioses, including mycorrhizae. Mycorrhizae are important for plant growth and will be featured in Chapter 36. In Chapter 30 general features of symbiotic associations are discussed more fully; here, we will explore examples of the symbioses fungi form with other organisms.

LICHENS ARE ASSOCIATIONS BETWEEN A FUNGUS AND ONE OR MORE PHOTOSYNTHETIC ORGANISMS Up until recently, it was thought that lichens were composed of two symbionts: a fungus (mycobiont), most commonly an ascomycete; and a unicellular green alga or blue-green bacteria (photobiont). A research group discovered that a third symbiont, a basidiomycete yeast, is also present in many lichens (see **Figure 25.20**).

Lichens grow as crusts on rocks, bark, or soil; as flattened leaflike forms; or as radially symmetrical cups, treelike structures, or hairlike strands **(Figure 25.21)**. This range of morphologies has intrigued scientists for years. Lichens have vital ecological roles and important human uses. They secrete acids that eat away at rock, breaking it down and converting it to soil that can support plants. Animals, such as caribou (*Rangifer tarandus*), rely on lichens for their winter forage. Some environmental chemists monitor air pollution by monitoring lichens, most of which cannot grow in heavily polluted air because they cannot discriminate between pollutants and mineral nutrients present in the atmosphere. Just as they do for mineral nutrients, lichens efficiently absorb airborne pollutants and concentrate them in their tissues. Humans use lichens as sources of dyes and perfumes, as well as medicines. Lichen chemicals are currently being explored as a source of natural pesticides.

How are lichens constructed? The primary fungus (called the **mycobiont**) makes up most of the body (**thallus**) of the lichen, with the photosynthetic partner (**photobiont**) usually confined to a thin layer inside the lichen thallus (Figure 25.21a). When present, the basidiomycete yeast cells are found in the cortex—the thick outer layer. To make matters more complicated, some lichens have two photobionts: a green algal photobiont inside the thallus and a cyanobacterial photobiont contained in "pockets" on or in the thallus. Because lichens are composite organisms, it may seem odd to talk of lichen

a.

b.

FIGURE 25.19 **(a)** Mould growth following flooding. **(b)** Mycelium of dry rot (*Serpula lacrymans*) emerging through a wall

FIGURE 25.20   **Experimental Research**

Hidden Third Partner in Lichen Symbiosis

Question: Why were two species of ascomycete lichens, while genetically identical, very different in appearance?

Experiment: *Bryoria tortuosa* **(a)** is yellow and produces an abundance of a nasty secondary compound, vulpinic acid, whereas *Bryoria fremontii* **(c)** is brown and produces the toxin in only small amounts. Initially, mRNA transcriptome analysis (Chapter 12) revealed no correlation between genotype and phenotype in the two lichens. Researchers broadened their analysis to include basidiomycete transcriptomes. Having discovered the presence of a basidiomycete yeast, they tested to see if there was a correlation between the presence of the yeast and the production of vulpinic acid.

Results: When the analysis included basidiomycete transcriptomes, researchers found a third partner in this symbiosis, a basidiomycete yeast (*Cyphobasidium*). The amount of vulpinic acid was correlated with the presence of the yeast; the yeast was more abundant in thalli with high concentrations of vulpinic acid **(b)** than in those with low concentrations **(d)**.

Conclusions: The discovery of an additional basidiomycete yeast symbiont was an unexpected outcome of this research, and has changed what we know about lichen symbiosis. The long-held assumption that the primary fungus (ascomycete) is responsible for the production of vulpinic acid has now been put into question. Is the yeast or the ascomycete responsible for its synthesis? To answer this question, the biosynthetic pathway of the compound will have to be elucidated.

Source: Toby Spribille, et al. 2016. Basidiomycete yeasts in the cortex of asco-mycete macrolichens. *Science* (July: published online); DOI: 10.1126/science. aaf8287.

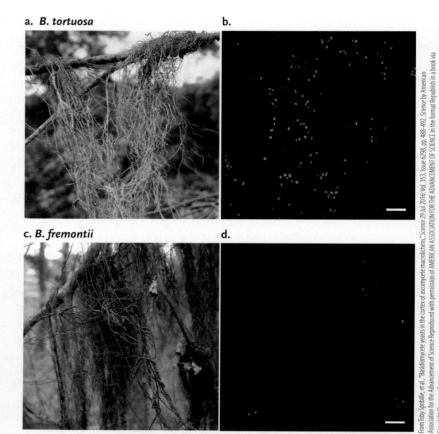

a. *B. tortuosa*   b.

c. *B. fremontii*   d.

From Toby Spribille, et al., "Basidiomycete yeasts in the cortex of ascomycete macrolichens," *Science* 29 Jul 2016: Vol. 353, Issue 6298, pp. 488-492. *Science* by American Association for the Advancement of Science Reproduced with permission of AMERICAN ASSOCIATION FOR THE ADVANCEMENT OF SCIENCE in the format Republish in a book via Copyright Clearance Center.

Differential abundance of Cyphobasidiales yeasts in B. *tortuosa* (b) and B. *fremontii* (d)

"species," but biologists do give lichens binomial names, which are based on the mycobiont. More than 13 500 different lichen species are recognized, each a unique combination of a particular species of fungus and one or more species of photobiont. As you might expect for a compound organism, reproduction can be complicated; it is not enough for each organism to reproduce itself, because formation of a new lichen requires that both partners be dispersed and end up together. Many lichens reproduce asexually by specialized fragments such as the **soredia** (singular, *soredium*; Figure 25.21b). Each soredium consists of photobiont cells wrapped in hyphae; the soredia can be dispersed by water, wind, or passing animals.

Inside the thallus, specialized hyphae of the mycobiont wrap around and sometimes penetrate photobiont cells, which become the fungus's sole source of carbon. Often the mycobiont absorbs up to 80% of the carbohydrates produced by the photobiont. Benefits for the photobiont are less clear-cut, in part because the drain on nutrients hampers its growth and because the mycobiont often controls reproduction of the photobiont. In one view, many and possibly most lichens are

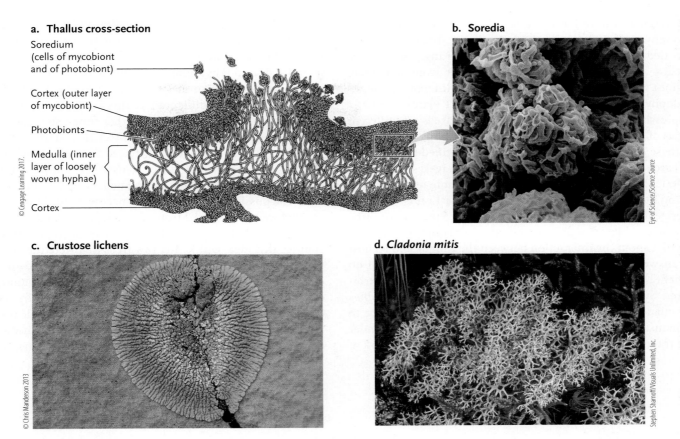

a. Thallus cross-section

Soredium
(cells of mycobiont
and of photobiont)

Cortex (outer layer
of mycobiont)

Photobionts

Medulla (inner
layer of loosely
woven hyphae)

Cortex

© Cengage Learning 2017.

b. Soredia

Eye of Science/Science Source

c. Crustose lichens

© Chris Manderson 2013

d. *Cladonia mitis*

Stephen Sharnoff/Visuals Unlimited, Inc.

FIGURE 25.21 Lichens. (a) Diagram of a cross-section through the thallus of the foliose lichen *Lobaria verrucosa*. **(b)** Soredia, which contain both hyphae and algal cells, are a type of dispersal fragment by which lichens reproduce asexually. **(c)** Crustose lichens. **(d)** Cladonia mitis, a branching, treelike lichen

parasitic symbioses, with the fungus enslaving the photobiont. On the other hand, although it is relatively rare to find a lichen photobiont species living independently in the same conditions under which the lichen survives, it may eke out an enduring existence as part of a lichen; some lichens have been dated as being more than 4000 years old! Studies have also revealed that at least some green algae clearly benefit from the relationship. Such algae are sensitive to desiccation and intense ultraviolet radiation. Sheltered by the lichen's fungal tissues, a green alga can thrive in locales where alone it would perish.

Lichens often live in harsh, dry microenvironments, including on bare rock and wind-whipped tree trunks. Some lichens actually live *inside* rocks. Unlike plants, lichens do not control water loss from their tissues; instead, their water status reflects that of their environment, and some lichens may dry out and re-wet several times a day. Lichens are very slow growing, even though the photobiont may have photosynthetic rates comparable to those of free-living species. What happens to all the carbohydrates made in photosynthesis if they are not used to fuel growth? The mycobiont takes much of the carbohydrate made by the photobiont and uses it to synthesize sec-

ondary metabolites and other compounds that allow the lichen to survive the repeated wet–dry cycles and extreme temperatures common in their habitats. These compounds give lichens their vibrant colours and may also inhibit grazing on lichens by slugs and other invertebrates. The mycobiont uses other lichen chemicals to control the photobiont; some chemicals regulate photobiont reproduction, whereas others cause photobiont cells to "leak" carbohydrates to the mycobiont. The transfer of nutrients and interactions between the basidiomycete yeast and the other partners in this symbiosis are unclear. In the lichens where they have been identified, it is apparent that they contribute to chemical defences and pigmentation. We still have much to learn about the physiological interactions between lichen partners.

ENDOPHYTES ARE FUNGI LIVING IN THE ABOVE-GROUND TISSUES OF PLANTS Just as the roots of many plants are colonized by fungi, so too are leaves and shoots **(Figure 25.22)**. Although some of these fungi are pathogens, many others evidently peacefully coexist with their plant hosts and in some cases are beneficial.

Biologists have known about the presence of these leaf endophytes for some time, but recent discoveries have revealed a startling diversity of these fungi, sometimes within a single plant. Samples of plants from temperate regions have been revealed to have tens of different species of endophytes in a single plant, but tropical plants are truly impressive, with several reports of hundreds of different types of endophytes being isolated from a single plant. Most of these endophytes have not yet been identified to species as researchers have not yet observed sexual stages, so it is difficult to know how many species of endophytes are really living in these tropical plants. A bigger question is, what are these endophytes doing in these leaves? Are they mutualists, like mycorrhizal fungi? In many cases, we simply don't know enough about the interaction between the fungus and its host to answer these questions but, in some cases, the fungi do benefit their plant hosts by producing toxins that deter herbivores. Synthesis of toxins and other secondary metabolites has made these endophytes of great potential importance to humans. For example, the anticancer drug taxol (sold under the tradename Taxol) was originally isolated from the bark of the Pacific yew tree (*Taxus brevifolia*). Production of taxol from this source was limited since the tree is quite rare and makes only a small amount of taxol. However, researchers later discovered that a fungal endophyte living in the needles of the Pacific yew also makes taxol, as do other endophytes living in completely different tree species. Evidence indicates that taxol inhibits the growth of other fungi, so these endophytes may be producing it to protect themselves. Did the genes to produce taxol get transferred from the fungi to the plant? Such horizontal gene transfer is known to have occurred in the evolution of organelles such as mitochondria. The possibility that the genes necessary for biosynthesis of taxol were transferred from the endophyte to its host plant is intriguing but, as of yet, there is no conclusive evidence to support this idea. Unlike the yew trees that were the original source of taxol, these endophytic fungi can be grown very easily in the lab, so we may be able to produce large amounts of this promising anti-cancer drug, also very easily. What other sources of medicines are out there, hiding inside plants? The possibility of finding new antibiotics and medicinal compounds makes saving rainforests even more urgent, as

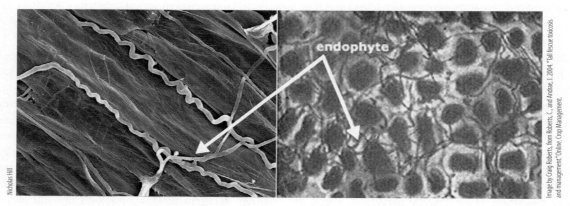

FIGURE 25.22 Endophytes growing inside stem (left) and seed (right)

FIGURE 25.23 **Rust fungus on a leaf**

not only the trees are disappearing but the endophytes inside them as well.

RUSTS AND CROPS Wheat, barley, oats, and rye are main crops on the Canadian prairies and are susceptible to a number of pathogens, including rust fungus. This fungus gets its name from the small spore producing lesions that are often reddish **(Figure 25.23)**. Rusts are basidiomycetes that often require two hosts to complete their life cycle and have five spore stages. For example, wheat rust (*Puccinia graminis*) lives within the shoot tissues of grasses such as wheat. It produces spores (Figure 25.23) to infect more wheat. As summer comes to an end, sexual spores are produced that end up overwintering in the dead shoots. These are the basidiospores and they can infect only the alternate host, barberry. The basidiospores germinate and hyphae grow through the barberry's leaf tissues, absorbing nutrients. Cup-shaped spore-producing structures are produced on the upper surface and are carried in a sticky exudate by insects (or rain water) to other leaves of the same plants or nearby barberry plants. This is the stage at which plasmogamy occurs. The spores act as gametes and are delivered to special receptive hyphae that project from these spore-producing structures. The spores and the receptive hyphae must be of different mating types for plasmogamy to occur. Like other basidiomycetes, the resulting dikaryotic mycelium will grow through the leaf (absorbing nutrients) and produce spore-producing structures on the lower side of the barberry leaf. These spores are wind dispersed and must land on wheat (or other grass) to germinate. Understanding this complicated life cycle was important, as huge crop losses were suffered due to wheat rust. In the early 1900s there was a major barberry eradication program that was very successful. By 1917 the growth of this plant was prohibited. Barberry is still on the Prohibited Plant List of Canada, but you can find rust-resistant varieties of barberry wheat in nurseries. Introduction of barberry is regulated through the Canadian Food Inspection Agency (CFIA). Many rust-resistant varieties of wheat have also been developed, but resistance by the rust is a continuing battle. Plant breeders must keep one step ahead of these constantly evolving fungi. Rust negatively impacts the health of wheat because it lowers yields by absorbing valuable nutrients needed in fruit development, reducing the photosynthetic tissue of the plants due to fungal growth, as well increasing water loss due to impairment of the epidermis.

Even though fungi are not closely related to plants in an evolutionary sense, you can see that relationships between fungi and plants play important roles in the lives of both types of organisms. Many saprotrophic and parasitic fungi depend on plants or their products as a source of carbon. Plants rely on fungi for nutrients, either directly through mycorrhizal relationships or indirectly through the role of fungi as decomposers. The very first land plants likely relied on mycorrhizal associations to survive in the harsh new environments they faced. In the next chapter, we look at how land plants evolved and diversified.

STUDY BREAK QUESTIONS

1. Describe the difference between a saprotroph and a symbiont. Discuss two examples of each type of life style.
2. What is a lichen? Explain how the partners contribute to the whole organism.
3. What is an endophyte? Why is its relationship with its plant hosts of interest to medical researchers?

Summary Illustration

Fungi occur as single-celled yeasts or multicellular filamentous organisms. They gain nutrition by extracellular digestion and absorption. Saprotrophic species feed on non-living organic matter, while others are symbionts.

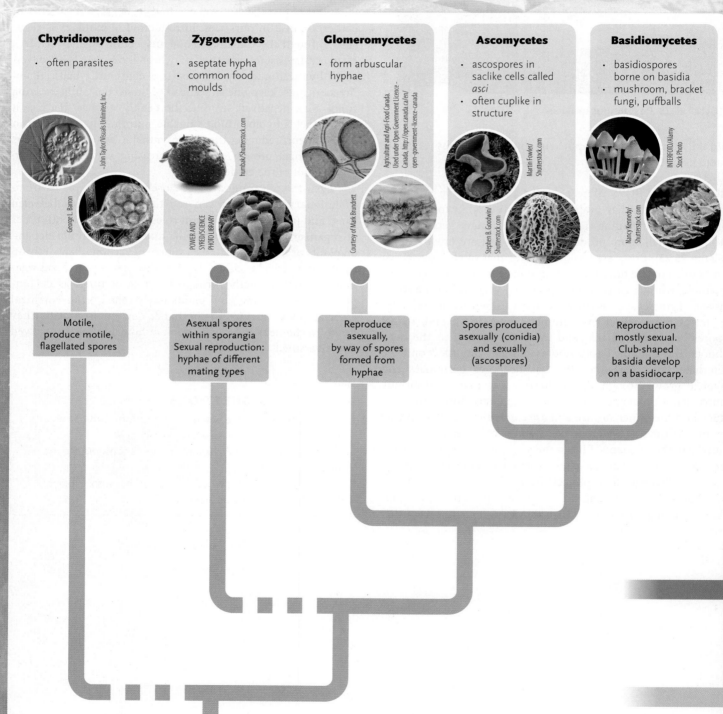

Chytridiomycetes
- often parasites

—John Taylor/Visuals Unlimited, Inc.

George L. Barron

Zygomycetes
- aseptate hypha
- common food moulds

humbak/Shutterstock.com

POWER AND SYRED/SCIENCE PHOTO LIBRARY

Glomeromycetes
- form arbuscular hyphae

Agriculture and Agri-Food Canada. Used under Open Government Licence – Canada, http://open.canada.ca/en/open-government-licence-canada

Courtesy of Mark Brundrett

Ascomycetes
- ascospores in saclike cells called *asci*
- often cuplike in structure

Martin Fowler/Shutterstock.com

Stephen B. Goodwin/Shutterstock.com

Basidiomycetes
- basidiospores borne on basidia
- mushroom, bracket fungi, puffballs

INTERFOTO/Alamy Stock Photo

Nancy Kennedy/Shutterstock.com

Motile, produce motile, flagellated spores

Asexual spores within sporangia Sexual reproduction: hyphae of different mating types

Reproduce asexually, by way of spores formed from hyphae

Spores produced asexually (conidia) and sexually (ascospores)

Reproduction mostly sexual. Club-shaped basidia develop on a basidiocarp.

Sexual Reproduction

**General Life Cycle
(Basidiomycetes and Ascomycetes)**

Mycelium or unicells

Plasmogamy between
compatible mycelium

Grows as dikaryon

Spores

MEIOSIS

Zygote

Cup fungus

Mushroom

Karyogamy occurs within
specialized cells or fruiting bodies

Asexual Reproduction is accomplished through the production of
asexual spores, budding, and fragmentation.

Saprotrophic species feed on non-living organic matter and are
key decomposers contributing to the recycling of carbon and other
nutrients in ecosystems.

Many fungi are **symbionts**, obtaining nutrients from organic matter
of living hosts. These symbioses range from parasitism, in which the
fungus benefits at the expense of its host, to mutualism, in which
both the fungus and its host benefit (e.g., mycorrhizae).

SELF-TEST QUESTIONS

Recall/Understand

1. Which of these traits is common to all fungi?
   a. parasitism
   b. septate hyphae
   c. reproduction via spores
   d. a prolonged dikaryotic phase

2. Which one of the following is/are the chief characteristic(s) traditionally used to classify fungi into the major fungal phyla?
   a. cell wall features
   b. sexual reproductive structures
   c. adaptations for obtaining water
   d. nutritional dependence on non-living organic matter

3. Which of these fungal reproductive structures is diploid?
   a. ascospore
   b. zygosporangium
   c. basidiocarp
   d. gametangium

4. Which of these features characterizes a zygomycete?
   a. septate hyphae
   b. + and − mating strains
   c. mostly sexual reproduction
   d. a life cycle in which karyogamy does not occur

5. Which of these statements *best* describes a lichen?
   a. an association between a green alga or a cyanobacterium, and one or more fungi
   b. an association between a basidiomycete and an ascomycete
   c. a fungus that breaks down rock to provide nutrients for an alga
   d. an organism that spends half its life cycle as a photosymbiont and the other half as a mycobiont

Apply/Analyze

6. At lunch, you eat a mushroom, some truffles, a little Camembert cheese, and, accidentally also a bit of mouldy bread. Which of these groups of fungi is represented in this meal?
   a. Zygomycota, Ascomycota, and Glomeromycota
   b. Ascomycota, Basidiomycota, and Glomeromycota
   c. Basidiomycota, and Glomeromycota, but not Zygomycota
   d. Zygomycota, Ascomycota, and Basidiomycota

7. Which of these statements is the reason that some fungi were placed in Deuteromycota, or Fungi Imperfecti, rather than in a phylum?
   a. They form flagellated spores.
   b. They grow as single cells, rather than as hyphae.

   c. The reproductive stage in their life cycle is unknown or absent.
   d. They lack an asexual reproductive stage in their life cycle.

8. In which of these ecosystems are mycorrhizal associations crucial for survival and why?
   a. in deserts, because the soils lack sugar
   b. in deserts, because of the drought
   c. in tropical rainforests, because soils are too damp
   d. in tropical rainforests, because soils are poor in mineral ions

Create/Evaluate

9. Which of these descriptions is the most accurate of a mushroom?
   a. a collection of saclike cells called *asci*
   b. the nutrient-absorbing region of an ascomycete
   c. the nutrient-absorbing region of a basidiomycete
   d. a reproductive structure formed only by basidiomycetes

10. Which form of nutrient acquisition classifies a fungus as a saprotroph?
    a. The fungus has external digestion.
    b. The fungus forms extensive mycelia in the soil.
    c. The fungus obtains carbon from non-living organisms.
    d. The fungus obtains carbon from a living organism.

11. What do mycorrhizal fungi obtain from the plants with which they associate?
    a. increased nitrogen uptake
    b. a regular supply of water
    c. carbon in the form of sugars
    d. the ability to decompose organic material

12. Contrast life cycles of humans with the general life cycle of fungi.

13. Compare and contrast arbuscular mycorrhizae with ectomycorrhizae.

14. Consider ways in which fungi affect humans, and evaluate their importance for us.

15. Suppose that you found a new organism and you want to determine if it belongs to Fungi. What evidence would you need to collect to confirm it is a fungus?

Chapter Roadmap

Plants

The advent of land plants made it possible for animals to diversify onto land.

From Chapter 6 →

26.1 Defining Characteristics of Land Plants

Land plants are multicellular eukaryotes with cellulose cell walls. Most, but not all, are photoautotrophs. All have an alternation of generations life cycle.

From Chapter 23 →

From Chapter 24 →

26.2 The Transition to Life on Land

Plants are thought to have evolved from charophyte green algae between 490 and 425 mya. Adaptations to terrestrial life in the earliest land plants include a poikilohydry, multicellular envelope that protects developing gametes, and an embryo sheltered inside a parent plant.

→ **To Chapter 33**

→ **To Chapter 34**

→ **To Chapter 36**

Ed Reschke

26.3 Bryophytes: Nonvascular Land Plants

Bryophytes differ from all other land plants by having no xylem or phloem tissues, as well as having a dominant gametophyte stage.

Dave Powell, USDA Forest Service, Bugwood.org

From Chapter 25 →

26.4 Seedless Vascular Plants

Seedless vascular land plants include the lycophytes (club mosses), whisk ferns, horsetails, and ferns. Like the bryophytes, they rely on water for fertilization.

Michael P. Gadomski/Science Source

→ **To Chapter 33**

→ **To Chapter 34**

26.5 Gymnosperms: The First Seed Plants

During the Mesozoic, gymnosperms were the dominant land plants. Today, conifers are the primary vegetation of forests at higher latitudes and elevations, and have important economic uses as sources of lumber and other products.

→ **To Chapter 35**

→ **To Chapter 36**

→ **To Chapter 37**

26.6 Angiosperms: Flowering Plants

Angiosperms (Anthophyta) have dominated the land for more than 100 million years and are currently the most diverse plant group.

Monotropa uniflora, a heterotrophic plant that lacks chlorophyll

Plants

26

Why it matters . . . You are out for a walk in Cathedral Grove on Vancouver Island, British Columbia; you are busy thinking about other things and so are not paying close attention to the plants that you're walking by—they are just a pleasing green background. Suddenly, a small white plant, like the one shown in the photo above, catches your eye. At least you think it's a plant. But aren't all plants green? How can there be a completely white plant?

What you have found is a plant known as *ghost flower* or *Indian pipe* (*Monotropa uniflora*), which does not produce chlorophyll and so cannot photosynthesize.

CONCEPT FIX We often assume that all plants are photoautotrophs, making their own organic carbon molecules from atmospheric CO_2 and sunlight. But some plants, such as *Monotropa*, are completely heterotrophic, living on organic carbon obtained from other plants. And other plants that do have chlorophyll supplement their carbon supply by being heterotrophic in low light levels or under other conditions that limit photosynthesis. How do heterotrophic plants get carbon? Some directly parasitize green plants, but others, like *Monotropa*, feed on neighbouring photosynthetic plants through shared root-colonizing fungi (mycorrhizal fungi; see Chapter 25). So, contrary to popular belief, not all plants are photosynthetic and green.

So, if being green isn't a unifying feature of all plants, what is? What features could you look for to determine whether this *Monotropa* is a plant? What characteristics set plants apart from other organisms? And how did plants evolve? In this chapter, we investigate these questions and look at the adaptations to terrestrial life that have made plants so successful. Their success is attributed in part to their ability to thrive in habitats where animals can't survive for long, and some plants are able to grow much larger and live much longer than any animal. Together with photosynthetic bacteria and protists, plant tissues provide the nutritional foundation for nearly all ecosystems on Earth. Humans also use plants as sources of medicinal drugs, wood for building, fibres for paper and clothing, and a wealth of other products. The partnership between humans and plants has a long evolutionary history: we first domesticated cereal plants 9000 years ago, but this was not the earliest relationship between humans and plants. Our early ancestors, like modern-day primates, would have relied heavily on plants in their diet.

Despite the long history between plants and humans, there is still much about plant biology that we don't understand and many questions that remain to be answered.

We start this chapter by considering the defining characteristics of plants and then look at the evolution of plants and their adaptations to life on land. We conclude by looking at the diversity of land plants.

26.1 Defining Characteristics of Land Plants

Land plants are eukaryotes. As we learned from the *Monotropa* example, not all are capable of photosynthesizing, but almost all plants are photoautotrophs (organisms that use light as their energy source and carbon dioxide as their carbon source; see Chapter 6). Like animals, all land plants are multicellular, but if you took a piece of tissue from *Monotropa* and looked at it under the microscope, you'd see that, unlike animal cells, plant cells have walls, which are made of cellulose. All plants are sessile, or stationary (not able to move around); no terrestrial animals are sessile, although some aquatic ones are. Plants also differ from animals in having an **alternation of generations** life cycle.

In most animals, the diploid stage dominates the life cycle and produces gametes (sperm or eggs) by meiosis. Gametes are the only haploid stage, and it is short-lived: fusion of gametes produces a new diploid organism. (Some animals, for example, social insects such as bees and wasps, have a different life cycle.) In other organisms, such as many green algae, the haploid stage dominates the life cycle; the haploid alga spends much of its life producing and releasing gametes into the surrounding water. The single-celled zygote is the only diploid stage, and it divides by meiosis to produce spores that give rise to the haploid stage again.

In contrast, land plants have two multicellular stages (generations) in their life cycles: one diploid and one haploid

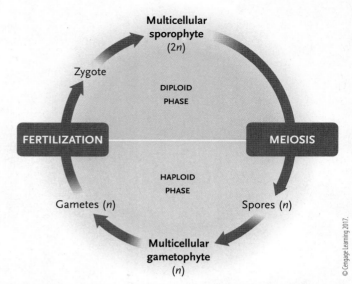

FIGURE 26.1 Overview of the alternation of generations, the basic pattern of the plant life cycle. The relative dominance of haploid and diploid phases is different for different plant groups.

(Figure 26.1). The diploid generation produces spores and is called a **sporophyte** (*phyte* = plant, hence, "spore-producing plant"). The haploid generation produces gametes by mitosis and is called a **gametophyte** ("gamete-producing plant"). The haploid phase of the plant life cycle begins within specialized structures on the sporophyte called *sporangia* (singular, *sporangium*). Within each sporangium (*angium* = vessel or chamber, hence, "spore-producing chambers"), haploid spores with thick cell walls are produced by meiosis. So, in plants, meiosis produces spores, not gametes. When a spore germinates, it divides by mitosis to produce a multicellular haploid gametophyte. The gametophyte produces structures called *gametangia*, which produce eggs and sperm. It also nourishes and protects the forthcoming sporophyte generation. Each generation gives rise to the other: hence the name *alternation of generations* for this life cycle.

The final defining feature of land plants is that the embryo (new sporophyte generation) is retained inside gametophyte tissue. The reasons for retention of embryos in parental tissue and for the rather complex life cycle will become clearer after we've looked at the evolution of plants and their transition onto land.

STUDY BREAK QUESTIONS

1. What features of land plants differentiate them from other eukaryotes, for example, from fungi? From animals?
2. What is an alternation of generations life cycle? How does this differ from the life cycle of most animals?
3. What does meiosis produce in plants?
4. Differentiate between a gametophyte and a sporophyte in terms of ploidy and what is produced.

26.2 The Transition to Life on Land

Along the shores of the ancient ocean, the only sound was the rhythmic muffled crash of waves breaking in the distance. There were no birds or other animals, no plants with leaves rustling in the breeze. In the preceding eons, cells that produce oxygen as a by-product of photosynthesis had evolved, radically changing Earth's atmosphere. Solar radiation had converted much of the oxygen into a dense ozone layer—a shield against lethal doses of ultraviolet radiation—that had kept early organisms below the water's surface. Now was the time to explore the land.

Cyanobacteria were probably the first to adapt to intertidal zones and then to spread into shallow, coastal streams. Later, green algae and fungi made the same journey. Around 480 million years ago (mya), one group of green algae living near the water's edge, or perhaps in a moist terrestrial environment, became the ancestors of modern plants. Several lines of evidence indicate that these algae were charophytes (a group discussed in Chapter 24): both charophytes and modern land plants have cellulose cell walls, they store energy captured during photosynthesis as starch, and their light-absorbing pigments include both chlorophyll *a* and chlorophyll *b*. Molecular genetic data also support the relationship between charophytes and land plants. Like other green algae, the charophyte lineage that produced the ancestor of land plants arose in water and has aquatic descendants today **(Figure 26.2)**. Yet, because terrestrial environments pose very different challenges than aquatic environments, evolution in land plants produced a range of adaptations crucial to survival on dry land.

The algal ancestors of plants probably invaded land about 450 mya. We say "probably" because the fossil record is inconclusive in pinpointing when the first truly terrestrial plants appeared, and many important stages in evolution are not represented in the fossil record. Even in more recent deposits, the most commonly found plant fossils are just microscopic bits and pieces; easily identifiable parts such as leaves, stems, roots, and reproductive parts seldom occur together. Whole fossilized plants are extremely rare. Adding to the challenge, some chemical and structural adaptations to life on land arose independently in several plant lineages. Despite these problems, botanists have been able to gain insight into several innovations and overall trends in plant evolution.

While the ancestors of land plants were making the transition to a fully terrestrial life, some remarkable adaptive changes unfolded. For example, the earliest land plants were exposed to higher levels of harmful UV radiation than their aquatic ancestors had experienced. Gradual changes in existing metabolic pathways resulted in the ability to synthesize simple phenylpropanoids—molecules that absorb UV radiation—which enhanced the plants' ability to live on land. Where did these new metabolic pathways and associated enzyme functions come from? They did not simply appear because the plants needed them.

CONCEPT FIX The idea that evolution involves organisms "trying" to adapt, or that natural selection gives organisms what they need to survive, is one of the major misconceptions about evolution. Natural selection cannot sense what a species "needs," and organisms cannot try to adapt: if some individual organisms in the population have traits that allow them to survive and reproduce more in that environment than other individuals, then they will pass on these traits to more offspring, and the frequency of the traits in the population will increase. But the organism cannot "try" to get the right genes. Research shows that new enzyme functions usually follow duplication of genes, which can occur in various ways (e.g., an error during crossing-over of meiosis). Mutations in the second copy of a gene will not have negative effects on the host because the other copy retains its original function; thus, over time the second copy tends to accumulate mutations. If the changes in this gene provide advantages to the host plant, then that gene is selected for. In this way, new enzyme functions and metabolic pathways evolve.

Eons of natural selection sorted out solutions to fundamental problems, among them, avoiding desiccation, physically supporting the plant body in air, obtaining certain nutrients from soil, and reproducing sexually in environments where water would not be available for dispersal of eggs and sperm. With time, plants evolved features that not only addressed these problems but also provided access to a wide range of terrestrial environments. Those ecological opportunities opened the way for a dramatic radiation (rapid evolution and divergence; see Chapter 19) of varied plant species, and for the survival of plant-dependent animal life. Today the **kingdom Plantae** encompasses more than 300 000 living species, organized in this textbook into 10 phyla. These modern plants range from mosses, horsetails, and ferns to conifers and flowering plants **(Figure 26.3)**.

FIGURE 26.2 *Chara*, a stonewort. This representative of the charophyte lineage is known commonly as a stonewort due to the calcium carbonate that accumulates on its surface.

BOB GIBBONS/SCIENCE PHOTO LIBRARY

a. Mosses growing on rocks

© Chris Manderson 1995

b. A jack pine

Michael P. Gadomski/Science Source

c. An orchid

iStockphoto.com/Don Enright

FIGURE 26.3 **Representatives of the kingdom Plantae. (a)** Mosses growing on rocks. Mosses evolved relatively soon after plants made the transition to land. **(b)** A jack pine (*Pinus banksiana*). This species and other conifers belonging to the phylum Coniferophyta represent the gymnosperms. **(c)** An orchid, *Calypso bulbosa*, is a showy example of a flowering plant.

a. Cuticle on the surface of a leaf

Cuticle   Epidermal cell

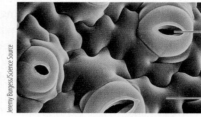

Jubal Harshaw/Shutterstock.com

b. Stomata

One stoma (opening in epidermis)

Epidermal cell

Jeremy Burgess/Science Source

FIGURE 26.4 **Adaptations for limiting water loss.** **(a)** A waxy cuticle covers the epidermis of land plants and helps reduce water loss. **(b)** Surface view of stomata in the epidermis (surface layer of cells) of a leaf. Stomata allow carbon dioxide to enter plant tissues and oxygen and water to leave.

26.2a Early Biochemical and Structural Adaptations Enhanced Plant Survival on Land

The greatest challenge plants had to overcome to thrive on land was how to survive in the dry terrestrial conditions. Unlike most modern-day plants, the earliest land plants had neither a waterproof **cuticle** (an outer waxy layer that prevents water loss from plant tissues) nor tissues with sufficient mechanical strength to allow for upright growth. These limitations restricted these early plants to moist habitats and made it necessary for them to stay small and grow close to the ground. Like modern-day mosses, these plants were **poikilohydric** (*poikilo* = variable; *hydric* = relating to water). Poikilohydric plants have little control over their internal water content and do not restrict water loss. Instead, their water content fluctuates with moisture levels in their environment: as their habitat dries out, so do their tissues, and their metabolic activities virtually cease. When external moisture levels rise, they quickly rehydrate and become metabolically active. In other words, poikilohydric plants are drought tolerators that can survive drying out; vascular plants, which regulate their internal water content and restrict water loss, are drought avoiders, with numerous adaptations to prevent drying out or with plant parts (e.g., underground stems) that can survive if the rest of the plant dries out.

Later-evolving plants were able to regulate water content and restrict water loss because they had cuticles covering their outer surfaces **(Figure 26.4a)**, as well as **stomata** (singular, *stoma*; *stoma* = mouth) pores in the cuticle-covered surfaces (Figure 26.4b) that open and close to regulate water loss (and are the main route for carbon dioxide to enter leaves; see Chapter 34). These plants also had water-transport tissues that also provided support for upright growth, described further in Section 26.2c.

26.2b Symbiotic Associations with Fungi Were Likely Required for Evolution of Land Plants

The ancestor of land plants was not the first organism to colonize terrestrial habitats; certain bacteria, protists, and fungi had been present at least since the late Proterozoic (around 540 mya). Almost all modern-day plants form symbiotic associations, known as *mycorrhizae*, with certain soil fungi (see Chapter 25). In these associations, the fungus colonizes the plant's roots and grows prolifically in the soil beyond the root system, producing a very large network that takes up soil nutrients. (See Chapter 37.) Both partners generally benefit by a two-way exchange of nutrients: the plant provides the fungus with carbon, and the fungus increases the plant's supply of soil nutrients, which it is able to obtain much more efficiently than the plant's own roots. Such mutually beneficial relationships may have been essential to the evolution of land plants and to their success in terrestrial habitats, given that the first land plants lacked roots and that the soils of early Earth were nutrient poor.

26.2c Lignified Water-Conducting Cells Provided Strength and Support for Plants to Grow Upright

The earliest land plants remained small because they lacked the mechanical support necessary to grow taller. Growing low to the ground helped them stay moist but was not very effective in capturing light: since all early land plants were low growing, there would have been intense competition for light. If any plant had been able to grow taller than its neighbours, it would have had a major advantage. But how could a plant support upright growth against the force of gravity? Plants require strengthening tissue to grow upright. And, since diffusion is not effective over longer distances, growing up and away from the ground surface also requires an internal water circulation system. Some of the early land plants did have specialized water-conducting cells that transported water through the plant body, but these cells did not provide mechanical strength. Later land plants synthesized lignin, a polymer of phenylpropanoids (the molecules mentioned earlier that absorb UV radiation). Lignin was deposited in cell walls, particularly in the water-conducting cells, providing support and rigidity to those tissues and allowing the plants to grow upright. These lignified water-conducting cells make up a tissue called *xylem*.

Xylem is one type of **vascular tissue** (*vas* = duct or vessel). Plants with this tissue (and the other type of vascular tissue, **phloem**, which conducts sugars through the plant body) are known as **vascular plants**. It is important to note that some plants, such as some mosses, that lack vascular tissues do have tissues that conduct water and sugars through their bodies. These tissues are not the same as xylem and phloem (e.g., their water-conducting cells do not have walls reinforced with lignin) and are likely not homologous with xylem and phloem, so they are not called vascular tissues. Thus, these plants are referred to as **nonvascular plants**. Chapter 34 explains how xylem and phloem perform these key internal transport functions.

Clearly, plants with lignified tissues had a benefit over plants lacking lignin and, over time, they evolved to become the dominant plants in most habitats on Earth. Ferns, conifers, and flowering plants—most of the plants you are familiar with—are vascular plants. Supported by lignin and with a well-developed vascular system, the body of a plant can grow very large. Extreme examples are the giant redwood trees of the northern California coast, some of which are more than 90 m tall. By contrast, nonvascular plants lack lignin, although some do have simple internal transport systems and are generally small **(Table 26.1)**.

Vascular plants also have **apical meristems**, regions of constantly dividing cells near the tips of shoots and roots that produce all tissues of the plant body. Meristem tissue is the foundation for a vascular plant's extensively branching stem and root systems and is a central topic of Chapter 33.

26.2d Root and Shoot Systems Were Adaptations for Nutrition and Support

The body of a nonvascular plant is not differentiated into true roots and stems, structures that are fundamental adaptations for absorbing nutrients from soil and for support of an erect

TABLE 26.1	Trends in Plant Evolution Traits Derived from Algal Ancestor: Cell Walls with Cellulose, Energy Stored in Starch, Chlorophylls *a* and *b* (main photosynthetic pigments).				
Bryophytes	Ferns and Their Relatives	Gymnosperms	Angiosperms		Functions of This Trait in Land Plants
Cuticle	⟶				Protection against water loss and pathogens
Stomata	⟶				Regulation of water loss and gas exchange (CO_2 in; O_2 out)
Nonvascular (although some have specialized water-conducting cells without lignin) ⟶	Vascular (have xylem and phloem) ⟶				Internal tubes that transport water and nutrients
	Lignin ⟶				Mechanical support for vertical growth
	Apical meristem ⟶				Branching shoot system
	Roots, stems, leaves ⟶				Enhanced uptake, transport of nutrients, and enhanced photosynthesis
Haploid phase dominant ⟶	Diploid phase dominant ⟶				Genetic diversity
One spore type (homospory) ⟶	Homospory in most but heterospory (two spore types) in some ⟶	Heterospory ⟶			Promotion of genetic diversity
Motile sperm ⟶		Nonmotile sperm ⟶			Protection of gametes within parent body
Seedless ⟶		Seeds ⟶			Protection of embryo

plant body. The evolution of sturdy stems, the basis of an aerial *shoot system,* went hand in hand with the capacity to synthesize lignin. To become large, land plants also require a means of anchoring aerial parts in the soil, as well as effective strategies for obtaining soil nutrients. **Roots**, anchoring structures that also absorb water and nutrients in association with mycorrhizal fungi, were the eventual solution to these problems. The earliest fossils showing clear evidence of roots are from vascular plants, although the exact timing of this change is uncertain. Ultimately, vascular plants developed specialized **root systems**, which generally consist of underground, cylindrical, absorptive structures with a large surface area that favours the rapid uptake of soil, water, and dissolved mineral ions. The root system has been called "the hidden half" of a plant: "half" refers to the fact that there is as much plant biomass below ground as there is above ground. And there are other similarities between above- and below-ground parts of plants: the fine roots of a root system go through regular cycles of growth and death, just as do the leaves of most plants. "Hidden" refers to the fact that the root system is hidden from our sight below ground, meaning that we cannot study it very easily. For this reason, we know less about root systems than about the above-ground parts of plants, although recent technological advances are changing this situation.

Above ground, the simple stems of early land plants also became more specialized, evolving into **shoot systems** in vascular plants. Shoot systems have stems and leaves that arise from apical meristems and that function in the absorption of light energy from the sun and carbon dioxide from the air. Stems grew larger and branched extensively after the evolution of lignin. The mechanical strength of lignified tissues almost certainly provided plants with several adaptive advantages. For instance, a strong internal scaffold could support upright stems

bearing leaves and other photosynthetic structures, and so help increase the surface area for intercepting sunlight. Also, reproductive structures borne on aerial stems might serve as platforms for more efficient launching of spores from the parent plant.

Structures we think of as "leaves" arose several times during plant evolution. In general, leaves represent modifications of stems and can be divided into two types: microphylls are narrow leaves with only one vein or strand of vascular tissue; megaphylls are broader leaves with multiple veins. **Figure 26.5** illustrates the basic steps of possible evolutionary pathways by which these two types of leaves evolved. In some early plants, microphylls may have evolved as flaplike extensions of the main stem. In contrast, megaphylls likely evolved from a modified branch system when photosynthetic tissue filled in the gaps between neighbouring branches.

Other land plant adaptations were related to the demands of reproduction in a dry environment. As described in more detail shortly, these adaptations included multicellular chambers that protect developing gametes, and a multicellular embryo that is sheltered inside the tissues of a parent plant.

26.2e In the Plant Life Cycle, the Diploid Phase Became Dominant

As early plants moved into drier habitats, their life cycles also modified considerably. The haploid gametophyte phase became physically smaller and less complex and had a shorter life span, whereas the opposite occurred with the diploid sporophyte phase. In mosses and other nonvascular plants, the sporophyte is a little larger and longer lived than in green algae, and in vascular plants, the sporophyte is clearly larger and more complex and lives much longer than the gametophyte **(Figure 26.6)**. When

a. Development of microphylls as an offshoot of the main vertical axis

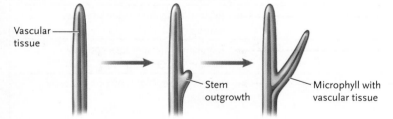

Vascular tissue · Stem outgrowth · Microphyll with vascular tissue

b. Development of megaphylls in a branching pattern

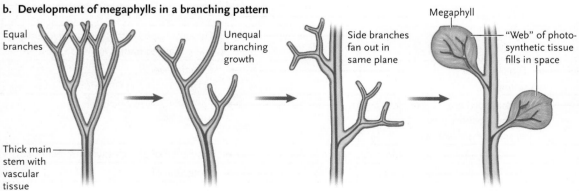

Equal branches · Unequal branching growth · Side branches fan out in same plane · Megaphyll · "Web" of photosynthetic tissue fills in space · Thick main stem with vascular tissue

FIGURE 26.5 Evolution of leaves. (a) One type of early leaflike structure may have evolved as offshoots of the plant's main vertical axis; there was only one vein (transport vessel) in each leaf. Today, the seedless vascular plants known as *lycophytes* (*club mosses*) have this type of leaf. **(b)** In other groups of seedless vascular plants, leaves arose in a series of steps that began when the main stem evolved a branching growth pattern. Small side branches then fanned out and photosynthetic tissue filled the space between them, becoming the leaf blade. With time, the small branches modified into veins.

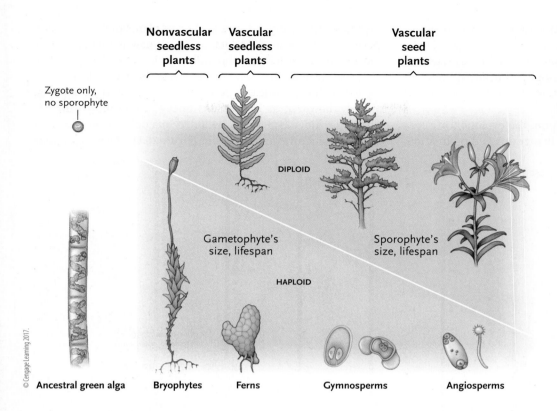

Nonvascular seedless plants | Vascular seedless plants | Vascular seed plants

Zygote only, no sporophyte

DIPLOID

Gametophyte's size, lifespan

Sporophyte's size, lifespan

HAPLOID

© Cengage Learning 2017.

Ancestral green alga | Bryophytes | Ferns | Gymnosperms | Angiosperms

FIGURE 26.6 Evolutionary trend from dominance of the gametophyte (haploid) generation to dominance of the sporophyte (diploid) generation, represented here by existing species ranging from a green alga (*Ulothrix*) to a flowering plant. This trend developed as early plants colonized habitats on land. In general, the sporophytes of vascular plants are larger and more complex than those of bryophytes, and their gametophytes are smaller and less complex. In this diagram, the fern represents seedless vascular plants.

you look at a pine tree, for example, you see a large, long-lived sporophyte. The sporophyte generation begins after fertilization, when the zygote divides by mitosis to produce a multicellular diploid organism. Its body will eventually develop sporangia, which produce spores by meiosis.

Why did the diploid phase become dominant over evolutionary time? Many botanists hypothesize that the trend toward "diploid dominance" reflects the advantage of being diploid in land environments; if there is only one copy of DNA, as in a haploid plant, and if a deleterious mutation occurs or if the DNA is damaged (e.g., by UV radiation, which is a greater problem on land than in aquatic habitats), the consequences could be fatal. In contrast, the sporophyte phase of that plant is diploid and so has a "backup" copy of the DNA that can continue to function normally even if one strand is damaged. However, it is important to remember that the land plants that do have a dominant haploid stage, such as mosses, are very successful plants in certain habitats. The lack of a dominant diploid stage has certainly not caused them to become extinct.

26.2f Some Vascular Plants Evolved Separate Male and Female Gametophytes

When a plant makes only one type of spore, it is said to be **homosporous** ("same spore"; **Figure 26.7a**). Usually, a gametophyte that develops from such a spore is bisexual—it can produce both sperm and eggs. However, some homosporous plants have ways to produce male and female sex organs on different gametophytes or to otherwise prevent self-fertilization, as described below in ferns. The sperm have flagella and are

a. *Lycopodium*

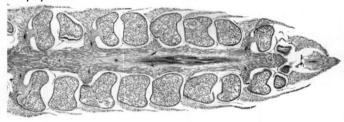

b. *Selaginella*

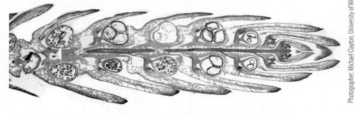

Photographer: Michael Clayton, University of Wisconsin Plant Teaching Collection, http://botit.botany.wisc.edu

FIGURE 26.7 Longitudinal sections through strobili of two lycophytes, (a) *Lycopodium* and (b) *Selaginella*. Lycopodium is a homosporous plant that produces spores of only one type, as can be seen in (a). Note that the sporangia of *Lycopodium* are all the same. The *Selaginella* strobilus shown here is from a heterosporous plant, which produces megasporangia (containing a few large megaspores) and microsporangia (containing numerous small microspores) in the same strobilus.

motile because they must swim through liquid water to encounter eggs.

Other vascular plants, including gymnosperms and angiosperms, are **heterosporous** (Figure 26.7b). They produce two types of spores—one type is smaller than the other—in two different types of sporangia. The smaller spores are **microspores**, which develop into male gametophytes, and the larger **megaspores** will develop into female gametophytes. Heterospory and the development of gametophytes inside spore walls are important steps in the evolution of the seed, as we will see further on.

As you will read in a later section, the evolution of seeds and related innovations, such as pollen grains and pollination, helped spark the rapid diversification of plants in the Devonian period, 360–408 mya. In fact, so many new fossils appear in Devonian rocks that paleobotanists—scientists who specialize in the study of fossil plants—have thus far been unable to determine which fossil lineages gave rise to the modern plant phyla. Clearly, however, as each major lineage came into being, its characteristic adaptations included major modifications of existing structures and functions **(Figure 26.8)**. The next sections

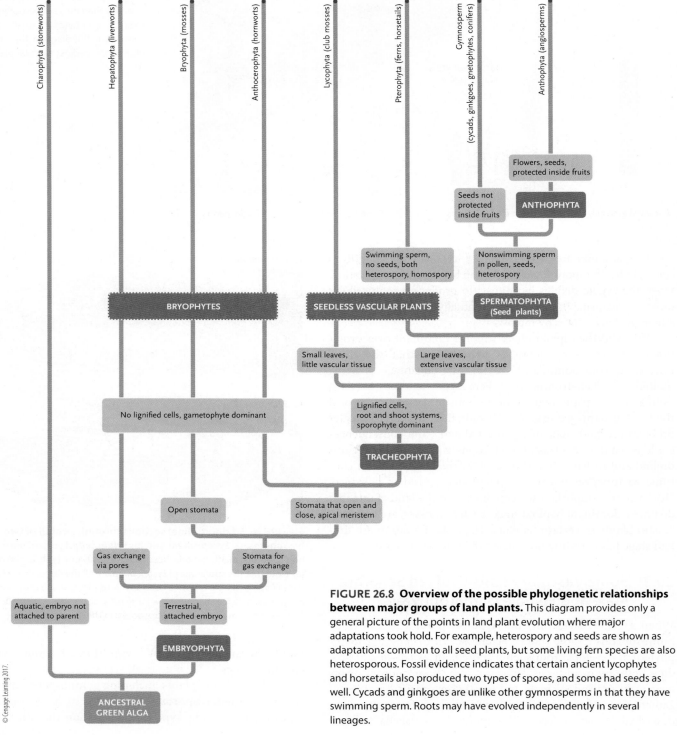

FIGURE 26.8 Overview of the possible phylogenetic relationships between major groups of land plants. This diagram provides only a general picture of the points in land plant evolution where major adaptations took hold. For example, heterospory and seeds are shown as adaptations common to all seed plants, but some living fern species are also heterosporous. Fossil evidence indicates that certain ancient lycophytes and horsetails also produced two types of spores, and some had seeds as well. Cycads and ginkgoes are unlike other gymnosperms in that they have swimming sperm. Roots may have evolved independently in several lineages.

fill out this general picture, beginning with the plants that are the living representatives of the earliest land plants.

STUDY BREAK QUESTIONS

1. What features do land plants share with their closest living relatives, the charophyte algae? What features differentiate the two groups?
2. How did mycorrhizal fungi fulfill the role we associate with roots in early land plants?
3. What is the main difference between the specialized water-conducting cells present in some nonvascular plants and those of vascular plants? How did this difference influence the evolution of vascular plants?
4. How did plant adaptations such as a root system, a shoot system, and a vascular system collectively influence the evolution of land plants?
5. Describe the difference between homospory and heterospory, and explain how heterospory paved the way for other reproductive adaptations in land plants.

26.3 Bryophytes: Nonvascular Land Plants

The **bryophytes** (*bryon* = moss)—liverworts, hornworts, and mosses—are important both ecologically and economically. As colonizers of bare land, their small bodies trap particles of organic and inorganic matter, helping to build soil on bare rock and stabilizing soil surfaces with a biological crust in harsh places such as coastal dunes, inland deserts, and embankments created by road construction. In boreal forests and Arctic tundras, bryophytes constitute as much as half the biomass, and they are crucial components of the **food web** that supports animals in these ecosystems. People have long used *Sphagnum* and other absorbent "peat" mosses (which typically grow in bogs and fens) for everything from primitive diapers and filtering whiskey to increasing the water-holding capacity of garden soil. Peat moss has also found use as a fuel; each day, the Rhode generating station in Ireland, one of several that use peat in that nation, burns 2000 tonnes of peat to produce electricity.

Bryophytes have a combination of traits that allow them to bridge aquatic and land environments. Because bryophytes lack cells strengthened by lignin and are poikilohydric, it is not surprising that they are small and commonly grow on wet sites along creek banks (see Figure 26.3a); in bogs, swamps, or the dense shade of damp forests; and on moist tree trunks or rooftops. However, some mosses live in very dry environments, such as **alpine tundra** and **arctic tundra (Figure 26.9)**. Being poikilohydric enables them to live in such seemingly inhospitable habitats.

Bryophytes retain many of the features of their algal ancestors: they produce flagellated sperm that must swim through water to reach eggs, which is another reason they are small: the

Figure 26.9 Bryophytes of arid habitats. (a) Moss growing on exposed rock. **(b)** Mosses and other plants in alpine tundra

sperm must be able to swim between plants in a film of water (e.g., from rain or dew), which is only possible if the plants are relatively close to the ground. They also lack xylem and phloem (although some do have specialized conductive tissues). Bryophytes have parts that are rootlike, stemlike, and leaflike. However, the "roots" are **rhizoids** that serve only to anchor the plant to its substrate and do not take up any water or nutrients from the substrate. Bryophyte "stems" and "leaves" are not considered to be true stems and leaves like those of vascular plants because they lack vascular tissue and because they did not evolve from the same structures as vascular plant stems and leaves did. (Said another way, stems and leaves are not homologous in bryophytes and vascular plants.)

In other ways, bryophytes are clearly adapted to land. The sporophytes (but not the longer-lived gametophytes) of some species have a water-conserving cuticle and stomata. And, as is true of all plants, the bryophyte life cycle has both multicellular gametophyte and sporophyte phases, but the sporophyte is permanently associated with the gametophyte (it never becomes independent of the gametophyte) and lives for a shorter time than the gametophyte. **Figure 26.10** shows the green, leafy gametophyte of a moss plant, with diploid sporophytes attached to it by slender stalks. Bryophyte gametophytes produce gametes inside a protective organ called a **gametangium** (plural, *gametangia*). The gametangia in which bryophyte eggs form are flask-shaped structures called **archegonia** (*archi* = first;

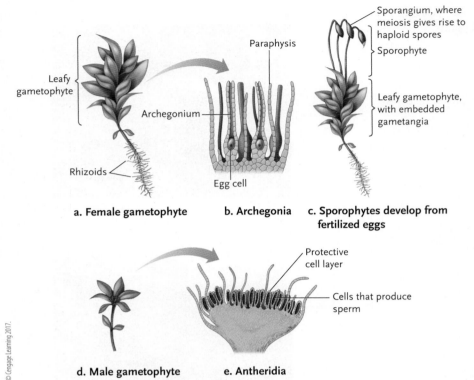

Paraphysis

Leafy gametophyte

Archegonium

Rhizoids

a. Female gametophyte

Egg cell

b. Archegonia

Sporangium, where meiosis gives rise to haploid spores

Sporophyte

Leafy gametophyte, with embedded gametangia

c. Sporophytes develop from fertilized eggs

Protective cell layer

Cells that produce sperm

d. Male gametophyte

e. Antheridia

FIGURE 26.10 Gametangia are multicellular structures that enclose and protect gametes—a bryophyte innovation. *Rhizomnium* bears gametangia (archegonia and antheridia) on separate gametophyte plants. **(a, b)** The archegonia are clustered in the tip of the female gametophyte interspersed with paraphyses (filaments that protect the archegonia). **(c)** A sporophyte develops from a fertilized egg. It has a sporangium in which meiosis occurs to produce haploid spores. **(d)** The antheridia are club-shaped gametangia that contain cells from which sperm arise. **(e)** The antheridia are clustered at the very tip of the male gametophyte plant and are interspersed with paraphyses.

© Cengage Learning 2017.

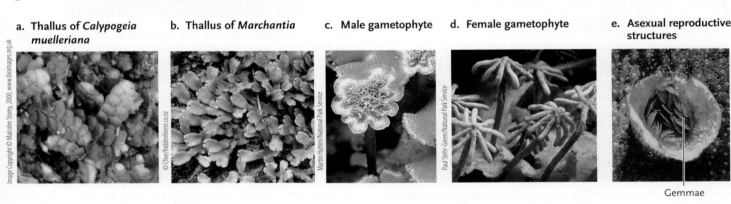

a. **Thallus of *Calypogeia muelleriana***

b. **Thallus of *Marchantia***

c. **Male gametophyte**

d. **Female gametophyte**

e. **Asexual reproductive structures**

Gemmae

FIGURE 26.11 Examples of liverworts. (a) Thallus of a leafy liverwort, *Calypogeia muelleriana*. **(b)** Thallus of the thalloid liverwort *Marchantia*, **(c)** male thallus with antheridia-bearing structures **(d)** female thallus with archegonia-bearing structures. *Marchantia* and some other liverworts also reproduce asexually by way of **(e)** gemmae, multicellular vegetative bodies that develop in tiny cups on the plant body. Gemmae can grow into new plants when splashing raindrops transport them to suitable sites.

gonos = seed). Flagellated sperm form in rounded gametangia called **antheridia** (*antheros* = flowerlike; singular, *antheridium*). The sperm swim through a film of water to the archegonia to fertilize eggs. Each fertilized egg gives rise to a diploid embryo sporophyte, which stays attached to the gametophyte and produces spores—and the cycle repeats.

Despite these similarities to more complex plants, bryophytes are unique in several ways. Unlike vascular plants, the gametophyte is much longer lived than the sporophyte and is photosynthetic, whereas the sporophyte remains attached to the gametophyte and depends on the gametophyte for much of its nutrition.

Bryophytes are not a monophyletic group (i.e., they did not all evolve from a common ancestor); instead, the various bryophytes evolved as separate lineages, in parallel with vascular plants.

26.3a Liverworts Resemble the First Land Plants

Liverworts make up the phylum **Hepatophyta**, so called because early herbalists thought that these small plants were shaped like the lobes of the human liver (*hepat* = liver; *wort* = herb). The resemblance might be a little vague to modern eyes. While some of the 6000 species of liverworts consist of a flat, branching, ribbonlike plate of tissue closely pressed against damp soil, other liverworts are leafy and superficially resemble mosses, although the arrangement of leaves is different **(Figure 26.11)**. This simple body, called a **thallus** (plural, *thalli*), is the gametophyte generation. Threadlike rhizoids anchor the gametophytes to their substrate. None have true stomata, the openings that regulate gas exchange in most other land plants, although some species do have pores. They lack some features present in the other two groups of bryophytes; this evidence, together with molecular data, suggests that the first land plants likely resembled modern-day liverworts.

We will look at one genus, *Marchantia* (Figure 26.11), as an example of liverwort reproduction. Separate male and female gametophytes produce sexual organs (antheridia and archegonia) on tall stalks (Figure 26.11c, d). The motile sperm released from antheridia are splashed and then swim through surface water to reach the eggs inside archegonia. After fertilization, a small diploid sporophyte develops inside the archegonium, matures there, and produces haploid spores by meiosis. During meiosis, sex chromosomes segregate, so some spores have the male genotype and others the female genotype. As in other liverworts, the spores develop inside jacketed sporangia that split open to release the spores. A spore that is carried by air currents to a suitable location germinates and gives rise to a haploid gametophyte, which is either male or female. *Marchantia* and some other liverworts can also reproduce asexually by way of **gemmae** (*gem* = bud; singular, *gemma*), small cell masses that form in cuplike growths on a thallus (Figure 26.11e). Gemmae can grow into new thalli when rainwater splashes them out of the cups and onto an appropriately moist substrate.

26.3b Many Mosses Have Specialized Cells for Water and Nutrient Transport

Chances are that you have seen, touched, or sat on at least some of the approximately 10 000 species of mosses. The use of the name **Bryophyta** for this phylum underscores the fact that mosses are the best-known bryophytes, forming tufts or carpets of vegetation on the surface of rocks, soil, or bark.

The moss life cycle, diagrammed in **Figure 26.12**, begins when a haploid (*n*) spore lands on a wet soil surface. After the

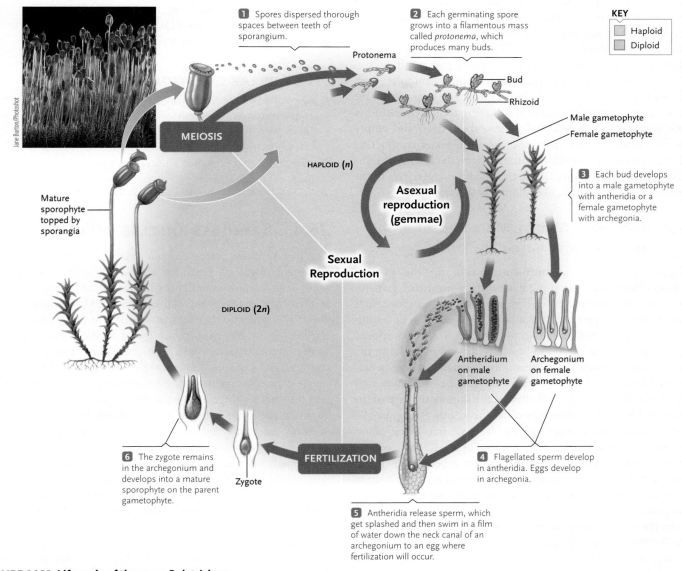

1 Spores dispersed thorough spaces between teeth of sporangium.

2 Each germinating spore grows into a filamentous mass called *protonema*, which produces many buds.

KEY

Haploid
Diploid

Protonema

Bud

Rhizoid

Male gametophyte

Female gametophyte

MEIOSIS

HAPLOID (*n*)

Asexual reproduction (gemmae)

3 Each bud develops into a male gametophyte with antheridia or a female gametophyte with archegonia.

Mature sporophyte topped by sporangia

Sexual Reproduction

DIPLOID (2*n*)

Antheridium on male gametophyte

Archegonium on female gametophyte

6 The zygote remains in the archegonium and develops into a mature sporophyte on the parent gametophyte.

Zygote

FERTILIZATION

4 Flagellated sperm develop in antheridia. Eggs develop in archegonia.

5 Antheridia release sperm, which get splashed and then swim in a film of water down the neck canal of an archegonium to an egg where fertilization will occur.

Jane Burton/Photoshot

© Cengage Learning 2017

FIGURE 26.12 Life cycle of the moss *Polytrichum*

spore germinates, it elongates and branches into a filamentous web of tissue called a **protonema** ("first thread"), which can become dense enough to colour the surface of soil, rocks, or bark visibly green. After several weeks of growth, the budlike cell masses on a protonema develop into leafy, green gametophytes anchored by rhizoids. A single protonema can be extremely prolific, producing bud after bud, thus giving rise to a dense clone of genetically identical gametophytes. Leafy mosses may also reproduce asexually by gemmae produced at the surface of rhizoids and on above-ground parts.

Antheridia and archegonia are produced at the tips of male and female gametophytes respectively. Propelled by flagella, sperm released from antheridia swim through a film of dew or rainwater and down a channel in the neck of the archegonium, attracted by a chemical gradient secreted by each egg. Fertilization produces the new sporophyte generation inside the archegonium in the form of diploid zygotes that develop into small mature sporophytes, each consisting of a sporangium on a stalk. Moss sporophytes may eventually develop chloroplasts and nourish themselves photosynthetically but, initially, they depend on the gametophytes for food. Even after a moss sporophyte begins photosynthesis, it still must obtain water, carbohydrates, and some other nutrients from the gametophyte.

Certain moss gametophytes are structurally complex, with features similar to those of higher plants. For example, some species have a central strand of conducting tissue. One kind of tissue is made up of elongated, thin-walled, dead and empty cells that conduct water. In a few mosses, the water-conducting cells are surrounded by sugar-conducting tissue resembling the phloem of vascular plants. These tissues did not give rise to the xylem and phloem of vascular plants, however.

26.3c Hornworts Share a More Recent Ancestor with Vascular Plants

Roughly 100 species of hornworts make up the phylum **Anthocerotophyta**. Like some liverworts, a hornwort gametophyte has a flat thallus, but the sporangium of the sporophyte phase is long and pointed, like a horn **(Figure 26.13)**, and splits into two or three ribbonlike sections when it releases spores. Sexual reproduction occurs in basically the same way as in liverworts, and hornworts also reproduce asexually by fragmentation as pieces of a thallus break off and develop into new individuals. While the gametophyte is the dominant stage of the hornwort life cycle, hornworts differ from other nonvascular plants in that their sporophytes can become free-living plants that are independent of the gametophyte! Recent genetic research into evolutionary relationships among the major groups of land plants indicates that hornworts are the group of bryophytes that have a more recent common ancestor with vascular plants.

In the next section, we turn to the vascular plants, which have lignified water-conducting tissue. Without the strength and support provided by this tissue, as well as its capacity to move water and minerals efficiently throughout the plant body,

FIGURE 26.13 The hornwort *Anthoceros*. The base of each long slender sporophyte is embedded in the flattened leafy gametophyte.

large sporophytes could not have survived on land. Unlike bryophytes, modern vascular plants are monophyletic—all groups are descended from a common ancestor.

STUDY BREAK QUESTIONS

1. Give some examples of bryophyte features that bridge aquatic and terrestrial environments.
2. Summarize the main similarities and differences among liverworts, hornworts, and mosses.
3. How do specific aspects of a moss plant's anatomy resemble those of vascular plants?

26.4 Seedless Vascular Plants

The first vascular plants did not produce seeds and were the dominant plants on Earth for almost 200 million years, until seed plants became abundant. The fossil record shows that seedless vascular plants were well established by the late Silurian, about 428 mya, and they flourished until the end of the Carboniferous, about 250 mya. Some living seedless vascular plants have certain bryophyte-like traits, whereas others have some characteristics of seed plants. On the one hand, like bryophytes, seedless vascular plants disperse themselves by releasing spores, and they have swimming sperm that require free water to reach eggs. On the other hand, as in seed plants, the sporophyte of a seedless vascular plant becomes independent of the gametophyte at a certain point in its development and has well-developed vascular tissues (xylem and phloem). Also, the sporophyte is the larger, longer-lived stage of the life cycle, and the gametophytes are very small, with some even lacking chlorophyll. **Table 26.2** summarizes these characteristics and gives an overview of seedless vascular plant features within the larger context of modern plant phyla.

In the late Paleozoic era, seedless vascular plants were Earth's dominant vegetation. Some lineages have endured to

TABLE 26.2	Plant Phyla and Major Characteristics		
Phylum	Common Name	Number of Species	Common General Characteristics
Bryophytes: nonvascular plants; gametophyte dominant, free water required for fertilization, cuticle and stomata present in some			
Hepatophyta	Liverworts	6 000	Leafy or simple flattened thallus, rhizoids; spores in capsules; moist, humid habitats
Bryophyta	Mosses	10 000	Simple flattened thallus, rhizoids; hornlike sporangia; moist, humid habitats
Anthocerotophyta	Hornworts	100	Flattened or frilly thallus; some have hydroids; spores in capsules; moist, humid habitats; colonizes bare rock, soil, or bark
Seedless vascular plants: sporophyte dominant, free water required for fertilization, cuticle and stomata present			
Lycophyta	Club mosses	1 000	Microphylls, true roots; most species have sporangia on sporophylls; mostly wet or shady habitats
Pterophyta	Ferns, whisk ferns, horsetails	13 000	*Ferns:* Finely divided, large megaphyllous leaves; sporangia often in sori; habitats from wet to arid. *Whisk ferns:* Branching stem from rhizomes; sporangia on stem scales; tropical to subtropical habitats. *Horsetails:* Hollow photosynthetic stem, scalelike leaves, sporangia in strobili; swamps, disturbed habitats
Gymnosperms: vascular plants with "naked" seeds; sporophyte dominant, fertilization by pollination, cuticle and stomata present, megaphylls present			
Cycadophyta	Cycads	185	Shrubby or treelike with palmlike leaves, pithy stems; male and female strobili on separate plants; widespread distribution
Ginkgophyta	Ginkgo	1	Woody-stemmed tree, deciduous fan-shaped leaves; male, female structures on separate plants; temperate areas of China
Gnetophyta	Gnetophytes	70	Shrubs or woody vines; one has strappy leaves; male and female strobili on separate plants; limited to deserts, tropics
Coniferophyta	Conifers	550	Mostly evergreen, woody trees and shrubs with needlelike or scalelike leaves; male and female cones usually on same plant
Angiosperms: plants with flowers and seeds protected inside fruits; sporophyte dominant, fertilization by pollination, cuticle and stomata present, megaphylls present; major groups: monocots and eudicots			
Angiosperms = Anthophytes	Flowering plants	268 500+ (including monocots and dicots, as well as magnoliids, other basal angiosperms)	Wood and herbaceous plants; nearly all land habitats, some aquatic
Monocots	Grasses, palms, lilies, orchids, and others	(60 000)	One cotyledon; parallel-veined leaves common; bundles of vascular tissue scattered in stem; flower parts in multiples of three
Eudicots	Most fruit trees, roses, beans, potatoes, and others	(200 000)	Most species have two cotyledons; net-veined leaves common; central core of vascular tissue in stem; flower parts in multiples of four or five

© Cengage Learning 2017.

the present but, collectively, these survivors total fewer than 14 000 species. The taxonomic relationships between various lines are still under active investigation, and comparisons of gene sequences from the genomes in chloroplasts, nuclei, and mitochondria are revealing previously unsuspected links between some of them. In this book, we assign seedless vascular plants to two phyla, the Lycophyta (club mosses and their close relatives; the common name "club moss" for lycophytes is misleading, as they are vascular plants, not mosses) and the Pterophyta (ferns, whisk ferns, and horsetails).

26.4a Early Seedless Vascular Plants Flourished in Moist Environments

What did the first vascular plant look like? There are no living relatives of the earliest vascular plants, so we rely on fossil data to answer this question. The extinct genus *Rhynia* was one of the earliest ancestors of modern seedless vascular plants. Based on fossil evidence, the sporophytes of the first vascular plants, such as *Rhynia* and related genera **(Figure 26.14)**, lacked leaves and roots. Above-ground photosynthetic stems produced sporangia

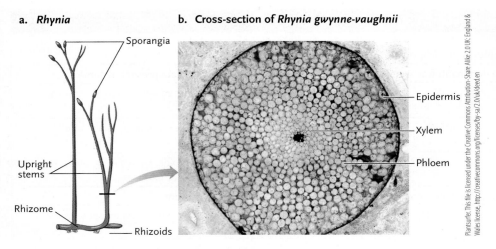

a. *Rhynia*

b. **Cross-section of *Rhynia gwynne-vaughnii***

Sporangia

Upright stems

Rhizome

Rhizoids

Epidermis

Xylem

Phloem

Plantsurfer. This file is licensed under the Creative Commons Attribution-Share Alike 2.0 UK: England & Wales license, http://creativecommons.org/licenses/by-sa/2.0/uk/deed.en

FIGURE 26.14 ***Rhynia*, an early seedless vascular plant. (a)** Fossil-based reconstruction of the entire plant, about 30 cm tall. **(b)** Cross-section of the stem, approximately 3 mm in diameter. This fossil was embedded in chert approximately 400 mya. Still visible in it are traces of the transport tissues xylem and phloem, along with other specialized tissues.

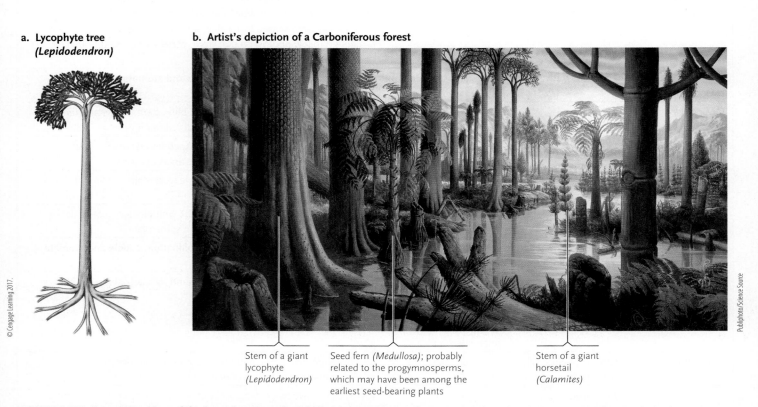

a. **Lycophyte tree (*Lepidodendron*)**

b. **Artist's depiction of a Carboniferous forest**

© Cengage Learning 2017.

Stem of a giant lycophyte (*Lepidodendron*)

Seed fern (*Medullosa*); probably related to the progymnosperms, which may have been among the earliest seed-bearing plants

Stem of a giant horsetail (*Calamites*)

Publiphoto/Science Source

FIGURE 26.15 Reconstruction of the lycophyte tree *Lepidodendron* and its environment. (a) Fossil evidence suggests that *Lepidodendron* grew to be about 35 m tall with a trunk 1 m in diameter. **(b)** Lush forests of the Carboniferous period were dominated by early seedless vascular plants.

at the tips of branches. Below ground, the plant body was supported by **rhizomes**, horizontal modified stems that can penetrate a substrate and anchor the plant. *Rhynia*'s simple stems had a central core of xylem, an arrangement seen in many existing vascular plants. Mudflats and swamps of the damp Devonian period were dominated by *Rhynia* and related plants (Figure 26.14). Although these and other now-extinct phyla came and went, ancestral forms of both modern phyla of seedless vascular plants appeared.

Carboniferous forests were swampy places dominated by members of the phylum **Lycophyta**, and fascinating fossil specimens of this group have been unearthed in North America and Europe. One example is *Lepidodendron*, which had broad, straplike leaves and sporangia near the ends of the branches **(Figure 26.15a)**. It also had xylem and other tissues typical of all modern vascular plants. Also abundant at the time were representatives of the phylum **Pterophyta**, including ferns and giants such as *Calamites*—huge horsetails that could have a trunk diameter of 30 cm. Some early seed plants were also present, including now-extinct fernlike plants, called *seed ferns*, that bore seeds at the tips of their leaves (Figure 26.15b).

Characterized by a moist climate over much of the planet and by the dominance of seedless vascular plants, the Carboniferous period continued for 150 million years, ending when climate patterns changed during the Paleozoic era. Most modern seedless vascular plants are confined largely to wet or humid environments because they require external water for reproduction. However, some are poikilohydric and can survive in a dehydrated state for long periods of time.

26.4b Modern Lycophytes Are Small and Have Simple Vascular Tissues

Lycophytes were highly diverse 350 mya, when some tree-sized forms inhabited lush swamp forests. Today, however, such giants are no more. The most familiar of the 1000 or so living species of lycophytes are club mosses (e.g., species of *Lycopodium* and *Selaginella*), which grow on forest floors, in alpine meadows, and in some prairie habitats **(Figure 26.16)**. For example, *Selaginella densa* (Figure 26.16b) is a dominant plant in shortgrass prairies of western North America. Club moss sporophytes have upright or horizontal stems that contain xylem and bear small green leaves and roots. Sporangia are clustered at the bases of specialized leaves, called **sporophylls** (*phyll* = leaf; thus, sporophyll = "spore-bearing leaf"). Sporophylls are clustered into a **cone** or **strobilus** (plural, *strobili*) at the tips of stems. Most lycophytes are homosporous, but some are heterosporous, producing two types of spores that will in turn produce separate male and female gametophytes.

26.4c Ferns, Whisk Ferns, Horsetails, and Their Relatives Make Up the Diverse Phylum Pterophyta

Second in size only to the flowering plants, the phylum Pterophyta (*pteron* = wing) contains a large and diverse group of vascular plants: the 13 000 or so species of ferns, whisk ferns, and horsetails. Most ferns, including some that are popular houseplants, are native to tropical and temperate regions. Some floating species are less than 1 cm across, whereas some tropical tree ferns grow to 25 m tall. Other species are adapted to life in Arctic and Alpine tundras, salty mangrove swamps, and semiarid deserts.

FEATURES OF FERNS. The familiar plant body of a fern is the sporophyte phase **(Figure 26.17)**, which produces an above-ground clump of leaves. Young leaves are tightly coiled, and as they emerge above the soil, these fiddleheads (so named because they resemble the scrolled pegheads of violins) unroll and expand. The fiddleheads of some species are edible when cooked, tasting similar to fresh asparagus, but be sure you have collected the right type of fiddlehead—some species contain a carcinogen.

Sporangia are produced on the lower surface or margins of leaves. Often, several sporangia are clustered into a rust-coloured **sorus** ("heap"; plural, *sori*; see Figure 26.17). Spores released from sporangia develop into gametophytes, which are typically small, heart-shaped, and anchored to the soil by rhizoids. Antheridia and archegonia develop on the underside of gametophytes, where moisture is trapped. Inside an antheridium is a globular packet of haploid cells, each of which develops into a helical sperm with many flagella. When water is present, the antheridium bursts, releasing the sperm. If mature archegonia are nearby, the sperm swim toward them, drawn by a chemical attractant that diffuses from the neck of the archegonium, which is open when free water is present.

In some ferns, antheridia and archegonia are produced on a single bisexual gametophyte. In other ferns, the first spores to germinate develop into bisexual gametophytes, which produce a chemical (antheridiogen) that diffuses through the substrate and causes all later-germinating spores to develop into male gametophytes. What is the advantage of producing a few bisexual gametophytes followed by many male gametophytes? If a bisexual gametophyte is surrounded by several male gametophytes that developed from other spores, it is more likely that eggs will be fertilized by sperm from one of the male

a. *Lycopodium* **sporophyte**

b. *Selaginella densa* **sporophytes**

Strobilus

FIGURE 26.16
Lycophytes. (a) *Lycopodium* sporophyte, showing the conelike strobili in which spores are produced. **(b)** *Selaginella* densa sporophytes

Ed Reschke

Dave Powell, USDA Forest Service, Bugwood.org

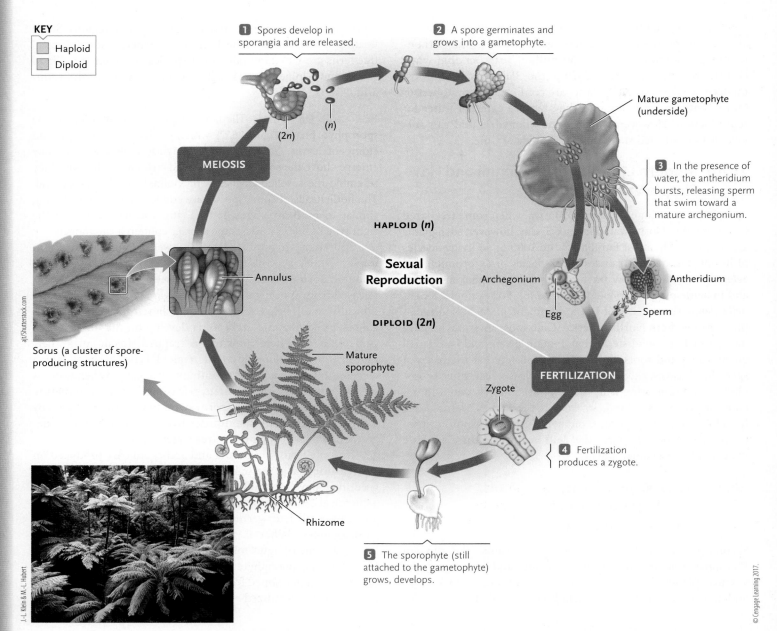

KEY
- Haploid
- Diploid

1 Spores develop in sporangia and are released.

2 A spore germinates and grows into a gametophyte.

Mature gametophyte (underside)

MEIOSIS

(2n) (n)

3 In the presence of water, the antheridium bursts, releasing sperm that swim toward a mature archegonium.

HAPLOID (n)

Sexual Reproduction

Annulus

Archegonium — Egg

Antheridium — Sperm

DIPLOID (2n)

FERTILIZATION

Sorus (a cluster of spore-producing structures)

Zygote

Mature sporophyte

4 Fertilization produces a zygote.

Rhizome

5 The sporophyte (still attached to the gametophyte) grows, develops.

Figure 26.17 Life cycle of a chain fern (*Woodwardia*). The photograph shows part of a forest of tree ferns (*Cyathea*) in Australia's Tarra-Bulga National Park.

gametophytes rather than by its own sperm, thus increasing the genetic diversity of the resulting zygote.

An embryo is retained on and nourished by the gametophyte for the first part of its life but soon develops into a young sporophyte larger than the gametophyte, with its own green leaf and root system. Once the sporophyte is nutritionally independent, the parent gametophyte degenerates and dies.

FEATURES OF WHISK FERNS The whisk ferns and their relatives are represented by only 2 genera, with about 10 species in total. They grow in tropical and subtropical regions, often as epiphytes. We will discuss one genus, *Psilotum* (**Figure 26.18**).

The sporophytes of *Psilotum* resemble the extinct vascular plants in that they lack true roots and leaves. Instead, small,

leaflike scales adorn an upright, green, branching stem, which arises from a horizontal rhizome system anchored by rhizoids. Symbiotic fungi colonize the rhizoids, increasing the plant's uptake of soil nutrients (read more about these mycorrhizal fungi in Chapter 25). The stem is photosynthetic and bears sporangia above the small scales. Gametophytes of *Psilotum* are non-photosynthetic and live underground (**Figure 26.19**); like the sporophyte, they obtain nutrients via symbioses with mycorrhizal fungi.

FEATURES OF HORSETAILS The ancient relatives of modern-day horsetails included treelike forms taller than a two-storey building. Only 15 species in a single genus, *Equisetum*, have survived to the present (**Figure 26.20**). Horsetails grow in moist soil

FIGURE 26.18 **Sporophyte of a whisk fern (*Psilotum*), a seedless vascular plant.** Three-lobed sporangia occur at the ends of stubby branchlets; inside the sporangia, meiosis gives rise to haploid spores.

a. **Sporophyte stem** b. **Sporangia**

Strobilus, an aggregation of sporangia and sporophylls at the tip of the horsetail sporophyte

c. This longitudinal section through a horsetail's strobilus shows sporangia containing spores formed by meiosis.

FIGURE 26.20 **A species of *Equisetum*, the horsetails. (a)** Vegetative stem. **(b)** Strobili, which bear sporangia. **(c)** Close-up of sporangium and associated structures on a strobilus

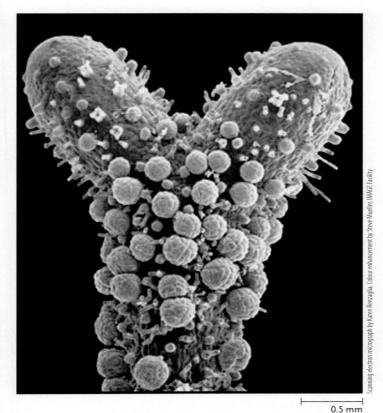

FIGURE 26.19 **Scanning electron micrograph image of the subterranean gametophyte of *Psilotum*.** Antheridia have been coloured blue, and the smaller archegonia have been coloured pink.

along streams and in disturbed habitats, such as roadsides and beds of railway tracks. Their sporophytes typically have underground rhizomes and roots that anchor the rhizome to the soil. Small, scalelike leaves are arranged in whorls about a photosynthetic stem that is stiff and gritty because horsetails accumulate silica in their tissues. Pioneers used them to scrub out pots and pans—hence their other common name, "scouring rushes."

As in lycophytes, *Equisetum* sporangia are borne in strobili. Haploid spores germinate within a few days to produce gametophytes, which are free-living plants about the size of a small pea.

26.4d Some Seedless Vascular Plants Are Heterosporous

Most seedless vascular plants are homosporous, but some (e.g., some lycophytes and some ferns) are heterosporous, producing microspores and megaspores in separate sporangia (see Figure 26.7). Both types of spores are usually shed from sporangia and germinate on the ground some distance from the parent plant. In many heterosporous plants, the gametophytes produced by the spores develop inside the spore wall; this **endosporous** development provides increased protection for the gametes and, later, for the developing embryo. The microspore gives rise to a male gametophyte, which produces motile sperm. At maturity, the microspore wall will rupture, releasing the sperm, which swim to the female gametophyte; water is thus still required for fertilization in these plants. The megaspore produces a female gametophyte inside the spore wall; archegonia of this gametophyte produce eggs, as in other seedless plants.

1. Compare the lycophyte and bryophyte life cycles with respect to the sizes and longevity of gametophyte and sporophyte phases.

2. Summarize the main similarities and differences in the life cycles of lycophytes, horsetails, whisk ferns, and ferns.

3. Define *sorus* and *strobilus*. How are these two structures similar?

26.5 Gymnosperms: The First Seed Plants

Gymnosperms include conifers and their relatives. The earliest fossils identified as gymnosperms are found in Devonian rocks. By the Carboniferous, when nonvascular plants were dominant, many lines of gymnosperms, including conifers, had also evolved. These radiated during the Permian period; the Mesozoic era that followed, 65–248 mya, was the age not only of the dinosaurs but of the gymnosperms as well.

The evolution of gymnosperms marked sweeping changes in plant structures related to reproduction. The evolution of gymnosperms included important reproductive adaptations: pollen and pollination, the ovule, and the seed. The fossil record has not revealed the sequence in which these changes arose, but all of them contributed to the radiation of gymnosperms into land environments.

As a prelude to our survey of modern gymnosperms, we begin by considering some of these innovations.

26.5a Major Reproductive Adaptations Occurred as Gymnosperms Evolved

The word *gymnosperm* is derived from the Greek *gymnos*, meaning "naked," and *sperma*, meaning "seed." As this name indicates, gymnosperms produce seeds that are exposed, not enclosed in fruit, as are the seeds of other seed plants.

OVULES: INCREASED PROTECTION FOR FEMALE GAMETO-PHYTE AND EGG How did seeds first arise? Think about the heterosporous plants described in the previous section and picture two steps that would lead us toward the development of a seed. In the first step, spores are not shed from the plant but instead are retained inside sporangia on the sporophyte. In the second step, the number of megaspores is reduced to just one per sporangium (i.e., four megaspores are produced by meiosis, but only one survives). These two steps result in retention of a single megaspore inside a megasporangium on a plant **(Figure 26.21)**. As in all land plants, the megaspore will give rise to a female gametophyte; because this is a heterosporous plant, the gametophyte will develop inside the megaspore wall and inside the megasporangium. Physically connected to the sporophyte and surrounded by protective layers, a female gametophyte

no longer faces the same risks of predation or environmental assault that can threaten a free-living gametophyte.

This new structure, an egg developing inside a gametophyte that is retained not only inside the spore wall but also inside integument and megasporangial tissues, is an **ovule**. When fertilized, an ovule becomes a **seed**; the fertilized egg will produce an embryo surrounded by nutritive tissue, encased in integument that becomes the seed coat.

Look at Figure 26.21 and note the megasporangium surrounded by integument. These layers provide protection for gametes and embryos, but they create a problem: How can sperm get to the egg now that the gametophyte is enclosed inside these layers of tissue? The solution is two-fold. First, there is a hole in the integument called the *micropyle* through which the pollen enters the ovule. Second, similar to internal fertilization in animals, there is penetration of the sporangial tissue and release of sperm inside the female gametophyte. In the next section, we look at the male gametophyte in seed plants.

POLLEN: ELIMINATING THE NEED FOR WATER IN REPRODUCTION As for megaspores, the microspores of seed plants are not dispersed. Instead, they are retained inside microsporangia and enveloped in additional layers of sporophyte tissue. As in other heterosporous plants, each microspore produces a male gametophyte, which develops inside the microspore wall. This male gametophyte is very small relative to those of nonseed plants—it is made of only a few cells—and is called a **pollen grain**. Pollen grains are transferred to female reproductive parts via air currents or on the bodies of animal pollinators; this transfer is known as **pollination**. When the pollen grain lands on female tissue, the pollen grain germinates to produce a **pollen tube (Figure 26.22)**, a cell that grows through female gametophyte tissue by invasive growth and carries the nonmotile sperm to the egg.

Pollen and pollination were enormously important adaptations for gymnosperms because the shift to non-swimming sperm, along with a means for delivering them to female gametes, meant that reproduction no longer required liquid water. The only gymnosperms that have retained swimming sperm are the cycads and ginkgoes described below, which have relatively few living species and are restricted to just a few native habitats.

SEEDS: PROTECTING AND NOURISHING PLANT EMBRYOS As described above, a seed is the structure that forms when an ovule matures, after a pollen grain reaches it and a sperm fertilizes the egg. Seeds consist of three basic parts: (1) the embryo sporophyte; (2) the tissues surrounding the embryo containing nutrients that nourish it until it becomes established as a seedling with leaves and roots; and (3) a tough, protective outer seed coat **(Figure 26.23)**. This complex structure makes seeds ideal packages for protecting an embryo from drought, cold, or other adverse conditions. As a result, seed plants enjoy a tremendous

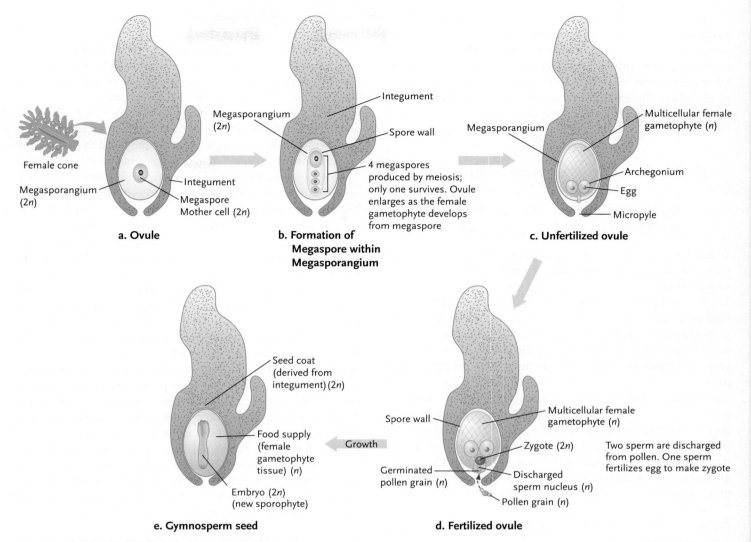

FIGURE 26.21 Structure of a gymnosperm ovule

a. Ovule

Female cone
Megasporangium (2n)
Integument
Megaspore Mother cell (2n)

b. Formation of Megaspore within Megasporangium

Megasporangium (2n)
Integument
Spore wall
4 megaspores produced by meiosis; only one survives. Ovule enlarges as the female gametophyte develops from megaspore

c. Unfertilized ovule

Megasporangium
Multicellular female gametophyte (n)
Archegonium
Egg
Micropyle

d. Fertilized ovule

Spore wall
Multicellular female gametophyte (n)
Zygote (2n)
Germinated pollen grain (n)
Discharged sperm nucleus (n)
Pollen grain (n)
Two sperm are discharged from pollen. One sperm fertilizes egg to make zygote

Growth

e. Gymnosperm seed

Seed coat (derived from integument) (2n)
Food supply (female gametophyte tissue) (n)
Embryo (2n) (new sporophyte)

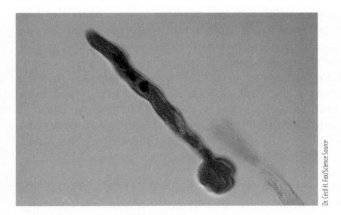

Dr. Cecil H. Fox/Science Source

FIGURE 26.22 Pollen tube extending from germinating pollen grain at bottom right

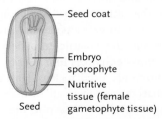

Seed coat
Embryo sporophyte
Nutritive tissue (female gametophyte tissue)
Seed

FIGURE 26.23 Generalized view of the seed of a pine, a gymnosperm

survival advantage over species that simply release spores to the environment. Encased in a seed, the embryo can also be transported far from its parent, as when ocean currents carry coconut seeds ("coconuts" protected in large, buoyant fruits) hundreds of kilometres across the sea. As discussed in Chapter 35, some plant embryos housed in seeds can remain dormant for months or years before environmental conditions finally prompt them to germinate and grow.

26.5b Modern Gymnosperms Include Conifers and a Few Other Groups Represented by Relatively Few Species That Tend to Be Restricted to Certain Climates

Today there are about 800 gymnosperm species. The sporophytes of nearly all are large trees or shrubs, although a few are woody vines.

Economically, gymnosperms, particularly conifers, are vital to human societies. They are sources of lumber, paper pulp, turpentine, and resins, among other products. They also have huge ecological importance. Their habitats range from **tropical forests** to deserts, but gymnosperms are most dominant in the cool-temperate zones of the Northern and Southern Hemispheres. They flourish in poor soils, where flowering plants don't compete as well. In Canada, for example, gymnosperms make up most of the boreal forests that cover about one-third of the country's landmass. Our survey of gymnosperms begins with the conifers, and then we will look at the cycads, ginkgoes, and gnetophytes; the latter two groups are remnants of lineages that have all but vanished from the modern scene.

CONIFERS ARE THE MOST COMMON GYMNOSPERMS About 80% of all living gymnosperm species are members of one phylum, the **Coniferophyta**, or conifers ("cone bearers"). Examples are pines, spruces, and firs. Coniferous trees and shrubs are longer lived and anatomically and morphologically more complex than any sporophyte phase we have discussed so far. Characteristically, they form woody cones, and most have needlelike leaves that are adapted to dry environments. For instance, needles have a thick cuticle, sunken stomata, and a fibrous epidermis, all traits that reduce the loss of water vapour.

Pines and many other gymnosperms produce resins, a mix of organic compounds that are by-products of metabolism. Resin accumulates and flows in long resin ducts through the wood, inhibiting the activity of wood-boring insects and certain microbes. Pine resin extracts are the raw material of turpentine, and (minus the volatile terpenes) the sticky rosin applied to violin bows enhances tone. Fossil resin is known as *amber* and is commonly used in jewellery; amber often contains fossilized insects or even small animals.

We know a great deal about the pine life cycle **(Figure 26.24)**, so it is a convenient model for gymnosperms. Male cones are relatively small and delicate (about 1 cm long) and are borne on the lower branches. Each cone consists of many sporophylls with two microsporangia on their undersides. Inside the microsporangia, **microspores** are produced by meiosis. Each microspore then undergoes mitosis to develop into a winged pollen grain—an immature male gametophyte. At this stage, the pollen grain consists of four cells, two that will degenerate and two that will function later in reproduction.

Young female cones develop higher in the tree, at the tips of upper branches. Two ovules are produced on each cone scale. Inside each ovule, four megaspores are produced by meiosis, but only one survives to develop into a megagametophyte. This female gametophyte develops slowly, becoming mature only when pollination is under way; in a pine, this process takes well over a year. The mature female gametophyte is a small oval mass of cells with several archegonia at one end, each containing an egg.

Each spring, air currents release vast numbers of pollen grains from male cones: by some estimates, billions may be released from a single pine tree. The extravagant numbers ensure that at least some pollen grains will land on female cones. The process is not as random as it might seem: studies have shown that the contours of female cones create air currents that can favour the "delivery" of pollen grains near the cone scales. After pollination, the two remaining cells of the pollen grain divide, one producing sperm by mitosis, the other producing the pollen tube that grows toward the developing gametophyte. When a pollen tube reaches an egg, the stage is set for fertilization, the formation of a zygote, and early development of the plant embryo. Fertilization occurs months to a year after pollination. Once an embryo forms, a pine seed—which, remember, includes the embryo, female gametophyte tissue, and seed coat—is eventually shed from the cone. The seed coat protects the embryo from drying out, and the female gametophyte tissue serves as its food reserve. This tissue makes up the bulk of a "pine nut."

CYCADS ARE RESTRICTED TO WARMER CLIMATES During the Mesozoic era, the **Cycadophyta** (*kykas* = palm), or cycads, flourished along with the dinosaurs. About 185 species have survived to the present, but they are confined to the tropics and subtropics.

At first glance, you might mistake a cycad for a small palm tree **(Figure 26.25)**. Some cycads have massive cones that bear either pollen or ovules. Air currents or crawling insects transfer pollen from male plants to the developing gametophyte on female plants. Poisonous alkaloids that may help deter insect predators occur in various cycad tissues. In tropical Asia, some people consume cycad seeds and flour made from cycad trunks, but only after rinsing away the toxic compounds. Much in demand from fanciers of unusual plants, cycads in some countries are uprooted and sold in what amounts to a black-market trade, greatly diminishing their numbers in the wild.

GINKGOES ARE LIMITED TO A SINGLE LIVING SPECIES The phylum **Ginkgophyta** has only one living species, the ginkgo (or maidenhair) tree (*Ginkgo biloba*), which grows wild today only in warm-temperate forests of central China. Ginkgo trees are large, diffusely branching trees with characteristic fan-shaped

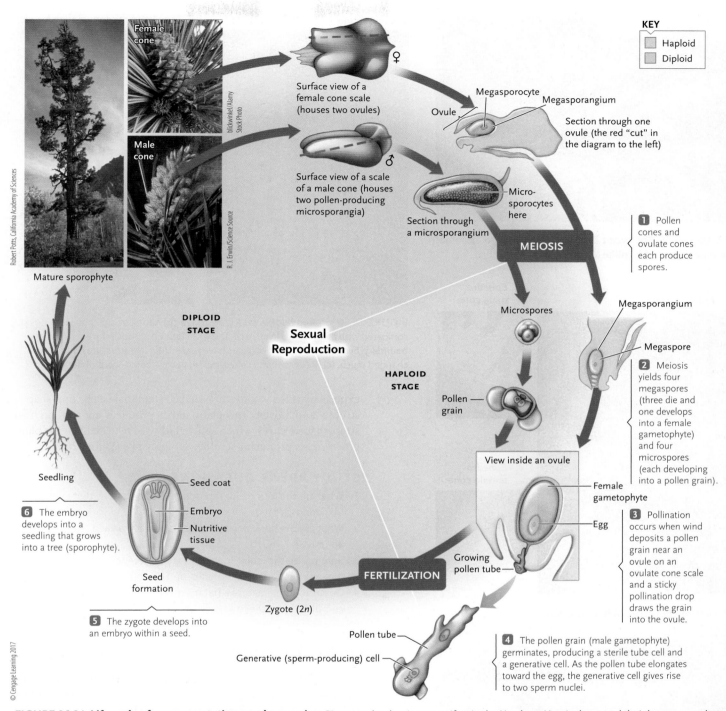

KEY
Haploid
Diploid

Surface view of a female cone scale (houses two ovules)

Surface view of a scale of a male cone (houses two pollen-producing microsporangia)

Section through a microsporangium

Micro-sporocytes here

Ovule

Megasporocyte

Megasporangium

Section through one ovule (the red "cut" in the diagram to the left)

MEIOSIS

1 Pollen cones and ovulate cones each produce spores.

Megasporangium

Microspores

Megaspore

2 Meiosis yields four megaspores (three die and one develops into a female gametophyte) and four microspores (each developing into a pollen grain).

Pollen grain

Sexual Reproduction

DIPLOID STAGE

HAPLOID STAGE

View inside an ovule

Female gametophyte

Egg

3 Pollination occurs when wind deposits a pollen grain near an ovule on an ovulate cone scale and a sticky pollination drop draws the grain into the ovule.

Growing pollen tube

Mature sporophyte

Seedling

Seed coat

Embryo

Nutritive tissue

Seed formation

6 The embryo develops into a seedling that grows into a tree (sporophyte).

5 The zygote develops into an embryo within a seed.

Zygote (2*n*)

FERTILIZATION

Pollen tube

Generative (sperm-producing) cell

4 The pollen grain (male gametophyte) germinates, producing a sterile tube cell and a generative cell. As the pollen tube elongates toward the egg, the generative cell gives rise to two sperm nuclei.

Female cone

Male cone

FIGURE 26.24 Life cycle of a representative ponderosa pine. Pines are the dominant conifers in the Northern Hemisphere, and their large sporophytes provide a heavily exploited source of wood.

leaves **(Figure 26.26)** that turn a brilliant yellow in autumn. Nursery-propagated male trees are often planted in cities because they are resistant to insects, disease, and air pollutants. The female trees are equally pollution resistant, but gardeners avoid them because their seeds produce a foul odour that only a ginkgo could love. The leaves and seeds have been used in traditional Chinese medicine for centuries. The extract of the leaves is one of the most intensely investigated herbal medicines; there

is some evidence that it assists in blood flow and so may be effective in the treatment of circulatory disorders.

GNETOPHYTES INCLUDE SIMPLE SEED PLANTS WITH INTRIGUING FEATURES The phylum Gnetophyta contains three genera—*Gnetum*, *Ephedra*, and *Welwitschia*—that together include about 70 species. Moist, tropical regions are home to about 30 species of *Gnetum*, which includes both trees and

FIGURE 26.25 **The cycad** *Zamia* **showing a large, terminal female cone and fernlike leaves**

a. *Ephedra* **plant**

b. *Ephedra* **male cone**

© William Ferguson

c. *Ephedra* **female cone**

Yang Y, Wang Q (2013) The Earliest Fleshy Cone of Ephedra from the Early Cretaceous Yixian Formation of Northeast China. PLoS ONE 8(1): e53652. https://doi.org/10.1371/journal.pone.0053652

d. *Welwitschia* **plant with female cones**

FIGURE 26.27 **Gnetophytes. (a)** Sporophyte of *Ephedra*, with close-ups of its **(b)** pollen-bearing cones and **(c)** seed-bearing cone, which develop on separate plants. **(d)** Sporophyte of *Welwitschia mirabilis*, with seed-bearing cones

a. Ginkgo tree

b. Fossil and modern ginkgo leaves

c. Male cone

© William Ferguson

d. Ginkgo seeds

FIGURE 26.26 *Ginkgo biloba.* **(a)** A ginkgo tree. **(b)** A fossilized ginkgo leaf compared with a leaf from a living tree. The fossil formed at the Cretaceous–Tertiary boundary. Even though 65 million years have passed, the leaf structure has not changed much. **(c)** Pollen-bearing cones and **(d)** fleshy-coated seeds of the *Ginkgo*

exposed part is a woody, disk-shaped stem that bears cone-shaped strobili and leaves. The plant never produces more than two strap-shaped leaves, which split lengthwise repeatedly as the plant grows older, producing a rather scraggly pile (Figure 26.27d).

STUDY BREAK QUESTIONS

1. What are the four major reproductive adaptations that evolved in gymnosperms?
2. What are the basic parts of a seed, and how is each one adaptive?
3. Summarize the main similarities and differences among ginkgoes, cycads, gnetophytes, and conifers.
4. Describe some features that make conifers structurally more complex than other gymnosperms.

26.6 Angiosperms: Flowering Plants

Of all plant phyla, the flowering plants, or **angiosperms**, are the most successful today. At least 260 000 species are known (**Figure 26.28** shows a few examples), and botanists regularly discover new ones in previously unexplored regions of the tropics. The word *angiosperm* is derived from the Greek *angeion* ("vessel") and *sperma* ("seed"). The "vessel" refers to the modified sporophyll, called a *carpel*, that surrounds and protects the ovules. Carpels are located in the centre of **flowers**—reproductive structures that are a defining feature of angiosperms. Another defining feature is the **fruit**—botanically speaking, a structure that helps protect and disperse seeds.

In addition to having flowers and fruits, angiosperms are the most ecologically diverse plants on Earth, growing on dry land and in **wetlands**, fresh water, and the seas. Angiosperms

leathery-leafed vines (lianas). About 35 species of *Ephedra* grow in desert regions of the world (**Figure 26.27a–c**).

Of all the gymnosperms, *Welwitschia* is the most bizarre. This seed-producing plant grows in the hot deserts of southwest Africa. The bulk of the plant is a deep-reaching taproot. The only

a. Flowering plants in a desert

b. Alpine angiosperms

c. Triticale, a grass

d. The carnivorous plant Venus flytrap

FIGURE 26.28 Flowering plants. Diverse photosynthetic species are adapted to nearly all environments, ranging from **(a)** deserts to **(b)** snowlines of high mountains. **(c)** Triticale, a hybrid grain derived from parental stocks of wheat (*Triticum*) and rye (*Secale*), is one example of the various grasses used by humans. **(d)** The carnivorous plant Venus flytrap (*Dionaea muscipula*) grows in nitrogen-poor soils and traps insects as an additional source of nitrogen.

range in size from tiny duckweeds that are about 1 mm long to towering *Eucalyptus* trees more than 60 m tall.

26.6a The Fossil Record Provides Little Information about the Origin of Flowering Plants

The evolutionary origin of angiosperms has confounded plant biologists for well over a hundred years. Charles Darwin called it the "abominable mystery" because flowering plants appear suddenly in the fossil record, without a fossil sequence that links them to any other plant groups. As with gymnosperms, attempts to reconstruct the earliest flowering plant lineages have produced several conflicting classifications and family trees. Some paleobotanists hypothesize that flowering plants arose during the Jurassic period; others propose that they evolved in the Triassic from now-extinct gymnosperms or from seed ferns. However, progress in this area does not rely solely on fossil evidence; molecular data can be used to test hypotheses, and the combination of molecular, morphological, and fossil evidence offers great promise in solving this mystery.

The fossil record has yet to reveal obvious transitional organisms between flowering plants and either gymnosperms or seedless vascular plants. As the Mesozoic era ended and the modern Cenozoic era began, great extinctions occurred among both plant and animal kingdoms. Gymnosperms declined and dinosaurs disappeared. Flowering plants, mammals, and social insects flourished, radiating into new environments. Today we live in what has been called "the age of flowering plants."

26.6b Angiosperms Are Subdivided into Several Groups, Including Monocots and Eudicots

Angiosperms are assigned to the phylum **Anthophyta**, a name that derives from the Greek *anthos*, meaning "flower." The great majority of angiosperms are classified as either monocots or eudicots, which are differentiated on the basis of morphological features such as the number of flower parts and the pattern of vascular tissue in stems and leaves. The two groups also differ in terms of the morphology of their embryos: **monocot** embryos have a single leaflike structure called a *cotyledon*, whereas **eudicot** ("true dicots") embryos generally have two cotyledons (see Table 26.2).

Botanists currently recognize several other groups of plants in addition to eudicots and monocots, but figuring out the appropriate classification for and relationships among these other groups is an ongoing challenge and an extremely active area of plant research. In this chapter, we focus only on monocots and eudicots.

There are at least 60 000 species of monocots, including 10 000 grasses and 20 000 orchids. **Figure 26.29a** gives some idea of the variety of living monocots, which include grasses, palms, lilies, and orchids. The world's major crop plants (wheat, corn, rice, rye, sugar cane, and barley) are all monocots and are all domesticated grasses. Eudicots are even more diverse, with nearly 200 000 species (Figure 26.29b). They include flowering shrubs and trees, most nonwoody (herbaceous) plants, and cacti. We will take a closer look at angiosperms in Chapter 35, which focuses on the structure and function of flowering plants.

26.6c Many Factors Contributed to the Adaptive Success of Angiosperms

Flowering plants likely originated about 140 mya. It took only about 40 million years—a short span in geologic time—for angiosperms to eclipse gymnosperms as the prevailing form of plant life on land. Several factors fuelled this adaptive success **(Figure 26.30)**. As with other seed plants, the large, diploid sporophyte phase dominates a flowering plant's life cycle, and the sporophyte retains and nourishes the much smaller gametophytes. But flowering plants also show some evolutionary innovations not seen in gymnosperms.

MORE EFFICIENT TRANSPORT OF WATER AND NUTRIENTS

Where gymnosperms have only one type of water-conducting cell in their xylem, angiosperms have an additional, more specialized type of cell that is larger and open ended and thus moves water more rapidly from roots to shoots (see Chapter 34). Also, modifications in angiosperm phloem tissue allow it to more efficiently transport sugars produced in photosynthesis through the plant body.

a. Representative monocots

Wheat (*Triticum*)

Trillium (*Trillium*)

Western wood lily (*Lilium philadelphicum*)

b. Representative eudicots

Wild rose (*Rosa acicularis*)

Twinflower (*Linnaea borealis*)

Claret cup cactus (*Echinocereus triglochidiatus*)

FIGURE 26.29 Examples of monocots and eudicots. (a) Representative monocots: wheat (*Triticum*), trillium (*Trillium*), and Western wood lily (*Lilium philadelphicum*). **(b)** Representative eudicots: wild rose (*Rosa acicularis*), twinflower (*Linnaea borealis*), and cactus (*Echinocereus triglochidiatus*)

FIGURE 26.30 **Experimental Research**

Exploring a Possible Early Angiosperm Adaptation for Efficient Photosynthesis in Dim Environments

Question: Did modifications in light-sensitive pigments shape the early evolution of flowering plants?

Experiment: Sarah J. Mathews and J. Gordon Burleigh, of the University of Missouri, and Michael J. Donoghue, of Yale University, hypothesized that the first angiosperms may have evolved in the dim understory of moist land habitats dominated by large Mesozoic gymnosperms and ferns.

1. The researchers began by looking at genes, designated *PHYA* and *PHYC*, that encode phytochromes (pigments) that allow seed plants to detect light of red and far-red wavelengths—wavelengths that predominate in dim light. The nucleotide sequences of *PHYA* and *PHYC* are about 50% identical and evidently are the descendants of a duplicated ancestral *PHY* gene. *PHYC* is sensitive to relatively bright light but apparently does not respond to dim light, and *PHYA* is highly sensitive to dim light and is inactivated by bright light.

2. The researchers obtained amino acid sequence data for key functional domains of the phytochrome proteins encoded by *PHYA* and *PHYC* in 45 plant species. Most of the species were angiosperms; several conifers represented the presumed ancestral gene. Analysis of the data focused on both the number of substitutions in the targeted phytochrome amino acid sequences and the biochemical effects of the substitutions.

Results: In the tree branch leading from the presumed ancestral *PHY* gene to *PHYA*, 32 amino acid substitutions occurred. Of these, 11 were best interpreted as shifts associated with selection pressure. In the branch leading to *PHYC*, only 7 substitutions occurred; 4 were best interpreted as associated with selection pressure. A phylogenetic tree based on these results displayed genetic divergences as branch points.

Amino acid sequences of key functional domains of phyA and phyC proteins from conifer, multiple angiosperms

Computer analysis

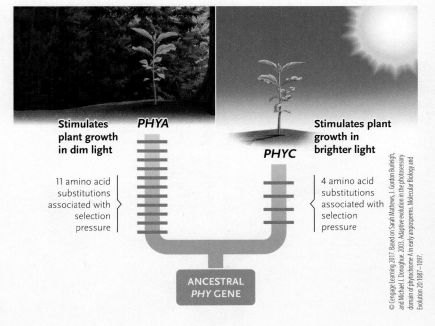

© Cengage Learning 2017. Based on Sarah Mathews, J. Gordon Burleigh, and Michael J. Donoghue. 2003. Adaptive evolution in the photosensory domain of phytochrome A in early angiosperms. Molecular Biology and Evolution 20:1087–1097.

Conclusion: Diverging molecular characteristics of *PHYA* and *PHYC* correlated with diverging functions of the phytochromes the genes encode. PHYA evidently evolved under strong selection pressure. The availability of phytochrome A (phyA) possibly allowed early angiosperm seedlings to grow in mostly dim light conditions, as in the shade of Mesozoic forests.

ENHANCED NUTRITION AND PHYSICAL PROTECTION FOR EMBRYOS Other changes in angiosperms increased the likelihood of successful reproduction and dispersal of offspring. For example, a two-step, double-fertilization process in the ovules of flowering plants produces both an embryo and a unique nutritive tissue (called *endosperm*) that nourishes the embryonic sporophyte **(Figure 26.31)**. The ovule containing a female gametophyte is enclosed within an ovary, made up of one or more carpels, depending on the plant, that shelters the ovule against desiccation and attack by herbivores or pathogens. After fertilization, an ovary develops into a fruit that not only protects seeds but also helps disperse them; for instance, when an animal eats a fruit, seeds may pass through the animal's gut none the worse for the journey and be released in a new location in the animal's feces. Above all, angiosperms have flowers, the unique reproductive organs that you will read much more about in Chapter 35.

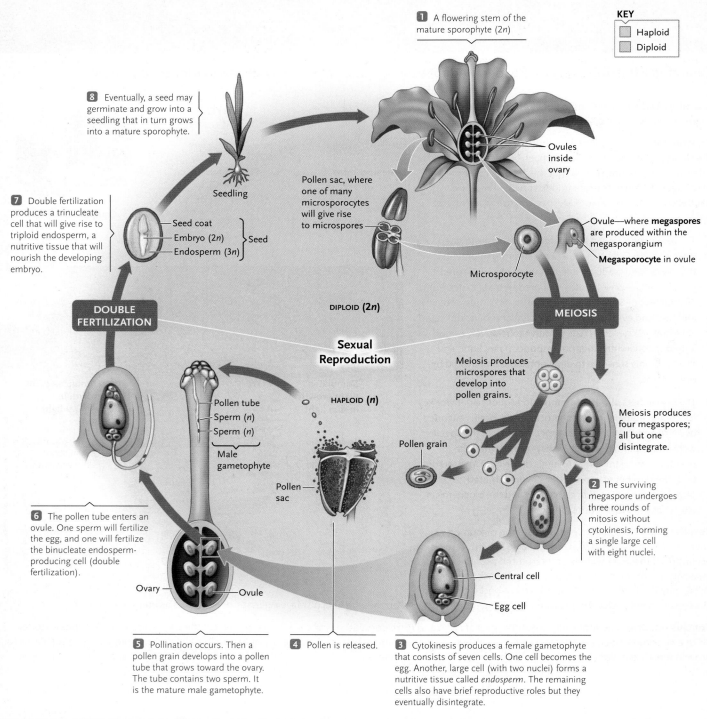

1 A flowering stem of the mature sporophyte (2*n*)

KEY
Haploid
Diploid

Ovules inside ovary

8 Eventually, a seed may germinate and grow into a seedling that in turn grows into a mature sporophyte.

Seedling

Pollen sac, where one of many microsporocytes will give rise to microspores

Ovule—where **megaspores** are produced within the megasporangium

Megasporocyte in ovule

7 Double fertilization produces a trinucleate cell that will give rise to triploid endosperm, a nutritive tissue that will nourish the developing embryo.

Seed coat
Embryo (2*n*)   Seed
Endosperm (3*n*)

Microsporocyte

DOUBLE FERTILIZATION

DIPLOID (2*n*)

MEIOSIS

Sexual Reproduction

Meiosis produces microspores that develop into pollen grains.

Meiosis produces four megaspores; all but one disintegrate.

HAPLOID (*n*)

Pollen tube
Sperm (*n*)
Sperm (*n*)

Male gametophyte

Pollen grain

Pollen sac

2 The surviving megaspore undergoes three rounds of mitosis without cytokinesis, forming a single large cell with eight nuclei.

6 The pollen tube enters an ovule. One sperm will fertilize the egg, and one will fertilize the binucleate endosperm-producing cell (double fertilization).

Central cell

Egg cell

Ovary
Ovule

5 Pollination occurs. Then a pollen grain develops into a pollen tube that grows toward the ovary. The tube contains two sperm. It is the mature male gametophyte.

4 Pollen is released.

3 Cytokinesis produces a female gametophyte that consists of seven cells. One cell becomes the egg. Another, large cell (with two nuclei) forms a nutritive tissue called *endosperm*. The remaining cells also have brief reproductive roles but they eventually disintegrate.

© Cengage Learning 2017

FIGURE 26.31 Life cycle of a typical flowering plant. Double fertilization is a notable feature of the cycle. The male gametophyte delivers two sperm to an ovule. One sperm fertilizes the egg, forming the embryo, and the other fertilizes the endosperm-producing cell, which nourishes the embryo.

26.6d Angiosperms Co-evolved with Animal Pollinators

The evolutionary success of angiosperms is due not only to the adaptations just described, but also to the efficient mechanisms of transferring pollen to female reproductive parts. Whereas a conifer depends on air currents to disperse its pollen, as do such

angiosperms as grasses, many angiosperms co-evolved with pollinators: insects, bats, birds, and other animals that transfer pollen from male floral structures to female reproductive parts, often while obtaining nectar. Nectar is a sugar-rich liquid secreted by flowers to attract pollinators. Pollen itself is a reward for some pollinators, such as bees, that use it as a food resource. So, while plants benefit from their animal pollinators, there is also a cost to the plant in providing a reward to the pollinator. Co-evolution occurs when two or more species interact closely in the same ecological setting. A heritable change in one species affects selection pressure operating between them, so that the other species evolves as well. Over time, plants have co-evolved with their pollinating animals.

In general, a flower's reproductive parts are positioned so that visiting pollinators will brush against them. In addition, many floral features correlate with the morphology and behaviour of specific pollinators. For example, reproductive parts may be located above nectar-filled floral tubes that are the same length as the feeding structure of a preferred pollinator. Nectar-sipping bats **(Figure 26.32a)** and moths forage by night. They pollinate intensely sweet-smelling flowers with white or pale petals that are more visible than coloured petals in the dark. The long thin mouthparts of moths and butterflies reach nectar in narrow floral tubes or floral spurs. The Madagascar hawkmoth uncoils a mouthpart the same length—an astonishing 22 cm—as the narrow flower of the orchid it pollinates, *Angraecum sesquipedale* (Figure 26.32b). Red and yellow flowers attract birds (Figure 26.32c), which have good daytime vision but a poor sense of smell. Hence, bird-pollinated plants do not squander metabolic resources to make fragrances. By contrast, flowers of species that are pollinated by beetles or flies may smell like rotten meat, dung, or decaying matter. This trickery by the plants is known as *signal mimicry*: the plant uses visual and olfactory signals to trick a pollinator into visiting it; some of these plants provide no nutritional reward for

their pollinators at all. Daisies and other fragrant flowers with distinctive patterns, shapes, and red or orange components attract butterflies, which forage by day.

Bees see ultraviolet light and visit flowers with sweet odours and parts that appear to humans as yellow, blue, or purple (Figure 26.32d). Produced by pigments that absorb ultraviolet light, the colours form patterns called "nectar guides" that attract bees, which may pick up or drop off pollen during the visit. Here, as in our other examples, flowers contribute to the reproductive success of plants that bear them.

In this chapter, we have introduced some of the strategies that plants use to meet the challenges of life on Earth; they face the same challenges as animals and other terrestrial organisms (attract a mate, reproduce, disperse offspring, and survive unfavourable conditions) but have had to find ways to do all of these without being able to move around (they are sessile). Many of these topics are followed up in more detail in the chapters dealing with plant biology (Chapters 33 to 37).

The next two chapters introduce animals. As you read these chapters, look for similarities and differences in how they have addressed the challenges of life compared to plants.

STUDY BREAK QUESTIONS

1. What are the advantages and costs to plants of using animals to disperse their pollen?
2. List at least three adaptations that have contributed to the evolutionary success of angiosperms as a group.

Figure 26.32 Co-evolution of flowering plants and animal pollinators. The colours and configurations of some flowers, and the production of nectar or odours, have co-evolved with specific animal pollinators. **(a)** At night, nectar-feeding bats sip nectar from flowers of the giant saguaro cactus (*Carnegiea gigantea*), transferring pollen from flower to flower in the process. **(b)** The hawkmoth (*Xanthopan morganii praedicta*) has a proboscis long enough to reach nectar at the base of the equally long floral spur of the orchid *Angraecum sesquipedale*. **(c)** A ruby-throated hummingbird (*Archilochus colubris*) sipping nectar from a hibiscus blossom (*Hibiscus*). The long narrow bill of hummingbirds co-evolved with long narrow floral tubes. **(d)** Under ultraviolet light, the bee-attracting pattern of a gold-petalled marsh marigold becomes visible to human eyes.

a. **Bat pollinating a giant saguaro**

b. **Hawkmoth pollinating an orchid**

c. **Hummingbird visiting a hibiscus flower**

d. **Bee-attracting pattern of a marsh marigold**

Visible light   UV light

Summary Illustration

Land plants are multicellular eukaryotes with cellulose cell walls and a number of adaptations to terrestrial life, including protecting gametes in multicellular chambers and sheltering embryos inside parent plants.

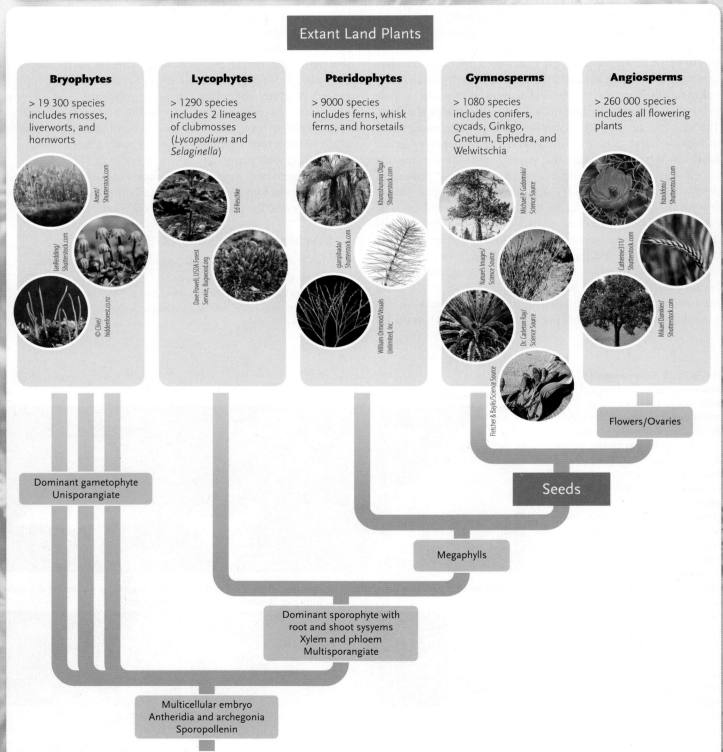

Extant Land Plants

Bryophytes
> 19 300 species includes mosses, liverworts, and hornworts

Lycophytes
> 1290 species includes 2 lineages of clubmosses (*Lycopodium* and *Selaginella*)

Pteridophytes
> 9000 species includes ferns, whisk ferns, and horsetails

Gymnosperms
> 1080 species includes conifers, cycads, Ginkgo, Gnetum, Ephedra, and Welwitschia

Angiosperms
> 260 000 species includes all flowering plants

Flowers/Ovaries

Seeds

Megaphylls

Dominant gametophyte
Unisporangiate

Dominant sporophyte with root and shoot sysyems
Xylem and phloem
Multisporangiate

Multicellular embryo
Antheridia and archegonia
Sporopollenin

Comparing the Gametophytes of the Main Lineages of Land Plants

	Mosses	Ferns	Conifers	Flowering Plants
Sporophyte				

Female gametophyte (Conifers)

Male gametophyte (Conifers)

Female gametophyte (Flowering Plants)

Male gametophyte (Flowering Plants)

Mosses

Gametophyte is dominant and photosynthetic; composed of stem, leaves, andrhizoids

- Archegonia contain eggs
- Antheridia produce flagellated sperm

Ferns

Gametophyte is free-living, photosynthetic, one cell layerthick, often heart-shaped, with rhizoids, mostly bisexual

- Archegonia contain eggs
- Antheridia produce flagellated sperm

Conifers

Female and male gametophytes separate

Female gametophyte: retained in ovule with several archegonia

Male gametophyte: pollen grain, 4-celled (no antheridia)

Flowering Plants

Female and male gametophytes separate

Female gametophyte (embryo sac): retained in ovule, often 7-celled with one egg.(no archegonia)

Male gametophyte: pollen grain 2-celled (no antheridia)

Recall/Understand

1. Which of the following occurred during land plant evolution?
   a. becoming seedless
   b. producing only one type of spore
   c. producing nonmotile gametes
   d. haploid generation becoming dominant

2. Which of the following occurs in the life cycle of *both* mosses and angiosperms?
   a. The sporophyte is the dominant generation.
   b. The gametophyte is the dominant generation.
   c. Spores develop into sporophytes.
   d. The sporophyte produces spores.

3. Which of these evolutionary innovations freed land plants from requiring water for reproduction?
   a. lignified stems
   b. fruits and roots
   c. seeds and pollen
   d. flowers and leaves

4. Which of these statements applies to archegonia?
   a. They are found in all land plants.
   b. They are found in all land plants except seed plants.
   c. They are found in all land plants except angiosperms.
   d. They are found in nonvascular land plants, but not in vascular plants.

5. Which of these statements applies to antheridia?
   a. They are found in all land plants.
   b. They are found in all land plants except seed plants.
   c. They are found in all land plants except angiosperms.
   d. They are found in nonvascular land plants, but not in vascular plants.

6. Which plant group is correctly paired with its phylum?
   a. cycads and Hepatophyta
   b. horsetails and Pterophyta
   c. gnetophytes and Bryophyta
   d. angiosperms and Coniferophyta

7. Horsetails are most closely related to which of the following plant groups?
   a. ferns and whisk ferns
   b. mosses and whisk ferns
   c. liverworts and hornworts
   d. gnetophytes and gymnosperms

8. In which of these groups is the evolution of true roots first seen?
   a. mosses
   b. conifers
   c. liverworts
   d. seedless vascular plants

Apply/Analyze

9. Your neighbour notices moss growing between bricks on her patio. Closer examination reveals tiny brown stalks with round tops emerging from leafy shoots. Which of the following are these brown structures most likely?
   a. antheridia
   b. archegonia
   c. a gametophyte generation
   d. a sporophyte generation

10. Which of the following is the order in which these features occurred during the evolution of land plants?
    a. seeds, vascular tissue, gametangia, flowers
    b. vascular tissue, gametangia, flowers, seeds
    c. gametangia, vascular tissue, flowers, seeds
    d. gametangia, vascular tissue, seeds, flowers

11. Which of these characteristics is most likely the reason that mosses are so short?
    a. lack of true leaves
    b. lack of vascular tissues
    c. lack of true roots
    d. lack of bark

12. Suppose that you found a leafless sporophyte with a waxy cuticle to reduce water loss, and stomata for gas exchange. Which of these plants is this plant most likely?
    a. a moss
    b. a fern
    c. a pine tree
    d. an angiosperm

13. Which of these factors is most likely a constraint for seedless vascular plants?
    a. short height
    b. dependence on moist environments
    c. dependence on shade
    d. decreased photosynthesis

Create/Evaluate

14. Which of these statements is most likely the advantage of taller plants over shorter plants?
    a. They can capture more CO_2.
    b. They can fertilize better.
    c. They can capture sunlight better.
    d. They can release seeds better.

15. Describe alternation of generations.

Animals

The kingdom Animalia is monophyletic, meaning that all animals share a common ancestry. Animals are eukaryotic, multicellular organisms. Animal cells may be organized into different morphological types, reflecting their role in the functioning of the animal as a single unit.

27.1 What Is an Animal?

27.2 Key Innovations in Animal Evolution

27.3 Molecular Phylogenetics and Classification

27.4 The Basal Phyla

27.5 The Protostomes

27.6 Lophotrochozoa Protostomes

27.7 Ecdysozoa Protostomes

27.8 The Deuterostomes

27.9 The Origin and Diversification of Vertebrates

27.10 Agnathans: The Jawless Fishes

27.11 Jawed Fishes: Jaws Meant New Feeding Opportunities

27.12 Early Tetrapods and Modern Amphibians

27.13 The Origin and Mesozoic Radiations of Amniotes

27.14 Turtles and Tortoises (Subclass Testudinata)

27.15 Living Diapsids: Sphenodontids, Squamates, and Crocodylians

27.16 Birds

27.17 Mammalia: Monotremes, Marsupials, and Placentals

Laitr Keiows/Shutterstock.com

EcoPrint/Shutterstock.com

M.B. Fenton

M.B. Fenton

Octopus, a highly evolved mollusc of the animal kingdom, capable of complex learning and behaviour

Animals

27

Why it matters . . . In 1977, the research submersible Alvin investigated a temperature anomaly in the Galapagos Rift, an area on the sea floor of the Pacific Ocean off the west coast of South America. This rift is where two of Earth's massive tectonic plates slowly moved apart, resulting in hydrothermal vents that spew out mineral-rich fluids that can be as hot as 400°C. In this unique environment, Alvin found a previously unimagined ecosystem, similar to that shown in **Figure 27.1**. A dominant member of this ecosystem is *Riftia pachyptila*, which is over 2 m long and has a plume of bright red tentacles extending from a chitinous tube.

Adult *Riftia* lack a gut, mouth, and anus. Is this an animal or a plant? You may be surprised to learn that it is an animal, a giant tubeworm. Like other animals, *Riftia* are multicellular and lack cell walls. Adult *Riftia* acquire food through a richly vascularized organ, the trophosome, which is home to millions of chemoautotrophic bacteria that oxidize sulfide, which is commonly found at hydrothermal vents. *Riftia* take up sulfide and the bacteria oxidize it to sulfate **(Figure 27.2)**. The energy released is used to fix carbon and synthesize organic molecules, a process analogous to photosynthesis (see Chapter 6). *Riftia* has a uniquely adapted hemoglobin that is not poisoned by sulfides and has separate binding sites for oxygen and for sulfides.

Riftia is one of many species fuelled by sulfide oxidation at deep-sea vent sites. Other species with symbiotic relationships with chemoautotrophic bacteria include giant clams (*Bathymodiolus*), which have bacteria in their gills. In addition, tube worms such as *Alvinella* (named after the submersible) have bacteria in their tubes. Yeti crabs (*Kiwa hirsuta*) culture bacteria on the fine

FIGURE 27.1 A large colony of *Riftia pachyptila* at a vent site on the Galapagos Rift

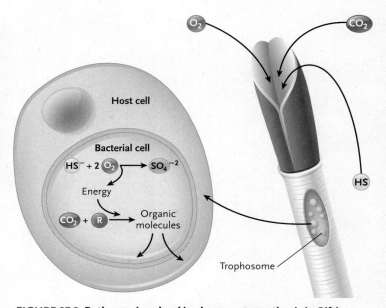

FIGURE 27.2 Pathways involved in chemoautosynthesis in *Riftia*

Source: Tunnicliffe, V. (1992). "Hydrothermal vent communities of the deep sea," *American Scientist*, 80: 336–349.

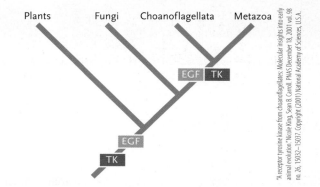

"A receptor tyrosine kinase from choanoflagellates: Molecular insights into early animal evolution." Nicole King, Sean B. Carroll. PNAS December 18, 2001 vol. 98 no. 26, 15032–15037. Copyright (2001) National Academy of Sciences, U.S.A.

FIGURE 27.3 Tyrosine kinase (TK) and epidermal growth factor (EGF) are found in most eukaryotic organisms. Only in Choanoflagellata and Metazoa are TK and EGF found as linked domains associated with a TK receptor. This, and other molecular evidence, supports placing the Choanoflagellata as a sister group to Metazoa.

setae covering their bodies. These species are the base of a food network that includes predators and scavengers in a complex community.

Riftia obviously belong to the kingdom Animalia because they lack cell walls and chloroplasts; however, they have undergone an almost unprecedented number of taxonomic reclassifications. Now molecular phylogenetic techniques—which involve studying DNA and RNA sequences—seem to have solved this taxonomic puzzle, classifying *Riftia pachyptila* as a sedentary annelid. Classifying animals to taxonomic groups is generally done based on body plans, a recurring theme in this chapter.

27.1 What Is an Animal?

The **kingdom Animalia** is monophyletic, meaning that all animals share a common ancestry. Animals are eukaryotic, multicellular organisms. Their cell membranes are in direct contact with one another, unlike plants and fungi, where walls surround individual cells. Animal cells may be organized into different morphological types (see Chapter 38), reflecting their role in the functioning of the animal as a single unit.

All animals are **heterotrophs**, which means they depend on other life forms for food, either by direct consumption or through a parasitic association. Most animals use oxygen to metabolize their food through aerobic respiration, and most store excess energy as glycogen, oil, or fat.

All animals are **motile**—able to move from place to place—at some time in their lives. Motile adults are most familiar but, in some species (e.g., mussels (Section 27.6e) and barnacles (Section 27.7h), only the young (larvae) are motile. These larvae eventually settle and turn into **sessile** (stationary) adults. Animals typically perceive and respond to information about the environment in which they live.

Animals reproduce either asexually or sexually, and many switch from one mode to the other. Sexually reproducing species produce haploid **gametes** (eggs and sperm) that fuse to form diploid **zygotes** (fertilized eggs). Many invertebrates are polymorphic and can exist as two or more distinct forms. Polymorphic development is important for the success of many of the inverte-

brate groups because it allows a species to use the resources of different habitats during different life stages (e.g., barnacles; Figure 27.62). This is particularly important for those living as parasites, since polymorphic larvae are part of a life cycle needs to reach a final host (e.g., tapeworms; Figure 27.34).

27.1a Animals Probably Arose from a Colonial Flagellate

Biologists agree that the common ancestor of all animals was probably a colonial, flagellated protist that lived in the Precambrian, at least 700 mya. Molecular evidence suggests that, from this unknown ancestor, there evolved the Choanoflagellata (see Chapter 24)—a group of flagellated protists found in aquatic environments—and a sister group, the Metazoa (multicellular animals; **Figure 27.3**).

Hypothesized evolution of a two-layered animal body plan

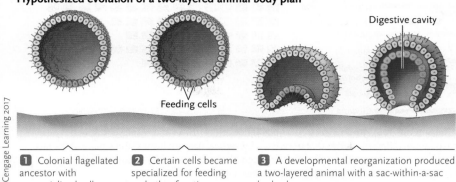

Feeding cells

Digestive cavity

1 Colonial flagellated ancestor with unspecialized cells

2 Certain cells became specialized for feeding and other functions.

3 A developmental reorganization produced a two-layered animal with a sac-within-a-sac body plan.

© Cengage Learning 2017

FIGURE 27.4 Animal origins. Animals may have arisen from a colonial, flagellated protist in which cells became specialized for specific functions. This putative ancestor would have had a developmental reorganization that resulted in two cell layers. The cell movements illustrated here are similar to those that occur during the development of many animals, as described in Chapter 44 and elsewhere in this chapter. Associated with this, cells became specialized for different functions, such as the feeding cells giving rise to the digestive cavity (shown here).

In 1874, the German embryologist Ernst Haeckel first proposed such a colonial, flagellated animal ancestor. He suggested that the ancestor was a hollow, ball-shaped organism with unspecialized cells. Over evolutionary time, its cells became specialized for particular functions, and a developmental reorganization produced a double-layered, sac-within-a-sac body plan **(Figure 27.4)**. The embryology of many living animals roughly parallels this hypothetical evolutionary transformation. Haeckel included this hypothetical organism among what he called the "Metazoa" (*meta* = more developed; *zoon* = animal) to distinguish them from the Protozoa, and this name is still used today.

STUDY BREAK QUESTIONS

1. What characteristics distinguish animals from plants?
2. What early steps may have led to the first metazoans?

27.2 Key Innovations in Animal Evolution

Once established, the animal lineage diversified quickly into many different **body plans**. Body plans describe the way that animals are built. They are the "blueprint" of cellular organization that encompasses such things as symmetry, segmentation, and formation and position of limbs. Several key morphological innovations help to unravel the evolutionary relationships among the major groups of animals. These innovations include the following:

- development of different tissues
- type of body symmetry
- presence or absence of a body cavity
- patterns of embryonic development
- body segmentation

27.2a Tissue Development

In most Metazoa, the process of development gives rise to two or three layers of cells. **Tissues**, which are groups of similarly differentiated cells that are specialized for particular functions, eventually arise from these layers of cells. In most metazoans, embryonic tissues form as either two or three concentric **germ layers** (see Chapter 44). The innermost layer, the **endoderm**, develops into the lining of the gut (digestive system) and, in some animals, respiratory organs. The outermost layer, the **ectoderm**, forms the external covering and the nervous system. Between the two, the **mesoderm** forms the muscles of the body wall and most other organs.

Some animals appear to have only a **diploblastic** body plan, a plan based on two embryonic layers: endoderm and ectoderm. However, most animals are **triploblastic**, having all three clearly identifiable germ layers.

27.2b Body Symmetry

The most obvious feature of an animal's body plan is its shape. Most animals are bilaterally symmetrical in that they can be divided vertically into two mirror image halves, with anterior, posterior, dorsal, and ventral regions **(Figure 27.5)**. Most animals also are **cephalized**—their sense organs are concentrated at the anterior end (i.e., the head).

Animal body plans are differentiated by a relatively small toolbox of genes. *Hox* genes are one group responsible for differentiating body parts along the anterior–posterior axis.

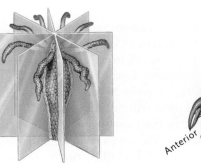

Radial symmetry

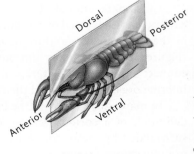

Dorsal · Posterior · Anterior · Ventral

Bilateral symmetry

© Cengage Learning 2017

FIGURE 27.5 Patterns of body symmetry. Most animals are bilaterally symmetrical.

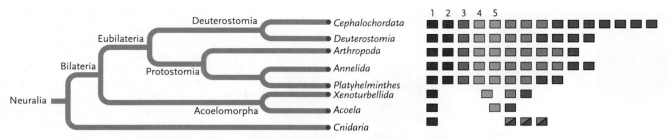

FIGURE 27.6 *Hox* genes of major eumetazoan groups. The anterior (red), group 3 (brown), and anterior central (*Hox*4 and *Hox*5; yellow) genes are arranged according to presumed orthologous genes. These are genes in different species that originated by vertical descent from a single gene of the last common ancestor. Only the numbers of the posterior central (green) and posterior (blue) genes are indicted. There is uncertainty about the orthology of genes shown in blue–green. More complex animals on the phylogenetic tree have a greater number of *Hox* genes.

Source: Nielsen, C., (2010), "After all" Xenoturbella is an acoelomoph!" *Evolution & Development.* 12(3): 241-243. ©2010 Wiley Periodicals, Inc. *Evolution & Development* by Society for Integrative and Comparative Biology Reproduced with permission of BLACKWELL PUBLISHING, INC. in the format Book via Copyright Clearance Center.

More complex animals have a greater number of *Hox* genes than simpler animals **(Figure 27.6).**

Radial symmetry means that body parts are regularly arranged around a central axis, like spokes on a wheel. Animals in the phylum Cnidaria (hydras, jellyfishes, and sea anemones) have traditionally been viewed as having radial symmetry. Challenging this view is the recognition that the primitive body plan of the Cnidaria, as seen in sea anemones (see Figure 27.19), is not fully radially symmetrical. Further, the homeobox (*Hox*) genes that determine body axes in bilaterally symmetrical animals are also part of the sea anemone genome. For example, the dorsal–ventral axis of both invertebrates and vertebrates is determined by the interaction of a pair of genes from the *Wnt* family of homeobox genes. In a sea anemone, genes orthologous to these genes are active but only in a small region that will become the lip of the mouth. It appears that the symmetry of Cnidaria (part bilateral, part radial), like that in other groups displaying a superficial radial symmetry, is an adaptation to life where environmental inputs may come from any direction.

27.2c Body Cavities

In most bilaterally symmetrical animals, a body cavity separates the gut from the muscles of the body wall. **Acoelomate** animals (*a* = without; *koiloma* = cavity), such as flatworms (phylum Platyhelminthes), lack such a cavity. A mass of cells derived largely from mesoderm pack the region between gut and body wall **(Figure 27.7a).**

Coelomate animals have a **coelom**, a fluid-filled body cavity completely lined by mesoderm. In vertebrates, this lining is the **peritoneum**, a thin tissue derived from mesoderm (Figure 27.7c). The inner and outer layers of the peritoneum connect and form **mesenteries**, membranes that surround the internal organs and suspend them within the coelom.

In many small animals, the body cavity does not meet the definition of a coelom because the cavity is not completely surrounded by mesoderm. Such a fluid-filled cavity, called a **pseudocoelom** (*pseudo* = false), commonly lies between the endoderm of the gut and the mesodermal musculature (Figure 27.7b). Pseudocoelomate groups appear in different

parts of the evolutionary tree, reflecting various levels of convergence. In Rotifers, the pseudocoelom is a remnant of part of the embryonic blastocoel. In Arthropoda and Mollusca, remnants of a true coelom remain in the reproductive system and around the heart. The rest of the body cavity is a hemocoel that supplies circulatory fluid and resembles a pseudocoel because it contacts all tissues and organs.

The body plan of coelomate and pseudocoelomate animals forms a "tube within a tube." The digestive system is the inner tube, and the body wall forms the outer tube. The body cavity, coelom or pseudocoelom, may serve at least four functions:

1. It can be used for transport of nutrients and products of metabolism.
2. It provides an environment in which eggs and sperm can develop.
3. It can serve as a **hydrostatic skeleton**, providing a basis for locomotion.
4. It provides space for the functioning of internal organs. The different parts of the digestive tract are muscular and use such movements as churning and peristalsis to process food. This can only occur if these structures are suspended and free to move.

27.2d Patterns of Embryological Development

Embryological evidence suggests that bilaterally symmetrical animals are divided into two lineages, **protostomes** (meaning "first opening," a reference to the initial development of the mouth) and **deuterostomes** (meaning "second opening," where the mouth develops later) **(Figure 27.8).**

After fertilization, the zygote undergoes a series of cell divisions, called **cleavage**. The first two cell divisions divide a zygote into four wedges from top to bottom. In animals with **spiral cleavage**, subsequent cell divisions occur at oblique angles to the vertical axis of the embryo, producing a mass in which each cell lies in the groove between the pair of cells below it (see Figure 27.8a, left side). Spiral cleavage is characteristic of most protostomes. **Radial cleavage** occurs in

a. In acoelomate animals, no body cavity separates the gut and body wall.

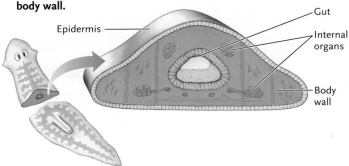

b. In pseudocoelomate animals, the pseudocoelom forms between the gut (a derivative of endoderm) and the body wall (a derivative of mesoderm).

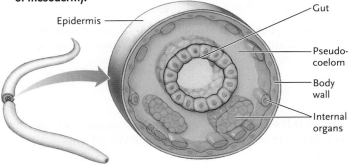

c. In coelomate animals, the coelom is completely lined by peritoneum (a derivative of mesoderm).

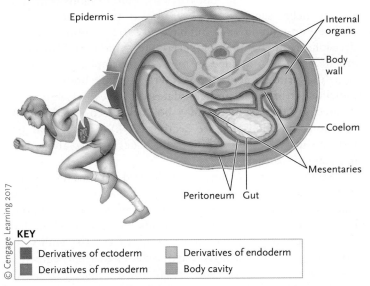

KEY

■ Derivatives of ectoderm	■ Derivatives of endoderm
■ Derivatives of mesoderm	■ Body cavity

© Cengage Learning 2017

FIGURE 27.7 Body plans for bilaterally symmetrical animals

Protostomes	Deuterostomes

a. Cleavage

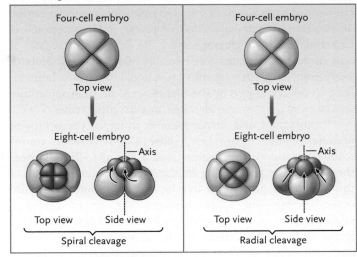

Four-cell embryo — Top view — Eight-cell embryo — Top view / Side view — Spiral cleavage

Four-cell embryo — Top view — Eight-cell embryo — Top view / Side view — Radial cleavage

b. Mesoderm and coelom formation

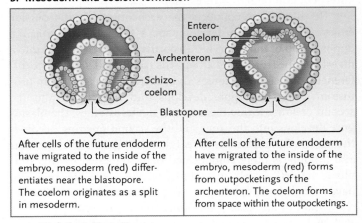

Entero-coelom · Archenteron · Schizo-coelom · Blastopore

After cells of the future endoderm have migrated to the inside of the embryo, mesoderm (red) differentiates near the blastopore. The coelom originates as a split in mesoderm.

After cells of the future endoderm have migrated to the inside of the embryo, mesoderm (red) forms from outpocketings of the archenteron. The coelom forms from space within the outpocketings.

c. Origin of mouth and anus

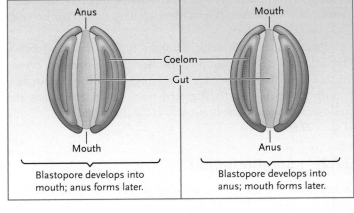

Anus — Coelom — Gut — Mouth

Mouth — Coelom — Gut — Anus

Blastopore develops into mouth; anus forms later.

Blastopore develops into anus; mouth forms later.

KEY

■ Derivatives of ectoderm	■ Derivatives of endoderm
■ Derivatives of mesoderm	■ Coelom (body cavity)

© Cengage Learning 2017

FIGURE 27.8 Protostomes and deuterostomes. The two lineages of coelomate animals differ in **(a)** cleavage patterns, **(b)** the origin of mesoderm and the coelom, and **(c)** the polarity of the digestive system.

---

deuterostomes. Here the third cell division is perpendicular to the vertical axis of the embryo. The fourth cell division is vertical, producing a mass of cells stacked directly above and below one another (see Figure 27.8a, right side).

Protostomes and deuterostomes differ in the timing of important developmental events. During cleavage, genes are activated at specific times, determining a cell's developmental path and ultimate fate. Many protostomes undergo **determinate cleavage**. Each cell's developmental path (what tissue it will become) is determined as the cell is being produced. Thus, one cell isolated from a two- or four-cell protostome embryo cannot develop into a functional embryo or a larva. Most deuterostomes have **indeterminate cleavage**. Here the developmental fates of cells are determined later. A cell isolated from a four-cell deuterostome embryo can develop into a functional embryo. In humans, the two cells produced by the first cleavage division sometimes separate and develop into identical (monozygotic) twins.

Protostomes and deuterostomes differ in the origin of mesoderm and coelom (see Figure 27.8b). In most protostomes, mesoderm originates from a few specific cells near the **blastopore**, an opening on the surface of the embryo. As the mesoderm grows and develops, it splits into inner and outer layers. The space between the layers forms a **schizocoelom** (*schizo* = split). In deuterostomes, mesoderm forms from outpocketings of the **archenteron** (developing gut). The space pinched off by an outpocketing forms an **enterocoelom** (*entero* = intestine).

The blastopore connects the archenteron to the outside environment. Later in development, a second opening at the opposite end of the embryo transforms the pouchlike gut into a digestive tube (see Figure 27.8c). The traditional view of the difference between protostomes and deuterostomes is that, in protostomes, the blastopore develops into the mouth and the second opening forms the anus. In deuterostomes, the blastopore develops into the anus and the second opening becomes the mouth. Recent studies reveal that the formation of the anus and hindgut is more complicated than suggested by this simplistic model. Acoela (e.g., *Praeconvoluta*, see Figure 27.26) have a single body opening serving as mouth and anus. Studies show that, in an acoel (*Convolutriloba longifissura*), the genes *Brachyury* and *Goosecoid* are expressed in part of the mouth. Mouth development in other bilaterians involves the same genes, making acoel mouth development homologous with those of other bilaterians.

Protostomes and deuterostomes differ in several other characteristics. For example, the nervous system of protostomes is on the ventral side of the body, and their brain surrounds the opening of the digestive tract. In deuterostomes, the nervous system and the brain are on the dorsal side of the body **(Figure 27.9)**.

27.2e Segmentation

A **segment** is a body structure that repeats along an anterior–posterior axis and itself has an anterior–posterior polarity. Annelid worms (see Section 27.6c), lobsters (see Section 27.7h), and chordates (see Section 27.8c) are animals with segmented body plans. These three animals are classified in different and separate lineages (Lophotrochozoa, Ecdysozoa, and Deuterostomia, respectively). In each lineage, there are closely related species that are not segmented. This means that either segmentation has evolved separately three times, or that the potential to be

a. Protostome

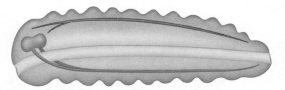

b. Deuterostome

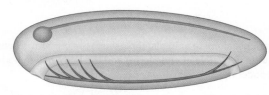

FIGURE 27.9 Body plans of a protostome (a) **and deuterostome** (b). The nerve cord is blue, the gut is yellow, and the heart and major blood vessels are red.

segmented was present in a common ancestor of the three examples and is suppressed in non-segmented forms.

Evidence supporting the common appearance of potential segmentation comes from other phyla. For example, Nemertea (see Section 27.6d) have a repeating pattern in their ventral nervous system. Superficially, mud dragons (Phylum Kinorhyncha; see Figure 27.49) appear to have segmented exoskeletons and muscles, but have no corresponding internal divisions. Note that the terms "serial repetition" and "metamerism" have been applied to levels of incomplete segmentation. The term segmentation is reserved for the body plans of annelids, arthropods, and chordates. In the evolution of segmented groups, segments may be specialized for different functions (e.g., lobsters; see Section 27.7h), or they may be reduced (e.g., leeches, see Section 27.6c) or lost altogether (e.g., spoon worms).

Segmentation is commonly associated with movement. In vertebrates, the articulated backbone and associated muscles combine to permit S-shaped side-to-side motion, as seen in the locomotion of fish or snakes. Annelids are capable of similar motion, but many live in burrows or tubes. The ability to expand segments by contracting muscles of adjacent segments assists this lifestyle (see Chapter 46). The articulated stiffened cuticle of arthropods serves as a point of attachment for muscles, providing significant leverage and strength. Arthropods have taken advantage of segmental appendages to assign special functions, such as feeding, locomotion, reproduction, or gas exchange, to particular appendages.

➲ **CONCEPT** Many people believe that all invertebrate animals are protostomes. The truth is that the deuterostomes include many species (some whole phyla) that lack backbones, some of which are invertebrates and some are protochordates, or members of the phylum Chordata. ⬡

STUDY BREAK QUESTIONS

1. What is a tissue, and what three primary tissue layers are present in the embryos of most animals? Explain the fate of each layer.
2. What kind of symmetry does an earthworm have?
3. What is the function of the coelom, and what is the importance of the fluid?

27.3 Molecular Phylogenetics and Classification

Traditionally, biologists have traced phylogenetic history using morphological innovations just described, along with embryological patterns and the fossil record (see Chapter 19). This evidence has been used to construct phylogenetic trees, which represent hypotheses about relatedness among phyla. Phyla with similar developmental and morphological patterns are presumed to share common ancestries. For example, annelids and arthropods are **schizocoelous** (they have a coelom formed by a split in the mesoderm) segmented coelomates, which are presumed to share a common ancestor. This interpretation is supported by the fossil record as well as by velvet worms (Phylum Onychophora) that appear to have characteristics of both phyla.

Increasingly, molecular sequence data are being used to determine relationships among groups of animals. Such analyses are commonly based on similarities in the nucleotide sequences in small subunit ribosomal RNA and mitochondrial DNA, as well as sequences of specific genes. These analyses are used to construct molecular cladograms. **Figure 27.10** is a

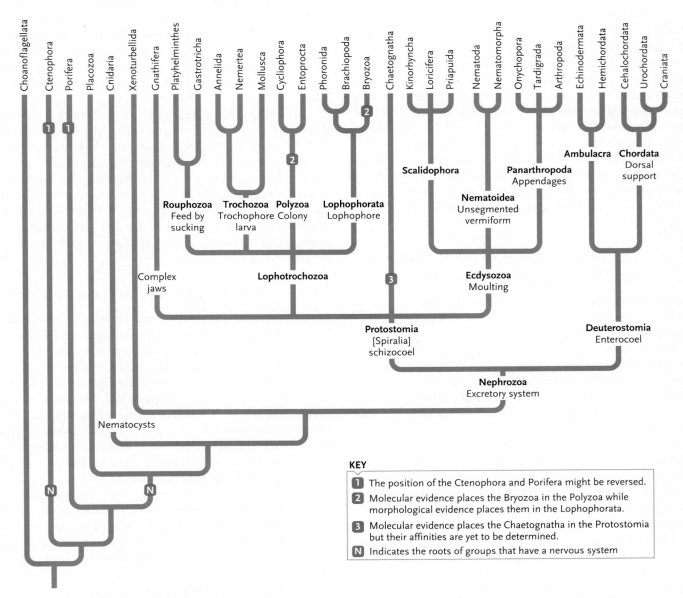

FIGURE 27.10 A molecular phylogeny for metazoans based on sequence data for several molecules. As new data are collected, continued revisions of phylogeny and taxonomic relationships will most likely continue.

phylogenetic tree developed from cladograms based on molecular sequences. This tree is a working hypothesis based on information currently available.

This phylogeny, based on molecular characters, includes major lineages originally defined by morphological innovations and embryological characters. In 2017, both molecular and traditional approaches confirmed the separation of phyla of deuterostomes from all other groups within Bilateria.

Currently, Protostomia and Deuterostomia are viewed as separate lineages within Metazoa. Protostomia is, in turn, subdivided into two major lineages: Lophotrochozoa and Ecdysozoa. The name Lophotrochozoa (*lophos* = crest; *troch* = wheel; *zoa* = animals, plural of zoon) refers to both the "lophophore," a feeding structure found in three phyla (see Figure 27.47), and the "trochophore," a type of larva found in annelids and molluscs (see Figure 27.29). The name Ecdysozoa (*ekdero* = strip off the skin) refers to the cuticle that these species secrete and periodically replace; the shedding of the cuticle is called **ecdysis**.

Interestingly, a 2016 paper questioned the apparent clear-cut separation of the protostomes and deuterostomes. Two species in the Phylum Brachiopoda (see Section 27.6i), *Terebratalia transversa* and *Novocrania anomala*, are about the same size, are found in similar habitats, have the same ecology, and have similar development times; however, the early development of *T. transversa* follows a protostome pattern, and that of *N. anomala* is deuterostomous. The difference correlates with developmental molecular signals and the timing and location of mesoderm formation. For the moment, protostomes and deuterostomes are considered separate, but this is likely to change in the future.

27.3a Surprising Patterns in the Evolution of Key Morphological Innovations

Molecular phylogeny has also forced a reevaluation of the evolution of several important morphological innovations. Traditional phylogenies implied that the absence of a body cavity was ancestral, and that the presence of a body cavity (whether pseudocoelom or coelom) was derived. Further, the molecular tree suggests that the schizocoelomate condition is ancestral, having evolved in the common ancestor of the lineage. If that hypothesis is correct, then the acoelomate condition of flatworms results from the evolutionary loss of the schizocoelom, rather than being an ancestral condition. Similarly, the molecular tree shows that a pseudocoelom evolved independently from modifications of the ancestral schizocoelom several times (e.g., Syndermata and Rotifera (see Section 27.5b); Ecdysozoa (see Section 27.7); and phylum Nematoda (see Section 27.7d).

The hypotheses presented in the phylogenetic tree in Figure 27.10 are the framework used for discussion of the major phyla in the remainder of this chapter. A key thing to remember, however, is that this phylogeny is provisional and new data may lead to revisions.

STUDY BREAK QUESTIONS

1. How is molecular analysis used in creating phylogenetic trees?
2. Describe the way molecular phylogeny has changed how biologists view the absence of the coelom.

27.4 The Basal Phyla

A major challenge in animal phylogeny lies in understanding the relationships among animal groups at the base of the phylogenetic tree. Included in this basal group are Porifera (sponges), Cnidaria (hydroids, jellies, anemones, and corals), Ctenophora (comb jellies), and Placozoa (*Trichoplax*).

Traditionally, the Porifera have been viewed as sister to the rest of Metazoa, and Cnidaria and Ctenophora seen as sister groups **(Figure 27.11a)**. However, analysis of a large number of transcriptosomes (complexes of RNA processing proteins within the nucleus) places Ctenophora as the sister group to the rest of Metazoa, and does not support a close relationship to Cnidaria. Data supporting a Ctenophora–Cnidaria relationship are artifacts arising from similarities in ribosomal protein genes.

Accepting Ctenophora as sister to Metazoa presents a problem. Ctenophores have a nervous system, unlike Porifera and Placozoa. This suggests that either the nervous system evolved twice or that it has been lost in sponges and placozoans. Some evidence supports the latter possibility because nervous system-associated genes have been identified in sponges and placozoans. While the arrangement in Figure 27.11b is currently the best supported by available data, some argue that the positions of ctenophores and sponges should be reversed (Figure 27.11c).

27.4a Phylum Ctenophora: The Comb Jellies

The Ctenophora (meaning "comb bearing") have recently become of major interest because phylogenetic studies have suggested that they are the sister group to all other animals. Ctenophores have a gelatinous body, and the "combs" are plates of fused cilia that project like a comb, arranged in rows (typically eight) on their outer surface **(Figure 27.12)**. Rhythmic beating of the comb plates, coordinated by neural inputs, propels a ctenophore. Ctenophores have clearly differentiated ectodermal and endodermal (gut lining) layers and some cells—differentiated from the endoderm—carry genetic markers that are associated with mesodermal cells in triploblastic animals.

Ctenophores have a through gut with a pair of anal pores (suggesting bilateral symmetry) and branches of the gut that carry nutrients to all regions of the body. They are carnivores, either using cells discharging a sticky thread to catch planktonic prey, or in some species swallowing larger prey by distension of the mouth.

Evidence that Ctenophora are the sister group to all other animals surprised biologists because ctenophores are

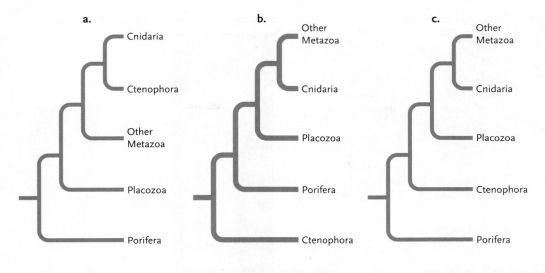

a.

Cnidaria
Ctenophora
Other Metazoa
Placozoa
Porifera

b.

Other Metazoa
Cnidaria
Placozoa
Porifera
Ctenophora

c.

Other Metazoa
Cnidaria
Placozoa
Ctenophora
Porifera

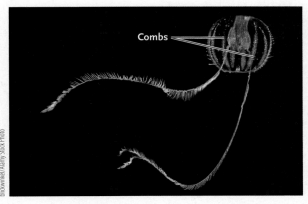

FIGURE 27.12 **Comb jellies, such as *Pleurobrachia pileus*, collect prey on their tentacles.**

Combs

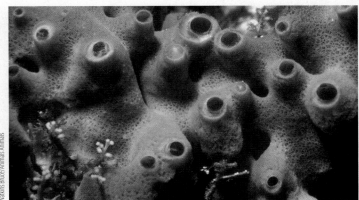

FIGURE 27.13 **Sponges are asymmetrical and sessile as adults.**

significantly more complex than Porifera (sponges), which were previously placed in this position (see Figure 27.11). *Hox* genes play a role in the organization of the body plan of all animal groups; however, no *Hox* type genes have been identified in ctenophores.

27.4b Phylum Porifera: The Sponges

Of the 8000 species of living sponges **(Figure 27.13)**, only a few species live in fresh water. Sponges are asymmetric and adults are sessile. They have been abundant since the Cambrian. The shapes of sponges vary with their habitats: they may be encrusting, barrel shaped, tubular, or stalked.

The development of more than one non-reproductive cell type is a metazoan characteristic. In sponges, an outer layer of epithelial cells (the **pinacoderm**) includes **porocytes**, cylindrical cells that allow water to pass **(Figure 27.14)**. This layer has a basement membrane in some sponges and must be regarded as a tissue layer, along with the organized inner cell lining. **Choanocytes**, food trapping cells with a collar of microtubules around a flagellum that drives water through the body cavity

(the **spongocoel**), are arranged in different ways in different groups. A gelatinous matrix, the **mesohyl** includes **amoeboid** cells called **archaeocytes** that transport nutrients and wastes. Most sponges depend on spicules for their rigidity. Spicules may be made of calcium or silica in different sponge groups and are secreted by specialized cells known as **sclerocytes**.

Sponges are typically **suspension feeders**. Choanocytes draw a current of water into the spongocoel through the porocytes that then leaves via the osculum. Cells inside the osculum have two cilia and have genetic characteristics common to sensory cells. Information from the osculum travels to the porocytes, which are contractile and regulate water flow rates through the sponge. Particles of food captured by choanocytes are passed to amoebocytes, which distribute food to all the cells throughout the sponge and may also store food reserves.

Sponges are typically **monoecious**, meaning individuals produce both sperm and eggs. Sperm are released into the environment, and eggs (**oocytes**) are retained in the mesohyl. Sperm are drawn in with water captured by choanocytes that carry sperm to oocytes. Sponges have various types of larvae. Some are free swimming, and others crawl over the substrate.

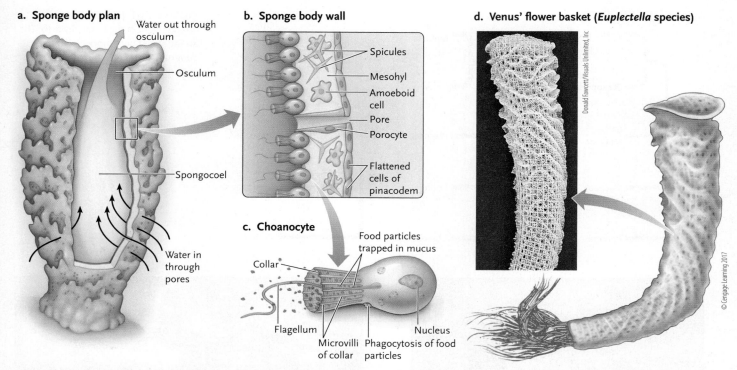

a. Sponge body plan

Water out through osculum

Osculum

Spongocoel

Water in through pores

b. Sponge body wall

Spicules

Mesohyl

Amoeboid cell

Pore

Porocyte

Flattened cells of pinacoderm

c. Choanocyte

Food particles trapped in mucus

Collar

Flagellum

Microvilli of collar

Phagocytosis of food particles

Nucleus

d. Venus' flower basket (*Euplectella* species)

Donald Fawcett/Visuals Unlimited, Inc

© Cengage Learning 2017

FIGURE 27.14 The body plan of sponges. Most sponges have **(a)** simple body plans and **(b)** relatively few cell types. **(c)** Beating flagella on the choanocytes create a flow of water through incurrent pores, into the spongocoel, and out through the osculum. **(d)** Venus's flower basket (*Euplectella* sp.), a marine sponge, has spicules of silica fused into a rigid framework.

Settled larvae develop into sessile adults. Sponges also reproduce asexually: small fragments break off an adult and grow into new sponges. Under difficult conditions, sponges may produce reduction bodies, which are clusters of food-filled archaeocytes enclosed by a membrane and a layer of pinacoderm. When favourable conditions return, archaeocytes are dispersed from the reduction body to develop directly into new sponges. In some freshwater sponges, reduction bodies have developed further into **gemmules**—thick-walled capsules that have spicules reinforcing the wall. Gemmules can withstand extreme conditions, such as a pond drying up in midsummer or freezing in winter.

Even with a very simple, basic body plan, sponges have achieved remarkable diversity. Sponges formed very large reefs during the Mesozoic, and a modern reef of glass sponges has been found off the west coast of Canada.

Sponges may serve as refuges for other species. Bacteria and cyanobacteria can be found in the mesohyl. Other species gain protection in the spongocoel. Male and female shrimp (*Spongicola* species) may enter the spongocoel of the Venus's flower basket when small, feed on material brought in by the sponge, and grow large enough that they are unable to leave. The pair of shrimp spend their entire lives in the prison formed by the elaborate basket of spicules. Some sponges are carnivorous and catch small arthropods by entangling them in hook-shaped spicules on the surface. Prey are then tangled in filamentous structures and digested.

Recent molecular evidence places sponges with other Metazoa in one monophyletic lineage. Sponges do not form distinct nervous tissue, but they have genes that are associated with nervous systems in other groups. Although sponges are asymmetric, each species has a particular body form. This demands intercellular communication of developmental information. A *Hox*-related gene identified in a sponge could play a role in regulating body form. Current interpretation of this and other molecular data confirms that sponges and other Metazoa share a common ancestry.

27.4c Phylum Placozoa: Plate Animals

For many years, *Trichoplax adherens* **(Figure 27.15)** was the only known species of placozoan. Found on hard substrata in shallow marine environments, *Trichoplax* has a worldwide distribution. Molecular studies of specimens collected from around the world show that, while there are only small differences in morphology, there are seven clades within the species and a number of genotypes within each clade.

Trichoplax has five cell types arranged in upper and lower epithelial layers, with three layers of fibre cells running across the central space. Shiny spheres, secreted in either the cavity of the animal or in association with a fibre layer, are on the upper surface and may release defensive chemicals that deter potential predators such as flatworms, polychaete worms, and small snails.

Trichoplax reproduces asexually by simple division of the body. While sperm have not been isolated from *Trichoplax*, a number of genetic markers for developing sperm have been identified, and oocyte development (accompanied by degeneration of the parent) can be induced in the laboratory. This provides strong evidence that sexual reproduction is also a part of *Trichoplax* biology.

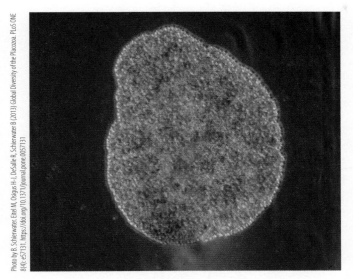

Photo by B. Schierwater, Eitel M, Osigus H-J, DeSalle R, Schierwater B (2013) Global Diversity of the Placozoa. PLoS ONE 8(4): e57131. https://doi.org/10.1371/journal.pone.0057131

FIGURE 27.15 *Trichoplax* **resembles a multicellular amoeba with two layers of cells.** Placozoans have no nervous system but cells are specialized for different functions. The refractile bodies on the upper surface of the animal are the shiny spheres.

27.4d Phylum Cnidaria: Hydroids, Jellies, Anemones, and Corals

Most of the over 10 000 species in the phylum Cnidaria (from the Greek word *knide* = nettle; the stem of *knizein* = to scratch or scrape) are marine. Cnidarians have a saclike body enclosing a gastrovascular cavity with one opening, the mouth, which is surrounded by food-collecting tentacles. Cnidarians may be vase-shaped with upward-pointing **polyps** or bell-shaped, with downward-pointing **medusae (Figure 27.16)**. Most polyps attach to a substrate at the *aboral* (opposite the mouth) end, while medusae are typically free-swimming.

Cnidarians are the simplest animals that have specialized tissues and nerve cells (see Figure 27.16c). The epidermis includes nerve cells, contractile cells, and **cnidocytes**, which are cells specialized for the capture of crustaceans, fish, and other prey. Each cnidocyte contains a **nematocyst (Figure 27.17)**. When a nematocyst is discharged, the capsule opens and three stylets spring together to form a beak that punctures the surface of the prey. This takes place within 1.5 microseconds and involves huge forces. Discharge of nematocysts may be triggered by touch, vibrations, or chemical stimuli. Nematocysts are not innervated but their sensitivity is regulated by the condition of the whole animal. Nematocyst toxins can paralyze small prey by disrupting nerve cell membranes, and some nematocysts are sufficiently potent to cause extreme pain to humans. Other types of nematocyst may be sticky or coil around objects.

The gastrodermis includes sensory receptor cells, gland cells, and phagocytic nutritive cells. Gland cells secrete enzymes

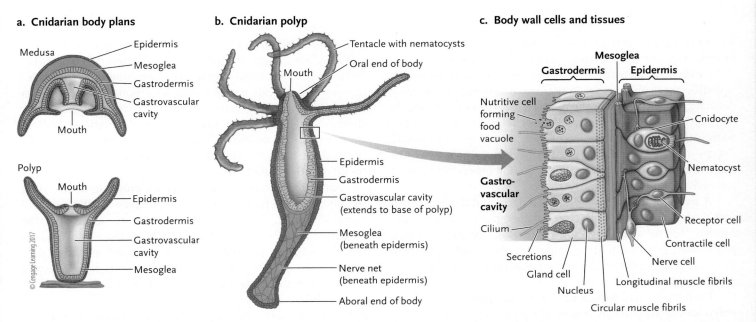

a. Cnidarian body plans

Medusa
— Epidermis
— Mesoglea
— Gastrodermis
— Gastrovascular cavity
Mouth

Polyp
Mouth
— Epidermis
— Gastrodermis
— Gastrovascular cavity
— Mesoglea

© Cengage Learning 2017

b. Cnidarian polyp

Tentacle with nematocysts
Oral end of body
Mouth
Epidermis
Gastrodermis
Gastrovascular cavity (extends to base of polyp)
Mesoglea (beneath epidermis)
Nerve net (beneath epidermis)
Aboral end of body

c. Body wall cells and tissues

Mesoglea
Gastrodermis | Epidermis
Nutritive cell forming food vacuole
Cnidocyte
Nematocyst
Gastro-vascular cavity
Cilium
Receptor cell
Secretions
Contractile cell
Gland cell
Nerve cell
Nucleus
Longitudinal muscle fibrils
Circular muscle fibrils

FIGURE 27.16 The cnidarian body plan. (a) Cnidarians exist in either polyp or medusa forms. **(b)** The body is organized around a gastrovascular cavity. **(c)** The two tissue layers in the body wall, the gastrodermis and the epidermis, include a variety of cell types.

a. *Hydra* consuming a crustacean

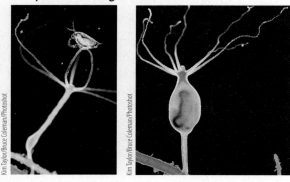

Kim Taylor/Bruce Coleman/Photoshot

Kim Taylor/Bruce Coleman/Photoshot

FIGURE 27.17 Predation by cnidarians.
(a) A polyp of a freshwater *Hydra* captures a small crustacean with its tentacles and swallows it whole. **(b)** Stages in nematocyst discharge: (i) undischarged nematocyst; (ii, iii) capsule opens and stylets are fired into prey; (iv) lamellae lock the nematocyst into the prey; (v) the stylets fold back and the hollow thread extends. The complete process is completed in about 700 nanoseconds and involves acceleration forces of over 5 million *g*.

b. Cnidocytes

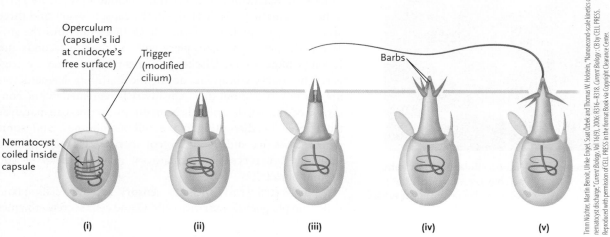

Timm Nüchter, Martin Benoit, Ulrike Engel, Suat Özbek and Thomas W. Holstein, "Nanosecond-scale kinetics of nematocyst discharge," *Current Biology*, Vol 16(9), 2006: R316–R318. *Current Biology* - CB by CELL PRESS. Reproduced with permission of CELL PRESS in the format Book via Copyright Clearance Center.

for the **extracellular digestion** of food, which is then engulfed by nutritive cells and exposed to **intracellular digestion**.

Cnidarian movement depends on contraction of fibres that resemble those in muscles contained in extensions of ectodermal cells. In medusae, the mesoglea serves as a deformable skeleton against which contractile cells act. Rapid contractions narrow the bell, forcing out jets of water that propel the animal. Polyps use their fluid-filled gastrovascular cavity as a hydrostatic skeleton. Coordinated cell contraction moves fluid within the cavity, changing the body's shape.

A **nerve net** lies between the ectoderm and the endoderm and has junctions with both layers. Although there is no recognizable "brain," there are control and coordination centres, particularly in a ring of nerves encircling the mouth. In spite of its structural simplicity, the nerve net permits directed swimming movements.

Cnidarians may have a life cycle that alternates between polyp and medusa forms **(Figure 27.18)** and some exist in only one form. Sexual reproduction typically produces a ciliated larval stage, the **planula**, that settles and undergoes metamorphosis into the polyp form.

CLASS ANTHOZOA There are over 6000 species of corals and sea anemones in the class Anthozoa **(Figure 27.19)**. Anthozoans vary from solitary sea anemones lacking skeletons to stony corals whose calcium carbonate skeletons can form gigantic underwater reefs. While some corals grow slowly in cold deep water, many species are restricted to clear shallow water. The energy needs of these corals are partly fulfilled through a symbiotic relationship with photosynthetic dinoflagellates.

Anthozoans have a more complex polyp structure than the Hydrozoa, which led to the assumption that they were more advanced. The Anthozoa are now recognized as the primitive form within the Cnidaria, with the evolution of a medusa stage in the other classes (grouped as the Medusozoa) coming later. Anthozoans have a muscular pharynx leading into the gastrovascular cavity, which is divided by septa, giving an increased surface area for food uptake. Asexual reproduction is by budding or fission, and sexual reproduction produces eggs that develop into ciliated larvae that settle and metamorphose into polyps that may produce colonies by budding.

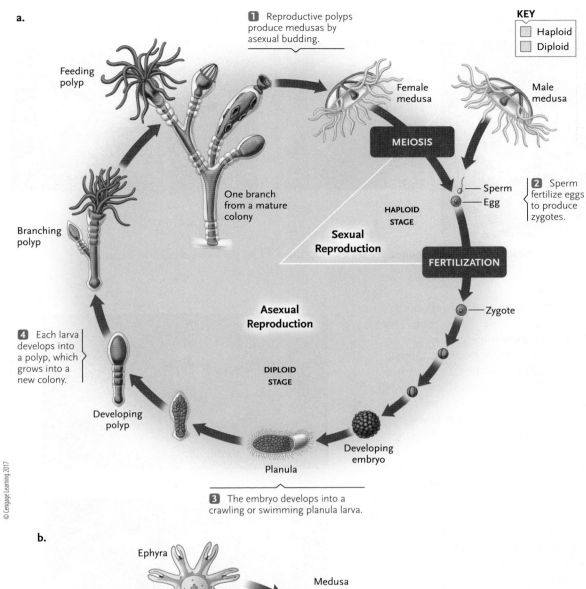

1 Reproductive polyps produce medusas by asexual budding.

KEY
- ☐ Haploid
- ☐ Diploid

Feeding polyp

Female medusa

Male medusa

One branch from a mature colony

MEIOSIS

2 Sperm fertilize eggs to produce zygotes.

Sperm

Egg

HAPLOID STAGE

Sexual Reproduction

FERTILIZATION

Branching polyp

Zygote

Asexual Reproduction

4 Each larva develops into a polyp, which grows into a new colony.

DIPLOID STAGE

Developing polyp

Planula

Developing embryo

3 The embryo develops into a crawling or swimming planula larva.

© Cengage Learning 2017

b.

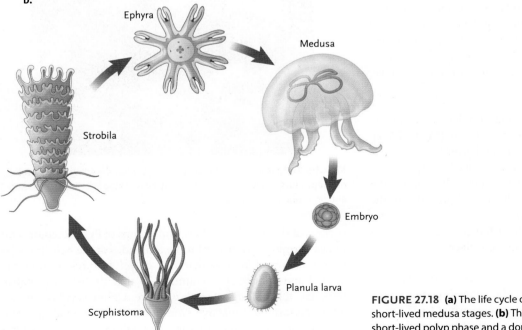

Ephyra

Medusa

Strobila

Embryo

Planula larva

Scyphistoma

FIGURE 27.18 (a) The life cycle of *Obelia* includes a dominant polyp and short-lived medusa stages. **(b)** The *Aurelia* (Scyphozoa) life cycle has a short-lived polyp phase and a dominant medusa phase.

a. Staghorn coral
(Acropora cervicornis)

b. Sea anemone (Urticina lofotensis) escape behaviour

Tentacle of one polyp

Interconnected
skeletons of polyps
of a colonial coral

FIGURE 27.19 **Anthozoans include** (a) **corals and** (b) **sea anemones.** The sea anemone shown here detaches to escape from the sea star.

CLASS HYDROZOA Among the almost 4000 species of Hydrozoa, there is a wide range of life cycles (e.g., see Figure 27.18 and **Figure 27.20**), including some species that are free-swimming polyps. A typical hydrozoan species is a sessile marine colony that develops asexually by budding. In many species, polyps are polymorphic (have different forms) and may be specialized for feeding, defence, or reproduction with food shared through connected gastrovascular cavities. A few warm-water species secrete a calcareous skeleton and resemble corals (Anthozoa).

Some pelagic hydrozoans have both polyp and medusoid forms in the same colony; for example, Portuguese man-of-war has a medusoid bell modified to form a carbon monoxide-filled sail surrounded by feeding and reproductive polyps.

Hydra **(Figure 27.21)** lives in fresh water and has solitary polyps that attach to rocks, twigs, and leaves. Under favourable conditions, *Hydra* reproduces by budding. Under adverse conditions, it produces eggs and sperm. Zygotes, formed by fertilization, are encapsulated in a protective coating but develop and grow when conditions improve. There is no larval stage; eggs hatch into small *Hydra*.

CLASS SCYPHOZOA The medusa stage predominates in the 200 species of the class Scyphozoa, or jellyfish **(Figure 27.22)**. They range from 2 cm to more than 2 m in diameter. Nerve cells near the margin of the bell control their tentacles and coordinate the rhythmic activity of contractile cells, which move the animal. Specialized sensory cells are clustered at the edge of the bell: statocysts sense gravity, and ocelli are sensitive to light. Scyphozoan medusae are either male or female, releasing gametes into the water, where fertilization takes place.

CLASS CUBOZOA Most of the 20 known species of box jellyfish, the Cubozoa **(Figure 27.23)**, are cube-shaped medusae only a few centimetres tall, but the largest species grows to 25 cm in height. Nematocyst-rich tentacles grow in clusters from the four

a.

b.

FIGURE 27.20 **Colonial hydroids. (a)** *Aegina citrea* feeding polyps, with one reproductive medusa being budded away on the left side. **(b)** Feeding and reproductive polyps of *Obelia* sp.

corners of the boxlike medusa, and groups of light receptors and image-forming eyes occur on the four sides of the bell. The eyes have lenses and retinas that can detect features around the animal and coordinate swimming so that the jelly can patrol back and forth along a length of shore. Unlike scyphozoan jellyfish, cubozoans are active swimmers. They eat small fish and invertebrates, immobilizing their prey with one of the deadliest

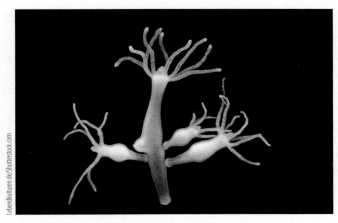

FIGURE 27.21 *Hydra* **exists as a solitary polyp with no medusa stage in its life cycle.**

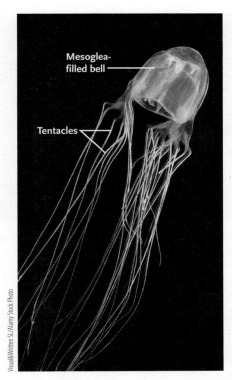

Figure 27.23 **Cubozoans, such as** *Chironex fleckeri*, **are strong swimmers that actively pursue prey.**

FIGURE 27.22 **Most species of Scyphozoa, such as** *Chrysaora quinquecirrha*, **live as free medusae.**

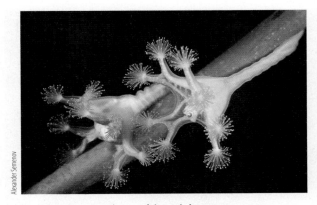

FIGURE 27.24 *Lucernaria quadricornis* **is a staurozoan.**

toxins produced by animals. Cubozoans live in tropical and subtropical coastal waters, where they sometimes pose a serious threat to swimmers. The nematocysts of some species (e.g., a group of species known as *Irukandji jellies*, which have a box less than a centimetre across but tentacles a metre long) can inflict considerable pain to, and may kill, humans.

CLASS STAUROZOA Recently separated from Scyphozoa, Staurozoa are viewed as the sister group to the Cubozoa. In these classes, unlike the Scyphozoa, the medusa forms as a single bud from the tip of a reduced polyp **(Figure 27.24)**.

Staurozoans are attached medusa with a stalk, originating at the apex of the medusa and attaching the animal to the substratum. The bell of the medusa divides to form eight arms, each tipped by a cluster of nematocytes that attack and hold prey.

CLASS MYXOZOA The Myxozoa, a group of parasites previously classified among Protista, are simplified medusozoans and truly cnidarians. What had been called "polar capsules" in protists are now recognized as nematocysts. These dark-stained inclusions are obvious in **Figure 27.25**, a typical parasitic myxozoan (*Myxobolus cerebralis*) found in salmon. These inclusions cause "whirling disease."

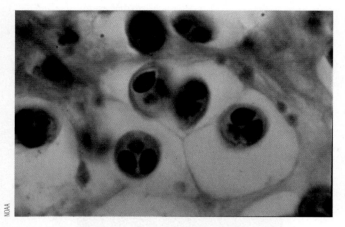

FIGURE 27.25 *Myxobolus cerebralis* **isolated from a salmon**

a.

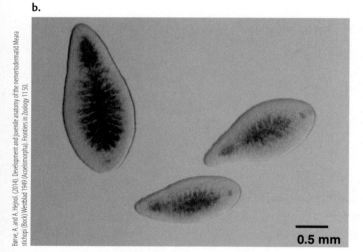

b.

0.5 mm

c.

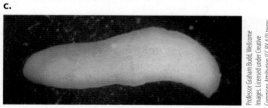

FIGURE 27.26 **(a)** *Praeconvoluta castinea* (Acoela): notice the single statocyst toward the left (anterior) end. Food is taken in through a mouth and held between the central parenchymal cells, where digestion is extracellular. **(b)** *Meara stichopi* (Nemertodermatidae). Paired statocysts are characteristic of this group; the mouth and pharynx are more developed than in the Acoela. **(c)** *Xenoturbella*. The groove around the middle of the animal appears to be sensory.

27.4e Phylum Xenacoelomorpha: Flatworms

The Xenacoelomorpha, a group of flatworms, is a sister grouping to the Bilateria. They are sometimes grouped with all other bilaterians, which have a specialized excretory system. Xenacoelomorpha includes three groups: the Acoela, the Nemertodermatidae, and the Xenoturbellida **(Figure 27.26)**. All three groups have a single opening to the gut and lack an anus. Xenoturbellids were initially classified as molluscs, because of mollusc DNA that the animals had obtained from their food. After suggestions that xenoturbellids were degenerate deuterostomes were disproved, the group found its proper position alongside Acoela.

STUDY BREAK QUESTIONS

1. Do sponges exhibit symmetry?
2. How does a sponge gather food from its environment?
3. How do cnidarians capture, consume, and digest their prey?
4. Describe the difference between a polyp and a medusa.

27.5 The Protostomes

Phyla viewed as more advanced than the basal phyla can be labelled as Nephrozoa on the basis that an excretory system is present. Nephrozoa are divided into two major groups: Protostomia and Deuterostomia **(Figure 27.27)**. The protostomes include the Gnathifera and phyla that are members of the Lophotrochozoa (Rouphozoa, Trochozoa, Polyzoa, Lophophorata) and Ecdysozoa (Scalidophora, Nematoidea, Panarthropoda) groups. At this time, Phylum Chaetognatha is classified as Protostomia.

27.5a Phylum Chaetognatha: Arrow Worms

Chaetognatha means "bristle jaws." In fact, the bristles are for capturing and holding prey; the true jaws are hidden below the hood of the head. Chaetognaths are marine predators, most in the plankton, a few species are benthic. Chaetognaths have a dartlike body, typically with two pairs of lateral fins and a tail fin; they swim rapidly but in short bursts. Chaetognaths have a muscular pharynx, a through gut, cerebral ganglia, nerve cords that have both dorsal and ventral elements, and a hermaphroditic reproductive system. There are only a small number of species of arrow worm (about 150), but they are ubiquitous and abundant in all oceans and are a major part of marine food chains.

The phylogeny of the chaetognaths remains uncertain. They have some deuterostome features (a post-anal tail and elements of a dorsal nervous system), but molecular evidence places them in the Protostomia.

27.5b Gnathifera

Gnathifera means "jaw bearing," and the clade includes the Gnathostomulida, Syndermata, and the recently described Micrognathozoa. In these groups, the jaws are complex and

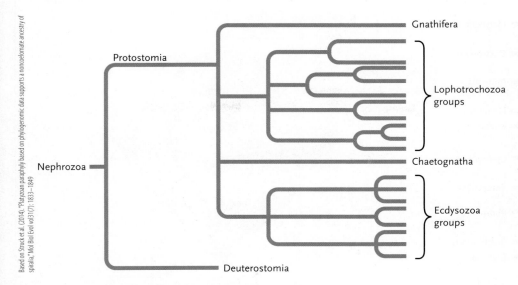

Based on Struck et al. (2014). "Platyzoan paraphyly based on phylogenomic data supports a noncoelomate ancestry of spiralia," Mol Biol Evol vol31(7): 1833–1849

FIGURE 27.27 Relationships of the higher animal phyla

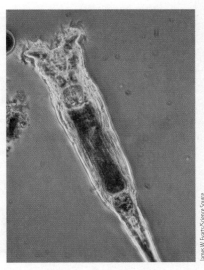

James W. Evarts/Science Source

FIGURE 27.28 A rotifer showing the corona (upper left)

located in the pharynx. In all three groups, the jaws are composed of similar microtubular elements.

Gnathostomulids are minute animals with a ferocious set of jaws. They have a mouth and gut but no anus. They expel undigested food material through their mouths. Micrognathozoa is known by a single genus, *Limnognathia*, which at 100 μm long may be the smallest known animal. These animals have the most complex jaws of any animal.

Syndermata combines two groups previously viewed as separate phyla: Rotifera and parasitic Acanthocephala. The Rotifera (meaning "wheel bearing") are named for the appearance of circular motion in the cilia, known as the *corona*, which set up feeding currents around the mouth **(Figure 27.28)**. There are over 2000 species of rotifers, mostly in freshwater (a few are marine) and usually less than 1 mm long. The pharynx includes a muscular bulb (the mastax) in which the jaws (trophi) break algal and bacterial cell walls in food collected by the corona. Rotifers are pseudocoelomate and have a protonephridial excretory system. Many rotifers are parthenogenetic, an asexual reproductive mode that allows rapid population increase under favourable conditions. Some species are polymorphic, with different morphs appearing under different environmental conditions. Acanthocephala (meaning "thorny headed") are endoparasitic worms. Their lack of jaws makes them a surprising inclusion in Gnathifera. Their position is based on molecular phylogeny data, combined with their morphological features being close to that of Rotifera.

STUDY BREAK QUESTIONS

1. What feature separates the basal phyla from the Nephrozoa?
2. What two major groups are the Nephrozoa divided into?

27.6 Lophotrochozoa Protostomes

This large grouping includes phyla with a **lophophore** feeding structure, which is a ring of ciliated feeding tentacles, and phyla that develop from a **trochophore** or modified trochophore larva **(Figure 27.29)**.

27.6a Phylum Platyhelminthes: The Flatworms

"Flatworms" is a direct translation of "platy" and "helminthes." There are over 20 000 species of platyhelminth described; of these, 80% are parasitic. Platyhelminthes are triploblastic, bilaterally symmetrical acoelomates **(Figure 27.30)**. They have a gut (lost in most parasitic species), an opening that acts as both a mouth and an anus, and a simple excretory system (called a **flame cell** system). The nervous system consists of two or more ventral nerve cords connected by nerve fibres. A concentration of nervous cell tissue, called the **ganglion**, acts as a primitive brain. Most free-living species have **ocelli**, or "eye spots." There is no circulatory system. Oxygen and carbon dioxide exchange occurs by diffusion over the body surface.

In traditional classifications, free-living species were grouped in the Turbellaria. **Figure 27.31** shows a simplified view of a current phylogeny.

Catenulida are a small group of aquatic flatworms that have a simple pharynx and a ciliated gut cavity. One genus, *Paracatenula*, has no gut but is packed with chemoautotrophic bacteria that derive energy from the oxidation of sulfide. Rhabditophora includes over a dozen orders of flatworms. They take their name from the rhabdites, which are rods formed in the epidermis and that are discharged when a predator threatens, dissolving to produce a chemical repellant. Order Tricladida (meaning "three branches") refers to the form of the gut with

a.

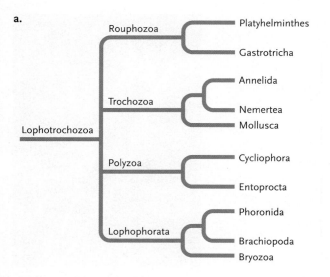

b.

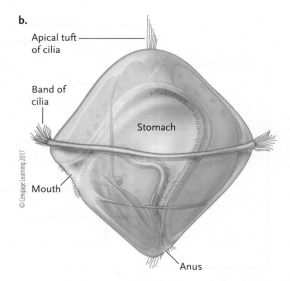

FIGURE 27.29 **(a)** The lophotrochozoan protostomes. **(b)** Animals such as molluscs and annelids pass through a trochophore larval stage at the conclusion of embryological development.

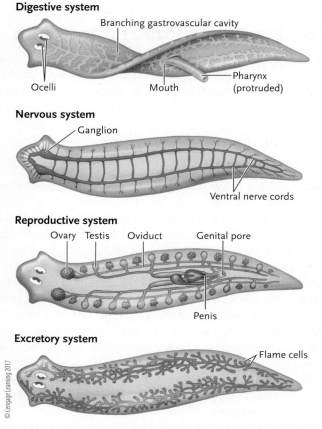

Digestive system

Branching gastrovascular cavity

Ocelli

Mouth

Pharynx (protruded)

Nervous system

Ganglion

Ventral nerve cords

Reproductive system

Ovary Testis Oviduct Genital pore

Penis

Excretory system

Flame cells

FIGURE 27.30 **Platyhelminthes, represented by this freshwater planarian, have digestive, nervous, reproductive, and excretory systems.**

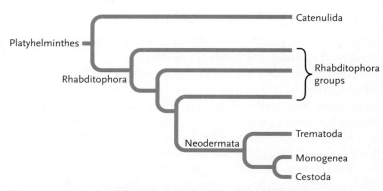

Platyhelminthes

Catenulida

Rhabditophora

Rhabditophora groups

Neodermata

Trematoda

Monogenea

Cestoda

FIGURE 27.31 **A simplified phylogeny of the Platyhelminthes**

a. *Microplana termitophaga*

b. *Pseudoceros dimidiatus*

FIGURE 27.32 **(a)** *Microplana termitophaga* attacking a termite nest. **(b)** *Pseudoceros dimidiatus*

one branch anterior to the pharynx and two branches posterior. Tricladida includes some flatworms living in damp terrestrial environments; an example is *Microplana termitophaga* **(Figure 27.32a)**, a predator of termites in southern Africa.

Polycladida (referring to a many-branched gut) are another large order of Rhabditophora. Many polyclads are brightly coloured (Figure 27.32b). There are many species in this group that have yet to be described.

Neodermata is a grouping within Rhabditophora that includes the three parasitic orders, Trematoda, Monogenea, and Cestoda. Trematodes are vertebrate parasites and many cause serious health problems. The Chinese liver fluke **(Figure 27.33)** is estimated to be found in the liver, bile ducts, and gall bladder of about 30 million people in Southeast Asia. Oral and ventral attachment suckers are characteristics of the trematodes.

a. Clonorchis sinensis

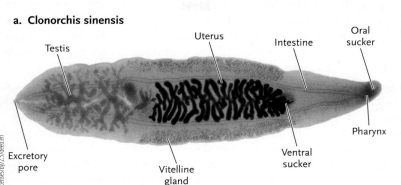

FIGURE 27.33 **(a)** A stained specimen of *Clonorchis sinensis* (Chinese liver fluke). **(b)** Life cycle of *Clonorchis*

b.

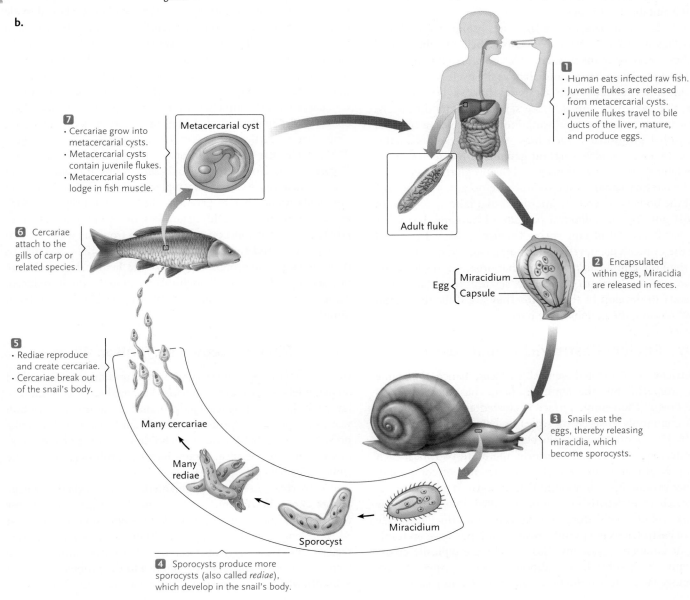

The life cycle of trematodes is complex and involves at least one intermediate host (usually a snail). Figure 27.33b shows the life cycle of *Clonorchis* and the stages that develop in the first intermediate host, a snail, and the second host, a freshwater fish, before the final human host is infected. It is typical of parasite life cycles that each passage from one host to another has a low probability of success. While many eggs are produced, few will be eaten by a snail. The stages in a snail involve asexual divisions to achieve a reproductive amplification that increases the probabilities of reaching the human host.

Monogenea have no intermediate host in their life cycle. Using hooks or suckers on attachment structures, monogeneans attach to the scales or gills of marine and freshwater fish. Fish gills are thin walled and richly vascularized; monogeneans break the epidermis and feed on blood leaking from the wound. Monogenean eggs hatch as ciliated larvae and may attach to the same host as the parent or develop from eggs stuck to the sea bed. Such eggs have the remarkable ability to hatch within seconds if a suitable host is nearby.

Cestoda, or tapeworms, are the sister group to the Monogenea **(Figure 27.34)**. "Cestoda" means a belt or ribbon and describes the shape of these worms. Cestodes are all parasitic in the intestines of vertebrates, and all have life cycles involving at least one intermediate host. Cestodes have a holdfast, the **scolex**, that may have hooks, suckers, and other modifications for attachment to the host gut wall. From the scolex, a series of units, called **proglottids**, each have a complete reproductive system. Tapeworms have cerebral ganglia in the scolex and a pair of lateral nerves runs through all the proglottids, as does a pair of excretory canals. Tapeworms have no gut, and the surface of the body is covered by microvilli that take up food from the host gut. *Taenia solium*, a parasite of humans, has a life cycle that is typical of tapeworms (Figure 27.34c). The larval stage, the cysticercus, develops in humans and may reach sites other than the gut. It can encyst in other organs and such cysts may have serious harmful effects (e.g., seizures when tapeworm cysts start to develop in the brain). They are difficult to treat without causing the patient more harm.

27.6b Phylum Gastrotricha: Hairy Backs

Gastrotricha have ciliated ventral surfaces, hence the name "hairy stomach," but the common name has these animals upside down! The ventral surface is ciliated and the body surface is commonly covered by scales or hairs. Gastrotrichs are small (< 3 mm) inhabitants of the benthic surface in marine and freshwater environments. Posteriorly, there are two toes, each with a pair of glands, one secreting an attachment compound, the other producing a compound that dissolves the attachment. Gastrotrichs are detritivores—food is taken into a muscular pharynx and crushed before passing to the intestine. The body cavity of gastrotrichs is a pseudocoelom, and they have no respiratory or circulatory systems. Gastrotrichs are typically cross-fertilizing hermaphrodites, although some species are parthenogenetic. Development is determinate and gastrotrichs

are eutelic (i.e., they have a fixed number of non-reproductive cells in their body).

27.6c Phylum Annelida: Segmented Worms

The phylum name comes from *anellus*, meaning "a small ring." This is a reference to the grooves between segments present in many annelids. More than 21 000 species of annelid have been described. Based on molecular data, the phylum has been enlarged through the inclusion of three groups that previously were separate phyla (Echiura, Sipunculidea, and Siboglinidae).

Annelids are highly segmented **(Figure 27.35)**. Segments are separated by intersegmental **septa**. A double ventral nerve cord runs from cerebral ganglia in the head and connects all segments. The gut runs from mouth to posterior anus and has regions specialized for food storage and breakdown in some species. The circulatory system is well developed, with vessels running above and below the gut and surrounding the gut. They lack a discrete respiratory system. Oxygen and carbon dioxide can be exchanged with the surrounding sea water by diffusion through the skin. The excretory system has open funnels (nephrostomes) in each segment, leading into nephridial tubes in the next segment. In freshwater and terrestrial annelids, the nephridial tubes may be elaborate and reabsorb salts and water.

Until recently, annelids were viewed as two classes, Polychaeta and Clitellata, with Clitellata including two subclasses, Oligochaeta (earthworms) and Hirudinea (leeches; see **Figure 27.36**). Molecular analysis produces a very different cladogram **(Figure 27.37)**. Notice that two basal groups (Oweniidae and Magelonidae) as well as Chaetopteridae, Amphinomidae, and Sipuncula branch before Errantia and Sedentaria separate. Sedentaria includes tube-building families, many of them with anterior tentacles that collect particles of food from the water, as well as scavengers and the ectoparasitic leeches in the Clitellata. In two quite separate groups, Sipuncula and Echiuridae, adults are not segmented, and in Siboglinidae segmentation is reduced, something seen also in small burrowing worms in the basal families.

27.6d Phylum Nemertea: Ribbon Worms

In Greek mythology, the sea god Nereus and his wife Doris had 50 daughters, known as the *nereids*. Among them was Nemertes, famed for her unerring legal judgements. A feature of the ribbon worms Nemertea is a proboscis that is rapidly extended to strike prey. It appears that the person who described the group transposed Nemertes' legal accuracy into the proboscis aim of the ribbon worms!

Nemertea are non-segmented, flat bodied worms **(Figure 27.38a, b)**. A nemertean may be the longest animal ever reported. A specimen of *Lineus longissimus* was measured at 54 m in length. Most are marine, although there are a few terrestrial and freshwater species. An alternative name for the Nemertea is Rhynchocoela, a reference to the proboscis (*rhynch* = snout), which is in a separate cavity from the gut. Some have a

a. Tapeworm

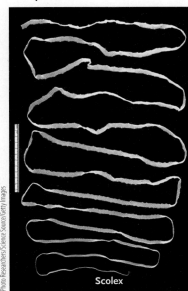

Photo Researchers/Science Source/Getty Images

Scolex

b. Scolex

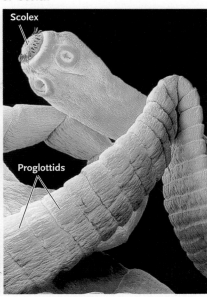

Andrew Syred/Science Source

Scolex

Proglottids

FIGURE 27.34 **(a)** Cestodas, or tapeworms, have long bodies that contain **(b)** a scolex that is used to attach to the host's intestinal wall. **(c)** The life cycle of *Taenia solium* is typical of tapeworms.

c.

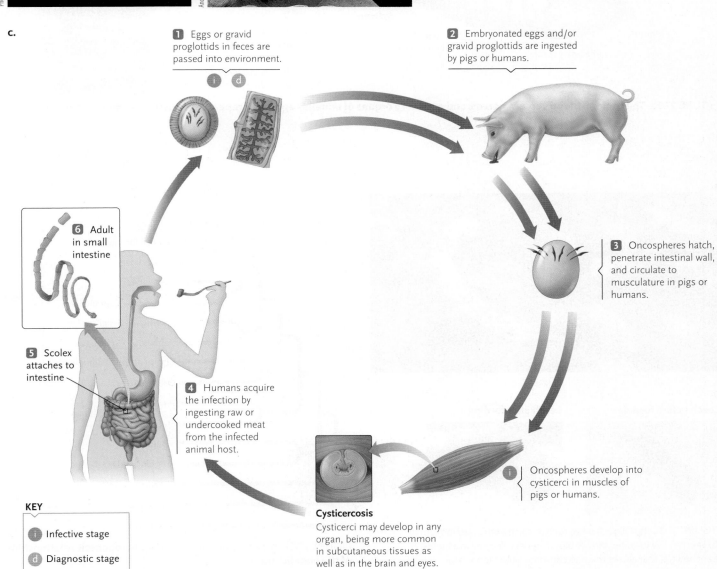

1 Eggs or gravid proglottids in feces are passed into environment.

2 Embryonated eggs and/or gravid proglottids are ingested by pigs or humans.

3 Oncospheres hatch, penetrate intestinal wall, and circulate to musculature in pigs or humans.

6 Adult in small intestine

5 Scolex attaches to intestine

4 Humans acquire the infection by ingesting raw or undercooked meat from the infected animal host.

Oncospheres develop into cysticerci in muscles of pigs or humans.

Cysticercosis
Cysticerci may develop in any organ, being more common in subcutaneous tissues as well as in the brain and eyes.

KEY

i Infective stage

d Diagnostic stage

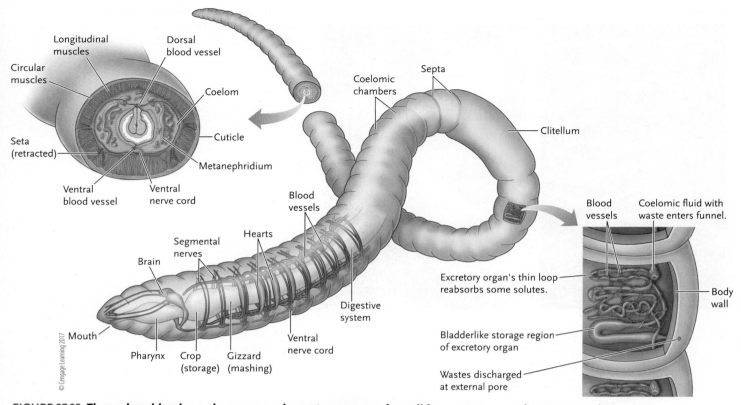

FIGURE 27.35 The coelom, blood vessels, nerves, and excretory organs of annelids appear as repeating structures in most segments.

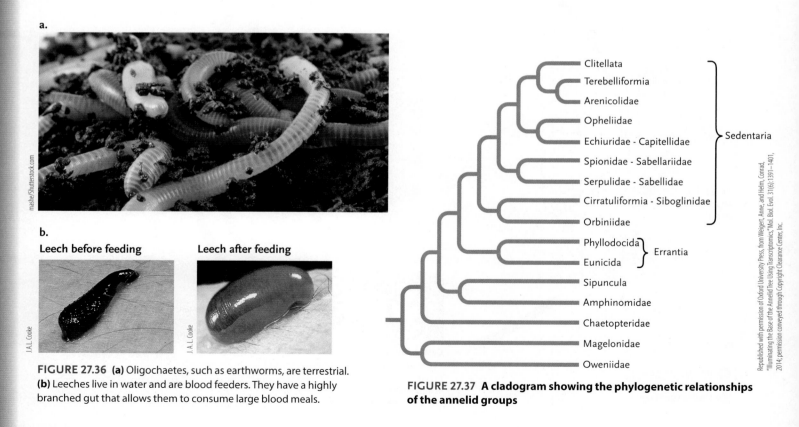

a.

b.

Leech before feeding

Leech after feeding

FIGURE 27.36 **(a)** Oligochaetes, such as earthworms, are terrestrial. **(b)** Leeches live in water and are blood feeders. They have a highly branched gut that allows them to consume large blood meals.

FIGURE 27.37 A cladogram showing the phylogenetic relationships of the annelid groups

Republished with permission of Oxford University Press, from Weigert, Anne, and Helm, Conrad, "Illuminating the Base of the Annelid Tree Using Transcriptomics," Mol. Biol. Evol. 31(6):1391−1401, 2014; permission conveyed through Copyright Clearance Center, Inc.

a. Ribbon worm (*Lineus* species)

b. Ribbon worm anatomy

Proboscis pore • Proboscis • Rhynchocoel

Mouth • Intestine • Proboscis retractor muscle • Anus

Everted proboscis

© Cengage Learning 2017

Figure 27.38 **(a)** Ribbon worms can be brightly coloured. **(b)** The rhynchocoel contains a proboscis.

barb that impales the prey, while in others the proboscis wraps around the prey. Nemertea are traditionally described as acoelomate, although the **rhynchocoel** is surrounded by mesoderm and hence a true coelom. The mouth of nemerteans is ventral and a little behind the front. In primitive nemertean groups, the proboscis extends from the rhynchocoel at the tip; in more evolved groups the proboscis and the mouth share a single ventral opening.

Nemerteans lack a cuticle, but ciliated epidermal cells, mucus-secreting cells, and rhabdites cover the body surface. They have a circulatory system whereby fluid flows through circulatory vessels that carry nutrients to tissues and remove waste. The fluid is moved through the vessels when the vessels are compressed by body movements.

Nemerteans reproduce asexually by fragmentation; even small pieces of a ribbon worm can regenerate to a complete individual. Sperm and ova are shed from males and females, and fertilization is external. A free-swimming larva develops, and a new adult differentiates within the body of the larva.

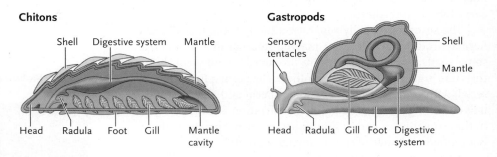

Chitons

Shell • Digestive system • Mantle

Head • Radula • Foot • Gill • Mantle cavity

Gastropods

Sensory tentacles • Shell • Mantle

Head • Radula • Gill • Foot • Digestive system

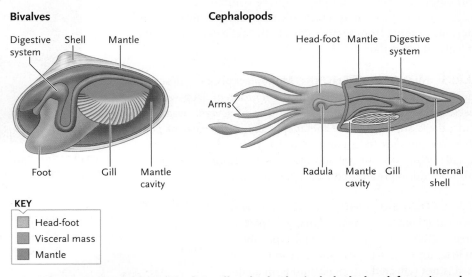

Bivalves

Digestive system • Shell • Mantle

Foot • Gill • Mantle cavity

Cephalopods

Head-foot • Mantle • Digestive system

Arms

Radula • Mantle cavity • Gill • Internal shell

KEY

- Head-foot
- Visceral mass
- Mantle

FIGURE 27.39 **Common features in the mollusc body plan include the head–foot, visceral mass, and mantle.**

27.6e Phylum Mollusca: Slugs, Snails, and Squid

The name Mollusca comes from the Latin *molluscus*, meaning "soft." Beneath or without their shell, molluscs are soft-bodied animals. Molluscs evolved as benthic animals at a time when the number, and variety, of predatory species was increasing.

Molluscs evolved a dorsal spicule covering, that later became a shell, as a defensive adaptation. Estimates suggest that there are 200 000 species of living mollusc living in all environments and about 70 000 in the fossil record.

The molluscan body plan has several common features **(Figure 27.39)**. Three regions are the visceral mass, head–foot, and mantle. The **visceral mass** contains the digestive, excretory, and reproductive systems, and the heart. The muscular **head–foot** often provides the major means of locomotion, except in cephalopods (e.g., octopuses, squid). In the more active groups, the head area of the head–foot region is well defined and carries sensory organs and a brain. The mouth often includes a toothed **radula**, which scrapes food into small particles or drills through the shells of prey. A well-known feature of this phylum is a shell. This protective shell of calcium carbonate is secreted by the **mantle**, a folding of the body wall that may enclose the visceral mass. The mantle also defines a space, the **mantle cavity**, that houses the gills (delicate respiratory structures). In most molluscs, cilia on the mantle and gills generate a steady flow of water into the mantle cavity. Most molluscs have an **open circulatory system** in which **hemolymph**, a bloodlike fluid, leaves the circulatory vessels and bathes tissues directly. Hemolymph pools in spaces called *sinuses* and then drains into vessels that carry it back to the heart.

The sexes are usually separate, although many snails are hermaphroditic. Fertilization may be internal or external. In some snails, eggs and sperm are produced simultaneously in the same organ, an ovotestis. In others, the hermaphroditism is serial, with younger snails producing sperm and older individuals switching to egg production. Fertilization is often internal in these organisms, and in simultaneous hermaphrodites, there is a mutual exchange of sperm during copulation.

There are eight classes of living molluscs (**Figure 27.40**). Although members of the phylum have common characteristics, they have evolved an extraordinary diversity in form and lifestyle, ranging from sessile clams to the agile octopus capable of learned behaviour.

CLASS MONOPLACOPHORA "Monoplacophora" describes the "single plate" shell form of this small group of deep-sea molluscs. Internally there is serial repetition of several organ systems: there are six pairs of metanephridia, eight pairs of pedal retractor muscles, two pairs of heart atria, and two pairs of gonads. While the advantages of serial repetition are not clear, this does not represent reduced segmentation.

CLASS POLYPLACOPHORA (THE CHITONS) *Polyplacophora* means "many plates" (**Figure 27.41**). In reality, the shell typically is divided into eight plates. The division of the shell is not reflected internally and is an adaptation to allow the animal to fit closely to rough rock surfaces where chitons browse on the algal and bacterial film. The mantle edge extends beyond the shell as a girdle that, in some species, may grow up and around the shell.

CLASS BIVALVIA (CLAMS, SCALLOPS, OYSTERS, AND MUSSELS) As their name implies, bivalves are enclosed within two shells that are hinged together by an elastic ligament (**Figure 27.42**). In the development of the shell, it first forms as a figure 8; the crossover in the eight is not calcified and forms the dorsal hinge when the two loops of the eight fold down and calcify. When **abductor muscles** contract the shell closes, and relaxation of the muscles allows the shell to open.

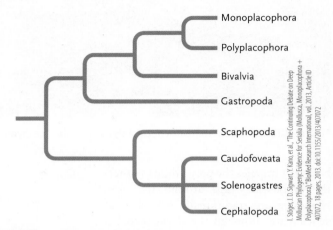

I. Stöger, J. D. Sigwart, Y. Kano, et al., "The Continuing Debate on Deep Molluscan Phylogeny: Evidence for Serialia (Mollusca, Monoplacophora + Polyplacophora)," BioMed Research International, vol. 2013, Article ID 407072, 18 pages, 2013. doi:10.1155/2013/407072

FIGURE 27.40 Molluscan phylogeny

George Wood/Dreamstime.com

FIGURE 27.41 Chitons use their foot and mantle to grip rocks and other surfaces.

a. Bivalve body plan

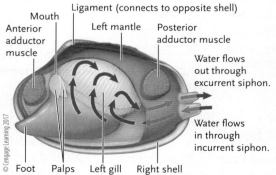

Mouth
Anterior adductor muscle
Ligament (connects to opposite shell)
Left mantle
Posterior adductor muscle
Water flows out through excurrent siphon.
Water flows in through incurrent siphon.
Foot Palps Left gill Right shell

© Cengage Learning 2017

b. Giant clam (*Tridachna gigas*)

treetstreet/iStock/Getty Images

FIGURE 27.42 (a) Bivalves are enclosed within two shells. **(b)** Although some bivalves are tiny, giant clams of the South Pacific can be more than 1 m across and weigh 225 kg.

666 | UNIT FIVE THE DIVERSITY OF LIFE

NEL

a. Gastropod body plan

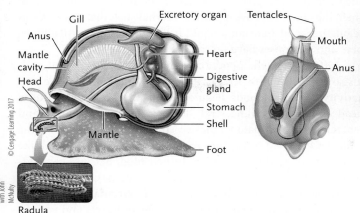

Gill
Anus
Mantle cavity
Head
Mantle
Radula

Excretory organ
Heart
Digestive gland
Stomach
Shell
Foot

Tentacles
Mouth
Anus

© Cengage Learning 2017

Danielle Zacherl with John McNulty

b. Terrestrial snail (*Helix pomatia*)

K00/Shutterstock.com

c. Marine nudibranch (*Flabellina iodinea*)

iStock.com/Thornberry

FIGURE 27.43 **(a)** Most gastropods have a coiled shell that contains the visceral mass. **(b)** The terrestrial snail (*Helix pomatia*) is a typical gastropod. **(c)** This marine nudibranch (*Flabellina iodine*) is an example of a shell-less marine snail.

Bivalves have evolved a highly modified molluscan form, specialized for burrowing and filter feeding. The foot is spade-like and can be expanded and contracted as blood is pumped in or as muscles contract, an alternating motion that penetrates the substratum and then anchors as the shell is pulled down. The hinge of the shell allows the valves to gape and form an anchor as the foot is extended.

Bivalves lack a distinct head and radula. Two tubes, called *siphons*, are formed from part of the mantle. Beating cilia on the gills draw water into the mantle cavity through the incurrent siphon. This water carries oxygen and nutrients. Water exits through the excurrent siphon, carrying away wastes. Primitive bivalves have palps on either side of the mouth that are extended into the substratum to collect food; in these species, the gills are small. In most bivalves, the gills are enormously expanded: an estimate has the gill area about 300 times that needed for gas exchange. The palps are reduced and sort food from the gills into the mouth.

Bivalves are a commercially important, including both harvested and cultured species of clams, oysters, scallops, and mussels.

CLASS GASTROPODA (SNAILS AND SLUGS) Gastropoda (*gastro* = stomach; *poda* = foot) are the largest molluscan group, containing around 75% of the described species. Gastropods, while mostly marine, have freshwater and terrestrial species and include predators, herbivores, filter feeders, and detritivores (consume dead or composing plant and animal matter). They exhibit a wide range of morphologies. Aquatic and marine gastropods use gills to obtain oxygen. Terrestrial gastropods have replaced gills by heavy vascularization of the mantle cavity, allowing the surface to operate like a lung **(Figure 27.43)**. The nervous and sensory systems of gastropods are well developed. Tentacles on the head include chemical and touch receptors; the eyes detect changes in light intensity but don't they form images. Many gastropods have lost or reduced shells, such as the terrestrial and sea slugs, which leaves them vulnerable to predators.

Understanding the appearance of the gastropods demands understanding two different processes of twisting. The most obvious is the coiling of the gastric hump from the conical form of a limpet **(Figure 27.44a)** to that of a snail (Figure 27.44b). The coiled shell allows expansion of the intestine, digestive

a. Common limpet

M. B. Fenton

b. Terrestrial snail

M. B. Fenton

FIGURE 27.44 **(a)** This common limpet is a gastropod that has a conical shell and lives on rocks in the intertidal zone. **(b)** Terrestrial snails, such as this *Helix pomatia,* have a coiled shell.

gland, and gonad in a way that allows them to be balanced above the foot. The second twist is less obvious and is a change that occurs during development. It involves rotation of the mantle cavity, gills, and anus from their posterior position to an anterior arrangement, a process known as *torsion*.

CLASS SCAPHOPODA (THE TOOTH SHELLS) The name Scaphopoda translates as "boat foot" and refers to the shape of the burrowing foot. The common name describes the tusklike shape of the shell. A scaphopod shell is a tapering tube, and the animal lives with the small end protruding above the substratum and the wide end buried. Seawater currents enter, and leave, the open end, and respiratory gas exchange occurs over the surface of the mantle. The foot is extended from the wide opening, as are a number of tentacles, known as **captacula**, that surround the mouth. The captacula extend into the seabed and collect small food items (particularly protists) and transfer them to the mouth. The anus opens into the mantle cavity, and wastes are washed out in the exhalant water stream.

CLASS CAUDOFOVEATA The name means a tail (*cauda*) pit (*fove*) and refers to the posterior chamber that encloses a pair of **ctenidia**, comb-like respiratory structures. The body has anterior, trunk, and posterior regions and is covered by spicules—perhaps a predecessor to the evolution of a rigid shell. Caudofoveates use the muscle of the anterior and trunk regions to burrow, leaving the gills above the substratum surface. They feed on foraminiferans, diatoms, and detritus. While only 120 species of Caudofoveata have been described, the majority of which are from the deep sea, it is probable that there are many species yet to be collected.

CLASS SOLENOGASTRES The Solenogastres are like the caudofoveates in having a wormlike shape and a body covered by spicules rather than a shell. The name comes from *solen* (= grooved) and *gaster* (= stomach), and it describes the way in which the foot is sunken into a groove on the ventral surface. Solenogastres are predators, feeding mostly on cnidarians either by direct predation or by sucking body fluid after penetrating the body wall of their prey.

CLASS CEPHALOPODA (SQUID AND OCTOPUS) Cephalopoda translates as "head footed" and describes the way in which the molluscan foot has evolved into the tentacles and head of the cephalopods. The group includes nautilus, squid, and octopus **(Figure 27.45)**, and there are about 1000 living species and more than 10 times as many fossil species. The evolutionary history of the cephalopods includes shell reduction.

Fossil belemnites (straight) and ammonites (coiled) had heavy shells. In modern groups, the nautiloids retain a light external shell, the cuttlefish have a porous internal shell that has a role in regulating their buoyancy, squid have only a thin cartilaginous pen, and octopuses have no shell.

Internally, cephalopod anatomy follows the standard molluscan model, with specializations that relate to the size and activity of cephalopods **(Figure 27.46)**. The body has a fused head and foot. The ancestral "foot" forms a set of arms and tentacles. Suction pads, adhesive structures, or hooks on the tentacles are used to capture prey. Cephalopods have beaklike jaws that are used to bite or crush their food. Because cephalopods are highly active, they need lots of oxygen. Unique to molluscan groups, they have a **closed circulatory system**: hemolymph is confined within the walls of hearts and vessels. The closed system allows cephalopods to have much smaller blood volumes and provides increased pressure to vascular fluid. The systemic heart is supplemented by two branchial

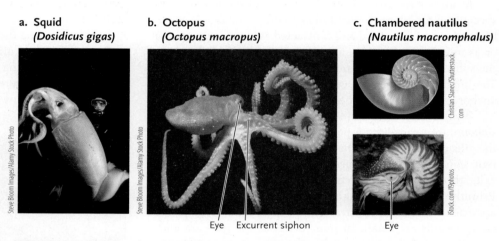

a. Squid *(Dosidicus gigas)*

b. Octopus *(Octopus macropus)*

c. Chambered nautilus *(Nautilus macromphalus)*

Eye   Excurrent siphon

Eye

FIGURE 27.45 (a, b) Squids and octopuses are the most familiar cephalopods. **(c)** The chambered nautilus retains a shell.

Internal anatomy of squid

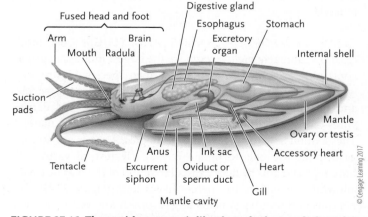

Fused head and foot

Arm

Mouth   Radula

Brain

Digestive gland

Esophagus

Excretory organ

Stomach

Internal shell

Suction pads

Tentacle

Anus

Excurrent siphon

Ink sac

Oviduct or sperm duct

Mantle cavity

Mantle

Ovary or testis

Accessory heart

Heart

Gill

© Cengage Learning 2017

FIGURE 27.46 The squid anatomy is like that of other cephalopods. It has a fused head and foot, and most organs are enclosed by the mantle.

hearts that pump hemolymph through the ctenidia. They speed the flow of hemolymph through blood vessels and gills, enhancing the uptake of oxygen and release of carbon dioxide. They have a discrete kidney that is closely associated with the circulatory system. Oxygen is carried by hemocyanin, a pigment that carries only 25% as much oxygen as hemoglobin.

Compared with other molluscs, cephalopods have large and complex brains, which connect to muscles of the mantle. This allows for quick response to food and danger. They are also highly intelligent: octopuses can learn to recognize shapes and can be trained to approach or avoid certain objects.

Cephalopods swim by jet propulsion. When muscles in the mantle relax, water is drawn into the mantle cavity and then expelled under pressure through the muscular siphon. Manipulating the position of the mantle and siphon allows a cephalopod to control the rate and direction of movement. Octopuses also walk on their arms, and squid and cuttlefish fins are involved in slow swimming.

The ink sac is a special feature of cephalopods. In shallow-water species, the ink sac contains a melanin suspension that can be released as a cloud, confusing a predator and allowing the cephalopod to escape. Deep-sea species have commonly replaced the ink with a colony of phosphorescent bacteria that produce a cloud of light when released, allowing escape into the darkness.

Cephalopods also have a remarkable ability to change colour. This is achieved through the expansion (by muscle strands) and contraction (by elasticity) of pigment containing chromatophores. Colour change is under neural control and, while mostly controlled through the highly developed eyes, can also be modulated by a general light sensitivity of the epidermis.

27.6f Phylum Entoprocta

The name Entoprocta means "inside anus" and describes the position of the anus inside the ring of tentacles. Entoprocts are colonial and almost all species are marine. Entoprocts lack a coelom; the space between gut and body wall is filled by connective-tissue strands. The tentacles are solid and are withdrawn by curling. Superficially, they resemble tube-dwelling annelid worms.

27.6g Phylum Cycliophora

The first described species of cycliophoran, *Symbion pandora*, lives commensally on the mouthparts of the Norway lobster (*Nephrops norvegicus*). *Symbion* has a complex life cycle that includes an asexual stage that multiplies on its lobster host. When the host is about to moult, the cycliophoran is triggered to move into a sexually reproductive phase. A male is produced that attaches to a bud that develops as a female; the fertilized female swims freely, its gut degenerates, and a larva develops in its place. The larva then swims free to seek another host. Adults resemble small hydralike cnidarians.

27.6h Phylum Phoronida: Horseshoe Worms

Phoronids are benthic worms that secrete a chitinous tube that is either attached to or buried in the substratum. Their common name comes from the shape of the lophophore that is coiled around the mouth in a horseshoe-like shape **(Figure 27.47)**. Phoronids have a U-shaped gut, with the anus outside the lophophore. A pair of metanephridial funnels discharge metabolic wastes near the anus. Phoronids live in low oxygen environments and, an adaptation unique among invertebrates, have hemoglobin in their blood system that is contained in corpuscles; weight for weight, a phoronid carries twice as much oxygen as a human.

27.6i Phylum Brachiopoda: Lamp Shells

Brachiopods resemble clams in having a bivalve shell. Unlike clams, where the shell valves are lateral, brachiopods have dorsal and ventral shell valves. The common name "lamp shells" comes from the shape of one valve resembling that of an oil lamp. The phylum name translates as "arm" (*brach*) "footed" (*pod*) and comes from the two arms of the lophophore that can be seen when the shell is open. There are about 400 living species of brachiopod, but the group was a dominant part of the Paleozoic

a. Phoronida (*Plumatella repens*)

b. Brachiopoda (*Terebratulina septentrionalis*)

c. Bryozoa (*Phoronis hippocrepia*)

FIGURE 27.47 The lophophore is a feathery structure that lophophorate animals use to obtain food.

fauna, with over 30 000 species described. Theories suggest competition between brachiopods and bivalve molluscs, combined with the great Permian extinction, led to the decline in brachiopod diversity.

27.6j Phylum Bryozoa: Moss Animals

Bryo- means "moss," which is how colonies of bryozoans appear. Bryozoans are colonial lophophorates found in marine and fresh waters. Individual zooids in the colony are protected by a body wall that may be of chitin or, in many cases, may be mineralized. Each zooid has a U-shaped gut and resembles a miniature phoronid. Bryozoans are polymorphic (composed of different individuals), with feeding zooids supplying food to reproductive zooids, defensive zooids, and zooids specialized for cleaning the surface of the colony. Zooids are able to coordinate their activities. While individual zooids collect food, they will cooperate with neighbours to use the tentacles to flick non-food items away from the colony.

STUDY BREAK QUESTIONS

1. What characteristic reveals the close evolutionary relationship of bryozoans, brachiopods, and phoronids?
2. Describe the three regions of the mollusc body.
3. Which organ systems exhibit segmentation in most annelid worms?

27.7 Ecdysozoa Protostomes

Twenty-five years ago, it was heretical to think that segmented arthropods and annelids might not be closely related. It followed that Onychophora, with features of both groups, were not associated with the evolutionary line between annelids and arthropods. An early contribution of using molecular analysis to understand phylogeny came from studies of 18S ribosomal DNA of protostome groups. The results showed that the protostomes must be divided into a clade of animals that moult a non-living cuticle (Ecdysozoa) and Lophotrochozoa. The analysis showed no support for a group that would link Arthropoda and Annelida.

Recent molecular studies support splitting Ecdysozoa into three groups: Scalidophora Nematozoa, and Panarthropoda **(Figure 27.48)**.

- Scalidophora includes the phyla Kinorhyncha, Loricifera, and Priapulida. Like other ecdysozoans they have a chitinous cuticle that is moulted. All three phyla have an anterior region (introvert) that can be retracted or extended and scalids—spines, hooks, or finger-like projects on the introvert that are continuous with the chitinous cuticle.
- Nematozoa includes the phyla Nematoda and Nematomorpha. Both lack circular muscle and have longitudinal muscle divided into four cords. Both have a cuticle supported

by a fibre lattice. While chitin is characteristic of all ecdysozoans, its presence is limited to the pharyngeal lining of nematodes and the larval cuticle of nematomorphs.
- Panarthropoda includes the phyla Onychophora, Tardigrada, and Arthropoda. Members of all three phyla have legs, claws, a double ventral nerve cord, and a segmented body plan. There is dispute over the relationship of the three phyla. Current evidence supports the tardigrades as being the sister group to the Arthropoda.

27.7a Phylum Kinorhyncha: Mud Dragons

The name of this phylum is based on the words *kines* (move) and *rhynch* (snout) and refers to the way in which the head is extended and retracted. There are about 250 described species of kinorhynch, living from the marine intertidal down to the deep sea. Kinorhynch adults have a head and neck and an 11-segmented body **(Figure 27.49)**. The head bears a group of anterior stylets and, behind them, numerous scalids (finger-like projections). Extension and withdrawal of the head moves the scalids to pull the animal through soft substrata.

Kinorhynchs feed on decaying organic material, algae, and bacteria as they burrow. They have a muscular pharynx and a simple through gut. Intersegmental muscles control movement of the body, the body cavity is a pseudocoel, and excretion is via a pair of protonephridial organs. Kinorhynchs are dioecious and hatch as small adult forms, although with fewer segments.

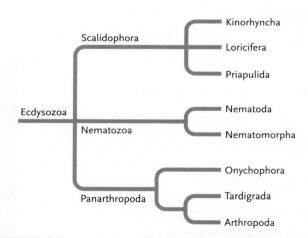

FIGURE 27.48 A current view of the phylogeny of the Ecdysozoa

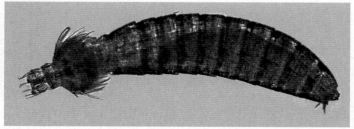

Michael Owen

FIGURE 27.49 A kinorhynch from the Bay of Fundy

27.7b Phylum Loricifera: The Brush Heads

A *lorica* is a corselet (part of a suit of armour), and in the case of loriciferans the outer sheath into which the animal can withdraw. Loriciferans have a frontal cone with two rings of scalids that, in some species, move the animal across the sea bed, and in others have been seen to be used in swimming. Loriciferans have a simple through gut, and some species are pseudocoelomate; others are acoelomate. Most species are dioecious and produce an egg that hatches to a form resembling a small adult. A few species are parthenogenetic.

The surprise finding from these animals is that they do not have mitochondria, normally present in all living eukaryotes. Instead, they have hydrogenosomes, organelles known only from some protists that supply energy through anaerobic pathways.

27.7c Phylum Priapulida: Penis Worms

The common name for Priapulida comes from the Greek god of fertility (*Priapus*), a figure depicted with a large penis. The rounded anterior part of a priapulid worm is suggested to resemble the head of a penis. Priapulids are a small group of marine, burrowing, predatory worms. There are about 25 living species. The body is divided into an anterior introvert, where the mouth is located. There are rings of scalids on the introvert, which grip the substrate as the introvert is moved in and out of the trunk. There is a simple through gut. The body cavity is undivided and is now thought to be a hemocoel. Cells carrying hemerythrin, a respiratory pigment, move through the fluid in the body cavity. Priapulans burrow by eversion and contraction of the introvert combined with peristaltic movements of the body. The body cavity fluid acts as a hydrostatic skeleton for movement.

27.7d Phylum Nematoda: Round Worms

Nematoda (*nemata* = thread) include about 30 000 described species, although estimates suggest that the phylum includes well over a million species, making it the second largest animal phylum. The phylum is distributed in all possible habitats, and over 50% of its members are parasitic **(Figure 27.50)**.

The upper 10 cm of a soil layer has been estimated to contain over a million nematodes per square metre. Nematodes constitute over 90% of the fauna of the sea bed and the group are well known as extremophiles, living in habitats where other organisms cannot survive. A frequently mentioned nematode is a species found in German beer coasters (now known to occur in other habitats, as it is also found living in the paste binding of library books). Cultures of the nematode *Caenorhabditis elegans* were on the ill-fated space shuttle Columbia. Nematodes in three of five containers found in the debris field in Texas were found to have survived the temperature conditions of Earth reentry as well as estimated forces of 2500*g*.

Nematodes are typically elongated, circular in cross-section, and tapered at both ends. Their body wall is protected by a cuticle that is moulted as they grow and reinforced by three layers of fibres arranged at alternating angles to each other. This arrangement gives strength while maintaining flexibility. The gut runs from an anterior mouth that opens into a muscular pharynx, leading to a thin-walled intestine and a posterior anus. Inside the body wall run four cords of longitudinal muscles, separated by dorsal and ventral nerve cords and lateral excretory canals **(Figure 27.51)**.

Nematode musculature is unusual in two ways. First, rather than nerves running to the muscle, the muscle itself has connectives that run to the nerve cords. Secondly, there is no circular muscle; differential contraction of the longitudinal muscle bends the worm, while hydrostatic pressure in the pseudocoelom opposes this change in shape and straightens the worm when the muscles relax. This hydrostatic mechanism is similar to that used in penis worms. High pressure in the pseudocoelom collapses the gut and the pharynx operates as a

Alistair Dove/Image Quest Marine

FIGURE 27.50 Some roundworms, such as these *Anguillicola crassus*, are parasites of plants or animals.

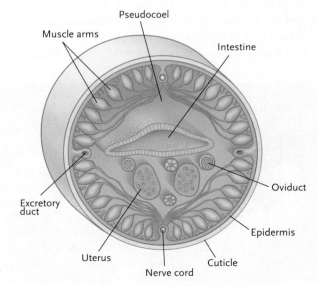

FIGURE 27.51 A cross-section of a typical nematode

pump, forcing food back into the intestine against the pressure. Free-living nematodes feed on decaying matter, fungi, bacteria, and other organic materials. A soil nematode has been shown to eat about 5000 bacterial cells a minute, a measure that shows the importance of nematodes in an ecosystem.

27.7e Phylum Nematomorpha: Horsehair Worms

As their name suggests, Nematomorpha are long (typically 50–100 cm), thin (usually only 2–3 mm diameter) worms. Adult nematomorphs are short-lived and have no excretory or circulatory system. There is a non-functional gut, and the worms do not eat. Females produce strings of eggs from which larvae hatch and then enter an intermediate host, frequently a beetle. Larvae grow in the host, absorbing food over their body wall, and will then moult to the adult form. At this time, they affect the behaviour of their host, stimulating movement and causing the host to seek water, where the newly emerged adult leaves through the host anus.

27.7f Phylum Onychophora: Velvet Worms

Onychophora means "claw bearing" and refers to the claws at the tip of each pair of the animal's lobe-like appendages **(Figure 27.52)**. Their common name, "velvet worm," comes from the soft appearance of their cuticle.

Onychophorans are segmented animals, although the only external evidence of segmentation lies in the pair of legs on each segment. The head has three pairs of modified appendages: a pair of sensory antennae, a pair of hardened mandibles within the mouth, and a pair of papillae through which a sticky slime can be discharged. Onychophorans are the champion spitters of the animal kingdom. A 5 cm animal can fire strands of slime at prey 50 cm away to immobilize the prey, which is then killed by an injection of toxic saliva.

Internally, the separation of the 13–43 segments (varying with species) is clear. There is a pair of glands opening at the base of each pair of legs, the neural supply and muscles associated with leg movement have a segmental arrangement, and on each segment there is an opening, the spiracle, into a tracheal system that resembles that of the insects. An important difference is that insect spiracles can be sealed shut, and onychophoran spiracles have no closing mechanism. This makes them a site for water loss, which restricts the habitats in which the onychophorans can live. Fertilization is internal, and in many onychophorans sperm is stored in a reservoir where it remains functional for several months. Some species are oviparous (egg laying), others ovoviviparous (eggs hatch in the uterus), and some viviparous (eggs hatch and young develop in the uterus). Some viviparous species actually have a placenta to provide food to the developing young.

27.7g Phylum Tardigrada: Water Bears

The name Tardigrada means "slow walker," an apt description of the locomotion of these small (0.05–1.5 mm long) animals. There are about 1000 described tardigrade species (and an estimated 10 000 species in total) living in marine, freshwater, and semi-terrestrial environments. Tardigrades **(Figure 27.53)** are segmented, with a head, three trunk segments, and a caudal segment; each segment behind the head bears a pair of lobe-like legs equipped with terminal claws, hooks, or suckers.

Tardigrades have a muscular pharynx that sucks food through the mouth from punctures, made by extending stylets through the mouth, in plant cells. There is a through gut, with tubular glands branching from the hindgut. Most tardigrade species are dioecious and oviparous (a few are parthenogenetic), and eggs are commonly thick walled. Like several other groups of small animals, tardigrades are eutelic (each species has a fixed number of non-reproductive cells).

Tardigrades are famous for their cryptobiotic adaptations. Difficult environmental conditions trigger a controlled dehydration, followed by loss of cuticular permeability and enormously reduced metabolism. Tardigrades in this state can withstand extreme challenges of heat, cold, noxious chemicals, radiation, and pressure. In this state, tardigrades can survive for up to 10 years and can still be revived when placed in water. Despite this adaptation, tardigrades are not viewed as extremophiles since they do not normally live in extreme environments.

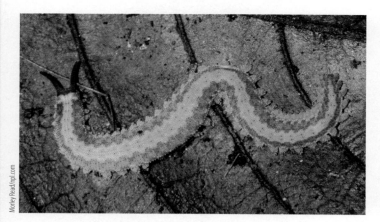

FIGURE 27.52 An onychophoran from Ecuador

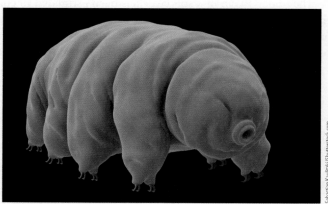

FIGURE 27.53 A tardigrade

27.7h Phylum Arthropoda: Joint-Legged Animals

The phylum Arthropoda (*arthro* = joint; *pod* = foot) includes four living groups (Chelicerata, Myriapoda, Crustacea, and Insecta) and has a species count vastly greater than any other phylum. Compare the species numbers in **Figure 27.54** to the roughly 5500 known species of mammals! This diagram shows only the living arthropod groups. The hard exoskeleton of arthropods results in their being common as fossils. Huge numbers of species (e.g., 17 000 species of trilobites) have been described from the early Cambrian onward in groups that became extinct, including some that played a dominant role in the ecosystem of the time.

Arthropods are segmented animals, frequently with some segments or groups of segments specialized for different functions; fusion of segments is common. Arthropod bodies are covered by an **exoskeleton**, a continuous layer of cuticle made of a mixture of chitin and proteins. Cuticle is commonly hardened by a process of tanning (sclerotization), which involves two dopamine derivatives, N-acetyldopamine and N-P-alanyldopamine, which are oxidized to quinones that cross-link with amino acids in the cuticular proteins. In crustaceans, the cuticle may be additionally thickened and hardened by the incorporation of calcium carbonate. Many factors affect cuticle hardness, particularly the relative amounts of chitin and protein, with more chitin (up to 4:1 ratio) making flexible cuticle and 1:1 chitin:protein making for rigid cuticle. If there were no flexible cuticle, arthropod bodies would be rigid and immobile. The demands of movement are met by the cuticle at joints (e.g., between segments and limb joints) being unsclerotized and flexible.

While an exoskeleton provides excellent protection, and muscles running between skeletal elements offer efficient locomotion, the exoskeleton makes growth impossible. Arthropods can grow only by a series of moults in which the old exoskeleton is shed. The body enlarges while its covering is soft, and the new cuticle hardens over the enlarged body. Moulting is regulated by a complex interaction between internal conditions and environmental conditions, and is controlled by neural and neurosecretory messages.

In soft-bodied animals, support comes from a hydrostatic skeleton formed by fluid in a gastric compartment (e.g., sea anemones), pseudocoel (e.g., nematodes), or coelom (e.g., annelid worms). In the arthropods, support comes from the exoskeleton. The coelom is greatly reduced and the body cavity is a hemocoel. Development of a circulatory system in arthropods may be minimal or may have a heart and a highly complex series of branching vessels that open into the hemocoel and transport materials throughout the body.

The exoskeleton is a barrier to the exchange of gasses and fluids over the body surface. These exchanges are performed by different excretory and respiratory structures in each arthropod group, and are discussed in the following sections.

Arthropods have a complex nervous system with a central nervous system developed by fusion of ganglia in the head segments, a double ventral nerve cord that includes giant neurons for fast conduction, segmental ganglia, and extensive neural development.

SUBPHYLUM CHELICERATA The name of this group comes from the first appendages, known as **chelicerae** (*chela* = claw; *cera* = horn). These are a small pair of pincerlike appendages used to bite or grasp prey. Chelicerates have a body that is divided into two main regions: a cephalothorax, also called a **prosoma** (formed from fusion of the head and thorax), and the abdomen, also called the **opisthosoma**. Chelicerata includes three classes: Pycnogonida, Xiphosura, and Arachnida.

Pycnogonids are known as *sea spiders*, although they are distantly related to true spiders. A typical pycnogonid **(Figure 27.55)** has four pairs of long thin legs. The head is small and bears a proboscis that is inserted into food (pycnogonids are predators or scavengers). The abdomen is vestigial. Liquid food is sucked into a gut that runs to a terminal anus, which has branches that extend into the basal parts of each leg.

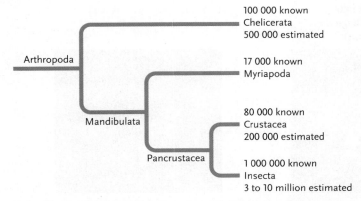

FIGURE 27.54 A current view of arthropod phylogeny showing the numbers of identified species, as well as estimates of the number of species still to be described

Figure 27.55 A pycnogonid (*Nymphon leptocheles*) feeding on a hydroid (*Tubularia* sp.)

Pycnogonids are gonochoristic—eggs are released and fertilized externally and are then carried to hatching by the male.

Xiphosurans, the horseshoe crabs **(Figure 27.56)**, are distantly related to true crabs (crustaceans). The name Xiphosura is based on the terms *xiphos* (= sword) and *uros* (= tail) and refers to the spinelike telson used to help right the animal if water movement turns it over. The body of a xiphosuran is divided into an anterior prosoma and a posterior opisthosoma (of which the spikelike telson is the last segment). There are five pairs of walking legs, and a pair of chelicerae on the ventral side of the prosoma. The leg bases are jawlike and grind food between them before passing it forward to the mouth. The ventral side of the opisthosoma has a series of flaplike gills. Although the cuticle is thick and hard, it is not strengthened by incorporation of calcium carbonate.

The arachnids represent almost all the chelicerates, which includes over 100 000 species in about 10 recognized orders. Arachnids have four pairs of legs on the prosoma, and most digest food to a liquid form before taking it into the gut. Included in this class are the mites, ticks, scorpions, and spiders **(Figure 27.57)**.

Spiders are unusual among animals in having only flexor muscles in their legs. They extend their legs by hydraulic action that depends upon on blood being pumped from the hemocoel. There is only one herbivorous species of spider, the rest are predatory, eating mostly other arthropods. A characteristic of the spiders is the modification of the chelicerae as fangs through which venom is injected into prey. Spider webs are a familiar mechanism of prey capture, although there are interesting variations in the use of silk. The jumping spiders (Salticidae) do not spin webs but actively pursue their prey and have exceptional vision for prey detection. The large eyes are telescopic and use differential focus of different colours to measure the distance to a prey.

FIGURE 27.56 *Limulus polyphemus* **is the only living xiphosuran.**

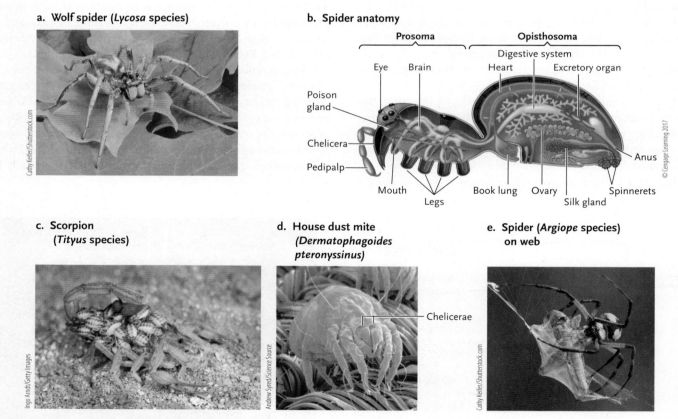

a. Wolf spider (*Lycosa* species)

b. Spider anatomy

FIGURE 27.57 **Examples of arachnids. (a)** Wolf spiders are harmless to humans. **(b)** The spider anatomy exemplifies the arachnid body plan. **(c)** Scorpions are nocturnal predators characterized by the grasping pedipalps and segmented tail tipped with a stinger. **(d)** This dust mite is viewed using a scanning electron microscope. **(e)** Spider webs are used to capture prey.

SUBPHYLUM MYRIAPODA The Myriapoda include the Chilopoda (centipedes), Diplopoda (millipedes), Pauropoda, and Symphyla (**Figure 27.58**). Myriapods have two body regions: a head and a segmented trunk. The head bears a single pair of antennae and a pair of eyes. Each segment bears a pair of legs, despite the appearance of the millipedes, whose name, Diplopoda, comes from the appearance of two pairs per segment (a result of segmental fusion). Millipedes, pauropods, and symphylans are herbivores and detritivores in leaf litter and in loose soil. Centipedes are predatory and have developed poison fangs through modification of the first pair of legs (**Figure 27.59**).

SUBPHYLUM CRUSTACEA This group name refers to the hardened exoskeleton of many crustaceans. The group is characterized by having two pairs of antennae and appendages that divide into two branches. The evolution of the Crustacea is one of specialization of body regions, segments, and appendages for different functions. Crustaceans have so many different body plans that they are divided into many groups and subgroups. The crabs, lobsters, and shrimps (examples of decapods; meaning "10 feet") number more than 10 000 species alone. The great majority of crustaceans are marine. There are freshwater species, such as crayfish, and some groups have invaded the terrestrial environment.

In Decapoda (**Figure 27.60**), the head bears the sensory antennae; the mandibles and food handling depends on the maxillae and the first three thoracic appendages (maxillipeds). Food is captured by the **chelipeds**, and there are four pairs of walking legs. The abdominal **swimmerets** circulate water (and in females ventilate eggs), and the telson and uropods allow for backward escape swimming. The exoskeleton forms a **carapace**, which is a protective covering that extends backward from the head. Most crustaceans exhibit complex movements and behaviours, and have elaborate sensory and nervous systems.

The extent, and nature, of segmental fusion and specialization is the basis of the separation of the groups within the Crustacea.

Many crustaceans, such as copepods (**Figure 27.61**), are present in the billions in freshwater and marine plankton. Most are only a few millimetres long. Plankton crustaceans are among the most abundant animals on Earth. They feed on microscopic algae and detritus and are themselves food for other animals.

Adult barnacles are sessile marine crustaceans that live within a shell (**Figure 27.62**). Their larvae are free swimming and attach permanently to substrates such as rocks and hulls of ships. They then secrete a shell, which is a modified exoskeleton. A barnacle feeds by opening the shell and using six pairs of feathery legs to capture plankton and transfer it to its mouth.

Two large orders of crustaceans are Isopoda and Amphipoda (*iso* = equal; *amphi* = around). Isopods are typically dorsoventrally flattened and have legs evenly spread to either side. Amphipods are typically laterally compressed and commonly lie on their sides in a curve around their legs. *Bathynomus* is a giant (~25 cm long) isopod from the deep ocean. The phenomenon of

a. **Millipede (*Spirobolus* species)**

b. **Centipede (*Scolopendra* species)**

FIGURE 27.58 (**a**) Millipedes and (**b**) centipedes have a head and a segmented body.

FIGURE 27.59 The forcipules (poison claws) of a centipede (*Scolopendra*)

deep-sea gigantism is not understood, but it is suggested that the size of this detritivore allows it to forage over a large area in search of scarce food. *Phronima* (**Figure 27.63**) is not a typical amphipod and is adapted for a predatory life, where it enters the body of a urochordate (see Section 27.8) and devours its prey from the inside. While only a few millimetres long, *Phronima* served as the model for the monster in the film *Aliens*.

SUBPHYLUM HEXAPODA The name of this group refers to arthropods that have three pairs of legs. It includes the Insecta (**Figure 27.64**) as well as some other smaller classes. Three groups

a. Crab (*Ocypode* species)

b. Lobster *(Homarus americanus)*

c. Lobster external anatomy

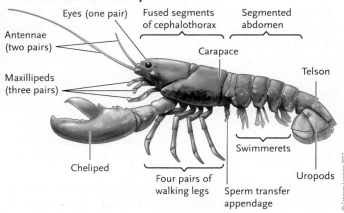

Eyes (one pair)
Fused segments of cephalothorax
Segmented abdomen
Antennae (two pairs)
Carapace
Maxillipeds (three pairs)
Telson
Cheliped
Four pairs of walking legs
Sperm transfer appendage
Swimmerets
Uropods

© Cengage Learning 2017

FIGURE 27.60 (a) Crabs and **(b)** lobsters are examples of decapods. **(c)** Lobster anatomy shows the main features of decapod crustaceans.

FIGURE 27.61 Copepods are tiny crustaceans that can be found by the billions in plankton.

FIGURE 27.62 These gooseneck barnacles attach themselves to the hulls of ships.

FIGURE 27.63 *Phronima* **sp., an Amphipoda**

have **entognathous** mouth parts, meaning the mouth parts can be withdrawn into a capsule in the head. There are also a large number of groups that are **ectognathous**, which have exposed mouth parts. These two divisions are almost synonymous with Apterygota (wingless) and Pterygota (winged).

The insect body plan includes a head, a thorax, and an abdomen **(Figure 27.65)**. Insects possess a pair of **compound eyes** and one pair of sensory antennae. The thorax contains three pairs of walking legs and often one or two pairs of wings. Segmentation has been reduced. Only some muscles, ventral nerve cord, and dorsal blood vessel are segmented. The insect respiratory system is a **tracheal system**. A branching network of tubes carry oxygen from openings in the exoskeleton to cells throughout the body. **Malpighian tubules** transport nitrogenous waste to the digestive system for excretion. Particularly fascinating about the insects is the specialized mouthparts, which reflect the nature of the food source. For example, insects that bite have piercing structures with a narrow channel to suck up blood, while butterflies have a long proboscis to drink nectar **(Figure 27.66)**.

a. Silverfish (Thysanura, *Lepisma saccharina*) are wingless, an ancestral trait within insects.

b. Dragonflies (Odonata, *Epitheca cynosura*) have aquatic larvae that are active predators; adults capture other insects in mid-air.

c. Male praying mantids (Mantodea, *Mantis religiosa*) are often eaten by the larger females during or immediately after mating.

d. This stag beetle (Coleoptera, *Lucanus cervus*) is one of more than 250,000 beetle species that have been described.

e. Fleas (Siphonaptera, *Ctenocephalides canis*) have strong legs with an elastic ligament that allows these parasites to jump on and off their animal hosts.

f. Crane flies (Diptera, *Tipula* species) look like giant mosquitoes, but their mouthparts are not useful for biting other animals; the adults of most species live only a few days and do not feed at all.

g. The luna moth (Lepidoptera, *Actias luna*), like other butterflies and moths, has wings that are covered with colourful microscopic scales.

h. Like many other ant species, fire ants (Hymenoptera, *Solenopsis invicta*) live in large cooperative colonies. Fire ants—named for their painful sting—were introduced into southeastern North America, where they are now serious pests.

FIGURE 27.64 There are about 30 subgroups of insects, eight of which are represented here.

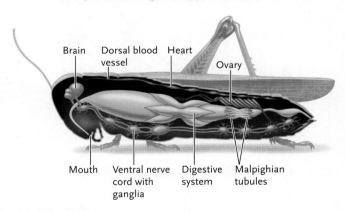

External anatomy of a grasshopper

Antenna — Head — Thorax — Abdomen — Tympanum (hearing organ) — Wing — Compound eye — Mouth parts — Legs

Internal anatomy of a female grasshopper

Brain — Dorsal blood vessel — Heart — Ovary — Mouth — Ventral nerve cord with ganglia — Digestive system — Malpighian tubules

FIGURE 27.65 The body plan of an insect includes a head, a thorax, and an abdomen.

A factor in the success of insects is the evolution of life cycles that allow developing stages to utilize resources from different environments than those of adults. Arthropod development depends on moulting (ecdysis) and is regulated through the pro-hormone ecdysone, a steroid, that is converted to the active moult hormone 20-hydroxyecdysone. After hatching from an egg, an insect passes through development stages called **instars**. There are three types of metamorphosis in the development of insects **(Figure 27.67)**. In each of these sequences, the moult from one stage to the next is regulated by physiological and environmental conditions that trigger a neurosecretory pathway from the brain that activates the prothoracic gland to secrete ecdysone.

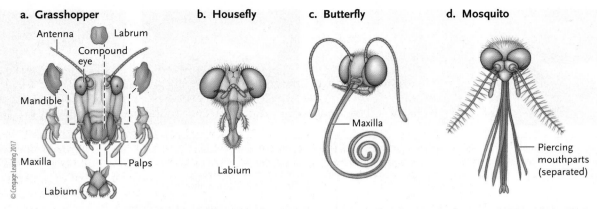

FIGURE 27.66 Insects have specialized mouth parts that have evolved over time to allow for different methods of feeding. (a) In plant feeders, the labrum covers the mouthparts and has sensory functions. The mandibles are for chewing, and paired maxillae, with palps, scoop the food. The labium is most posterior, represents a fused pair of appendages, and contains many sensory structures and palps. This basic plan has evolved and allowed insects to **(b)** sponge up food, **(c)** drink nectar, and **(d)** pierce skin to consume blood.

a. No metamorphosis

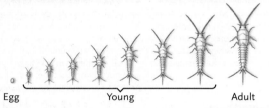

Some wingless insects, like silverfish (Thysanura), do not undergo a dramatic change in form as they grow.

b. Metamorphosis without a pupa (hemimetaboly)

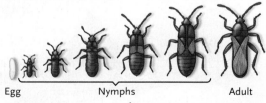

Other insects, such as true bugs (Hemiptera), have incomplete metamorphosis; they develop from nymphs into adults with relatively minor changes in form.

c. Metamorphosis with a pupa (holometaboly)

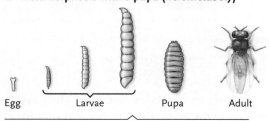

Fruit flies (Diptera) and many other insects have complete metamorphosis; they undergo a total reorganization of their internal and external anatomy when they pass through the pupal stage of the life cycle.

FIGURE 27.67 Patterns of postembryonic development in insects

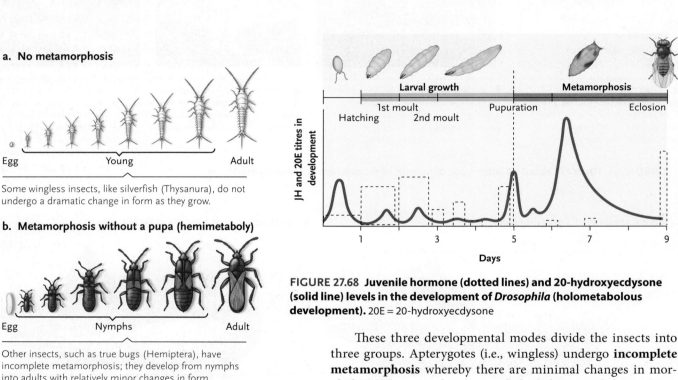

Edward B. Dubrovsky, "Hormonal cross talk in insect development," *Trends in Endocrinology & Metabolism*, 16(1): 6–11. Copyright © 2004 Elsevier Ltd. *Trends in Endocrinology and Metabolism*. TEM by ELSEVIER SCIENCE PUBLISHERS Reproduced with permission of ELSEVIER LTD. in the format Book via Copyright Clearance Center.

FIGURE 27.68 Juvenile hormone (dotted lines) and 20-hydroxyecdysone (solid line) levels in the development of *Drosophila* (holometabolous development). 20E = 20-hydroxyecdysone

These three developmental modes divide the insects into three groups. Apterygotes (i.e., wingless) undergo **incomplete metamorphosis** whereby there are minimal changes in morphology. They simply grow and shed their exoskeleton. Most insects undergo **complete metamorphosis**. In this case, the larvae that hatch are very different from the adults; they live in different habitats and eat different food. The Exopterygota (meaning that the wings develop externally) metamorphose without a pupa; and in the Endopterygota, the wings develop internally in the **pupa** stage, which is a sessile stage before larva transform into sexually mature adults.

Juvenile hormone (JH) is a sesquiterpenoid hormone secreted into the blood from the corpora allata (behind the brain). Levels of JH determine the outcome of each moult. In a hemimetabolous life cycle, metamorphosis is gradual from one instar to the next; JH levels decline a little at each instar. In a holometabolous life cycle (**Figure 27.68**), there is a major decline in JH when the final larva moults to produce a pupal stage.

Flight is a major factor in the success of insects in the terrestrial environment. Flight provides a way of escaping danger, as well as searching for food, mates, or suitable environments. Fossil evidence does not provide a clear picture of how insect wings evolved. The probability is that flat lateral cuticular extensions first provided stability in jumps and falls, and that these evolved into static surfaces for gliding and then into moving wings. Muscles power the wings directly in dragonflies (Odonata; see **Figure 27.69a**) but, in most advanced insect orders, the muscles are arranged indirectly (Figure 27.69b) and wing movement is a response to deformation of the thorax. Vertical muscles compress the thorax dorsoventrally and raise the wings, and horizontal muscles restore the thorax shape and power the downstroke. The extremes of insect flight include sphynx moths reaching speeds of 50 km/hour (house flies are slow at 6–8 km/hour), painted lady butterflies migrating 6400 km from Iceland to North Africa, small fly wing beats of 600 Hz (compared to the slowest butterfly rates of 5 Hz), and fossil dragon flies that had a 60 cm wingspan.

Insects demonstrate remarkable communication abilities in various modes, including chemical messages (pheromones), sound, and light signals. Pheromones may convey many types of information, including mate attraction, alarm, and food locations. Many male moths have featherlike antennae that have evolved to detect minute amounts of pheromone from a female. Gypsy moths may sense just a few molecules of pheromone from a female a kilometre away. In flying toward the source of the scent, they zigzag to maintain an average path along the line of greatest concentration. The gypsy moth pheromone has been identified and produced synthetically as gyplure for use in traps for pest control. Pheromones can provide directional information on the ground as well as in the air. Leafcutter ants mark a trail from a food source to the nest. The trail pheromone is secreted from the venom gland and includes volatile and non-volatile components. Pheromones may also carry an alarm message. When a honeybee stings a vertebrate **(Figure 27.70)**, the barbs of the sting catch in the flesh and the sting is torn from the body. As the sting attachment breaks, a pheromone sac at its base is ruptured to release an alarm pheromone; this triggers a response from other bees to attack the threat to the hive.

The sounds of summer include a background of grasshopper chirps and the metallic buzz of cicadas. Grasshopper sounds are produced by stridulation—a mechanism in which a file (rough surface) on the hind legs is rubbed against a scraper at the base of the forewings. Male grasshoppers stridulate to attract females and, in some species, females also stridulate in response. Grasshoppers hear sounds through a tympanal organ at the base of the abdomen. Cicadas use a different mechanism to produce sounds that may be as loud as 120 dB, about the sound level of a jet plane taking off. Male cicadas have a membrane, supported by ribs, known as the *tymbal*, in the anterior region of the abdomen. This membrane is vibrated by a tymbal muscle at frequencies between 2 and 10 kHz, and sound production is amplified by a large air cavity in the abdomen. Female cicadas do not produce calls and hear the male call through a tympanal organ similar to that of grasshoppers.

In fireflies, which are actually beetles, flashing light signals are the basis of communication between females and males **(Figure 27.71)**. Light is produced by a light organ in the abdomen and depends on the action of an enzyme, luciferase, on a luciferin substrate, a reaction that requires ATP, Mg^{2+}, and oxygen. Different species have different patterns of flash duration and frequency. Some female fireflies in the genus *Photuris* imitate the flash patterns of other species to attract them as prey—leading to these insects being called *femmes fatales*!

a.

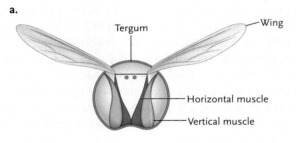

b.

FIGURE 27.69 **(a)** Direct flight muscles connect directly to the wings at either side of their pivot point. **(b)** Indirect flight muscles move the wings through changes in the shape of the thorax.

FIGURE 27.70 **A honeybee (*Apis mellifera*) with its sting embedded in a human**

CHAPTER 27 ANIMALS |

FIGURE 27.71 Ventral view of a female *Photinus* sp. flashing light

The examples insect biology described in this section have been drawn from the larger and more familiar orders of insects. There are over a million described species of insects classified in about 29 orders, some including only a few species while the largest group, the Coleoptera (beetles), includes well over 300 000 species. Insect biology fills libraries and many careers—a world worthy of exploration.

STUDY BREAK QUESTIONS

1. If an arthropod's rigid skeleton cannot be expanded, how does the animal grow?
2. Compare the body plans of the four groups of living arthropods.
3. How do the life stages differ between insects that have incomplete metamorphosis and those that have complete metamorphosis?

27.8 The Deuterostomes

Membership in the Deuterostomia (**Figure 27.72**) is restricted to animals in which the anus develops from the blastopore, and the mouth from a second opening. The body plans of these animals vary from star shaped and radially symmetrical, through asymmetrical to bilaterally symmetrical. At first glance, deuterostome animals, such as echinoderms, chordates, and hemichordates, are not obviously similar. This reflects modifications of their bodies that mask underlying developmental and genetic features (**Figure 27.73**).

27.8a Phylum Echinodermata

The phylum Echinodermata (*echino* = spiny; *derm* = skin) includes 6500 species of sea stars, sea urchins, sea cucumbers, brittle stars, and sea lilies. These slow-moving or sessile bottom-dwelling animals are important herbivores and predators living in oceans, from the shallow coastal waters to the depths. The phylum was diverse in the Paleozoic, but only a remnant of that fauna remains. Echinoderms vary in size from less than 1 cm in diameter to more than 50 cm long. Adult echinoderms develop from bilaterally symmetrical, free-swimming larvae. As the larvae develop, they assume a secondary radial symmetry, often organized around five rays, or "arms" (**Figure 27.74**). Many echinoderms have an oral surface, with the mouth facing the substrate, and an aboral surface facing in the opposite direction. Virtually all echinoderms have an internal skeleton made of calcium-stiffened ossicles that develop from mesoderm. In some groups, fused ossicles form a rigid container called a *test*. In most species with these features, spines or bumps project from the ossicles.

The internal anatomy of echinoderms is unique among animals. They have a well-defined coelom and a complete digestive system, but they lack both excretory and respiratory systems. Most species have a minimal circulatory system. In many species, gases are exchanged and metabolic wastes are eliminated through projections of the epidermis and peritoneum near the base of the spines. These radially symmetrical animals have no obvious head or central brain. The nervous system is organized around nerve cords that encircle the mouth and branch into the radii. Sensory cells are abundant in the skin.

Echinoderms move using tube feet operated by a system of fluid-filled canals, the **water vascular system** (see Figure 27.74e). In a sea star, for example, water enters the system through the madreporite, a sievelike plate on the aboral surface. A short tube connects it to the ring canal, which surrounds the **esophagus**. The ring canal branches into five radial canals that extend into the arms. Each radial canal is connected to numerous tube feet that protrude through holes in the plates. Each tube foot has a mucus-covered, suckerlike tip and a small muscular bulb, the ampulla, lying inside the body. Contraction of an ampulla forces fluid into the tube foot, causing it to lengthen and attach to the substrate (see Figure 27.74f). When the tube foot contracts, it pulls the animal along. As the tube foot shortens, water is forced back into the ampulla, and the tube foot releases its grip on the substrate. The tube foot can then take another step forward, reattaching to the substrate. Although each tube foot has limited strength, the coordinated action of hundreds or even thousands of them is so strong that they can hold an echinoderm to a substrate even against strong wave action.

Echinoderms have separate sexes, and most reproduce by releasing gametes into the water. Radial cleavage is so clearly apparent in the transparent eggs of some sea urchins that they are commonly used to demonstrate cleavage in introductory biology laboratories. A few echinoderms reproduce asexually by splitting in half and regenerating the missing parts. Other echinoderms regenerate body parts lost to predators. Four-day-old sand dollars (*Dendraster excentricus*) asexually clone themselves in response to the odour of fish (in mucus), apparently a defensive response.

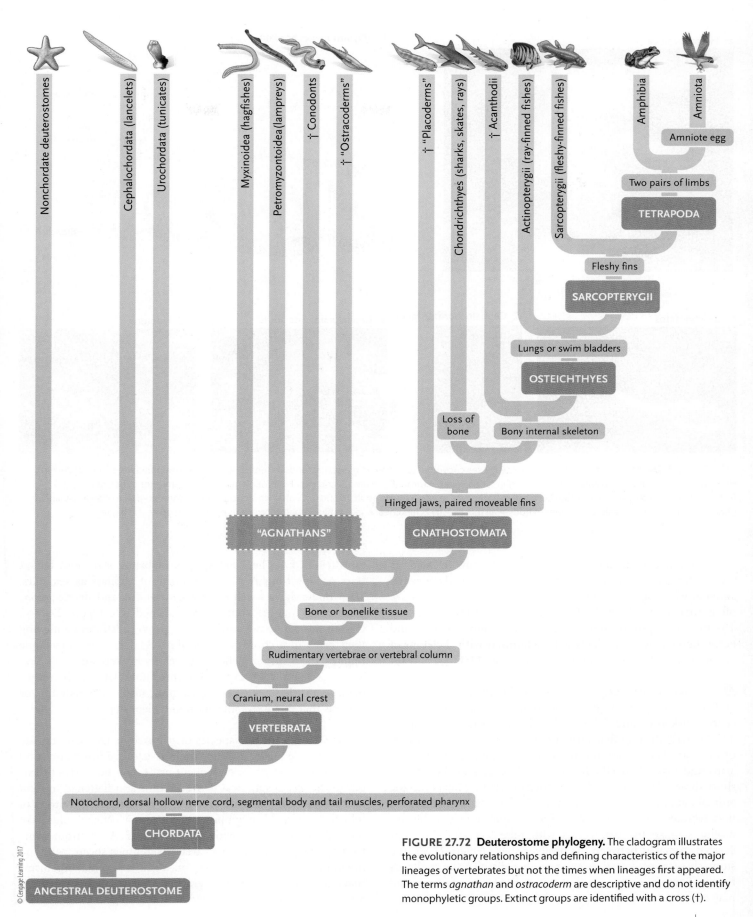

FIGURE 27.72 Deuterostome phylogeny. The cladogram illustrates the evolutionary relationships and defining characteristics of the major lineages of vertebrates but not the times when lineages first appeared. The terms *agnathan* and *ostracoderm* are descriptive and do not identify monophyletic groups. Extinct groups are identified with a cross (†).

© Cengage Learning 2017

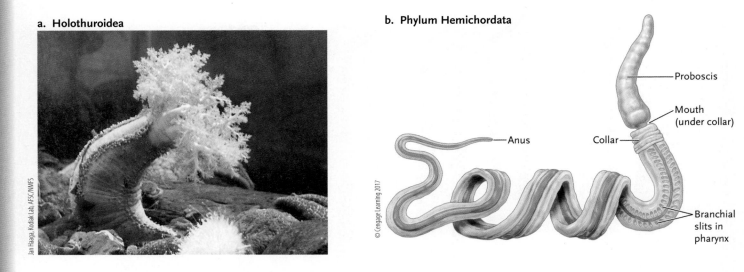

a. Holothuroidea

b. Phylum Hemichordata

- Proboscis
- Mouth (under collar)
- Anus
- Collar
- Branchial slits in pharynx

© Cengage Learning 2017

Jan Haaga, Kodiak Lab, AFSC/NMFS

c. Urochordates

d. Cephalochordate larva

e. Cephalochordate adult

f. Echinoidea

D.P. Wilson/FLPA/Science Source

Ethan Daniels/Shutterstock.com

Natural Visions/Alamy Stock Photo

Edward Snow/Bruce Coleman/Photoshot

FIGURE 27.73 Deuterostomes. (a) Holothuroidea. A sea cucumber (*Cucumaria miniata*) extends its tentacles, which are modified tube feet. **(b)** Phylum Hemichordata. Acorn worms draw food- and oxygen-laden water in through the mouth and expel it through gill slits in the anterior region of the trunk. **(c)** Urochordates. A tadpolelike tunicate larva will metamorphose into a sessile adult. **(d** and **e)** Cephalochordates. The unpigmented skin of an adult lancelet (*Brachiostoma species*) reveals its segmented body-wall muscles. **(f)** Echinoidea. A sea urchin (*Strongylocentrotus purpuratus*) grazes on algae.

Echinoderms include the sea daisies, now treated as Asteroidea. These small, medusa-shaped animals occupy sunken, waterlogged wood in the deep sea. Sunken ships are often important habitats for these and other marine organisms. The five other groups, described below, are more diverse and better known. Some students will be familiar with skeletons of echinoderms often found on beaches **(Figure 27.75)**.

ASTEROIDEA Sea stars live on rocky shorelines to depths of 10 000 m. Many are brightly coloured. The body consists of a central disk surrounded by 5–20 radiating "arms" (see Figure 27.74a), with the mouth centred on the oral surface. The ossicles of the endoskeleton are not fused, permitting flexibility of the arms and disk. **Pedicellariae** are small pincers at the base of short spines. They are used to remove debris that falls onto the animal's aboral surface (see Figure 27.74f). Many sea stars eat invertebrates and small fishes. Species that consume bivalve molluscs grasp the two valves with tube feet and slip their everted stomachs between the bivalve's shells **(Figure 27.76)**. The stomach secretes digestive enzymes that dissolve the mollusc's tissues. Some sea stars are destructive predators of corals and may endanger many reefs.

OPHIUROIDEA The 2000 species of brittle stars and basket stars occupy roughly the same range of habitats as sea stars. Their bodies have a well-defined central disk and slender, elongated arms that are sometimes branched (see Figure 27.74b). Ophiuroids can crawl fairly swiftly across substrates by moving their arms in a coordinated fashion. As their common name implies, the arms are delicate and easily broken, an adaptation allowing them to escape from predators with only minor damage. Brittle stars feed on small prey, suspended plankton, or detritus that they extract from muddy deposits.

ECHINOIDEA The 950 species of sea urchins and sand dollars lack arms (see Figure 27.73f). Their ossicles are fused into solid tests (shells) that provide excellent protection but restrict flexibility. The test is spherical in sea urchins and flattened in sand dollars. These animals use tube feet in locomotion. Five rows of tube feet emerge through pores in the test. Most echinoids have movable spines, some with poison glands. A jab from some tropical species can cause a careless swimmer severe pain and inflammation. Echinoids graze on algae and other organisms that cling to surfaces. In the centre of an urchin's oral surface is a five-part nipping jaw that is controlled by powerful muscles.

a. Asteroidea: This sea star (*Fromia milleporella*) lives in the intertidal zone.

b. Ophiuroidea: A brittle star (*Ophiothrix suensonii*) perches on a coral branch.

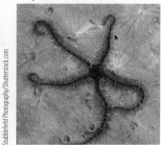

c. Crinoidea: A feather star (*Himerometra robustipinna*) feeds by catching small particles with its numerous tentacles.

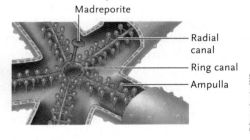

d. Internal anatomy

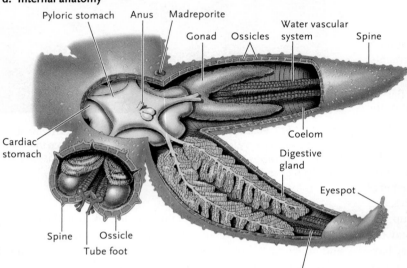

Pyloric stomach · Anus · Madreporite · Gonad · Ossicles · Water vascular system · Spine · Cardiac stomach · Coelom · Digestive gland · Eyespot · Spine · Ossicle · Tube foot · Row of ampullae

e. Water vascular system

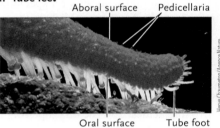

Madreporite · Radial canal · Ring canal · Ampulla

f. Tube feet

Aboral surface · Pedicellaria · Oral surface · Tube foot

FIGURE 27.74 Echinoderm diversity. (a–c) Echinoderms exhibit secondary radial symmetry, usually organized as five rays around an oral–aboral axis. The coelom **(d)** is well developed in echinoderms, as illustrated by this cutaway diagram of a sea star. The water vascular system **(e)**, unique in the animal kingdom, operates the tube feet. Tube feet **(f)** are responsible for locomotion. Note the pedicellariae on the upper surface of the star's arm.

FIGURE 27.75 Shown here are skeletons of echinoderms that are often found on beaches, including a sea urchin, two sand dollars, and three starfish.

FIGURE 27.76 Sea star feeding on a mussel. Even when the tide is out in Haida Gwaii, sea stars hunt mussels.

Some species damage kelp beds, disrupting the habitat of young lobsters and other crustaceans. Echinoid ovaries are a gourmet delicacy in many countries, making these animals a prized natural resource.

HOLOTHUROIDEA Sea cucumbers are elongated animals that lie on their sides on the ocean bottom; they number about 1500 species. Although they have five rows of tube feet, their endoskeleton is reduced to widely separated microscopic plates. The body, which is elongated along the oral–aboral axis, is soft and fleshy, with a tough, leathery covering. Modified tube feet form a ring of tentacles around the mouth. The central disk and mouth point upward rather than toward the substrate (see Figure 27.73a). Some species secrete a mucus net that traps plankton or other food particles. The net and tentacles are inserted into the mouth, where the net and the trapped food are ingested. Other species extract food from bottom sediments. Many sea cucumbers exchange gases through an extensively branched respiratory tree arising from the rectum, the part of the digestive system just inside the anus at the aboral end of the animal. A well-developed circulatory system distributes oxygen and nutrients to tissues throughout the body.

Sea cucumbers are actually home for a specialized symbiotic fish. *Carapus bermudensis,* the pearl fish, enters sea cucumber's cloacal opening tail-first, allowing them to emerge head-first. The cloaca is the chamber receiving urine, feces, and reproductive products. Pearl fish are members of a group that usually live in the tubes of other animals, including the cavities of bivalves. These fishes have thin, elongated bodies. They have lost the pelvic fins and scales, and the anal opening has moved forward to a position under the head. This adaptation ensures that the fish defecates outside the body of the sea cucumber. These fishes use olfactory cues to find the "correct" host.

CRINOIDEA The 600 living species of sea lilies and feather stars are the surviving remnants of a diverse and abundant fauna that lived 500 million years ago (mya; see Figure 27.74c). Most species occupy marine waters of medium depth. Between five and several hundred branched arms surround the disk that contains the mouth. New arms are added as a crinoid grows larger. The branches of the arms are covered with tiny, mucus-coated tube feet that trap suspended microscopic organisms. Sessile sea lilies have the central disk attached to a flexible stalk that can reach 1 m in length. By contrast, adult feather stars can swim or crawl weakly, attaching temporarily to substrates. The disks making up sea lily stalks, called *ossicles*, are common fossils in many deposits **(Figure 27.77)**.

27.8b Phylum Hemichordata

The 80 species of **acorn worms** comprising this phylum have a dorsally situated stiffening rod, or chord. Compared to the chordates, this short rod, called the *stomochord*, is reflected in the name "hemichord" (*hemi* = half). Acorn worms are sedentary marine animals living in U-shaped tubes or burrows in coastal

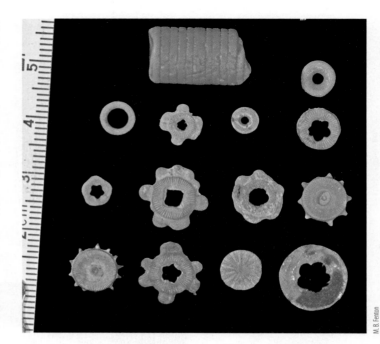

FIGURE 27.77 Fossil crinoid stems. Ossicles making up the stems of crinoids are commonly fossilized. The individual ossicles are from the Devonian of Ontario. The section of complete stem is *Encrinus liliiformis*, from the Triassic of Germany. Scale is in millimetres.

M. B. Fenton

sand or mud. Their soft bodies range in length from 2 cm to 2 m and are organized into an anterior proboscis, a tentacled collar, and an elongated trunk (see Figure 27.73b). They use the muscular, mucus-coated proboscis to construct burrows and trap food particles. Acorn worms also have pairs of gill slits in the pharynx, the part of the digestive system just posterior to the mouth. Beating cilia create a flow of water, which enters the pharynx through the mouth and exits through the gill slits. As water passes through, suspended food particles are trapped and shunted into the digestive system, and gases are exchanged across the partitions between gill slits. The dorsal nerve cord, coupled with feeding and respiration, reflects a close evolutionary relationship between hemichordates and chordates. Pterobranchia are the other class of animals in this phylum. These uncommon marine animals are colonial and live in tubes. They superficially resemble some cnidarians.

27.8c Phylum Chordata

This phylum includes the evolutionary lines of invertebrates, the Urochordata and the Cephalochordata, as well as the more diverse line, the Vertebrata (animals with backbones). A notochord, a dorsal hollow nerve cord, and pharyngeal slits (a perforated pharynx) are three key morphological features distinguishing chordates from all other deuterostomes. These features occur during at least some time in a chordate's life cycle. Chordates also have segmental muscles in the body wall and tail **(Figure 27.78)**. Collectively, these structures enable higher levels of activity and unique modes of aquatic locomotion, as well as

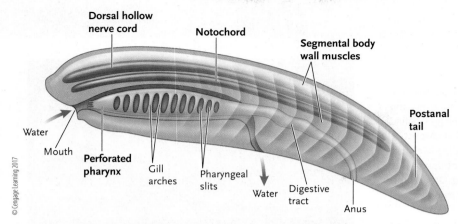

FIGURE 27.78 Diagnostic chordate characteristics. Chordates have a notochord, a dorsal hollow nerve cord, pharyngeal (gill) slits (a perforated pharynx), and a muscular post-anal tail with segmental body wall and tail muscles. Other basic features also are shown but they are not unique to chordates.

Labels in figure: Dorsal hollow nerve cord; Notochord; Segmental body wall muscles; Postanal tail; Water; Mouth; Perforated pharynx; Gill arches; Pharyngeal slits; Water; Digestive tract; Anus

more efficient feeding and acquisition of oxygen. In the past, cephalochordates were considered to be the sister group to the chordates. Recent analyses suggest that the Urochordata are sister to the Chordata.

Early in chordate embryonic development, the **notochord** (*noto* = back; *chord* = string), a flexible rod, develops from mesoderm dorsal to the developing digestive system (see Research in Biology). The notochord is constructed of fluid-filled cells surrounded by tough connective tissue. It supports the embryo from head to tail. The notochord is the skeleton of invertebrate chordates, serving as an anchor for body-wall muscles. When these muscles contract, the notochord bends but does not shorten. Waves of contractions pass down one side of the animal and then up the other, sweeping the body and tail back and forth in a smooth and continuous movement. Thus, the chordate body swings left and right during locomotion, propelling the animal forward. The chordate tail, which is posterior to the anus, provides most of the propulsion in some aquatic species. Segmentation allows each muscle block to contract independently. Unlike the bodies of annelids and other nonchordate invertebrates, the chordate body does not shorten when the animal is moving. Remnants of the notochord persist as gelatinous disks between the vertebrae of some adult vertebrates.

The central nervous system of chordates is a hollow nerve cord on the dorsal side of the embryo (Chapter 45). Most nonchordate invertebrates have ventral, solid nerve cords. In vertebrates, an anterior enlargement of the nerve cord forms the brain. In invertebrates, an anterior concentration of nervous system tissue is a ganglion and may be referred to as a "brain."

Gill (pharyngeal) slits perforate the chordate pharynx. The pharynx is part of the digestive system and is located just behind the mouth. **Gill slits** are paired openings originating as exit holes for water that carried particulate food into the mouth, allowing chordates to gather food by filtration. Invertebrate chordates also collect oxygen and release carbon dioxide across the walls of the pharynx. In fishes, gill arches have evolved as supporting structures between the slits in the pharynx.

Invertebrate chordates and fishes retain a perforated pharynx throughout their lives. In most air-breathing vertebrates, the slits are present only during embryonic development and in some larvae.

SUBPHYLUM UROCHORDATA The 2500 species of urochordates (*uro* = tail) float in surface waters or attach to substrates in shallow marine habitats. Sessile adults of many species secrete a gelatinous or leathery "tunic" around their bodies and squirt water through a siphon when disturbed. Adults can attain lengths of several centimetres. In the most common group of sea squirts (Ascidiacea), swimming larvae have notochords, dorsal hollow nerve cords, and gill slits, features lacking in the sessile adults. Larvae eventually attach to substrates and transform into sessile adults. During metamorphosis, larvae lose most traces of the notochord and tail as their basketlike pharynx enlarges. The nerve chord remains but is no longer dorsal. In adults, beating cilia pull water into the pharynx through an incurrent siphon. A mucus net traps particulate food, which is carried with the mucus to the gut. Water passes through the gill slits, enters a chamber called the **atrium**, and is expelled through the **atrial siphon** along with digestive wastes and carbon dioxide **(Figure 27.79)**. Oxygen is absorbed across the walls of the pharynx. In some urochordates, the larvae are neotenous, acquiring the ability to reproduce and remaining active throughout their life cycles.

SUBPHYLUM CEPHALOCHORDATA All 28 species of cephalochordates (*cephalo* = head) live in warm, shallow, marine habitats, where they lie mostly buried in sand (see Figure 27.73e). Although generally sedentary, they have well-developed body-wall muscles and a prominent notochord. Most species are included in the genus *Branchiostoma* (formerly *Amphioxus*). Lancelet bodies, which are 5–10 cm long, are pointed at both ends, like the double-edged surgical tools for which they are named **(Figure 27.80)**. Adults have light receptors on the head as well as chemical sense organs on tentacles that grow from the **oral hood**. Lancelets use cilia to draw food-laden water through hundreds of pharyngeal slits; water flows into the atrium and is expelled through the **atriopore**. Most gas exchange occurs across the skin.

SUBPHYLUM VERTEBRATA (CRANIATA) Species in this subphylum have a distinct head, making them craniate, and most have a **backbone (spine)** made up of individual bony vertebrae (Chapters 19 and 45). This internal skeletal feature provides structural support for muscles and protects the nervous system and other organs. In addition, the internal skeleton and attached muscles allow most vertebrates to move rapidly. Vertebrates are the only animals with bone, a connective tissue in which cells secrete the mineralized matrix that surrounds them

The Tully Monster

The Tully monster, *Tullimonstrum gregarium* (**Figure 1**), is from the Late Carboniferous of Illinois in the United States. Since its fossil discovery and description, this mainly soft-bodied animal has been tentatively classified with species in five different groups of animals (phyla). Tully Monsters have been considered to be nemerteans (see Section 27.6d), polychaete annelids, gastropod molluscs (see Section 27.6e), conodonts (see Section 27.10), and some early arthropods (Section 27.7h). Other interpretations suggested that the Tully Monster was the only evidence of a now extinct phylum of animals.

The correct phylogenetic placement of an organism should reflect and convey information about its evolutionary relationship(s) to other organisms. Considerable energy and technological prowess is expended in the development of accurate phylogenies. When the organism, such as a Tully Monster, is known only as a fossil, some evidence is not available.

In 2016, the results of further close examination of the fossil Tully Monster revealed characteristics that clearly place these animals in the phylum Chordata (see Section 27.8c), the phylum that includes vertebrates such as humans. The fine-grained fossil Tully Monster reveals that the structure of the eyes, especially the retinae, unambiguously indicate that this animal was a vertebrate. There is no evidence of a notochord in Tully Monsters, probably reflecting lack of fossilization, the same situation that occurs in fossil lamprey and hagfish. The Tully Monster specimens also lack details of the branchial area, again suggesting lack of pigmentation and fossilization. Some biologists argue that lampreys are the closest living relatives of Tully Monsters.

Tully Monsters' lack of notochord and gill slits complicated correct assignment of the creature to a phylum. But the evidence from the eyes,

Figure 1 A reconstruction of the Tully Monster, front and rear views. Note the gill openings along the side of the body and the extraordinary stalked eyes.

in particular the retinae, were pivotal in assigning Tully Monsters to Vertebrata in the phylum Chordata. The movement of Tully Monsters among animal phyla is but one recent example of ongoing changes to the classification of animals. A more profound change is the current recognition that the historical (and traditional) grouping of animals into protostomes (see Section 27.2d) and deuterostomes (see Section 27.2d) is more artificial than real.

---

a. Larval tunicate (*Oikopleura* species)

Mouth   Atriopore   **Dorsal hollow nerve cord**   **Segmental body wall and tail muscles**

Pharynx with slits   Gut   **Notochord**   **Postanal tail**

b. Adult tunicate (*Rhopalaea crassa*)

Water enters.

Water exits.

Atrial siphon

Incurrent siphon

Pharynx with slits

Atrium

Tunic

Gut

Heart

FIGURE 27.79 (a) The tadpolelike tunicate larva metamorphoses into an adult, a sessile filter feeder. **(b)** In the adult, the atriopore becomes the atrial siphon.

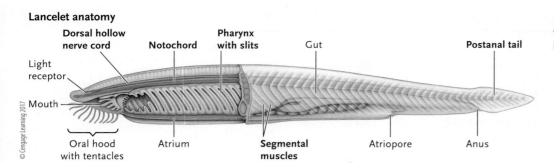

Lancelet anatomy

Light receptor

Dorsal hollow nerve cord

Mouth

Notochord

Pharynx with slits

Gut

Postanal tail

Oral hood with tentacles

Atrium

Segmental muscles

Atriopore

Anus

© Cengage Learning 2017

FIGURE 27.80 A drawing showing the internal anatomy of an adult lancelet (*Branchiostoma*)

(Chapter 46). One vertebrate lineage, the cartilaginous fishes (class Chondrichthyes), may have lost its bone over evolutionary time. These animals, mostly sharks and rays, have skeletons of cartilage, a dense, flexible connective tissue that can be a developmental precursor of bone (Chapters 45 and 46).

At the anterior end of the vertebral column, the head is usually protected by a bony **cranium**, or skull. The backbone surrounds and protects the dorsal nerve cord, and the bony cranium surrounds the brain. The cranium, vertebral column, ribs, and sternum (breastbone) make up the **axial skeleton**. Most vertebrates also have a **pectoral girdle** anteriorly and a **pelvic girdle** posteriorly that attach bones in the fins or limbs to the axial skeleton. The bones of the two girdles and the appendages constitute the appendicular skeleton.

Vertebrates have neural crest cells (Chapter 45), a unique cell type distinct from endoderm, mesoderm, and ectoderm. Neural crest cells arise next to the developing nervous system but migrate throughout the body. Neural crest cells ultimately contribute to uniquely vertebrate structures, such as parts of the cranium, teeth, sensory organs, **cranial nerves**, and the medulla (the interior part) of the adrenal glands.

The brains of vertebrates are larger and more complex than those of invertebrate chordates. Moreover, the vertebrate brain is divided into three regions, the forebrain, midbrain, and hindbrain, each governing distinct nervous system functions (Chapter 45).

STUDY BREAK QUESTIONS

1. What are echinoderms? How do adult echinoderms develop?
2. Use a table to compare an echinoderm and a human by system: (a) digestive, (b) excretory, (c) respiratory, (d) circulatory, and (e) nervous.
3. Using a sea star as an example, describe how echinoderms move.
4. How do hemichordates feed?
5. List four morphological features distinguishing chordates from other deuterostomes.
6. Explain the purpose and structure of gill slits.
7. What is the function of a backbone?

27.9 The Origin and Diversification of Vertebrates

Biologists have used embryological, molecular, and fossil evidences to trace the origin of vertebrates and to chronicle the evolutionary diversification of the group that includes humans. We suspect that vertebrates arose from a cephalochordate-like ancestor through duplication of genes that regulate development. The change to vertebrates was marked by the emergence of neural crest cells, bone, and other vertebrate traits. Biologists hypothesize that an increase in the number of genes that control the expression of other genes (homeotic) may have facilitated the development of more complex anatomy. In terms of organization, remember that there is no compelling reason to believe that "more complex" is superior to "simple."

Hox genes are homeotic genes that influence the three-dimensional shape of the animal and the locations of important structures such as eyes, wings, and legs, particularly along the head-to-tail axis of the body. *Hox* genes are arranged on chromosomes in a particular order, forming the *Hox* gene complex. Each gene in the complex governs the development of particular structures. Animal groups with the simplest structure, such as cnidarians, have 2 *Hox* genes; those with more complex anatomy, such as insects, have 10; chordates typically have up to 13 or 14. Lineages with many *Hox* genes generally have more complex anatomy than those with fewer *Hox* genes.

Molecular analyses reveal that the entire *Hox* gene complex was duplicated several times in the evolution of vertebrates, producing multiple copies of all the genes in the *Hox* complex **(Figure 27.81)**. The cephalochordate *Branchiostoma* has one *Hox* gene complex, whereas hagfish, the most ancestral living vertebrate, has two. All vertebrates with jaws have at least four sets of *Hox* genes, and some fishes have seven. Evolutionary biologists who study development hypothesize that the duplication of *Hox* genes and other tool-kit genes allowed the evolution of new structures. Although original copies of these genes maintained their ancestral functions, duplicate copies were available to assume *new* functions, leading to the development of novel structures such as the vertebral column and jaws. These changes coincided with the adaptive radiation of vertebrates.

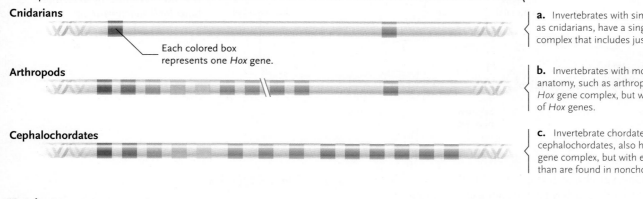

Each row of colored boxes represents one *Hox* gene complex.

Cnidarians

Each colored box
represents one *Hox* gene.

a. Invertebrates with simple anatomy, such as cnidarians, have a single *Hox* gene complex that includes just a few *Hox* genes.

Arthropods

b. Invertebrates with more complicated anatomy, such as arthropods, have a single *Hox* gene complex, but with a larger number of *Hox* genes.

Cephalochordates

c. Invertebrate chordates, such as cephalochordates, also have a single *Hox* gene complex, but with even more *Hox* genes than are found in nonchordate invertebrates.

Vertebrates

d. Vertebrates, such as the laboratory mouse, have numerous *Hox* genes, arranged in two to seven *Hox* gene complexes. The additional *Hox* gene complexes are products of wholesale duplications of the ancestral *Hox* gene complex.

© Cengage Learning 2017

FIGURE 27.81 ***Hox* genes and the evolution of vertebrates.** The *Hox* genes in different animals appear to be homologous, indicated here by their colour and position in the complex. Vertebrates have many more individual *Hox* genes than invertebrates, and the entire *Hox* gene complex was duplicated in the vertebrate lineage.

The oldest known vertebrate fossils are from the early Cambrian (about 550 mya) in China. Both *Myllokunmingia* and *Haikouichthys* were fish-shaped animals about 3 cm long **(Figure 27.82)**. In both species, the brain was surrounded by a cranium of fibrous connective tissue or cartilage. They also had segmental body-wall muscles and fairly well-developed fins, but neither shows any evidence of bone. In 2014 Morris and Caron redescribed *Metaspriggina* based on new fossil material, much of it from the Burgess Shales. This animal resembled the slightly older *Myllokunmingia* and *Haikouichthys* but had more prominent eyes and may have been more basal to the origin of vertebrates than the older forms. Again, the discovery of new fossil material often changes our view of the relationships among animals.

The early vertebrates gave rise to numerous descendants that varied greatly in anatomy, physiology, and ecology. New feeding mechanisms and locomotor structures were correlated with their success. Today, vertebrates occupy nearly every habitat on Earth and eat virtually all other organisms. Biologists tend to identify vertebrates with four key morphological innovations: cranium, vertebrae, bone, and neural crest cells. Important biological changes during the evolution of vertebrates included improved access to energy (food), which involved mobility and jaws, combined with effective aerobic metabolism (access to oxygen).

The earliest vertebrates lacked jaws (Agnatha, *a* = not; *gnath* = jawed), but Agnatha is not a monophyletic group. Although most became extinct by the end of the Paleozoic, two ancestral lineages, Myxinoidea (hagfishes) and Petromyzontidae (lampreys), survive today. All other vertebrates have

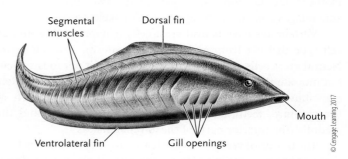

Segmental muscles — Dorsal fin

Mouth

Ventrolateral fin — Gill openings

© Cengage Learning 2017

FIGURE 27.82 Cambrian agnathan, *Haikouichthys*, was more like a hagfish than a lamprey, but generally similar to an ammocoetes larva of lampreys, living agnathans.

movable jaws and form the monophyletic lineage **Gnathostomata** (*gnath* = jawed; *stoma* = mouth). The first jawed fishes, the Acanthodii and the Placodermi, are now extinct, but several other lineages of jawed fishes are still abundant. Included are Chondrichthyes, fishes with cartilaginous skeletons (sharks, skates, chimaeras), and Teleostei (actinopterygians and sarcopterygians), with bony endoskeletons. Although all jawless vertebrates and most jawed fishes live mainly in water, mudskippers (*Periophthalmus* species), climbing perch (*Anabas* species), and some eels regularly venture onto land. Many fish have developed lunglike structures for breathing atmospheric oxygen, but most use gills to extract dissolved oxygen from water. Lungs may be an ancestral trait in vertebrates.

Gnathostomata also includes the monophyletic lineage **Tetrapoda** (*tetra* = four; *pod* = foot), most of which use four limbs for locomotion. Many tetrapods are amphibious, semi-terrestrial, or terrestrial, although some, such as sea turtles and porpoises, are secondarily aquatic. Adult tetrapods generally use lungs to breathe atmospheric oxygen. Within the Tetrapoda, one lineage, the Amphibia (such as frogs and salamanders), typically needs standing water to complete its life cycle. Another lineage, the Amniota, comprises animals with specialized eggs that can develop on land. Shortly after their appearance, amniotes diversified into three lineages: one ancestral to living mammals; another to living turtles; and a third to lizards, snakes, alligators, and birds.

STUDY BREAK QUESTIONS

1. What are the four key morphological innovations that are used to identify vertebrates?
2. What is a *Hox* gene, and how does it influence the diversity of vertebrates?

27.10 Agnathans: The Jawless Fishes

Lacking jaws, the earliest vertebrates used a muscular pharynx to suck water containing food particles into the mouth, and used gills both to acquire dissolved oxygen and to filter food from the water. The agnathans that flourished in the Paleozoic varied greatly in size and shape and possessed different combinations of vertebrate characters.

Lampreys and hagfishes, the two living groups of agnathans, have skeletons composed entirely of cartilage. Although fossil lampreys or hagfishes older than the Devonian have been found, the absence of bone in their living descendants suggests that they arose early in vertebrate history, before the evolution of bone. The first fossil lamprey from the Devonian of South Africa is unmistakably a lamprey. Hagfishes and lampreys have a well-developed notochord but no true vertebrae or paired fins. Their skin lacks scales. Individuals grow to a maximum length of about 1 m **(Figure 27.83)**. Two possible phylogenies for hagfishes and other vertebrates are presented, but at this time, there are too few data to decide which is most likely to be correct.

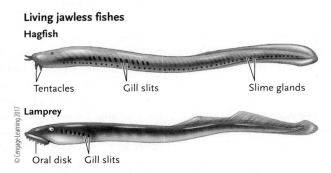

Living jawless fishes

Hagfish

Tentacles   Gill slits   Slime glands

Lamprey

Oral disk   Gill slits

FIGURE 27.83 Two groups of jawless fishes are the hagfish and lamprey

© Cengage Learning 2017

The axial skeletons of the 60 living species of hagfishes include only a cranium and a notochord. No specialized structures surround the dorsal nerve cord. Hagfishes are marine scavengers that burrow in sediments on continental shelves. They eat invertebrate prey and dead or dying fishes. In response to predators, they secrete immense quantities of sticky, noxious slime. When no longer threatened, a hagfish ties itself into a knot and wipes the slime from its body. The life cycle of a hagfish lacks a larval stage.

The 38 living species of lamprey have a more specialized axial skeleton than hagfishes. Their notochord is surrounded by dorsally pointing cartilage that partially covers the nerve cord, perhaps representing an early stage in the evolution of the vertebral column. About half the living lamprey species are parasitic as adults and use the sucking disk around their mouths to attach to the bodies of fish (or other prey), rasp a hole in the host's body, and ingest body fluids. In most species, sexually mature adults migrate from the ocean or a lake to the headwaters of a stream, where they reproduce and then die. The filter-feeding **ammocoetes** larvae of lampreys resemble adult cephalochordates. They burrow into mud and develop for as long as seven years before metamorphosing and migrating to the sea or lake to live as adults.

Conodonts and ostracoderms were early jawless vertebrates with bony structures. Conodonts are mysterious bonelike fossils, mostly less than 1 mm long, occurring in oceanic rocks from the early Paleozoic through the early Mesozoic. Called **conodont** elements, these abundant fossils were originally described as supporting structures of marine algae or feeding structures of ancient invertebrates. Recent analyses of their mineral composition reveal that they were made of dentine, a bonelike component of vertebrate teeth. In the 1980s and 1990s, many questions about conodonts were answered by the discovery of fossils of intact conodont animals with these elements.

We now know that conodonts were elongate, soft-bodied animals 3–10 cm long. They had a notochord, a cranium, segmental body-wall muscles, and large, movable eyes **(Figure 27.84a)**. The conodont elements at the front of the mouth were forward-pointing, hook-shaped structures (the original fossils) apparently used in the collection of food. Conodont elements in the pharynx were stouter, making them suitable for crushing food. Paleontologists now classify conodonts as vertebrates, the earliest ones with bonelike structures.

Ostracoderms (*ostrac* = shell; *derm* = skin) include an assortment of jawless fishes representing several evolutionary lines that lived from the Ordovician through the Devonian (Figure 27.84b). Like their invertebrate chordate ancestors, ostracoderms probably used the pharynx to draw water with food particles into the mouth, and used gills to filter food from water. The muscular pharynx was more efficient than that of agnathans, using currents generated by cilia. Greater flow rates allowed ostracoderms to collect food more rapidly and achieve larger body sizes. Although most ostracoderms were much smaller, some were 2 m long.

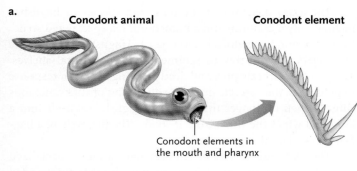

a.

Conodont animal

Conodont element

Conodont elements in
the mouth and pharynx

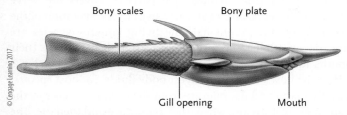

b. **Ostracoderm**

Bony scales

Bony plate

Gill opening

Mouth

© Cengage Learning 2017

FIGURE 27.84 Extinct agnathans. (a) Conodonts were elaborate, soft-bodied animals with bonelike feeding structures in the mouth and pharynx. **(b)** *Pteropsis*, an ostracoderm, had large bony plates on its head and small body scales on the rest of its body. It was about 6 cm long.

The skin of ostracoderms was heavily armoured with bony plates and scales. Although some had paired lateral extensions of their bony armour, they could not move them in the way living fishes move paired fins. Ostracoderms lacked a true vertebral column, but they had rudimentary support structures surrounding the nerve cord. Ostracoderms had other distinctly vertebrate-like characteristics. Their head shields indicate that their brains had the three regions (forebrain, midbrain, and hindbrain) typical of all later vertebrates (see Chapter 45).

STUDY BREAK QUESTIONS

1. How did the earliest vertebrates feed without jaws?
2. Compare the hagfish and the lamprey based on body structure, feeding habits, and life cycles.

27.11   Jawed Fishes: Jaws Meant New Feeding Opportunities

The first gnathostomes were jawed fishes. Jaws meant that they could eat more than just filtered food particles and take larger food items with higher energy content. The renowned anatomist and paleontologist Alfred Sherwood Romer described the evolution of jaws as "perhaps the greatest of all advances in vertebrate history." Hinged jaws allow vertebrates to grasp, kill, shred, and crush large food items. Some species also use their jaws for defence, for grooming, to construct nests, and to transport young. Jaws may serve more than one purpose. Another important development is tooth-on-tooth contact, which increases the

effectiveness of chewing, particularly cutting and grinding. This is a recurrent theme among gnathostome vertebrates from fish to reptiles and mammals.

Embryological evidence suggests that jaws evolved from paired gill arches in the pharynx of a jawless ancestor **(Figure 27.85)**. One pair of ancestral **gill arches** formed bones in the upper and lower jaws, whereas a second pair was transformed into the **hyomandibular bones** that braced the jaws against the cranium. Nerves and muscles of the ancestral suspension-feeding pharynx control the movement and actions of jaws. Jawed fishes also had fins, first appearing as folds of skin and movable spines that stabilized locomotion and deterred predators. Movable fins appeared independently in several lineages, and by the Devonian, most jawed fishes had unpaired (dorsal, anal, and caudal) and paired (pectoral and pelvic) fins **(Figure 27.86)**.

27.11a   Classes Acanthodii and Placodermi Were Early Lineages

The spiny "sharks" (*acanth* = spine) persisted from the late Ordovician through the Permian. Most of these sharklike fishes were less than 20 cm long, with small, light scales, streamlined bodies, well-developed eyes, large jaws, and numerous teeth. Although acanthodians were not true sharks, they were probably fast swimmers and efficient predators. Many of them lived in fresh water. Most had a row of ventral spines and fins with internal skeletal support on each side of the body. The anatomy of acanthodians suggests a close relationship to bony fishes of today.

The placoderms (*plac* = plate; *derm* = skin) appeared in the Silurian and diversified in the Devonian and Carboniferous, but left no direct descendants. Some species of *Dunkleosteus* **(Figure 27.87)** were huge. The bodies of placoderms were covered with large, heavy plates of bone anteriorly, and smaller scales posteriorly. Their jaws had sharp cutting edges but no separate teeth, and their paired fins had internal skeletons and powerful muscles.

27.11b   Class Chondrichthyes Includes Sharks and Rays

The cartilaginous fishes (*chondr* = cartilage; *ichthy* = fish) are represented today by about 850 living species of sharks, skates and rays, and chimeras. As the name implies, their skeletons are entirely cartilaginous. However, the absence of bone is a derived trait because all earlier fishes had bony armour or bony endoskeletons. Most living chondrichthyans are grouped into two subclasses, the **Elasmobranchii** (skates, rays, and sharks) and the **Holocephali** (chimeras) **(Figure 27.88)**. Most are marine predators. With about 40 living species, holocephalians are the only cartilaginous fishes with an operculum (gill cover). Sharks, rays, and chimeras are often exhibited at aquaria.

Skates and rays are dorsoventrally flattened (see Figure 27.88b) and swim by undulating their enlarged pectoral fins.

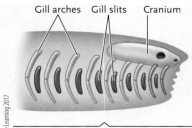
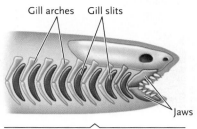
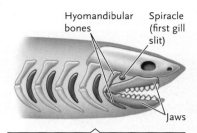

Gill arches Gill slits Cranium

a. Jaws evolved from the anterior pair of gill arches in the pharynx of jawless fishes.

© Cengage Learning 2017

Gill arches Gill slits

Jaws

b. In early jawed fishes, the upper jaw was firmly attached to the cranium.

Hyomandibular bones Spiracle (first gill slit)

Jaws

c. In later jawed fishes, the jaws were supported by the hyomandibular bones, which were derived from a second pair of gill arches.

FIGURE 27.85 The evolution of jaws. In two early lineages of jawed fishes (Acanthodii and Placodermi), the upper jaw (**maxillae, premaxillae**) was firmly attached to the cranium, and the lower jaw moved up and down. This meant an inflexible mouth that simply snapped open and shut. Acanthodians and placoderms had bony internal skeletons.

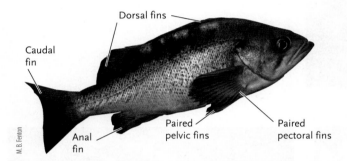

Dorsal fins

Caudal fin

Anal fin

Paired pelvic fins

Paired pectoral fins

M. B. Fenton

FIGURE 27.86 Fish fins. Most fishes have both paired and unpaired fins.

Skull of *Dunkleosteus*

M. B. Fenton

FIGURE 27.87 The placoderm *Dunkleosteus* was gigantic, growing to 10 m long. Although some acanthodians had teeth, placoderms had only sharp cutting edges. The 3 m long skull of a *Dunkleosteus* demonstrates how impressive placoderms could be.

Most are bottom dwellers that often lie partly buried in sand. They eat hard-shelled invertebrates (such as molluscs), which they crush with rows of flattened teeth **(Figure 27.89a)**. The largest species, the manta ray (*Manta birostris*), measures 6 m across and eats plankton in the open ocean. Some rays have electric organs that stun prey with shocks of as much as

200 volts. There are species of freshwater skates and rays in some rivers in the tropics. For example, in the Mekong River basin, some *Himantura chaophraya* are 2 m across.

Sharks (see Figure 27.88a) are among the ocean's dominant predators. Flexible fins, lightweight skeletons, streamlined bodies, and the absence of heavy body armour allow most sharks to rapidly pursue prey. Their livers often contain **squalene**, an oil that is lighter than water, which increases their buoyancy. The great white shark (*Carcharodon carcharias*), the largest living predatory species of shark, can be 10 m long. At 18 m, the whale shark (*Rhincodon typus*) is the world's largest fish, and it eats only plankton. Sharks' teeth are designed for cutting. *Isistius plutodus,* the cookie-cutter shark, uses piercing teeth in its upper jaw to attach to its prey, biting with the lower jaw and its cutting teeth while rotating its body (see Figure 27.89b). The feeding process removes a disk of flesh from the prey. The combination of serrated teeth and flexible, extensible jaws makes the effects of shark bites astonishing and frightening. The insatiable human market for shark fin soup has drastically reduced populations of sharks worldwide. This has changed marine ecosystems (see Chapter 31).

Elasmobranchs have remarkable adaptations for acquiring and processing food. Their teeth develop in whorls under the fleshy parts of the mouth. New teeth migrate forward as old worn teeth break free (see Figure 27.89). In many sharks, the upper jaw is loosely attached to the cranium, and it swings down during feeding. As the jaws open, the mouth spreads wide, sucking in large, hard-to-digest chunks of prey, which are swallowed intact, allowing for hurried eating. Although the elasmobranch digestive system is short, it includes a corkscrew-shaped **spiral valve** that slows the passage of material and increases the surface area available for digestion and absorption (see Chapter 39).

Elasmobranchs also have well-developed sensory systems. In addition to vision and olfaction, they use **electroreceptors** to detect weak electric currents produced by other animals. Their **lateral line system**, a row of tiny sensors in canals along both sides of the body, detects vibrations in water (see Figure 45.19).

a. Grey reef shark
(*Carcharhinus amblyrhynchos*)

b. Manta ray

c. Sawfish

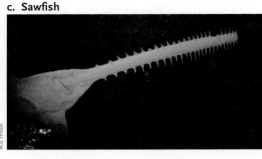

FIGURE 27.88 **Chondrichthyes include (a) sharks,** (b) **skates and rays,** (c) **sawfish, and** (d) **chimeras, or ratfish.** The eggs of many sharks **(e)** include a large visible yolk that nourishes the developing embryo.

d. Chimaera

e. Shark egg

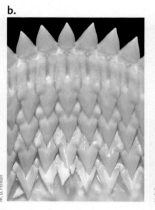

a.

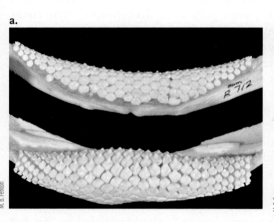

b.

c.

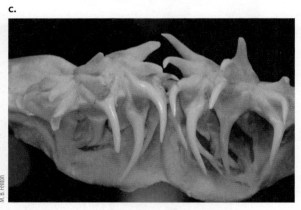

FIGURE 27.89 **Elasmobranch teeth. (a)** The teeth of barndoor skates (*Dipturus laevis*; see also Chapter 28) are specialized for crushing hard prey, such as bivalve molluscs. **(b)** Cookie-cutter sharks (*Isistius plutodus*) use cutting teeth to remove disks of flesh. **(c)** The goblin shark, *Mitsukurina owstoni*, eats soft-bodied prey. In **(a)** and **(b)**, the replacement pattern of the teeth (from back to front of the jaws) is obvious.

They use urea as an osmolyte that makes their body fluids more concentrated than sea water. Freshwater skates have much lower concentrations of urea in their blood than their saltwater relatives do. (For more about osmoregulation, see Chapter 42.)

People of the Gilbert Islands in the South Pacific made fearsome weapons by attaching shark teeth to clubs made of palm wood **(Figure. 27.90)**. These weapons provide modern biologists with a window on the shark community of the waters around the islands over 100 years ago. The weapons, known as *terbutjes*, were festooned with shark teeth set in grooves and held in place with braided palm fibres. Terbutjes made in the last half of the nineteenth century included teeth of spot-tail (*Carcharinus sorrah*) and dusky sharks (*Carcharhinus obscurus*),

two species not currently known to occur in those waters. Thus, these terbutjes provide an unexpected glimpse into changes in the predator assemblages of the region.

Anyone who has seen sharks in action will appreciate that many of them are enthusiastic biters. The all-too-often gory sight of the results of shark bites furthers this impression. Small wonder that some people have made weapons whose cutting edges are made of shark teeth. The effectiveness of the cutting edges of the weapons appears clear, but terbutjes were probably designed to draw blood rather than deliver killing blows.

Chondrichthyans have evolved numerous reproductive specializations. Males have a pair of organs, **claspers**, the pelvic fins, which help transfer sperm into the female. Fertilization occurs internally. In many species, females produce yolky eggs with tough leathery shells. Others retain the eggs within the oviduct until the young hatch. A few species nourish young in utero (see Chapter 44).

27.11c The Bony Fishes Represent Over 95% of Fish Today

Fishes with bony endoskeletons (cranium, vertebral column with ribs, and bones supporting their movable fins) are the most successful of all vertebrates, whether the count is of numbers of species or of individuals. The endoskeleton provides lightweight support compared with the bony armour of ostracoderms and placoderms, enhancing their locomotor efficiency.

Bony fishes have numerous adaptations that increase swimming efficiency. The scales of most bony fishes are small, smooth, and lightweight, and their bodies are covered with a protective coat of mucus that retards bacterial growth and minimizes drag as water flows past the body.

Bony fishes first appeared in the Silurian and rapidly diversified into two lineages, Actinopterygii and Sarcopterygii. The ray-finned fishes (Actinopterygii; *acti* = ray; *ptery* = wing) have fins supported by thin and flexible bony rays, whereas the fleshy-finned fishes (Sarcopterygii; *sarco* = flesh) have fins supported by muscles and an internal bony skeleton. Ray-finned fishes are more diverse as measured by numbers of species, and today vastly outnumber fleshy-finned fishes. The approximately 30 000 living species of bony fishes occupy nearly every aquatic habitat and represent more than 95% of living fish species. Adults range from 1 cm to more than 6 m in length. In the Yangtze River basin, *Psephurus gladius,* the Chinese paddlefish, can weigh up to 500 kg. The fleshy-finned fishes were on the evolutionary lineage that led to amphibians. In some Devonian fossil species, the lobe fins have bones that are precursors to limbs and digits.

CLASS ACTINOPTERYGII Sturgeons **(Figure 27.91a)** and paddlefishes, the most ancestral members of this group, are characterized by mostly cartilaginous skeletons. These large fishes live in rivers and lakes of the Northern Hemisphere. Sturgeons eat detritus and invertebrates, whereas paddlefish eat plankton. Gars (Figure 27.91b) and bowfins are remnants of a more recent radiation. They occur in the eastern half of North America, where they eat fish and other prey. Gars are protected from predators by a heavy coat of bony scales.

The subclass Teleostei represents the latest radiation of Actinopterygii, one that produced a wide range of body forms

FIGURE 27.90 **(a)** April Hawkins of the Royal Ontario Museum in Toronto provides an indication of the size of a terbutje. **(b)** Braided palm fibres hold three shark teeth in grooves in a palm wood terbutje.

a. Sevruga sturgeon (*Accipenser stellatus*)

b. Long-nosed gar (*Lepisosteus osseus*)

FIGURE 27.91 **Ancestral actinopterygians (ray-finned bony fishes) are represented today by sturgeons** (a) **and gars** (b).

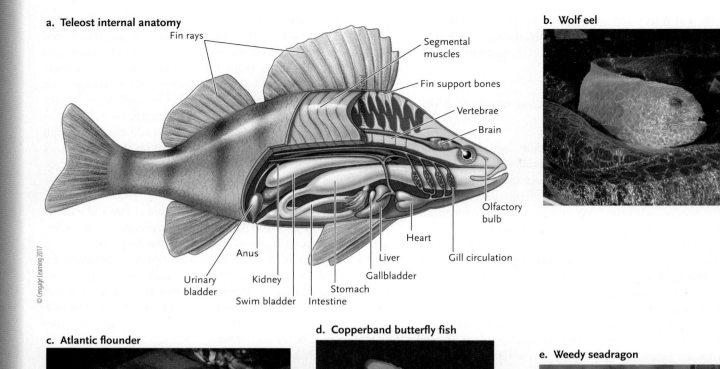

a. Teleost internal anatomy

Fin rays

Segmental muscles

Fin support bones

Vertebrae

Brain

Olfactory bulb

Gill circulation

Heart

Liver

Gallbladder

Stomach

Intestine

Swim bladder

Kidney

Anus

Urinary bladder

© Cengage Learning 2017

b. Wolf eel

M. B. Fenton

c. Atlantic flounder

M. B. Fenton

d. Copperband butterfly fish

M. B. Fenton

e. Weedy seadragon

M. B. Fenton

FIGURE 27.92 **This range of bony fishes provides an indication of the range of body forms in the groups. (a)** The basic anatomy provides a map to "typical" fish. **(b)** The wolf eel (*Anarrhichthys ocellatus*) is predatory, **(c)** as is the Atlantic flounder (*Paralichthys* spp.). **(d)** The copperband butterfly fish (*Chelmon rostratus*) is a denizen of coral reefs. **(e)** The weedy seadragon (*Phyllopteryx taeniolatus*) is closely related to sea horses.

(Figure 27.92). Teleosts have an internal skeleton made almost entirely of bone. On either side of the head, the **operculum**, a flap of the body wall, covers a chamber that houses the gills. Sensory systems (see Chapter 45) generally include large eyes, a lateral line system, sound receptors, chemoreceptive nostrils, and taste buds.

Variations in jaw structure and teeth give different species of teleosts access to a wide range of food from plankton, macroalgae, invertebrates, or other vertebrates. Teleosts exhibit remarkable adaptations for feeding and locomotion. When some teleosts open their mouths, bones at the front of the jaws swing forward to create a circular opening. Folds of skin extend backward, forming a tube through which they suck food. Like Chondrichthyes, Actinopterygii exhibit great variation in tooth structure **(Figure 27.93)**. Species such as piranhas (*Serrasalmus*) are notorious for their bites. Other species have teeth specialized for crushing hard prey, such as bivalve molluscs. Whereas the piranha's teeth are on the premaxilla, maxilla, and mandible (as they are in mammals and many other vertebrates), the crushing teeth of ray-finned fishes often occur on the bones of the pharynx.

In many modern ray-finned fishes, a gas-filled **swim bladder** serves as a hydrostatic organ that increases buoyancy (see Figure 27.92a). The swim bladder is derived from an ancestral air-breathing lung that allowed early actinopterygians to gulp air, supplementing gill respiration in aquatic habitats where dissolved oxygen concentration is low.

Many have symmetrical tail fins posterior to the vertebral column that provide power for locomotion. Their pectoral fins often lie high on the sides of the body, providing fine control over swimming. Some species use pectoral fins for acquiring food, for courtship, and for care of eggs and young. Some teleosts use pectoral fins for crawling on land (e.g., mudskippers, *Periophthalmus* species; and climbing perch, *Anabas* species) or gliding in the air (flying fish, family Exocoetidae).

Most marine species produce small eggs that hatch into larvae that live among the plankton. Eggs of freshwater teleosts are generally larger and hatch into tiny versions of the adults.

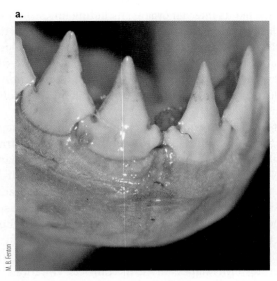

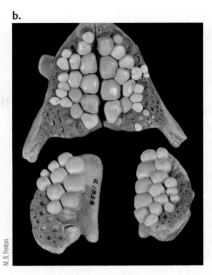

FIGURE 27.93 **Teleost teeth.** Like Chondrichthyes, bony fishes have also developed cutting **(a)** and crushing **(b)** teeth. The cutting teeth are those of a piranha (*Serrasalmus* species). The crushing teeth are from a black drum (*Pogonias cromis*).

a. Coelacanth

b. Australian lungfish

FIGURE 27.94 **Sarcopterygians. (a)** The coelacanth (*Latimeria chalumnae*) is now one of eight living species of lobe-finned fishes. **(b)** The Australian lungfish (*Neoceratodus forsteri*) is one of six living lungfish species.

Parents often care for their eggs and young, fanning oxygen-rich water over them, removing fungal growths, and protecting them from predators. Some freshwater species, such as guppies, give birth to live young.

CLASS SARCOPTERYGII The two groups of fleshy-finned fishes, lobe-finned fishes and lungfishes, are represented by eight living species **(Figure 27.94)**. Although lobe-finned fishes were once thought to have been extinct for 65 million years, a living coelacanth (*Latimeria chalumnae*) was discovered in 1938 near the Comoros Islands, off the southeastern coast of Africa. A population of these metre-long fishes live at depths of 70–600 m, feeding on other fishes and squid. Remarkably, a second population of coelacanths was discovered in 1998, 10 000 km east of the Comoros, when a specimen was found in an Indonesian fish market. Analyses of the DNA of the Indonesian specimen indicated that it is a distinct species (*Latimeria menadoensis*).

Lungfishes have changed relatively little over the past 200 million years. Six living species are distributed on southern continents. Australian lungfishes live in rivers and pools, using their lungs to supplement gill respiration when dissolved oxygen concentration is low. South American and African species live in swamps and use their lungs for breathing during the annual dry season, which they spend encased in a mucus-lined burrow in the dry mud. When the rains begin, water fills the burrow and the fishes awaken from dormancy. During their periods of dormancy, these fishes excrete urea.

STUDY BREAK QUESTIONS

1. What did the evolution of jaws mean for fish?
2. What anatomical and physiological characteristics make sharks dominant ocean predators?
3. What is the lateral line system? What does it do?

27.12 Early Tetrapods and Modern Amphibians

The fossil record suggests that tetrapods evolved in the late Devonian from a group of lobe-finned fishes (also known as *fleshy-finned*), called the "Osteolepiformes." Osteolepiformes and early tetrapods shared several derived characteristics, including dental and cranial features. In both groups, infoldings of tooth surfaces probably increased the functional area of the tooth. They also shared shapes and positions of bones on the dorsal side of their crania and in their appendages.

Some problems of moving onto land were identified earlier. During dry periods in swampy, late Devonian habitats, drying pools may have forced osteolepiform ancestors to move overland to adjacent pools that still had water. During these excursions, the fish may have found that land plants, worms, and arthropods provided abundant food, and oxygen was more readily available in air than in water. Furthermore, there may well have been fewer terrestrial predators at that time, but this interpretation is open to question.

Osteolepiformes usually had strong, stout fins that allowed them to crawl on mud. Of particular importance were crescent-shaped bones in their vertebral columns that provided strong intervertebral connections. Their nostrils led to sensory pits housing olfactory (odour) receptors (see Chapter 45). They almost certainly had lungs, allowing them to breathe atmospheric oxygen. Like living lungfishes, they could also have excreted urea or uric acid rather than ammonium, which is toxic.

The earliest tetrapod with nearly complete skeletal data is the semi-terrestrial, metre-long *Ichthyostega*. Compared with its fleshy-finned ancestors, *Ichthyostega* had a more robust vertebral column, sturdier limb girdles and appendages, a ribcage that protected its internal organs (including lungs), and a neck. Fishes lack necks because the pectoral girdle is fused to the cranium. In *Ichthyostega*, several vertebrae separated the pectoral girdle and the cranium, allowing the animal to move its head to scan the environment and capture food. *Ichthyostega* retained a fishlike lateral line system, caudal fin, and scaly body covering.

Life on land also required changes in sensory systems. In fishes, the body wall picks up sound vibrations and transfers them directly to sensory receptors. Sound waves are harder to detect in air. The appearance of a **tympanum** (ear drum) in early tetrapods apparently allowed them to detect vibrations in air associated with airborne sounds. The tympana are specialized membranes on either side of the head. The tympanum connects to the **stapes**, a bone homologous to the hyomandibula, which had supported the jaws of fishes (see Figure 19.5, Chapter 19). The stapes, in turn, transfers vibrations to the sensory cells of an inner ear. In mammals, as we will see (Chapter 45), there are three auditory ossicles.

27.12a Class Amphibia Includes Frogs, Toads, Salamanders, and Caecilians

Most of the over 6000 living species of amphibians (*amphi* = both; *bios* = life) are small, and their skeletons contain fewer bones than those of Paleozoic tetrapods, such as *Ichthyostega*. All living amphibians are carnivorous as adults, but the aquatic larvae of some are herbivores. Fossil amphibians, such as *Eryops* **(Figure 27.95)**, were large and predatory.

The thin, scaleless skin of most living amphibians is well supplied with blood vessels and can be a major site of gas exchange. To operate in oxygen uptake, the skin must be moist and thin enough to bring blood into close contact with air.

FIGURE 27.95 A fossil amphibian. This amphibian, *Eryops,* from the Texas Permian, was about 1.8 m long and was strikingly different from living amphibians.

Having moist skin limits amphibians to moist habitats. Many species of living amphibians keep their skin surfaces moist, and some are lungless, but most use lungs in gaseous exchange. The evolution of lungs was accompanied by modifications of the heart and circulatory system that increased the efficiency with which oxygen is delivered to body tissues (see Chapter 44). Some adult frogs have a waxy coating on their skin, making them as waterproof as lizards (**Figure 27.96**).

The life cycles of many amphibians include larval and adult stages. In frogs, larvae (tadpoles) hatch from fertilized eggs and eventually metamorphose into adults (see Chapter 44). The larvae of most frog species are aquatic, but adults may live their lives in water (be aquatic), move between land and water (be amphibious), or live entirely on land (be terrestrial). Some salamanders are paedomorphic (see Chapter 16), which means that the larvae attain sexual maturity without changing to the adult form or moving to land. On the other hand, some frogs and salamanders reproduce on land, omitting the larval stage altogether. In these species, tiny adults emerge directly from fully developed eggs. However, the eggs of terrestrial breeders dry out quickly unless they are laid in moist places.

Modern amphibians are represented by three lineages (**Figure 27.97**), but the evolutionary origin of frogs, salamanders, and caecilians has remained unresolved. The 2008 description of a small fossil from the Lower Permian of Texas suggests that frogs and salamanders have a relatively close common ancestor, and that caecilians are distantly related to them.

Populations of practically all amphibians have declined rapidly in recent years. These declines are probably due to exposure to acid rain, high levels of ultraviolet B radiation, and fungal and parasitic infections. Another major factor in the decline of amphibians may be habitat splitting, the human-induced disconnection of habitats essential to the survival of amphibians can cause adult amphibians to move across inhospitable habitats (roads, power line rights-of-way) to reach breeding habitats.

ANURA The 3700 species of frogs and toads (*an* = without; *uro* = tail) have short, compact bodies, and the adults lack tails.

FIGURE 27.96 Waterproof frogs. (a) *Chiromantis xerampelina* from southern Africa and **(b)** *Phyllomedusa sauvagii* from South America make their skin waterproof with a waxy secretion. These frogs are as waterproof as chameleons. They also excrete uric acid to further conserve water.

a. A frog

b. A salamander

c. A caecilian

FIGURE 27.97 Living amphibians. Anurans, such as **(a)** a red-eyed frog (*Agalychnis callidryas*) and **(b)** a tiger salamander from Riding Mountain National Park in Manitoba (*Amblystoma tigrinum*), and caecilians, such as **(c)** *Caecilia nigricans* from Colombia

Their elongated hind legs and webbed feet allow them to hop on land or to swim. A few species are adapted to dry habitats, encasing themselves in mucus cocoons to withstand periods of drought. The Pacific tailed frog, *Ascaphus truei*, occurs in coastal British Columbia.

URODELA The 400 species of newts and salamanders (*uro* = tail; *del* = visible) have an elongated, tailed body and four legs. They walk by alternately contracting muscles on either side of the body, much the way fishes swim. Species in the most diverse group, the lungless salamanders, are fully terrestrial throughout their lives, using their skin and the lining of the throat for gas exchange.

GYMNOPHIONA The 200 species of caecilians (*gymn* = naked; *ophioneos* = snakelike) are legless, burrowing animals with wormlike bodies. They occupy tropical habitats throughout the world. Unlike other extant amphibians, caecilians have small bony scales embedded in their skin. Fertilization is internal, and females give birth to live young. In some species, the mother's skin produces a milk-like substance for the young, which use specialized teeth to collect it from the mother's body.

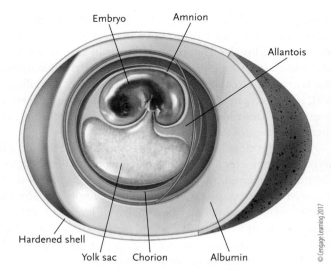

FIGURE 27.98 The amniote egg. A water-retaining egg with four specialized membranes surrounded by a hard or leathery shell allowed amniotes and their descendants to reproduce in dry environments. The chorion surrounds the amnion, which in turn surrounds the amniotic fluid.

> **STUDY BREAK QUESTIONS**
>
> 1. Present four lines of evidence suggesting that tetrapods arose from Osteolepiformes.
> 2. Why was the development of the tympanum important to life on land?
> 3. What characteristics allow amphibians to use their skin as a major site of gas exchange?

27.13 The Origin and Mesozoic Radiations of Amniotes

The amniote lineage that today includes reptiles, birds, and mammals arose during the Carboniferous. Then seed plants and insects began to invade terrestrial habitats, providing additional food and cover for early terrestrial vertebrates. Amniotes take their name from the amnion, a fluid-filled sac that surrounds the embryo during development (see Chapter 44). Although the fossil record includes many skeletal remains of early amniotes, it provides little direct information about soft body parts and physiology. Four key features of living amniotes allow life on dry land and liberate them from reliance on standing water:

1. Skin is waterproof: keratin and lipids in the cells make skin relatively impermeable to water.
2. **Amniote (amniotic) eggs** can survive and develop on dry land because they have four specialized membranes and a hard or leathery shell perforated by microscopic pores **(Figure 27.98)**. Amniote eggs are resistant to desiccation. The membranes protect the developing embryo and

facilitate gas exchange and excretion. The shell mediates the exchange of air and water between the egg and its environment. Developing amniote embryos can excrete uric acid, which is stored in the allantois of the embryo, which will later become the bladder. Generous supplies of **yolk** in the egg are the developing embryo's main energy source, whereas **albumin** supplies water and other materials. There is no larval stage, and hatchling amniotes are miniature versions of the adult. Amniote eggs are the ancestral condition, but in some reptiles and most mammals, development takes place within the body of the mother (see Chapter 44).

3. Some amniotes produce urea and/or uric acid as a waste product of nitrogen metabolism (see Chapter 42). Although ammonia (NH_3^+) is less expensive (metabolically) to produce, it is toxic and must be flushed away with water. Urea is much less toxic than ammonia and therefore easier to store and to void. Uric acid is even less toxic and, because it is insoluble, it can be stored or voided without risk while conserving water.
4. A skeleton provides support and points of attachment for muscles, allowing locomotion and survival on land.

The abundance and diversity of fossils of amniotes indicate that they were extremely successful, quickly replacing many nonamniote species in terrestrial habitats. During the Carboniferous and Permian, amniotes produced three major radiations: synapsids, anapsids, and diapsids **(Figure 27.99)**, distinguishable by the numbers of bony arches in the temporal region of the skull (in addition to the openings for the eyes; **Figure 27.100**). The bony arches demarcate fenestrae, openings in the skull that allow space for contraction (and expansion) of large and powerful jaw muscles.

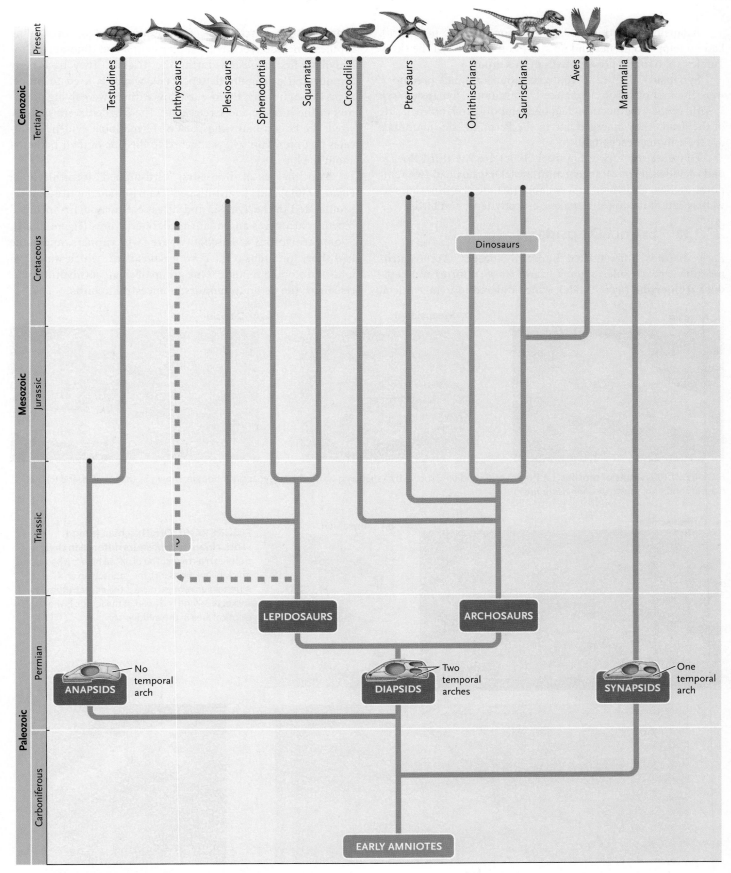

FIGURE 27.99 Amniote ancestry. The early amniotes gave rise to three lineages (anapsids, synapsids, and diapsids) and numerous descendants. The lineages are distinguished by the number of bony arches in the temporal region of the skull (indicated on the small icons).

Anapsida (Figure 27.100a), the second lineage (*an* = not), had no temporal arches and no spaces on the sides of the skull. Turtles are living representatives of this group.

Synapsida (Figure 27.100b), a group of small predators, were the first offshoot from ancestral amniotes. Synapsids (*syn* = with; *apsid* = connection) had one temporal arch on each side of the head. They emerged late in the Permian, and mammals are their living descendants.

Diapsida (*di* = two; Figure 27.100c) are the third lineage and included most Mesozoic amniotes. Diapsids had two temporal arches, and their descendants include the dinosaurs as well as extant lizards and snakes, crocodylians, and birds.

27.13a Extinct Diapsids

Early diapsids differentiated into two lineages, **Archosauromorpha** (*archo* = ruler; *sauro* = lizard; *morph* = form) and **Lepidosauromorpha** (*lepi* = scale), which differed in many skeletal characteristics. Archosaurs (archosauromorphs), or "ruling reptiles," include crocodylians, pterosaurs, and dinosaurs. Crocodylians first appeared during the Triassic. They have bony armour and a laterally flattened tail, which is used to propel them through water. Pterosaurs, now extinct, were flying predators of the Jurassic and Cretaceous. The smallest were sparrow sized; the largest had wingspans of 11 m. Some evidence indicates that pterosaur wings attached to the side of their bodies at about the hips.

Two lineages of dinosaurs, "bird-hipped" (ornithischian; **Figure 27.101a**) and "lizard-hipped" (saurischian; Figure 27.101b) proliferated in the Triassic and Jurassic. Saurischians included bipedal carnivores and quadrupedal herbivores **(Figure 27.102)**. Some carnivorous saurischians were swift runners, and some had short forelimbs (e.g., *Tyrannosaurus rex*, which was 12 m long and stood 6 m high). One group of small carnivorous saurischians, the deinonychusaurs, is ancestral to birds.

a. Anapsid

b. Synapsid

c. Diapsid

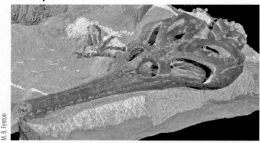

FIGURE 27.100 Skulls of reptiles. (a) The anapsid condition, shown by a snapping turtle; **(b)** the synapsid condition, shown by *Dimetrodon;* and **(c)** the diapsid condition, shown by *Champsosaurus*

a. Ornithischian

b. Saurischian

FIGURE 27.101 Ornithischian (a) **and saurischian** (b) **dinosaurs differed in their pelvic structures.** The ornithischian is a hadrosaur (duck-billed dinosaur), the saurischian an Albertosaurus. In each case, the **acetabulum**, the socket receiving the head of the femur, is the large elliptical area in the middle.

a.

b.

FIGURE 27.102 Saurischian dinosaurs. While *Ornitholestes hermanni* **(a)** stood less than 1 m at the shoulder, the fearsome *Tyrannosaurus rex* **(b)** was about 12 m long. Both were carnivores.

a. *Lambeosaurus*

b. *Stegoceras*

c. *Triceratops*

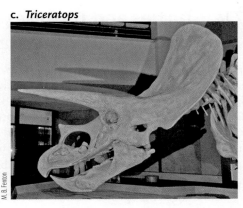

FIGURE 27.103 Ornithischian dinosaurs. These herbivores varied in size: **(a)** the 15 m long *Lambeosaurus lambei*; **(b)** the smaller, thick-skulled *Stegoceras*; and **(c)** the 10 m long *Triceratops horridus*.

a.

b.

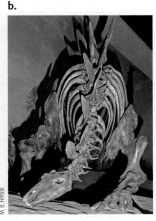

FIGURE 27.104 Large, lumbering herbivores. Other ornithischian dinosaurs included the 18 m long *Camarasaurus supremus* **(a)** and the 9 m long *Stegosaurus armatus* **(b)**. The latter had distinctive plates along its back.

a.

b.

c.

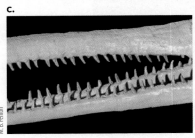

d.

FIGURE 27.105 Reptile teeth. As usual, teeth reflect the dietary habits of dinosaurs. Herbivorous dinosaurs, *Diplodocus longus* **(a)** and hadrosaur **(b)**, had teeth adapted for gathering plant material (a) and grinding it (b). These teeth differed from those of a fish-eating reptile such as a champsosaur **(c)**. A tooth of a *Tyrannosaurus rex* changed distinctly over its length. The biting part of the tooth **(d)** had enamel and serrated edges. There was no enamel on the part of the tooth located within the socket of the skull.

By the Cretaceous, some herbivorous saurischians were gigantic, and many had long, flexible necks **(Figure 27.103)**. *Apatosaurus* (previously known as *Brontosaurus*) was 25 m long and may have weighed 50 000 kg. The largely herbivorous ornithischian dinosaurs had large, chunky bodies **(Figure 27.104)**. This lineage included armoured, or plated, dinosaurs (*Ankylosaurus* and *Stegosaurus*), duck-billed dinosaurs (*Hadrosaurus*), horned dinosaurs (*Styracosaurus*), and some with remarkably thick skulls (*Pachycephalosaurus*). Ornithischians were most abundant in the Jurassic and Cretaceous.

Lepidosaurs (Lepidosauromorpha) are the second major lineage of diapsids. This diverse group included both marine and terrestrial animals. Fossil lepidosaurs include champsosaurs, which were freshwater fish eaters, and the marine fish-eating plesiosaurs, with long, paddle-like limbs that they used like oars. Fossil lepidosaurs also included ichthyosaurs, porpoise-like animals with laterally flattened tails. Like today's whales, ichthyosaurs were highly specialized for marine life and did not return to land to lay eggs. Indeed, it appears that ichthyosaurs, like today's whales, gave birth to live young. Squamates, the living lizards and snakes, are the third important group within this lineage. *Sphenodon,* the tuatara, is the last living genus of a once diverse group of lizard-like squamates.

The teeth of reptiles provide important clues about their diets **(Figure 27.105)** and show interesting parallels with the teeth of other vertebrates.

STUDY BREAK QUESTIONS

1. Where do amniotes get their name? Why are amniote eggs resistant to desiccation?
2. What four key features liberate living amniotes from reliance on standing water?
3. Name and describe three major radiations of amniotes during the Carboniferous and Permian.

27.14 Turtles and Tortoises (Subclass Testudinata)

The turtle body plan, defined largely by a bony, boxlike shell, has changed little since the group first appeared during the Triassic (**Figure 27.106**). A turtle's ribs are fused to the inside of the shell and, in contrast to other tetrapods, the pectoral and pelvic girdles lie within the ribcage. The shell is formed from large, keratinized scales covering the bony plates. It includes a dorsal carapace and a ventral **plastron**. Like living birds, turtles have keratinized beaks and lack teeth.

The 250 living species occupy terrestrial, fresh-water, and marine habitats. They range from 8 cm to 2 m in length. Turtles use a keratinized beak in feeding, whether they eat animal or plant material. When threatened, most species retract into their shells. Many species are now endangered because adults are hunted for meat and their eggs are eaten by humans and other predators. Young are often collected for the pet trade, and the beaches favoured as nesting sites by marine species are too often used as tourist attractions.

STUDY BREAK QUESTION

1. Describe the body plan of a turtle.

27.15 Living Diapsids: Sphenodontids, Squamates, and Crocodylians

Sphenodon punctatus is one of two living species of sphenodontids (*sphen* = wedge; *dont* = tooth), or tuataras, a lineage that was diverse in the Mesozoic (**Figure 27.107a**). These lizardlike animals are best known as tetrapods with a "third," or pineal, eye, a reflection of earlier vertebrates such as lampreys with pineal eyes (see also photoreceptors in Chapter 1). They survive on a few islands off the coast of New Zealand. Adults are about 60 cm long. They live in dense colonies, where males and females defend small territories. They often share underground burrows with seabirds and eat invertebrates and small vertebrates. They are primarily nocturnal and maintain low body temperatures during periods of activity. Their survival is threatened by two introduced predators, cats and rats.

27.15a Lizards and Snakes

Lizards and snakes (Figure 27.107b, c) are covered by overlapping, keratinized scales (*squam* = scale) that protect against dehydration. Squamates periodically shed their skin while growing, much the way arthropods shed their exoskeletons (see Section 27.7h). Most squamates regulate their body temperature behaviourally (see Chapter 42), so they are active only when weather conditions are favourable. They shuttle between sunny and shady places to warm up or cool down as needed.

a. The turtle skeleton

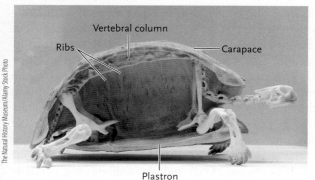

b. Spiny softshell turtle (*Apalone spinifera*)

c. Green sea turtle (*Chelonia mydas*)

FIGURE 27.106 Testudines. (a) The turtle skeleton. **(b)** Most turtles can withdraw their heads and legs into a bony shell, for example this spiny softshell *Apalone spinifera*. **(c)** But marine (sea) turtles, like green turtles (*Chelonia mydas*), cannot withdraw their heads into their shells.

a. Tuartara (*Sphenodon punctatus*)

b. Zebra-tailed lizard (*Callisaurus draconoides*)

c. Western diamondback rattlesnake

FIGURE 27.107 (a) Sphenodontia includes the tuartara (*Sphenodon punctatus*) and one other species. **(b)** Zebra-tailed lizard (*Callisaurus draconoides*). **(c)** Western diamondback rattlesnakes have fangs that are used to inject toxin into prey.

a.

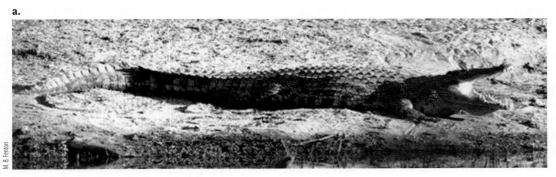

b.

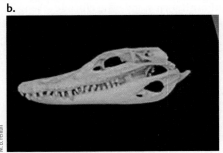

c.

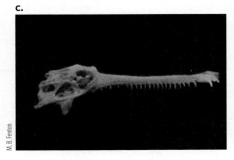

FIGURE 27.108 Crocodylians. (a) A 3 m long Nile crocodile (*Crocodylus niloticus*) basks in Kruger National Park, South Africa. **(b)** The skull of an alligator (*Alligator mississippiensis*) and **(c)** a gavial (*Gavialis gangeticus*) illustrate the range of variation among living crocodylians. In the Cretaceous, the group was much more diverse, exhibiting a greater variety of morphology and locomotion.

Most of the 3700 lizard species are less than 15 cm long, but Komodo dragons (*Varanus komodoensis*) grow to nearly 3 m in length (see Figure 45.24, Chapter 45). Lizards occupy a wide range of habitats and are especially common in deserts and the tropics. One species (*Lacerta vivipara*) occurs within the Arctic Circle. Most lizards eat insects, although some consume leaves or meat.

The 2300 species of snakes evolved from a lineage of lizards that lost their legs over evolutionary time. Streamlined bodies make snakes efficient burrowers or climbers. Many subterranean species are 10 or 15 cm long, whereas giant constrictors may grow to 10 m. Unlike lizards, all snakes are predators that swallow prey whole. Compared with their lizard ancestors, snake skull bones are reduced in size and connected to each other by elastic ligaments. This gives snakes a remarkable capacity to stretch their mouths. Some snakes can swallow food items that are larger than their heads (see Chapter 39). Snakes also have well-developed sensory systems for detecting prey. The flicking tongue carries airborne molecules to sensory receptors in the roof of the mouth. Most snakes can detect vibrations on the ground and some, such as rattlesnakes, have heat-sensing organs (see Figure 45.39, Chapter 45). Many snakes kill by constriction, which suffocates prey. Other species produce venoms, toxins that immobilize, kill, and partially digest prey. Snakes that take larger prey tend to be ambush hunters.

27.15b Crocodiles and Alligators

The 21 species of alligators and crocodiles, along with birds, are the living remnants of the archosaurs **(Figure 27.108)**. Crocodylians are aquatic predators that eat other vertebrates. Striking anatomical adaptations distinguish them from living lepidosaurs, including a four-chambered heart (see Chapters 19 and 41) that is homologous to the heart in birds, analogous to this structure in mammals. In some crocodylians, muscles that originate on the pubis insert on the liver and pericardium. When these muscles contract, the liver moves toward the tail, creating negative pressure in the chest cavity and drawing air in. This situation is analogous to the role of the diaphragm in mammals.

The snouts of alligators are broad compared to those of crocodiles. But the gavial has the longest and narrowest snout of living crocodylians. Saltwater crocodiles (*Crocodylus porosus*) and Nile crocodiles are the largest living reptiles, reaching up to 8 m in length.

American alligators (*Alligator mississippiensis*) exhibit strong maternal behaviour, perhaps reflecting their relationship to birds. Females guard their nests ferociously and, after the young hatch, free their offspring from the nest. The young stay close to the mother for about a year, feeding on scraps that fall from her mouth and living under her watchful protection.

Many species of alligators and crocodiles are endangered because their habitats have been disrupted by human activities. They have been hunted for their meat and leather and because larger individuals are predators of humans. There is hope, however, as some populations of American alligators have recovered in the wake of efforts to protect them. In Africa and Australia, crocodiles are farmed for their meat and skin.

In the past, crocodylians were more diverse in body form than modern species. During the Mesozoic, there were running (cursorial) species as well as others showing specializations of teeth strikingly similar to those of mammals. These included teeth with narrow cutting edges, like the carnassial teeth (see Section 27.17b) of carnivorous mammals.

STUDY BREAK QUESTIONS

1. How do snakes kill their prey?
2. What features of crocodilians are homologous to those of birds? Which ones are analogous to those of mammals?

27.16 Birds

Birds (or aves) appeared in the Jurassic as descendants of carnivorous, bipedal, theropod dinosaurs (see Figure 19.9, Chapter 19). Birds belong to the archosaur lineage, and their evolutionary relationship to dinosaurs is evident in their skeletal anatomy and in the scales on their legs and feet. Powered flight gave birds access to new **adaptive zones**, likely contributing to their astounding evolutionary success. Some species of birds are flightless, and some of these are bipedal runners. Other birds are weak fliers.

Three skeletal features associated with flight in birds are the **keeled sternum** (breastbone), the **furculum** (wishbone), and the **uncinate processes** on the ribs **(Figure 27.109)**. The keel on the sternum anchors the flight muscles, and the furculum acts like a spring, storing and releasing energy and making muscle contraction more efficient. The uncinate processes, which effect overlap of adjoining ribs, give the ribcage strength

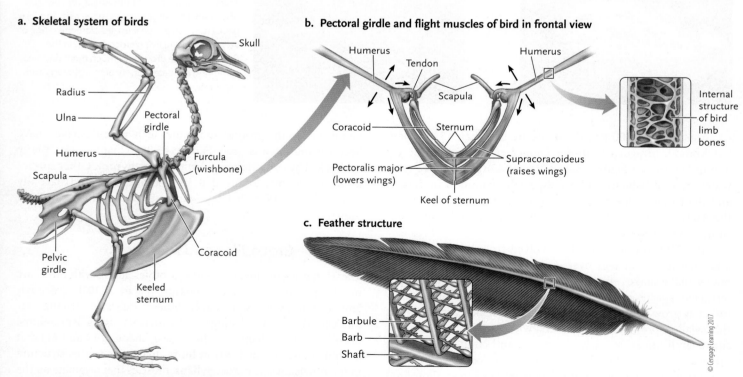

a. Skeletal system of birds

Skull
Radius
Ulna
Pectoral girdle
Humerus
Scapula
Furcula (wishbone)
Pelvic girdle
Coracoid
Keeled sternum

b. Pectoral girdle and flight muscles of bird in frontal view

Humerus
Tendon
Humerus
Scapula
Coracoid
Sternum
Pectoralis major (lowers wings)
Supracoracoideus (raises wings)
Keel of sternum
Internal structure of bird limb bones

c. Feather structure

Barbule
Barb
Shaft

© Cengage Learning 2017

FIGURE 27.109 Flying birds generate lift and propulsion by flapping their wings. (a) The bird skeleton includes a boxlike trunk, short tail, long neck, lightweight skull and beak, and well-developed limbs. In large birds, limb bones are hollow. **(b)** Two sets of flight muscles originate on the keeled sternum: one set raises the wings; the other lowers them. **(c)** Flexible feathers form an airfoil on the wing surface.

and they anchor intercostal muscles. In flightless species, the sternum often lacks a keel **(Figure 27.110)**, penguins that "fly" through the water retain the keel, making them an exception. However, flightless species often have uncinate processes.

Birds' skeletons are light and strong. The skeleton of a 1.5 kg frigate bird (*Fregata magnificens*) weighs just 100 g, far less than the mass of its feathers. The bones of birds tend to be lighter and less dense than those of mammals. Most birds have hollow limb bones with small supporting struts that crisscross the internal cavities. Birds have reduced numbers of separate bony elements in the wings, skull, and vertebral column (especially the tail), so the skeleton is rigid. The bones associated with flight are generally large, and the wing bones are long. In general, the skeleton reflects the bird's way of life. Note that many birds have sclerotic rings, which are bones in the eye.

The approximately 9000 living bird species show extraordinary ecological specializations built on the same body plan. Living birds are traditionally classified into nearly 30 orders **(Figure 27.111)**. Rather than teeth, all extant birds use a dense, heavy, keratinized bill for feeding. Bird bills show considerable diversity, reflecting different feeding behaviours. Birds offer many examples of convergence, such as species that feed at flowers: the hummingbirds of the New World and the sunbirds of the Old World. Many species have a long, flexible neck that allows them to use their bills for feeding, grooming, nest building, and social interactions. Keratinized bills can also be very light, even the spectacular bills of hornbills and toucans **(Figure 27.112)**. A bird's bill usually reflects its diet. Seed and nut eaters, such as finches and

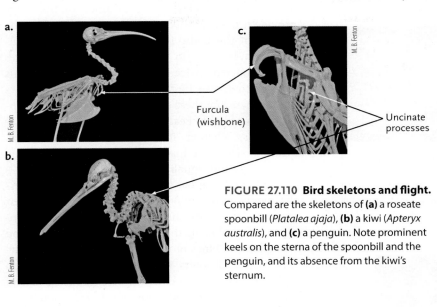

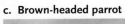

FIGURE 27.110 Bird skeletons and flight. Compared are the skeletons of **(a)** a roseate spoonbill (*Platalea ajaja*), **(b)** a kiwi (*Apteryx australis*), and **(c)** a penguin. Note prominent keels on the sterna of the spoonbill and the penguin, and its absence from the kiwi's sternum.

Furcula (wishbone)

Uncinate processes

a. European starling

b. Downy woodpecker

c. Brown-headed parrot

d. Turkey vulture

e. White-bellied sunbird

f. Ruby-throated hummingbird

FIGURE 27.111 The six species shown here illustrate some of the diversity of bills of extant birds. Included are **(a)** the generalist European starling (*Sturnus vulgaris*), **(b)** a downy woodpecker (*Picoides pubescens*), **(c)** a brown-headed parrot (*Poicephalus cryptoxanthus*), **(d)** a turkey vulture (*Cathartes aura*), **(e)** a white-bellied sunbird (*Cinnyris talatala*), and **(f)** a ruby-throated hummingbird (*Archilochus colubris*).

a.

b.

c.

d.

FIGURE 27.112 Both green aracari, such as **(a)** the toucan (*Pteroglossus viridis*), and hornbills, such as **(b)** the yellow-billed hornbill (*Tockus leucomelas*), have enlarged bills. **(c)** A Malabar pied hornbill, *Anthracoceros coronatus*. The details of the bill of a Malabar pied hornbill **(d)** show how the keratinized bill overlies porous bone, making the whole structure strong but lightweight.

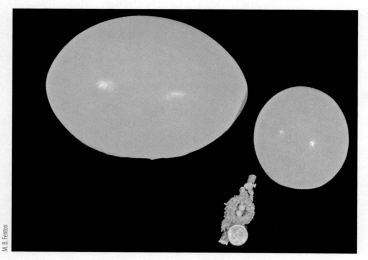

FIGURE 27.113 Bird eggs range in size from those of elephant birds (*Aepyornis* of Madagascar, left) to ostriches (*Struthio camelus*, right) to hummingbirds (bottom). The scale: a Canadian $2 coin is 2.8 cm in diameter.

parrots, have deep, stout bills that crack hard shells. Carnivorous hawks and carrion-eating vultures have sharp beaks to rip flesh. Nectar-feeding hummingbirds and sunbirds have long slender bills to reach into flowers, although many perching birds also have slender bills to feed on insects. The bills of ducks are modified to extract particulate matter from water.

Birds' soft internal organs are modified to reduce mass. Most birds lack a urinary bladder, so uric acid paste is eliminated with digestive wastes. Females have only one ovary and never carry more than one mature egg at a time. Eggs are laid as soon as they are shelled. Egg sizes give an indication of the

range of size in birds **(Figure 27.113)**. Birds range in size from a bee hummingbird (*Mellisuga helenae*) at 2 g, to ostriches (*Struthio camelus*) at about 150 kg.

All living birds have **feathers (Figure 27.114)**, sturdy, lightweight structures derived from scales in the skin of their reptilian ancestors. Each feather has numerous barbs and barbules with tiny hooks and grooves that maintain the feathers' structures, even during vigorous activity. Flight feathers on the wings provide lift, whereas contour feathers streamline the surface of the body. Down feathers form an insulating cover close to the skin. Moulting replaces feathers once or twice each year. But not all animals with feathers are birds. Several extinct archosaurs had feathers, but these animals had none of the adaptations for flight. Feathers may have originated as insulators, whether for keeping heat out or in. Feathers also serve many other functions, including camouflage and signalling.

Other adaptations for flight allow birds to harness the energy needed to power their flight muscles. Their metabolic rates are 8–10 times as high as those of comparably sized reptiles, allowing them to process energy-rich food rapidly. A complex and efficient respiratory system and a four-chambered heart (see Chapters 40, 19, and 41) enable them to consume and distribute oxygen efficiently. As a consequence of high rates of metabolic heat production, most birds maintain a high and constant body temperature (see Chapter 42).

Flying birds were abundant by the Cretaceous. Even in the Jurassic, *Archaeopteryx* had a furculum and was capable of at least limited flight. Until 2008, two main theories purported to explain the evolution of flight in birds. Proponents of the *top-down* theory argued that ancestral birds lived in trees and glided down from them in pursuit of insect prey. Gliding and access to prey are key elements of this theory. Proponents of the *bottom-up* theory proposed that a protobird was a runner (cursorial) and ran in pursuit of prey and jumped up to catch it.

In 2008, Kenneth P. Dial and two colleagues proposed the *ontogenetic-transitional wing* (OTW) hypothesis to explain the evolution of flight in birds. They asserted that the transitional stages leading to the development of flight in modern birds corresponded to its evolutionary development. Key to the OTW theory is the observation that, in developing from flightless hatchlings to flight-capable juveniles, individual birds move their protowings in the same ways as adults move fully developed wings. Dial and his colleagues noted that flap-running allows as yet flightless birds to move over obstacles. The OTW theory provides another look at the evolution of flight, and its predictions can be tested with fledglings of extant species. The combination of wings and bipedalism is central to the OTW hypothesis. Birds are bipedal, and pterosaurs may have been. Bats, however, are not bipedal, so the OTW hypothesis does not explain the evolution of flight in that group.

The first known radiation of birds produced the enantiornithines ("opposite" birds), the dominant birds of the

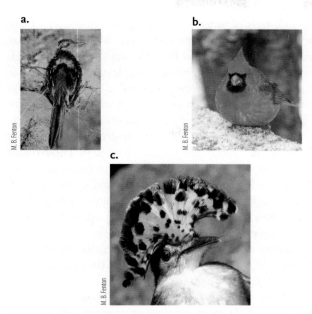

M. B. Fenton (appears for images a, b, c)

FIGURE 27.114 Feathers can serve a thermoregulatory and/or a signalling function. (a) A roadrunner (*Geococcyx californianus*) lifts feathers on its back to warm up by exposing underlying dark areas to the morning sun. Contrasting colour patterns enhance communication in **(b)** a male northern cardinal (*Cardinalis cardinalis*) and **(c)** a female royal flycatcher (*Onychorhynchus coronatus*).

Jurassic and Cretaceous. Ornithurines are modern birds **(Figure 27.115)**. Like dinosaurs, many mammals, and other organisms, the enantiornithines did not survive the extinctions that marked the end of the Cretaceous (see Chapter 28). Many enantiornithines flew, reflected by keeled sterna, furcula, and other "modern" skeletal features. Others, such as *Hesperornis*, were swimmers that used their feet for propulsion and, unlike penguins, had unkeeled sterna. Ornithurines include modern groups of wading birds and seabirds, first known from late Cretaceous rocks. Woodpeckers, perching birds, birds of prey, pigeons, swifts, the flightless ratites, penguins, and some other groups were all present by the end of the Oligocene. Birds continued to diversify through the Miocene.

All birds have well-developed sensory and nervous systems, and their brains are proportionately larger than those of comparably sized diapsids. Large eyes provide sharp vision, and most species also have good hearing, which nocturnal hunters such as owls use to locate prey. Vultures and some other species have a good sense of smell, which they use to find food. Migrating birds use polarized light, changes in air pressure, and Earth's magnetic field for orientation.

Many birds exhibit complex social behaviour, including courtship, territoriality, and parental care. Many species use vocalizations and visual displays to challenge other individuals

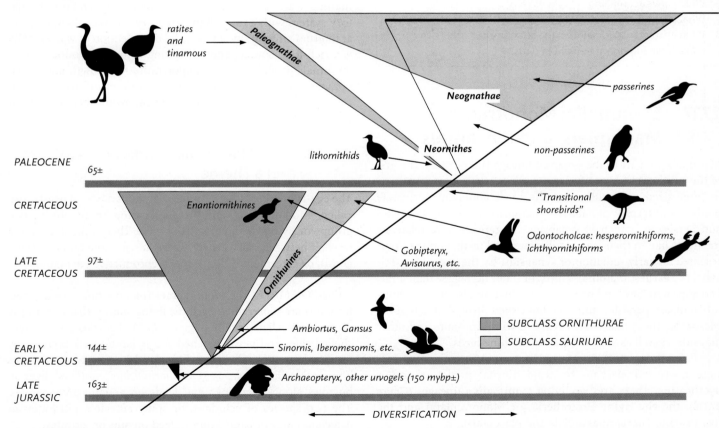

FIGURE 27.115 Evolution of birds. Enantiornithines, or opposite birds, were dominant in the Mesozoic but coexisted with ornithurine (more modern) birds in the early Cretaceous. The enantiornithines did not survive the extinctions at the end of the Cretaceous. By the Miocene, passerine birds had become the dominant land birds. Names of genera for some fossil birds make it easier to find more information about these animals.

Source: From Alan Feduccia, "Explosive Evolution in Tertiary Birds and Mammals," *Science* 3 February 1995: Vol. 267 no. 5198 pp. 637-638. *Science* by American Association for the Advancement of Science Reproduced with permission of AMERICAN ASSOCIATION FOR THE ADVANCEMENT OF SCIENCE in the format Republish in a book via Copyright Clearance Center.

or attract mates. Most raise their young in nests, using body heat to incubate eggs. The nest may be a simple depression on a gravel beach, a cup woven from twigs and grasses, or a feather-lined hole in a tree.

Many bird species make semi-annual, long-distance migrations (see Chapter 32). Golden plovers (*Pluvialis dominica*) and the godwit (*Limosa lapponica*) migrate over 20 000 km a year going to and from their summer and winter ranges. Migrations are a response to seasonal changes in climate. Birds travel toward the tropics as winter approaches; in spring, they return to high latitudes to breed and to use seasonally abundant food sources.

Some people think that birds can fly because of air spaces within their bones. In reality, many of the bones of birds are laminated structures with hollows that reduce the density of their skeletons, but this is true even of flightless birds such as ostriches. Birds, bats, pterosaurs, and insects fly because they have wings and muscles to flap them, in addition to other morphological and physiological specializations. ⬢

STUDY BREAK QUESTIONS

1. What three skeletal features are associated with bird flight? Which ones are missing in flightless birds?
2. What adaptations make flight possible in birds and pterosaurs?
3. What characteristics maintain the structure of feathers and make them important to flight in birds?

27.17 Mammalia: Monotremes, Marsupials, and Placentals

Mammals are part of the synapsid lineage (therapsids), the first of the amniotes to diversify. During the late Paleozoic, medium- to large-sized synapsids were the most abundant vertebrate predators in terrestrial habitats. Therapsids were one successful and persistent branch of synapsids. Therapsids were relatively mammal-like in their legs, skulls, jaws, and teeth, and they represented an early radiation of synapsids. By the end of the Triassic, the earliest mammals (most of them no bigger than a rat) had appeared. Several lineages of early mammals, such as multituberculates, persisted and even flourished through much of the Mesozoic. These mammals coexisted with dinosaurs and other diapsids, as well as with the enantiornithine birds.

Paleontologists hypothesize that most Mesozoic mammals were nocturnal, perhaps to avoid diurnal predators and/or overheating. There are two living mammalian lineages **(Figure 27.116)**: the egg-laying Prototheria (or Monotremata) and the live-bearing Theria (marsupials and placentals).

Several features distinguish mammals from other vertebrates, but mammalian diversity makes it difficult to generalize absolutely about definitive characteristics. Living mammals are relatively easy to recognize. They are usually furry and have a diaphragm (a sheet of muscle separating the chest cavity from the viscera); most are **endothermic** (warm blooded) and bear live young. In mammals, most blood leaves the heart through the **left aortic arch** (the main blood vessel leaving the heart; see Chapter 41). Mammals have two occipital condyles where the skull attaches to the neck, as well as a secondary palate (the plate of bones forming the roof of the mouth). They are **heterodont** and **diphyodont (Figure 27.117)**. Heterodont means that different teeth are specialized for different jobs. Diphyodont means that there are two generations of teeth (milk or deciduous teeth, and adult teeth). But some mammals have no teeth and others lay eggs. The secondary palate allows mammals to breathe and chew, or breathe while sucking without releasing hold on the nipple, an essential part of nursing.

Endothermy means that mammals typically maintain an elevated and stable body temperature so that they can be active under different environmental conditions. They can do this because of their metabolic rates and insulation. Heterodont teeth make mammals more efficient at mechanically dealing with their food (chewing), reducing the lag between the time food is consumed and when the energy in it is available to the consumer. Heterodont teeth are correlated with improved jaw articulation, in mammals between the dentary (lower jaw) and squamosal (bone on the skull). The diaphragm means that mammals are reasonably efficient at breathing, and the circulatory system with a four-chambered heart makes them efficient at internal circulation of resources or collection of wastes. Milk is a rich food source, and by feeding it to their young, female mammals provide the best opportunity for growth and development. The **cortex** of the brain is central to information processing and learning. Mammals' brains are another key to their evolutionary success.

27.17a The Mammalian Radiation: Variations on a Theme

The egg-laying Prototheria (*proto* = first; *theri* = wild beast), also called "Monotremata," and the live-bearing Theria are the two groups of living mammals. Among the Theria, the Metatheria (*meta* = between), also called *marsupials*, and the Eutheria (*eu* = good), or placentals, differ in their reproductive adaptations.

MONOTREMATA The **monotremes** (*mono* = one; *trema* = perforation) are represented by three living species that occur only in the Australian region **(Figure 27.118)**. Females lay leathery shelled eggs, and newly hatched young lap up milk secreted by modified sweat glands (mammary glands) on the mother's belly. The duck-billed platypus (*Ornithorhynchus anatinus*) lives in burrows along riverbanks and feeds on aquatic invertebrates. The two species of echidnas, or spiny anteaters (*Tachyglossus aculeatus* and *Zaglossus bruijni*), feed on ants or termites.

MARSUPIALIA Represented by 240 species, marsupials (*marsupion* = purse; Metatheria) are characterized by short **gestation** periods. The young are briefly (as few as 8–10 days in some

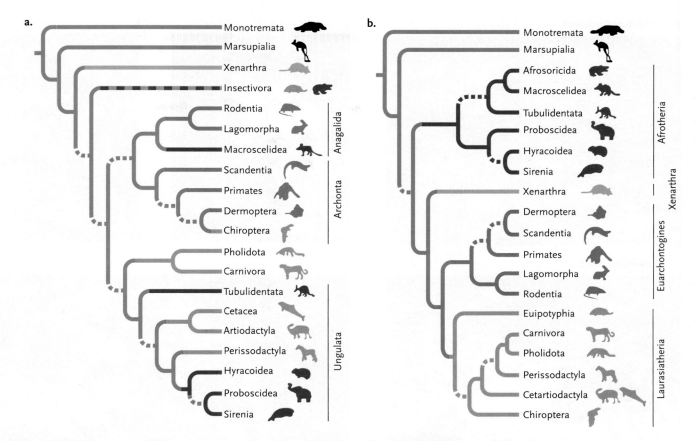

FIGURE 27.116 Modern mammals. Prevailing phylogenies of mammals derived from **(a)** morphological and **(b)** molecular data

Source: Mark S. Springer, Michael J. Stanhope, Ole Madsen and Wilfried W. de Jong, "Molecules consolidate the placental mammal tree," 19(8), 2004: 430-438, *Trends in Ecology & Evolution* by TRENDS JOURNALS. Reproduced with permission of TRENDS JOURNALS in the format Book via Copyright Clearance Center.

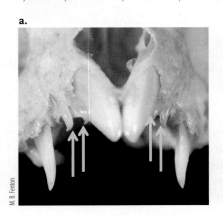

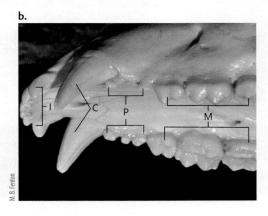

FIGURE 27.117 Mammal teeth. In most mammals, the teeth are diphyodont, meaning that milk (deciduous) teeth are replaced by permanent teeth. **(a)** The skull of a vampire bat (*Desmodus rotundus*) clearly shows four deciduous teeth (arrows), as well as permanent teeth. The teeth of mammals are also heterodont, meaning that different teeth are specialized to do different jobs. **(b)** In this bear (*Ursus americanus*), incisors (I), a canine (C), **premolars** (P), and molars (M) are obvious.

species and up to 30 days in others) nourished in the uterus via a placenta and are then born at an early stage of development. Newborns use their forelimbs to drag themselves from the vagina and across the mother's belly fur to her abdominal pouch, the marsupium, where they complete their development attached to a teat. Marsupials are prevalent among the native mammals of Australia and are also diverse in South America **(Figure 27.119)**. One species, the opossum (*Didelphis virginiana*), occurs as far north as Canada. South America once had a diverse marsupial fauna, which declined after the Isthmus of Panama bridged the seaway between North America and South America (see Chapter 18), allowing placental mammals to move southward.

EUTHERIA Placental mammals are represented by 4000 living species. They complete embryonic development in the mother's uterus, nourished through a **placenta**, until they reach an advanced stage of development (**viviparous**). Some species, such as humans, are helpless at birth (**altricial**), but others, such as horses, are born with fur and are quickly mobile (**precocial**). Biologists divide the eutherians into about 18 orders, of which only 8 have more than 50 living species **(Figure 27.120)**. Rodents (Rodentia) make up about 45% of eutherian species, and bats (Chiroptera) make up another 22%. We belong to the primates, along with 169 other species, representing about 5% of the current mammalian diversity.

a. Short-nosed echidna

b. Duck-billed platypus

FIGURE 27.118 Monotremes. (a) The short-nosed echidna (*Tachyglossus aculeatus*) is terrestrial. **(b)** The duck-billed platypus (*Ornithorhynchus anatinus*) raises its young in a streamside burrow.

The diversity of eutherian mammals is reflected partly in modes of locomotion. Whales and dolphins (order Cetacea) and manatees and dugongs (order Sirenia) are descended from terrestrial ancestors, but live their entire lives in water. They can no longer function on land, unlike seals and walruses (order Carnivora), which feed under water but rest and breed on land. Bats (order Chiroptera) use wings for powered flight, and mammals from several lineages can glide.

Although early mammals appear to have been insectivorous, the diets of modern eutherians are diverse. Odd-toed ungulates (*ungula* = hoof) such as horses and rhinoceroses (order Perissodactyla), even-toed ungulates such as cows and

a.

b.

c.

FIGURE 27.119 Marsupials. (a) A kangaroo (*Macropus giganteus*) carries her joey in her pouch; **(b)** a male koala (*Phascolarctos cinereus*) naps; and **(c)** an opossum from Guyana (*Didelphis* species) emerges from its den after dark to feed.

camels (order Artiodactyla), and rabbits and hares (order Lagomorpha) are mainly vegetarian. Some of the vegetarians use fermentation to digest cellulose (see Chapter 39). **Carnivores** (order Carnivora) usually consume other animals, but some, such as the giant panda (*Ailuropoda melanoleuca*), are vegetarians. Most bats eat insects, but some feed on flowers, fruit, or nectar, and some, the vampires, consume blood. Many whales and dolphins prey on fishes and other animals, but some eat plankton. Some groups, including rodents and primates, feed opportunistically on both plant and animal matter. Ants and termites are the preferred food of a variety of mammals, both prototherian and therian.

27.17b Evolutionary Convergence and Mammalian Diversity

Eating mainly ants and termites is a common mammalian approach across the tropics and subtropics. This is true in the New World (South and Central America) and in Africa, Southeast Asia, and Australia **(Figure 27.121)**. Ant-eating mammals

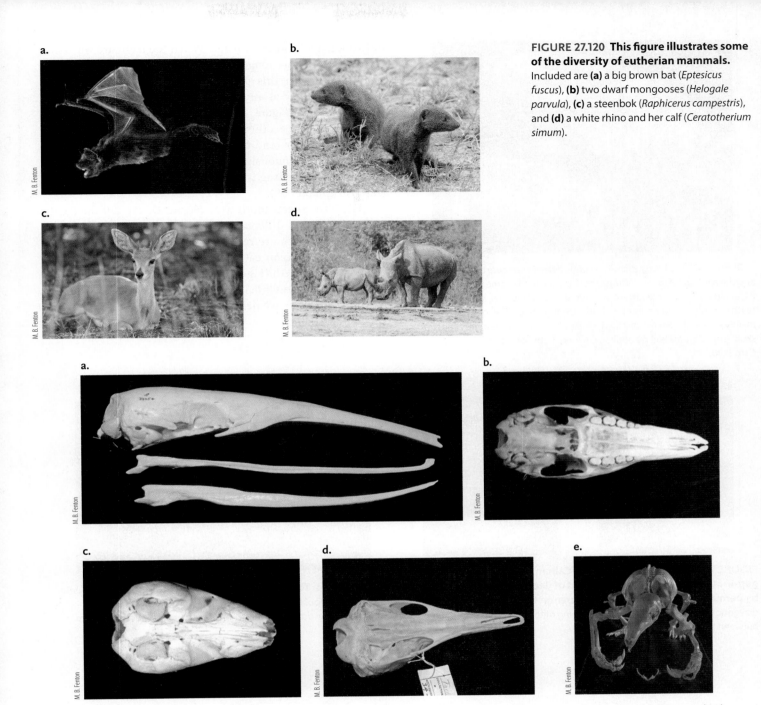

FIGURE 27.120 This figure illustrates some of the diversity of eutherian mammals. Included are **(a)** a big brown bat (*Eptesicus fuscus*), **(b)** two dwarf mongooses (*Helogale parvula*), **(c)** a steenbok (*Raphicerus campestris*), and **(d)** a white rhino and her calf (*Ceratotherium simum*).

FIGURE 27.121 Included here are ventral (palatal) views of the skulls and dentitions of **(a)** a giant anteater (*Myrmecophaga tridactyla*), **(b)** an aardvark (*Orycteropus afer*), **(c)** a pangolin (*Manis* spp), and **(d)** a spiny anteater (*Tachyglossus aculeatus*). **(e)** Also shown is a front view of a lesser anteater (*Tamandua tetradactyla*), showing forelimbs specialized for digging.

typically have no teeth or small peglike teeth, combined with long, extensible tongues. These animals often are excellent diggers, a reality reflected by specialized forelimbs (Figure 27.121e). Among the ant and termite eaters, aardwolves are the most strikingly different **(Figure 27.122)**. Aardwolves are most closely related to hyenas, species that eat larger prey and are equipped with very large teeth. Ants and termites are large, predictable, energy-rich foods, so it is little wonder that mammalian lineages

such as monotremes, marsupials, and eutherians have specialized on them as food. Specializations for eating ants and termites appear in four eutherian orders.

Mammals with teeth typically have two generations, milk teeth and permanent teeth **(Figure 27.123)**. This occurs because, in young mammals, the jaw bones are too small to accommodate permanent teeth. Whereas reptiles, amphibians, fish, and sharks can replace teeth many times, mammals replace them

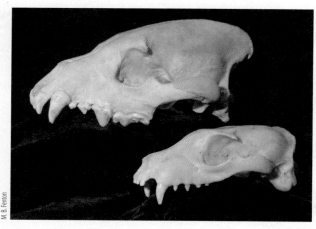

FIGURE 27.122 **Divergence.** The spotted hyena (*Crocuta crocuta;* top) and the aardwolf (*Proteles cristatus;* bottom) are in the same family (Hyaenidae). The spotted hyena is a carnivorous scavenger with massive teeth capable of cutting tendons and crushing bones. The aardwolf eats mainly ants and termites and has reduced teeth (and a differently shaped skull). The *Crocuta* skull is about 30 cm long. Both belong to the order Carnivora.

only once. Teeth wear with age. When the teeth are worn out, the animal can no longer feed itself properly and dies. Elephants deal with this problem by having only four active molars in the jaw at any one time. The new molar grows in from the back **(Figure 27.124)**, replacing the worn one. In rodents and some other mammals (and also in hadrosaur dinosaurs), molar (and for rodents and lagomorphs, incisor) teeth grow continuously. Here the teeth are curved so that pressure during biting is not directed at the points of growth (see also Chapter 39).

Diet also affects tooth wear **(Figure 27.125)**. Off the Pacific coast of Canada, different groups of killer whales have different diets, which are reflected by tooth wear. Killer whales from the open ocean eat mainly sharks whose abrasive skin causes wear on teeth (Figure 27.125a). The patterns of wear are different on resident killer whales that eat mainly fish (salmon), or transient killer whales that eat mainly marine mammals (Figure 27.125b, c).

a.

b.

FIGURE 27.123 **In mammals, such as Callum** (a) **and Iain** (b) **Downie, gap-toothed grins show replacement of deciduous (or milk) teeth by permanent teeth.** These pictures, taken on 16 July 2011, show dizygotic twins and illustrate that the timing of tooth replacement differs between them.

FIGURE 27.124 **Tooth wear and replacement.** Elephants (*Loxodonta africana*) have four functional molars in the mouth at any one time (one in each jaw quadrant). New molars push into the tooth row from the back.

FIGURE 27.125 Tooth wear on killer whales varies widely, depending on diet. For more information, see Ford et al., (2011) "Shark predation and tooth wear in a population of northeastern Pacific killer whales." *Aquatic Biology*. Vol. 11: 213–224 (dos: 10.3354/ab00307).

STUDY BREAK QUESTIONS

1. What features are found in most mammals and distinguish them from other vertebrates?
2. How is heterodont different from diphyodont?
3. Distinguish among monotremes, marsupials, and placentals.

Summary Illustration

Animals are heterotrophic, multicellular organisms that usually produce gametes and are grouped in about 40 phyla. Groupings by phylum reflect key characters and shared features. Arrangement by phylum typically has reflected body plans and symmetry as well as patterns of development, including number of germ layers. The types of body cavities also influence classification, as does genetic and molecular relatedness. Variability in life style and life history reflect the diversity of animals.

Key Innovations of Animals

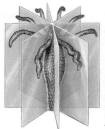

Symmetry
Animals can be asymmetric, radially symmetric, or bilaterally symmetric.

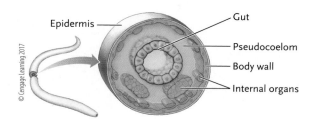

Body plans
Animals can have two or three germ layers. If an animal has three layers, it can be a pseudocoelomate, such as this worm, or a coelomate, such as a human. If only two germ layers are present, such as in flatworms, then these organisms are acoelomates.

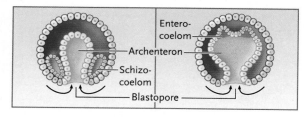

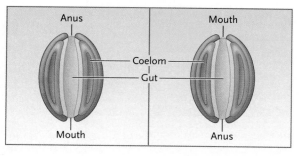

Protostomes vs. deuterostomes
What makes an animal a protostome or a deuterostome depends on how cleavage proceeds and how the archenteron, coelom, and the gut form in early development.

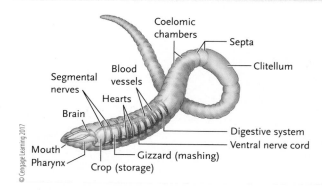

Segmentation
Some animals are segmented, and this separates some groups from others that are not. Segmentation divides the body into a series of repeating units, such as the worm shown here. Other annelids, the arthropods, and chordates (think vertebral column) are also segmented.

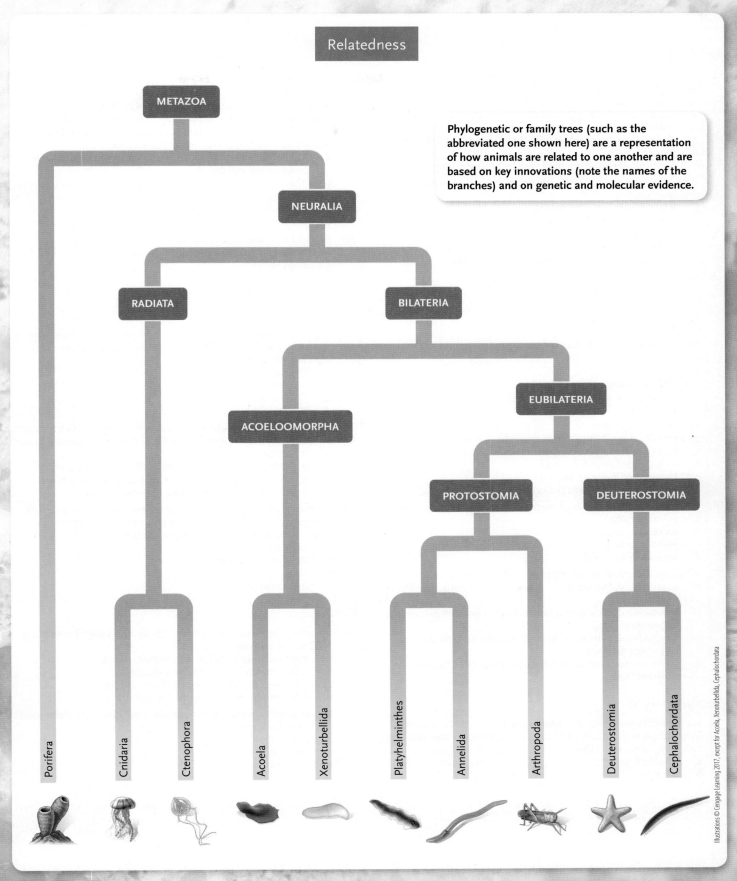

Relatedness

METAZOA

NEURALIA

RADIATA

BILATERIA

EUBILATERIA

ACOELOOMORPHA

PROTOSTOMIA

DEUTEROSTOMIA

Porifera

Cnidaria

Ctenophora

Acoela

Xenoturbellida

Platyhelminthes

Annelida

Arthropoda

Deuterostomia

Cephalochordata

Phylogenetic or family trees (such as the abbreviated one shown here) are a representation of how animals are related to one another and are based on key innovations (note the names of the branches) and on genetic and molecular evidence.

Illustrations © Cengage Learning 2017, except for Acoela, Xenoturbellida, Cephalochordata

Recall/Understand

1. Which of the following are considered to be key innovations in animal evolution?
   a. segmented bodies, patterns of body symmetry, heterotrophy
   b. segmented bodies, patterns of body symmetry, presence of different tissues
   c. multicellularity, segmented bodies, presence of different tissues
   d. multicellularity, segmented bodies, heterotrophy

2. Which of these characteristics distinguishes a protostome from a deuterostome?
   a. Protostomes are not animals.
   b. A protostome coelom forms from space within the outpocketing.
   c. Protostomes undergo spiral cleavage of the embryo.
   d. A protostome blastopore develops into an anus.

3. How many basal phyla do scientists identify?
   a. 1
   b. 2
   c. 3
   d. 4

4. Which phylum has a species count vastly greater than any other phylum?
   a. Cnidaria
   b. Echinodermata
   c. Arthropoda
   d. Chordata

5. Which of these features is an example of a unique internal anatomy of echinoderms among animals?
   a. lack of excretory and respiratory systems
   b. well-defined pseudocoelom
   c. incomplete digestive system
   d. lack of sensory cells in the skin

6. Which one of these body symmetries do echinoderms exhibit?
   a. primary radial
   b. secondary radial
   c. primary bilateral
   d. secondary bilateral

7. Which of these features are unique to all chordates?
   a. a notochord, but not a dorsal hollow nerve cord, gill slits, or a post-anal tail
   b. a notochord and a dorsal hollow nerve cord, but not gill slits or a post-anal tail
   c. a notochord, a dorsal hollow nerve cord, and gill slits, but not a post-anal tail
   d. a notochord, a dorsal hollow nerve cord, gill slits, and a post-anal tail

Apply/Analyze

8. Suppose that you found an unknown organism that is a motile heterotroph without cell walls in its body. Which of the following is this organism most likely?
   a. a bacterium
   b. a fungus
   c. an animal
   d. a plant

9. Suppose that you isolate one cell from a starfish embryo, and you continue culturing it in the lab, separate from the original embryo. What is most likely going to happen with the embryo and the isolated cell?
   a. The original embryo will develop into a starfish, but the isolated cell will die.
   b. The cell will develop into a starfish, but the original embryo will die.
   c. Each will develop into a starfish.
   d. Both will die.

10. Suppose that your friend found a medusa and you want to impress her. Which of these phyla can you correctly tell her that it belongs to?
    a. Cnidaria
    b. Arthropoda
    c. Echinodermata
    d. Porifera

11. Suppose that you go out for dinner and you order a seafood dish that contains clams, scallops, and mussels. Which class of animals are you about to eat?
    a. Cephalopoda
    b. Scaphopoda
    c. Gastropoda
    d. Bivalvia

12. Suppose that you expose a tardigrade to an extreme dehydration. Which of the following will most likely happen to the tardigrade?
    a. It will die right away.
    b. It will become more active and will search for water.
    c. It will dry out and turn into a dust in about a few hours.
    d. It will dry out, but will revive if placed in water.

13. Suppose that your friend asks you to provide one characteristic of insects that has a special importance for coevolution with plants. Which of the following could it be?
    a. mouthparts
    b. Malpighian tubules
    c. wings
    d. metamorphosis

Create/Evaluate

14. Which of these statements is the reason why a pseudocoelom is NOT a true coelom?
    a. It is not completely lined by the mesoderm.
    b. It is completely lined by the endoderm.
    c. It is not completely lined by the endoderm.
    d. It is completely lined by the mesoderm.

15. In which of these animals would you most likely find flame cells?
    a. round worms
    b. flatworms
    c. arrow worms
    d. tapeworms

16. In which of these animals would you most likely find a toothed radula?
    a. lobsters
    b. slugs
    c. worms
    d. corals

17. Animals may have arisen from a colonial, flagellated protist in which cells became specialized for specific functions. Explain why we think this might be true.

18. Provide an analogy for radial symmetry. Justify your selection.

19. What are *Hox* genes? Use examples to describe their importance.

20. Four key features of living amniotes allow life on dry land and liberate them from reliance on standing water. Describe these four features.

Chapter Roadmap

Conservation of Biodiversity

At almost every turn, there are examples of human activities driving other species to extinction. A range of examples associated with extinction and the threat of extinction are introduced in this chapter. Steps that can be taken to protect biodiversity, including some successes and some failures, are also considered.

28.1 The Anthropocene → To Chapter 30

28.2 Vulnerability to Extinction

From Chapter 8 → **28.3 Climate Change Can Cause Extinction**

28.4 Protecting Species

28.5 Protecting What?

28.6 Conservation and Agriculture

28.7 Contaminating Natural Systems

28.8 Motivation

28.9 Effecting Conservation

28.10 Human Population: A Root Problem for Conservation

28.11 Signs of Stress: Systems and Species

28.12 Taking Action

M.B. Fenton

M.B. Fenton

Two mounted specimens of passenger pigeons. These specimens are in the Zoological Collections of the Department of Biology at The University of Western Ontario. Unfortunately, specimens like these are all that remains of a once abundant species. The importance of such collections is obvious to those who try to understand evolution and extinction.

Conservation of Biodiversity

28

Why it matters . . . Martha, the last passenger pigeon (*Ectopistes migratorius*), died in the Cincinnati Zoo on 1 September 1914. This marked the death of a species, which is also known as an *extinction*. In the early 1800s, there may have been as many as 3.5 billion passenger pigeons in the wild in North America. These abundant and widespread birds seemed unlikely candidates for extinction. Human overharvesting of these tasty animals has been invoked to explain their disappearance. Huge flocks and breeding colonies made these birds easy targets for hunters. This pressure, combined with land clearing for agriculture, appeared to account for the birds' rapid extinction. Female passenger pigeons laid one egg a year (= clutch size of 1), making the species even more vulnerable to rapid declines in population.

In 2014, analysis of ancient DNA obtained from specimens of passenger pigeons allowed biologists and computer scientists to examine the details of populations of these birds. The results provide a different view of this extinction event. Various analyses using ecological niche models supported the view that populations of passenger pigeons showed dramatic oscillations in size. Genetic analyses indicated that the population of passenger pigeons showed no evidence of structures into sub-populations or subspecies. Further genetic analysis indicated a relatively small number of individuals contributing offspring to the population. Known as the *effective population size*, for passenger pigeons this was about 3.3×10^5. These analyses indicated a long-term, effective population size varying from 0.5 to 1.7×10^5 over the last million years, with a minimum of 2.1×10^4 at the end of the last glacial maximum. These estimates of effective population size are consistently about 1/10 000 of the census population presumed in the 1800s. By comparison, the effective population size for humans is 1.7×10^4, while the census population exceeds 7×10^9.

The extinction of the passenger pigeon should alert us to the reality that being abundant and widespread does not necessarily make a species secure in a conservation sense. Indeed, declines in populations can identify vulnerable species and alert us to the importance of taking steps to protect them. In the absence of information about population declines, population sizes can be misleading. For example, in 2005 in Ontario, Canada, the population estimate of an open field songbird, the bobolink (*Dolichonyx oryzivorus*; **Figure 28.1**), was 400 000 breeding pairs. By 2010 this had declined to 285 000 breeding pairs. Our experience with the passenger pigeon should alert us to the importance of using a steep decline in population to identify species that appear to be numerous yet are vulnerable to declining to extinction. And yet, listing the bobolink as a threatened species was not uniformly regarded as a prudent, timely step.

The onus is on us as citizens of the planet to conserve biodiversity, whether the focus is species or habitats. One of the main problems we must overcome is the attitude of many humans. Today a common reflection of this attitude is that being able to do something (afford to, have the means to) is justification enough for doing it—whether the project involves making space for a shopping mall by draining a wetland or cutting down the trees in a woodlot.

If we as a species can recognize the importance of biodiversity and accept that the world is not ours to do with as we please, what would we do next? What is the best route to protecting and conserving biodiversity? Should we focus on species? On genetic diversity? On ecosystems? How should we blend these approaches to achieve the best support for the endeavour? How can we engage people in this important activity and perhaps move them away from a human-centric view of the world?

As we shall see, at almost every turn there are examples of human activities driving other species to extinction. The motivations for human actions range from little more than greed to people's daily efforts to survive. The purpose of this chapter is to introduce you to a range of situations and examples associated with the reduction of biodiversity by extinction and the threat of extinction. We also consider steps that can be taken to protect biodiversity, including some successes and some failures.

28.1 The Anthropocene

In the past 500 years there has been a large increase in the size of the human population (see Figure 29.21). This increase coincides with greater habitat destruction and disruption as well as other by-products of human civilization. The trend continues, and further increases in the human population coincide with further destruction and modification of habitats. The period of the past 500 years is known as the *Anthropocene*. During this time, at least 322 species of terrestrial vertebrates have gone extinct, and the populations of an additional 25% of living species have declined considerably. The same general patterns emerge from data about invertebrate animals as those from plants. To many biologists, the Anthropocene is the "sixth major extinction," caused directly and indirectly by one species, *Homo sapiens*. But extinctions are an ongoing part of Earth's history, reflected in background rates of extinction. David Raup of the University of Chicago has estimated background rates at about 10% of species every one million years, 50% every 100 million years.

A mass extinction occurs when the rate of extinction rises well above the background rate. Before the Anthropocene, the fossil record indicates that there were at least five mass extinctions in Earth's history:

- First at the end of the Ordovician and beginning of the Devonian
- Second at the end of the Devonian
- Third at the end of the Permian
- Fourth at the end of the Triassic
- Fifth at the end of the Cretaceous.

The Permian extinction was the most severe, and more than 85% of the species alive then disappeared forever. This extinction was the end of the trilobites, many amphibians, and the trees of the coal swamp forests. At the end of the Cretaceous, the last mass extinction, half the species on Earth disappeared, including most dinosaurs.

Mass extinctions have a huge impact on the species that survive them. The losses of biodiversity (the numbers of species) affect the productivity and stability of ecosystems. At this stage in the Anthropocene, at least 50% of ice-free ecosystems have been converted to cropland and pasture. The remaining ecosystems are in varying stages of disturbance, which means changes in nutrient eutrophication, fire suppression, frequency of fire, decimation of predators, climate warming, and drought. Changes in plant diversity influence the levels of nitrogen, carbon dioxide, fire, levels of herbivory, and the availability of water.

An analysis of the situation documented by 12 multiyear studies revealed that changes in the diversity of plants (primary producers) profoundly affect the global environment. Work on

FIGURE 28.1 Bobolink

FotoRequest/Shutterstock.com

islands in the West Indies revealed that human factors more than geographic area and isolation determine species compositions of island communities of anole lizards. Today, foremost among the human-related factors are those relating to economic isolation and the introduction of exotic species.

Many researchers believe that an asteroid impact caused the Cretaceous mass extinction. The resulting dust cloud could have blocked the sunlight necessary for photosynthesis. This would have started a chain reaction of extinctions that began with microscopic marine organisms. Geologic evidence supports this hypothesis. Rocks dating to the end of the Cretaceous period (65 mya) contain a highly concentrated layer of iridium, a metal that is rare on Earth but common in asteroids. The impact from an iridium-laden asteroid only 10 km in diameter could have caused an explosion equivalent to a billion tonnes of TNT, scattering iridium dust around the world. Geologists have identified the likely site of the impact: the 180 km diameter submarine Chicxulub crater off Mexico's Yucatán peninsula.

Although scientists agree that an asteroid struck Earth then, many question its precise relationship to the mass extinction. Dinosaurs had begun their decline at least 8 million years earlier, and many persisted for at least 40 000 years after the impact. Moreover, other groups of organisms did not suddenly disappear, as one would expect after a global calamity. The Cretaceous extinction took place over tens of thousands of years. Furthermore, some organisms survived periods of extinction, such as ginkgo trees (*Ginkgo biloba*), horseshoe crabs (*Limulus polyphemus*), and coelacanths (*Latimeria chalumnae*).

Even today we cannot blame the extinctions of most species on the activities of humans. But our increasing technological capability and prowess coincide with a burgeoning population of people. This situation is exacerbated by the philosophical view that humans are disconnected from nature. Thus, we are becoming better and better at destroying the biota of the planet. Taking action requires identifying root causes and then trying to make changes that will alleviate the problems.

STUDY BREAK QUESTIONS

1. What is extinction?
2. What is the Anthropocene?
3. When did three major extinctions occur?
4. Why is iridium important in identifying the cause for the extinction of dinosaurs?

28.2 Vulnerability to Extinction

The passenger pigeon, a widespread and abundant species, was vulnerable because of a combination of human impact, small clutch size, and dramatic oscillations in sizes of populations. Here are five examples of pending, imminent, or recent extinctions. They illustrate the diversity of threats and the vulnerabilities of species.

28.2a Pacific Water Shrew

We expect that species occurring in small populations with a limited geographic distribution (range) are more vulnerable to extinction than species such as the passenger pigeon. Limited geographic distribution and specific habitat requirements typify the Pacific water shrew (*Sorex bendirii*; **Figure 28.2**), but other factors pose immediate threats to the species in Canada.

Pacific water shrews occur in a small area along the Pacific coast of North America (**Figure 28.3a**); there are few actual records of specimens of the animal in Canada (Figure 28.3b), suggesting a small population. To make matters worse, the prime habitat for Pacific water shrews in Canada is directly threatened by the urban sprawl of the city of Vancouver (Figure 28.3c). How long will they last?

28.2b Black Rhino

Black rhinos (*Diceros bicornis*) were widespread in Africa. Like the four other species of living rhinos, black rhinos teeter on the brink of extinction. In 1960 there may have been 60 000 black rhinos living in the wild (**Figure 28.4a**). This large (1.5 m at the shoulder, 1400 kg) browsing mammal was widespread in sub-Saharan Africa (Figure 28.4b). Adult males and females have two distinctive "horns" (**Figure 28.5a**; see also Figure 28.4a), actually formed from hair. Rhinos use the horns to protect themselves and their young from predators and other rhinos. By 1981, the populations in the wild had been reduced to between 10 000 and 15 000, and reduced further to about 3500 by 1987. In less than 30 years, the species was almost exterminated in the wild. Although black rhinos had been hunted as trophies, this source of mortality did not drive them to the brink of extinction.

People use rhino horn (Figure 28.5a) in different ways and it commands a high price in a competitive market. In China, bowls made from rhino horn (Figure 28.5b) were believed to have had magical properties, removing or neutralizing poisons. Therefore, travelling nobles were served wine in their own rhino horn bowls to minimize the chances of their being poisoned. In India and other areas, from India to the Koreas,

FIGURE 28.2 Pacific water shrew, a 10 g mammal with a small geographic range

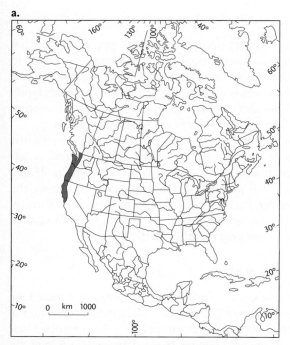

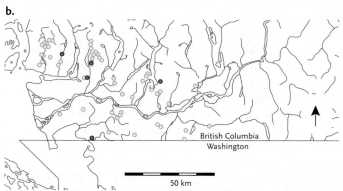

Baseline Thematic Mapping Present Land Use Mapping
at 1:220 000

COSEWIC Assessment and Update Status Report on the Pacific Water Shrew Sorex bendirii in Canada. 2006. Figure 2, p. 6.
© Her Majesty The Queen in Right of Canada, Environment Canada, 2014. Reproduced with the permission of the Minister
of Public Works and Government Services Canada.

COSEWIC Assessment and Update Status Report on the Pacific Water Shrew Sorex bendirii in Canada. 2006. Figure 5, p. 15. © Her Majesty The Queen in Right of
Canada, Environment Canada, 2014. Reproduced with the permission of the Minister of Public Works and Government Services Canada.

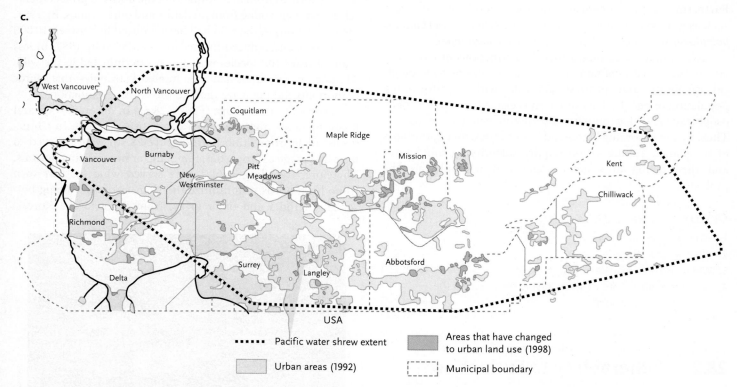

COSEWIC Assessment and Update Status Report on the Pacific Water Shrew Sorex bendirii in Canada. 2006. Figure 6, p. 18. Map prepared by Susan Jesson, BC Conservation Foundation 13-Oct. -04, while under contract with Environment Canada. © Her Majesty The Queen in Right of Canada, Environment Canada, 2014.
Reproduced with the permission of the Minister of Public Works and Government Services Canada.

FIGURE 28.3 **(a)** The distribution of *Sorex bendirii*, the Pacific water shrew. **(b)** Lower Fraser Valley locations where it was found (solid circles) or not found (open circles). **(c)** For comparison, the same area is shown with changes in the availability of urban lands in 1992 and 1998. Data on the map are from 2004.

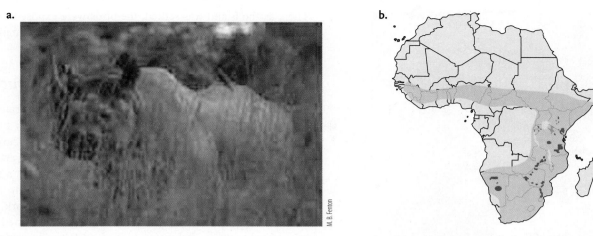

FIGURE 28.4 **(a)** Black rhinos (*Diceros bicornis*) were widespread and common in Africa in 1960 (orange area on the map in (b)). **(b)** Today their range (dark spots in orange areas) is much reduced, reflecting diminished populations. Note the oxpecker (*Buphagus africanus*; see Chapter 30) sitting on the rhino.

FIGURE 28.5 **(a)** A horn from a black rhino in Zimbabwe is shown with **(b)** a rhino horn bowl from China and **(c)** a jambiya with a rhino horn handle.

powdered rhino horn is used as a fever suppressant. Contrary to popular belief, rhino horn does not appear to have been used as an aphrodisiac, an early version of Viagra.

To some people of the Arabian Peninsula, a ceremonial dagger, a jambiya, is a symbol of status. Jambiyas with rhino horn handles (Figure 28.5c) are particularly highly prized. In 1973, when the price of oil jumped from US$4 to US$12 a barrel, the ensuing "energy crisis" meant a larger market for jambiyas because more people could afford them. Increased cash flow and easy access to military weapons such as Kalashnikov assault rifles (**Figure 28.6**) provided an incentive and a means to kill rhinos. The epidemic of poaching started in northern Kenya and spread southward throughout the continent. Poaching for their horns catastrophically reduced populations of black rhinos. Although black rhinos had long survived in the presence of predators, including *Homo sapiens*, they could not survive the poachers. In 1984, going for a walk at night around the headquarters of Mana Pools National Park in Zimbabwe almost always meant meeting a black rhino. By 1987, the rhinos were very scarce, and by 1990 they were gone from there.

FIGURE 28.6 A Kalashnikov assault rifle (an AK), a weapon widely used in the poaching of animals in many parts of the world

28.2c American Ginseng

The case of the black rhino demonstrated how targeted harvesting can drive a species to the brink of extinction even when it is protected and lives mainly in national parks or game reserves. American ginseng (**Figure 28.7**) is another target species, now Endangered in Canada because of harvesting. The species used to grow wild from southwestern Quebec and southern Ontario south to Louisiana and Georgia. This 20- to 70 cm-tall perennial

FIGURE 28.7 **A herbarium specimen of American ginseng (*Panax quinquefolius*) collected in southwestern Ontario on 5 July 1890.** Herbarium collections too often are the only way to see specimens of plants that used to be common and abundant.

is long lived in rich, moist, mature, sugar maple–dominated woods. In Canada, the species has been protected since 1973, but populations continued to decline. In 2000, there were 22 viable populations in Ontario and Quebec, but none was secure. Black rhinos and ginseng had been common about 50 years ago, but by 2008, both demonstrated the risks of being rare and valuable. They are also examples of the need for immediate on-the-ground enforcement of regulations and laws protecting species and habitats.

28.2d Mauritian Calvaria Tree

If you visit the island of Mauritius, you might notice that the few remaining Mauritian Calvaria trees (*Sideroxylon majus*) are slowly dying of old age. Their passing will mark the extinction of this species. This will occur even though the trees have continued to bloom and produce seeds. The key to the pending extinction of the Mauritian Calvaria tree is the earlier extinction of dodos. To germinate, seeds of these trees had to pass through the dodo's digestive tract. The dodo (**Figure 28.8**) was a medium-sized flightless bird that lived on the island of Mauritius. When European sailors first visited the island, they used dodos as fresh meat.

Then, as the island was settled, the birds were exposed to introduced predators (cats, dogs, rats) and an expanding human population. Dodos had vanished by 1690.

28.2e Little Brown Myotis (*Myotis lucifugus*)

Like many other species of bats living in the temperate zones of the world, little brown myotis (*Myotis lucifugus*) pass the winter hibernating in underground sites, typically caves and abandoned mines. This behaviour and strategy for overwintering was the norm for these bats, but the arrival of a fungus from Europe turned what had been safe sites into deadly places. In March 2006, at sites near Albany, New York, biologists counting bats hibernating in caves and abandoned mines were shocked to find thousands of dead bats where they had expected thousands of live ones. The bats had died from white-nose syndrome (WNS), caused by a cold-loving fungus (*Pseudogymnoascus destructans*; formerly *Geomyces destructans*) that interrupted their rhythm of hibernation. Some infected bats were easy to recognize by the white fungus like structures around their nostrils (**Figure 28.9**). To survive hibernation, bats minimize the number of times they arouse from torpor because of the metabolic cost of waking up (raising the body temperature from 2°C–5°C to over 35°C). At most Canadian hibernation sites, bats normally go about 90 days between arousals because each arousal costs them energy that they would use in 60 days of hibernation. WNS causes them to arouse much more often and exhaust their stores of body fat in January or February, well before spring and the re-appearance of insect prey.

The initial focal area for WNS in North America was specific sites around Albany. By March 2010, WNS had spread to underground hibernation sites in Ontario and Quebec, as well as many other sites in the United States. In March 2016, WNS had been reported from hibernation sites in Washington State. In the intervening years, WNS continued to spread, in Canada arriving at sites at the west end of Lake Superior by March 2015. In March 2016, WNS had not yet been reported from sites in Newfoundland and Labrador.

FIGURE 28.8 (a) **A reconstruction of a *Raphus cucullatus*, the dodo, an extinct, flightless bird from** (b) **Mauritius**

Photo by Lesley Hale

FIGURE 28.9 Five little brown myotis, one (middle) showing characteristic signs of infection by the fungus *Pseudogymnoascus destructans* that causes white-nose syndrome (WNS) in bats that hibernate underground in the United States and Canada

The spread of WNS surely reflects the movements and behaviour of the bats. American bat biologists estimate that, in 2005, there were over 6 million little brown myotis in the American northeast. These bats may well be extirpated (wiped out) from there by 2020.

At known hibernation sites, populations of little brown myotis declined by over 95%. Professor Craig Willis from the University of Winnipeg and his colleagues demonstrated that the strain of the fungus causing WNS in North American bats originated in Europe. It was presumably inadvertently transferred to the sites near Albany by cave explorers or bat biologists. The European strain did not cause WNS in bats there, just as the North American strain did not cause WNS in bat species from North America.

Can the populations of little brown myotis recover? Probably not, because, like most bats, little brown myotis live in the slow life-history lane (see Chapter 29). They reproduce slowly (a single young per year) and, like most species of bats of the temperate regions, up to 60% of young do not survive their first year. The combination of low reproductive output and low survival of first year translates into low potential for increase of their populations.

There are 19 species of bats in Canada but not all are exposed to WNS because only some hibernate underground. So, perhaps WNS does not mean the end of our bats, but likely the loss of more than half the species. WNS is a stark example of how a widespread and abundant species can become endangered.

Other species of fungi put other wildlife at risk. Perhaps best known is *Batrachochytrium dendrobatidis*, a pathogenic fungus apparently responsible for a global decline in populations of amphibians. Still other pathogenic fungi affect snakes, corals, and bees.

STUDY BREAK QUESTIONS

1. What do ginseng and black rhinos have in common?
2. What harm can pathogenic fungi do?
3. What is causing the extinction of the Mauritian Calvaria tree?
4. What role do AKs play in poaching?

28.3 Climate Change Can Cause Extinction

Failure to reproduce can drive a species to extinction. Anything that interferes with reproduction can threaten a species' survival (e.g., Mauritian Calvaria tree). Genetic recombination is a fundamental benefit of sexual reproduction, enabling increases in genetic diversity and elimination of deleterious mutants. Effective sexual reproduction means having male and female systems, sometimes in one individual (hermaphrodites), more often in different individuals. Males and females differ in many fundamental ways: genetically, hormonally, physiologically, and anatomically.

In humans and many other animals, gender is determined by genotype, with males having an X and a Y chromosome and females having two X chromosomes. The reverse is true in many other animals, for example in birds. In many reptiles, gender is determined environmentally. Eggs incubated at some temperatures develop into males; when incubated at other temperatures, they produce females.

In 2008, D. A. Warner and R. Shine reported the results of experiments done with jacky dragons (*Amphibolurus muricatus*; **Figure 28.10**), Australian lizards in which gender is determined by temperature. Eggs incubated at 23°C–26°C or 30°C–33°C produce females; those incubated at 27°C–29°C produce males. Warner and Shine tested the hypothesis that temperature-dependent sex determination ensured production of females when they had an advantage and males when the advantage was to them. Using a combination of temperature and hormonal manipulations, Warner and Shine could produce males or females at any temperature. They analyzed paternity to assess the reproductive output of these males, and observed eggs laid and hatched to document these females' reproductive output.

In female jacky dragons, larger body sizes occur at higher temperatures, and larger females have higher fecundity than smaller ones. Higher temperatures also correlate with larger body size in males. However, males hatched from eggs incubated

Belle Ciezak/Shutterstock.com

FIGURE 28.10 A jacky (or tree) dragon

between 27°C and 29°C sired more offspring than those hatched from eggs incubated at lower or higher temperatures.

Change in climate, such as global warming, could put species with temperature-dependent sex determination at risk by effectively eliminating males or females from the population. Eggs incubated at the wrong temperatures would fail to hatch. The importance of variation in temperature during development in ectothermic organisms could explain the prevalence of genotypic-dependent sex determination in euthermic (homeothermic) viviparous animals. Viviparous or ovoviviparous ectotherms (fish, amphibians, reptiles, other animals) could also rely on temperature-dependent gender determination, provided that their developing young experience an appropriate range of temperatures.

Recent work from Mexico reveals that, since 1975, 12% of local populations of lizards have disappeared, likewise 4% of worldwide local populations. Like other ectotherms, lizards have a narrow thermal range in which they thrive, and climate change has altered the thermal niches available to them. This and temperature-dependent gender determination put lizards in double jeopardy.

Long term observations across Europe and North America reveal that, over 110 years, there have been changes in the geographic distributions of 67 species of bumblebees. In both areas, compression of geographic ranges coincides with negative effects of climate change. These changes in the distributions of bumblebees are over and above those caused by the use of insecticides. Climate change also has affected marine vertebrates. The most prevalent mechanisms of change are physiological responses and changes in predator–prey interactions associated with changes in climate.

STUDY BREAK QUESTIONS

1. What is temperature-dependent sex determination?
2. How does temperature-dependent sex determination relate to climate change?

28.4 Protecting Species

The widespread recognition of trademarks such as the World Wildlife Fund (WWF) panda is an example of successfully associating a cause with an icon. It is not surprising that many conservation efforts began with a focus on one species—such as giant pandas (*Ailuropoda melanoleuca*; **Figure 28.11**), polar bears (*Ursus maritimus*), and redwood trees (*Sequoia sempervirens*). The lure of conservation movements that focus on charismatic species is very strong. But some charismatic organisms may not need protection, while other species that are unattractive, dangerous, or mundane desperately need our assistance. Unfortunately, mundane, ugly, and dangerous (to us) species are unlikely to serve as a call to arms (or to attract financial support). Worldwide, the WWF panda is one of the most recognized logos, whether or not pandas are in the neighbourhood.

FIGURE 28.11 A giant panda

A critical first step toward conservation is the development and adoption of objective, data-based criteria for assessing the risk posed to different species. This process has been developed on several fronts around the world. Governments and nongovernmental organizations (NGOs) focused on conservation typically use the criteria and assessment procedures perfected by the International Union for Conservation of Nature (IUCN). Conservation actions have sometimes successfully halted the march to extinction, but there are many more examples where we have failed. Making arguments based on data does not guarantee success. Using a data-based approach, some species emerge as being in need of protection, but others do not. Being rare or unusual, by itself, will not warrant protection. The species concept and the Linnaean system of nomenclature (see Chapter 19) are fundamental to conservation.

In Canada, federal and provincial committees are charged with assessing conservation status of species. Federally, recommendations about the conservation status of species involve the Committee on the Status of Endangered Wildlife in Canada (COSEWIC). The definition of wildlife includes plants and animals. Like IUCN, COSEWIC recognizes six categories for assessing species at risk:

- **Extinct** wildlife species no longer exist.
- **Extirpated** species no longer exist in one location/area in the wild but occur elsewhere.
- **Endangered** species face imminent extirpation or extinction.
- **Threatened** species are likely to become endangered if limiting factors are not reversed.
- **Special concern** species may become threatened or endangered because of a combination of biological characteristics and identified threats.
- **Data deficient** is a category used when available information is insufficient either to resolve a wildlife species' eligibility of assessment or to permit an assessment of its risk of extinction.

A seventh category, **not at risk**, identifies species not at risk of extinction under current circumstances.

Members of COSEWIC vote on the appropriate conservation category for each species whose status they review. The members review as many aspects of the situation as possible, including the area of occupancy, an indication of the geographic range of a species, as well as the availability of suitable habitat. They consider data about the population(s) of the species, including trends in the numbers of organisms. This information is corrected for species showing extreme fluctuations in numbers from year to year. Members also consider the demographics of the species and how these vary in the habitat where the species occur. Generation time is also considered, along with specific habitat features essential for the species' survival. The effective population size—the numbers of reproducing adults—is important, as are risks to the survival of the species under consideration.

You may recognize this litany from Chapter 29, on populations. The assessment criteria used by COSEWIC (and similar agencies elsewhere) describe the numbers of individuals in the population, fecundity, mortality, and the intrinsic rate of increase. Carrying capacity is also important, as is the area (range) over which the species occurs. These criteria are designed to support making data-based decisions about the conservation status of species.

STUDY BREAK QUESTIONS

1. How does extinction differ from extirpation?
2. What is COSEWIC? What does it do?
3. What is the difference between Not at Risk and Data Deficient?

28.5 Protecting What?

Before data are used to address questions about the status of species at risk, conservation biologists must decide about eligibility. The conservation jargon for this is "designatable unit." Are the organisms "real" species? Are they subspecies? Are they distinct populations? Are they really Canadian? Do they regularly occur in Canada or perhaps turn up here by accident? If the species does not breed here, is the habitat they use in Canada essential to their survival? Most species of wildlife in Canada occur close to the border with the United States, and many species widespread in the United States just make it

into Canada. In some cases, a distinct population is treated as a designatable unit. Distinct populations may be recognized by their geographic distribution and/or their genetic structure.

Questions about what units are designatable echo those raised in discussions about the definition of species (see Chapter 18). Off the west coast of Canada, biologists use striking differences in behaviour to distinguish among three "kinds" of killer whales. Resident killer whales eat mainly fish and often echolocate. Transient killer whales eat mainly marine mammals and rarely produce echolocation signals. Open-ocean killer whales eat mainly sharks. Individual killer whales often have distinct marks; repeated sightings of recognizable individual whales reveals that different groups of these animals live in different areas along the coast (**Figure 28.12**).

Based on behaviour and geographic distribution, there appear to be three designatable units of killer whales in the Pacific Ocean off Canada's west coast. The different units face different threats to their survival even though they appear to represent a single species.

Questions about what to protect often reflect different realities of biology. Migrating birds may be blown off course and end up in southern Ontario instead of their usual habitat much farther south. Marine birds and mammals may feed in Canadian waters but breed elsewhere. Many organisms commonly hitchhike, using ocean vessels, aircraft, or automobiles as vehicles of dispersal. But some hitchhikers, for example, some snails, travel with birds, making the association and the dispersal more "natural."

People can be quick to try to protect species they consider to be important or distinctive. In 2003, the Ontario Ministry of Natural Resources reported 4–6 white-coloured moose (*Alces alces*) among the approximately 1900 moose in two wildlife management areas near Foleyet, in northeastern Ontario. Should white-coloured moose be protected? There was local

FIGURE 28.12 Two views of a killer whale (*Orcinus orca*). (a) A captive animal in Vancouver and **(b)** a wild orca swimming off the Queen Charlotte Islands. The captive orca raises challenging questions about the appropriateness of keeping captive animals as part of an overall conservation strategy.

support for protecting the white moose, animals that have cultural and spiritual significance for First Nations communities. White moose also have been reported from other places in northern Ontario, Newfoundland and Labrador, and elsewhere. Although the population of white moose is small and widespread, there is no evidence that they are a designatable unit. In Canada, they have not been accorded special protection.

CITES, the Convention on International Trade in Endangered Species of Wild Fauna and Flora, plays a pivotal role in protecting species at the international level. Here, countries signatory to the CITES agreement enforce bans forbidding international trade in endangered species. International trade in wildlife is an important threat to biodiversity. In addition to directly affecting local populations of threatened species, it can also spread infectious diseases and promote the spread of invasive species. Membership in CITES includes 180 countries, and CITES tries to regulate trade in almost 36 000 species. Basic, accurate, and reliable biological data about species are essential for informing decisions about which species should be protected. Yet, decisions about what species are protected by CITES are political and not necessarily uniformly acclaimed. Between 2014 and 2016, the annual budget of the secretariat of CITES averaged US$6.2 million, coming from donations. But budget restrictions still influenced the effectiveness of CITES at the secretariat level by affecting capacity for detailed collection and analysis of basic data.

The Linnaean system of nomenclature is used to name species (see Chapter 19). Once a species has a name, however acquired, it may benefit from protection under CITES. But will data-based decisions about what counts as endangered be consistent and predictable? The answer is "yes and no." Black rhinos were not effectively protected under CITES, even though horns and products from the horns were moved across international borders to markets outside Africa.

28.5a Leopards and CITES

In Africa, the leopard (*Panthera pardus*; **Figure 28.13**) was protected under CITES. This effectively banned importation of

FIGURE 28.13 A leopard photographed in a game reserve in South Africa

leopard skins to the United States after passage of the Endangered Species Act there. The ban extended to the trophy skins of leopards shot by Americans on safari. The safari hunts were legal in the countries where the leopards had been shot. The CITES listing reflected the belief that leopards were endangered and that hunting threatened their survival.

Two groups immediately reacted negatively to the ban. First, predictably, were the hunting and related associations and lobbies. They objected to the ban because their members were anxious to import the trophies they had acquired on safari. Second were leaders and governments in many African countries. They objected to the ban because safaris were (and still are) an important source of foreign exchange. In many of these countries, large tracts of land, "safari hunting areas," have been set aside to accommodate visitors. These areas also protected populations of nongame species as well as appropriate habitat.

What did the data show? Leopards are 40 to 80 kg solitary cats that hunt by stealth. They are widespread in Africa. The estimate is that there are more than 700 000 leopards in the wild in Africa, with resident populations in all but very small countries with high human population densities. In 2000, Zimbabwe alone had a population of more than 16 000 leopards in the wild. The 1969 safari harvest of 6100 leopards throughout Africa and the export of their skins were no threat to the population in Zimbabwe, let alone to leopards in the whole continent.

Ecologists studied the population of leopards in the Matetsi Safari Area in Zimbabwe. Before 1974, the 4300 km^2 area had been a cattle ranch whose operators made strong efforts to eradicate leopards to protect their livestock. After conversion to a hunting area, people on the first safaris rarely shot leopards. By 1984, the leopard population in this safari area was 800–1000; in 1988, the annual safari quota was 12–28 leopards (3.6% of the estimated population). There was no change in the sizes of leopards shot in the mid-1980s compared with those taken in the 1970s. But by 1986, the average age of leopards taken as trophies was 5.4 years, compared with 3.2 years from the earlier period. These data show that leopards can persist even when subjected to heavy hunting pressure. On average, leopards live longer in a safari hunting regime than when they are hunted in the context of predator control operations. Other evidence suggests that populations of leopards persist even in urban areas; trapping evidence, for example, suggests that resident leopards live in Nairobi, the capital of Kenya.

Leopards are an interesting example of human responses to conservation. Hunting or some other form of harvesting is not necessarily a threat to their survival. Indeed, some harvesting may be critical to the livelihood of some people, and can advance efforts to protect some species. But decisions about harvesting made in one part of the world can influence what happens elsewhere.

Today, there are quotas for the numbers of leopards that can be harvested in different countries in Africa. Safari hunters

FIGURE 28.14 **A polar bear**

In the European Economic Community, setting aside 5% of agricultural land as natural habitat is an effective way to conserve biodiversity. Set-asides can be an important part of worldwide efforts to advance conservation. Mosaics of land use often provide suitable habitat for many organisms, with smaller species probably benefitting more than larger ones. Comparing bat communities between islands in water and those in agricultural landscapes revealed interesting

a.

b.

c.

FIGURE 28.15 **Agricultural landscapes in southwestern Ontario** (a) **and Orange Walk County in Belize** (b, c). In (a) and (b), note the mosaic of land use and forest cover. In (c), note ongoing slash-and-burn land clearing.

must obtain licences to take trophies, and skins exported must be accompanied by paperwork showing that the harvest was legal. The documentation allows a citizen, for example, of Canada or of a European Union country, to import a leopard skin. This was not possible in the United States in the 1970s, but it is now. In Africa, local farmers are permitted to kill "problem" animals that threaten their livestock or themselves and their families. These actions may be supported by government officials.

Key elements in the success of harvesting include having data about the population of organisms, the rates of reproduction, and the rates of harvest. Enforcement of quotas is essential if this approach is to succeed. Legal harvest quotas do not require people who object to hunting to be hunters. Trophy hunting is not the exclusive preserve of countries in Africa. On 3 April 2007, *The Globe and Mail* reported that the economy of Nunavut received C$3.9 million from polar bear (**Figure 28.14**) hunting; hunters can pay US$20 000 for a polar bear hunt.

STUDY BREAK QUESTIONS

1. Are species the same as designated units? Explain.
2. What is CITES? How did it figure in the conservation of leopards? Did it work in the conservation of black rhinos?
3. Does hunting threaten the survival of leopards?

28.6 Conservation and Agriculture

Using land to grow crops to feed people was a reality long before the "beginning" of the Anthropocene, arguably 500 years ago. In some situations, for example in southwestern Ontario (**Figure 28.15a**) or in Belize (Figure 28.15b), agricultural landscapes may be a mosaic of habitats. In many other cases, land is cleared and devoted to growing crops (e.g., Figure 28.15c).

differences. For 66 species of bats, degrees of the evenness and species richness was high among islands in agricultural systems. This was significantly different from prevailing data for islands in lakes.

The proliferation and diversity of edge habitats can both enrich opportunities for some species and threaten those of others. For example, in eastern Canada, songbirds that breed in continuous forest (e.g., hooded warblers, *Wilsonia citrina*; **Figure 28.16a**) are more exposed to nest parasitism by brown-headed cowbirds (*Molothrus ater*; Figure 28.16b) when they nest closer to forest edges.

As important as set-asides can be, they often involve a direct cost to the landowner. For the Brazilian Atlantic forest, a widely recognized system under pressure from expanding human populations and operations, annually spending about 6.5% of what Brazil spends on subsidies to agriculture would greatly enhance conservation efforts there. Set-asides also can be important jumping-off points for restoring threatened habitats in agricultural landscapes.

In September 2014, at the climate summit convened by the United Nations, there was general agreement with the New York Declaration on Forests. This document identified restoration of degraded ecosystems as one approach to dealing with climate change. There are four basic principles associated with restoration. First, the reality that restoration can increase ecological integrity. Second, restoration can be sustainable over a longer term. Third, restoration draws heavily on historical information, which can guide specific goals. Fourth, restoration provides general benefits and leads to societal engagement. Many human activities cause habitat degradation, but starting with agricultural impacts overtly recognizes this operation as a fundamental contributor.

STUDY BREAK QUESTIONS

1. What are set-asides? How do they serve conservation?
2. What is restoration?

28.7 Contaminating Natural Systems

Contamination of natural systems is one obvious by-product of the spread of humans in the world. This impact is compounded by population growth, habitat destruction, and the demand for resources. Further complicating the picture is our use of technology. To some extent, the resiliency of natural systems dampens some of our negative impact. Resiliency is one of the most impressive features of life at the species and/or ecosystem levels. In one respect, this feature complicates the challenges of conserving biodiversity. Introduced species are a form of contamination, and some of them are very invasive and adaptable and have huge negative impacts where they are released.

28.7a 2,4-Dichlorophenoxyacetic Acid (2,4-D)

Humans first identified 2,4-D (**Figure 28.17**) in 1942, and from 1944, it was marketed as a herbicide. Technically, 2,4-D is a hormone absorbed by the plant and translocated to the growing points of roots and shoots. 2,4-D kills weeds by inhibiting growth. The global market for 2,4-D is probably more than US$300 million, and it is used mainly to control broad-leaved weeds in cereal crops. According to the World Health Organization (WHO), 2,4-D is a "moderately hazardous pesticide" known to affect a variety of animals (e.g., dogs but not rats). Curiously, it turns out that other animals use 2,4-D for their own ends.

a.

b.

FIGURE 28.16 A hooded warbler (a) **and a brown-headed cowbird** (b)

2, 4-D

(2,4-dichlorophenoxy)acetic acid

FIGURE 28.17 2,4-Dichlorophenoxyacetic acid (2,4-D)

In 1971, Thomas Eisner and colleagues reported that a grasshopper (*Romalea microptera*; **Figure 28.18**) produced a froth of chemicals (**Figure 28.19**) for protection against ants. One of the main ingredients in the froth was 2,5-dichlorophenol, apparently derived from 2,4-D. This is an astonishing demonstration of adaptability that can underlie resiliency.

Resiliency and the recuperative powers of ecosystems are demonstrated by stories of "lost cities," for example, structures built by Maya in Central America, being found in a jungle. Archaeological evidence reveals that, in some habitats, these buildings and pyramids were overgrown by the rain forest in about 100 years. The Great Zimbabwe Ruins in southern Africa were overgrown by savannah woodland in a period of 100–200 years and only latterly "discovered" by European explorers.

28.7b Plastic Microbeads

Plastics are another example of contamination. Worldwide, polyethylene terephthalate (PET) is used in plastic products, and over 55 million tons of PET was produced in 2013 alone. Many plastics persist in the environment because they are chemically inert. Huge quantities of PET have been released into the environment as microbeads, used in consumer products such as facial soaps and toothpastes. These tiny (< 2 mm diameter) particles of plastic pose an immediate threat to many living species (**Figure 28.20**). Persistence in the environment makes plastics, including those made of PET, chemically inert and resistant to microbial degradation.

In 2016, a team of Japanese scientists described *Ideonella sakaiensis 201-F6*, a species of bacteria new to science. This is an important discovery because *I. sakaiensis 201-F6* produces enzymes that can hydrolyze PET and convert it to terephthalic acid and ethylene glycol, two environmentally benign monomers. The researchers collected samples of debris contaminated with PET at a bottle recycling site. In this case, resiliency of a natural system resulted in what could be the first step in reducing environmental persistence of PET. Investigation of the evolutionary history of the capacity of *I. sakaiensis 201-F6* to digest PET suggested that this species emerged at the contaminated site through lateral gene transfer and natural selection favouring its ability to exploit a new energetic opportunity.

28.7c Alien Species

Humans cause extinction through overexploitation of food species and by introducing other species. House cats, *Felis catus*, are among the worst introductions

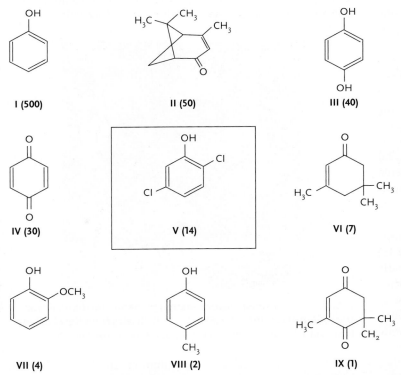

FIGURE 28.18 *Romalea microptera,* a grasshopper that uses an ant repellent with a 2,4-D derivative

I (500)   II (50)   III (40)

IV (30)   V (14)   VI (7)

VII (4)   VIII (2)   IX (1)

FIGURE 28.19 Active ingredients in the defensive froth of the grasshopper *Romalea microptera.* 2,5-Dichlorophenol (boxed) is apparently derived from 2,4-D.

FIGURE 28.20 A cartoon about plastic microbeads

FIGURE 28.21 **Stephen's Island wren, *Xenicus lyalli*.** This species was exterminated by one cat.

FIGURE 28.22 **(a)** Shells of zebra mussels (Dreissena polymorpha) on a beach on Pelee Island in Lake Erie. These mussels were introduced to the Great Lakes in North America, where they have spread rapidly. Their arrival coincided with steep declines in populations of native mussels such as, in **(b)** from left front to right back, kidneyshell (*Ptychobranchus fasciolaris*), eastern pondmussel (*Ligumia nasuta*), rainbow mussel (*Villosa iris*), round pigtoe (*Pleurobema sintoxia*), and maple leaf (*Quadrula quadrula*).

FIGURE 28.23 **This earthworm-eating planarian (*Arthurdendyus triangulatus*) was introduced to the British Isles from New Zealand.** It has had a devastating effect on local populations of earthworms.

people have made (and continue to make). Anecdotal records suggest that, in 1894, one house cat named Tibbles exterminated an entire population of flightless wrens (**Figure 28.21**) on Stephen's Island, a 2.6 km² island off the north shore of New Zealand. Fossils indicate that the wrens had occurred widely in New Zealand. This record stands for one individual, Tibbles, taking out the remaining approximately 10 pairs and exterminating the species.

The negative impacts occur whether the introductions were intentional or accidental, and whether the anticipated outcome was positive or negative. The invaders, once arrived and established, may outcompete resident species, devastating native species and ecosystems. The list of introduced organisms is very long and includes many domesticated or commensal species of animals and plants. Zebra mussels (**Figure 28.22a**) provide an example. These immigrant mussels outcompeted and overgrew the native ones, reducing their range and populations to levels that threatened the survival of several endemic species (Figure 28.22b).

Meanwhile, in parts of the British Isles, flatworms (*Arthurdendyus triangulatus*; **Figure 28.23**; see also Chapters 39 and 45) introduced from New Zealand in the soil plant pots, are deadly predators of earthworms. Since their arrival the flatworms have thrived and spread rapidly, coinciding with the demise of earthworms. We may think of gardeners as individuals in touch with nature; unfortunately, their propensity to introduce exotic species often conflicts with conservation.

Some organisms move about in ballast water in ships. Since about 1880, ships have regularly used water for ballast. Ships without cargo tend to ride high on the water, resulting in low fuel efficiency. Ballast keeps unladen ships riding lower in the water, reducing their fuel consumption. In the early 1990s, biologists surveyed ballast water in 159 cargo ships in Coos Bay, Oregon. They found 367 taxa representing 16 animal and 3 protist phyla, as well as 3 plant divisions. The samples included all major and most minor phyla. Organisms in the ballast water included carnivores, herbivores, omnivores, deposit feeders, scavengers, suspension feeders, primary producers, and parasites. Ballast water is taken on in one port and discharged in another, providing many species with almost open access to waters around the world.

Meanwhile, introduced diseases (and the organisms that cause them) have decimated, if not obliterated, resident species. When Europeans arrived in the New World, *Castanea dentata*, the American chestnut tree, was widespread in forests from southern Ontario to Alabama. This large tree of the forest canopy grew to heights of 30 m. Often most abundant on prime agricultural soils, the species' distribution and density were reduced as settlers from Europe cleared more and more land for agriculture. *Endothia parasitica*, the chestnut blight, was introduced around 1904 from Asian nursery stock. This introduced blight killed the American chestnut trees by the 1930s. By 2000, only scattered American chestnut trees remained, most of them sprouts from stumps.

Why are invading species so successful? Does the spread of starlings (*Sturnus vulgaris*; **Figure 28.24**) or dandelions (*Taraxacum officinale*) after introduction to new continents suggest that they moved into vacant niches? Does it mean that they are better competitors? In the case of starlings, 13 birds were introduced to Central Park in New York City in 1890, and they have spread far and wide. Once established, invading or introduced species can pose huge conservation problems because of their impact on ecosystems and diversity.

Although many invaders arrive, only a few are widely successful and become large-scale problems in their new settings. Invading plants are most often successful in nutrient-rich habitats, where they can achieve high growth rates, early reproduction, and maximal production of offspring. What happens in resource-poor settings? In the past, conventional wisdom had suggested that low-resource settings could be reservoirs for native species that could outcompete invaders.

However, an experimental examination of the responses of native and introduced species to challenging conditions revealed that invasive plant species almost always fared better (**Figure 28.25**). Resource use efficiency (RUE), calculated by measuring carbon assimilation per unit of resource, is an indicator of success. Many invasive species, such as ferns, C_3 and C_4 grasses, herbs, shrubs, and trees, were more successful in low-resource systems than native species were.

This research was conducted in Hawaii, where there are many invasive species. Among the invaders were *Bromus tectorum* (cheatgrass), *Heracleum mantegazzianum* (cartwheel flower or giant hogweed), and *Pinus radiata* (Monterey pine). Humans have introduced these plants for gardening (cheatgrass and cartwheel flower) or commercial timber production (Monterey pine). The data demonstrate that attempting to restore ecosystems and exclude invading species by reducing resource availability does not succeed because of the efficiency with which some species use resources.

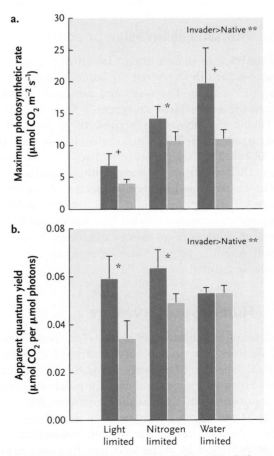

FIGURE 28.25 (a) **Photosynthetic rates (RUE) and** (b) **light-use efficiency of invasive plant species (blue bars) make them more competitive than native species (yellow bars).** The plants were from three different habitats in Hawaii. In the graphs, + denotes $P < 0.01$; *denotes $P < 0.05$. **Indicates that, in both instances, invaders are significantly more efficient than native species.

FIGURE 28.24 A starling, photographed in Toronto, introduced from Europe

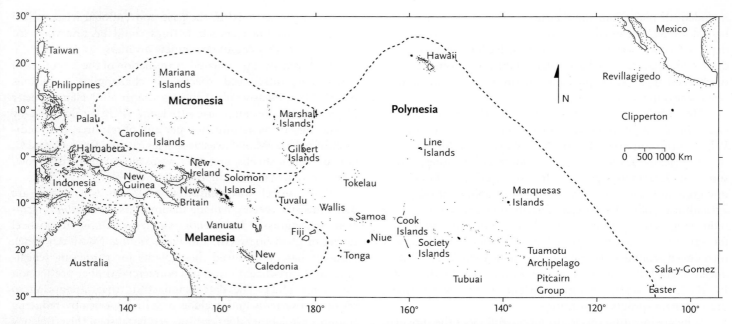

FIGURE 28.26 Islands in the South Pacific where the arrival of Polynesians coincided with the extinction of many island species of birds

Source: From David W. Steadman, "Prehistoric Extinctions of Pacific Island Birds: Biodiversity Meets Zooarchaeology," *Science*, vol. 267, Feb 24, 1995, pp. 1123 - 1131. *Science* by American Association for the Advancement of Science Reproduced with permission of AMERICAN ASSOCIATION FOR THE ADVANCEMENT OF SCIENCE in the format Republish in a book via Copyright Clearance Center.

28.7d Humans as Invasive Species

Species confined to islands often have small populations and are unaccustomed to terrestrial predators, making them vulnerable to extinction. The fossil and subfossil records show that many species of birds disappeared from islands in the South Pacific as Polynesians arrived there from the west. This occurred from Tonga to Easter Island and beyond (**Figure 28.26**). The Galápagos, only discovered by people in 1535, was sheltered from the wave of human-induced extinctions. On Easter Island, **endemic species** of sea birds and other species disappeared soon after people settled there. These examples demonstrate that humans do not have to be industrial or "high tech" to effect extinctions. Meanwhile, in the North Atlantic, people hunted *Pinguinus impennis*, the Great Auk, to extinction.

28.7e Humans as Harvesters

Populations of organisms we harvest for food often show marked declines. The annual harvest of bivalve molluscs has been a local fishery in Chesapeake Bay in the United States and elsewhere along the eastern seaboard for hundreds of years. In 1999, populations of bay scallops (*Argopecten irradians*; **Figures 28.27** and **28.28**), a main target of the fishery, were very low. The immediate reason for the low populations was the impact of predation by skates and rays that feed heavily on bivalve molluscs. Skates and rays are tertiary consumers and in turn are eaten by larger elasmobranchs, specifically various species of sharks.

Among tertiary consumers, the cownose ray (**Figure 28.29**) shows a marked increase in population. Evidence from surveys

FIGURE 28.27 A handful of bay scallops (*Argopecten irradians*)

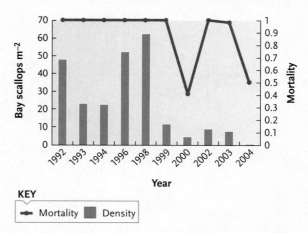

FIGURE 28.28 Numbers of bay scallops off the east coast of the United States

Source: From Ransom A. Myers, Julia K. Baum, Travis D. Shepherd, Sean P. Powers, Charles H. Peterson, "Cascading Effects of the Loss of Apex Predatory Sharks from a Coastal Ocean," *Science*, vol. 315, Mar 30, 2007, pp. 1846 - 1850. *Science* by American Association for the Advancement of Science Reproduced with permission of AMERICAN ASSOCIATION FOR THE ADVANCEMENT OF SCIENCE in the format Republish in a book via Copyright Clearance Center.

FIGURE 28.29 A cownose ray (*Rhinoptera bonasus*)

on the U.S. Atlantic coast estimates an order-of-magnitude increase in populations of cownose rays, and that the total population of 14 species of rays and skates exceeds 40 million. So, the decline in scallop (and other bivalve) populations can be explained by the increase in predation by tertiary consumers, especially skates and rays.

The picture becomes clearer when the population data for the local great sharks are added to the mix (**Figure 28.30**). Prolonged and intensive fishing of 12 species of sharks accounts for a 35-year decline in their populations (see Figure 28.30, top row). The sharks have been taken primarily for their fins and meat. In some parts of the world, shark fins sell for around US$700 per kilogram and are used to make shark fin soup.

The data demonstrate how removal of a top predator (sharks) destroyed a century-old scallop fishery. Fewer sharks meant increased predation by tertiary consumers, whose populations, in turn, increased (see Figure 28.30, middle row). The data illustrate a cascading ecological effect and demonstrate the potential long-term harm that our species can do to ecosystems and the species inhabiting them. The demise of bay scallops and other bivalves can be attributed to the impact of large-scale harvesting of marine resources. The late Ransom Myers and his colleagues documented this cascade of effects.

Bycatch: One unfortunate reality of harvesting is collateral damage. People fishing for one species may catch another, with unfortunate consequences. Changes in hook design may reduce some incidences of bycatch. Altering the curvature of a hook

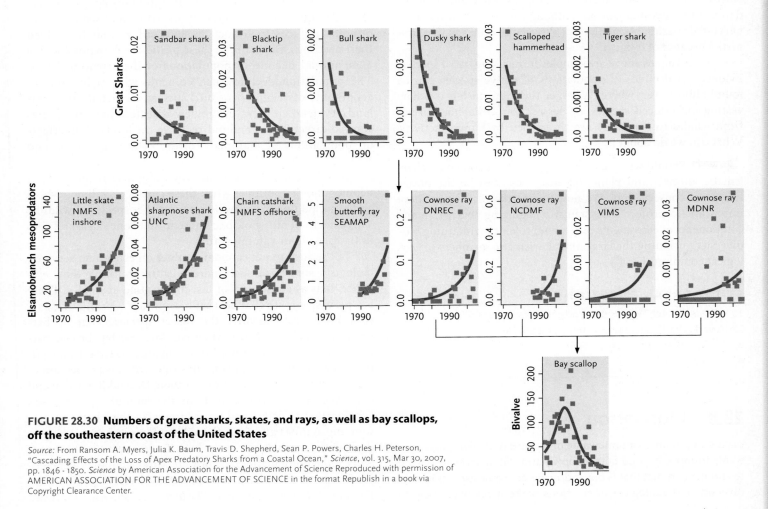

FIGURE 28.30 **Numbers of great sharks, skates, and rays, as well as bay scallops, off the southeastern coast of the United States**

Source: From Ransom A. Myers, Julia K. Baum, Travis D. Shepherd, Sean P. Powers, Charles H. Peterson, "Cascading Effects of the Loss of Apex Predatory Sharks from a Coastal Ocean," *Science*, vol. 315, Mar 30, 2007, pp. 1846 - 1850. *Science* by American Association for the Advancement of Science Reproduced with permission of AMERICAN ASSOCIATION FOR THE ADVANCEMENT OF SCIENCE in the format Republish in a book via Copyright Clearance Center.

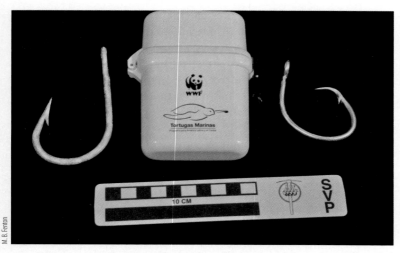

FIGURE 28.31 Sea turtles and longlining. Conventional longline hooks (left) readily catch sea turtles, whereas the hook on the right does not. The World Wildlife Fund is promoting the use of hooks (right) that are friendly to sea turtles in an effort to reduce their losses to longline fishing.

can make it less likely to catch sea turtles and not interfere with catching the target fish (**Figure 28.31**). The demise of barndoor skates (*Dipterus laevis*), a species formerly widespread in the North Atlantic, from Canada to Europe, is an example of the damage that bycatch can do. Although never a commercially harvested species, populations of these large skates have plummeted because of bycatch.

The examples above are samples from a long list of species. Evidence of declines of populations of native species can be found almost everywhere. Whether the root cause is overharvesting, introduced species, or destruction of habitat, species from whales to songbirds are threatened by human activity. What can we do about it?

CONCEPT FIX Should we focus conservation efforts on large, charismatic animals and plants because these can be the poster images of conservation? We now realize that it is often more important to protect ecosystems, recognizing that the many components of ecosystems play a vital role in maintaining biodiversity, including the large and charismatic members of ecological communities. ⬡

STUDY BREAK QUESTIONS

1. What is bycatch? Why is it important in conservation?
2. How do sharks affect populations of scallops?
3. Are humans an invasive species?
4. What is RUE?

28.8 Motivation

Trying to put an economic value on nature is challenging if one wants to move beyond cutting down and selling trees or paying to shoot an animal that is big and/or fierce. Some aspects of biodiversity and ecological interactions make it relatively easy to

appreciate the value-added involved with nature and ecosystems services. Others do not.

Data on the value of pollination to many agricultural enterprises illustrate why we should protect pollinators. It is easy to think of honeybees (*Apis mellifera*) as producers of honey, but the value of the crops they pollinate vastly exceeds revenue from honey and related products. Treatment with neonicotinoid pesticides (e.g., imidacloprid and clothianidin) caused a significant reduction in the number of visits by bumblebees to apple blossoms. Apples are grown commercially in 95 countries, and in 2012 the apple crop was estimated to be worth over US$350 billion.

Many insects visit flowers and, in doing so, pollinate plants and contribute directly to their reproduction. Somehow, bees are champion pollinators even though other insects also are involved. Bee–plant relationships are the product of over 200 million years of coevolution. These interactions provide some of the most exquisite examples of interactive diversification, partly accounting for the over 20 000 species of bees in the world. But the survival of bees is threatened by human activity. For example, 23 species of bees had disappeared from Britain by 2013.

Neonicotinoids also are harmful to many species of vertebrate wildlife. In the Netherlands, treatment with neonicotinoids reduces food such as caterpillars that birds feed their nestlings. Exposure to these pesticides coincided with a 3.5% annual decline in populations of insectivorous birds. The population declines also coincide with reductions in geographic distribution of bird species, especially in farmlands. A detailed literature review revealed that 150 studies showed direct (toxic) and indirect (via the food chain) effects on populations of mammals, birds, fish, amphibians, and reptiles.

It is difficult to understand why using insecticides such as neonicotinoids continues when these chemicals kill honeybees and other pollinators as well as many other species of wildlife. This smacks of biting off one's nose to spite one's face and flies in the face of our valuing nature.

In the rush to put economic values on ecosystem services, biologists sometimes use more wishful thinking than evidence. Bats as consumers of insects are good examples. There is a pervasive myth that bats eat mosquitoes. Use of DNA barcode analysis to identify the insect species eaten by bats revealed that two North American species, big brown bats (*Eptesicus fuscus*) and little brown myotis, rarely eat mosquitoes. The idea that bats are big consumers of mosquitoes comes from work on bat echolocation. In 1960, Donald R. Griffin and colleagues demonstrated that, in the laboratory, bats used echolocation to detect and track insects. In the lab, the targets were mosquitoes and fruit flies. The research had nothing to do with the normal prey of the bats. To demonstrate that predators reduce populations of prey requires actual evidence of consumption and associated reduction in target populations. For Brazilian free-tailed bats (*Tadarida brasiliensis*) in Texas, there is the necessary evidence of the impact of these of bats on populations of insects that are pests of corn and cotton. The fact that these bats live in colonies of millions of individuals probably explains the population control the bats effect. Comparable evidence is rarely available for the effects of other bats on other insects.

One robust example of ecosystem services is provided from coffee plantations in Costa Rica. There, forest patches in coffee plantations provide a reservoir of insectivorous birds that eat the coffee berry borer beetles (*Hypothenemus hampei*), providing a valuable service to coffee growers. In the end, choosing to support conservation activities is more a political than an economic undertaking. Ecosystem service is one argument in support of conservation.

STUDY BREAK QUESTIONS

1. What are ecosystem services?
2. What are neonicotinoids? Why are they important in conservation?

28.9 Effecting Conservation

Today we face many challenges when trying to protect biodiversity. Too many of the immediate threats are the direct or indirect consequences of human activities. We must protect species by acting at levels ranging from species to populations and habitats. Sometimes the route to saving one species appears to necessitate killing another.

Across northern Canada and the United States, many populations of caribou (*Rangifer tarandus caribou*; **Figure 28.32a**) are in sharp decline. Herds that had numbered in the thousands have dwindled to hundreds of individuals. Some isolated populations in southern Canada have disappeared, and none seems to have a secure future. Operations associated with oil and gas exploration in Alberta directly threaten the survival of caribou through habitat destruction and fragmentation. But there, predation by grey wolves (*Canis lupus*; Figure 28.32b) is the immediate cause of caribou mortality.

To assess the impact of wolf predation on populations of caribou, Dave Hervieux and four other biologists compared two herds of caribou in west-central Alberta. The Little Smoky Mountain and the Red Rock Prairie Creek herds were studied from 2000 to 2012. Wolf populations in the area of the Little Smoky Mountain caribou herd were reduced by hunting and poisoning wolves. This did not happen in the area of the Red Rock Prairie Creek herd. Reducing populations of grey wolves coincided with a 4.6% increase in the Little Smoky Mountain herd, while the Red Rock Prairie Creek herd declined by 4.7% during the same period. Survival of calves appeared to explain the differences in the two populations. The results of the wolf cull on the Little Smoky Mountain herd were clear, but would it ensure the long-term survival of the caribou? Does the end justify the means?

a.

b.

FIGURE 28.32 **A woodland caribou** (a) **and a grey wolf** (b)

Earlier, in Baja California, biologists resorted to culling golden eagles (*Aquila chrysaetos*) to preserve populations of Channel Island foxes (*Urocyon littoralis*). In that situation, the eagles had increased their predation on the foxes in the wake of reduced food supply caused by culling feral pigs (*Sus scrofa*). Use of words such as "killing" somewhat minimizes the extent of the killing that is involved, however.

The survival of predators is a matter of great concern for those interested in conservation (e.g., leopards). At least one-third of the countries in Europe have wild populations of at least one large carnivore: brown bears (*Ursus arctos*), grey wolves, Eurasian lynx (*Lynx lynx*), or wolverines (*Gulo gulo*). In Sweden this survival is achieved by various actions, including electric fencing to exclude predators as well as paying subsidies to those who harbour large carnivores on their land. In some jurisdictions in the United States, grey wolves can be hunted

FIGURE 28.33   **Observational Research**

Near-Complete Extinction of Small Mammals in Tropical Forest Fragments

Question: How long do populations of small mammals persist in small fragments of tropical forests?

Hypothesis: Populations of small mammals will eventually become extinct on small islands that were created when a large patch of forest was flooded to establish a reservoir **(a)**.

Prediction: Using principles from the theory of island biogeography, Gibson and his colleagues predicted that extinctions would be more rapid in small forest fragments than in large fragments.

Method: The researchers conducted on-the-ground surveys on 16 small islands (red) of varying size (0.3–56.3 ha) five times over a period of 20 years, recording all the small mammal species they encountered. The first surveys took place 5–7 years after the forest fragments were formed.

a. Islands in Chiew Larn Reservoir

b. Extinction of small mammals

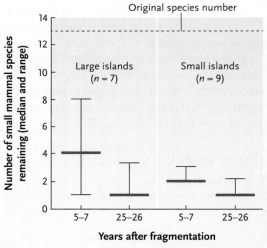

L. Gibson et al. 2013. "Near-complete extinction of native small mammal fauna 25 years after forest fragmentation," *Science* 341:1508–1510. *Science* by American Association for the Advancement of Science. Reproduced with permission of AMERICAN ASSOCIATION FOR THE ADVANCEMENT OF SCIENCE in the format Republish in a book via Copyright Clearance Center.

Result: Small mammal populations quickly became extinct in the habitat fragments **(b)**. Extinction varied with the size of habitat fragments such that most species disappeared from small islands within the first 5–7 years after fragmentation. By 25 years after forest fragmentation, nearly all small native mammals had become extinct on islands of any size. The Malayan field rat (*Rattus tiomanicus*) was the only mammal that persisted in all fragments; researchers believe that it colonized the fragments after they were separated from each other and from the surrounding forest.

Conclusion: Habitat fragments experienced size-dependent rates of extinction, but all habitat fragments in this study eventually lost all their native small mammals.

---

legally but there is considerable concern about the levels harvested.

Reactions to the paper about wolves and caribou focused mainly on the means of culling. These included using strychnine and shooting wolves from helicopters. Hervieux and his coauthors did not contend that culling wolves would ensure the future of caribou. Their data did, however, demonstrate that managing populations of predators could have a positive effect on populations of prey. Everyone seemed to acknowledge that, until there are changes in policies about land use, habitat destruction, and disturbance, killing wolves will not save caribou.

The survival of populations of Pacific water shrews in Canada was more a matter of habitat destruction than direct mortality. Fragmentation of populations is an important factor in conservation. Mountain lions (*Felis concolor*) provide an excellent example.

Mountain lions are large predators (130 kg) that once occurred widely in North and South America. Today, there is a small population of mountain lions in the Santa Monica Mountains in California, and their range occurs within

Greater Los Angeles. A genetic analysis combined with data about the movements of tagged individuals revealed that these mountain lions are genetically isolated and show inbreeding depression. The combination of urban development and large freeways effectively contains the Santa Monica Mountain population of mountain lions. Here the immigration of a single male in 2009 increased the genetic diversity of the population. This situation provides at least one solution to isolated populations.

Issues surrounding conservation continue to generate considerable debate. It seems obvious that one size does not fit all when it comes to protecting species and habitats **(Figure 28.33)**.

STUDY BREAK QUESTIONS

1. How can culling wolves help populations of caribou?
2. What is fragmentation of habitat? How is it important in conservation?

28.10 Human Population: A Root Problem for Conservation

The increasing human population is a fundamental root cause of declining biodiversity. Visit the website http://www.ined.fr/en/everything_about_population/population-games/world-population-me/ and use it to determine the estimated human population in the year you were born, and then for the years in which your parents and grandparents were born. Even when many people are killed, the momentum of our population increase does not slow down. The December 2004 tsunami killed approximately 250 000 people at a time when the world population was estimated at 6 billion. By comparison, the 1883 explosion of Krakatoa (and resulting tsunamis) is thought to have killed 35 000 people when the global human population was about 1.5 billion. If these estimates are correct, $4.1 \times 10^{-3}\%$ of the human population at the time was killed by the 2004 tsunami and $2.3 \times 10^{-3}\%$ by the explosion of Krakatoa. Neither calamity caused the human population growth curve (see Chapter 29) to waver.

If human population growth continues at the same rate it is growing now, it will double in 40 years. However, studies show that our population is not growing as quickly as it did during much of the twentieth century. The United Nations Development Program (UNDP) has released data on human fertility (the total number of births per woman) for 162 countries (**Table 28.1**). Compared with 1970–1975, 152 countries had lower human fertility in 2000–2005, 3 countries showed increases in fertility, and 7 showed no change.

Concerned about the global population and its effect on Earth, world leaders adopted the United Nations Millennium Development Goals in 2000, committing their nations to achieving the following goals by 2015:

- end poverty and hunger
- universal education
- gender equality
- child health
- maternal health
- combat HIV/AIDS
- environmental sustainability
- global partnerships

These goals can be achieved only if reproduction is controlled (see Chapter 29). Go to the United Nations Millennium Goals website at http://www.un.org/millenniumgoals/bkgd.shtml to see how we are faring. In 1994, the United Nations held the International Conference on Population and Development (ICPD), which set a target for global investment in family planning. By 2004, the amount spent had fallen to 13% of this target. Consequently, family planning information and devices (usually for fertility control) are not readily available in many of the lowest-income countries. In 1950, Sri Lanka and Afghanistan had the same population. Sri Lanka began strong efforts to make family planning available in culturally acceptable ways. This did not happen in Afghanistan. By 2050, Afghanistan will have four times as many people as Sri Lanka. The solution centres around controlling the fertility of women, but more particularly on giving them the power to control their own fertility in culturally acceptable ways. As seen in Chapter 29, the growth potential of a population is determined by the numbers of females of reproductive age. Why females? Because in mammals, females are the limiting step in reproduction—the ones who produce the eggs and young and milk as food.

STUDY BREAK QUESTIONS

1. What is HDI? What can we learn from it?
2. Why is education important in the dynamics of human populations?

28.11 Signs of Stress: Systems and Species

People's demand for food, water, and energy puts thousands of other species at risk. We do not have to look far to see examples of species and ecosystems under stress (see Chapter 31). For example, we are losing birds. We know this because for years, birdwatchers and ornithologists have counted them and monitored their behaviour and activity. Locally, birds are affected by changes in habitat availability as cities and towns and their suburbs expand into adjoining land. Birds also lose habitat when agricultural operations expand to increase productivity. Birds that make annual migrations from temperate areas of the world to tropical and subtropical ones must survive the changes that accumulate across their entire circuit of habitats, each one essential to their survival.

Avian influenza (also called *bird flu*) is a looming crisis for humans, one that appears to involve birds as central players. The issue here is another one involving basic biology, namely, the outcome when a disease-causing organism jumps from one

TABLE 28.1	Variations in Fertility Rate (Total Births per Woman): A Sample of UNDP Data for 162 Countries		
Country	Human Development Index (HDI) Rank	1970–1975	2000–2005
Norway	2	2.2	1.8
Canada	4	2.0	1.5
United States	12	2.0	2.0
Portugal	29	2.7	1.5
Brazil	70	4.7	2.3
China	81	4.9	1.7
Indonesia	107	5.2	2.4
India	128	5.4	3.1

species (host) to another. Bird flu could have as much to do with our insatiable demand for poultry as food as it does with birds. In 2006, 12 billion chickens were farmed in China. Worldwide, poultry farms housed over 100 billion broiler chickens. Raising organisms at very high densities (see Chapter 29) provides an ideal setting for the spread of disease. Humans have responded to the threat of bird flu by wholesale slaughter of fowl, raising concerns about the roles played by migrating birds, and efforts to develop a vaccine that will protect humans from bird flu. All involve basic biology.

Drylands are arid, semiarid, and subhumid areas where precipitation is scarce and more or less unpredictable. In drylands, the combination of high temperatures, low relative humidities, and abundant solar radiation means high potential evapotranspiration. Drylands cover approximately 41% of Earth's land surface and are home to about 38% of the human population. Drylands are not just a problem of deserts but cover large expanses, for example, of Canada's Prairie Provinces. However, between 10% and 20% of the drylands are subject to some form of severe land degradation, directly affecting the lives of at least 250 million people. Climate change, combined with increasing pressure on water resources for these people, their crops, and their animals, compounds the problems that confront them. Competition for limited resources, such as water, can generate local and international strife.

We have seen that complexity is an important and pervasive feature of ecosystems. Biodiversity is intimately associated with complexity, and disruption of this complexity often translates into reduced biodiversity and decay of ecosystems. Ironically, many social and economic systems that humans have developed are also subject to disruption by stress. This places the onus on our species to develop sustainable operations, whether in the area of agriculture, resource use and exploitation, or conservation.

STUDY BREAK QUESTIONS

1. How is reproductive effort different between males and females in birds and in mammals?
2. How are drylands at risk?

28.12 Taking Action

Do individuals have the power to effect change? Think of things that have changed dramatically in a relatively short time. Two good examples are the abolition of slavery and the emancipation of women. In a way, these demonstrate humans' capacity for effecting change. On a more local level, the acceptance of the use of tobacco in public has declined remarkably in the past 20 years—in Canada and elsewhere. We also have seen the abolition of capital punishment and much more ready access to abortion in Canada.

But none of these changes is universal. In the daily news we find stories about people living in virtual slavery, of people

executed in public, of women with few or no rights in their home countries. To complicate the matter, not everyone agrees that the changes listed above are for the better.

Effecting changes in our approach to conservation means identifying the root causes for the erosion of biodiversity and the things that are impediments to conservation. This means starting by changing our own lifestyles, including the food we eat and our use of energy. We must be wary of simple, and often misleading, solutions and avoid blaming someone else as a way of self-exoneration. We must respect the rights of others; use education and training to become informed; and learn to be objective, to examine and evaluate data or evidence. The outpouring of support for victims of the 2004 tsunami demonstrated that humans have great empathy for their fellows, and we need to extend this concern to the other species with whom we share the planet.

We have seen that action is needed at the species and the habitat level, and there is a propensity to focus more on species. But in the human view, all species are not equal. The 2006 IUCN list of threatened species shows that, whereas 20% of the described species of mammals were listed as threatened, only 0.07% of the insect species received this level of attention. Other interesting numbers from this table are 12% of described species of birds listed as threatened, 4% of fish species, 3.5% of dicotyledonous plants, and 0.006% of species of mushrooms. In Canada, the same situation prevails, with mammals and birds dominating the list of threatened species, with other taxa receiving less attention. Do these data about threatened species mean that mammals are more vulnerable than insects? That we care more about mammals than about insects? Or does it mean that there are more "experts" to offer opinions and data about mammals than about insects? Are the possibilities mutually exclusive?

The success of some native species, for example, Canada geese (**Figure 28.34**), is encouraging for many reasons. However, there can be downsides to large numbers of geese. Anyone who has walked barefoot on the grass in a park with lots of geese

FIGURE 28.34 Three Canada geese (*Branta canadensis*) landing on the Humber River in Toronto

will be familiar with one obvious problem posed by geese. Effective population management means finding humane ways to control populations of Canada geese and other species (e.g., raccoons, *Procyon lotor*) that thrive in urban and suburban habitats. In Toronto, Canada, there are ongoing biodiversity programs about native flora and fauna, from bats to bees, from native plants to restoration operations.

Biology can be at the centre of the movement to achieve conservation of biodiversity while being part of our efforts to achieve sustainable use of the resources we need as a species. Conservation begins at home when we modify our lifestyles and become active on any front, from protecting local habitat and species to protecting charismatic species elsewhere.

Our ability to make data-based decisions about conservation can increase the credibility of initiatives and the chances of their being successful. It is important to remember that one size does not fit all when it comes to conservation, whether focused at the species, habitat, or ecosystem level.

STUDY BREAK QUESTIONS

1. Name three things you could change in your lifestyle to improve your impact on biodiversity.
2. Name three things that your local member of parliament might do to advance conservation of biodiversity.
3. What about the prime minister?

Summary Illustration

Before humans, the conservation of any one species depended on that species surviving whatever environmental challenges came its way (survival of the fittest). Human population growth and technological advances have superimposed onto this dynamic additional stressors to species. Species are now disappearing at exacerbated rates due to land development (habitat destruction), climate change, overhunting, and other human-induced causes.

Early humans essentially lived in harmony with nature.

Humans arrive

Extinction Events

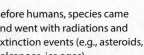

Before humans, species came and went with radiations and extinction events (e.g., asteroids, volcanoes, ice ages).

Pollution

Wastes

CO_2

Anthropocene: sixth extinction?

Heats up threats to habitats and species

Extinct

Endangered

Threatened

Special concern

Globalization and transportation of goods facilitates invasive species.

Conservationists can try to work outside of all of the cumulative impacts to conserve species, but will this stop extinctions?

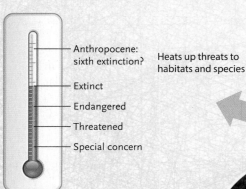

As human populations grew, the threat to biological conservation began.

The Harvesters. Pieter Bruegel the Elder. Metropolitan Museum of Art. Rogers Fund, 1919.

As human culture evolved, so did humans' ability to "tame" the land for their own purposes—the threat to biological conservation began to grow.

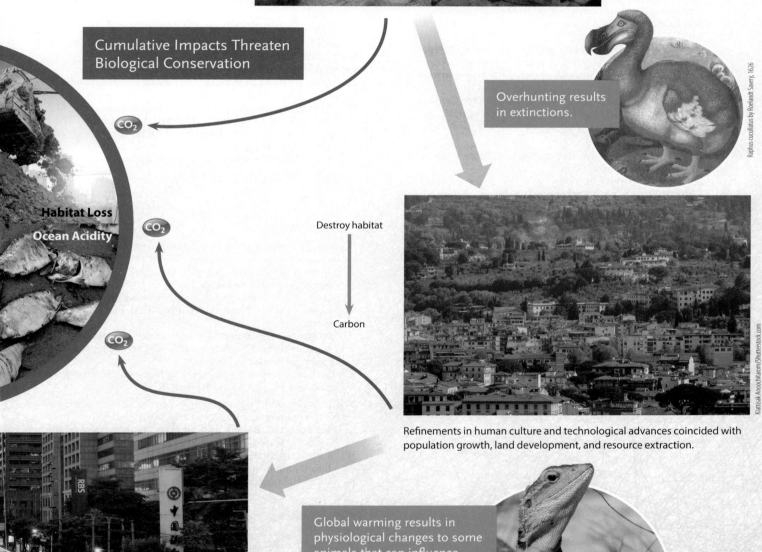

Cumulative Impacts Threaten Biological Conservation

CO_2

CO_2

CO_2

Habitat Loss

Ocean Acidity

Overhunting results in extinctions.

Raphus cucullatus by Roelandt Savery, 1626

Destroy habitat

Carbon

Refinements in human culture and technological advances coincided with population growth, land development, and resource extraction.

Kiattisak Anoochitarom/Shutterstock.com

Global warming results in physiological changes to some animals that can influence reproductive capacity.

Belle Ciezak/Shutterstock.com

More humans leads to more habitat conversion and more resource extraction, which threatens more species.

SELF-TEST QUESTIONS

Recall/Understand

1. How many mass extinctions were in Earth's history before the Anthropocene?
   a. 1
   b. 3
   c. at least 5
   d. at least 8

2. Which of these groups is an example of organisms pending imminent extinction or recently extinct?
   a. Pacific water shrew (*Sorex bendirii*), black rhino (*Diceros bicornis*), American ginseng (*Panax quinquefolius*), Mauritian Calvaria tree (*Sideroxylon majus*), Egyptian fruit bat (*Rousettus aegyptiacus*)
   b. Pacific water shrew (*Sorex bendirii*), white rhino (*Ceratotherium simum*), American ginseng (*Panax quinquefolius*), Mauritian Calvaria tree (*Sideroxylon majus*), Egyptian fruit bat (*Rousettus aegyptiacus*)
   c. Pacific water shrew (*Sorex bendirii*), black rhino (*Diceros bicornis*), American ginseng (*Panax quinquefolius*), Mauritian Calvaria tree (*Sideroxylon majus*), little brown myotis (*Myotis lucifugus*)
   d. Pacific water shrew (*Sorex bendirii*), white rhino (*Ceratotherium simum*), American ginseng (*Panax quinquefolius*), Mauritian Calvaria tree (*Sideroxylon majus*), little brown myotis (*Myotis lucifugus*)

3. Which of the following makes leopards an interesting example of human responses to conservation?
   a. Humans do not hunt leopards.
   b. Leopards are not a vulnerable species.
   c. Leopards live only in Africa.
   d. Hunting is not necessarily a threat to the survival of leopards as a species.

4. Which of these action steps is an effective way to conserve biodiversity in the European Economic Community?
   a. turning natural habitats completely into human-controlled land
   b. creating islands artificially
   c. setting aside 5% of agricultural land as natural habitat
   d. breaking landscapes into smaller areas of land

5. What is the significance of ballast water in ships?
   a. Ballast water is stagnant water, which provides life to a variety of organisms, allowing us to learn about their biodiversity.
   b. Ballast water is taken on in one port and discharged in another, providing many species with great opportunities to move around the world.
   c. Ballast water is a great source of preserved animal and plant remains.
   d. Ballast water is a great source of viruses.

6. If human population growth continues at the same rate as it is growing now, when is it most likely that it will double?
   a. in 20 years
   b. in 40 years
   c. in 60 years
   d. in 80 years

7. CITES is designed to stop international trade of endangered species. Which of these species was effectively protected by CITES?
   a. passenger pigeons
   b. black rhinos
   c. Canada geese
   d. leopards

8. In 1950, Sri Lanka and Afghanistan had the same population. By 2050, Afghanistan will have four times as many people as Sri Lanka. What is the main reason for this?
   a. Afghanistan began strong efforts to make family planning available.
   b. Sri Lanka began strong efforts to make family planning available.
   c. The Sri Lankan government imposed a rule of one child per family.
   d. Afghanistan males have not undergone sterilization.

9. Which of these pairs of species were common about 50 years ago, but by 2008 both demonstrated risks of being rare and vulnerable?
   a. African savannah elephant (*Loxodonta Africana*) and white rhino (*Ceratotherium simum*)
   b. African savannah elephant (*Loxodonta Africana*) and Mauritian Calvaria tree (*Sideroxylon majus*)
   c. black rhino (*Diceros bicornis*) and American ginseng (*Panax quinquefolius*)
   d. white rhino (*Ceratotherium simum*) and American ginseng (*Panax quinquefolius*)

Apply/Analyze

10. What is the connection between iridium and dinosaur extinction?
    a. Iridium ended up in the water on early Earth, which poisoned all the dinosaurs.
    b. Iridium dust is flammable, and it probably caused massive fires on Earth, which drove dinosaurs to extinction.
    c. Iridium is rare on Earth but common in asteroids, which suggests that an iridium-laden asteroid could have hit Earth, causing dinosaur extinction.
    d. Iridium is radioactive, suggesting that its radioactivity was enough to kill all dinosaurs on Earth.

11. Which of the following is good evidence that the Cretaceous mass extinction was caused by an asteroid impact?
    a. high concentration of iridium in rocks and a crater off the coast of Mexico
    b. earthquakes and volcano eruptions
    c. floods and fires
    d. dust, darkness, and cooling

12. Which tertiary consumers have experienced increases in populations that may explain the demise of scallops off the southeastern coast of the United States?
    a. skates and rays
    b. sharks
    c. killer whales
    d. pelagic seabirds

13. Which of these environmental factors is particularly important for reptiles, and why?
    a. humidity, because it determines their body temperature
    b. humidity, because it determines their food quality
    c. temperature, because it determines their gender
    d. temperature, because it determines their nesting sites

Create/Evaluate

14. Suppose that a species no longer occurs in Canada but still lives in the United States. Which of these terms best describes the status of this species?
    a. extinct
    b. extirpated
    c. highly endangered
    d. not at risk

15. What is the difference between an extirpated species and an endangered species?

Chapter Roadmap

Population Ecology

The realities of population biology underlie many of the challenges facing our species in general, and biologists in particular.

29.1 Introduction

29.2 Population Characteristics

29.3 Demography

29.4 Evolution of Life Histories

29.5 Models of Population Growth

29.6 Population Regulation → To Chapter 30

29.7 Human Administered Population Control

29.8 Human Population Growth

29.9 The Future: Where Are We Going?

29.10 The Pill

NASA

M.B Fenton

Populations have characteristics that transcend those of the individuals comprising the populations.

Population Ecology

29

Why it matters . . . The realities of population ecology underlie many of the challenges facing our species in general, and biologists in particular. Malaria is a good example of the range of realities for at least three reason: first, its impact on millions of humans; second, the resilience of the parasites (mainly *Plasmodium falciparum* and *Plasmodium vivax*) that cause malaria; third, the ubiquity and resilience of the blood-eating insects (the vectors: mosquitoes, mainly *Anopheles* spp.) that move the parasites among prey. Malaria is mainly a disease of the tropics and subtropics **(Figure 29.1)**. One indication of the importance of malaria is that human deaths from malaria have affected the outcomes of wars in many parts of the world.

In 2015, the WHO (World Health Organization) estimated that almost half the world's human population is at risk of being exposed to malaria. Children, pregnant women, and travellers from more temperate parts of the world are most often severely affected by malaria. Today, malaria has the greatest impact on humans in Africa. In 2015, 89% of 214 million cases of malaria occurred there, as well as 91% of 438 000 human deaths from the disease. The numbers side of the impact of malaria on human mortality is clear.

What can we do about this life-threatening disease that is both preventable and curable? The simplest way to avoid exposure to malaria is to ensure that you are not bitten by a mosquito carrying the parasite. Virtually all the vector species bite between dusk and dawn. This means that using an insect repellent and sleeping under an insect net treated with insecticide are good preventative measures. But, as anyone who has worked or slept in areas with mosquitoes will know, neither approach is guaranteed to provide protection. The nets have to be treated and maintained and the repellent applied repeatedly.

Controlling populations of mosquitoes is another avenue of defence against malaria. This may mean minimizing sites for them to breed (females lay eggs in stagnant water) or spraying

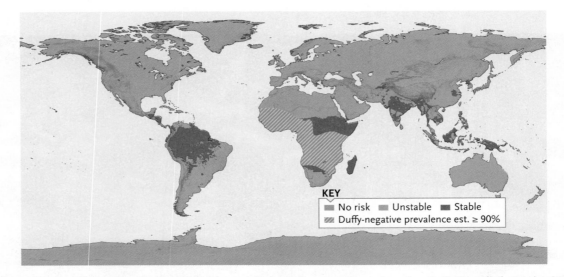

FIGURE 29.1 **An estimation of the risks of exposure to vivax malaria.** Duffy-negative prevalence is an indication of infection by vivax malaria.

Source: Guerra CA, Howes RE, Patil AP, Gething PW, Van Boeckel TP, Temperley WH, et al. (2010) The International Limits and Population at Risk of Plasmodium vivax Transmission in 2009. *PLoS Negl Trop Dis* 4(8): e774. https://doi.org/10.1371/journal.pntd.0000774

them with insecticides. Increasing incidences of mosquito resistance to insecticides, including those in bed nets, erodes the effectiveness of control by insecticides.

Malaria is treatable, usually with an artemisinin-based combination therapy (ACT), but resistance to ACTs and other treatments poses an ongoing problem for this line of defence. Antimalarial medicines suppress the blood stage of the *Plasmodium* and, again, resistance to these drugs makes this approach less effective. Furthermore, antimalarial drugs have significant side effects, another weakness of this approach to controlling malaria.

Dealing with malaria is an ongoing challenge for public health authorities because it requires engaging on the level of treating the disease, controlling the vector, and reducing human exposure to the vector. The need for continuous vigilance and treatment places a large burden on the economies of some of the countries hardest hit by malaria. Indeed, malaria control is an example of a Sisyphean problem.

According to the myth, Zeus, the supreme Greek God, punished Sisyphus, the King of what is now Corinth, for craftiness and deceitfulness. In Hades, Sisyphus faced a life of eternal frustration because the boulder he had to push up a hill always rolled back down. Sisyphean problems are common in population ecology. Controlling malaria is an example of a Sisyphean problem.

For example, consider the incidence of malaria in Zanzibar **(Figure 29.2)**. Zanzibar, an archipelago of several islands off the east coast of Africa, has a population of 1.3 million people,

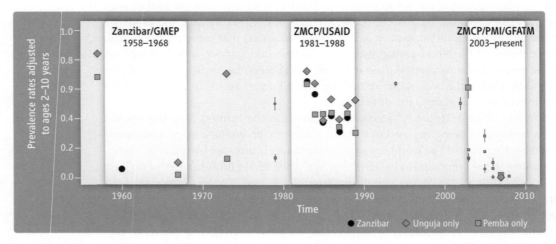

FIGURE 29.2 **Incidence of malaria parasites in children between 1958 and 2010.** During periods of concerted efforts to reduce or eliminate malaria, the incidence of parasites in children drops, only to rebound when control measures are stopped. Large symbols represent regional and national surveys; smaller symbols, smaller-scale surveys. GMEP was part of the Global Malaria Eradication Programme, ZMCP was the Zanzibar Malaria Control Programme assisted by USAID, and ZMCP/PMI/GFATM is the Zanzibar Malaria Control Programme assisted by the U.S. President's Malaria Initiative and the Global Fund to Fight AIDS, Tuberculosis, and Malaria. Here, Zanzibar refers to all the islands; Pemba and Unguja are specific islands in the archipelago.

Source: From Smith, D.L., J.M. Cohen, B. Moonen, A.J. Tatem, O.J. Sabot, A. Ali and S.M. Mugheiry. 2011. "Solving the Sisyphean problem of malaria in Zanzibar." *Science*, vol. 332: 1384–1385. *Science* by American Association for the Advancement of Science Reproduced with permission of AMERICAN ASSOCIATION FOR THE ADVANCEMENT OF SCIENCE in the format Republish in a book via Copyright Clearance Center.

compared to 1.1 billion in Africa. Annual antimalarial efforts in Zanzibar prevent about 600 000 cases of, and about 3300 deaths from, malaria. The cost is about US$1183 per death averted and US$34.50 per impact of reducing the incidence of the disease.

Data on the prevalence of the malarial parasite in children (Figure 29.2) demonstrate why it is essential to maintain antimalarial programs. This is vital even in the face of success measured as fewer cases of malaria and fewer deaths from it. Arrival of people already infected with the malarial parasite in Zanzibar results in new cases of the disease and is part of the problem. This problem is Sisyphean because, as soon as efforts to control malaria are cut back, the incidence of disease increases, along with deaths from it.

To further complicate the situation, malaria caused by *Plasmodium falciparum* has received more attention than the apparently less lethal malaria caused by *Plasmodium vivax*. Vivax malaria is widespread (Figure 29.1) and any overall program to control malaria must consider both variants of the disease. Global warming adds another dimension to issues related to malaria. An obvious example is the consequences of warming that allows vector species to overwinter in areas that used to be too cold.

29.1 Introduction

The population ecology roots of such problems lie in patterns of population growth: the impact of *r* (intrinsic rate of increase), *N* (population size), and *K* (carrying capacity). Perhaps Sisyphus's challenge was modest compared to that posed by some problems in population ecology! As we shall see, the growing population of humans remains an urgent and pressing problem.

29.2 Population Characteristics

We can describe at least eight characteristics of any population, including geographic range, size, density, dispersion, age structure, generation time, sex ratio, and incidence of reproducing individuals. Populations have characteristics that transcend those of the individuals comprising the populations. Every population has a **geographic range** (the overall space in which it lives) and this can vary considerably. A population of snails might inhabit a small tide pool, whereas a population of marine phytoplankton might occur over a much, much larger area. Every population also occurs in a **habitat** or range of habitats that offers the necessary biotic and abiotic features. Some animals occupy widely separated habitats and migrate between them.

Population size is the number of individuals making up the population at a specified time (N_t). **Population density** is the number of individuals per unit area or per unit volume of habitat. Species with a large body size generally have lower population densities than those with a small body size **(Figure 29.3)**. Although population size and density are related measures, knowing a population's density provides more information about its relationship to the resources it uses. If a population of 200 oak trees occupies one hectare (ha; 10 000 m²), the population density

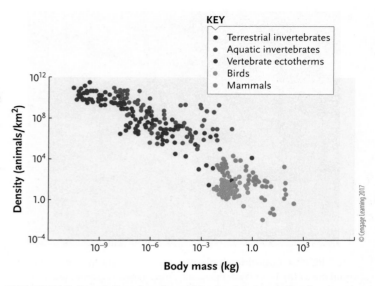

FIGURE 29.3 **Population density and body size.** Population density generally declines with increasing body size among animal species. There are similar trends for other organisms.

is $200 \times 10\,000$ m^{-2}, or 1 tree per 50 m². But if 200 oaks are spread over 5 ha, the density is 1 tree per 250 m². Clearly, the second population is less dense than the first, and its members will have greater access to sunlight, water, and other resources.

Ecologists use population size and density to monitor and manage populations of endangered species, economically important species, and agricultural pests. For large-bodied species, a simple head count may provide accurate information about population size. For example, ecologists survey the size and density of populations of African elephants by flying over herds and counting individuals **(Figure 29.4)**. Researchers use a variation on that technique to estimate population size in tiny organisms that live at high population densities. To estimate the density of aquatic phytoplankton, for example, you might collect water samples of known volume from representative areas in a lake and count them by looking through a microscope. These data allow you to estimate population size and density based on the estimated volume of the entire lake. One ongoing challenge is measuring population size in organisms that are clones, for example, stands of poplar trees (*Populus* spp.).

Populations can vary in their **dispersion** (the spatial distribution of individuals within the geographic range). Some populations are clumped, reflecting different situations. Clumped populations may reflect the distribution of essential resources. Certain pasture plants, for instance, are clumped in small, scattered areas where cowpats had fallen and locally enriched the soil. Some animals are social, occurring together in groups of varying size. In some cases the essential resources are food or shelter, or sometimes mates. Social individuals may cooperate in rearing offspring, feeding, or defence against predators. Other clumped distributions occur in species that reproduce by asexual clones and remain attached to the parents. Aspen trees and sea anemones reproduce this way and often occur in large aggregations (see Chapter 18). Clumping may also occur in species in

FIGURE 29.4 **Counting elephants.** It is easy to think that large animals such as African elephants (*Loxodonta africana*) would be easy to count from the air **(a)**. This may or may not be true, depending on vegetation. But it can be easy to overlook animals, particularly young ones **(b)**, in the shade.

which seeds, eggs, or larvae lack dispersal mechanisms and offspring grow and settle near their parents **(Figure 29.5)**.

Uniform distributions can occur when individuals repel or avoid one another because resources are in short supply. Creosote bushes are uniformly distributed in the dry scrub deserts of the U.S. Southwest. Mature bushes deplete the surrounding soil of water and secrete toxic chemicals, making it impossible for seedlings to grow. This chemical warfare is called *allelopathy*. Moreover, seed-eating ants and rodents living at the bases of mature bushes eat any seeds that fall nearby. In these situations, the distributions of species of plants and animals can be uniform and interrelated. Territorial behaviour (the defence of an area and its resources) can also produce **uniform dispersion** in some species of animals, such as nests in colonies of colonial birds (see Chapter 32).

FIGURE 29.5 **(a)** Populations of the mushroom *Craterellus tubaeformis* are associated with pitcher plants (*Sarracenia purpurea*) in bogs. Both tend to be clumped. **(b)** Other species, such as toque macaques (*Macaca sinica*), are social. **(c)** In other species, aggregations of individuals reflect the availability of food and water (ducks, *Anas platyrhynchos*).

Random dispersion occurs when environmental conditions do not vary much within a habitat, and individuals are neither attracted to nor repelled by others of their species (conspecifics). Ecologists use formal statistical definitions of *random* to establish a theoretical baseline for assessing the pattern of distribution. In cases of random dispersion, individuals are distributed unpredictably. Some spiders, burrowing clams, and rainforest trees exhibit random dispersion.

Whether the spatial distribution of a population appears to be clumped, uniform, or random depends partly on the size of the organisms and of the study area. Oak seedlings may be randomly dispersed on a spatial scale of a few square metres, but over an entire mixed hardwood forest, they are clumped under the parent trees. Therefore, dispersion of a population depends partly on the researcher's scale of observation.

In addition, the dispersion of animal populations often varies through time in response to natural environmental rhythms. Few habitats provide a constant supply of resources throughout the year, and many animals move from one habitat to another on a seasonal cycle, reflecting the distribution of resources such as food. Tropical birds and mammals are often widely dispersed in deciduous forests during the wet season, when food is widely available. During the dry season, these species crowd into narrow gallery forests along watercourses, where evergreen trees provide food and shelter.

All populations have an **age structure**, a statistical description of the relative numbers of individuals in each age class (see also Section 29.8). Individuals can be categorized generally as pre-reproductive (younger than the age of sexual maturity), reproductive, or post-reproductive (older than maximum age of reproduction). The age structure of a population reflects its recent growth history and can be used to predict future growth. Populations composed of many pre-reproductive individuals must have grown rapidly in the recent past. These populations will continue to grow as individuals mature and reproduce.

Generation time also influences a population's potential for growth or decline. Generation time is the average time between the birth of an organism and the birth of its offspring. Generation time usually is short in species that reach sexual maturity at a small body size **(Figure 29.6)**. Their populations often grow rapidly because of the speedy accumulation of reproducing individuals.

The proportions of males and females may vary in populations of sexually reproducing organisms. In a species where only females produce young, the number of females has a larger impact on population growth than the number of males. Moreover, in many species, one male can mate with several females, and the number of males may have little effect on the population's reproductive output. In northern elephant seals (see Chapter 17), mature bulls fight for dominance on the beaches

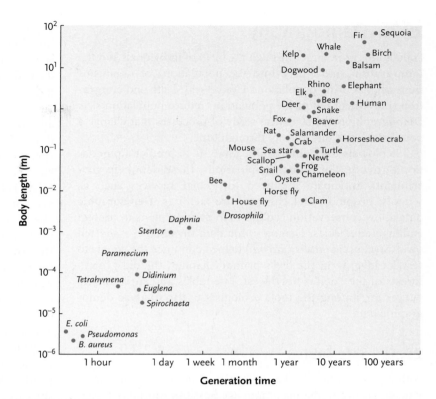

FIGURE 29.6 Generation time and body size. Generation time increases with body size among bacteria, protists, plants, and animals. The logarithmic scale on both axes compresses the data into a straight line.

where the seals mate. While a few males each may inseminate many females and sire many young, most males do not. Thus, the presence of other males in the group may have little effect on the size of future generations. In animals that form lifelong pair bonds, such as geese and swans, the number of pairs influences reproduction in the population.

Population ecologists try to determine the **proportion of reproducing individuals** in a population. This issue is particularly relevant to the conservation of any species in which individuals are rare or widely dispersed (see Chapter 32).

CONCEPT FIX Many people believe that the sizes of populations of animals and plants will increase until net demands for food (and other resources) exceed the supply. This crisis of carrying capacity leads to crashes in populations and even to extinction. Under natural conditions, however, interactions among individuals (of the same or different species) usually cause populations to stop growing well before they reach carrying capacity. In many populations, there are natural cycles of numbers. ⬡

STUDY BREAK QUESTIONS

1. What is the difference between geographic range and habitat?
2. What are the three types of dispersion? What is the most common pattern found in nature? Why?
3. What is the common pattern of generation time among bacteria, protists, plants, and animals?

29.3 Demography

Populations grow larger through the birth of individuals and the **immigration** (movement into the population) of organisms from neighbouring populations. Conversely, death and **emigration** (movement out of the population) reduce population size. **Demography** is the statistical study of processes that change a population's size and density through time.

Ecologists use demographic analysis to predict a population's growth. For human populations, these data help governments anticipate the need for social services such as schools, hospitals, and chronic care facilities. Demographic data allow conservation ecologists to develop plans to protect endangered species. Demographic data on northern spotted owls (*Strix occidentalis caurina*) helped convince the courts to restrict logging in the owl's primary habitat, the old-growth forests of the Pacific Northwest. Life tables and survivorship curves are among the tools ecologists use to analyze demographic data.

29.3a Life Tables

Although every species has a characteristic lifespan, few individuals survive to the maximum age possible. Mortality results from starvation, disease, accidents, predation, or inability to find a suitable habitat. Life insurance companies first developed techniques for measuring mortality rates (known as *actuarial science*), and ecologists adapted these approaches to study populations of other organisms.

A **life table** summarizes the demographic characteristics of a population **(Table 29.1)**. To collect life table data for short-lived organisms, demographers typically mark a **cohort** (a group of individuals of similar age) at birth and monitor their survival until all members of the cohort die. For organisms that live more than a few years, a researcher might sample the population for one or two years, recording the ages at which individuals die and then extrapolating these results over the species' lifespan. The approach to the timing of collection of data about reproduction and longevity will depend on the details of the species under study.

In any life table, lifespans of organisms are divided into age intervals of appropriate length. For short-lived species, days, weeks, or months are useful, whereas for longer-lived species, years or groups of years will be better. Mortality can be expressed in two complementary ways: **age-specific mortality** is the proportion of individuals alive at the start of an age interval that died during that age interval. Its more cheerful reflection, **age-specific survivorship**, is the proportion of individuals alive at the start of an age interval that survived until the start of the next age interval. Thus, for the data shown in Table 29.1, the age-specific mortality rate during the three- to six-month age interval is 195/722 = 0.270, and the age-specific survivorship rate is 527/722 = 0.730. For any age interval, the sum of age-specific mortality and age-specific survivorship must equal 1. Life tables also summarize the proportion of the cohort that survived to a particular age, a statistic identifying the probability that any randomly selected newborn will still be alive at that age. For the three- to six-month age interval in Table 29.1, this probability is 722/843 = 0.856.

Life tables also include data on **age-specific fecundity**, the average number of offspring produced by surviving females during each age interval. Table 29.1 shows that plants in the three- to six-month age interval produced an average of 300 seeds each. In some species, including humans, fecundity is highest in individuals of intermediate age. Younger individuals have not yet reached sexual maturity, and older individuals are past their reproductive prime. However, fecundity increases steadily with age in some plants and animals.

TABLE 29.1	Life Table for a Cohort of 843 Individuals of the Grass *Poa annua* (Annual Bluegrass)					
Age Interval (in months)	Number Alive at Start of Age Interval	Number Dying during Age Interval	Age-Specific Mortality Rate	Age-Specific Survivorship Rate	Proportion of Original Cohort Alive at Start of Age Interval	Age-Specific Fecundity (Seed Production)
0–3	843	121	0.144	0.856	1.000	0
3–6	722	195	0.270	0.730	0.856	300
6–9	527	211	0.400	0.600	0.625	620
9–12	316	172	0.544	0.456	0.375	430
12–15	144	90	0.625	0.375	0.171	210
15–18	54	39	0.722	0.278	0.064	60
18–21	15	12	0.800	0.200	0.018	30
21–24	3	3	1.000	0.000	0.004	10
24–	0	—	—	—	—	—

Source: *Population Ecology : A Unified Study of Animals and Plants* by BEGON, MICHAEL ; MORTIMER, MARTIN Reproduced with permission of BLACKWELL SCIENCE in the format Book via Copyright Clearance Center.

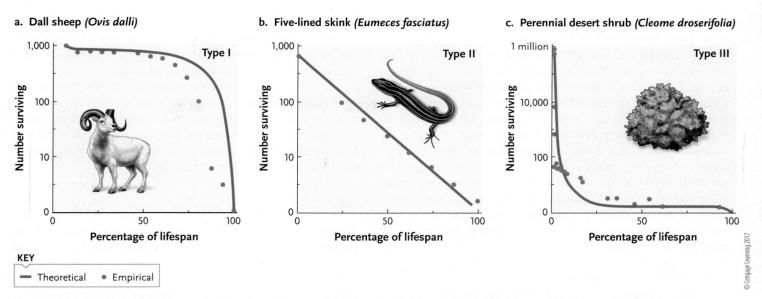

a. Dall sheep *(Ovis dalli)*

Type I

b. Five-lined skink *(Eumeces fasciatus)*

Type II

c. Perennial desert shrub *(Cleome droserifolia)*

Type III

KEY

— Theoretical   • Empirical

© Cengage Learning 2017

FIGURE 29.7 Survivorship curves. The survivorship curves of many organisms (pink) roughly match one of three idealized patterns (blue).

29.3b Survivorship Curves

Survivorship data are depicted graphically in a **survivorship curve**, which displays the rate of survival for individuals over the species' average lifespan. Ecologists have identified three generalized survivorship curves (blue lines in **Figure 29.7**), although most organisms exhibit survivorship patterns falling between these idealized patterns.

Type I curves reflect high survivorship until late in life (see Figure 29.7a). They are typical of large animals that produce few young and reduce juvenile mortality with extended care. Large mammals, such as Dall mountain sheep, produce only one or two offspring at a time and nurture them through their first year. At that time, the young are better able to fend for themselves and are at lower risk for mortality (compared with younger animals). The picture of survivorship in mammals could change if one starts with the time of conception, as opposed to birth. The change would reflect problems of pregnancy (see Chapter 44) and health of mothers.

Type II curves reflect a relatively constant rate of mortality in all age classes, a pattern that produces steadily declining survivorship (see Figure 29.7b). Many lizards, such as the five-lined skink, as well as songbirds and small mammals face a constant probability of mortality from predation, disease, and starvation and show a type II pattern.

Type III curves reflect high juvenile mortality, followed by a period of low mortality once offspring reach a critical age and size (see Figure 29.7c, in which the vertical scale is logarithmic). *Cleome droserifolia*, a desert shrub from the Middle East, experiences extraordinarily high mortality in its seed and seedling stages. Researchers estimate that, for every 1 million seeds produced, fewer than 1000 germinate, and only about 40 individuals survive their first year. Once a plant becomes established, however, its likelihood of future survival is higher, and the survivorship curve flattens out. Many plants, insects, marine invertebrates, and fishes exhibit type III survivorship.

STUDY BREAK QUESTIONS

1. What is the relationship between age-specific mortality and age-specific survivorship? If the age-specific mortality is 0.384, what is the age-specific survivorship?
2. What is age-specific fecundity?
3. Describe three survivorship curves. Which curve describes humans? Songbirds? Insects?

29.4 Evolution of Life Histories

Analysis of life tables reveals how natural selection affects an organism's life history, which includes the lifetime patterns of growth, maturation, and reproduction. Ecologists study life histories to understand trade-offs in the allocation of resources to these three activities. The results of their research suggest that natural selection adjusts the allocation of resources to maximize an individual's number of surviving offspring.

Every organism is constrained by a finite **energy budget**, the total amount of energy it can accumulate and use to fuel its activities. An organism's energy budget is like a savings account. When the individual accumulates more energy than it needs, it makes deposits to this account, storing energy as starch, glycogen, or fat. When the individual expends more energy than it harvests, it makes withdrawals from its energy stores. But unlike a bank account, an organism's energy budget cannot be overdrawn, and no loans against future "earnings" are possible.

Just as humans find clever ways to finance their schemes, many organisms use different ways to mortgage their operations. Organisms that enter states of inactivity or dormancy can maximize the time over which they use stored energy. An extreme example is animals and plants that can survive freezing, an obvious strategy for conserving energy. Hibernation and estivation in animals are other examples (see Chapter 42). Hibernating animals use periods of reduced body temperature to weather prolonged periods of cold weather. Estivation is inactivity during prolonged periods of high temperatures. Specialized spores can be resistant to heat and desiccation. Migrating birds on long flights get energy by metabolizing fat as well as other body structures, such as muscle or digestive tissue. Organisms use the energy they harvest for three broadly defined functions: maintenance (the preservation of good physiological condition), growth, and reproduction. When an organism devotes energy to any one of these functions, the balance in its energy budget is reduced, leaving less energy for other functions.

A fish, a deciduous tree, and a mammal illustrate the dramatic variations existing in life history patterns. Larval coho salmon (*Oncorhynchus kisutch*) hatch in the headwaters of a stream, where they feed and grow for about a year before assuming their adult body form and swimming to the ocean. They remain at sea for a year or two, feeding voraciously and growing rapidly. Eventually, using a Sun compass and geomagnetic and chemical cues, salmon return to the rivers and streams where they hatched. The fishes swim upstream. Males prepare nests and try to attract females. Each female lays hundreds or thousands of relatively small eggs. After breeding, the body condition of males and females deteriorates, and they die.

Most deciduous trees in the temperate zone, such as oaks (genus *Quercus*), begin their lives as nuts (acorns) in late summer. The acorns remain metabolically inactive until the following spring or a later year. After germinating, seedling trees collect nutrients and energy and continue to grow throughout their lives. Once they achieve a critical size, they may produce thousands of acorns annually for many years. Thus, growth and reproduction occur simultaneously through much of the trees' life.

European red deer (*Cervus elaphus*) are born in spring and the young remain with their mothers for an extended period, nursing and growing rapidly. After weaning, the young feed on their own. Female red deer begin to breed after reaching adult size in their third year, producing one or two offspring annually until they die at about 16 years of age, the usual maximum lifespan.

How can we summarize the similarities and differences in the life histories of these organisms? All three species harvest energy throughout their lives. Salmon and deciduous trees continue to grow until old age, whereas deer reach adult size fairly early in life. Salmon produce many offspring in a single reproductive episode, whereas deciduous trees and deer reproduce repeatedly. However, most trees produce thousands of seeds annually, whereas deer produce only one or two young each spring.

What factors have produced these variations in life history patterns? Life history traits, like all population characteristics, are modified by natural selection. Thus, organisms exhibit evolutionary adaptations that increase the fitness of individuals. Each species' life history is, in fact, a highly integrated "strategy," or suite of selection-driven adaptations.

In analyzing life histories, ecologists compare the number of offspring with the amount of care provided to each offspring by the parents. They also determine the number of reproductive episodes in the organism's lifetime and the timing of first reproduction. Because these characteristics evolve together, a change in one trait is likely to influence others.

29.4a Fecundity versus Parental Care

A female with a fixed amount of energy for reproduction can package it in various ways. A female duck with 1000 units of energy for reproduction might lay 10 eggs, each with 100 units of energy. A salmon, which has higher fecundity, might lay 1000 eggs each with 1 unit of energy. Energy invested in each offspring before birth is **passive parental care**, usually provided by the female. Passive parental care is provided through yolk in an egg; endosperm in a seed; or, in mammals, nutrients that cross the placenta.

Many animals also provide **active parental care** after birth. In general, species producing many offspring in a reproductive episode (e.g., the coho salmon) provide relatively little active parental care to each offspring. In fact, female coho salmon, each producing 2400 to 4500 eggs, die before their eggs even hatch. Conversely, species producing few offspring at a time (e.g., European red deer) provide much more care to each one. A red deer doe nurses its single fawn for up to eight months before weaning it.

29.4b How Often to Breed

The number of reproductive episodes in an organism's lifespan is a second life history characteristic acted on by natural selection. Some organisms, such as coho salmon, devote all their stored energy to a single reproductive event. Any adult that survives the upstream migration is likely to leave some surviving offspring. Other species, such as deciduous trees and red deer, reproduce more than once. In contrast to salmon, individuals of these species devote only some of their energy budget to reproduction at any time, with the balance allocated to maintenance and growth. Moreover, in some plants, invertebrates, fishes, and reptiles, larger individuals produce more offspring than smaller ones. Thus, one advantage of using only part of the energy budget for reproduction is that continued growth may result in greater fecundity at a later age. But organisms that do not survive until the next breeding season lose the potential advantage of putting energy into maintenance and growth.

29.4c Age at First Reproduction

Individuals that first reproduce at the earliest possible age may have a good chance of leaving some surviving offspring. But the energy they use in reproduction is not available for maintenance and growth. Thus, early reproducers may be smaller and less healthy than individuals that delay reproduction in favour of other functions. Conversely, an individual that delays reproduction may increase its chance of survival and its future fecundity by becoming larger or more experienced. But there is always a chance that it will die before the next breeding season, leaving no offspring at all. Therefore, a finite energy budget and the risk of mortality establish a trade-off in the timing of first reproduction. Mathematical models suggest that delayed reproduction will be favoured by natural selection, when a sexually mature individual is likely to survive to an older age. This can be correct if organisms grow larger as they age and if larger organisms have higher fecundity. Early reproduction will be favoured if adult survival rates are low, if animals do not grow larger as they age, or if larger size does not increase fecundity. These characteristics apply more readily to some animals and plants than they do to others. Among animals, the features discussed above apply more readily to vertebrate than to invertebrate animals. Parasitic organisms may have quite different patterns of life history.

GUPPY LIFE HISTORY Life history characteristics vary from one species to another, and they can vary among populations of a single species. Predation differentially influences life history characteristics in natural populations of guppies (*Poecilia reticulata*) in Trinidad. Some years ago, drenched with sweat and with fishnets in hand, two ecologists studied guppies and fish communities on the Caribbean island of Trinidad. In their native habitats, guppies bear live young in shallow mountain streams, and John Endler and David Reznick were studying the environmental variables influencing the evolution of their life history patterns.

Male guppies are easy to distinguish from females. Males stop growing at sexual maturity; they are smaller and their scales have bright colours that serve as visual signals in intricate courtship displays. Females are drably coloured and continue to grow larger throughout their lives. In the mountains of Trinidad, guppies live in different streams, even in different parts of the same stream. Two other species of fish eat guppies **(Figure 29.8)**. In some streams, a small killifish (*Rivulus hartii*) preys on immature guppies but does not have much success with the larger adults. In other streams, a large pike–cichlid (*Crenicichla alta*) prefers mature guppies and rarely hunts small, immature ones.

Reznick and Endler found that the life history patterns of guppies vary among streams with different predators. In streams with pike–cichlids, male and female guppies mature faster and begin to reproduce at a smaller size and younger age than their counterparts in streams where killifish live. Female guppies from pike–cichlid streams reproduce more often, producing smaller and more numerous young. These differences allow guppies to avoid some predation. Those in pike–cichlid streams begin to reproduce when they are smaller than the size preferred by that predator. Those from killifish streams grow quickly to a size that is too large to be consumed by killifish.

FIGURE 29.8 **Male guppies from streams where pike–cichlids live** (a) **are smaller and more streamlined, and have duller colours than those from streams where killifish live** (b)**.** The pike–cichlid prefers to eat large guppies; the killifish feeds on small guppies. Guppies are shown approximately life sized; adult pike–cichlids grow to 16 cm in length; adult killifish grow to 10 cm.

Although these life history differences were correlated with the distributions of the two predatory fishes, they might result from some other, unknown differences between the streams. Endler and Reznick investigated this possibility with controlled laboratory experiments. They shipped groups of live guppies to California, where they bred guppies from each kind of stream for two generations. Both types of experimental populations were raised under identical conditions in the absence of predators. Even in the absence of predators, the two types of experimental populations retained their life history differences. These results provided evidence of a genetic (heritable) basis for the observed life history differences.

Endler and Reznick also examined the role of predators in the *evolution* of the size differences**.** They raised guppies for many generations in the laboratory under three experimental conditions: some alone, some with killifish, and some with pike–cichlids. As predicted, the guppy lineage subjected to predation by killifish became larger at maturity. Individuals that were small at maturity were frequently eaten, and their reproduction was limited. The lineage raised with pike–cichlids showed a trend toward earlier maturity. Individuals that matured at a larger size faced a greater likelihood of being eaten before they had reproduced.

STUDY BREAK QUESTIONS

1. Organisms use energy for what three main operations?
2. Explain passive and active parental care in humans.
3. When would early reproduction be favoured?

29.5　Models of Population Growth

Now we move to exponential and logistic growth, two mathematical models of population growth. **Exponential** models apply when populations experience unlimited growth. **Logistic** models apply when population growth is limited, often because available resources are finite. These simple models are tools that help ecologists refine their hypotheses, but neither provides entirely accurate predictions of population growth in nature. In the simplest versions of these models, ecologists define births as the production of offspring by any form of reproduction and ignore the effects of immigration and emigration.

29.5a　Exponential Models

Populations sometimes increase in size for a period of time with no apparent limits on their growth. In models of exponential growth, population size increases steadily by a constant ratio. Populations of bacteria and prokaryotes provide the most obvious examples, but multicellular organisms also sometimes exhibit exponential population growth.

Bacteria reproduce by binary fission. A parent cell divides in half, producing two daughter cells, and each can divide to produce two granddaughter cells. When bacteria all survive and generation time is the time between successive cell divisions, when no bacteria die, the population doubles in size in each generation.

Bacterial populations grow quickly under ideal temperatures and with unlimited space and food. Consider a population of the human intestinal bacterium *Escherichia coli*, for which the generation time could be 20 minutes. If we start with one bacterium, the population doubles to two cells after one generation (20 minutes), to four cells after two generations (40 minutes), and to eight cells after three generations (**Figure 29.9**). After 8 hours (24 generations), the population will number almost 17 million. And after one day (72 generations), the population will number nearly 5×10^{21} cells. Although other bacteria grow more slowly than *E. coli*, it is no wonder that pathogenic bacteria, such as those causing cholera or plague, can quickly overtake the defences of an infected animal.

When populations of multicellular organisms are large, they can grow exponentially, as we shall see below for our own species. In any event, over a given time period, change in population size = number of births – number of deaths. We express this relationship mathematically by defining N as the population size; ΔN (pronounced "delta N") as the change in population size; Δt as the time period during which the change occurs; and B and D as the numbers of births and deaths, respectively, during that time period. Thus, $\Delta N/\Delta t$ symbolizes the change in population size over time, and

$$\Delta N/\Delta t = B - D.$$

The above equation applies to any population for which we know the exact numbers of births and deaths. Ecologists usually express births and deaths as per capita (per individual) rates,

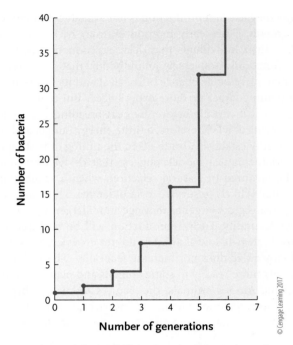

FIGURE 29.9　Bacterial population growth. If all members of a bacterial population divide simultaneously, a plot of population size over time forms a stair-stepped curve in which the steps get larger as the number of dividing cells increases.

allowing them to apply the model to a population of any size. The per capita birth rate (b) is the number of births in the population during the specified time period divided by the population size: $b = (B/N)$. Similarly, the per capita death rate (d) is the number of deaths divided by the population size: $d = (D/N)$.

If in a population of 2000 field mice, 1000 mice are born and 200 mice die during one month: $b = 1000/2000 = 0.5$ births per individual per month, and $d = 200/2000 = 0.1$ deaths per individual per month. Of course, no mouse can give birth to half an offspring, and no individual can die one-tenth of a death. But these rates tell us the per capita birth and death rates averaged over all mice in the population. Per capita birth and death rates are always expressed over a specified time period. For long-lived organisms, such as humans, time is measured in years. For short-lived organisms, such as fruit flies, time is measured in days. We can calculate per capita birth and death rates from data in a life table.

Now we can revise the population growth equation to use per capita birth and death rates instead of the actual numbers of births and deaths. The change in a population's size during a given time period ($\Delta N/\Delta t$) depends on the per capita birth and death rates, as well as on the number of individuals in the population. Mathematically, we can write

$$\Delta N/\Delta t = B - D = bN - dN = (b - d)N$$

or, in the notation of calculus,

$$dN/dt = (b - d)N.$$

This equation describes the **exponential model of population growth**. (Note that, in calculus, dN/dt is the notation for the population growth rate. The d in dN/dt is not the same d we use to symbolize the per capita death rate.)

The difference between the per capita birth rate and the per capita death rate, $b - d$, is the **per capita growth rate** of the population, symbolized by r. Like b and d, r is always expressed per individual per unit time. Using the per capita growth rate, r, in place of $b - d$, the exponential growth equation is written

$$dN/dt = rN.$$

If the birth rate exceeds the death rate, r has a positive value ($r > 0$), and the population is growing. In our example with field mice, r is $0.5 - 0.1 = 0.4$ mice per mouse per month. When the birth rate is lower than the death rate, r has a negative value ($r < 0$) and the population is shrinking. In populations in which the birth rate equals the death rate, r is zero and the population's size is not changing, a situation known as **zero population growth** (ZPG). Even under ZPG, births and deaths still occur, but the numbers of births and deaths may cancel each other out.

Populations will grow as long as the per capita growth rate is positive ($r > 0$). In our hypothetical population of field mice, we started with $N = 2000$ mice and calculated a per capita growth rate of 0.4 mice per individual per month. In the first month, the population grows by $0.4 \times 2000 = 800$ mice **(Figure 29.10)**. At the start of the second month, $N = 2800$ and r is still 0.4. Thus, in the second month, the population grows by $0.4 \times 2800 = 1120$ mice. Notice that, even though r remains constant, the increase in population size grows each month because more individuals are reproducing. In less than two years, the mouse population will be more than one million! A graph of exponential population growth has a characteristic J shape, getting steeper through time. The population grows at an ever-increasing pace because the change in a population's size depends on the number of individuals in the population and its per capita growth rate.

Imagine a hypothetical population living in an ideal environment with unlimited food and shelter; no predators, parasites, or disease; and a comfortable abiotic environment. Under such circumstances (admittedly unrealistic), the per capita birth rate is very high; the per capita death rate is very low; and the per capita growth rate, r, is as high as it can be. This maximum per capita growth rate, symbolized r_{max}, is the population's **intrinsic rate of increase**. Under these ideal conditions, our exponential growth equation is

$$dN/dt = r_{max}N.$$

When populations grow at their intrinsic rate of increase, population size increases very rapidly. Across a wide variety of protists and animals, r_{max} varies inversely with generation time: species with a short generation time have higher intrinsic rates of increase than those with a long generation time **(Figure 29.11)**.

The exponential model predicts unlimited population growth. But we know from even casual observations that population sizes of most species are somehow limited. We are not knee-deep in bacteria, rosebushes, or garter snakes. What factors limit the growth of populations? As a population gets larger, it uses more vital resources, perhaps leading to a shortage of resources. In this situation, individuals may have less energy available for maintenance and reproduction, causing decreases in per capita birth rates and increases in per capita death rates. Energy in food is not always equally available, and when an animal spends time handling food to eat it, the ratio of cost (handling) to benefit (energy in the food) diminishes, affecting return on investment. Such rate changes can affect a population's per capita growth rate, causing population growth to slow or stop.

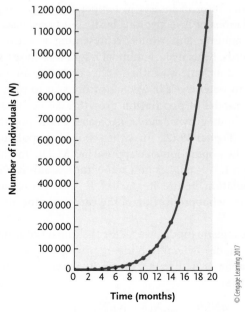

Month	Old Population Size		Net Monthly Increase		New Population Size
1	2 000	+	800	=	2 800
2	2 800	+	1 120	=	3 920
3	3 920	+	1 568	=	5 488
4	5 488	+	2 195	=	7 683
5	7 683	+	3 073	=	10 756
6	10 756	+	4 302	=	15 058
7	15 058	+	6 023	=	21 081
8	21 081	+	8 432	=	29 513
9	29 513	+	11 805	=	41 318
10	41 318	+	16 527	=	57 845
11	57 845	+	23 138	=	80 983
12	80 983	+	32 393	=	113 376
13	113 376	+	45 350	=	158 726
14	158 726	+	63 490	=	222 216
15	222 216	+	88 887	=	311 102
16	311 102	+	124 441	=	435 543
17	435 543	+	174 217	=	609 760
18	609 760	+	243 904	=	853 664
19	853 674	+	341 466	=	1 195 1340

© Cengage Learning 2017

FIGURE 29.10 Exponential population growth. Exponential population growth produces a J-shaped curve when population size is plotted against time. Although the per capita growth rate (r) remains constant, the increase in population size gets larger every month because more individuals are reproducing.

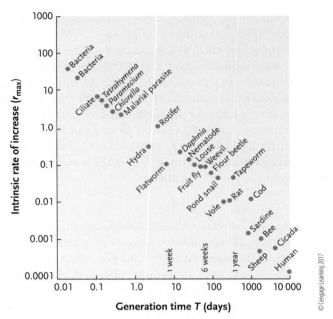

FIGURE 29.11 **Generation time and r_{max}.** The intrinsic rate of increase (r_{max}) is high for protists and animals with short generation times and low for those with long generation times.

29.5b Logistic Models: Populations and Carrying Capacity (K)

Environments may provide enough resources to sustain only a finite population of any species. The maximum number of individuals that an environment can support indefinitely is termed its **carrying capacity**, symbolized as K. K is defined for each population. It is a property of the environment that can vary from one habitat to another and in a single habitat over time. The spring and summer flush of insects in temperate habitats supports large populations of insectivorous birds. But fewer insects are available in autumn and winter, representing a seasonal decline in K for birds. Birds make autumnal migrations in search of food and to avoid inclement weather. Other cycles are annual, such as variation in water levels in wetlands from year to year.

The **logistic model of population growth** assumes that a population's per capita growth rate, r, decreases as the population gets larger **(Figure 29.12)**. In other words, population growth slows as the population size approaches K. The mathematical expression $K - N$ tells us how many individuals can be added to a population before it reaches K. The expression $(K - N)/K$ indicates what proportion of the carrying capacity is still available.

To create the logistic model, we factor the impact of K into the exponential model by multiplying r_{max} by $(K - N)/K$ to reduce the per capita growth rate (r) from its maximum value (r_{max}) as N increases:

$$dN/dt = r_{max}N(K - N)/K.$$

Calculating how r varies with population size is straightforward **(Table 29.2)**. In a very small population (N much

a. The predicted effect of N on r

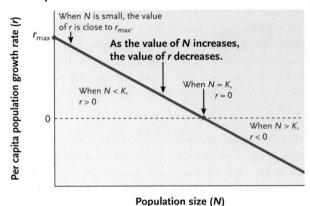

b. Population size through time

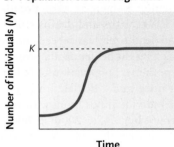

FIGURE 29.12 **The logistic model of population growth.** The logistic model **(a)** assumes that the per capita population growth rate (r) decreases linearly as population size (N) increases. The logistic model also predicts that population size **(b)** increases quickly at first but then slowly approaches carrying capacity (K).

TABLE 29.2	The Effect of N on r and ΔN* in a Hypothetical Population Exhibiting Logistic Growth in which K Equals 2000 and r_{max} Is 0.04 per Capita per Year		
N (population size)	$(K-N)/K$ (% of K available)	$r = r_{max}(K-N/K)$ (per capita growth rate)	$\Delta N = rN$ (change in N)
50	0.975	0.0390	2
100	0.950	0.0380	4
250	0.875	0.0350	9
500	0.750	0.0300	15
750	0.625	0.0250	19
1000	0.500	0.0200	20
1250	0.375	0.0150	19
1500	0.250	0.0100	15
1750	0.125	0.0050	9
1900	0.050	0.0020	4
1950	0.025	0.0010	2
2000	0.000	0.0000	0

*ΔN rounded to the nearest whole number

smaller than K), plenty of resources are available and the value of $(K - N)/K$ is close to 1. Here the per capita growth rate (r) approaches the maximum possible (r_{max}). Under these conditions, population growth is close to exponential. If a population is large (N close to K), few additional resources are available. Now the value of $(K - N)/K$ is small, and the per capita growth rate (r) is very low. When the size of the population exactly equals K, $(K - N)/K$ becomes 0, as does the population growth rate, the situation defined as ZPG.

The logistic model of population growth predicts an S-shaped graph of population size over time, with the population slowly approaching K and remaining at that level **(Figure 29.13)**. According to this model, the population grows slowly when the population size is small because few individuals are reproducing. It also grows slowly when the population size is large because the per capita population growth rate is low. The population grows quickly (dN/dt is highest) at intermediate population sizes, when a sizable number of individuals are breeding and the per capita population growth rate (r) is still fairly high (see Table 29.2).

The logistic model assumes that vital resources become increasingly limited as a population grows. Thus, the model is a mathematical portrait of **intraspecific** (within species) **competition**, the dependence of two or more individuals in a population on the same limiting resource. For mobile animals, limiting resources could be food, water, nesting sites, and refuges from predators. For sessile species, space can be a limiting resource. For plants, sunlight, water, inorganic nutrients, and growing space can be limiting. The pattern of uniform dispersion described earlier often reflects intraspecific competition for limited resources.

In some very dense populations, accumulation of poisonous waste products may reduce survivorship and reproduction. Most natural populations live in open systems where wastes are consumed by other organisms or flushed away. But the buildup of toxic wastes is common in laboratory cultures of microorganisms. For example, yeast cells ferment sugar and produce ethanol as a waste product. Thus, the alcohol content of wine usually does not exceed 13% by volume, the ethanol concentration that poisons yeasts that are vital to the wine-making process.

How well do species conform to the predictions of the logistic model? In simple laboratory cultures, relatively small organisms, such as *Paramecium* spp., some crustaceans, and flour beetles, often show an S-shaped pattern of population growth (Figure 29.13, left, middle). Moreover, large animals introduced into new environments sometimes exhibit a pattern of population growth that matches the predictions of the logistic model (Figure 30.13, right).

Nevertheless, some assumptions of the logistic model are unrealistic. For example, the model predicts that survivorship and fecundity respond immediately to changes in a population's density. Many organisms exhibit a delayed response (a **time lag**) because fecundity has been determined by resource availability sometime in the past. This may reflect conditions that prevailed when individuals were adding yolk to eggs or endosperm to seeds. Moreover, when food resources become scarce, individuals may survive and reproduce using reserves of stored energy. This delays the impact of crowding until stored reserves are depleted and means that population size may overshoot K (see Figure 29.13, middle). When deaths outnumber births, the population size drops below K, at least temporarily. Time lags often cause a population to oscillate around K.

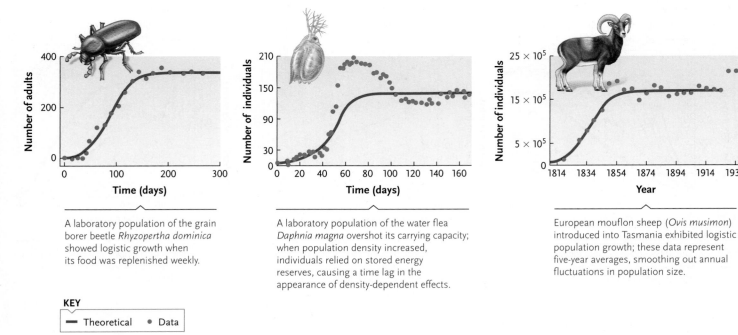

A laboratory population of the grain borer beetle *Rhyzopertha dominica* showed logistic growth when its food was replenished weekly.

A laboratory population of the water flea *Daphnia magna* overshot its carrying capacity; when population density increased, individuals relied on stored energy reserves, causing a time lag in the appearance of density-dependent effects.

European mouflon sheep (*Ovis musimon*) introduced into Tasmania exhibited logistic population growth; these data represent five-year averages, smoothing out annual fluctuations in population size.

KEY
— Theoretical   • Data

FIGURE 29.13 Examples of logistic population growth

© Cengage Learning 2017

The assumption that the addition of new individuals to a population always decreases survivorship and fecundity is unrealistic. In small populations, modest population growth may not have much impact on survivorship and fecundity. In fact, most organisms probably require a minimum population density to survive and reproduce. Some plants flourish in small clumps that buffer them from physical stresses, whereas a single individual living in the open would suffer adverse effects. In some animal populations, a minimum population density is necessary for individuals to find mates. Determining the minimum viable population for a species is an important issue in conservation biology (see Chapter 28).

STUDY BREAK QUESTIONS

1. When do you use an exponential model rather than a logistic one?
2. Define the terms in the equation $dN/dt = (b - d)N$.
3. What does it mean when $r < 0$, $r > 0$, or $r = 0$? What is r_{max}, and how does it vary with generation time?

29.6 Population Regulation

What environmental factors influence population growth rates and control fluctuations in population size? The influence of **density dependent** factors can increase or decrease with population density; either way can be an example of a density-dependent environmental factor. The logistic model includes the effects of density dependence in its assumption that per capita birth and death rates change with population density.

Numerous laboratory and field studies have shown that crowding (high population density) decreases individual growth rate, adult size, and survival of plants and animals **(Figure 29.14)**. Organisms living in very dense populations are unable to harvest enough resources; they grow slowly and tend to be small, weak, and less likely to survive. Gardeners understand this relationship and thin out their populations of plants to achieve a density that maximizes the number of vigorous individuals available for harvest.

Crowding has a negative effect on reproduction **(Figure 29.15)**. When resources are in short supply, each individual has less energy for reproduction after meeting its basic needs for maintenance. Hence, females in crowded populations produce either fewer offspring or smaller offspring that are less likely to survive.

In some species, crowding stimulates developmental and behavioural changes that can influence population density. Migratory locusts can develop into either solitary or migratory forms in the same population. Migratory individuals have longer wings and more body fat, characteristics that allow long-distance dispersal. High population density increases the frequency of the migratory form, so many locusts move away from the area of high density **(Figure 29.16)**, reducing the size and thus the density of the original population.

Although these data about locusts confirm the assumptions of the logistic equation, they do not prove that natural populations are regulated by density-dependent factors. Experimental evidence is necessary to provide a convincing

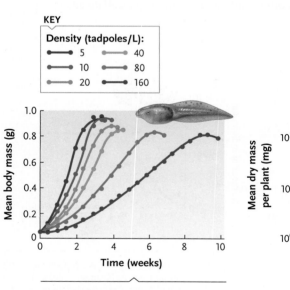

Tadpoles of the frog *Rana tigrina* grew faster and reached larger adult body size at low densities than at high densities.

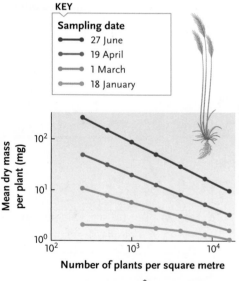

The size of the annual dune grass *Vulpia fasciculata* decreased markedly when plants were grown at high density. Density effects became more accentuated through time as the plants grew larger (indicated by the progressively steeper slopes of the lines).

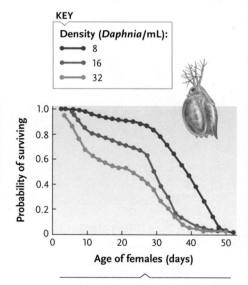

The water flea *Daphnia pulex* had higher survivorship at a density of 8/mL than at densities of 16/mL or 32/mL.

FIGURE 29.14 Effects of crowding on individual growth, size, and survival

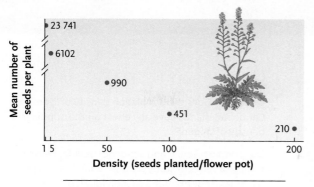

The number of seeds produced by shepherd's purse (*Capsella bursa-pastoris*) decreased dramatically with increasing density in experimental plots.

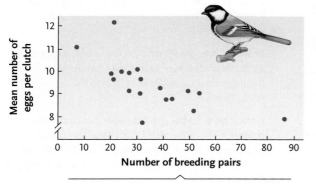

The mean number of eggs produced by the Great Tit (*Parus major*), a woodland bird, declined as the number of breeding pairs in Marley Wood increased.

© Cengage Learning 2017

FIGURE 29.15 Effects of crowding on fecundity

Gianni Tortoli/Science Source

FIGURE 29.16 A swarm of locusts. Migratory locusts (*Locusta migratoria*) moving across an African landscape can devour their own weight in plant material every day.

demonstration that an increase in population density causes population size to decrease, whereas a decrease in density causes it to increase.

In the 1960s, Robert Eisenberg experimentally increased the numbers of aquatic snails (*Lymnaea elodes*) in some ponds and decreased them in others. He also maintained natural densities in control ponds. Adult survivorship did not differ between experimental and control treatments. But there was a gradient in egg production, from few eggs (snails in high-density ponds) to more (control density) to most (low density). Furthermore, survival rates of young snails declined as density increased. After four months, densities in the two experimental groups converged on those in the control, providing strong evidence of density-dependent population regulation.

At this stage, intraspecific competition appears to be the primary density-dependent factor regulating population size. Competition between populations of different species can also exert density-dependent effects on population growth (see Chapter 30). The Allee effect occurs when *r* begins to decline after *N* falls below some threshold. This is another example of a density-dependent regulator.

Predation can also cause density-dependent population regulation. As a particular prey species becomes more numerous, predators may consume more of it because it is easier to find and catch. Once a prey species exceeds some threshold density, predators may consume a larger percentage of its population, amounting to a density-dependent effect. On rocky shores in California, sea stars feed mainly on the most abundant available invertebrates. When one prey species becomes common, predators feed on it disproportionately, reducing its numbers. Then they switch to now more abundant alternative prey.

Sometimes several density-dependent factors influence a population at the same time. On small islands in the West Indies, spiders are rare wherever lizards (*Ameiva festiva*, *Anolis carolinensis*, and *Anolis sagrei*) are abundant, but common where the lizards are rare or absent. To test whether the presence of lizards limits the abundance of spiders, David Spiller and Tom Schoener built fences around plots on islands where these species occur. They eliminated lizards from experimental plots but left them in control plots. After two years, spider populations in some experimental plots were five times denser than those in control plots, suggesting a strong impact of lizard populations on spider populations **(Figure 29.17)**. In this situation, lizards had two density-dependent effects on spider populations. First, lizards ate spiders; second, they competed with them for food. Experimental evidence made it possible for biologists to better understand the situation.

Predation, parasitism, and disease can cause density-dependent regulation of plant and animal populations. Infectious microorganisms (e.g., those causing malaria) can spread quickly in a crowded population. In addition, if crowded individuals are weak or malnourished, they are more susceptible

FIGURE 29.17 **Experimental Research**

Evaluating Density-Dependent Interactions between Species

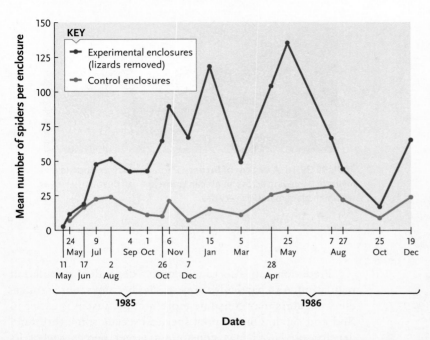

Source: D. A. Spiller and T. W. Schoener. 1998. An experimental study of the effects of lizards on web-spider communities. Ecological Monographs 58:57–77. Ecological monographs by ECOLOGICAL SOCIETY OF AMERICA Copyright 1988. Reproduced with permission of ECOLOGICAL SOCIETY OF AMERICA in the format Textbook via Copyright Clearance Center.

Question: Does the population density of lizards on Caribbean islands have any effect on the population density of spiders?

Experiment: Spiller and Schoener built fences to enclose a series of study plots on a small island in the Bahamas. They excluded all individuals of three lizard species from the experimental enclosures, but left resident lizards undisturbed in the control enclosures. They then made monthly measurements of population densities of the web-building spider *Metepeira daytona* in both experimental enclosures and control enclosures.

Results: Over the 20-month course of the experiment, spider densities were as much as five times higher in the experimental enclosures than in the control enclosures.

Conclusion: Spiller and Schoener concluded that the presence of lizards has a large impact on spider populations. The lizards not only compete with the spiders for insect food, but they also appear to prey on the spiders.

---

to infection and may die from diseases that healthy organisms would survive. Effects on survival can be direct or indirect.

29.6a Populations and Density

Some populations are affected by **density-independent** factors that reduce the size of a population regardless of its density. If an insect population is not physiologically adapted to high temperature, a sudden hot spell may kill 80% of them, whether they number 100 or 100 000. Fires, earthquakes, storms, and other natural disturbances can contribute directly or indirectly to density-independent mortality. Because such factors do not cause a population to fluctuate around its *K,* these density-independent factors can reduce but do not regulate population size.

Density-independent factors have a particularly strong effect on populations of small-bodied species that cannot buffer themselves against environmental change. Their populations may grow exponentially for a time, then shifts in climate or random events may cause high mortality before populations reach a size at which density-dependent factors would regulate their numbers. When conditions improve, populations grow exponentially, at least until another density-independent factor

causes them to crash again. A small Australian insect, a thrip (*Thrips imaginis*), eats the pollen and flowers of plants in the rose family. These thrips can be abundant enough to damage blooms. Populations of thrips grow exponentially in spring, when many flowers are available and the weather is warm and moist **(Figure 29.18)**. But their populations crash predictably during summer because thrips do not tolerate hot and dry conditions. After the crash, a few individuals survive in remaining flowers, and they are the stock from which the population grows exponentially the following spring.

29.6b Density-Dependent and Density-Independent Factors

Density-dependent factors can interact with density-independent factors and limit population growth. Food shortage caused by high population density (a density-dependent factor) may lead to malnourishment. Malnourished individuals may be more likely to succumb to the stress of extreme weather (a density-independent factor).

Populations can be affected by density-independent factors in a density-dependent manner. Some animals retreat into

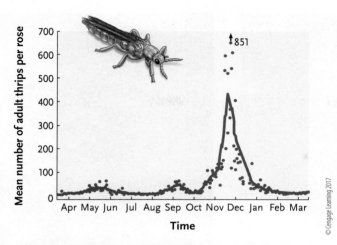

FIGURE 29.18 Booms and busts in a population of thrips.
Populations of the Australian insect *Thrips imaginis* grow exponentially when conditions are favourable during spring (which begins in September in the southern hemisphere). But the populations crash in summer when hot and dry conditions cause high mortality.

TABLE 29.3	Characteristics of *r*-Selected and *K*-Selected Species	
Characteristic	*r*-Selected Species	*K*-Selected Species
Maturation time	Short	Long
Lifespan	Short	Long
Mortality rate	Usually high	Usually low
Reproductive episodes	Usually one	Usually several
Time of first reproduction	Early	Late
Clutch or brood size	Usually large	Usually small
Size of offspring	Small	Large
Active parental care	Little or none	Often extensive
Population size	Fluctuating	Relatively stable
Tolerance of environmental change	Generally poor	Generally good

shelters to escape environmental stresses, such as floods or severe heat. If a population is small, most individuals can be accommodated in available refuges. But if a population is large (exceeds the capacity of shelters), only some individuals will find suitable shelter. The larger the population, the greater the percentage of individuals exposed to the stress(es). Thus, although the density-independent effects of weather limit populations of thrips, the availability of flowers in summer (a density-dependent factor) regulates the size of the starting populations of thrips the following spring. Thus both density-dependent and density-independent factors influence the size of populations of thrips.

Other explanations focus on extrinsic control, such as the relationship between a cycling species and its food or predators. A dense population may exhaust its food supply, increasing mortality and decreasing reproduction. The die-off of large numbers of African elephants in Tsavo National Park in Kenya is an example of the impact of overpopulation. There, elephants overgrazed vegetation in most of the Park habitat. In 1970, the combination of overgrazing and a drought caused high mortality of elephants. The picture is not always clear because experimental food supplementation does not always prevent decline in mammal populations, suggesting some level of intrinsic control.

29.6c Strategies for Population Growth

Even casual observation reveals considerable variation in the rapidity of changes in sizes of populations in different species. New weeds often appear in a vegetable garden overnight, whereas the number of oak trees in a forest may remain relatively stable for years. Why do some species have the potential for explosive population growth? The answer lies in how natural selection has moulded life history strategies adapted to different ecological conditions. Some ecologists recognize two quite

different life history patterns: *r*-selected species and *K*-selected species (**Table 29.3** and **Figure 29.19**).

On the face of it, *r*-selected species are adapted to rapidly changing environments, and many have at least some of the features outlined in Table 29.3. The success of an *r*-selected life history depends on flooding the environment with a large quantity of young because only some may be successful. Small body size means that, compared with larger-bodied species, *r*-selected species lack physiological mechanisms to buffer themselves from environmental variation. Populations of *r*-selected species can be reduced by changes in abiotic environmental factors (e.g., temperature or moisture) so that they may never grow large enough to reach *K* and face a shortage of limiting resources. In these cases, *K* cannot be estimated by researchers, and changes in population size are not accurately described by the logistic model of population growth. Although *r*-selected species appear to have poor tolerance of environmental change, they appear adaptable to rapidly changing environments.

At the same time, *K*-selected species have at least some of the features outlined for them in Table 29.3. These organisms survive the early stages of life (type I or type II survivorship), and a low r_{max} means that their populations grow slowly. The success of a *K*-selected life history is linked to the production of a relatively small number of high-quality offspring that join an already well-established population. Generalizations about *r*-selected and *K*-selected species are misleading. We can recognize this when we compare two species of small mammals.

Peromyscus maniculatus, deer mice, occur widely in North America. In southern Ontario, adults weigh 12–31 g, females produce average litters of four (range two to eight), and each can bear four or five litters a year. Females become sexually mature at age two months and breed in their first year. Occasionally, deer mice live to age three years in the wild.

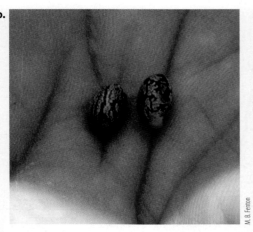

FIGURE 29.19 Life history differences. (a) An *r*-selected species, a castor bean (*Ricinus communis*) matures in one growing season and produces many small seeds (two in palm of hand) **(b)**. **(c)** A *K*-selected species, a coconut palm (*Cocos nucifera*) grows slowly and produces a few large seeds repeatedly during its long life.

Throughout their extensive range in North America, *Myotis lucifugus*, little brown myotis, weigh 7–12 g. Females bear a single young per litter and have one litter per year. Females may breed a year after they are born, but many wait until they are two years old. In the wild, little brown myotis can live over 30 years. Using these data, one small mammal (deer mouse) is an *r*-strategist, whereas another (little brown bat) is a *K*-strategist. To complicate matters, deer mice living in Kananaskis in the mountains near Calgary mature at one year and may have two litters per year, typically five young per litter. Compared to little brown bats, Kananaskis deer mice are *r*-strategists. Compared to Ontario deer mice, they are more like *K*-strategists.

Biologists may find the idea of *r*-strategists and *K*-strategists useful, but too often the idea means imposing some human view of the world on a natural system. *K*-strategists and *r*-strategists may be more like beauty, defined by the eye of the beholder. Elephants (*Loxodonta africana*, *Loxodonta cyclotis*, *Elephas maximus*) are big and meet all *K*-strategist criteria. Many insects are small but in all other respects meet the criteria considered typical of *K*-strategists because of their patterns of reproduction. Codfish (*Gadus morhua*) are big (compared to insects or bats) but meet most of the criteria used to identify *r*-strategists, such as their patterns of reproduction.

29.6d Population Cycles

Population densities of many insects, birds, and mammals in the northern hemisphere fluctuate between species-specific lows and highs in a multiyear cycle. Arctic populations of small rodents (*Lemmus lemmus*) vary in size over a 4-year cycle, whereas snowshoe hares (*Lepus americanus*), ruffed grouse (*Bonasa umbellus*), and lynx have 10-year cycles. Ecologists documented these cyclic fluctuations more than a century ago, but none of the general hypotheses proposed to date explain cycles in all species. Availability and quality of food, abundance of predators, prevalence of disease-causing microorganisms, and variations in weather can influence population growth and declines. Furthermore, food supply and predators for a cycling population are themselves influenced by a population's size.

Theories of intrinsic control suggest that, as an animal population grows, individuals undergo hormonal changes that increase aggressiveness, reduce reproduction, and foster dispersal. The dispersal phase of the cycle may be dramatic. When populations of Norway lemming (*Lemmus lemmus*), a rodent that lives in the Scandinavian Arctic, reach their peak density, aggressive interactions drive younger and weaker individuals to disperse. The dispersal of many thousands of lemmings during periods of population growth has sometimes been incorrectly portrayed in nature films as a suicidal mass migration.

Cycles in populations of predators could be induced by time lags between populations of predators and prey, and vice versa **(Figure 29.20)**. The 10-year cycles of snowshoe hares and their feline predators, Canada lynx, were often cited as a classic example of such an interaction. But snowshoe hare populations can exhibit a 10-year fluctuation even on islands where lynx are absent. Thus, lynx are not solely responsible for population cycles in snowshoe hares. To further complicate matters, the database demonstrating fluctuations was often the numbers of pelts purchased by the Hudson's Bay Company. Here, fur price

Ed Cesar/Science Source

FIGURE 29.20 **The predator–prey model.** Predator–prey interactions may contribute to density-dependent regulation of both populations. **(a)** A mathematical model predicts cycles in the numbers of predators and prey because of time lags in each species' responses to changes in the density of the other. (Predator population size is exaggerated in this graph.) **(b)** Canada lynx (*Lynx canadensis*) and snowshoe hare (*Lepus americanus*) were often described as a typical cyclic predator–prey interaction. The abundances of lynx (red line) and snowshoe hares (blue line) are based on counts of pelts that trappers sold to the Hudson's Bay Company over a 90-year period. Recent research shows that population cycles in snowshoe hares are caused by complex interactions between the snowshoe hare, its food plants, and its predators.

a. Predictions of a predator–prey model

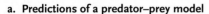

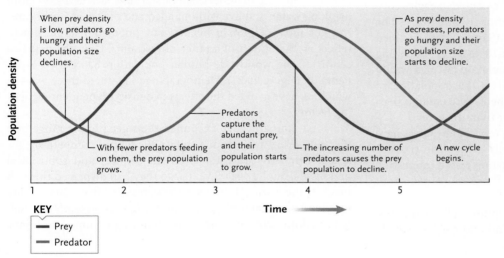

When prey density is low, predators go hungry and their population size declines.

With fewer predators feeding on them, the prey population grows.

Predators capture the abundant prey, and their population starts to grow.

The increasing number of predators causes the prey population to decline.

As prey density decreases, predators go hungry and their population size starts to decline.

A new cycle begins.

KEY
— Prey
— Predator

b. Lynx and hare population sizes through time

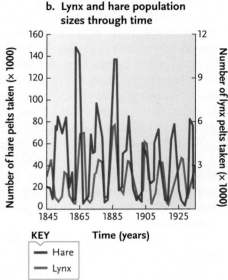

KEY
— Hare
— Lynx

influenced the trapping effort and the numbers of animals harvested. This economic reality brought into question the relationship between the numbers of pelts and actual population densities of lynx and snowshoe hares.

Charles Krebs and his colleagues studied hare and lynx interactions with a large-scale, multiyear experiment in Kluane, in the southern Yukon. Using fenced experimental areas, they could add food for snowshoe hares, exclude mammalian predators, or apply both experimental treatments while monitoring unmanipulated control plots. When mammalian predators were excluded, densities of snowshoe hares approximately doubled relative to controls. Where food was added, densities of snowshoe hares tripled relative to controls. In plots where food was added and predators were excluded, densities of snowshoe hares increased 11-fold compared with controls. Krebs and his colleagues concluded that neither food availability nor predation is solely responsible for population cycles in snowshoe hares. They postulated that complex interactions between snowshoe hares, their food plants, and their predators generate cyclic fluctuations in populations of snowshoe hares.

STUDY BREAK QUESTIONS

1. What are density-dependent factors? Why do dense populations tend to decrease in size?
2. Define *density-independent factors* and give some examples.
3. Describe two key differences between *r*-selected species and *K*-selected species.

29.7 Human Administered Population Control

People commonly expect that predators play an active role in controlling populations of prey. This misconception was one reason that mongooses (*Herpestes auropunctatus*) were introduced from India to Central America. In this case, the mongoose's reputation as a killer of snakes appeared to offer the promise that mongooses would at least reduce populations of fer-de-lances (*Bothrops asper*). These venomous relatives of rattlesnakes were a hazard to cane workers. The mongooses thrived in the New World but did not do well against fer-de-lances, whose strikes were faster than those of cobras. The mongooses were very effective predators of other snakes as well as ground-nesting birds, leading to the extinction of several species. This made the introductions disastrous from a conservation standpoint.

Predators can seriously deplete populations of prey, and this can precipitate dilemmas about conservation and the management of wildlife. One well-known example is the decline of island foxes (*Urocyon littoralis*), a species endemic to the Channel Islands in California. Each of the six islands had a distinct population (subspecies) of foxes. Island foxes were considered to be threatened with imminent extinction, partly reflecting the impact of feral pigs (*Sus scrofa*) that had been introduced to the islands.

After golden eagles (*Aquila chrysaetos*) colonized the Channel Islands, their numbers increased, reflecting the abundant food supply, the pigs. The population of golden eagles continued to increase and they began eating island foxes. The population of the foxes on one island (Santa Cruz) declined from 1500 to less than 100 in less than 10 years. A modelling study suggested that reducing the population of pigs would increase the pressure on the foxes unless the population of eagles also was decreased. As long as there were enough pigs, the eagles preyed mainly on them rather than the foxes.

In the United States, golden eagles (and bald eagles) have special legal protection, making it legally difficult to translocate or otherwise harass them. This situation raised interesting legal, political, and social challenges to those concerned about conservation.

In Alberta, Canada, human disruptions of ecosystems, largely associated with exploration for oil and gas, are largely responsible for drastic declines in herds of woodland caribou (*Rangifer tarandus caribou*). Roadways associated with exploration operations offer wolves (*Canis lupus*) linear features for travel but also facilitate human harvesting of caribou. A study published in 2014 reported the results of monitoring adult survival in a herd of 172 adult female caribou from 2000 to 2012. During the winters of 2005–2006, the researchers reduced populations of wolves, which coincided with a 4.6% increase in the growth rate of the herd of caribou. In a comparable control area where there was no focused reduction of populations of wolves, another herd of caribou declined by 4.7% in the same period.

Unfortunately, human activities in much of the world negatively affect ecosystems and wild populations of organisms. In some cases, control of predators may be one of the main options open to those trying to conserve wild systems.

Actions associated with predator control often stir heated debates. In Canada, we can expect more confrontations around predator control, which often are intended to protect woodland caribou. But population control by culling can be as contentious when the targets are other animals, from white-tailed deer (*Odocoileus virginianus*) to double-crested cormorants (*Phalacrocorax auritus*). There is less contention about the control of weeds.

29.8 Human Population Growth

How do human populations compare with those of other species? The worldwide human population was over 7 billion in 2014. Like many other species, humans live in somewhat isolated populations that vary in their demographic traits and access to resources. Although many live comfortably, at least a billion people are malnourished or starving, lack access to clean drinking water, and live without adequate shelter or healthcare.

For most of human history, our population grew slowly, reflecting the impact of a range of restraints. Over the past two centuries, the worldwide human population has grown exponentially **(Figure 29.21)**. Demographers identified three ways in which we have avoided the effects of density-dependent regulating factors.

First, humans have expanded their geographic range into virtually every terrestrial habitat, alleviating competition for space. Our early ancestors lived in tropical and subtropical grasslands, but by 40 000 years ago they had dispersed through much of the world. Humans' success resulted from their ability to solve ecological problems by building fires, assembling shelters, making clothing and tools, planning community hunts,

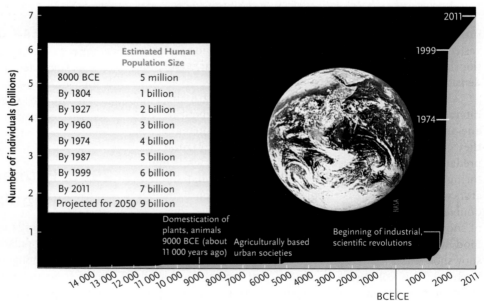

Estimated Human Population Size	
8000 BCE	5 million
By 1804	1 billion
By 1927	2 billion
By 1960	3 billion
By 1974	4 billion
By 1987	5 billion
By 1999	6 billion
By 2011	7 billion
Projected for 2050	9 billion

FIGURE 29.21 Human population growth. The worldwide human population grew slowly until 200 years ago, when it began to increase explosively. The dip in the mid-fourteenth century represents the death of 60 million Asians and Europeans from the bubonic plague. The table shows how long it took for the human population to add each billion people.

and sharing information. Vital survival skills spread from generation to generation and from one population to another because language allowed communication of complex ideas and knowledge.

Second, we have increased K in habitats we occupy, isolating us, as a species, from restrictions associated with access to resources. This change began to occur about 11 000 years ago, when populations in different parts of the world began to shift from hunting and gathering to agriculture. At that time, our ancestors cultivated wild grasses and other plants, diverted water to irrigate crops, and used domesticated animals for food and labour. Innovations such as these increased the availability of food, raising both K and rates of population growth. In the mid-eighteenth century, people harnessed the energy in fossil fuels, and industrialization began in Western Europe and North America. Food supplies and K increased again, at least in industrialized countries, largely through the use of synthetic fertilizers, pesticides, and efficient methods of transportation and food distribution.

Third, advances in public health reduced the effects of critical population-limiting factors such as malnutrition, contagious diseases, and poor hygiene. Over the past 300 years, modern plumbing and sewage treatment, removal of garbage, and improvements in food handling and processing, as well as medical discoveries, have reduced death rates sharply. Births now greatly exceed deaths, especially in more industrialized countries, resulting in rapid population growth. Note, however, that problems of hygiene and access to fresh water and food had been solved in some societies at least hundreds of years ago. Rome, for example, had a population of about 1 million people by 2 CE, and this was supported by an excellent infrastructure for importing and distributing food, providing fresh water, and dealing with human wastes.

29.8a Age Structure and Economic Growth

Where have our migrations and technological developments taken us? It took about 2.5 million years for the human population to reach 1 billion, 80 years to reach the second billion, and only 12 years to jump from 5 billion to 6 billion, and another 12 years to reach 7 billion (see the inset table in Figure 29.21). Rapid population growth now appears to be an inevitable consequence of our demographic structure and economic development.

29.8b Population Growth and Age Structure

In 2011, the worldwide annual growth rate for the human population averaged about 1.15% ($r = 0.0115$ new individuals per individual per year). Population experts expect that rate to decline, but even so, the human population will probably exceed 9 billion before 2050.

In 2000, population growth rates of individual nations varied widely, ranging from much less than 1% to more than 3% **(Figure 29.22)**. Industrialized countries of Western Europe have achieved nearly ZPG, but other countries, particularly those in Africa, Latin America, and Asia, will experience huge increases over the next 20 or 25 years (Figure 29.22b).

For all long-lived species, differences in age structure are a major determinant of differences in population growth rates **(Figure 29.23)**. There are three basic patterns in the graphs in

a. Mean annual population growth rates, 2013

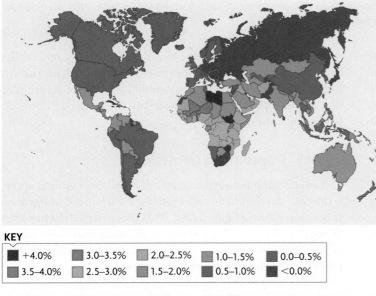

KEY

■ +4.0%	■ 3.0–3.5%	■ 2.0–2.5%	■ 1.0–1.5%	■ 0.0–0.5%
■ 3.5–4.0%	■ 2.5–3.0%	■ 1.5–2.0%	■ 0.5–1.0%	■ <0.0%

b. Actual and projected population sizes for major world regions

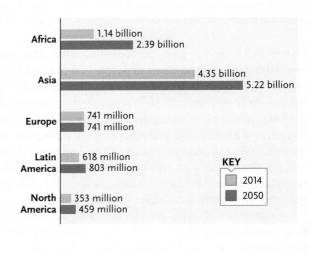

KEY
■ 2014
■ 2050

FIGURE 29.22 Local variation in human population growth rates. In 2001, **(a)** average annual population growth rates varied among countries and continents. In some regions **(b)**, the population is projected to increase greatly by 2025 (red) compared with the population size in 2001 (orange). The population of Europe is likely to decline.

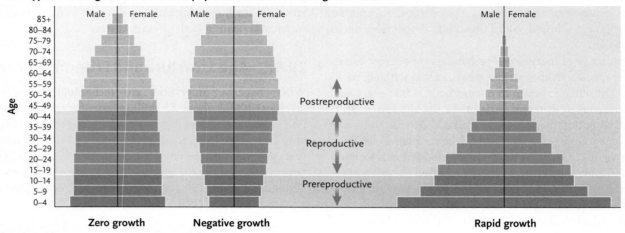

a. Hypothetical age distributions for populations with different growth rates

Zero growth   **Negative growth**   **Rapid growth**

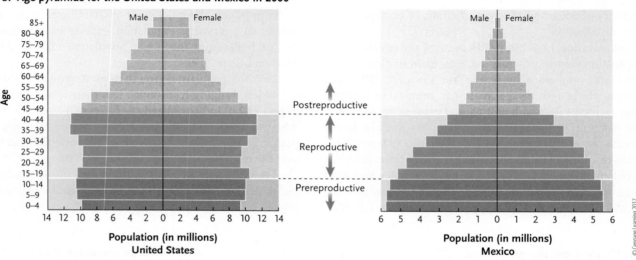

b. Age pyramids for the United States and Mexico in 2000

Population (in millions)
United States

Population (in millions)
Mexico

© Cengage Learning 2017

FIGURE 29.23 Age structure diagrams. Age structure diagrams **(a)** differ for countries with zero, negative, and rapid population growth rates. The width of each bar represents the proportion of the population in each age class. Age structure diagrams for the United States and Mexico **(b)** in 2000 (measured in millions of people) suggest that these countries will experience different growth rates.

Figure 29.23. In the first, in countries with ZPG, there are approximately equal numbers of people of reproductive and pre-reproductive ages. The ZPG situation is exacerbated when reproductives have very few offspring, meaning that pre-reproductives may not even replace themselves in the population. Second, in countries with negative growth (without immigration), post-reproductives outnumber reproductives, and these populations will not experience a growth spurt when today's children reach reproductive age. Third are countries with rapid growth, where reproductives vastly outnumber post-reproductives.

Countries with rapid growth have a broad-based age structure (pattern three, above), with many youngsters born during the previous 15 years. Worldwide, more than one-third of the human population falls within this pre-reproductive base. This age class will soon reach sexual maturity. Even if each woman produces only two offspring, populations will continue to grow rapidly because so many individuals are reproducing. This situation is a population bomb.

The age structures of the United States and Mexico differ, and this has consequences for population growth in the two jurisdictions. Remember the potential importance of immigration and emigration when considering the longer-term impact of the population bomb.

29.8c Population Growth

The relationship between a country's population growth and its economic development can be depicted by the **demographic transition model (Figure 29.24)**. This model describes historical changes in demographic patterns in the industrialized countries of Western Europe. Today, we do not know whether it accurately predicts the future for developing nations.

According to this model, during a country's pre-industrial stage, birth and death rates are high, and the population grows slowly. Industrialization begins a transitional stage, when food production rises and healthcare and sanitation improve, and

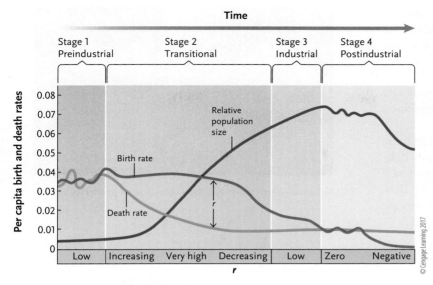

Time →

| Stage 1 Preindustrial | Stage 2 Transitional | Stage 3 Industrial | Stage 4 Postindustrial |

Birth rate

Death rate

Relative population size

r

| Low | Increasing | Very high | Decreasing | Low | Zero | Negative |

r

© Cengage Learning 2017

FIGURE 29.24 The demographic transition. The demographic transition model describes changes in the birth and death rates and relative population size as a country passes through four stages of economic development. The bottom bar describes the net population growth rate, *r*.

death rates decline, resulting in increased rates of population growth. Later, as living conditions improve, birth rates decline, causing a drop in rates of population growth. When the industrial stage is in full swing, population growth slows dramatically. Now people move from countryside to cities, and urban couples often choose to accumulate material goods instead of having large families. ZPG is reached in the post-industrial stage. Eventually, the birth rate falls below the death rate, *r* falls below zero, and population size begins to decrease.

Today, the United States, Canada, Australia, Japan, Russia, and most of Western Europe are in the industrial stage: their growth rates are slowly decreasing. In Germany, Bulgaria, and Hungary (and other European countries), birth rates are lower than death rates and populations are shrinking, indicating entry into the post-industrial stage. Kenya and other less-industrialized countries are in the transitional stage, but they may not have enough skilled workers or enough capital to make the transition to an industrialized economy. For these reasons, many poorer nations may be stuck in the transitional stage. Developing countries experience rapid population increase because they experience declines in death rates associated with the transitional stage without the decreases in birth rates typical of industrial and post-industrial stages.

Stable population in humans can be achieved with an average of 2.1 births per woman, the replacement level. A study published in 2014 reported that, in at least 40 countries, the rate exceeded 2.1 births per woman. Another important factor in a human population is the potential support ratio (PSR). This depicts the ratio of working people (number aged 20–64 years) to older people (number older than 65 years). The economic and social implications of the PSR are becoming more and more apparent.

29.8d Controlling Reproductive Output

Most governments realize that increased population size is now the major factor causing resource depletion, excessive pollution, and an overall decline in quality of life. The principles of population ecology demonstrate that slowing the rate of population growth and effecting an actual decline in population size can be achieved only by decreasing the birth rate and/or increasing the death rate. Increasing mortality is neither a rational nor a humane means of population control. Some governments use **family planning programs** in an attempt to lower birth rates. In other countries, any form of family planning is unlawful. This topic is discussed further in Chapter 28, where we will see that education of women is a vital undertaking.

To achieve ZPG, the average replacement rate should be just slightly higher than two children per couple. This is necessary because some female children die before reaching reproductive age. Today's replacement rate averages about 2.5 children in less industrialized countries with higher mortality rates in pre-reproductive cohorts, and 2.1 in more industrialized countries. However, even if each couple on Earth produced only two children, the human population would continue to grow for at least another 60 years (the impact of the population bomb). Continued population growth is inevitable because today's children, who outnumber adults, will soon mature and reproduce. The worldwide population will stabilize only when the age distributions of all countries resemble that for countries with ZPG.

Family planning efforts encourage women to delay their first reproduction. Doing so reduces the average family size and slows population growth by increasing generation time (see Figure 29.10). Imagine two populations in which each woman produces two offspring. In the first population, women begin reproducing at age 32 years, and in the second they begin reproducing at age 16 years. We can begin with a cohort of newborn baby girls in each population. After 32 years, women in the first population will be giving birth to their first offspring, but women in the second population will be new grandmothers. After 64 years, women in the first population will be new grandmothers, but women in the second population will witness the birth of their first great-great grandchildren (if their daughters also bear their first children at age 16 years). Obviously, the first population will grow much more slowly than the second.

Age at menarche (first menstruation) is an important factor in determining the trajectory of growth of human populations. There is evidence of selection for age at menarche in some human populations. In 2015, analysis of 182 416 European women performed in the course of 57 separate studies confirmed that at least 123 signals at 106 genetic loci were involved in determining age at menarche. Furthermore, there is evidence that parasitic infections by roundworms (*Ascaris lumbricoides*) are associated with earlier first births and shorter interbirth intervals. In contrast, infections by hookworms (*Ancylostoma duodenale* and *Necator americanus*) coincide with delayed first birth and longer interbirth intervals. This evidence illustrates the importance of health and hygiene and the role that helminth parasites can play in population ecology.

A 2014 analysis of data collected to 2012 offered little prospect of stabilization of human populations. The analysis indicated an 80% probability that the human global population will grow from 7.2 billion to between 9.6 and 12.3 billion by 2100. The population in Africa is central to these projections because of higher fertility there. The prospect is daunting.

29.9 The Future: Where Are We Going?

Homo sapiens has arrived at a turning point in our cultural evolution and in our ecological relationship with Earth. Hard decisions await us, and we must make them soon. All species face limits to their population growth, and it is naive to assume that our unique abilities exempt us from the laws of population growth. We have postponed the action of most factors that limit population growth, but no amount of invention and intervention can expand the ultimate limits set by resource depletion and a damaged environment. We now face two options for limiting human population growth: we can make a global effort to limit our population growth, or we can wait until the environment does it for us.

STUDY BREAK QUESTIONS

1. In what three ways have humans avoided the effects of density-dependent regulation factors?
2. What is a population bomb?
3. What does family planning encourage women to do?

29.10 The Pill

The advent of birth control pills **(Figure 29.25)** had a great impact on the behaviour of people. Women using birth control pills had more control over their fertility than others. Central to the development of an effective oral contraceptive was a change in the molecular structure of progesterone **(Figure 29.26)**. Specifically, the addition of a CH_3 group (Figure 29.26b) meant that the new molecule, megestrol, had the same effect on a woman's reproductive system, but it was not quickly metabolized and remained in the system long enough to have the desired effect (suppressing ovulation). Similarly, slight modifications to the estradiol molecule turned it into ethinylestradiol **(Figure 29.27)**. Megestrol is an analogue of progesterone, and ethinylestradiol is an analogue of estradiol.

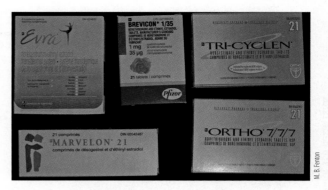

FIGURE 29.25 Birth control pills, a selection of products

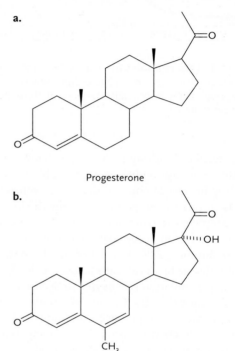

a.

Progesterone

b.

Megestrol

FIGURE 29.26 Progesterone and the synthetic megestrol

Source: Professor John Wiebe

For animals whose populations are growing at a rapid pace, birth control gives keepers the chance to control growth of the populations. The same principles apply to working with organisms in the wild, but getting African elephants to take their birth control pills has not proven to be easy.

Hormones and their analogues are common in untreated municipal wastewaters. But the pill can have unexpected consequences. In some cases, male fish exposed to these wastewaters are feminized. Specifically, some male fish produce vitellogenin mRNA and protein, substances normally associated with the maturation of oocytes in females. Males thus exposed produce early-stage eggs in their testes. This feminization occurs in the presence of estrogenic substances, including

a.

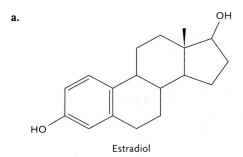

Estradiol

b.

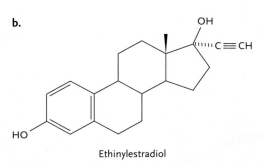

Ethinylestradiol

FIGURE 29.27 Estradiol and the synthetic ethinylestradiol

Source: Professor John Wiebe

FIGURE 29.28 *Pimephales promelas*, the fathead minnow

natural estrogen (17b-estradiol) and the synthetic estrogen 17a-ethynylestradiol.

Do a few feminized male fish in the population matter? Karen A. Kidd and six colleagues conducted a seven-year, whole-lake experiment in northwestern Ontario (the Experimental Lakes Area). Male fathead minnows (*Pimephales promelas*) **(Figure 29.28)** chronically exposed to low levels (5–6 ng/L) of estrogenic substances showed feminizing effects and the development of intersex males, whereas females had altered oogenesis. The situation led to the near-extinction of fathead minnows in the experimental lake.

Summary Illustration

Population ecology is rooted in patterns of population growth—represented by the equation at the centre of the illustration. At least eight characteristics (shown here encircling the equation) define populations and influence the parameters of the equation. These characteristics in turn are influenced by climate and weather, food, immigration and emigration, predation and parasites, and disease.

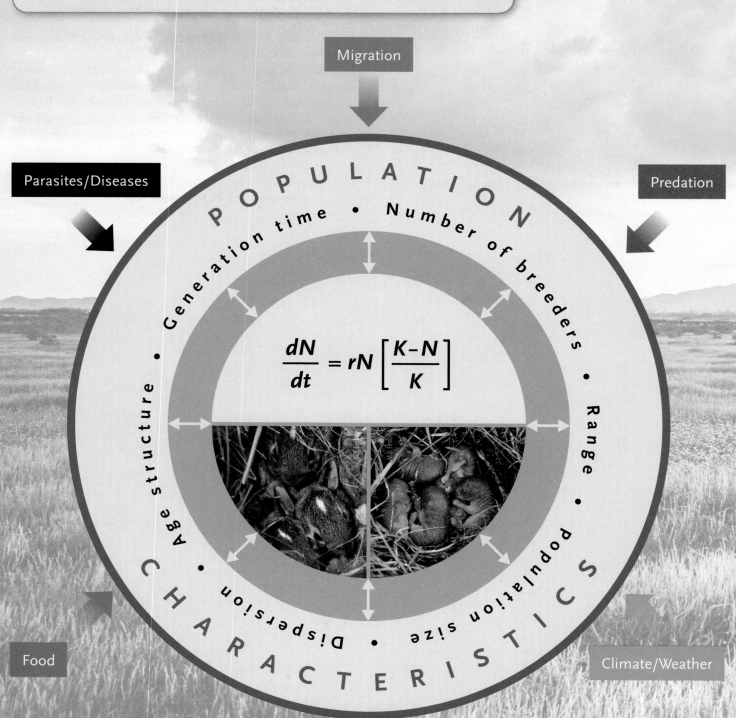

Migration

Parasites/Diseases

Predation

POPULATION

Generation time • Number of breeders

Age structure

Range

$$\frac{dN}{dt} = rN\left[\frac{K-N}{K}\right]$$

Dispersion • Population size

CHARACTERISTICS

Food

Climate/Weather

Migration
Population size is increased when animals move into the population (immigration) and is decreased when they move out (emigration).

Predation
Population size is decreased with increased predation and is increased when predation pressures relax.

Climate/Weather
Shifts in climate and/or adverse weather conditions can cause high mortality events or add stress to population health, which can influence reproductive productivity.

Food
When food resources are sufficient, competition for food is reduced. When food is limited, competition reduces the amount of food available for individuals, leading to reduced individual health, reduced reproductive rates, and even starvation.

Parasites/Diseases
Populations contract with increased incidence of disease and with elevated parasite loads, and expand when parasites and disease are reduced.

SELF-TEST QUESTIONS

Recall/Understand

1. Which of these factors refers to the number of individuals making up the population at a specified time?
   a. size
   b. density
   c. dispersion pattern
   d. age structure

2. Which of these terms can be used to describe the number of individuals per unit area or volume of habitat?
   a. dispersion pattern
   b. density
   c. size
   d. age structure

3. Half the world's human population is at risk of being exposed to which of these diseases?
   a. malaria
   b. HIV
   c. disease caused by Zika virus
   d. disease caused by West Nile virus

4. Which of the following is paired according to what it stands for?
   a. K and population size
   b. K and carrying capacity
   c. r and carrying capacity
   d. r and population size

Apply/Analyze

5. Suppose that one day you caught and marked 90 butterflies in a population. A week later, you returned to the population and caught 80 butterflies, including 16 that had been marked previously. What is the size of the butterfly population?
   a. 154
   b. 170
   c. 450
   d. 486

6. Which of these statements describes what a uniform dispersion pattern implies about the members of a population?
   a. They work together to escape from predators.
   b. They use resources that are patchily distributed.
   c. They may experience intraspecific competition for vital resources.
   d. They have no ecological interactions with each other.

7. Which of these statements does the model of exponential population growth predict about the per capita population growth rate (r)?
   a. r does not change as a population gets larger.
   b. r gets larger as a population gets larger.
   c. r gets smaller as a population gets larger.
   d. r is always at its maximum level (r_{max}).

8. If a population of 1000 individuals experiences 452 births and 380 deaths in 1 year, what is the value of r for this population?
   a. 0.009/individual/year
   b. 0.072/individual/year
   c. 0.380/individual/year
   d. 0.452/individual/year

9. According to the logistic model of population growth, which of the following happens to the absolute number of individuals by which a population grows during a given time period?
   a. It gets steadily larger as the population size increases.
   b. It gets steadily smaller as the population size increases.
   c. It remains constant as the population size increases.
   d. It is highest when the population is at an intermediate size.

10. Which of these patterns is a K-selected species likely to exhibit?
    a. a type I survivorship curve and a short generation time
    b. a type II survivorship curve and a short generation time
    c. a type III survivorship curve and a short generation time
    d. a type I survivorship curve and a long generation time

11. Suppose that you are researching populations of king penguins (*Aptenodytes patagonicus*) and their predator, leopard seals (*Hydrurga leptonyx*). How would you expect the populations to change in relation to each other?
    a. When the king penguin population density is low, the leopard seal population size increases.
    b. When the king penguin population density is stable, the leopard seal population size increases.
    c. When the king penguin population density is stable, the leopard seal population size decreases.
    d. When the king penguin population density is low, the leopard seal population size also decreases.

Create/Evaluate

12. Suppose that you observe an animal that gives birth to many young, but does not care for them. Which survivorship curve is it most likely that this animal represents?
    a. type I or type II
    b. type II or type III
    c. type I
    d. type III

13. Which of these examples might reflect density-dependent regulation of population size?
    a. An exterminator uses a pesticide to eliminate carpenter ants from a home.
    b. Mosquitoes disappear from an area after the first frost.
    c. Northeast storms blow over and kill all willow trees along a lake.
    d. A clam population declines in numbers in a bay as the number of predatory herring gulls increases.

14. Which one of these statements is *most* likely a reason that human populations have sidestepped factors that usually control population growth?
    a. Agriculture and industrialization have increased the carrying capacity for our species.
    b. The population growth rate (r) for the human population has always been small.
    c. The age structure of human populations has no impact on its population growth.
    d. Plagues have killed off large numbers of humans at certain times in the past.

15. Compare survivorship curves I, II, and III.

Chapter Roadmap

Species Interactions and Community Ecology

Earth is a huge ecosystem consisting of many communities of sympatric organisms interconnected by the flow of energy and wastes.

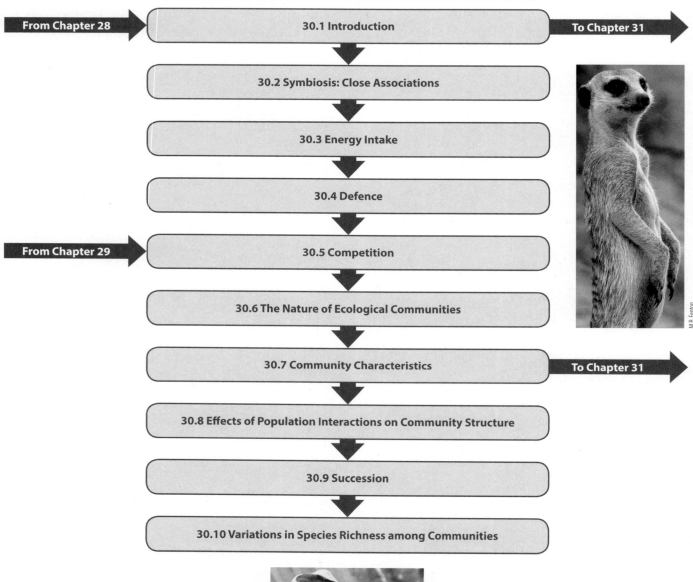

From Chapter 28 → **30.1 Introduction** → To Chapter 31

30.2 Symbiosis: Close Associations

30.3 Energy Intake

30.4 Defence

From Chapter 29 → **30.5 Competition**

30.6 The Nature of Ecological Communities

30.7 Community Characteristics → To Chapter 31

30.8 Effects of Population Interactions on Community Structure

30.9 Succession

30.10 Variations in Species Richness among Communities

M.B. Fenton

M.B. Fenton

Five red-billed oxpeckers (*Buphagus erythrorhynchus*) moving around on a giraffe (*Giraffa camelopardalis*). Oxpeckers, also known as tick birds, remove ticks and other ectoparasites from some large mammals. But is the relationship between oxpeckers and large mammals mutually beneficial?

Species Interactions and Community Ecology

30

Why it matters . . . Mutualism describes interactions between organisms that benefit both participants. One commonly cited example is tickbirds, the oxpeckers that eat the ticks they find on their hosts, large mammals such as giraffes. Do the oxpeckers benefit the host? Paul Weeks, a zoologist at Cambridge University, set out to answer this question using experimental manipulation of oxpeckers' access to cattle. He expected that, if hosts, in his case cattle, were well served by oxpeckers, the incidence of ticks would be higher on cattle without the services of oxpeckers. Working in Zimbabwe, Paul Weeks found that exposure to oxpeckers did not coincide with lower tick infestations in cattle. Furthermore, he observed that wounds on cattle exposed to these birds took longer to heal than those on cattle not so exposed. This raised the possibility that oxpeckers feed at wounds where their actions would give them access to blood and this would result in slower healing. The oxpeckers also could obtain insects at wounds. Weeks' data do not support the suggestion that the hosts benefit from the interaction with oxpeckers.

Many other animals use ectoparasites of other animals as a source of food. Cleaner fish are one of the best known. As the name implies, cleaner fish **(Figure 30.1)** remove parasites from the bodies and gills of other fish. On coral reefs, cleaner stations are sites where fish find the cleaner fish and benefit from their feeding activity. The interaction between cleaner fish and their hosts is mutualistic because both appear to benefit from the cleaning behaviour. But, if oxpeckers do not reduce tick infestations and even eat the host's blood, the situation is not mutualistic because there is little if any benefit to the host.

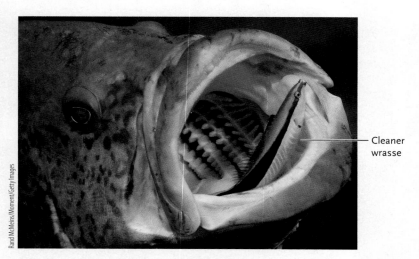

—— Cleaner
   wrasse

FIGURE 30.1 Mutualism between animal species. A large potato cod (*Epinephelus tukula*) from the Great Barrier Reef in Australia remains nearly motionless in the water while a striped cleaner wrasse (*Labroides dimidiatus*) carefully removes and eats ectoparasites attached to its lip. The potato cod is a predator; the striped cleaner wrasse is a potential prey. Here the mutualistic relationship supersedes the possible predator–prey interaction.

To determine the nature of the relationship between oxpeckers and their host requires knowledge of exactly what oxpeckers eat. Modern techniques for analyzing isotopes in the birds' feathers could shed light on the importance of blood in oxpeckers' diets. DNA barcode analysis (see Section 30.1a) could provide details of what species of arthropods the birds eat. To get answers means catching some oxpeckers, taking some feathers to analyze for isotopes, and some of their droppings to learn just what arthropods they ate. Stay tuned; perhaps we will learn the answer.

30.1 Introduction

Earth is a huge ecosystem consisting of many communities of sympatric organisms interconnected by the flow of energy and wastes that are by-products of energy production and use. Ironically, DDT (see Chapter 31) provided an early demonstration of connectivity among Earth's ecosystems and communities. The diversity of Earth's biological communities is astonishing, reflecting a wide range of conditions from bright, hot, and humid to cold, dark, and dry. In most communities, photosynthetic autotrophs (plants and cyanobacteria) are the **primary producers** of energy and oxygen. Exceptionally, other sources of energy are found around hydrothermal vents in the ocean floor; and, as we have seen in caves, bats (their droppings) are the principal energy source for specialized ecosystems (see Chapter 31).

Organisms can be generally classified according to the trophic role they play in an ecosystem. Primary producers supply energy (e.g., a plant), **primary consumers** eat primary producers (e.g., a rabbit), and **secondary consumers** eat primary consumers (e.g., a lynx). Animals are generally **herbivores** because

they eat primary producers or **predators** that eat other animals. Both predators and herbivores have characteristics allowing them to feed effectively and catch food or avoid being caught and eaten. Meat eaters use sensory systems to locate animal prey and specialized behaviours and anatomical structures to capture and consume it. Herbivores use sensory systems to identify preferred food or to avoid food that is toxic. Their anatomical specializations for feeding often are associated with obtaining and chewing food. **Detritus** feeders and **decomposers** are other main components in food chains, and also exhibit a range of specializations.

Although sometimes neutral, interactions among species typically benefit or harm the organisms involved (**Table 30.1**). Furthermore, where interactions with other species affect individuals' survival and reproduction, many relationships we witness today are the products of long-term evolutionary modification. Remember that interactions among species occur at the individual level. Some individuals of a species may be better adapted to survive when individuals of another species exert selection pressure on them. **Co-evolution** occurs when genetically based, reciprocal adaptation occurs in two or more interacting species. Many good examples of co-evolution are provided by interactions among plants and their animal pollinators.

Ecologists describe the co-evolutionary interactions between some predators and their prey as a race in which each species evolves adaptations that temporarily allow it to outpace another. When antelope populations suffer predation by cheetahs, natural selection fosters the evolution of faster antelopes. Faster cheetahs may be the result of this situation; and if their offspring are also fast, then antelopes will also become more fleet of foot. Other co-evolved interactions provide benefits to both partners. Flower structures of different monkey-flower species have evolved characteristics that allow them to be visited by either bees or hummingbirds (see Figure 18.6, Chapter 18).

TABLE 30.1	Population Interactions and Their Effects	
Interaction		Effects on Interacting Populations
Predation	+/−	Predators gain nutrients and energy; prey are killed or injured.
Parasitism	+/−	Parasites gain nutrients and energy; hosts are injured or killed.
Herbivory	+/−	Herbivores gain nutrients and energy; plants are killed or injured.
Competition	−/−	Both competing populations lose access to some resources.
Commensalism	−/0	One population benefits; the other population is unaffected.
Mutualism	+/+	Both populations benefit.

© Cengage Learning 2017

One can hypothesize a co-evolutionary relationship between any two interacting species, but it can be challenging to document the evolution of reciprocal adaptations. Co-evolutionary interactions often involve more than two species, and most organisms experience complex interactions with numerous other species in their communities. Cheetahs take several prey species. Antelopes are prey for many species of predators, from cheetahs to lions, leopards, and hyenas, as well as some larger birds of prey. Not all predators use the same hunting strategy; therefore, the simple portrayal of co-evolution as taking place between two species rarely does justice to the complexity of these relationships.

30.1a The CO1 Gene: Barcode of Life

Whether the challenge is answering a question such as, How many species are there in my sample? or What did that bat actually eat?, the Barcode of Life work with the CO1 gene has provided a means to obtain accurate answers (**Figure 30.2**). The diversity of species can be overwhelming, so it is difficult to provide a confident estimate of how many species remain undescribed. For many groups of organisms, there may be very few authorities able to identify species and provide descriptions of "new" species, the ones not yet described and therefore nameless. The Barcode of Life Data Systems, based in Guelph, Ontario, offers one alternative to the challenge of knowing how many species are in the sample you have just acquired, or the origin of a mystery mouse found in a shipment of frozen chickens from Thailand.

The Barcode of Life project depends upon variation in the mitochondrial cytochrome *c oxidase 1* (CO1) gene consisting of about 650 nucleotides. This genetic barcode is embedded in almost every cell and offers biologists a chance to identify a species even if they have only a small sample of feathers or fur, a leaf, a seed, or a caterpillar. Since identification of some species depends upon having a whole adult specimen, being able to make an identification from an egg, a larva, or a hair offers enormous potential. Identification of organisms with different life stages can be particularly challenging. Using morphology, it can be easy to identify a butterfly or a frog, but much more difficult to identify its caterpillar or its tadpole.

The Barcode of Life project is based on polymerase chain reaction (PCR) technology, which allowed biologists to process 100 samples every three hours. Subsequent advances in genomic technology have increased our capacity for efficient sequencing of DNA. The combination of this potential, an army of researchers collecting specimens, and Global Positioning Satellite (GPS) technology to document locations means that the Barcode of Life project can deliver accurate (to 97.5%) identifications of specimens in a short time. Further developments could see biologists and naturalists armed with appropriately programmed handheld devices to obtain in-field identifications.

One important consequence of this project is that biologists will have a fighting chance to document more fully the diversity of life on Earth. On one hand, this means realizing that one species of the butterfly *Astraptes fulgerator* is actually 10 species, or that what people had thought were several species is, in fact, one. Protecting species through CITES, the Convention on International Trade in Endangered Species, means being able to name them so that they can be placed on a protected list. The Barcode of Life project should allow a merchant to be sure that the ivory being sold in her shop is from an extinct mammoth, rather than a living species said to be endangered. The same applies to food species in a market: Is that fish really what the label says?

Everyone has experience with barcode operations because they are used in many retail outlets and therefore we all know that barcodes and readers do not always work. These limitations, as well as biological ones associated with genetics of different species, make some organisms more appropriate for Barcode of Life approaches than others.

STUDY BREAK QUESTIONS

1. What are the basic components of biological communities?
2. What is co-evolution? Is it usually restricted to two species?

30.2 Symbiosis: Close Associations

Symbiosis occurs when one species has a physically close ecological association with another (*sym* = together; *bio* = life; *sis* = process). Biologists define three types of symbiotic interactions: commensalism, mutualism, and parasitism (see Table 30.1). Oxpeckers are a good introduction to the problem of drawing boundaries among different types of interactions.

In **commensalism**, one species benefits from and the other is unaffected by the interactions. Commensalism appears to be rare in nature because few species are unaffected by interactions with another. If oxpeckers eat mainly ectoparasites that

a.

International Barcode of Life

b.

M. B. Fenton

FIGURE 30.2 Shown here is (a) **the bar code of** (b) **a flying fringe-lipped bat (*Trachops cirrhosus*).**

they remove from their hosts, and cause no harm to the hosts, the relationship would be commensal.

In **mutualism**, both partners benefit. Mutualism appears to be common and includes co-evolved relationships between flowering plants and animal pollinators. Animals that feed on a plant's nectar or pollen carry the plant's pollen from one flower to another. Similarly, animals that eat fruits disperse the seeds and "plant" them in piles of nutrient-rich feces. Mutualistic relationships between plants and animals do not require active cooperation, as each species simply exploits the other for its own benefit. Some associations between bacteria and plants are mutualistic. The association between *Rhizobium* and leguminous plants such as peas, beans, and clover is very important for agricultural operations (see Chapter 36).

Mutualistic relationships among animal species are common, as are mutualistic relationships between animals and plants. One example of mutualism is the relationship between the bull's horn acacia tree (*Acacia cornigera*) of Central America and small ants (*Pseudomyrmex ferruginea*) (**Figure 30.3**). Each acacia is inhabited by an ant colony that lives in hollows in the tree's swollen thorns. Ants swarm out of the thorns to sting, and sometimes kill, herbivores that touch the tree. Ants also clip any vegetation that grows nearby. Acacia trees colonized by ants grow in a space free of herbivores and competitors, and occupied trees grow faster and produce more seeds than unoccupied trees. In return, the plants produce sugar-rich nectar consumed by adult ants and protein-rich structures that the ants feed to their larvae. Ecologists describe the co-evolved mutualism between these species as obligatory, at least for the ants, because they cannot subsist on any other food sources.

Many animals eat honey and sometimes the bees that produce it. In Africa, greater honeyguide birds (*Indicator indicator*) use a special guiding display to lead humans to beehives. Individuals in one tribe of Kenyans, the honey-gathering Borans, call honeyguides with a special whistle. Boran honey gatherers that follow greater honeyguides are much more efficient at finding beehives than those working alone. When the honey gatherer goes to the hive and raids it to obtain honey, greater honeyguides help themselves to bee larvae, left-over honey, and wax. Although greater honeyguides are said to guide ratels (honey badgers, *Mellivora capensis*) to beehives, there are no firm data supporting this position.

If oxpeckers benefit from eating ectoparasites taken from their hosts, and if the hosts benefit by incurring fewer ectoparasites, then the relationship would be mutualistic. But if the oxpeckers benefit at the hosts' expense, then the relationship is more parasitic.

In **parasitism**, one species, the parasite, uses another, the host, in a way that harms the host. A parasite is an organism whose survival depends upon exploitation of its host. Parasite–host interactions can be considered to be specialized predator–prey relationships because one population of organisms feeds on another. Parasites differ from predators because they do not directly kill their prey. A dead host typically is not a continuing source of nourishment such as blood.

Many animals eat blood (**Figure 30.4**). Ticks, leeches, insects, and vampire bats are on the list. Blood-feeding insects include mosquitoes, black flies, bed bugs, fleas, and kissing bugs among others and number about 10 000 species. This is less than 1% of all species of insects. Are blood feeders parasites or just crafty predators? The three species of vampire bats stand out among blood feeders because they are warm blooded. This means that they must ingest larger quantities of blood than cold-blooded blood feeders. One species of Darwin's finches, the vampire finch (*Geospiza difficilis septentrionalis*), eats blood. The vampire bats are parasites because their survival depends upon obtaining blood from their host(s). This may or may not be true of vampire finches. Interestingly it is true of many female mosquitoes, but not the males that eat nectar.

While blood is arguably an ideal food and a renewable resource, various defence mechanisms protect animals' blood. Blood feeders typically have chemicals in their saliva that prevent clotting. For example, a leech bite typically bleeds for some time after the leech stops feeding (Figure 30.4e). Digesting blood also is a challenge, and it is interesting to see that leeches and vampire bats have similar bacteria in their digestive tracts. To obtain a blood meal, blood feeders must overcome clotting and clustering of red blood cells, and counter peripheral

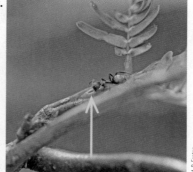

FIGURE 30.3 Highly co-evolved mutualisms. (a) Bull's horn acacia trees (*Acacia cornigera*) provide colonies for small ants (*Pseudomyrmex ferruginea*). In addition to providing homes (domatia: yellow arrow in **(b)**) in hollow thorns, the acacia also provides food for ants (nectar: yellow arrow in **(c)**).

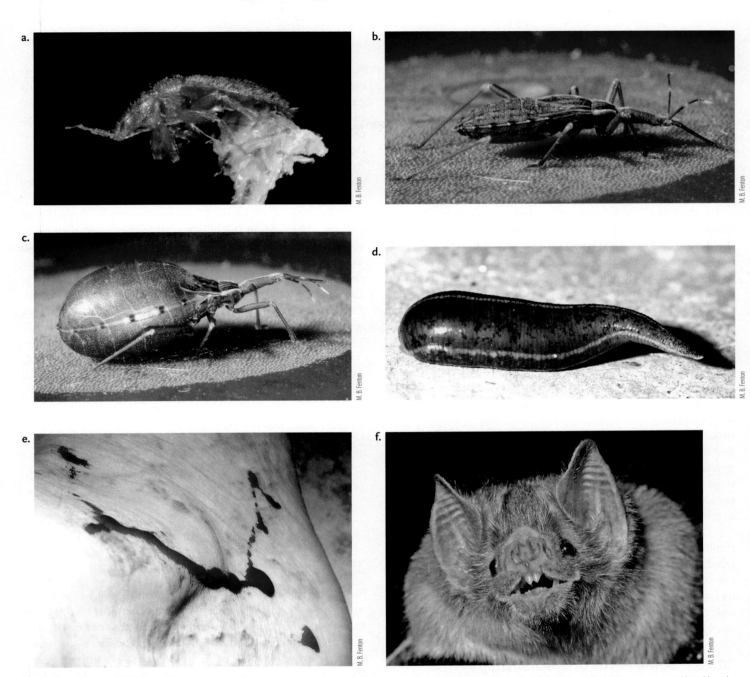

FIGURE 30.4 A sample of blood feeders including a bat bug **(a)**; two kissing bugs (*Rhodnius prolixus*), one unfed **(b)** and one fed **(c)**; an engorged land leech and **(d)** blood marking the site of a bite from the land leech **(e)**; and a vampire bat (*Desmodus rotundus* **(f)**). A comparison of the two pictures of the kissing bug (b, c) and the distended leech (d) illustrate just how much blood may be consumed at one time.

vasoconstriction that reduces blood flow to a wounded area. The limitations appear to more directly affect warm-blooded blood feeders, which must ingest more blood. A vampire bat (30 g) eats about 25 g of blood a day and cannot go two days without feeding. Vampire bats appear to be one stop shoppers, getting their daily blood meal from one prey.

Diseases can complicate the relationship of blood feeders to their hosts. A mosquito taking a blood meal can transfer a disease such as malaria that may kill the host. There are many examples of disease-causing agents being transmitted by blood-feeding animals. But this situation does not address the issue of whether the victim is a prey or a host.

Endoparasites, such as tapeworms, flukes, and round-worms, live within a host. Many endoparasites acquire their hosts passively when a host accidentally ingests the parasites' eggs or larvae. Endoparasites generally complete their life cycle in one or two host individuals. Ectoparasites, such as leeches, aphids, and mosquitoes, feed on the exterior of the host. Most animal ectoparasites have elaborate sensory and behavioural mechanisms, allowing them to locate specific hosts, and they

CHAPTER 30 SPECIES INTERACTIONS AND COMMUNITY ECOLOGY | **781** feed on numerous host individuals during their lifetimes. Plants such as mistletoes (genus *Phoradendron*) live as ectoparasites on the trunks and branches of trees; their roots penetrate the host's xylem and extract water and nutrients. These differ from epiphytes, such as bromeliads or Spanish moss, that use the host only as a base. Other plants are root parasites, for example, *Conopholis americana*.

Not all parasites eat a host's tissues. Some bird species are brood parasites, laying their eggs in the host's nest. It is quite common for female birds such as canvasback ducks (*Aythya valisineria*), brown-headed cowbirds, and Kirtland's warblers to lay their eggs in the nests of conspecifics (members of the same species). Some species of songbirds often lay some eggs in the nests of others, a variation on hedging of genetic bets and on extra-pair copulations (see Chapter 32 respectively). Brood parasitism is the next level of escalation in this spectrum of parasitism. Brown-headed cowbirds (*Molothrus ater*), like other brood parasites, always lay their eggs in the nest of other species, leaving it to the host parents to raise their young. This behaviour can have drastic repercussions for host species. Brown-headed cowbirds, for instance, have played a large role in the near-extinction of Kirtland's warblers (*Dendroica kirtlandii*).

The feeding habits of insects called *parasitoids* fall somewhere between true parasitism and predation. A female parasitoid lays her eggs in a larva or pupa of another insect species, and her young consume the tissues of the living host. But the parasitoid spends part of its life cycle as free living. The larval stage usually kills the host. Because the hosts chosen by most parasitoids are highly specific, agricultural ecologists often try to use parasitoids to control populations of insect pests.

One of the most striking and perhaps startling example of symbioses is the rich biota of prokaryotes and Protozoa that inhabit our digestive tracts. This biota significantly expands our capacity for extracting nutrients and other important factors from the food we ingest. The producers of "probiotic" foods depend upon our being impressed by the importance of our symbionts.

30.2a   Some Perils of Mutualism

Living organisms offer many examples of mutualistic interactions in which one species (or group of species) shows varying levels of dependence on another or others. Mutualistic situations can place species on the edge of survival. Where one species depends entirely on another, the extinction of one must lead to change or the extinction of both (e.g., dodos, discussed in Chapter 28, and yucca plants and their moths). There are many other examples of close relationships, including a desert melon (*Cucumis humifructus*) that depends perhaps entirely on aardvarks (*Orycteropus afer*) for dispersal of its seeds. Aardvarks sniff out the underground melons, dig them up, and eat them to obtain water. When aardvarks bury their dung, they plant the melon's seeds and fertilize them. The survival of the melon depends on the aardvark but not vice versa.

Mutualistic interactions between species can be even more complex. In the African **savannah**, ants often live in mutualistic relationships with trees. In east Africa, whistling thorn acacia trees (*Acacia drepanolobium*) are host to four species of ants (see Figure 30.4). One species of ant (*Crematogaster mimosae*) in particular depends on room (hollows in swollen thorns, called *domatia*) and board (carbohydrates secreted from extrafloral glands and the bases of leaves) provided by the trees. Another species of ant (*Crematogaster sjostedti*) also lives on the trees but usually nests in holes made by cerambycid beetles that burrow into and harm the trees.

The ants, particularly *C. mimosae*, attack animals that attempt to browse on the foliage or branches of *A. drepanolobium*. They deter many herbivores, from large mammals to wood-boring beetles (such as cerambycids). If large, browsing mammals are excluded from the area, *A. drepanolobium* produce fewer domatia and fewer carbohydrates for *C. mimosae*. The decline in this species of ant leads to higher damage by cerambycid beetles and increases in populations of *C. sjostedti*.

Many other plants also use ants as mercenaries (see Figure 30.4), and it is becoming clear that survival of these systems depends on the continued presence of participating species.

STUDY BREAK QUESTIONS

1. How do commensalism, mutualism, and parasitism differ?
2. Give examples of each. What sets the boundaries among them?
3. How do parasites differ from predators?
4. Why is blood often exploited as food? Give examples of blood-feeding animals.

30.3   Energy Intake

Plants and some other organisms use photosynthesis to trap the sun's rays and convert them from light to chemical energy. Some animals harvest chloroplasts; for example, solar sea slugs harvest chloroplasts and use them to emulate green plants. Some plants, notably pitcher plants, use photosynthesis to obtain energy and obtain nitrogen from animal excretory products. This includes rotifers living in pitchers of pitcher plants (**Figure 30.5**).

In Borneo, biologists have discovered two astonishing variations on the pitcher plant story. Specifically, one species, *Nepenthes lowii*, provides pit toilets for tree shrews (*Tupaia* spp.). Nectaries around the pitcher attract the shrews and provide them with a snack as they deposited feces and urine in the pitcher. Another species, *Nepenthes hemsleyana*, has pitchers modified to accommodate roosting bats (*Kerivoula hardwickii*), which urinate and defecate into the pitcher. In both cases, isotopic analysis reveals that nitrogen from the tree shrews and the bats is used by the plants.

Animals typically select food from a variety of potential items. Some species, specialists, eat one or just a few types of food. Among birds, Everglades kites (*Rostrhamus sociabilis*) eat

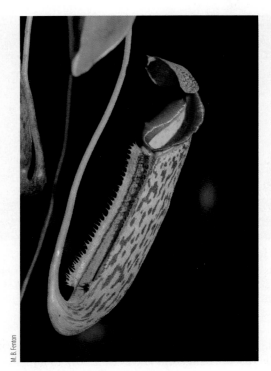

FIGURE 30.5 Pitcher of a *Nepenthes* spp.

only apple snails (*Pomacea paludosa*). Koalas (see Figure 27.119b, Chapter 27) eat the leaves of only a few of the many available species of *Eucalyptus*. Other species, generalists, have broader tastes. Crows (genus *Corvus*) take food ranging from grain to insects to carrion. Bears (genus *Ursus*) and pigs (genus *Sus*) are as omnivorous as humans.

Herbivores are adapted to locate and process their food plants. Insects use chemical sensors on their legs and mouthparts to identify edible plants, and sharp mandibles or sucking mouthparts to consume plant tissues or sap. Herbivorous mammals have specialized teeth to harvest and grind tough vegetation (see Chapter 27). Herbivores such as farmer ants, ruminants, and termites (see "Digesting Cellulose: Fermentation," Chapter 39) may co-opt other species to gain access to nutrients locked up in plant materials.

How does an animal select its food? Why eat pizza rather than salad? Mathematical models, collectively described as **optimal foraging theory**, predict that an animal's diet is a compromise between the costs and benefits associated with different types of food. Assuming that animals try to maximize their energy intake at any meal, their diets should be determined by the ratio of costs to benefits; in short, the costs of obtaining the food versus the benefits of consuming it. Costs are the time and energy it takes to pursue, capture, consume, and digest a particular kind of food. Benefits are the energy provided by that food. A cougar (*Felis concolor*) will invest more time and energy hunting and attacking a mountain goat (*Oreamnos americanus*) than a jackrabbit (*Lepus townsendii*), but the payoff for the cat is a bigger meal. One important element in food choice is the relative abundance of prey, referred

to as encounter rate. This usually is influenced by population density of prey and can influence a predator's diet. For the cougar, encounter rate determines the time between jackrabbits, and when they are abundant, they can be a more economical meal than larger, scarcer prey.

Food abundance affects food choice. When prey are scarce, animals often take what they can get, settling for food with a higher cost-to-benefit ratio. When food is abundant, they may specialize, selecting types that provide the largest energetic return. Bluegill sunfishes eat *Daphnia* spp. and other small crustaceans. When crustacean density is high, these fishes take mostly large *Daphnia*, which provide a higher energetic return than small ones. When prey density is low, bluegills eat *Daphnia* of all sizes (**Figure 30.6**).

Think of yourself at a buffet. The array of food can be impressive, if not overwhelming. But your state of hunger, the foods you like, the ones you do not like, and any to which you are allergic all influence your selection. You may also be influenced by choices made by others. In your feeding behaviour, you betray your animal heritage.

For predators, finding food is one thing, capturing and subduing it is another. Rattlesnakes, such as species in the genus *Crotalus*, use heat sensors in pits in their faces (see Figure 45.39, Chapter 45) to detect warm-blooded prey. The snakes deliver venom through fangs (hollow teeth) by open-mouthed strikes

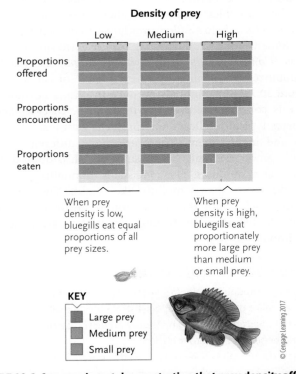

FIGURE 30.6 An experiment demonstrating that prey density affects predator food choice. Bluegill sunfishes (*Lepomis macrochirus*) were offered equal numbers of small, medium, and large prey (*Daphnia magna*) at three different total densities of prey. Because large prey are easy to find, the fishes encountered them more often, especially at the highest prey densities, than either medium-sized or small prey. The fishes' choice of prey varied with prey density, but they always chose the largest prey available.

CHAPTER 30 SPECIES INTERACTIONS AND COMMUNITY ECOLOGY |

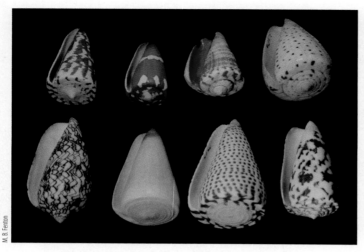

FIGURE 30.7 Shells of cone snails (*Conus* spp.)

FIGURE 30.8 Protective latex sap. Milky sap laced with cardiac glycosides oozes from a cut milkweed (*Asclepias* species) leaf. Milky sap does not always mean dangerous chemicals; for example, the sap of dandelions is benign.

on prey. After striking, the snakes wait for the venom to take effect and then use chemical sensors on the roofs of their mouths to follow the scent trail left by the dying prey. Venom is produced in the snakes' salivary glands. Venom typically is a cocktail of proteins, including neurotoxins that paralyze prey and protease enzymes that begin to digest it. The specific components vary among venomous species. Elastic ligaments connecting the bones of the snakes' jaws (mandibles) to one another and the mandibles to the skull allow snakes to open their mouths very wide to swallow prey larger than their heads.

Some venoms are surprising. At least two species of cone snails (*Conus geographus* and *Conus tulipa*) use insulin to immobilize fish, facilitating the challenge of catching them (**Figure 30.7**). Most animals produce insulin, a hormone, but there is considerable diversity in insulins. Diseases such as diabetes typically reflect some problem with insulin production and management. There are many different kinds of insulin among animals. The insulin of fish is quite different from that of molluscs. The cone snails immobilize fish with a fish-like rather than a mollusc-like insulin. The cone snails release insulin into the water around the fish; the insulin enters the fish through its gills, causing hypoglycemic shock and immobilizing it.

STUDY BREAK QUESTIONS

1. How do predators differ from herbivores? How are they similar?
2. Is a koala a generalist or a specialist? What is the difference?
3. What does optimal foraging theory predict? Describe the costs and benefits central to this theory.
4. How do animals use venoms? How do venoms work?

30.4 Defence

CONCEPT FIX Some people believe that "natural" products (chemicals) are beneficial to us, while artificial ones are potentially harmful. In reality, many plants produce chemicals (natural products) that are dangerous and even deadly, to humans and to other animals and to some plants. Contact with the leaves (or stems, roots, flowers, or berries) of poison ivy may be enough to convince you that not all plant products are beneficial. If not, you can read about coniine, an active ingredient in poison hemlock, the poison that killed Socrates. ⬡

Predation and herbivory negatively affect the species being eaten, so it is no surprise that animals and plants have evolved mechanisms to avoid being caught and eaten. Some plants use spines, thorns, and irritating hairs to protect themselves from herbivores. Plant tissues often contain poisonous chemicals that deter herbivores from feeding. When damaged, milkweed plants (family Asclepiadaceae) exude a milky, irritating sap (**Figure 30.8**) that contains poisons that affect the heart (cardiac glycosides). Even small amounts of cardiac glycosides are toxic to the heart muscles of some vertebrates. Other plants have compounds that mimic the structure of insect hormones, disrupting the development of insects that eat them. Most poisonous compounds are volatile, giving plants their typical aromas. Some herbivores recognize these odours and avoid toxic plants. Some plants increase their production of toxic compounds in response to herbivore feeding. Potato and tomato plants damaged by herbivores have higher levels of protease-inhibiting chemicals. These compounds prevent herbivores from digesting the proteins they have eaten, reducing the food value of these plants.

30.4a Be Too Big to Tackle

Size can be a defence. At one end of the spectrum, this means being too small to be considered food. At the other end, it means being so big that few predators can succeed in attacking and killing the prey. Relative size of predator and prey is central to this situation. Today, elephants and some other large herbivores (megaherbivores) are species with few predators (other than humans). But 50 thousand years ago, there were larger predators, including one species of "lion" that was one-third larger than an African lion.

30.4b Eternal Vigilance: Always Be Alert

A first line of defence of many animals is avoiding detection. This often means not moving, as well as keeping a sharp lookout for the danger presented by approaching predators (**Figure 30.9**). Animals that live in groups benefit from the multitude of eyes and ears that can detect approaching danger, so the risk of predation influences group size and social interactions.

30.4c Avoid Detection: Freeze—Movement Invites Discovery

Many animals are cryptic, camouflaged so that a predator does not distinguish them from the background (**Figure 30.10**). Patterns such as the stripes of a zebra (*Equus burchellii*) make the animal conspicuous at close range, but at a distance, patterns break up the outline, rendering the animals almost invisible.

FIGURE 30.10 **A camouflaged praying mantis is almost invisible on the trunk of a tree in Belize.**

Many other animals look like something that is not edible. Some caterpillars look like bird droppings, whereas other insects look like thorns or sticks. Neither bird droppings nor thorns are usually eaten by insectivores.

30.4d Thwarting Attacks: Take Evasive Action

Animals resort to other defensive tactics once they have been discovered and recognized. Running away is a typical next line of defence. Taking refuge in a shelter and getting out of a predator's reach are alternatives. African pancake tortoises (*Malacochersus tornieri*) are flat, as the name implies. When threatened, they retreat into rocky crevices and puff themselves up with air, becoming so tightly wedged that predators cannot extract them.

If cornered by a predator, offence is the next line of defence. This can involve displays intended to startle or intimidate by making the prey appear large and/or ferocious. Such a display might dissuade a predator or confuse it long enough to allow the potential victim to escape. Many animals use direct attack in these situations, engaging whatever weapons they have (biting, scratching, stinging, etc.). Direct attacks are not usually a good primary defence because they involve getting very close to the predator, something prey usually avoid doing.

30.4e Spines and Armour: Be Dangerous or Impossible to Attack

Other organisms use active defence in the form of spines or thorns (**Figure 30.11**). North American porcupines (genus *Erethizon*) release hairs modified into sharp, barbed quills that, when stuck into a predator, cause severe pain and swelling. The spines detach easily from the porcupine, and the nose, lips, and tongue of an attacker are particularly vulnerable. In Israel, there are records of leopards (*Panthera pardus*) being killed by

FIGURE 30.9 **Eternally vigilant.** The sentry of a group of meerkats (*Suricata suricatta*)

CHAPTER 30 SPECIES INTERACTIONS AND COMMUNITY ECOLOGY

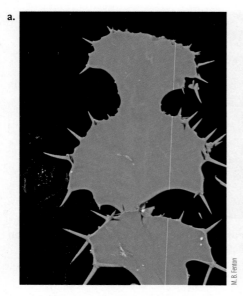

a.

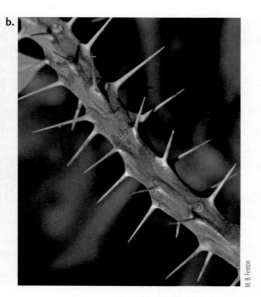

b.

c.

d.

FIGURE 30.11 **Defensive spines.** Plants such as **(a)** the cow horn euphorb (*Euphorbia grandicornis*) and **(b)** crown of thorns (*Euphorbia milii*), and animals such as **(c)** spiny anteaters (*Tachyglossus* species) and **(d)** porcupines (*Hystrix* species) use thorns or spines in defence. Pen shown for scale with quills in (d)

30.4f Chemical Defence Ranges from Bad Taste to Deadly

Like plants that produce chemicals to repel herbivores, many animals make themselves chemically unattractive. At one level, this can be as simple as smelling or tasting bad. Have you ever had a dog or a cat that was sprayed by a skunk (*Mephitis mephitis*)? Many animals vomit and defecate on their attackers. Skunks and bombardier beetles escalate this strategy by producing and spraying a noxious chemical. Other animals go beyond spraying. Many species of cnidarians, annelids, arthropods, and chordates produce dangerous toxins and deliver them directly into their attackers. These toxins may be synthesized by the user or sequestered from other sources, often plants or other animals (see "Nematocysts"; Chapter 27). Caterpillars of monarch butterflies are immune to the cardiac glycosides in the milkweed leaves they eat. They extract, concentrate, and store these chemicals, making the caterpillars themselves poisonous to potential predators. The concentrations of defensive chemicals may be higher in the animal than they were in its food. Cardiac glycosides persist through metamorphosis, making adult monarchs poisonous to vertebrate predators.

porcupine spines. In these instances, the damage to the leopards' mouths, combined with infection, was probably the immediate cause of death. Many other mammals, from monotremes (spiny anteaters) to tenrecs (insectivores from Madagascar, *Tenrec* species and *Hemicentetes* species), hedgehogs (*Erinaceus* species), and porcupines in the Old World, use the same defence. So do some fishes and many plants.

Other organisms are armoured (**Figure 30.12**). Examples include bivalve and gastropod molluscs, chambered nautiluses, arthropods such as horseshoe crabs (*Limulus* species), trilobites (see Chapter 27), fishes such as catfish (Siluriformes), reptiles (turtles; see Figure 27.106, Chapter 27), and mammals (armadillos, scaly anteaters). We know a great deal about extinct species that were armoured (see Chapter 19) because they often made good fossils.

FIGURE 30.12 **Even life in a shell does not make leopard tortoises immune to mishaps.** Turtles and their allies live inside shells. This leopard tortoise (*Stigmochelys pardalis*) is inspecting the remains of a conspecific. Armour does not guarantee survival.

FIGURE 30.13 Warning colours. (a) This arrowhead frog (*Dendrobates tinctorius*) gets its name from toxins in its skin that were used to poison arrowheads. **(b)** Three wasps on their nest; their black and yellow colouring advertises their ability to sting. **(c)** The grasshopper nymph also is black and yellow, but to date we do not know whether this is an aposematic signal or false advertising.

30.4g   Warnings Are Danger Signals

Many noxious or dangerous animals are **aposematic**: they advertise their unpalatability with an appropriate display (**Figure 30.13**; see Chapter 17). Aposematic displays are designed to "teach" predators to avoid the signaller, reducing the chances of harm to would-be predators and prey. Predators that attack a brightly coloured bee or wasp and are stung learn to associate the aposematic pattern with the sting. Many predators quickly learn to avoid black-and-white skunks, yellow-banded wasps, or orange monarch butterflies because they associate the warning display with pain, illness, or severe indigestion.

But for every ploy there is a counter-ploy, and some predators eat mainly dangerous prey. Bee-eaters (family Meropidae) are birds that eat hymenopterans (bees and wasps). Some individual African lions specialize in porcupines, and animals such as hedgehogs (genus *Erinaceus*) seem able to eat almost anything and show no ill effects. Indeed, some hedgehogs first lick toads and then their own spines, anointing them with toad venom. Hedgehog spines treated with toad venom are more irritating (at least to people) than untreated ones, enhancing their defensive impact.

30.4h   Mimicry Is Advertising, Whether True or False

If predators learn to recognize warning signals, it is no surprise that many harmless animals' defences are based on imitating (mimicking) dangerous or distasteful species. Mimicry occurs when one species evolves to resemble another (**Figure 30.14**). Batesian mimicry, named for English naturalist Henry W. Bates, occurs when a palatable or harmless species (the mimic) resembles an unpalatable or poisonous one (the model). Any predator that eats the poisonous model and suffers accordingly will subsequently avoid other organisms that resemble it. However, the predator must survive the encounter. Müllerian mimicry, named for German zoologist Fritz Müller, involves two or more unpalatable species looking the same, presumably to reinforce lessons learned by a predator that attacks any species in the mimicry complex.

For mimicry to work, the predator must learn (see Chapter 32) to recognize and then avoid the prey. The more deadly the toxin, the less likely an individual predator is to learn by its experience. In many cases, predators learn by watching the discomfort of a conspecific that has eaten or attacked an aposematic prey.

Plants often use toxins to protect themselves against herbivores. Is this also true of toxins in mushrooms (see Chapter 18)?

30.4i   There Is No Perfect Defence

Helmets protect soldiers, skiers, motorcyclists, and cyclists, but not completely; no defence provides perfect protection. Some predators learn to circumvent defences. Many predators learn to deal with a diversity of prey species and a variety of defensive tactics. Orb web spiders confronting a captive in a web adjust their behaviour according to the prey. They treat moths differently from beetles, and they treat bees in yet another way. When threatened by a predator, headstand beetles raise their rear ends and spray a noxious chemical from a gland at the tip of the abdomen. This behaviour deters many would-be predators. But experienced grasshopper mice from western North America circumvent this defence. An experienced mouse grabs the beetle, averts its face (to avoid the spray), turns the beetle upside down so that the gland discharges into the ground, and eats the beetle from the head down.

STUDY BREAK QUESTIONS

1. List the eight defence techniques used by animals and/or plants. Provide an example of each.
2. How do animals obtain the chemicals they use in chemical defences?
3. What is the purpose of aposematic displays?
4. What do aposematic displays depend upon?

FIGURE 30.14 **If you closely watch insects visiting goldenrod (*Solidago* spp.) flowers, you can see both Batesian and Müllerian mimics.** Stinging hymenoptera that visit flowers include wasps **(a)**, bumblebees **(b)**, and honey bees **(c)**. These are Müllerian mimics. Syrphid flies **(d)** are stingless Batesian mimics whose general behaviour and colour resembles stinging hymenoptera. Note the differences in the eyes, antennae, and heads. A fly that does not mimic hymenoptera **(e)** does not have black and yellow colouring. The ambush bug **(f)** hunts other insects, including bees, at flowers.

30.5 Competition

When access to resources limits populations (Chapter 32), individuals of the same species (**intraspecific**) may compete among themselves for limiting resources such as food and shelter. Individuals of different species using the same limiting resources experience **interspecific** competition (competition between species). Competing individuals may experience increased mortality and decreased reproduction, responses similar to the effects of intraspecific competition. Interspecific competition can reduce the size and population growth rate of one or more of the competing populations.

Community ecologists identify two main forms of interspecific competition. In **interference competition**, individuals of one species directly harm individuals of another species. Here animals may fight for access to resources, as when lions chase smaller predators, such as hyenas, jackals, and vultures, from their kills. Many plant species, including creosote bushes, release toxic chemicals into the soil, preventing other plants from growing nearby.

In **exploitative competition**, two or more populations use (exploit) the same limiting resource, and the presence of one

species reduces resource availability for others. Exploitative competition need not involve snout-to-snout or root-to-root confrontations. In the deserts of the U.S. Southwest, many bird and ant species eat mainly seeds, and each seed-eating species may deplete the food supply available to others without necessarily encountering each other.

To further explore the role of competition, ecologists undertook field experiments on competition in natural populations. The experiment on barnacles (**Figure 30.15**) is typical of this approach: the impact on one species' potential competitors of adding or removing another species changed patterns of distribution or population size. The picture that emerges from the results of these experiments is not clear, even to ecologists. In the early 1980s, Joseph Connell surveyed 527 published experiments on 215 species. He found that competition was demonstrated in roughly 40% of the experiments and more than 50% of species. At the same time, Thomas W. Schoener used different criteria to evaluate 164 experiments on approximately 400 species. He found that competition affected more than 75% of species.

Data on resource partitioning and character displacement suggest, but do not prove, that interspecific competition is an

FIGURE 30.15 **Experimental Research**

Demonstration of Competition between Two Species of Barnacles

Question: Do two barnacle species limit one another's realized niches in habitats where they coexist?

Experiment: Connell observed a difference in the distributions of two barnacle species on a rocky coast: *Chthamalus stellatus* occupies shallow water, and *Balanus balanoides* lives in deeper water. He then determined the fundamental niche of each species by removing either *Chthamalus* or *Balanus* from rocks and monitoring the distribution of each species in the absence of the other.

Results: When Connell removed *Balanus* from rocks in deep water, larval *Chthamalus* colonized the area and produced a flourishing population of adults. By contrast, the removal of *Chthamalus* from rocks in shallow water did not result in colonization by *Balanus*.

Control: No treatment. *Chthamalus* occupies only shallow water and *Balanus* occupies only deep water.

Treatment 1: Remove *Balanus*. In the absence of *Balanus*, *Chthamalus* occupies both shallow water and deep water.

Treatment 2: Remove *Chthamalus*. In the absence of *Chthamalus*, *Balanus* still occupies only deep water.

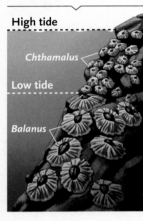

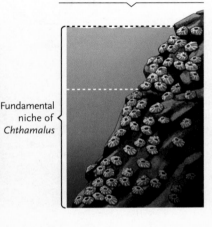

Conclusion: In habitats where *Balanus* and *Chthamalus* coexist, the realized niche (see Section 30.5a) of *Chthamalus* is smaller than its fundamental niche (see Section 30.5a) because of competition from *Balanus*. The realized niche of *Balanus* is similar to its fundamental niche because it is not affected by the competitive interaction.

important selective force in nature. To demonstrate conclusively that interspecific competition limits natural populations, one must show that the presence of one population reduces the population size or density of its presumed competitor. In a classic field experiment, Joseph Connell examined competition between two barnacle species (Figure 30.15). Connell first observed the distributions of both species of barnacles in undisturbed habitats to establish a reference baseline. *Chthamalus stellatus* is generally found in shallow water on rocky coasts, where it is periodically exposed to air. *Balanus balanoides* typically lives in deeper water, where it is usually submerged.

In the absence of *Balanus* on rocks in deep water, larval *Chthamalus* colonized the area and produced a flourishing population of adults. *Balanus* physically displaced *Chthamalus* from these rocks. Thus, interference competition from *Balanus* prevents *Chthamalus* from occupying areas where it would

otherwise live. Removal of *Chthamalus* from rocks in shallow water did not result in colonization by *Balanus*. *Balanus* apparently cannot live in habitats that are frequently exposed to air. Connell concluded that there was competition between the two species. But competition was asymmetrical because *Chthamalus* did not affect the distribution of *Balanus*, whereas *Balanus* had a substantial effect on *Chthamalus*.

Not surprisingly, there is no single answer to the question about how competition works in and influences communities. Plant and vertebrate ecologists working with *K*-selected species generally believe that competition has a profound effect on species distributions and resource use. Insect and marine ecologists working with *r*-selected species argue that competition is not the major force governing community structure, pointing instead to predation or parasitism and physical disturbance. We know that even categorizing a species as *r*- or *K*-selected is open to discussion (see Chapter 29).

© Cengage Learning 2017. Based on J. H. Connell. 1961. The influence of interspecific competition and other factors on the distribution of the barnacle Chthamalus stellatus. *Ecology* 42:710–723.

FIGURE 30.16   **Experimental Research**

Gause's Experiments on Interspecific Competition in *Paramecium*

Question: Can two species of *Paramecium* coexist in a simple laboratory environment?

Experiment: Gause grew populations of two species, *Paramecium aurelia* and *Paramecium caudatum,* alone (single species cultures) or together (mixed cultures) in small bottles in his laboratory. To determine whether the growth of these populations followed the predictions of the logistic equation, Gause had to maintain a reasonably constant carrying capacity in each culture. Thus, he fed the cultures a broth of bacteria, and he eliminated their waste products (by centrifuging the cultures and removing some of the culture medium) on a regular schedule. He then monitored their population sizes over time.

Results: When grown separately, *P. caudatum* **(a)** and *P. aurelia* **(b)** each exhibited logistic population growth. But when the two species were grown together in a mixed culture **(c)**, *P. aurelia* persisted and *P. caudatum* was nearly eliminated from the culture.

Conclusion: Because one species was almost always eliminated from mixed species cultures, Gause formulated the competitive exclusion principle: Populations of two or more species cannot coexist indefinitely if they rely on the same limiting resources and exploit them in the same way.

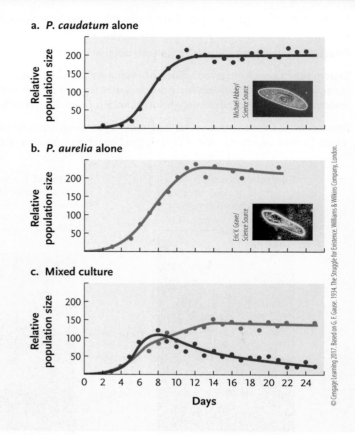

30.5a   Competition and Niches: When Resources Are Limited

In the 1920s, the Russian mathematician Alfred J. Lotka and the Italian biologist Vito Volterra independently proposed a model of interspecific competition, modifying the logistic equation (see Chapter 29) to describe the effects of competition between two species. In their model, an increase in the size of one population reduces the population growth rate of the other.

In the 1930s, Russian biologist G. F. Gause tested the model experimentally. He grew cultures of two *Paramecium* species (ciliate protozoans) under constant laboratory conditions, regularly renewing food and removing wastes. Both species ate bacteria suspended in the culture medium. When grown alone, each species exhibited logistic growth. When grown together in the same dish, *Paramecium aurelia* persisted at high density, but *Paramecium caudatum* was almost eliminated **(Figure 30.16).** These results inspired Gause to define the **competitive exclusion principle.** Populations of two or more species cannot coexist indefinitely if they rely on the same limiting resources and exploit them in the same way. One species inevitably harvests resources more efficiently; produces more offspring than the other; and, by its actions, negatively affects the other species.

Ecologists developed the concept of the **ecological niche** to visualize resource use and the potential for interspecific competition in nature. They define a species' niche by the resources it uses and the environmental conditions it requires over its lifetime. In this context, niche includes food, shelter, and nutrients, as well as non-depletable abiotic conditions such as light intensity and temperature. In theory, an almost infinite variety of conditions and resources could contribute to a species' niche. In practice, ecologists usually identify the critical resources for which populations might compete. Sunlight, soil moisture, and inorganic nutrients are important resources for plants, so differences in leaf height and root depth, for example, can affect plants' access to these resources. Food type, food size, and nesting sites are important for animals. When several species coexist, they often use food and nest resources in different ways.

Ecologists distinguish the **fundamental niche** of a species, the range of conditions and resources it could tolerate and use, from its **realized niche,** the range of conditions and resources it actually uses in nature. Realized niches are smaller than fundamental niches, partly because all tolerable conditions are not always present in a habitat and partly because some resources are used by other species. We can visualize competition between two populations by plotting their fundamental and realized niches with respect to one or more resources

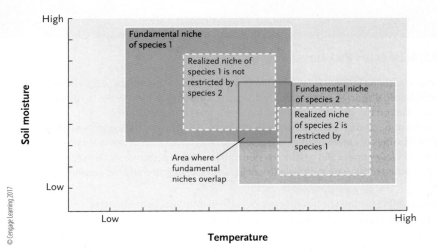

FIGURE 30.17 **Fundamental versus realized niches.** In this hypothetical example, both species 1 and species 2 can survive intermediate temperature conditions, as indicated by the shading where their fundamental niches overlap. Because species 1 actually occupies most of this overlap zone, its realized niche is not much affected by the presence of species 2. In contrast, the realized niche of species 2 is restricted by the presence of species 1, and species 2 occupies warmer and drier parts of the habitat.

(Figure 30.17). If the fundamental niches of two populations overlap, they might compete in nature.

Observing that several species use the same resource does not demonstrate that competition occurs (or does not occur). All terrestrial animals consume oxygen but do not compete for oxygen because it is usually plentiful. Nevertheless, two general observations provide indirect evidence that interspecific competition may have important effects.

Resource partitioning occurs when several sympatric (living in the same place) species use different resources or the same resources in different ways. Although plants might compete for water and dissolved nutrients, they may avoid competition by partitioning these resources, collecting them from different depths in the soil **(Figure 30.18)**. This allows coexistence of different species.

Character displacement can be evident when comparing species that are sometimes sympatric and sometimes allopatric (living in different places). Allopatric populations of some animal species are morphologically similar and use similar resources, whereas sympatric populations are morphologically different and use different resources. Differences between sympatric species allow them to coexist without competing. To illustrate this situation, Allen Keast studied honeyeaters (family Meliphagidae), a group of birds from Australia. In mainland Australia, up to six species in the genus *Melithreptus* occur in some habitats. On the coast of Kangaroo Island, there are two species. When two species are sympatric, each feeds in a wider range of situations than when six species live in the same area, reflecting the use of broader niches. Behavioural and morphological differences are evident when species are compared between the different situations. Although well known for his work on birds, Keast also studied communities of fish. He spent most of his academic career at Queen's University in Kingston, Ontario.

Which might be more important, competition or predation? In 2010, Ryan Calsbeek and Robert M. Cox reported their work with lizards (*Anolis* spp.) on islands in the Caribbean. In this system, competition between species altered their morphological traits, while predation did not.

Predators can influence the species richness and structure of communities by reducing the sizes of prey populations. On the rocky coast of British Columbia, different species that fill different trophic roles compete for attachment sites on rocks, a requirement for life on a wave-swept shore. Mussels are the strongest competitors for space, eliminating other species from the community. At some sites, predatory sea stars preferentially eat mussels, reducing their numbers and creating space for other species to grow. Because the interaction between *Pisaster* and *Mytilus* affects other species as well, it qualifies as a strong interaction.

In the 1960s, Robert Paine used removal experiments to evaluate the effects of predation by *Pisaster*. In predator-free experimental plots, mussels outcompeted barnacles, chitons, limpets, and other invertebrate herbivores, reducing species richness from 15 species to 8. In control plots containing predators, all 15 species persisted. Ecologists describe predators such as *Pisaster* as **keystone species**, defined as species with a greater effect on community structure than their numbers might suggest. Snowshoe hares (Chapter 29) are candidates to be keystone species in boreal forest ecosystems because they are prey for a range of predators. Pallas' long-tongued bats may emerge as keystone species because, as we have seen, they eat insects and fruit as well as nectar and pollen.

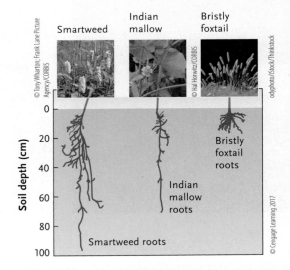

FIGURE 30.18 **Resource partitioning.** The root systems of three plant species that grow in abandoned fields partition water and nutrient resources in soil. Bristly foxtail grass (*Setaria faberi*) has a shallow root system, Indian mallow (*Abutilon theophrasti*) has a moderately deep taproot, and smartweed (*Polygonum pensylvanicum*) has a deep taproot that branches at many depths.

FIGURE 30.19   **Experimental Research**

The Complex Effects of a Herbivorous Snail on Algal Species Richness

Jane Lubchenco made enclosures that prevented periwinkle snails (*Littorina littorea*) from entering or leaving study plots in tide pools and on exposed rocks in rocky intertidal habitat **(a)**. She then monitored the algal species composition in the plots, comparing them to the density of the periwinkles. In this way, she examined the influence of the periwinkles on the species richness of algae in intertidal communities.

The results varied dramatically between the study plots in tide pools and on exposed rocks. In tide pools, periwinkle snails preferentially ate *Enteromorpha*, the competitively dominant alga. At intermediate densities of *Enteromorpha*, the periwinkles remove some of these algae, allowing weakly competitive species to grow. The snails' grazing increases species richness. But grazing by periwinkles when *Enteromorpha* is at low or high densities reduces the species richness of algae in tide pools. On exposed rocks, where periwinkle snails rarely eat the competitively dominant alga *Chondrus*, feeding by snails reduces algal species richness **(b)**.

Question: How does feeding by periwinkle snails (*Littorina littorea*) influence the species richness of algae in intertidal communities?

Experiment: Lubchenco manipulated the densities of periwinkle snails in tidepools and on exposed rocks in a rocky intertidal habitat by creating enclosures that prevented snails from either entering or leaving her study plots. She then monitored the species composition of algae in the study plots and graphed them against periwinkle density.

Results: The effects of periwinkle density on algal species richness varied dramatically between study plots in tidepools and on exposed rocks.

Conclusion: Grazing by periwinkle snails has complex effects on the species richness of competing algae. In tidepools, where periwinkle snails preferentially feed on *Enteromorpha*, the competitively dominant alga, snails at an intermediate density remove some *Enteromorpha*, which allows weakly competitive algae to grow, increasing species richness. Feeding by snails at either low or high densities reduces algal species richness. On exposed rocks, where periwinkle snails rarely eat the competitively dominant alga *Chondrus*, feeding by snails reduces algal species richness.

a. The distribution of periwinkle snails and two kinds of algae

Periwinkle snails (*Littorina littorea*)

Enteromorpha growing in tide pools

Chondrus growing on exposed rocks

b. Density of periwinkles versus algal species richness in tide pools and on exposed rocks

In tide pools

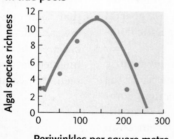

In tide pools, snails at low densities eat little algae and *Enteromorpha* competitively excludes other algal species, reducing species richness. At high snail densities, heavy feeding on all species reduces algal species richness. At intermediate snail densities, grazing eliminates some *Enteromorpha*, allowing other species to grow.

On exposed rocks

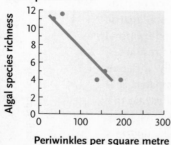

On exposed rocks, periwinkles don't eat much *Chondrus*, but they consume the tender, less successful competitors. Thus, feeding by periwinkles reinforces the competitive superiority of *Chondrus*: as periwinkle density increases, algal species richness declines.

Herbivores also exert complex effects on communities. In the 1970s, Jane Lubchenco studied herbivory in a periwinkle snail, believed to be a keystone species on rocky shores in Massachusetts **(Figure 30.19)**. The features of plants and algae and the food preferences of animals that eat them can influence community structure.

STUDY BREAK QUESTIONS

1. How does the importance of competition vary between *K*-selected and *r*-selected species?
2. Does predation or herbivory increase or decrease species richness? Explain.
3. What is a keystone species?

© Cengage Learning 2017

30.6 The Nature of Ecological Communities

The interactions among species in an ecological community can be broadly categorized as antagonistic or mutually beneficial (Table 30.1; **Figure 30.20**). Trophic interactions are associated with consumption (antagonistic; one species eating another), the usual situation portrayed in food webs. Mutually beneficial interactions include, for example, those between flowering plants and their insect pollinators. Understanding community dynamics requires knowledge of the structure of community networks (e.g., food webs; see Chapter 31) as well as information about how structure influences the extinction or persistence of species. An overview of the dynamics of an ecological community is obtained through a combination of fieldwork and attendant statistical analysis of data to document ecosystem architecture. The second element, knowledge of the influence of architecture on species persistence, emerges from mathematical modelling.

To explore the nature of ecosystems, Elisa Thébault and Colin Fontaine examined pollination (mutualistic) and plant–herbivore (trophic) systems (Figure 30.20). They found that the structure of the network favouring ecosystem **stability** differs between trophic (herbivore) and mutually beneficial

(pollination) networks. In pollination networks, the elements are highly connected and nested, promoting stability of communities. In herbivore networks, stability is greater in structures that are compartmentalized and weakly connected. The work identifies features that affect the stability of ecosystems, potentially informing those working to effect conservation at the system level.

Ecotones, the borders between communities, are sometimes wide transition zones. Ecotones are generally species rich because they include plants and animals from both neighbouring communities, as well as some species that thrive only under transitional conditions. Although ecotones are usually relatively broad, places where there is a discontinuity in a critical resource or important abiotic factor may have a sharp community boundary. Chemical differences between soils derived from serpentine rock and sandstone establish sharp boundaries between communities of native California wildflowers and introduced European grasses (See **Figure 30.21**).

STUDY BREAK QUESTIONS

1. Distinguish between antagonistic and mutualistic architectural structures in ecosystems.
2. Are ecotones generally species rich or species poor?

30.7 Community Characteristics

Growth forms (sizes and shapes) of plants vary markedly in different environments, so the attributes of plants often can be used to characterize communities. Warm, moist environments support complex vegetation with multiple vertical layers. Tropical forests include a canopy formed by the tallest trees, an understory of shorter trees and shrubs, and a herb layer under openings in the canopy. Vinelike lianas and epiphytes grow on the trunks and branches of trees (**Figure 30.22**). In contrast, physically harsh environments are occupied by low vegetation with simple structure. Trees on mountainsides buffeted by cold winds are short, and the plants below them cling to rocks and soil. Other environments support growth forms between these extremes.

In 2016, there were important advances in the study of vascular plants. Sandra Diaz and colleagues reported the results of a global look at plant form and function. They used an analysis of six major traits critical to the growth, survival, and reproduction of vascular plants to show the importance of coordination and trade-offs. About 75% of the variation in traits related directly to plant form and function. One important element is the sizes of plants and their parts. Another involves leaf operations, as

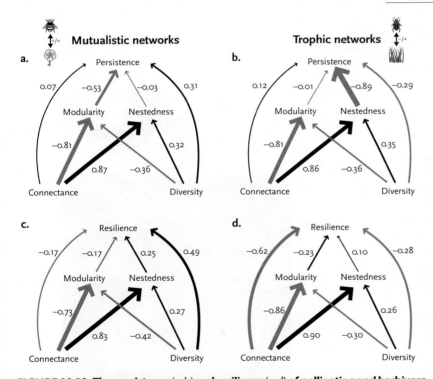

FIGURE 30.20 **The persistence** (a, b) **and resilience** (c, d) **of pollinating and herbivore ecosystem patterns are summarized, revealing important differences.** The thickness of arrows, scaled to standardized coefficients, illustrates the relative strength of the effects. Red identifies negative effects; black, positive ones. There is a further comparison of the effects of connectance and diversity, comparing direct and indirect effects, considering modularity and nestedness. The numbers in each diagram indicate the coefficients along the path.

Source: From Elisa Thébault, Colin Fontaine, "Stability of Ecological Communities and the Architecture of Mutualistic and Trophic Networks," *Science* 13 August 2010, Vol. 329 no. 5993 pp. 853-856. *Science* by American Association for the Advancement of Science Reproduced with permission of AMERICAN ASSOCIATION FOR THE ADVANCEMENT OF SCIENCE in the format Republish in a book via Copyright Clearance Center.

a. Interactive hypothesis

Environmental Gradient

The interactive hypothesis predicts that species within communities exhibit similar distributions along environmental gradients (indicated by the close alignment of several curves over each section of the gradient) and that boundaries between communities (indicated by arrows) are sharp.

b. Individualistic hypothesis

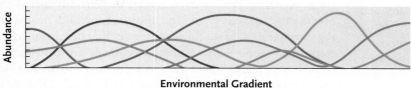

Environmental Gradient

The individualistic hypothesis predicts that species distributions along the gradient are independent (indicated by the lack of alignment of the curves) and that sharp boundaries do not separate communities.

c. Siskiyou Mountains

Moisture Gradient

Most gradient analyses support the individualistic hypothesis, as illustrated by distributions of tree species along moisture gradients in Oregon's Siskiyou Mountains and Arizona's Santa Catalina Mountains.

d. Santa Catalina Mountains

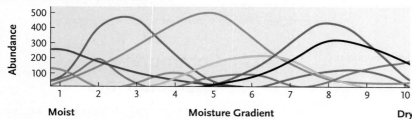

Moist   Moisture Gradient   Dry

© Cengage Learning 2017

FIGURE 30.21 Two views of ecological communities. Each graph line indicates a different species.

they reflect the cost of development relative to growth potential. Meanwhile, Kunstler and colleagues used data from more than 3 million trees to show how the outcome of wood density, leaf area, and maximum height affect the outcome of competition among species. Their analysis revealed that intraspecific competition was more important than interspecific competition. Farrior and colleagues examined the size distributions of tropical trees. Faster-growing species fill gaps in the forest canopy, and the species forming the understory scale themselves to fit within the relationship of the ratio of diameters of crown to trunk.

Collectively these species illustrate the importance of modelling to understand the dynamics of communities of plants.

Communities differ greatly in **species richness**, the number of species that live within them. The harsh environment on a low desert island may support just a few species of microorganisms, fungi, algae, plants, and arthropods. In contrast, tropical forests that grow under milder physical conditions include many thousands of species. Ecologists have studied global patterns of species richness (see Chapter 28) for decades. Today, as human disturbance of natural communities has reached a crisis point, conservation biologists try to understand global

FIGURE 30.22 Layered forests. Tropical forests, such as one near the Mazaruni River in Guyana (South America), include a canopy of tall trees and an understorey of short trees and shrubs. Huge vines (lianas) climb through the trees, eventually reaching sunlight in the canopy. Epiphytic plants grow on trunks and branches, increasing the structural complexity of the habitat.

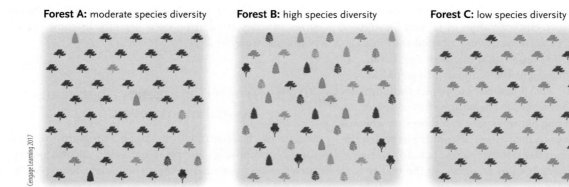

Forest A: moderate species diversity **Forest B:** high species diversity **Forest C:** low species diversity

FIGURE 30.23 Species diversity. In this hypothetical example, each of the 3 samples of forest communities (A, B, and C) contains 50 trees. Indices allow biologists to express the diversity of species and evenness of numbers (see Table 30.2).

patterns of species richness to determine which regions of Earth are most in need of preservation.

The relative abundances of species vary across communities. Some communities have one or two abundant species and a number of rare species. In others, the species are represented by more equal numbers of individuals. In a **temperate deciduous forest** in southern Quebec, red oak trees (*Quercus rubra*) and sugar maples (*Acer saccharum*) might together account for nearly 85% of the trees. A tropical forest in Costa Rica may have more than 200 tree species, each making up a small percentage of the total.

The factors underlying diversity and community structure can be expected to vary among groups of organisms, and the interactions between very different groups of organisms can have positive effects on both. Using an experimental mycorrhizal plant system (see Chapter 25), H. Maherali and J. N. Klironomos found that, after one year, the species richness of mycorrhizal fungi correlated with higher plant productivity. In turn, the diversity and species richness of mycorrhizal fungi were highest when their starting community had more distinct evolutionary lineages. This example illustrates the importance of diversity and interactions.

30.7a Measuring Species Diversity and Evenness: Calculating Indices

The number of species is the simplest measure of diversity, so a forest with four tree species has higher **species diversity** than one with two tree species. But there can be more to measuring diversity than just counting species. Biologists use indices of diversity to facilitate comparison of data sets documenting the numbers of species and of individuals. Shannon's index of diversity (H'), one commonly used measure, is calculated using the formula

$$H' = -\sum_{i=1}^{s} p_i \ln p_i$$

where S is the total number of species in the community (richness), p_i is the proportion of S made up by species i, and ln is the natural logarithm.

Another index, Shannon's evenness index (E_H), is calculated using the formula

$$E_H = \frac{H'}{\ln S}$$

where ln S is the natural logarithm of the number of species. Evenness is an indication of the mixture of species. Indices of diversity and evenness allow population biologists to objectively portray and compare the diversity of communities.

Use the two indices to compare the 3 forests of 50 trees each in **Figure 30.23**. The number of species and the number of individuals of each species in each forest are shown in **Table 30.2**. In Table 30.2, the values of H' and E_H indicate the diversity of the three hypothetical forests and the evenness of species representations. Lower values of H' and E_H suggest

TABLE 30.2	Shannon's Indices for Measuring Diversity and Evenness		
Numbers of Individuals per Species			
	Forest A*	Forest B*	Forest C*
Species 1	39	5	25
Species 2	2	5	25
Species 3	2	5	0
Species 4	1	5	0
Species 5	1	5	0
Species 6	1	5	0
Species 7	1	5	0
Species 8	1	5	0
Species 9	1	5	0
Species 10	1	5	0
Shannon Indices			
H' diversity	0.6	2.3	0.7
E_H evenness	0.26	1.0	1.0

*Forests from Figure 30.23

communities with few species (low H' values) or uneven distribution (low E_H values). Higher values of H' and E_H suggest a richer array of species with evenly distributed individuals.

Measures of diversity can be used to advantage. Ecologists refer to α diversity to represent the numbers of sympatric species in one community, and β diversity to depict the numbers in a collection of communities. The number of herbivorous Lepidoptera species in one national park is α diversity, whereas β diversity is the number of species in the country in which the park is located. The trend to establish parks that cross international boundaries is a step toward recognizing the reality that political and biological boundaries can be quite different. Measures of diversity can be used directly in some conservation plans (see Chapter 28).

30.7b Trophic Interactions between Nourishment Levels

Every ecological community has trophic structure (*troph* = nourishment), comprising all plant–herbivore, predator–prey, host–parasite, and potential competitive interactions (**Figure 30.24**).

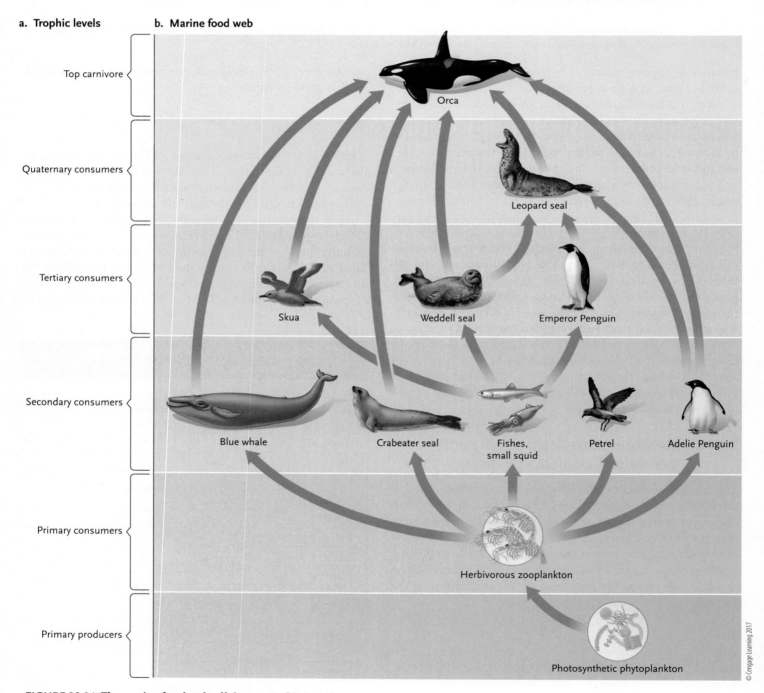

a. Trophic levels

- Top carnivore
- Quaternary consumers
- Tertiary consumers
- Secondary consumers
- Primary consumers
- Primary producers

b. Marine food web

Orca

Leopard seal

Skua · Weddell seal · Emperor Penguin

Blue whale · Crabeater seal · Fishes, small squid · Petrel · Adelie Penguin

Herbivorous zooplankton

Photosynthetic phytoplankton

© Cengage Learning 2017

FIGURE 30.24 The marine food web off the coast of Antarctica

We can visualize the trophic structure of a community as a hierarchy of **trophic levels**, defined by the feeding relationships among its species (see Figure 30.24a). Photosynthetic organisms are primary producers, the first trophic level. Primary producers are photoautotrophs (*auto* = self) because they capture sunlight and convert it into chemical energy, which is used to make larger organic molecules that plants can use directly. Plants are the main primary producers in terrestrial communities. Multicellular algae and plants are the major primary producers in shallow freshwater and marine environments, whereas photosynthetic protists and cyanobacteria play that role in deep open water.

All **consumers** in a community (animals, fungi, and diverse microorganisms) are heterotrophs (*hetero* = other) because they acquire energy and nutrients by eating other organisms or their remains. Animals are consumers. Herbivores (primary consumers) feed directly on plants and form the second trophic level. Secondary consumers (mesopredators) eat herbivores and form the third trophic level. Animals that eat secondary consumers make up the fourth trophic level, the **tertiary consumers**. In one meal, animals that are omnivores (e.g., humans, pigs, and bears) can act as primary, secondary, and tertiary consumers.

Detritivores (scavengers) form a separate and distinct trophic level. These organisms extract energy from organic detritus produced at other trophic levels. Detritivores include fungi, bacteria, and animals such as earthworms and vultures that ingest dead organisms, digestive wastes, and cast-off body parts such as leaves and exoskeletons. Decomposers, a type of detritivore, are small organisms, such as bacteria and fungi, that feed on dead or dying organic material. Detritivores and decomposers serve a critical ecological function because their activity reduces organic material to small inorganic molecules that producers can assimilate (see Chapter 23).

Although omnivores obviously do not fit exclusively into one trophic level, this can also be true of other organisms. Carnivorous plants and sea slugs that use chloroplasts are examples of species that do not fit readily into trophic categories.

30.7c Food Chains and Webs: Connections In Ecosystems

Ecologists use food chains and webs to illustrate the trophic structure of a community. Each link in a food chain is represented by an arrow pointing from food to consumer (see Figure 30.24b). Simple, straight-line food chains are rare in nature because most consumers feed on more than one type of food and because most organisms are eaten by more than one type of consumer. Complex relationships are portrayed as food webs—sets of interconnected food chains with multiple links.

In the food web for the waters off the coast of Antarctica (see Figure 30.24), primary producers and primary consumers are small organisms occurring in vast numbers. Microscopic diatoms (phytoplankton) are responsible for most photosynthesis, and small shrimplike krill (zooplankton) are the major primary consumers. These tiny organisms, in turn, are eaten by larger species such as fish and seabirds, as well as by suspension-feeding baleen whales. Some secondary consumers are eaten by birds and mammals at higher trophic levels. The top carnivore in this ecosystem, the orca, feeds on carnivorous birds and mammals.

Ideally, depictions of food webs would include all species in a community, from microorganisms to top consumer. But most ecologists simply cannot collect data on every species, particularly those that are rare or very small. Instead, they study links between the most important species and simplify analysis by grouping trophically similar species. Figure 30.24 categorizes the many different species of primary producers and primary consumers as phytoplankton and zooplankton respectively.

Many biological hot spots (areas with many species) exist, from thermal vents on the floor of some oceans to deposits of bat guano in some caves. A more recently described example is icebergs drifting north from Antarctica. The icebergs can be hot spots of enrichment because of the nutrients and other materials they shed into surrounding waters. The water around two free-drifting icebergs (0.1 km² and 30.8 km² in area) was sampled in the Weddell Sea. High concentrations of chlorophyll, krill, and seabirds extended about 3.7 km around each iceberg. These data, reported by K. L. Smith Jr. and seven colleagues, demonstrate that icebergs can have substantial effects on pelagic ecosystems.

In the late 1950s, Robert MacArthur analyzed food webs to determine how the many links between trophic levels may contribute to a community's stability. The stability of a community is defined as its ability to maintain **species composition** and relative abundances when environmental disturbances eliminate some species from the community. MacArthur hypothesized that, in species-rich communities, where animals feed on many food sources, the absence of one or two species would have only minor effects on the structure and stability of the community as a whole. He proposed a connection between species diversity, food web complexity, and community stability.

Subsequent research has confirmed MacArthur's reasoning. The average number of links per species generally increases with increasing species richness. Comparative food web analysis reveals that the relative proportions of species at the highest, middle, and lowest trophic levels are reasonably constant across communities. In 92 communities, MacArthur found two or three prey species per predator species, regardless of species richness.

Interactions among species in most food webs can be complex, indirect, and hard to unravel. In contrast, rodents and ants living in desert communities of the U.S. Southwest potentially compete for seeds, their main food source. Plants that produce the seeds compete for water, nutrients, and space. Rodents generally prefer to eat large seeds, whereas ants prefer small seeds. Thus, feeding by rodents reduces the potential population sizes of plants that produce large seeds. As a result, the population sizes of plants that produce small seeds may increase, ultimately providing more food for ants (see Chapter 39). Compared with the Antarctic system described above (see Figure 30.24), this community is not particularly complex.

STUDY BREAK QUESTIONS

1. Why are indices important for population biologists? What do Shannon's indices measure?
2. Differentiate between α and β diversity.
3. Are herbivores primary or secondary consumers? Which trophic level do they form? Where do omnivores belong?

30.8 Effects of Population Interactions on Community Structure

Observations of resource partitioning and character displacement suggested that some process had fostered differences in resource use among coexisting species, and competition provided the most straightforward explanation of these patterns.

Interspecific competition can cause local extinction of species or prevent new species from becoming established in a community, reducing its species richness. During the 1960s and early 1970s, ecologists emphasized competition as the primary factor structuring communities.

30.8a Effects of Disturbance on Community Characteristics

Recent research tends to support the individualistic view that many communities are not in equilibrium and that species composition changes frequently. Environmental disturbances such as storms, landslides, fires, floods, avalanches, and cold spells often eliminate some species and provide opportunities for others to become established. Frequent disturbances keep some ecological communities in a constant state of flux.

Physical disturbances are common in some environments. Lightning-induced fires commonly sweep through grasslands, powerful hurricanes often demolish patches of forest and coastal habitats, and waves wash over communities at the edge of the sea and sweep away organisms as well as landforms and other structures.

Joseph Connell and his colleagues conducted an ambitious long-term study of the effects of disturbance on coral reefs, shallow tropical marine habitats that are among the most species-rich communities on Earth. In some parts of the world, reefs are routinely battered by violent storms that wash corals off the substrate, creating bare patches in the reef. The scouring action of storms creates opportunities for coral larvae to settle on bare substrates and start new colonies.

From 1963 to 1992, Connell and his colleagues tracked the fate of the Heron Island Reef at the south end of Australia's Great Barrier Reef (**Figure 30.25**). The inner flat and protected crests of the reef are sheltered from severe wave action during storms, whereas some pools and crests are routinely exposed to physical disturbance. Because corals live in colonies of variable size, the researchers monitored coral abundance by measuring the percentage of the substrate (i.e., the sea floor) that colonies covered. They revisited marked study plots at intervals, photographing and identifying individual coral colonies.

Five major cyclones crossed the reef during the 30-year study period. Coral communities in exposed areas of the reef were in a nearly continual state of flux. In exposed pools, four of the five cyclones reduced the percentage of cover, often drastically. On exposed crests, the cyclone of 1972 eliminated virtually all corals, and subsequent storms slowed the recovery of these areas for more than 20 years. In contrast, corals in sheltered areas suffered much less storm damage. Nevertheless, their coverage also declined steadily during the study as a natural consequence of the corals' growth. As colonies grew taller and closer to the ocean's surface, their increased exposure to air resulted in substantial mortality.

Connell and his colleagues also documented recruitment, the growth of new colonies from settling larvae, in their study plots. They discovered that the rate at which new colonies developed was almost always higher in sheltered than in exposed areas. Recruitment rates were extremely variable, depending in part on the amount of space that storms or coral growth had made available.

This long-term study of coral reefs illustrates that frequent disturbances prevent some communities from reaching an equilibrium determined by interspecific interactions. Changes in the coral reef community at Heron Island result from the effects of external disturbances that remove coral colonies from the reef, as well as internal processes (growth and recruitment) that either eliminate colonies or establish new ones. In this community, growth and recruitment are slow processes and disturbances are frequent. Thus, the community never attains equilibrium, and moderate levels of disturbance can foster high species richness.

The **intermediate disturbance hypothesis**, proposed by Connell in 1978, suggests that species richness is greatest in communities experiencing fairly frequent disturbances of moderate intensity. Moderate disturbances create openings for r-selected species to arrive and join the community while allowing K-selected species to survive. Thus, communities that experience intermediate levels of disturbance contain a rich mixture of species. Where disturbances are severe and frequent, communities include only r-selected species that complete their life cycles between catastrophes. Where disturbances are mild and rare, communities are dominated by long-lived K-selected species that competitively exclude other species from the community.

Several studies in diverse habitats have confirmed the predictions of the intermediate disturbance hypothesis. Colin R. Townsend and his colleagues studied the effects of disturbance at 54 stream sites in the Taieri River system in New Zealand.

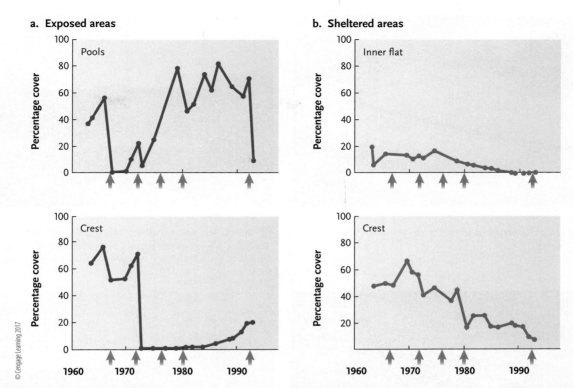

a. Exposed areas

Pools

Crest

b. Sheltered areas

Inner flat

Crest

1960   1970   1980   1990   1960   1970   1980   1990

© Cengage Learning 2017

FIGURE 30.25 Major hydrodynamic disturbances to coral reefs, such as tsunamis and severe storms, have important impacts on coral reefs. Using oceanographic and engineering models, it is possible to predict the degree of dislodgement of benthic reef corals and, in this way, predict how coral shape and size indicate vulnerability to major disturbances. The use of these models is particularly important during times of climate change. The graphs show the effects of storms on corals. Five tropical cyclones (marked by grey arrows) damaged corals on the Heron Island Reef during a 30-year period. Storms reduced the percentage cover of corals in **(a)** exposed parts of the reef much more than in **(b)** sheltered parts of it. These data show that the 1970 event had the largest impact on some exposed and sheltered areas.

Disturbance occurs in these communities when water flow from heavy rains moves rocks, soil, and sand in the streambed, disrupting animal habitats. Townsend and his colleagues measured how much the substrate moved in different streambeds to develop an index of the intensity of disturbance. Their results indicate that species richness is highest in areas that experience intermediate levels of disturbance (**Figure 30.26**).

Some ecologists have suggested that species-rich communities recover from disturbances more readily than less diverse communities. In the United States, David Tilman and his colleagues conducted large-scale experiments in Midwestern grasslands. They examined relationships between species number and the ability of communities to recover from disturbance. Grassland plots with high species richness recover from drought faster than plots with fewer species.

STUDY BREAK QUESTIONS

1. What did Connell's 30-year study of coral reefs illustrate about the ability of communities to reach a state of equilibrium?
2. What is the intermediate disturbance hypothesis? Describe one study that supports this hypothesis.
3. How does species richness affect the rate of recovery following a disturbance?

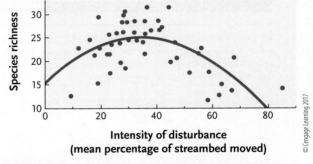

© Cengage Learning 2017

FIGURE 30.26 An observational study that supports the intermediate disturbance hypothesis. In the Taieri River system in New Zealand, species richness was highest in stream communities that experienced an intermediate level of disturbance.

30.9   Succession

Ecosystems change over time in a process called **succession**, the change from one community type to another.

30.9a   Primary Succession: The First Steps

Primary succession begins when organisms first colonize habitats without soil, such as those created by erupting volcanoes and retreating glaciers (**Figure 30.27**). Lichens are often among

1 The glacier has retreated about 8 m per year since 1794.

2 This site was covered with ice less than 10 years before this photo was taken. When a glacier retreats, a constant flow of melt water leaches minerals, especially nitrogen, from the newly exposed substrate.

3 Once lichens and mosses have established themselves, mountain avens (genus *Dryas*) grows on the nutrient-poor soil. This pioneer species benefits from the activity of mutualistic nitrogen-fixing bacteria, spreading rapidly over glacial till.

4 Within 20 years, shrubby willows (genus *Salix*), cottonwoods (genus *Populus*), and alders (genus *Alnus*) take hold in drainage channels. These species are also symbiotic with nitrogen-fixing microorganisms.

5 In time, young conifers, mostly hemlocks (genus *Tsuga*) and spruce (genus *Picea*), join the community.

6 As the years progress, the smaller trees and shrubs are gradually replaced by larger trees.

FIGURE 30.27 Primary succession following glacial retreat. The retreat of glaciers at Glacier Bay, Alaska, has allowed ecologists to document primary succession on newly exposed rocks and soil.

the very first colonists (see Chapter 25), deriving nutrients from rain and bare rock. They secrete mild acids that erode rock surfaces, initiating the slow development of soil, which is enriched by the organic material lichens produce. After lichens modify a site, mosses (see Chapter 26) colonize patches of soil and grow quickly.

As soil accumulates, hardy, opportunistic plants (grasses, ferns, and broad-leaved herbs) colonize the site from surrounding areas. Their roots break up rock, and when they die, their decaying remains enrich the soil. Detritivores and decomposers facilitate these processes. As the soil becomes deeper and richer, increased moisture and nutrients support bushes and, eventually, trees. Late successional stages are often dominated by K-selected species with woody trunks and branches that position leaves in sunlight and large root systems that acquire water and nutrients from soil.

In the classical view of ecological succession, long-lived species, which replace themselves over time, eventually dominate a community, and new species join it only rarely. This relatively stable, late successional stage is called a **climax community** because the dominant vegetation replaces itself and persists until an environmental disturbance eliminates it and allows other species to invade. Local climate and soil conditions, the surrounding communities where colonizing species originate, and chance events determine the species composition of climax communities. We now know that even climax communities change slowly in response to environmental fluctuations.

30.9b Secondary Succession: Changes after Destruction

Secondary succession occurs after existing vegetation is destroyed or disrupted by an environmental disturbance, such as a fire, a storm, or human activity. The presence of soil makes disturbed sites ripe for colonization and may contain numerous seeds that germinate after disturbance. Early stages of secondary succession proceed rapidly, but later stages parallel those of primary succession.

30.9c Climax Communities: The Ultimate Ecosystems until Something Changes

Similar climax communities can arise from several different successional sequences. Hardwood forests can also develop in sites that were once ponds. During **aquatic succession**, debris from rivers and runoff accumulates in a pond, filling it to its margins. Ponds are first transformed into swamps, inhabited by plants adapted to a semisolid substrate. As larger plants get established, their high transpiration rates dry the soil, allowing other plant species to colonize.

Given enough time, the site may become a meadow or forest in which an area of moist, low-lying ground is the only remnant of the original pond.

Because several characteristics of communities can change during succession, ecologists try to document how patterns change. First, because r-selected species are short lived and K-selected species are long lived, species composition changes rapidly in the early stages and more slowly in the later stages of succession. Second, species richness increases rapidly during early stages because new species join the community faster than resident species become extinct. In later stages, species richness stabilizes or may even decline. Third, in terrestrial communities receiving sufficient rainfall, the maximum height and total mass of the vegetation increase steadily as large species replace small ones, creating the complex structure of the climax community.

Because plants influence the physical environment below them, the community itself increasingly moderates its **microclimate**. The shade cast by a forest canopy helps retain soil moisture and reduce temperature fluctuations. The trunks and canopy also reduce wind speed. In contrast, the short vegetation in an early successional stage does not effectively shelter the space below it.

Although ecologists usually describe succession in terms of vegetation, animals can show similar patterns. As the vegetation shifts, new resources become available, and animal species replace each other over time. Herbivorous insects, often with strict food preferences, undergo succession along with their food plants. And as herbivores change, so do their predators, parasites, and parasitoids. In old-field succession in eastern North America, different vegetation stages harbour a changing assortment of bird species (**Figure 30.28**).

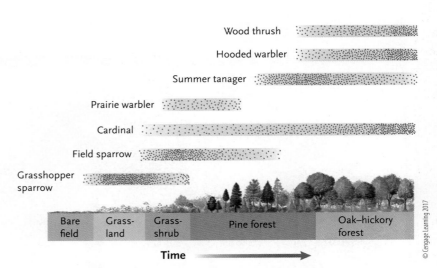

FIGURE 30.28 Succession in animals. Successional changes in bird species composition in an abandoned agricultural field in eastern North America parallel the changes in plant species composition. The residence times of several representative species are illustrated. The density of stippling inside each bar illustrates the density of each species through time.

Differences in dispersal abilities (see "Dispersal," Section 30.9e), maturation rates, and life spans among species are partly responsible for ecological succession. Early successional stages harbour many *r*-selected species because they produce numerous small seeds that colonize open habitats and grow quickly. Mature successional stages are dominated by *K*-selected species because they are long lived. Nevertheless, coexisting populations inevitably affect one another. Although the role of population interactions in succession is generally acknowledged, ecologists debate the relative importance of processes that either facilitate or inhibit the turnover of species in a community.

30.9d Facilitation Hypothesis: One Species Makes Changes That Help Others

The **facilitation hypothesis** suggests that species modify the local environment in ways that make it less suitable for themselves but more suitable for colonization by species typical of the next successional stage. When lichens first colonize bare rock, they produce a small quantity of soil that is required by mosses and grasses that grow there later. According to this hypothesis, changes in species composition are both orderly and predictable because the presence of each stage facilitates the success of the next one. Facilitation is important in primary succession, but it may not be the best model of interactions that influence secondary succession.

30.9e Inhibition Hypothesis: One Species Negatively Affects Others

The **inhibition hypothesis** suggests that new species are prevented from occupying a community by species that are already present. According to this hypothesis, succession is neither orderly nor predictable because each stage is dominated by the species that happened to have colonized the site first. Species replacements occur only when individuals of dominant species die of old age or when an environmental disturbance reduces their numbers. Eventually, long-lived species replace short-lived species, but the precise species composition of a mature community is open to question. Inhibition appears to play a role in some secondary successions. The interactions among early successional species in an old field are highly competitive. Horseweed inhibits the growth of asters that follow them in succession by shading aster seedlings and releasing toxic substances from their roots. Experimental removal of horseweed enhances the growth of asters, confirming the inhibitory effect.

DISPERSAL In other situations, plants disperse with the assistance of animals through pollination and seeds. Using the Mahaleb cherry (*Prunus mahaleb*) and genetic techniques, P. Jordano and two colleagues examined the role of birds and mammals in pollination and the dispersion of seeds (**Figure 30.29**). Small passerine birds dispersed seeds short distances (most less than 50 m) from the parent tree, whereas medium-sized birds (*Corvus corone* and *Turdus viscivorus*) usually dispersed seeds over longer distances (more than 110 m). Mammals (usually *Martes foina* and *Vulpes vulpes* but sometimes *Meles meles*) dispersed seeds about 500 m. The genetic work also indicated the extent of gene flow during pollination.

It is obvious that plants capable of self-fertilization or vegetative reproduction can be more effective colonists than those depending on outcrossing, especially with the help of animal pollinators.

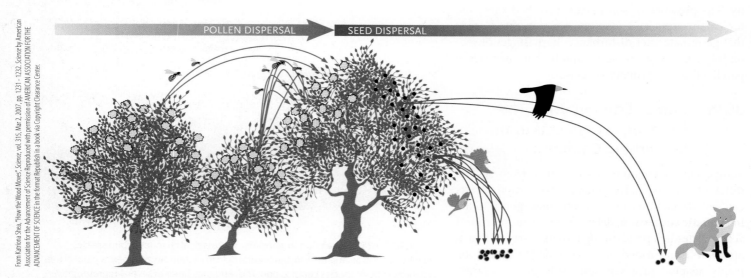

From Katriona Shea, "How the Wood Moves", *Science*, vol. 315, Mar 2, 2007, pp. 1231 – 1232. *Science* by American Association for the Advancement of Science Reproduced with permission of AMERICAN ASSOCIATION FOR THE ADVANCEMENT OF SCIENCE in the format Republish in a book via Copyright Clearance Center.

POLLEN DISPERSAL → SEED DISPERSAL

FIGURE 30.29 The movement of pollen and seeds from Mahaleb cherry trees. Gene flow occurs through pollination and seed dispersal (see Chapter 17).

30.9f Tolerance Hypothesis: Species Tolerate One Another

The **tolerance hypothesis** asserts that succession proceeds because competitively superior species replace competitively inferior ones. According to this model, early-stage species neither facilitate nor inhibit the growth of later-stage species. Instead, as more species arrive at a site and resources become limiting, competition eliminates species that cannot harvest scarce resources successfully. In the Piedmont region of North America, young hardwood trees are more tolerant of shade than are young pine trees, and hardwoods gradually replace pines during succession. Thus, the climax community includes only strong competitors. Tolerance may explain the species composition of many transitional and mature communities.

At most sites, succession probably results from some combination of facilitation, inhibition, and tolerance, coupled with interspecific differences in dispersal, growth, and maturation rates. Moreover, within a community, the patchiness of abiotic factors strongly influences plant distributions and species composition. In deciduous forests of eastern North America, maples (*Acer* species) predominate on wet, low-lying ground, but oaks (*Quercus* species) are more abundant at higher and drier sites. Thus, a mature deciduous forest is often a mosaic of species and not a uniform stand of trees.

Disturbance and density-independent factors play important roles, in some cases speeding successional change. Moose (*Alces alces*) prefer to feed on deciduous shrubs in northern forests. This disturbance accelerates the rate at which conifers replace deciduous shrubs. On Isle Royale in Lake Superior, however, grazing by moose strongly affects balsam fir (*Abies balsamea*), their preferred food there. The net effect is a severe reduction in conifers and an increase in deciduous shrubs. Disturbance can also inhibit successional change, establishing a **disturbance climax** or **disclimax community.** In many grassland communities, periodic fires and grazing by large mammals kill seedlings of trees that would otherwise become established. Thus, disturbance prevents the succession from grassland to forest, and grassland persists as a disclimax community.

Animals such as moose can alter patterns of succession and vegetation in some communities, but the effect also extends to small mammals. Removal experiments involving kangaroo rats and plots of shrubland in the Chihuahuan Desert (southeastern Arizona) allowed J. H. Brown and E. J. Heske to demonstrate that these rodents were keystones in some systems where they occur. Kangaroo rats affect the plants in several ways. They are seed predators, and their burrowing activities disturb soils. Excluding kangaroo rats from experimental plots led to a threefold increase in the density of tall perennials and annual grasses **(Figure 30.30)**, suggesting that, by predation on seeds and burrowing, these rodents affected the vegetation in the experimental areas.

On a local scale, disturbances often destroy small patches of vegetation, returning them to an earlier successional stage. A hurricane, tornado, or avalanche may topple trees in a forest, creating small, sunny patches of open ground. Locally occurring *r*-selected species take advantage of newly available resources and quickly colonize the openings. These local patches then undergo succession that is out of step with the immediately surrounding forest. Thus, moderate disturbance, accompanied by succession in local patches, can increase species richness in many communities.

FIGURE 30.30 **Predation and succession.** Kangaroo rats (*Dipodomys*) were removed from the left side of the fence, which excluded them from the plot on the left. The top photograph was taken 5 years after the removal and the bottom one 13 years after. A large-seeded annual (after 5 years) and tall grasses are present in the *Dipodomys*-free plots.

From James H. Brown, Edward J. Heske, "Control of a Desert-Grassland Transition by a Keystone Rodent Guild," *Science*, vol. 250, Dec 21, 1990, pp. 1705–1707. *Science* by American Association for the Advancement of Science. Reproduced with permission of AMERICAN ASSOCIATION FOR THE ADVANCEMENT OF SCIENCE in the format Republish in a book via Copyright Clearance Center.

STUDY BREAK QUESTIONS

1. What are the two types of succession? How do they differ?
2. What is a climax community? What determines the species composition of a climax community?
3. Identify and briefly describe the three hypotheses used to explain how succession proceeds.

30.10 Variations in Species Richness among Communities

Species richness often varies among communities according to a recognizable pattern. Two large-scale patterns of species richness—latitudinal trends and island patterns—have captured the attention of ecologists for more than a century.

30.10a Latitudinal Effects: From South to North

Ever since Darwin and Wallace travelled the globe (see Chapter 16), ecologists have recognized broad latitudinal trends in species richness. For many but not all plant and animal groups, species richness follows a latitudinal gradient, with the most species in the tropics and a steady decline in numbers toward the poles (**Figure 30.31**). Several general hypotheses may explain these striking patterns.

Some hypotheses propose historical explanations for the *origin* of high species richness in the tropics. The benign climate in tropical regions allows some tropical organisms to have more generations per year than their temperate counterparts. Small seasonal changes in temperature mean that tropical species may be less likely than temperate species to migrate from one habitat to another, reducing gene flow between geographically isolated populations (see Chapter 17). These factors may have fostered higher speciation rates in the tropics, accelerating the accumulation of species. Tropical communities may also have experienced severe disturbance less often than communities at higher latitudes, where periodic glaciations have caused repeated extinctions. Thus, new species may have accumulated in the tropics over longer periods of time.

Other hypotheses focus on ecological explanations for the *maintenance* of high species richness in the tropics. Some resources are more abundant, predictable, and diverse in tropical communities. Tropical regions experience more intense sunlight, warmer temperatures in most months, and higher annual rainfall than temperate and polar regions (see *The Purple Pages*). These factors provide a long and predictable growing season for the lush tropical vegetation that supports a rich assemblage of herbivores and, through them, many carnivores and parasites. Furthermore, the abundance, predictability, and year-round availability of resources allow some tropical animals to have specialized diets. Tropical forests support many species of fruit-eating bats and birds that could not survive in temperate forests where fruits are not available year-round.

Species richness may be a self-reinforcing phenomenon in tropical communities. Complex webs of population interactions and interdependency have co-evolved in relatively stable and predictable tropical climates. Predator–prey, competitive, and symbiotic interactions may prevent individual species from dominating communities and reducing species richness.

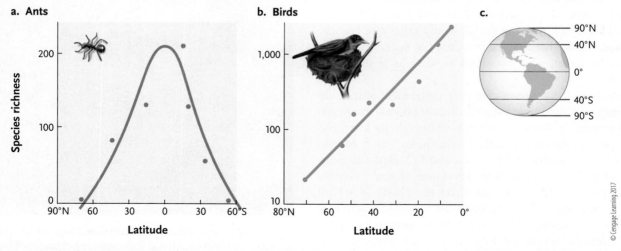

FIGURE 30.31 Latitudinal trends in species richness. The species richness of many animals and plants varies with latitude **(c)** as illustrated here for **(a)** ants in North, Central, and South America and **(b)** birds in North and Central America. The species richness data used in (b) are based on records of where these birds breed.

30.10b Equilibrium Theory of Island Biogeography

In 1883, a volcanic eruption virtually obliterated the island of Krakatoa. Within 50 years, what was left of Krakatoa had been recolonized by plants and animals, providing biologists with a clear demonstration of the dispersal powers of many living species. The colonization of islands and the establishment of biological communities there have provided many natural experiments that have advanced our knowledge of ecology and populations. Islands are attractive sites for experiments because, although the species richness of communities may be stable over time, the species composition is often in flux as new species join a community and others drop out. In the 1960s, Robert MacArthur and Edward O. Wilson used islands as model systems to address the question of why communities vary in species richness. Islands provide natural laboratories for studying ecological phenomena, just as they do for evolution (see Chapter 16). Island communities can be small, with well-defined boundaries, and are isolated from surrounding communities.

MacArthur and Wilson developed the **equilibrium theory of island biogeography** to explain variations in species richness on islands of different size and different levels of isolation from other landmasses. They hypothesized that the number of species on any island was governed by give and take between two processes: the immigration of new species to an island and the extinction of species already there (**Figure 30.32**).

According to their model, the mainland harbours a *species pool* from which species immigrate to offshore islands.

Seeds and small arthropods are carried by wind or floating debris. Animals such as birds arrive under their own power. When only a few species are on an island, the rate at which new species immigrate to the island is high. But as more species inhabit the island over time, the immigration rate declines because fewer species in the mainland pool can still arrive on the island as *new* colonizers (see Chapter 16). Once some species arrive on an island, their populations grow and persist for variable lengths of time. Other immigrants die without reproducing. As the number of species on an island increases, the rate of species extinction also rises. Extinction rates increase over time partly because more species can go extinct there. In addition, as the number of species on the island increases, competition and predator–prey interactions can reduce the population sizes of some species and drive them to extinction.

According to MacArthur and Wilson's theory, an equilibrium between immigration and extinction determines the number of species that ultimately occupy an island (see Figure 30.32a). Once that equilibrium has been reached, the number of species remains relatively constant because one species already on the island becomes extinct in about the same time it takes a new one to arrive. The model does not specify which species immigrate or which ones already on the island become extinct. It simply predicts that the number of species on the island is in equilibrium, although species composition is not. The ongoing processes of immigration and extinction establish a constant turnover in the roster of species that live on any island.

The MacArthur–Wilson model also explains why some islands harbour more species than others. Large islands have

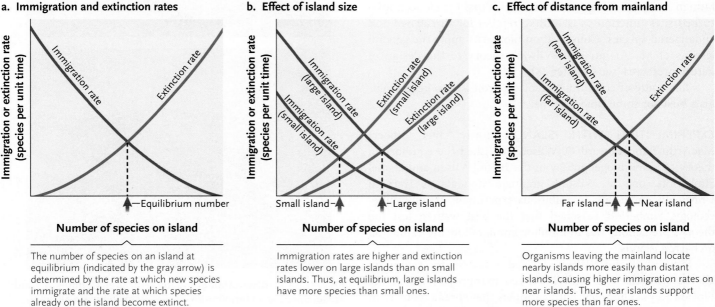

a. Immigration and extinction rates

The number of species on an island at equilibrium (indicated by the gray arrow) is determined by the rate at which new species immigrate and the rate at which species already on the island become extinct.

b. Effect of island size

Immigration rates are higher and extinction rates lower on large islands than on small islands. Thus, at equilibrium, large islands have more species than small ones.

c. Effect of distance from mainland

Organisms leaving the mainland locate nearby islands more easily than distant islands, causing higher immigration rates on near islands. Thus, near islands support more species than far ones.

© Cengage Learning 2017

FIGURE 30.32 Predictions of the theory of island biogeography. The horizontal axes of the graphs are time.

higher immigration rates than small islands because they are larger targets for dispersing organisms. Moreover, large islands have lower extinction rates because they can support larger populations and provide a greater range of habitats and resources. At equilibrium, large islands have more species than small islands do (see Figure 30.32b). Islands near the mainland have higher immigration rates than distant islands because dispersing organisms are more likely to arrive at islands close to their point of departure. Distance does not affect extinction rates, so, at equilibrium, nearby islands have more species than distant islands (see Figure 30.32c).

The equilibrium theory's predictions about the effects of area and distance are generally supported by data on plants and animals (Figure 30.32). Experimental work has verified some of the theory's basic assumptions. Amy Schoener found that more than 200 species of marine organisms colonized tiny artificial islands (plastic kitchen scrubbers) within 30 days after she placed them in a Bahamian lagoon. Her research also confirmed that immigration rate increases with island size. Daniel Simberloff and Edward O. Wilson exterminated insects on tiny islands in the Florida Keys and monitored subsequent immigration and extinction (see next section, "Experimenting with Islands"). Their research confirmed the equilibrium theory's predictions that an island's size and distance from the mainland influence how many species will occupy it.

The equilibrial view of species richness can also apply to mainland communities that exist as islands in a metaphorical sea of dissimilar habitat. Lakes are "islands" in a "sea" of dry land, and mountaintops are habitat "islands" in a "sea" of low terrain. Species richness in these communities is governed partly by the immigration of new species from distant sources and partly by the extinction of species already present. As human activities disrupt environments across the globe, undisturbed sites function as islandlike refuges for threatened and endangered species. Conservation biologists apply the general lessons of MacArthur and Wilson's theory to the design of nature preserves (see Chapter 28).

The study of community ecology promises to keep biologists busy for some time to come.

EXPERIMENTING WITH ISLANDS Shortly after Robert MacArthur and Edward O. Wilson published the equilibrium theory of island biogeography in the 1960s, Wilson and Daniel Simberloff, one of Wilson's graduate students at Harvard University, undertook an ambitious experiment in community ecology. Simberloff reasoned that the best way to test the theory's predictions was to monitor immigration and extinction on barren islands.

Simberloff and Wilson devised a system for removing all the animals from individual red mangrove trees in the Florida Keys. The trees, with canopies that spread from 11 to 18 m in diameter, grow in shallow water and are isolated from their neighbours. Thus, each tree is an island that harbours an arthropod community. The species pool on the Florida mainland includes about 1000 species of arthropods, but each mangrove island contains no more than 40 species at one time.

After cataloguing the species on each island, Simberloff and Wilson hired an extermination company to erect large tents over each mangrove island and fumigate them to eliminate all arthropods on them **(Figure 30.33)**. The exterminators used methyl bromide, a pesticide that does not harm trees or leave any residue. The tents were then removed.

Simberloff then monitored both the immigration of arthropods to the islands and the extinction of species that became established on them. He surveyed four islands regularly for two years and at intervals thereafter.

The results of this experiment confirm several predictions of MacArthur and Wilson's theory **(Figure 30.34)**: Arthropods rapidly recolonized the islands, and within eight or nine months the number of species living on each island had reached an

FIGURE 30.33 **After cataloguing the arthropods, Simberloff and Wilson hired an extermination company to eliminate all living arthropods.**

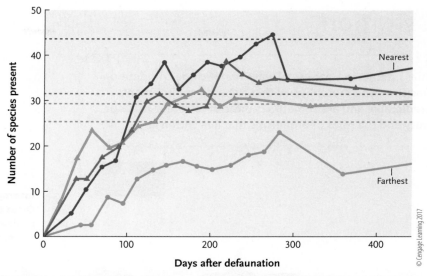

FIGURE 30.34 On three of four islands, species richness slowly returned to the pre-defaunation level (indicated by colour-coded dotted lines). The most distant island had not reached its pre-defaunation species richness after two years.

equilibrium that was close to the original species number. The island nearest the mainland had more species than the most distant island. However, immigration and extinction were rapid, and Simberloff and Wilson suspected that some species went extinct even before they had noted their presence. The researchers also discovered that three years after the experimental treatments, the species composition of the islands was still changing constantly and did not remotely resemble the species composition on the islands before they were defaunated.

Simberloff and Wilson's research was a landmark study in ecology because it tested the predictions of an important theory using a field experiment. Although such efforts are now almost routine in ecological studies, this project was one of the first to demonstrate that large-scale experimental manipulations of natural systems are feasible and that they often produce clear results.

STUDY BREAK QUESTIONS

1. How does species richness change with increasing latitude?
2. In the island biogeography model proposed by MacArthur and Wilson, what processes govern the number of species on an island? What happens to the number of species once equilibrium is reached?
3. What effect do island size and distance from the mainland have on immigration and extinction of colonizing species?

Summary Illustration

Species within communities interact in a variety of ways that include competition, predation, herbivory, parasitism, and mutualism within a shared environment. All interactions are not predictable and are sometimes difficult to categorize, but these define the community and the roles of organisms that live within it.

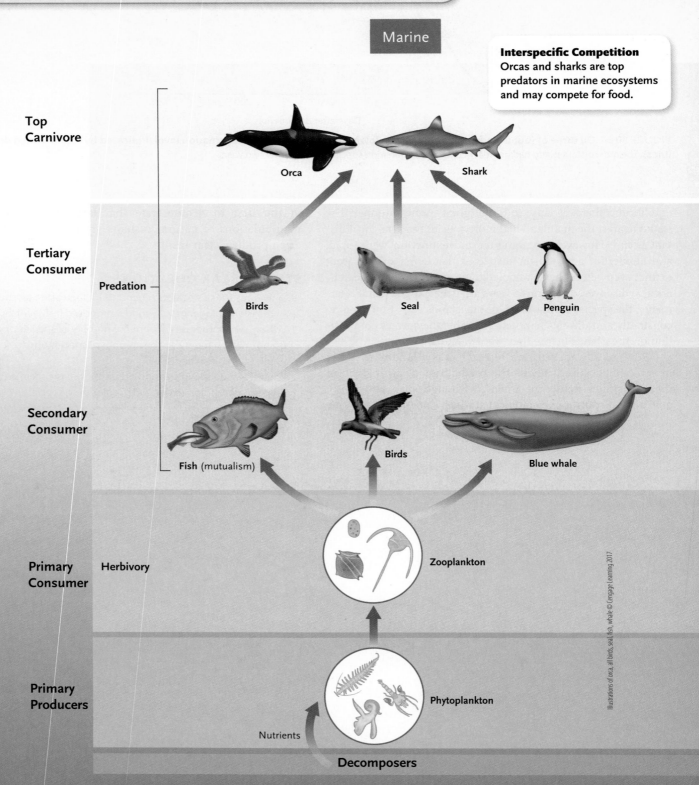

Marine

Interspecific Competition
Orcas and sharks are top predators in marine ecosystems and may compete for food.

Top Carnivore

Orca   Shark

Tertiary Consumer

Predation

Birds   Seal   Penguin

Secondary Consumer

Fish (mutualism)   Birds   Blue whale

Primary Consumer   Herbivory

Zooplankton

Primary Producers

Phytoplankton

Nutrients

Decomposers

Illustrations of orca, all birds, seal, fish, whale © Cengage Learning 2017

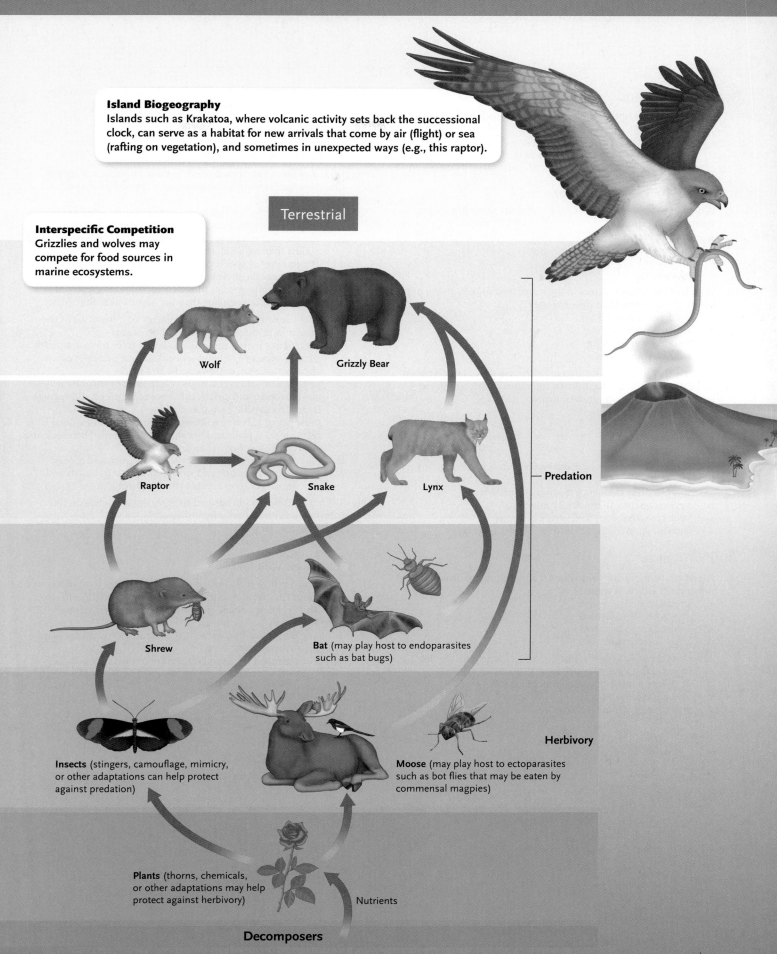

Island Biogeography
Islands such as Krakatoa, where volcanic activity sets back the successional clock, can serve as a habitat for new arrivals that come by air (flight) or sea (rafting on vegetation), and sometimes in unexpected ways (e.g., this raptor).

Terrestrial

Interspecific Competition
Grizzlies and wolves may compete for food sources in marine ecosystems.

Wolf

Grizzly Bear

Predation

Raptor

Snake

Lynx

Shrew

Bat (may play host to endoparasites such as bat bugs)

Herbivory

Insects (stingers, camouflage, mimicry, or other adaptations can help protect against predation)

Moose (may play host to ectoparasites such as bot flies that may be eaten by commensal magpies)

Plants (thorns, chemicals, or other adaptations may help protect against herbivory)

Nutrients

Decomposers

Recall/Understand

1. According to the optimal foraging theory, which of the following do predators do?
   a. always eat the largest prey possible
   b. always eat the prey that are easiest to catch
   c. choose prey based on the costs of consuming it compared to the energy it provides
   d. eat plants when animal prey is scarce

2. Which of these terms refers to the use of the same limiting resource by two species?
   a. brood parasitism
   b. exploitative competition
   c. symbiosis
   d. mutualism

3. Which of these terms refers to the range of resources that a population of one species can possibly use?
   a. fundamental niche
   b. realized niche
   c. resource partitioning
   d. relative abundance

4. Bacteria that live in the human intestine assist human digestion and eat nutrients that the human consumes. Which of these terms best describes this relationship?
   a. commensalism
   b. mutualism
   c. endoparasitism
   d. ectoparasitism

5. Which type of community disturbance causes species richness to be the highest?
   a. intermediate frequency and severe intensity
   b. very frequent and moderate intensity
   c. very rare frequency and severe intensity
   d. intermediate frequency and moderate intensity

Apply/Analyze

6. Adaptations in molar (tooth) structure of sympatric mammals may reflect which of these factors?
   a. predation
   b. character displacement
   c. interference competition
   d. cryptic coloration

7. Which of these statements best describes a keystone species?
   a. It is usually a primary producer.
   b. It always plays a critically important role.
   c. It is always a predator.
   d. It is usually the most abundant.

8. Which term refers to a community's change in species composition from bare and lifeless rock to climax vegetation?
   a. competition
   b. secondary succession
   c. primary succession
   d. facilitation

9. Which of these statements refers to the equilibrium theory of island biogeography prediction about the number of species found on an island?
   a. The number of species found on an island increases steadily until it equals the number in the mainland species pool.
   b. The number of species found on an island is greater on large islands than on small ones.
   c. The number of species found on an island is smaller on islands near the mainland than on distant islands.
   d. The number of species found on an island is greater for islands near the equator than for islands near the poles.

10. Consider the retreat of glaciers at Glacier Bay. In which of the following orders did primary succession occur?
    a. presence of lichen and mosses; larger trees replace smaller shrubs; presence of hemlock and spruce; presence of shrubby willows, cottonwoods, and alders
    b. presence of lichen and mosses; presence of shrubby willows, cottonwoods, and alders; presence of hemlock and spruce; larger trees replace smaller shrubs
    c. presence of shrubby willows, cottonwoods, and alders; larger trees replace smaller shrubs; presence of hemlock and spruce; presence of lichen and mosses
    d. presence of shrubby willows, cottonwoods, and alders; presence of hemlock and spruce; presence of lichen and mosses; larger trees replace smaller shrubs

11. Which of these people has had the greatest influence on the intermediate disturbance hypothesis?
    a. Charles Darwin
    b. Jane Lubchenco
    c. Joseph Connell
    d. Robert Whittaker

12. A fly and a yellow jacket resemble each other. If Henry Bates were told about this, what might you reasonably expect him to say?
    a. This is only a coincidence resulting from a mutation.
    b. Neither fly nor yellow jacket is venomous.
    c. The fly is most likely harmful because it resembles a venomous yellow jacket.
    d. The harmless fly resembles the venomous yellow jacket.

Create/Evaluate

13. In the table below, the letters refer to four communities, and the numbers indicate how many individuals were recorded for each of five species in those communities. Which of the four communities has the highest species diversity?

	Species 1	Species 2	Species 3	Species 4	Species 5
a.	80	10	10	0	0
b.	25	25	25	25	0
c.	0	4	6	8	80
d.	20	20	20	20	20

14. Compare realized niche and fundamental niche.

15. Describe Gause's experiments and explain the principle behind their results.

Chapter Roadmap

Ecosystems

Ecosystems are based on connections among the diversity of species comprising the systems. Ecosystems can be studied by following the movement of energy from one level to another.

31.1 Connections Within and Among Ecosystems

Natural systems provide many examples of biological magnification. DDT, mercury, and pesticides are examples of contaminants that undergo biological magnification.

From Chapter 30

31.2 Ecosystems and Energy

Food webs define the pathways by which energy and nutrients move through an ecosystem's biotic components.

31.3 Nutrient Cycling in Ecosystems

The availability of nutrients is as important to ecosystem function as the input of energy. Earth is essentially a closed system with respect to matter; nutrients constantly circulate between biotic and abiotic organisms.

To Chapter 36

31.4 Carbon: A Disrupted Cycle

CO_2 and other compounds act like a pane of glass in a greenhouse, trapping much of their energy as heat. The rising atmospheric levels of CO_2 could change the composition and dynamics of communities.

31.5 Ecosystem Modelling

Ecologists use modelling to make predictions about how an ecosystem will respond to specific changes in physical factors, energy flow, or nutrient availability.

31.6 Scale, Ecosystems, Species

The complex interactions between and among species combine with abiotic and biotic factors to produce even more complex situations.

31.7 Three Sample Ecosystems

Clumps of white seedlings on the floor of a cave in Cuba mark the areas under roosts used by Jamaican fruit bats. The seedlings and bat droppings are the main energy input into a totally dark system. Guano and seedlings support a community of cave-loving organisms, including detritivores as well as primary and secondary consumers.

Ecosystems

31

Why it matters . . . Photosynthetic organisms are absent from places with perpetual darkness, such as ocean depths and caves. In caves of the tropics and subtropics, bat droppings are the primary energetic (and biomass) inputs. Caves with large populations of active bats are showered with bat guano and often support considerable biomass, diversity, and well-developed food webs. Caves of the cooler temperate regions are typically too cold for active bats, lack bat guano-driven systems, and have much less diversity and biomass. Caves in glaciers and those with year-round ice support even lower levels of biomass. These are, effectively, refrigerated dark systems with very low biodiversity. In intermediate areas, probably best defined by temperature, there are cave ecosystems with low biomass and low energy.

Caves are interesting natural laboratories for studying ecosystems, communities, diversity, and energy flow. The topic is enriched by variation in cave size and the degree of isolation from the surrounding surface habitat. The spectrum of cave-dwelling organisms reflects levels of specialization for life in the dark. Troglobites are obligatory cave dwellers that complete their entire life cycles underground. Many troglobitic species lack eyes and pigments. Troglophiles, cave lovers, use caves but do not complete their life cycles underground. Trogloxenes are animals that visit caves. Worldwide, there are many species of troglobitic arthropods, fish, and amphibians; some bats and cave crickets are examples of troglophiles. Many other organisms, including humans, are trogloxenes, occasionally visiting caves. As usual in biology, the differences among categories are subjective.

a.

b.

FIGURE 31.1 Two species of cavefishes, one from Mexico (a) **and the other from the south central United States** (b)**.** Both species are troglobitic, obligatory, cave dwellers but they are classified in two different families (Characidae and Amblyopsidae respectively); they are not closely related in an evolutionary sense. These troglobites lack eyes and pigment.

Mexican cavefish (*Astyanax mexicanus*; **Figure 31.1a**) are often sold in pet stores. These fish occur in caves in Mexico where they live in a soup of bat droppings and the many organisms supported by this input. In some cases, cave and surface waters are connected and there is a spectrum of Mexican cavefish from individuals with well-developed eyes to eyeless fish. Mexican cavefish swim continuously propelled by lateral movements of their tail (caudal) fins. They appear to find food by random searching, an effective strategy when you live in an energy-rich soup of bat droppings.

Other species of cavefish occur elsewhere in the world. In the central United States (e.g., Kentucky, Indiana), there is no bat enrichment of the waters. The troglobitic southern cavefish (*Typhlichthys subterraneus*; Figure 31.1b) eat mainly aquatic crustaceans such as amphipods. These fish use specialized sensory cells to detect the vibrations generated by swimming prey. They are slow and deliberate swimmers, propelling themselves with enlarged pectoral fins.

Perhaps as interesting are communities of eukaryotes living in biofilms, in the dark, in rocks 1.4 km below Earth's surface. These communities were discovered in the depths of gold mines in South Africa. The fissure waters in which they live are up to 12 300 years old. These biofilm communities include protozoans and fungi as well as species of platyhelminths, rotifers, annelids, and arthropods. The organisms all appear to have originated from surface waters, and their populations are limited by access to food rather than oxygen.

Caves and deep subsurface biofilms are examples of life in the dark. These systems illustrate the diversity of life and the different situations in which some forms of life can thrive. The deep subsurface biofilms may set the stage for different approaches to searches for life on other planets.

Ecosystems are based on connections among the diversity of species comprising the systems. In a setting as large as planet Earth, it could be easy to dismiss the proposal that different species are connected in ecosystems. Ironically, the prevalence

and importance of the connections was forcefully illustrated by a poison named DDT (dichloro-diphenyl-trichloroethane).

Originally formulated in 1873, DDT's potential as an insecticide was recognized in 1939. DDT (**Figure 31.2**), the first of the chlorinated insecticides, was used extensively in some theatres of World War II. In 1943 in southern Italy, DDT was instrumental in controlling populations of lice that plagued Canadian troops there. Widespread application of DDT in Burma (now Myanmar) reduced the incidence of malaria by killing mosquitoes, the vectors of the disease. After World War II, the use of DDT spread rapidly, and the World Health Organization (WHO) credited this molecule with saving 25 million human lives (mainly through control of mosquitoes that carry malaria). As we shall see, DDT rapidly spread well beyond the locations where it had been used, directly illustrating connections among species.

Ecosystems can be studied by following the movement of energy from one level to another. Photosynthetic organisms form the energetic basis for ecosystems, providing sources of food for other organisms (usually animals). Levels of biomass at different trophic levels (primary producers; primary, secondary, and tertiary consumers) generally reflect the movement of energy.

FIGURE 31.2 A molecule of DDT

31.1 Connections Within and Among Ecosystems

At first, DDT seemed an ideal insecticide. In addition to being inexpensive to produce, it had low toxicity to mammals. For mammals, 300–500 mg/kg is the LD_{50} of DDT, the amount required to kill half the target population. But many insects subsequently developed immunity to DDT, reducing its effectiveness.

DDT is chemically stable and soluble in fat. Mammals store DDT in their fat rather than metabolizing it. The biological half-life of DDT is approximately eight years. It takes about eight years for a mammal to metabolize half the amount of DDT it has assimilated. DDT is released when fat is metabolized, so when mammals metabolize fat (e.g., when humans go on a diet), they are exposed to higher concentrations of DDT in their blood. DDT had dramatic effects on some birds, notably those higher up the food chain. Eggshell thinning was a consequence of exposure to DDT. Populations of birds such as peregrine falcons (*Falco peregrinus*) and bald eagles (*Haliaeetus leucocephalus*) plummeted.

DDT provided a graphic example of **biological magnification**. Consumers accumulate DDT from all the organisms they eat in their lifetimes. Primary consumers, such as herbivorous insects, may ingest relatively small amounts of DDT. But a songbird that eats many of these insects accumulates all the collected DDT consumed by its prey. A predator such as a raptor that eats songbirds accumulates even more DDT. This biomagnification occurs whether the food chain (web) is aquatic or terrestrial. The net effect on higher-level consumers is the same (**Figure 31.3**) and can be debilitating or lethal.

Natural systems provide many examples of biological magnification. In cities where DDT was used to control the spread of Dutch elm disease, songbirds died from DDT poisoning after eating insects that had been sprayed (whether or not they were involved in spreading the disease). In forests, DDT was used in an effort to control spruce budworm moths (*Choristoneura occidentalis*). Here the salmon died because runoff carried DDT into their streams and rivers, where their herbivorous prey consumed it.

Despite the ban on the use of DDT in the United States in 1973, in 1990, the California State Department of Health recommended closing a fishery off the coast of California because of DDT accumulating there. DDT discharged in industrial waste 20 years earlier was still moving through the ecosystem.

Biological magnification occurs with other contaminants. Mercury contamination is a common by-product of the pulp and paper industry. Minamata, the disease humans get from

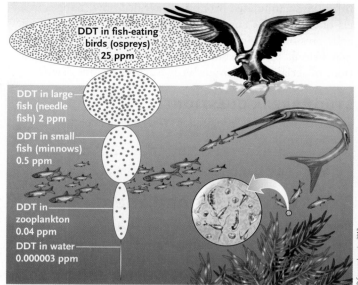

FIGURE 31.3 **Biological magnification.** In this marine food web in northeastern North America, DDT concentration (measured in parts per million, ppm) was magnified nearly 10 million times between zooplankton and the osprey (*Pandion haliaetus*).

DDT in fish-eating birds (ospreys) 25 ppm

DDT in large fish (needle fish) 2 ppm

DDT in small fish (minnows) 0.5 ppm

DDT in zooplankton 0.04 ppm

DDT in water 0.000003 ppm

© Cengage Learning 2017.

mercury poisoning, is usually linked to the consumption of fish taken from contaminated watersheds. Eating fish contaminated with mercury can result in mercury concentrations in people's hair (0.9–94 mg/kg) and in otters' fur (*Lontra canadensis*; 0.49–54.37 mg/kg). In southern Ontario, hair of bats that eat insects that emerge from mercury-contaminated sediments contain concentrations up to 13 mg/kg. These data illustrate that fish are not essential to this chain of biomagnification.

Since 1985, the use of DDT has been totally banned in Canada, and it is now banned in many other countries. But DDT is still produced in countries such as the United States, and still used where malaria is a prominent problem because the ecological costs of DDT are considered secondary to the importance of controlling the mosquitoes. By the early 1970s, cetaceans in the waters around Antarctica had DDT in their body fat even though DDT had never been used there. The movement of DDT up the food chain and through food webs demonstrated the interconnections in biological systems. The movement of DDT also provides a graphic demonstration of the transfer of materials from one trophic level to another.

Removing DDT from the arsenal of products used to control insects had other impacts. For example, an upsurge in the number of houses, apartments, and hotel rooms infested by bedbugs (*Cimex lectularius*). DDT had been very effective in the control of bedbugs but, in its absence, populations of these insects have rebounded, renewing old challenges that our grandparents experienced.

Evidence for the impact of pesticides often comes from unexpected sources. An excellent example is the accumulation of chimney swift (*Chaetura pelagica*) droppings at the bottom of a chimney in Kingston, Ontario. As their name implies, chimney swifts often nest in chimneys, and analysis of samples from the accumulated droppings revealed how changes in levels of insecticides coincided with changes in the birds' diets and, presumably, in populations of their prey. This research may help us to understand the reasons for declines in populations of aerial insectivorous birds (such as chimney swifts).

STUDY BREAK QUESTION

1. What is biological magnification? What does it imply about ecosystems?

31.2 Ecosystems and Energy

Ecosystems receive input of energy from an external source, usually the Sun. Energy flows through an ecosystem but, as dictated by the laws of thermodynamics (see Chapter 3), much of it is lost without being used by organisms. In contrast, materials cycle between living and nonliving reservoirs, both locally and on a global scale. The flow of energy through, and the cycling of materials around, an ecosystem make resident organisms highly dependent on one another and on their physical surroundings.

Food webs define the pathways by which energy and nutrients move through an ecosystem's biotic components. In most ecosystems, nutrients and energy move simultaneously through a grazing food web and a detrital food web (**Figure 31.4**). The grazing food web includes the producer, herbivore, and secondary consumer trophic levels. The detrital food web includes detritivores and decomposers. Because detritivores and decomposers subsist on the remains and waste products of organisms at every trophic level, the two food webs are closely interconnected. Detritivores also contribute to the grazing food web when carnivores eat them.

All organisms in a particular trophic level are the same number of energy transfers away from the ecosystem's ultimate energy source. Photosynthetic plants are one energy transfer removed from sunlight, herbivores (primary consumers) are two, secondary consumers are three, and tertiary consumers are four.

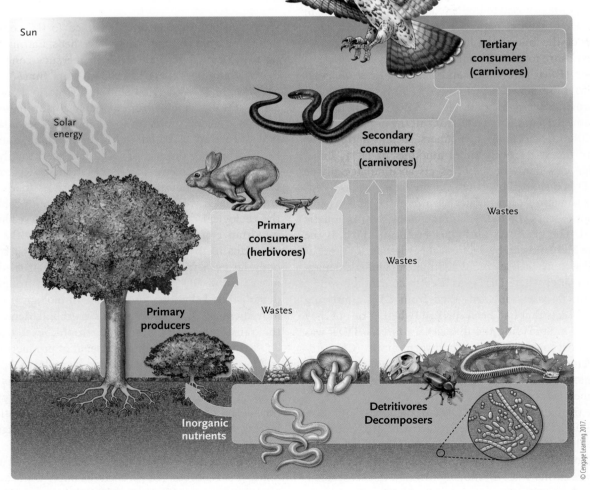

FIGURE 31.4 Grazing and detrital food webs. Energy and nutrients move through two parallel food webs in most ecosystems. The grazing food web includes producers, herbivores, and carnivores. The detrital food web includes detritivores and decomposers. Each box in this diagram represents many species, and each arrow represents many arrows.

31.2a Primary Productivity Involves Fixing Carbon

Almost all life on Earth depends directly or indirectly on the input of solar energy. Every minute of every day, Earth's atmosphere intercepts roughly 80 kJ (kilojoules) of energy per square metre (see Chapter 1). About half that energy is absorbed, scattered, or reflected by gases, dust, water vapour, and clouds before it reaches the planet's surface (see *The Purple Pages*). Most energy reaching the surface falls on bodies of water or bare ground, where it is absorbed as heat or reflected back into the atmosphere. Reflected energy warms the atmosphere. Only a small percentage contacts primary producers, and most of that energy evaporates water, driving transpiration in plants (see Chapter 6).

Ultimately, photosynthesis converts less than 1% of the solar energy arriving at Earth's surface into chemical energy. But primary producers still capture enough energy to produce an average of several kilograms of dry plant material per square metre per year. On a global scale, they produce more than 150 billion tonnes of new biological material annually. Some of the solar energy that producers convert into chemical energy is transferred to consumers at higher trophic levels.

The rate at which producers convert solar energy into chemical energy is an ecosystem's **gross primary productivity**. But, like other organisms, producers use energy for their own maintenance functions. After deducting energy used for these functions (see Chapter 5), the remaining chemical energy is the ecosystem's **net primary productivity**. In most ecosystems, net primary productivity is 50%–90% of gross primary productivity. In other words, producers use between 10% and 50% of the energy they capture for their own respiration.

Ecologists usually measure primary productivity in units of energy captured ($kJ/m^2/year$) or in units of biomass created ($kg/m^2/year$). **Biomass** is the dry mass of biological material per unit area or volume of habitat. Do not confuse an ecosystem's productivity with its **standing crop biomass**, the total dry mass of plants present at a given time. Net primary productivity is the *rate* at which the standing crop produces *new* biomass (see Chapter 6).

Energy captured by plants is stored in biological molecules, mostly carbohydrates, lipids, and proteins. Ecologists can convert units of biomass into units of energy or vice versa as long as they know the total amounts of carbohydrate, protein, and lipid in a sample of biological material. For reference, 1 g of carbohydrate and 1 g of protein each contains about 17.5 kJ of energy. Thus, net primary productivity indexes the rate at which producers accumulate energy as well as the rate at which new biomass is added to an ecosystem. Ecologists measure changes in biomass to estimate productivity because it is far easier to measure biomass than energy content. New biomass takes at least three forms, including:

- growth of existing producers,
- creation of new producers by reproduction, and
- storage of energy as carbohydrates.

Because herbivores eat all three forms of new biomass, net primary productivity also measures how much new energy is available for primary consumers.

The potential rate of photosynthesis in any ecosystem is proportional to the intensity and duration of sunlight, which varies geographically and seasonally (see Chapter 5, Chapter 6, and *The Purple Pages*). Sunlight is most intense and day length is least variable near the equator. In contrast, the intensity of sunlight is weakest and day length is most variable near the poles. This means that producers at the equator can photosynthesize for nearly 12 hours a day, every day of the year, whereas near the poles, photosynthesis is virtually impossible during the long dark winter. In summer, however, photosynthesis occurs virtually around the clock.

Sunlight is not the only factor influencing the rate of primary productivity. Temperature and the availability of water and nutrients also affect this rate. Many of the world's **deserts** receive plenty of sunshine but have low rates of productivity because water is in short supply and the soil is poor in nutrients. Mean annual primary productivity varies greatly on a global scale (**Figure 31.5**), reflecting variations in these environmental factors (see *The Purple Pages*).

On a finer geographic scale, within a particular terrestrial ecosystem, mean annual net productivity often increases with the availability of water (**Figure 31.6**). In systems with sufficient water, a shortage of mineral nutrients may be limiting. All plants need specific ratios of macronutrients and micronutrients for maintenance and photosynthesis (see Chapter 6). But plants withdraw nutrients from soil, and if nutrient concentration drops below a critical level, photosynthesis may decrease or stop altogether. In every ecosystem, one nutrient inevitably runs

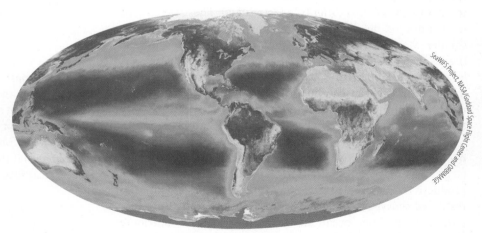

FIGURE 31.5 Global variation in primary productivity. Satellite data from 2002 provide a visual portrait of net primary productivity across Earth's surface. High-productivity regions on land are dark green; low-productivity regions are yellow. For aquatic environments, the highest productivity is red, down through orange, yellow, green, blue, and purple (lowest).

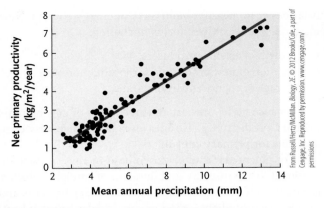

FIGURE 31.6 **Water and net primary productivity.** Mean annual precipitation at 100 sites in the Great Plains of North America. These data include only above-ground productivity.

From Russell/Hertz/McMillan. *Biology, 2E.* © 2012 Brooks/Cole, a part of Cengage, Inc. Reproduced by permission. www.cengage.com/permissions

out before the supplies of other nutrients are exhausted. The element in shortest supply is a **limiting nutrient** because its absence curtails productivity. Productivity in agricultural fields is subject to the same constraints as productivity in natural ecosystems. Farmers increase productivity by irrigating (adding water to) and fertilizing (adding nutrients to) their crops.

In freshwater and marine ecosystems, depth of water and combined availability of sunlight and nutrients govern the rate of primary productivity. Productivity is high in near-shore ecosystems, where sunlight penetrates shallow nutrient-rich waters. Kelp beds and coral reefs along temperate and tropical marine coastlines, respectively, are among the most productive ecosystems on Earth (**Table 31.1**). In contrast, productivity is low in the open waters of a large lake or ocean. There, sunlight penetrates only the upper layers, and nutrients sink to the bottom; thus, the two requirements for photosynthesis—sunlight and nutrients—are available in different places.

Although ecosystems vary in their rates of primary productivity, these differences are not always proportional to variations in their standing crop biomass (see Table 31.1). For example, biomass amounts in temperate deciduous forests and **temperate grasslands** differ by a factor of 20. The difference in their rates of net primary productivity, however, is much smaller. Most biomass in trees is present in non-photosynthetic tissues such as wood, so their ratio of productivity to biomass is low (12 kg/m^2/300 kg/m^2 = 0.04). Grasslands do not accumulate much biomass because annual mortality, herbivores, and fires remove plant material as it is produced. Here the productivity to biomass ratio is much higher (6.0 kg/m^2/16 kg/m^2 = 0.375).

Some ecosystems contribute more than others to overall net primary productivity (**Figure 31.7**). Ecosystems covering large areas make substantial total contributions, even if their productivity per unit area is low. Conversely, geographically restricted ecosystems make large contributions if their productivity is high. Open ocean and tropical rainforests contribute about equally to total global productivity, but for different reasons. Open oceans have low productivity, but they cover nearly two-thirds of Earth's surface. Tropical rainforests are highly productive but cover only a relatively small area.

TABLE 31.1	Standing Crop Biomass and Net Primary Productivity of Different Ecosystems	
Ecosystem	Mean Standing Crop Biomass (kg/m^2)	Mean Net Primary Productivity (kg/m^2/y)
Terrestrial Ecosystems		
Tropical rainforest	450	22.0
Tropical deciduous forest	350	16.0
Temperate rainforest	350	13.0
Temperate deciduous forest	300	12.0
Savannah	40	9.0
Boreal forest (**taiga**)	200	8.0
Woodland and shrubland	60	7.0
Agricultural land	10	6.5
Temperate grassland	16	6.0
Tundra and Alpine tundra	6.0	1.4
Desert and thornwoods	7.0	0.9
Extreme desert, rock, sand, ice	0.2	0.03
Freshwater Ecosystems		
Swamp and marsh	150	20
Lake and stream	0.2	2.5
Marine Ecosystems		
Open ocean	0.03	1.3
Upwelling zones	0.2	5.0
Continental shelf	0.1	3.6
Kelp beds and reefs	20	25
Estuaries	10	15
World Total	**36**	**3.3**

Source: Based on Whittaker, R.H. 1975. *Communities and Ecosystems.* 2nd ed. Macmillan.

Net primary productivity ultimately supports all consumers in grazing and detrital food webs. Consumers in the grazing food web eat some biomass at every trophic level except the highest. Uneaten biomass eventually dies and passes into detrital food webs. Moreover, consumers assimilate only a portion of the material they ingest, and unassimilated material passed as feces also supports detritivores and decomposers.

31.2b Secondary Productivity: Animals Eating Plants

As energy is transferred from producers to consumers, some is stored in new consumer biomass, **secondary productivity**. Nevertheless, two factors cause energy to be lost from the

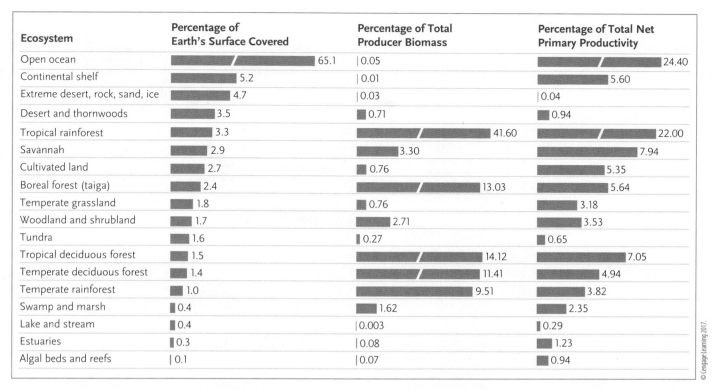

Ecosystem	Percentage of Earth's Surface Covered	Percentage of Total Producer Biomass	Percentage of Total Net Primary Productivity
Open ocean	65.1	0.05	24.40
Continental shelf	5.2	0.01	5.60
Extreme desert, rock, sand, ice	4.7	0.03	0.04
Desert and thornwoods	3.5	0.71	0.94
Tropical rainforest	3.3	41.60	22.00
Savannah	2.9	3.30	7.94
Cultivated land	2.7	0.76	5.35
Boreal forest (taiga)	2.4	13.03	5.64
Temperate grassland	1.8	0.76	3.18
Woodland and shrubland	1.7	2.71	3.53
Tundra	1.6	0.27	0.65
Tropical deciduous forest	1.5	14.12	7.05
Temperate deciduous forest	1.4	11.41	4.94
Temperate rainforest	1.0	9.51	3.82
Swamp and marsh	0.4	1.62	2.35
Lake and stream	0.4	0.003	0.29
Estuaries	0.3	0.08	1.23
Algal beds and reefs	0.1	0.07	0.94

© Cengage Learning 2017.

FIGURE 31.7 Biomass and net primary productivity. An ecosystem's percentage coverage of Earth's surface is not proportional to its contribution to total biomass of producers or its contribution to the total net primary productivity.

ecosystem every time it flows from one trophic level to another. First, animals use much of the energy they assimilate for maintenance and locomotion rather than for production of new biomass. Second, as dictated by the second law of thermodynamics, no biochemical reaction is 100% efficient, so some of the chemical energy liberated by cellular respiration is converted to heat, which most organisms do not use.

31.2c Ecological Efficiency Is Measured by Use of Energy

Ecological efficiency is the ratio of net productivity at one trophic level to net productivity at the trophic level below. If plants in an ecosystem have a net primary productivity of 1.0 kg/m^2/year of new tissue, and the herbivores that eat these plants produce 0.1 kg of new tissue per square metre per year, the ecological efficiency of the herbivores is 10%. The efficiencies of three processes (harvesting food, assimilating ingested energy, and producing new biomass) determine the ecological efficiencies of consumers.

Harvesting efficiency is the ratio of the energy content of food consumed to the energy content of food available. Predators harvest food efficiently when prey are abundant and easy to capture (see Chapter 30).

Assimilation efficiency is the ratio of the energy absorbed from consumed food to the total energy content of the food. Because animal prey is relatively easy to digest, carnivores absorb between 60% and 90% of the energy in their food.

Assimilation efficiency is lower for prey with indigestible parts such as bones or exoskeletons. Herbivores assimilate only 15% to 80% of the energy they consume because cellulose is not very digestible. Herbivores lacking cellulose-digesting systems are on the low end of the scale, whereas those that can digest cellulose are at the higher end.

Production efficiency is the ratio of the energy content of new tissue produced to the energy assimilated from food. Production efficiency varies with maintenance costs. Endothermic animals often use less than 10% of their assimilated energy for growth and reproduction because they use energy to generate body heat (see Chapter 42). Ectothermic animals channel more than 50% of their assimilated energy into new biomass.

The overall ecological efficiency of most organisms is 5%–20%. As a rule of thumb, only about 10% of energy accumulated at one trophic level is converted into biomass at the next higher trophic level. This is illustrated by energy transfers at Silver Springs, Florida (**Figure 31.8**), an ecosystem studied for many years. Producers in the Silver Springs ecosystem convert 1.2% of the solar energy they intercept into chemical energy (represented by 86 986 kJ/m^2/year of gross primary productivity). However, plants use about two-thirds of this energy for respiration, leaving a net primary productivity, one-third of which is to be included in new plant biomass. All consumers in the grazing food web (on the right in Figure 31.8) ultimately depend on this energy source, which diminishes with each transfer between trophic levels. Energy is lost to respiration and export at each trophic level. In addition, organic wastes

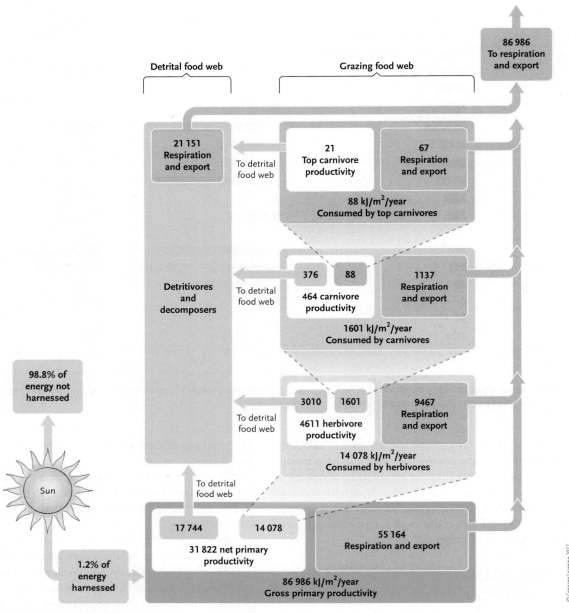

FIGURE 31.8 Energy flow through the Silver Springs ecosystem

and uneaten biomass represent substantial energy that flows into the detrital food web (on the left in Figure 31.8). To determine the ecological efficiency of any trophic level, we divide its productivity by the productivity of the level below it. The ecological efficiency of midlevel carnivores at Silver Springs is 10.06%: 464 kJ/m²/year/4611 kJ/m²/year.

31.2d Pyramids in Ecosystems: Energy, Biomass, and Numbers

As energy works its way up a food web, energy losses are multiplied in successive energy transfers (**Figure 31.9**). Consider a hypothetical example with ecological efficiency of 10% for all consumers. Assume that the plants in a small field annually

produce new tissues containing 100 kJ of energy. Because only 10% of that energy is transferred to new herbivore biomass, the 100 kJ in plants produces 10 kJ of new herbivorous insects, 1 kJ of new songbirds that eat insects, and only 0.1 kJ of new falcons that eat songbirds. About 0.1% of the energy from primary productivity remains after three trophic levels of transfer. If the energy available to each trophic level is depicted graphically, the result is a **pyramid of energy**, with primary producers on the bottom and higher-level consumers on the top (Figure 31.9).

The low ecological efficiencies that characterize most energy transfers illustrate one advantage of eating "lower on the food chain." This reality accounts for major adaptive radiations of lineages of animals where ancestors were secondary

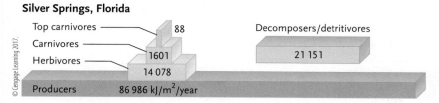

Silver Springs, Florida

FIGURE 31.9 **Pyramids of energy.** The pyramid of energy for Silver Springs, Florida, shows that the amount of energy (kJ/m²/year) passing through each trophic level decreases as it moves up the food web.

consumers that then switched to being primary consumers. Good examples of such radiations occur, for example, among insects, fish, dinosaurs, and mammals.

Humans digest and assimilate meat more efficiently than vegetables. But we could feed more people if we ate more primary producers rather than secondary consumers. Being a secondary consumer means passing carbohydrates through another trophic level, such as cattle or chickens. Production of animal protein is costly because much of the energy fed to livestock is used for their own maintenance rather than production of new biomass. But despite the economic and health-related logic of a more vegetarian diet, changing our eating habits alone will not eliminate food shortages or the frequency of malnutrition. Many regions of Africa, Australia, North America, and South America support vegetation that is suitable only for grazing by large herbivores. These areas could not produce significant quantities of edible grains and vegetables without significant additions of water and fertilizer (see Chapter 36).

Inefficiency of energy transfer from one trophic level to the next has profound effects on ecosystem structure. Ecologists illustrate these effects in diagrams called **ecological pyramids**. Trophic levels are drawn as stacked blocks, with the size of each block proportional to the energy, biomass, or numbers of organisms present. Pyramids of energy typically have wide bases and narrow tops (Figure 31.9) because each trophic level contains only about 10% as much energy as the trophic level below it.

Progressive reduction in productivity at higher trophic levels usually establishes a **pyramid of biomass (Figure 31.10)**. The biomass at each trophic level is proportional to the amount of chemical energy temporarily stored there. Thus, in terrestrial ecosystems, the total mass of producers is generally greater than the total mass of herbivores, which, in turn, is greater than the total mass of predators (Figure 31.10a). Populations of top predators, from killer whales to lions and crocodiles, contain too little biomass and energy to support another trophic level; thus, they have no nonhuman predators.

Freshwater and marine ecosystems sometimes exhibit inverted pyramids of biomass (Figure 31.10b). In the open waters of a lake or ocean, primary consumers (zooplankton) eat primary producers (phytoplankton) almost as soon as they are produced. As a result, the standing crop of primary consumers at any time is actually larger than the standing crop of primary producers. Food webs in these ecosystems are stable because producers have exceptionally high **turnover rates**. In other words, producers divide and their populations grow so quickly that feeding by zooplankton does not endanger their populations or reduce the producers' productivity. However, on an annual basis, the cumulative total biomass of primary producers far outweighs that of primary consumers.

The reduction of energy and biomass affects sizes of populations of organisms at the top of a food web. Top predators can be relatively large animals, so the limited biomass present in the highest trophic levels is concentrated in relatively few animals **(Figure 31.11)**. The extremely narrow top of this **pyramid of numbers** has grave implications for conservation biology (see Chapter 28). Top predators tend to be large animals with small population sizes. And because each individual must patrol a large area to find sufficient food, members of a population are often widely dispersed within their habitats. As a result, they are subject to genetic drift (see Chapter 17) and are highly sensitive to hunting, habitat destruction, and random events that can lead to extinction. Top predators may also suffer from the accumulation of poisonous materials that move through food webs (biomagnification). Even predators that feed below the top trophic level often suffer the ill effects of human activities. Consumers sometimes regulate ecosystem processes.

Numerous abiotic factors, such as the intensity and duration of sunlight, rainfall, temperature, and the availability of nutrients, significantly affect primary productivity. Primary productivity, in turn, profoundly affects the populations of herbivores

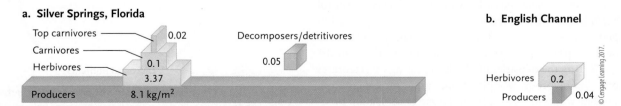

FIGURE 31.10 **Pyramids of biomass. (a)** The pyramid of standing crop biomass for Silver Springs is bottom heavy, as it is for most ecosystems. **(b)** Some marine ecosystems, such as that in the English Channel, have an inverted pyramid of biomass because producers are quickly eaten by primary consumers. Only the producer and herbivore trophic levels are illustrated here. The data for both pyramids are given in kilograms per square metre of dry biomass.

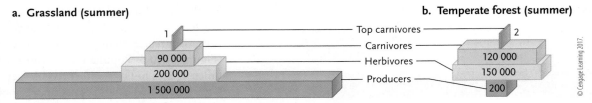

a. Grassland (summer)

1	Top carnivores
90 000	Carnivores
200 000	Herbivores
1 500 000	Producers

b. Temperate forest (summer)

2	
120 000	
150 000	
200	

© Cengage Learning 2017.

FIGURE 31.11 Pyramids of numbers. (a) The pyramid of numbers (numbers of individuals per 1000 m²) for temperate grasslands is bottom heavy because individual producers are small and very numerous. **(b)** The pyramid of numbers for forests may have a narrow base because herbivorous insects usually outnumber the producers, many of which are large trees. Data for both pyramids were collected during summer. Detritivores and decomposers (soil animals and microorganisms) are not included because they are difficult to count. Parasites are another example of an inverted pyramid.

and the predators that feed on them. But what effect does feeding by these consumers have on primary productivity?

Consumers sometimes influence rates of primary productivity, especially in ecosystems with low species diversity and relatively few trophic levels. Food webs in lake ecosystems depend primarily on the productivity of phytoplankton (**Figure 31.12**). Phytoplankton, in turn, are eaten by herbivorous zooplankton, which themselves consumed by predatory invertebrates and fishes. The top nonhuman carnivore in these food webs is usually a predatory fish.

Herbivorous zooplankton play a central role in regulation of lake ecosystems. Small zooplankton species consume only small phytoplankton. Thus, when small zooplankton are especially abundant, large phytoplankton escape predation and survive, and the lake's primary productivity is high. Large zooplankton are voracious, eating both small and large phytoplankton. When large zooplankton are abundant, they reduce the overall biomass of phytoplankton and lower the ecosystem's primary productivity.

In this **trophic cascade**, predator–prey effects reverberate through population interactions at two or more trophic levels. Feeding by plankton-eating invertebrates and fishes directly affects populations of herbivorous zooplankton and indirectly affects populations of phytoplankton (the ecosystem's primary producers). Invertebrate predators prefer small zooplankton, and when they dominate an ecosystem, large zooplankton become more abundant. In turn, the larger zooplankton eat many phytoplankton and cause a decrease in productivity in the ecosystem. But plankton-eating fishes prefer to eat large zooplankton (Figure 31.12), so when they are abundant, small zooplankton become the dominant herbivores. This leads to more numerous large phytoplankton, which in turn raises the lake's productivity.

Large predatory fishes may add an additional level of control to the system because they eat and thus regulate the population sizes of plankton-eating invertebrates and fishes. The effects of feeding by the top predator can cascade downward through the food web, affecting the densities of plankton-eating invertebrates and fishes, herbivorous zooplankton, and phytoplankton. Research in Norway with brown trout (*Salmo trutta*), a top predator, and Arctic char (*Salvelinus alpinus*), the prey, demonstrated how culling prey can promote the recovery of top predators. Removal of older, stunted, prey individual Arctic char from Lake

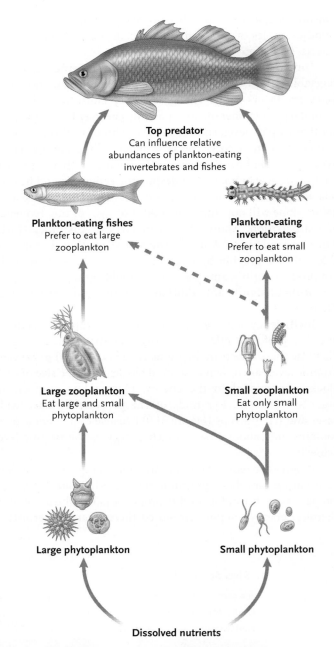

Top predator
Can influence relative abundances of plankton-eating invertebrates and fishes

Plankton-eating fishes
Prefer to eat large zooplankton

Plankton-eating invertebrates
Prefer to eat small zooplankton

Large zooplankton
Eat large and small phytoplankton

Small zooplankton
Eat only small phytoplankton

Large phytoplankton

Small phytoplankton

Dissolved nutrients

FIGURE 31.12 Consumer regulation of primary productivity.
A simplified food web illustrates that lake ecosystems have relatively few trophic levels. The effects of feeding by top carnivores can cascade downward, exerting an indirect effect on the phytoplankton and thus on primary productivity.

Takvatn resulted in an increase in the availability of prey and recovery of the predator. Here brown trout were the top predators. Culling Arctic char, an introduced species, rejuvenated the lake ecosystem. This example shows how addition of a fish-eating fish to a lake successfully restored ecosystem balance.

STUDY BREAK QUESTIONS

1. What are primary producers? Secondary producers? Detritivores?
2. What is gross primary productivity?
3. What is standing crop biomass?
4. What is a limiting nutrient?
5. What is secondary productivity?
6. What are the differences between harvesting efficiency, assimilation efficiency, and production efficiency?
7. What are the differences between energy, biomass, and numbers pyramids?
8. How is the pyramid for the English Channel different from that of a grassland community?
9. How do these pyramids relate to biomagnification?

31.3 Nutrient Cycling in Ecosystems

The availability of nutrients is as important to ecosystem function as the input of energy. Photosynthesis requires carbon, hydrogen, and oxygen, which producers acquire from water and air. Primary producers also need nitrogen, phosphorus, and other minerals. A deficiency in any of these minerals can reduce primary productivity.

Earth is essentially a closed system with respect to matter, even though cosmic dust enters the atmosphere. Thus, unlike energy, for which there is a constant cosmic input, virtually all the nutrients that will ever be available for biological systems are already present. Nutrient ions and molecules constantly circulate between the abiotic environment and living organisms in **biogeochemical cycles**. And, unlike energy, which flows through ecosystems and is gradually lost as heat, matter is conserved in biogeochemical cycles. Although there may be local shortages of specific nutrients, Earth's overall supplies of these chemical elements are never depleted or increased.

Nutrients take various forms as they pass through biogeochemical cycles. Materials such as carbon, nitrogen, and oxygen form gases that move through global atmospheric cycles. Geologic processes move other materials, such as phosphorus, through local sedimentary cycles, carrying them between dry land and the sea floor. Rocks, soil, water, and air are the reservoirs where mineral nutrients accumulate, sometimes for many years.

Ecologists use a **generalized compartment model** to describe nutrient cycling (**Figure 31.13**). Two criteria divide ecosystems into four compartments in which nutrients accumulate: (1) Nutrient molecules and ions are either *available* or *unavailable*, depending on whether they can be assimilated by organisms.

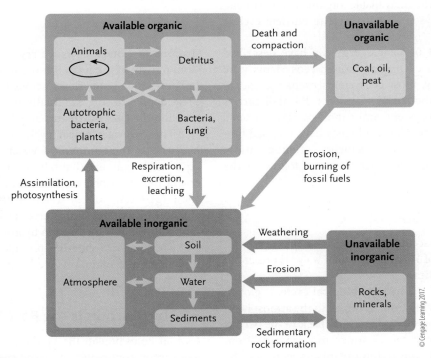

FIGURE 31.13 A generalized compartment model of nutrient cycling. Nutrients cycle through four major compartments within ecosystems. Processes that move nutrients from one compartment to another are indicated on the arrows. The circular arrow under "Animals" represents animal predation on other animals.

(2) Nutrients are present in either *organic* material, such as living or dead tissues of organisms, or *inorganic* material, such as rocks and soil. Minerals in dead leaves on the forest floor are in the available–organic compartment because they are in the remains of organisms that can be eaten by detritivores. Calcium ions in limestone rocks are in the unavailable–inorganic compartment because they are in a non-biological form that producers cannot assimilate.

Nutrients move rapidly within and between the available compartments. Living organisms are in the available–organic compartment, and whenever heterotrophs consume food, they recycle nutrients within that reservoir (indicated by the circular arrow in the upper left of Figure 31.13). Producers acquire nutrients from the air, soil, and water of the available–inorganic compartment. Consumers acquire nutrients from the available–inorganic compartment when they drink water or absorb mineral ions through their integument. Several processes routinely transfer nutrients from organisms to the available–inorganic compartment. Respiration releases carbon dioxide, moving both carbon and oxygen from the available–organic compartment to the available–inorganic compartment.

The exchange of materials into and out of the unavailable compartments is generally slow. Sedimentation, a long-term geologic process, converts ions and particles of the available–inorganic compartment into rocks of the unavailable–inorganic compartment. Materials are gradually returned to the available–inorganic compartment when rocks are uplifted and eroded or weathered. Similarly, over millions of years, the remains of organisms in the available–organic compartment were converted into the coal, oil, and peat of the unavailable–organic compartment. In many systems, fire plays an essential role in nutrient cycling (**Figure 31.14**).

Except for the input of solar energy, we have described energy flow and nutrient cycling as though ecosystems were closed systems. In reality, most ecosystems exchange energy and nutrients with neighbouring ecosystems. Rainfall carries nutrients into a forest ecosystem, and runoff carries nutrients from a forest into a lake or river. Ecologists have mapped biogeochemical cycles of important elements, often by using radioactively labelled molecules that they can follow in the environment.

31.3a Water Is the Staff of Life

Water is the universal intracellular solvent for biochemical reactions, but only a fraction of 1% of Earth's total water is present in biological systems at any time.

The cycling of water, the **hydrogeological cycle**, is global, with water molecules moving from oceans into the atmosphere, to land, through freshwater ecosystems, and back to the oceans (**Figure 31.15**). Solar energy causes water to evaporate from oceans, lakes, rivers, soil, and living organisms, entering the atmosphere as a vapour and remaining aloft as a gas, as

M. B. Fenton

FIGURE 31.14 A ghostly heap of ash starkly demonstrates the importance of fire in releasing materials, in this case locked up in a tree trunk. Regular fires are part of the cycle in ecosystems like this savanna in South Africa.

droplets in clouds, or as ice crystals. Water falls as precipitation, mostly in the form of rain and snow. When precipitation falls on land, water flows across the surface or percolates to great depths in soil, eventually reentering the ocean reservoir through the flow of streams and rivers.

The hydrogeological cycle maintains its global balance because the total amount of water entering the atmosphere is equal to the amount that falls as precipitation. Most water that enters the atmosphere evaporates from the oceans, which are the largest reservoir of water on the planet. A much smaller fraction evaporates from terrestrial ecosystems, and most of that is through transpiration by green plants.

Constant recirculation provides fresh water to terrestrial organisms and maintains freshwater ecosystems such as lakes and rivers.

31.3b Carbon Is the Backbone of Life

Carbon atoms provide the backbone of most biological molecules, and carbon compounds store the energy captured by photosynthesis (see Chapter 6). Carbon enters food webs when producers

a. The water cycle

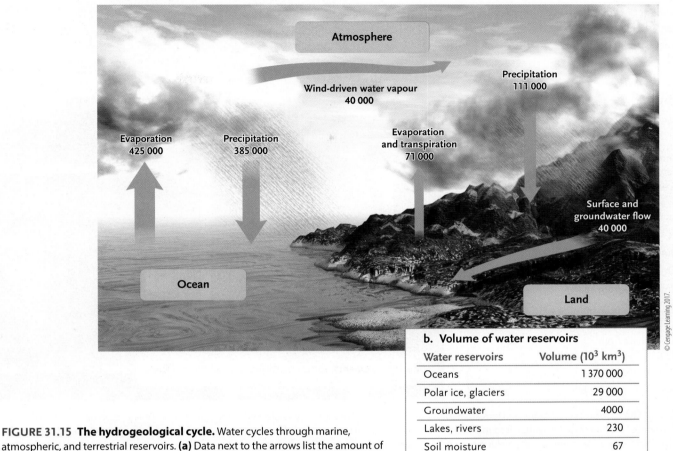

b. Volume of water reservoirs

Water reservoirs	Volume (10^3 km³)
Oceans	1 370 000
Polar ice, glaciers	29 000
Groundwater	4000
Lakes, rivers	230
Soil moisture	67
Atmosphere (water vapour)	14

FIGURE 31.15 The hydrogeological cycle. Water cycles through marine, atmospheric, and terrestrial reservoirs. **(a)** Data next to the arrows list the amount of water (in km³/year) moved among the reservoirs by various processes. **(b)** The oceans are by far the largest of the six major reservoirs of water on Earth.

convert atmospheric carbon dioxide (CO_2) into carbohydrates. Heterotrophs acquire carbon by eating other organisms or detritus. Although carbon moves somewhat independently in sea and on land, a common atmospheric pool of CO_2 creates a global **carbon cycle (Figure 31.16)**.

The largest reservoir of carbon is sedimentary rock, such as limestone. Rocks are in the unavailable–inorganic compartment, and they exchange carbon with living organisms at an exceedingly slow pace. Most available carbon is present as dissolved bicarbonate ions (HCO_3^-) in the ocean. Soil, atmosphere, and plant biomass are significant, but much smaller, reservoirs of available carbon. Atmospheric carbon is mostly in the form of molecular CO_2, a product of aerobic respiration. Volcanic eruptions also release small quantities of CO_2 into the atmosphere.

Carbon atoms sometimes leave organic compartments for long periods of time. Some organisms in marine food webs build shells and other hard parts by incorporating dissolved carbon into calcium carbonate ($CaCO_3$) and other insoluble salts. When shelled organisms die, they sink to the bottom and

are buried in sediments. Other animals, notably vertebrates, store calcium in bone. Insoluble carbon that accumulates as rock in deep sediments may remain buried for millions of years before tectonic uplifting brings it to the surface, where erosion and weathering dissolve sedimentary rocks and return carbon to an available form.

Carbon atoms are also transferred to the unavailable–organic compartment when soft-bodied organisms die and are buried in habitats where low oxygen concentration prevents decomposition. In the past, under suitable geologic conditions, these carbon-rich tissues were slowly converted to gas, petroleum, or coal, which we now use as fossil fuels. Human activities, especially burning fossil fuels, are transferring carbon into the atmosphere at an unnaturally high rate. The resulting change in the worldwide distribution of carbon is having profound consequences for Earth's atmosphere and climate, including a general warming of the climate and a rise in sea level.

Changes in land use can affect carbon cycles. An analysis of above-ground biomass at 45 forest sites in the

c. The global carbon cycle

a. Amount of carbon in major reservoirs

Carbon Reservoirs	Mass (10^{12} g)
Sediments and rocks	770 000 000
Ocean (dissolved forms)	397 000
Soil	15 000
Atmosphere	7 500
Biomass on land	7 150

b. Annual global carbon movement between reservoirs

Direction of Movement	Mass (10^{12} kg)
From atmosphere to plants (carbon fixation)	1200
From atmosphere to ocean	1070
To atmosphere from ocean	1050
To atmosphere from plants	600
To atmosphere from soil	600
To atmosphere from burning fossil fuel	50
To atmosphere from burning plants	20
To ocean from runoff	4
Burial in ocean sediments	1

Diffusion between atmosphere and ocean

Combustion of fossil fuels

Dissolved in ocean water (bicarbonate and carbonate)

Photosynthesis

Aerobic respiration

Marine food webs

Incorporation into sediments

Death, sedimentation

Uplifting over geological time

Marine sediments, including formations with fossil fuels

Sedimentation

FIGURE 31.16 The carbon cycle. Marine and terrestrial components of the global carbon cycle are linked through an atmospheric reservoir of carbon dioxide. **(a)** By far the largest amount of Earth's carbon is found in sediments and rocks. **(b)** Earth's atmosphere mediates most of the movement of carbon. **(c)** In this illustration of the carbon cycle, boxes identify major reservoirs, and labels on arrows identify the processes that cause carbon to move between reservoirs.

Neotropics was published in 2016. During the development of second-growth (secondary; **Figure 31.17**) forests, the rate of carbon uptake was 11 times higher than in old-growth forest. After 20 years, recovery of above-ground biomass averaged 122 Mg per hectare. These results have important implications for conservation and patterns of land use. Promoting

FIGURE 31.17 A Mayan temple emerges from partly cleared, second-growth forest in Belize. At the time the temple was built, about 800 years ago, much of the surrounding area would have been cleared for human habitation and agricultural operations.

regeneration and restoration of second-growth forest is an important positive strategy.

31.3c Nitrogen Is a Limiting Element

All organisms require nitrogen to construct nucleic acids, proteins, and other biological molecules (see Chapter 39). Earth's atmosphere had a high nitrogen concentration long before life began. Today, a global **nitrogen cycle** moves this element between the huge atmospheric pool of gaseous molecular nitrogen (N_2) and several much smaller pools of nitrogen-containing compounds in soils, marine and freshwater ecosystems, and living organisms (**Figure 31.18**).

Molecular nitrogen is abundant in the atmosphere, but triple covalent bonds bind its two atoms so tightly that most organisms cannot use it. Only certain microorganisms, volcanic action, and lightning can convert N_2 into ammonium (NH_4^+) and nitrate (NO_3^-) ions. This conversion is called **nitrogen fixation** (see Chapter 36). Once nitrogen is fixed, primary producers can incorporate it into biological molecules such as proteins and nucleic acids. Secondary consumers obtain nitrogen by consuming these molecules.

Several biochemical processes produce different nitrogen-containing compounds and thus move nitrogen through

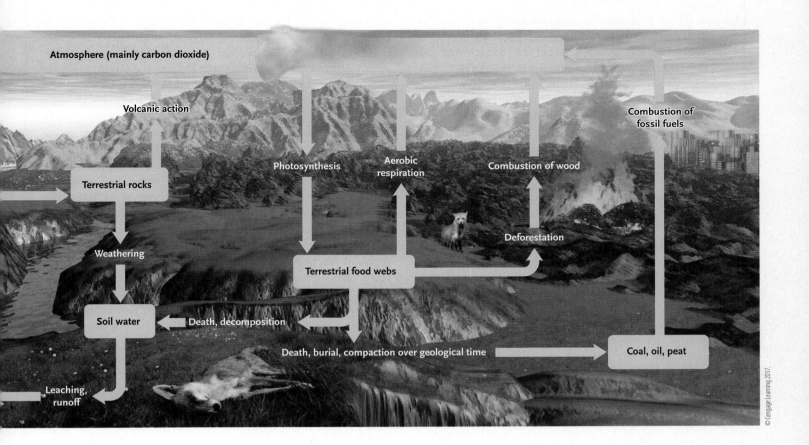

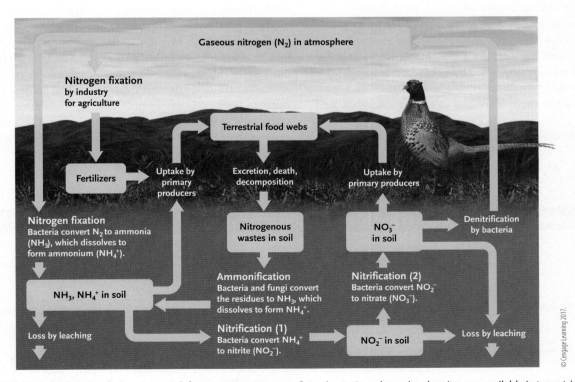

FIGURE 31.18 The nitrogen cycle in a terrestrial ecosystem. Nitrogen-fixing bacteria make molecular nitrogen available in terrestrial ecosystems. Other bacteria recycle nitrogen within the available–organic compartment through ammonification and two types of nitrification, converting organic wastes into ammonium ions and nitrates. Denitrification converts nitrate to molecular nitrogen, which returns to the atmosphere. Runoff carries nitrogen from terrestrial ecosystems into aquatic ecosystems, where it is recycled in freshwater and marine food webs.

ecosystems. These processes are nitrogen fixation, ammonification, nitrification, and denitrification (**Table 31.2**).

In nitrogen fixation, several kinds of microorganisms convert molecular nitrogen (N_2) to ammonium ions (NH_4^+). Certain bacteria, which collect molecular nitrogen from the air between soil particles, are the major nitrogen fixers in terrestrial ecosystems (see Table 31.2). The cyanobacteria partners in some lichens (see Chapter 25) also fix molecular nitrogen. Other cyanobacteria are important nitrogen fixers in aquatic ecosystems, whereas the water fern (genus *Azolla*) plays that role in rice paddies. Collectively, these organisms fix an astounding 200 million tonnes of nitrogen each year. Plants and other primary producers assimilate and use this nitrogen in the biosynthesis of amino acids, proteins, and nucleic acids, which then circulate through food webs.

Some plants, including legumes (such as beans and clover), alders (*Alnus* species), and some members of the rose family (Rosaceae), are mutualists with nitrogen-fixing bacteria. These plants acquire nitrogen from soils much more readily than plants that lack such mutualists. Although these plants have the competitive edge in nitrogen-poor soil, non-mutualistic species often displace them in nitrogen-rich soil. In an interesting twist on the usual predator–prey relationships, several species of flowering plants living in nitrogen-poor soils capture and digest insects.

In addition to nitrogen fixation, other biochemical processes make large quantities of nitrogen available to producers. **Ammonification** of detritus by bacteria and fungi converts organic nitrogen into ammonia (NH_3), which dissolves in water to produce ammonium ions (NH_4^+) that plants can assimilate. Some ammonia escapes into the atmosphere as a gas. **Nitrification** by certain bacteria produces nitrites (NO_2^-), which are then converted by other bacteria to usable nitrates (NO_3^-). All these compounds are water soluble, and water rapidly leaches them from soil into streams, lakes, and oceans.

Under conditions of low oxygen availability, **denitrification** by still other bacteria converts nitrites or nitrates into nitrous oxide (N_2O) and then into molecular nitrogen (N_2), which enters the atmosphere (see Table 31.2). This action can deplete supplies of soil nitrogen in waterlogged or otherwise poorly aerated environments, such as bogs and swamps.

In 1909, Fritz Haber developed a process for fixing nitrogen and, with the help of Carl Bosch, the process was commercialized for fertilizer production. The Haber–Bosch process has altered Earth's nitrogen cycles and is said to be responsible for the existence of 40% of the people on Earth. Before the implementation of the Haber–Bosch process, the amount of nitrogen available for life was limited by the rates at which N_2 was fixed by bacteria or generated by lightning strikes. Today, spreading fertilizers rich in nitrogen is the basis for most of agriculture's productivity. This practice has quadrupled some yields over the past 50 years. Of all nutrients required for primary production, nitrogen is often the least abundant. Agriculture routinely depletes soil nitrogen, which is removed from fields through the harvesting of plants that have accumulated nitrogen in their tissues. Soil erosion and leaching remove more. Traditionally, farmers rotated their crops, alternately planting legumes and other crops in the same fields. In combination with other soil conservation practices, crop rotation stabilized soils and kept them productive, sometimes for hundreds of years. Some of the most arable land in New York State was farmed by members of the Mohawk Iroquois First Nations. The evidence of this comes from the locations of palisaded villages. The people moved their villages and farming operations every 10–20 years, changing fields repeatedly over hundreds of years.

The production of synthetic fertilizers is expensive, using fossil fuels as both raw material and an energy source. Fertilizer becomes increasingly costly as supplies of fossil fuels dwindle. Furthermore, rain and runoff leach excess fertilizer from agricultural fields and carry it into aquatic ecosystems. Nitrogen has become a major pollutant of freshwater ecosystems, artificially enriching the waters and allowing producers to expand their populations. Human activities have disrupted the global nitrogen cycle (**Figure 31.19**).

TABLE 31.2	Biochemical Processes That Influence Nitrogen Cycling in Ecosystems		
Process	**Organisms Responsible**	**Products**	**Outcome**
Nitrogen fixation	Bacteria: *Rhizobium, Azotobacter, Frankia* Cyanobacteria: *Anabaena, Nostoc*	Ammonia (NH_3), ammonium ions (NH_4^+)	Assimilated by primary producers
Ammonification of organic detritus	Soil bacteria and fungi	Ammonia (NH_3), ammonium ions (NH_4^+)	Assimilated by primary producers
Nitrification			
(1) Oxidation of NH_3	Bacteria: *Nitrosomonas, Nitrococcus*	Nitrite (NO_2^-)	Used by nitrifying bacteria
(2) Oxidation of NO_2^-	Bacteria: *Nitrobacter*	Nitrate (NO_3^-)	Assimilated by primary producers
Denitrification of NO_3^-	Soil bacteria	Nitrous oxide (N_2O), molecular nitrogen (N_2)	Released to atmosphere

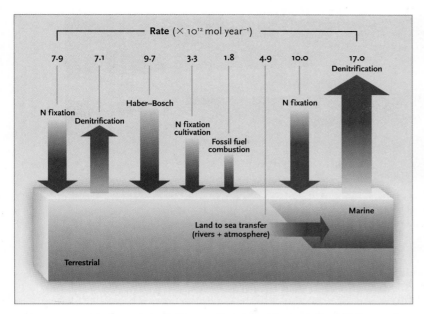

Rate ($\times\ 10^{12}$ mol year^{-1})

7.9 7.1 9.7 3.3 1.8 4.9 10.0 17.0

N fixation
Denitrification
Haber–Bosch
N fixation cultivation
Fossil fuel combustion
N fixation
Denitrification

Land to sea transfer (rivers + atmosphere)

Marine

Terrestrial

FIGURE 31.19 Modern global nitrogen flux depends upon the efficiency of transfer of N between reservoirs. Thickness of arrows indicates relative size of flux. Anthropogenic inputs are shown as dark brown arrows.

Source: From Canfield, D.E., A.N. Glazer and P.G. Falkowski. "The evolution and future of Earth's nitrogen cycle," *Science* 8 October 2010, Vol. 330 no. 6001 pp. 192-196. *Science* by American Association for the Advancement of Science Reproduced with permission of AMERICAN ASSOCIATION FOR THE ADVANCEMENT OF SCIENCE in the format Republish in a book via Copyright Clearance Center.

31.3d Phosphorus Is Another Essential Element

Phosphorus compounds lack a gaseous phase, and this element moves between terrestrial and marine ecosystems in a sedimentary cycle (**Figure 31.20**). Earth's crust is the main reservoir of phosphorus, as it is for other minerals, such as calcium and potassium, that also undergo sedimentary cycles.

Phosphorus is present in terrestrial rocks in the form of phosphates (PO_4^{3-}). In the **phosphorus cycle**, weathering and erosion add phosphate ions to soil and carry them into streams and rivers, which eventually transport them to the ocean. Once there, some phosphorus enters marine food webs, but most of it precipitates out of solution and accumulates for millions of years as insoluble deposits, mainly on continental shelves. When parts of the sea floor are uplifted and exposed, weathering releases the phosphates.

Plants absorb and assimilate dissolved phosphates directly, and phosphorus moves easily to higher trophic levels. All heterotrophs excrete some phosphorus as a waste product in urine and feces; the phosphorus becomes available after decomposition. Primary producers readily absorb the phosphate ions, so phosphorus cycles rapidly *within* terrestrial communities.

Supplies of available phosphate are generally limited, however, and plants acquire it so efficiently that they reduce soil phosphate concentration to extremely low levels. Thus, like nitrogen, phosphorus is a common ingredient in agricultural fertilizers, and excess phosphates are pollutants of freshwater ecosystems. A particularly good example is Lake Erie, a Great Lake that was heavily affected by accumulations of phosphorus. The example here is more convincing because the problem has largely been resolved over the years.

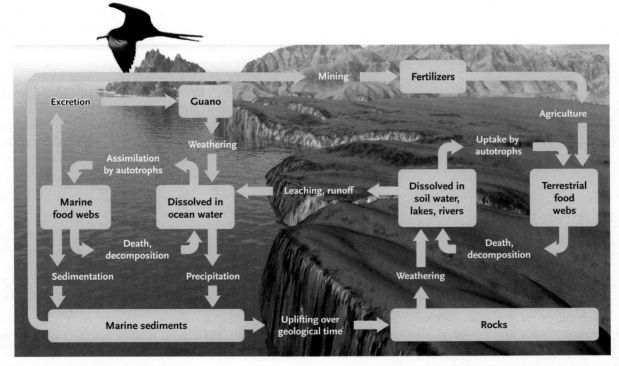

FIGURE 31.20 The phosphorus cycle. Phosphorus becomes available to biological systems when wind and rainfall dissolve phosphates in rocks and carry them into adjacent soil and freshwater ecosystems. Runoff carries dissolved phosphorus into marine ecosystems, where it precipitates out of solution and is incorporated into marine sediments.

Sunlight penetrates the atmosphere and warms Earth's surface.

Earth's surface radiates heat (infrared wavelengths) to the atmosphere. Some heat escapes into space. Greenhouse gases and water vapour absorb some infrared energy and reradiate the rest of it back toward Earth.

When atmospheric concentrations of greenhouse gases increase, the atmosphere near Earth's surface traps more heat. The warming causes a positive feedback cycle in which rising ocean temperatures cause increased evaporation of water, which further enhances the greenhouse effect.

FIGURE 31.21 The greenhouse effect

For many years, phosphate for fertilizers was obtained from guano (the droppings of seabirds that consume phosphorus-rich food), which was mined on small islands that hosted seabird colonies, for example, in Polynesia and Micronesia. We now obtain most phosphate for fertilizer from phosphate rock mined in places such as Saskatchewan that have abundant marine deposits.

STUDY BREAK QUESTIONS

1. What is a generalized compartment model?
2. How does evaporation play into the hydrogeological cycle?
3. What is secondary forest? Why is it important in the Neotropics?
4. Why is carbon referred to as "the backbone of life"?
5. What is nitrification?
6. Why was the Haber–Bosch process so important?
7. What is nitrogen fixation?
8. Why is phosphorus important?
9. Why were accumulations of phosphorus lethal?
10. What is the role of cyanobacteria in the nitrogen cycle?

31.4 Carbon: A Disrupted Cycle

Concentrations of gases in the lower atmosphere have a profound effect on global temperature, in turn affecting global climate. Collectively, molecules of CO_2, water vapour, ozone, methane, nitrous oxide, and other compounds act like a pane of glass in a greenhouse. These "greenhouse gases" allow short wavelengths of visible light to reach Earth's surface while impeding the escape of longer, infrared wavelengths into space, trapping much of their energy as heat (**Figure 31.21**). Greenhouse gases foster the accumulation of heat in the lower atmosphere, a warming action known as the **greenhouse effect**. This natural process prevents Earth from being a cold and lifeless planet.

Data from air bubbles trapped in glacial ice indicate that atmospheric CO_2 concentrations have fluctuated widely over Earth's history (**Figure 31.22**). Since the late 1950s, scientists have measured atmospheric concentrations of CO_2 and other greenhouse gases at remote sampling sites such as the top of Mauna Loa in the Hawaiian Islands. These sites are free of local contamination and reflect average global conditions. Concentrations of greenhouse gases have increased steadily for as long as they have been monitored (**Figure 31.23**).

The graph for atmospheric CO_2 concentration has a regular zigzag pattern that follows the annual cycle of plant growth (Figure 31.23). The concentration of CO_2 decreases during the summer because photosynthesis withdraws so much from the atmospheric available–inorganic pool. The concentration of CO_2 is higher during the winter when photosynthesis slows

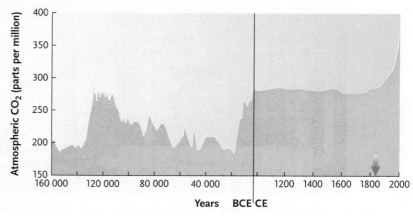

FIGURE 31.22 Carbon dioxide levels over time. The amount of atmospheric CO_2 has risen dramatically since about 1850 (arrow).

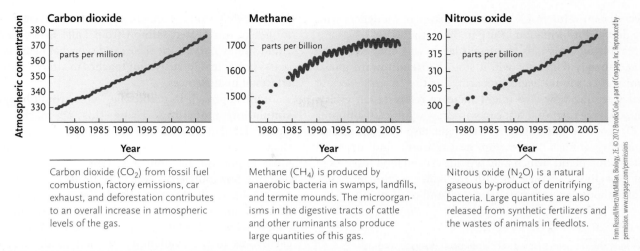

From Russell/Hertz/McMillan. Biology, 2E. © 2012 Brooks/Cole, a part of Cengage, Inc. Reproduced by permission. www.cengage.com/permissions

Carbon dioxide (CO$_2$) from fossil fuel combustion, factory emissions, car exhaust, and deforestation contributes to an overall increase in atmospheric levels of the gas.

Methane (CH$_4$) is produced by anaerobic bacteria in swamps, landfills, and termite mounds. The microorganisms in the digestive tracts of cattle and other ruminants also produce large quantities of this gas.

Nitrous oxide (N$_2$O) is a natural gaseous by-product of denitrifying bacteria. Large quantities are also released from synthetic fertilizers and the wastes of animals in feedlots.

FIGURE 31.23 Increases in atmospheric concentrations of three greenhouse gases, mid-1970s through 2004. The data were collected at a remote monitoring station in Australia (Cape Grim, Tasmania) and compiled by scientists at the Commonwealth Scientific and Industrial Research Organization, an agency of the Australian government.

while aerobic respiration continues, returning carbon to the atmospheric available–inorganic pool. Whereas the zigs and zags in the data for CO$_2$ represent seasonal highs and lows, the midpoint of the annual peaks and troughs has increased steadily for 40 years. These data are evidence of a rapid buildup of atmospheric CO$_2$, representing a shift in the distribution of carbon in the major reservoirs on Earth. The best estimates suggest that CO$_2$ concentration has increased by 35% in the past 150 years, and by more than 10% in the past 30 years.

The increase in the atmospheric concentration of CO$_2$ appears to result from combustion, whether we burn fossil fuels or wood. Today, humans burn more wood and fossil fuels than ever before. Vast tracts of tropical forests are being cleared and burned (see Chapter 28). To make matters worse, deforestation reduces the world's biomass of plants that assimilate CO$_2$ and help maintain the carbon cycle as it existed before human activities disrupted it.

The increase in the concentration of atmospheric CO$_2$ is alarming because plants with C$_3$ metabolism respond to increased CO$_2$ concentrations with increased growth rates. This is not true of C$_4$ plants (see Chapter 6). Thus, rising atmospheric levels of CO$_2$ will probably alter the relative abundances of many plant species, changing the composition and dynamics of their communities.

Simulation models suggest that increasing concentrations of any greenhouse gas may intensify the greenhouse effect, contributing to a trend of global warming. Should we be alarmed about the prospect of a warmer planet? Some models predict that the mean temperature of the lower atmosphere will rise by 4°C, enough to increase ocean surface temperatures. In some areas, such as the Canadian Arctic and the Antarctic, warming has occurred much more rapidly than predicted or expected. Water expands when heated, and global sea levels could rise as much as 0.6 m just from this expansion. In addition, atmospheric temperature is rising fastest near the poles. Thus, global warming may also foster melting of glaciers and

the Antarctic ice sheet, which might raise sea levels as much as 50–100 m, inundating low coastal regions. Waterfronts in Vancouver, Los Angeles, Hong Kong, Durban, Rio de Janeiro, Sydney, New York, and London would be submerged. So would agricultural lands in India, China, and Bangladesh, where much of the world's rice is grown. Moreover, global warming could disturb regional patterns of precipitation and temperature. Areas that now produce much of the world's grains would become arid scrub or deserts, and the now-forested areas to their north would become dry grasslands.

Many scientists believe that atmospheric levels of greenhouse gases will continue to increase at least until the middle of the twenty-first century, and that global temperature may rise by several degrees. At the Earth Summit in 1992, leaders of the industrialized countries agreed to try to stabilize CO$_2$ emissions by the end of the twentieth century. We have already missed that target, and some countries, including the United States (then the largest producer of greenhouse gases), have now forsaken that goal as too costly.

Marked seasonal variation in CO$_2$ occurs in many parts of the world, especially in northern terrestrial ecosystems. Since 1960, the marked increase in the amplitude of seasonal variation in CO$_2$ reflects upward trends in CO$_2$ because of climate warming. Changes in vegetation cover in northern ecosystems appear to be responsible for the increasing amplitude. This reality emphasizes the importance of feedbacks between climate, vegetation, and carbon cycle at high latitudes. The change in amplitude informs us that photosynthetic carbon uptake has reacted more strongly than processes that release carbon.

Seasonality of photosynthesis in evergreen forests of the Amazon basin have been a matter of some discussion. In 2016, the results of a detailed analysis of photographic observations and measures of fluctuations in CO$_2$ revealed an unexpected reality. Changes in the patterns of leaf development and demography explained the large changes (27%) in photosynthesis in the ecosystem. This result provided ecosystem modellers with more detailed information to use in their studies.

Stabilizing emissions at current levels will not reverse the damage already done, nor will it stop the trend toward global warming. We should begin preparing for the consequences of global warming now. We might increase reforestation efforts because a large tract of forest can withdraw significant amounts of CO_2 from the atmosphere. We might also step up genetic engineering studies to develop heat-resistant and drought-resistant crop plants, which may provide crucial food reserves in regions of climate change. In 2016, the issues of climate change and greenhouse gases remain persistent and challenging.

STUDY BREAK QUESTIONS

1. What is the greenhouse effect? How does it relate to global warming?
2. What is a greenhouse gas?
3. Is *climate warming* synonymous with *climate change*?

31.5 Ecosystem Modelling

Ecologists use modelling to make predictions about how an ecosystem will respond to specific changes in physical factors, energy flow, or nutrient availability. Analyses of energy flow and nutrient cycling allow us to create a conceptual model of how ecosystems function (**Figure 31.24**). Energy that enters ecosystems is gradually dissipated as it flows through a food web. By contrast, nutrients are conserved and recycled among the system's living and nonliving components. This general model does not include processes that carry nutrients and energy out of one ecosystem and into another.

More important, the model ignores the nuts-and-bolts details of exactly how specific ecosystems function. Although it is a useful tool, a conceptual model does not really help us

predict what would happen, say, if we harvested 10 million tonnes of introduced salmon from Lake Erie every year. We could simply harvest the fishes and see what happens. But ecologists prefer less intrusive approaches to studying the potential effects of disturbances.

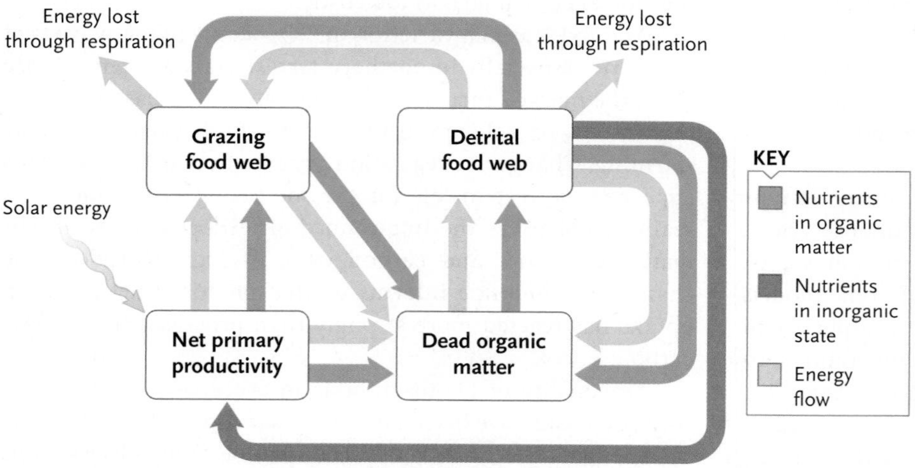

One approach to predicting "what would happen if..." is **simulation modelling**. Using this approach, researchers gather detailed information about a specific ecosystem. They then derive a series of mathematical equations that define its most important relationships. One set of equations might describe how nutrient availability limits productivity at various trophic levels. Another might relate the population growth of zooplankton to the productivity of phytoplankton. Other equations would relate the population dynamics of primary carnivores to the availability of their food, and still others would describe how the densities of primary carnivores influence reproduction in populations at both lower and higher trophic levels. Thus, a complete simulation model is a set of interlocking equations that collectively predict how changes in one feature of an ecosystem might influence other features.

Creating a simulation model is a challenge because the relationships within every ecosystem are complex. First you must identify the important species, estimate their population sizes, and measure the average energy and nutrient content of each. Next you must describe the food webs in which they participate, measure the quantity of food each species consumes, and estimate the productivity of each population. And, for the sake of completeness, you must determine the ecosystem's energy and nutrient gains and losses caused by erosion, weathering, precipitation, and runoff. You must repeat these measurements seasonally to identify annual variation in these factors. Finally, you might repeat the measurements over several years to determine the effects of year-to-year variation in climate and chance events.

After collecting these data, you must write equations that quantify the relationships in the ecosystem, including information about how temperature and other abiotic factors influence the ecology of each species. Having completed that job, you would begin to predict, for example, possibly in great detail, the effects of adding 1000 new housing units to an area of native prairie or boreal forest. Of course, you must refine the model whenever new data become available.

Some ecologists devote their professional lives to studying ecosystem processes and creating simulation models. Modelling becomes an increasingly important tool as we attempt to understand larger and more complex ecosystems. These systems bring more challenging environmental problems. A model based on well-defined ecological relationships and good empirical data can allow us to make accurate predictions about

FIGURE 31.24 **A conceptual ecosystem model.** A simple conceptual model of an ecosystem illustrates how energy flows through the system and is lost from both detrital and grazing food webs. Nutrients are recycled and conserved.

Energy lost through respiration

Energy lost through respiration

Solar energy

Grazing food web

Detrital food web

Net primary productivity

Dead organic matter

KEY
- Nutrients in organic matter
- Nutrients in inorganic state
- Energy flow

ecosystem changes without the need for costly and environmentally damaging experiments. But, like all ideas in science, a model is only as good as its assumptions, and models must constantly be adjusted to incorporate new ideas and recently discovered facts.

STUDY BREAK QUESTIONS

1. Briefly describe the process of simulation modelling.
2. Why is simulation modelling necessary?

31.6 Scale, Ecosystems, Species

As we have seen, the complex interactions between and among species combine with abiotic and biotic factors to produce even more complex situations. Several questions emerge from this situation: What determines which species occur in an ecosystem? What controls the size of the populations of species in an ecosystem? How do species in an ecosystem interact? What effect does scale have on the situation?

Ecosystems span scales from millimetres to kilometres. Consider the microorganisms in a biofilm of water compared to the species, some of them microorganisms, in the water contained in the pitcher of a pitcher plant. Furthermore, the community of organisms may vary among pitchers on one plant. Like the pitcher-based community, terrestrial organisms living on an island may be relatively isolated. Consider the differences among islands, such as the British Isles, the Hawaiian Islands, or the Galapagos Islands, with respect to the combination of size (area), degree of isolation (distance from mainland), and range of habitats.

Variations in the scale of interactions (**Figure 31.25**) help to put the nature of ecosystems in context. Compare Figure 31.25 to Figure 30.29—about pollen and seed dispersal. More obvious in the latter is the influence of mobility on patterns of dispersal and connections. Large animals disperse seeds farther than small ones. Animals that can fly have greater potential as dispersers of seeds and pollen than those that walk or run. Data on the distribution and habitat associations of terrestrial birds in Denmark reveal how species in the same genus and those filling similar niches have more influence on the patterns of distribution of one another than less similar species.

Studies of salmon along the northwest coast of North America (Great Bear Rainforest in British Columbia and sites around Bristol Bay in Alaska) reveal how salmon, fish in the genus *Oncorhynchus*, can influence the plant communities bordering the streams in which they spawn. Nutrients from salmon enter these communities when salmon die after spawning and/ or when they are taken and eaten by predators such as bears. Healthy populations of salmon affect the nutrient loading in terrestrial plants along the rivers and streams. The density of salmon and the characteristics of the watershed (steep versus shallow banks) influence the situation. Nutrient input from

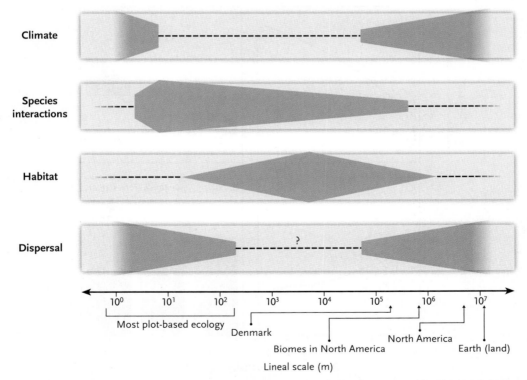

FIGURE 31.25 Climate, species interactions, habitat, and dispersal are four main factors controlling the distribution of species (vertical axis). Note the variation in scale (horizontal axis) across which these factors can act.

Source: From McGill, B.J., "Matters of scale," *Science* 30 April 2010, Vol. 328 no. 5978 pp. 575-576. *Science* by American Association for the Advancement of Science Reproduced with permission of AMERICAN ASSOCIATION FOR THE ADVANCEMENT OF SCIENCE in the format Republish in a book via Copyright Clearance Center.

salmon leads to an increase in plants, such as salmonberry, associated with nutrient-rich soils. Lower input from salmon is associated with plants associated with nutrient-poor soils (e.g., blueberries). Increases in nutrient-rich soils coincide with decreases in plant diversity (**Figure 31.26**).

The above data from salmon at sites along 50 watersheds in British Columbia demonstrate the local impact that species in one genus can have. Work from sites in Alaska shows how the inherent diversity of populations of sockeye salmon (*Oncorhynchus nerka*) is vital to the survival of the species and, by extension, the ecosystem. The data from sockeye salmon show how damping variance in the population provides stability. One example of variance is the timing of returns of salmon to the streams in which they hatched. The diversity is part of the portfolio effect, named because it is analogous to the impact of asset diversity on the stability of financial portfolios.

The diversity inherent in several hundred discrete watershed-based populations of sockeye is less than half the diversity that would occur if the sockeye were a single homogeneous population. The diversity also makes sockeye more resilient to pressures of fishing. Studies of food webs in the watersheds provide further evidence of diversity and extend the portfolio effect.

In short, work with salmon advances our knowledge of the fundamental nature of ecosystems and helps us to appreciate the importance of maintaining biodiversity, which sets the stage for Chapter 28.

STUDY BREAK QUESTIONS

1. Why do ecosystems range so greatly in scale?
2. How do salmon have such a great influence on ecosystems around the streams in which they spawn?

31.7 Three Sample Ecosystems

Now we use three sample ecosystems to illustrate the guiding points presented above. We will move across a scale from individual leaves, to caves and to cityscapes.

31.7a Pitcher Plant Ecosystems

Pitcher plants have modified leaves (pitchers) that act as pitfall traps for drowning and digesting insect prey. Pitchers have developed in at least five different evolutionary lines of vascular plants (see Chapter 34). Throughout much of North America,

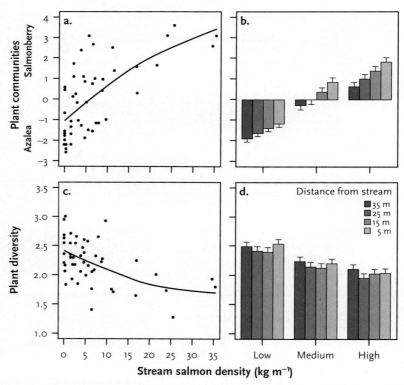

FIGURE 31.26 **The influence of stream level density of spawning salmon (horizontal axis) on the structure of the community of understorey plants (a, b) and on the diversity of plants (c, d; vertical axis). Note the impact of distance from the stream.**

Source: From Hocking, M.D. and J.D. Reynolds, "Impacts of salmon on riparian plant diversity," *Science* 25 March 2011, Vol. 331 no. 6024 pp. 1609-1612. *Science* by American Association for the Advancement of Science Reproduced with permission of AMERICAN ASSOCIATION FOR THE ADVANCEMENT OF SCIENCE in the format Republish in a book via Copyright Clearance Center.

a.

b.

FIGURE 31.27 *Sarracenia purpurea*, a pitcher plant, showing the flower (a) on the end of a long stalk, and a pitcher (b). Note the water in the pitcher.

pitcher plants (the provincial flower of Newfoundland and Labrador; **Figure 31.27**) are common in bogs. *Sarracenia purpurea*, like other carnivorous plants, obtain much of their nitrogen from the insects they capture.

The captured arthropod prey, mainly ants and flies, is the base of a food web inside the pitchers (**Figure 31.28**). These are shredded and partly consumed by larvae of midges (*Metriocnemus knabi*) and sarcophagid flies. A soup of bacteria and protozoa processes shredded prey, which are eaten by filter-feeding rotifers (*Habrotrocha rosa*; **Figure 31.29**) and mites (*Sarraceniopus gibsonii*). Mosquito larvae (*Wyeomyia smithii*) eat the bacteria, protozoa, and rotifers, whereas the larger sarcophagid fly larvae eat the rotifers and smaller mosquito larvae. Populations of bacteria, protozoa, and rotifers grow much more rapidly than populations of mosquito or midge larvae, making the system sustainable.

Pitchers are essential to the life cycles of two species of insects whose larvae live in them. A mosquito and a midge

coexist in the same pitchers, and their populations are limited by the availability of insect carcasses. In any pitcher, growth in populations of the midge larvae is not affected by increases in the numbers of mosquito larvae. But, as shown in Figure 31.28 populations of mosquito larvae increase as populations of midge larvae increase.

The situation is an example of processing-chain commensalism (see also Chapter 30) because the action of one species creates opportunities for another. In this case, midge larvae feed on the hard parts of insect carcasses and break them up in the process. Mosquito larvae are filter feeders, consuming particles derived from the decaying matter. The feeding of the midges generates additional food for the mosquito larvae. Although the populations of midge and mosquito larvae can be large in any pitcher, only a single sarcophagid fly larva occurs in any pitcher. *Fletcherimyia fletcheri* is a *K*-strategist (see Chapter 29) and gives birth to larvae. If you place more than one *F. fletcheri* larva in a pitcher, a fight ensues. The larger larva either wins or leaves the pitcher to pupate in the sphagnum around it.

These insects do not appear to compete with their hosts, the pitcher plants. The abundance of rotifers living in the pitchers of *S. purpurea* is negatively associated with the presence of midge and mosquito larvae (which eat the rotifers). Rotifers are detritivores, and their excretory products (NO_3^--N, NH_4OH, P) account for a major portion of the N acquired by the plants from their insect prey.

Two species of moths also exploit *S. purpurea* (**Figure 31.30**). *Exyra fax* and *Papaipema appassionata* do not live in the pitchers. *Exyra fax* caterpillars eat the interior surface of the pitcher chambers, whereas *P. appassionata* caterpillars consume the rhizomes. Although predation by *E. fax* caterpillars does not kill the plants, predation by *P. appassionata* does. To what trophic level does one

a.

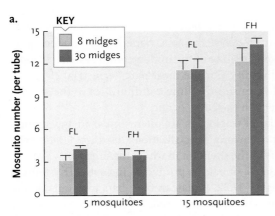

b.

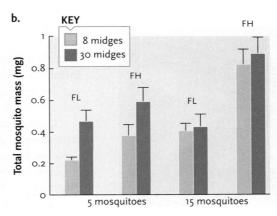

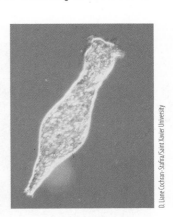

FIGURE 31.29 **A bdelloid rotifer, *Habrotrocha rosa*, from a *Sarracenia purpurea* pitcher**

FIGURE 31.28 **Midge and mosquito larvae in pitchers. (a)** The density and **(b)** total dry mass of mosquito larvae are the same whether the population of midges is low (8 midges) or high (30 midges). FH = high food availability; FL = low food availability. Error bars show standard errors of the mean.

FIGURE 31.30 Moths whose caterpillars eat *Sarracenia purpurea.* The caterpillars of **(a)** *Exyra fax* and **(b)** *Papaipema appassionata* feed on pitcher plants, either (a) the lining of pitchers or (b) the rhizomes.

assign moths whose caterpillars are herbivores feeding on primary producers that eat insects?

At this point, remember other interactions involving pitcher plants and tree shrews and bats (see Chapter 30). The leaves of pitcher plants provide an excellent illustration of the complexity of a small, self-contained ecosystem.

31.7b Cave Ecosystems

Mexican cavefish and southern cavefish (Figure 31.1) illustrate two quite different energy regimes that can occur in cave ecosystems. The tendency for troglobitic species to lack pigment and vision appears to reflect the costs of maintaining these features in situations where they serve no purpose. Mexican cavefish are part of a species complex that includes both cave and surface populations occurring in several neighbouring systems in the area of Sierra de El Abra in south central Mexico. Lineages of these fish have lost eyes at least three times in the last one million years, and there is a range of eye conditions in today's populations (**Figure 31.31**).

FIGURE 31.31 This grouping of captive Mexican cavefish photographed in a pet store illustrates the range of eye development.

The situation in cavefish supports the view that the cost of maintaining eyes (for example) explains the lack of eyes for organisms living in perpetual darkness. Expression of *Pax6* genes (see Chapter 1) as well as fate determination of the optic primordia are responsible for the loss of eyes in different populations of Mexican cavefish. It appears that both natural selection and neutral mutations are responsible for loss of eyes in these fish.

A comparison of eyed and eyeless populations of Mexican cavefish revealed that, while the eyed fish showed a typical circadian rhythm, the eyeless fish did not. Circadian rhythms are daily patterns of activity and energy expenditure. The blind Mexican cavefish achieve a 27% savings in daily energetic expenditure compared to eyed forms.

Compared to surface ecosystems, cave ecosystems have truncated food webs. They lack primary producers and consumers and they have few strictly top level predators. This means that cave systems depend upon input from elsewhere. This input is known as **allochthonous** and could be considered a subsidy. Allochthonous input can be bat guano or material washed in by floods. Cave ecosystems are isolated from surface systems and appear protected from environmental changes that affect surface systems. Biodiversity of cave systems is low compared to surface systems, but nonetheless can be quite high. The energetic regime of the underground system strongly influences biodiversity. For the most part, terrestrial cave faunas are derived from soil-dwelling communities in the surface systems below which the caves occur.

Communities of troglobites are often similar in appearance, physiology, and behaviour. Specializations for a troglobitic existence usually reflect the situation in which the organisms live.

The importance of bats as producers in cave ecosystems is illustrated in **Figure 31.32**. Jamaican fruit bats feed outside the cave and return with fruit and seeds, which they eat as they roost. In some cases the bats deposit only guano (**Figure 31.33a**), or a mixture of guano, pellets of chewed fruit fibre, and seeds (Figure 31.33b).

FIGURE 31.32 Guano and pellets of fruit fibre (each about 1 cm long) cover the floor of a cave room where Jamaican fruit bats (inset: *Artibeus jamaicensis*) roost.

a.

b.

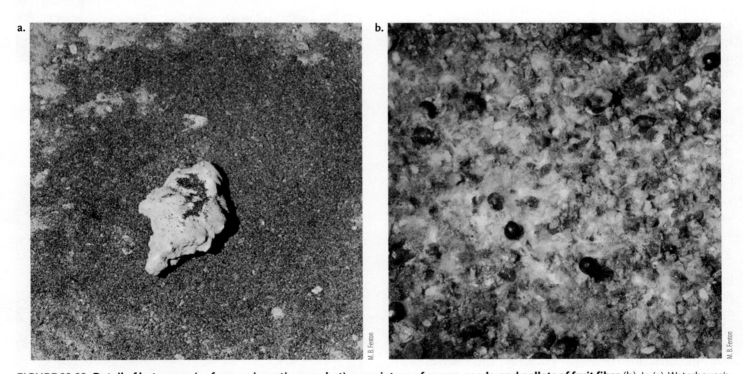

FIGURE 31.33 **Detail of bat guano (a., from an insectivorous bat) or a mixture of guano, seeds, and pellets of fruit fibre** (b). In (a), Waterhouse's leaf-nosed bat (*Macrotus waterhousii*) produces pellets consisting of insect fibres. In (b), Jamaican fruit bats drop guano, seeds (black and shiny), and pellets of fruit fibre (yellowish). The bats make the pellets by chewing on the fruit while sucking out the pulp and juices. The bats then spit out the pellets.

Cave communities include many detritivores, and species that are usually herbivorous (e.g., cave crickets: *Amphiacusta* spp.) also may eat fresh bat guano. Predatory troglobitic grotto salamanders (*Eurycea spelaea*) also feed on bat guano; isotopic analysis reveals that material from the guano is assimilated into muscle.

Bats themselves are important food resources for scavengers and detritivores living in caves. They also serve as food for opportunistic predators, ranging from feral cats (*Felis catus*) to snakes that live in caves (**Figure 31.34**). Around the world, especially in the tropics and subtropics, concentrations of bats attract predators such as snakes. None of the bat-eating snakes is troglobitic.

The other major energetic input to caves is materials swept in by floods, or that fall into entrances. This input can include materials brought into caves by animals, including humans, taking shelter there.

FIGURE 31.34 **Cuban dwarf boa (*Epicrates angulifer*) photographed in a cave where it preyed on passing bats**

Four features appear to account for the patterns of biodiversity in caves and thus the structures of the ecosystems that occur there. First is environmental harshness, reflecting mainly darkness. Second is a high level of endemic species and allopatric vicariant species usually associated with habitat fragmentation and isolation. Third is a high level of relict taxa, which reflects the relative stability and antiquity of cave environments. Fourth is the truncated ecosystem. Some of these features also occur in other systems, such as the depths of Lake Baikal.

In any event, cave ecosystems provide a clear demonstration of how energy input affects biodiversity and food webs. Of special note is the fact that a cave in southern Romania has chemoautotrophic bacteria that can fix inorganic carbon. These bacteria use hydrogen sulfide as an energy source. Isotopic analysis reveals that production from these bacteria provides a food base for troglobitic animals. It seems that not all cave ecosystems are created equal.

31.7c Cities: Urban Ecosystems

In a 2013 model, Luís Bettencourt identified four simple assumptions that could be used to advantage in understanding the dynamics of cities. First, cities have the capacity for mixing populations of citizens that live there. This presumes that citizens can afford to fully explore the city and use it to advantage. Second, infrastructure develops gradually and incrementally, accommodating the expanding population. The mainstay of this assumption is a city's network of roads. Third, *G* (the product of gross domestic product and road volume per capita) is mainly independent of *N* (population size). *G* reflects an increasing demand by cities on the mental and physical efforts of their citizens. This also involves communication networks. Fourth, socioeconomic outputs are proportional to local social interactions. In other words, cities are concentrations of social interactions, not just of people. Unlike biological systems that appear to minimize dissipation of energy, cities are systems in which the opposite is true: energy dissipation is maximized. This reflects ongoing processes such as transportation, as well as heating and cooling.

Waste disposal is one harsh reality of the energy side of cities (**Figure 31.35**). Landfill sites attract large numbers of animals searching for food. At the Thunder Bay site, gulls and ravens are both conspicuous and numerous. Rats also abound at the site, but are less visible. In December 2015, about 100 bald eagles also converged on the landfill site (**Figure 31.36**). These birds showed little interest in the other

FIGURE 31.35 **Operations at a landfill site near Thunder Bay, Ontario, illustrate the scale of the accumulated refuse as well as fuel consumption associated with maintaining the site.** The attendant birds hint at another side of the garbage we produce.

FIGURE 31.36 **Eight of approximately 100 bald eagles (*Haliaeetus leucocephalus*) loitering at a landfill in Thunder Bay in December 2015**

birds and appeared to scavenge a living from the accumulated garbage.

Cities share many features with more biological ecosystems, and thinking of them in this way may teach us more about these different kinds of systems and how they operate. Just as intriguing are the reasons that some organisms thrive in cities (**Figure 31.37**) while others do not. This is a critical problem in conservation biology because cities are the fastest growing ecosystems in the world.

STUDY BREAK QUESTIONS

1. What do pitcher plant, cave, and city ecosystems have in common?
2. How do they differ?
3. Which would you choose as a "model" system?

FIGURE 31.37 A view of an urban techno ecosystem, specifically the campus of Western University as seen in 2007. The expanses of woodland may be more extensive in cities than they are in agroecosystems.

Summary Illustration

Pyramids of energy biomass and numbers have the same basic shape. Each category of organism in these pyramids is part of an ecosystem and plays a role in the cycling of ecosystem nutrients. Consider the role of each category of organism in each of these cycles.

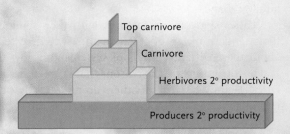

Top carnivore

Carnivore

Herbivores 2° productivity

Producers 2° productivity

Water Cycle

Water cycles through marine, atmospheric, and terrestrial reservoirs. The numbers next to the arrows indicate the amount of water (in km³/year) moved among the reservoirs by various processes.

The six major reservoirs of water are the oceans, polar ice and glaciers, groundwater, lakes and rivers, soil moisture, and the atmosphere. The oceans are by far the largest of the major reservoirs.

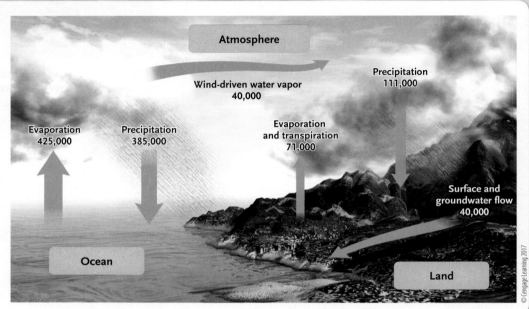

Atmosphere

Wind-driven water vapor
40,000

Precipitation
111,000

Evaporation
425,000

Precipitation
385,000

Evaporation
and transpiration
71,000

Surface and
groundwater flow
40,000

Ocean

Land

© Cengage Learning 2017

Carbon Cycle

Marine and terrestrial components of the global carbon cycle are linked through an atmospheric reservoir of carbon dioxide. The largest amount of Earth's carbon is found in sediments and rocks. Earth's atmosphere mediates most of the movement of carbon.

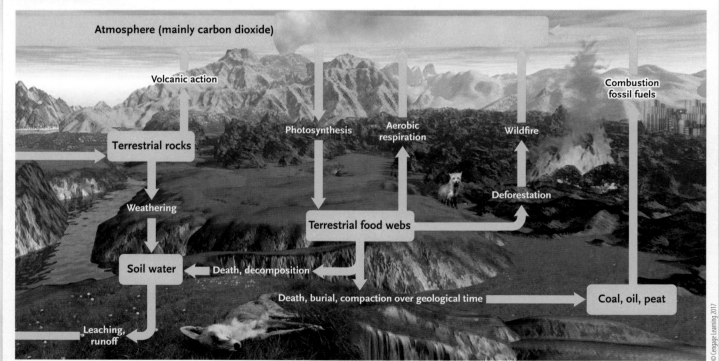

Atmosphere (mainly carbon dioxide)

Volcanic action

Combustion
fossil fuels

Terrestrial rocks

Photosynthesis

Aerobic
respiration

Wildfire

Weathering

Deforestation

Terrestrial food webs

Soil water

Death, decomposition

Death, burial, compaction over geological time

Coal, oil, peat

Leaching,
runoff

(Background) Ninafotoart/Shutterstock.com

© Cengage Learning 2017

Nitrogen-fixing bacteria produce molecular nitrogen. Other bacteria recycle nitrogen through ammonification and two types of nitrification. Denitrification converts nitrate to molecular nitrogen. Runoff carries nitrogen from terrestrial ecosystems into aquatic ecosystems.

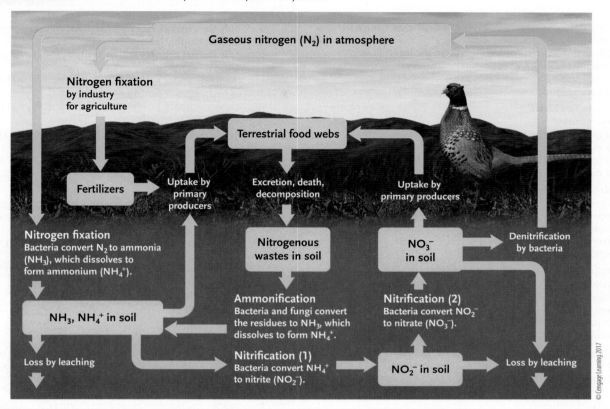

Gaseous nitrogen (N_2) in atmosphere

Nitrogen fixation by industry for agriculture

Fertilizers

Uptake by primary producers

Terrestrial food webs

Excretion, death, decomposition

Uptake by primary producers

Nitrogen fixation Bacteria convert N_2 to ammonia (NH_3), which dissolves to form ammonium (NH_4^+).

Nitrogenous wastes in soil

NO_3^- in soil

Denitrification by bacteria

NH_3, NH_4^+ in soil

Ammonification Bacteria and fungi convert the residues to NH_3, which dissolves to form NH_4^+.

Nitrification (2) Bacteria convert NO_2^- to nitrate (NO_3^-).

Loss by leaching

Nitrification (1) Bacteria convert NH_4^+ to nitrite (NO_2^-).

NO_2^- in soil

Loss by leaching

© Cengage Learning 2017

Phosphorous Cycle

Phosphorus becomes available when wind and rainfall dissolve phosphates in rocks and carry them into soil and freshwater ecosystems. Runoff carries dissolved phosphorus into marine ecosystems, where it precipitates and is incorporated into marine sediments.

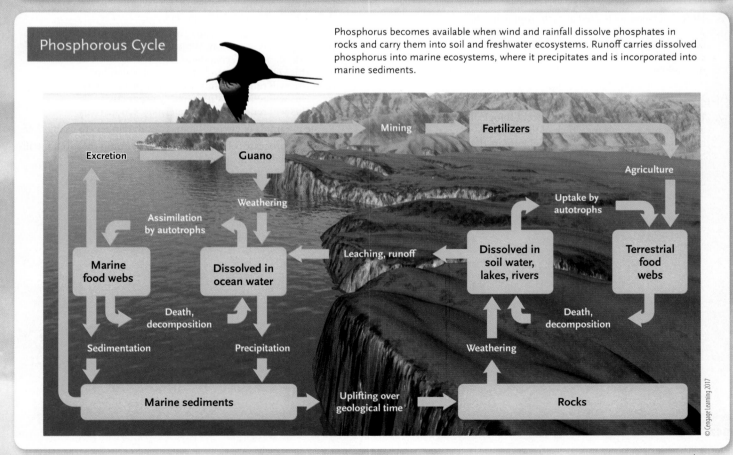

Mining

Fertilizers

Excretion

Guano

Agriculture

Weathering

Assimilation by autotrophs

Uptake by autotrophs

Leaching, runoff

Marine food webs

Dissolved in ocean water

Dissolved in soil water, lakes, rivers

Terrestrial food webs

Death, decomposition

Death, decomposition

Sedimentation

Precipitation

Weathering

Marine sediments

Uplifting over geological time

Rocks

© Cengage Learning 2017

SELF-TEST QUESTIONS

Recall/Understand

1. Which of these events moves energy and material from a detrital food web into a grazing food web?
   a. an earthworm eating dead leaves on the forest floor
   b. a robin catching and eating an earthworm
   c. a crow eating a dead robin
   d. a bacterium decomposing the feces of an earthworm

2. Which of these statements defines the total dry mass of plant material in a forest?
   a. a measure of the forest's gross primary productivity
   b. a measure of the forest's net primary productivity
   c. a measure of the forest's standing crop biomass
   d. a measure of the forest's ecological efficiency

3. Which of these ecosystems has the highest rate of net primary productivity?
   a. open ocean
   b. temperate deciduous forest
   c. tropical rainforest
   d. agricultural land

4. Which pyramid is inverted in some freshwater and marine ecosystems?
   a. biomass
   b. energy
   c. numbers
   d. ecological efficiency

5. Which process moves nutrients from the available–organic compartment to the available–inorganic compartment?
   a. respiration
   b. assimilation
   c. sedimentation
   d. photosynthesis

6. How much energy is used at each trophic level?
   a. ~10%
   b. ~30%
   c. ~50%
   d. ~90%

Apply/Analyze

7. Endothermic animals exhibit a lower ecological efficiency than ectothermic animals for which of these reasons?
   a. Endotherms are less successful hunters than ectotherms.
   b. Endotherms eat more plant material than ectotherms eat.
   c. Endotherms are larger than ectotherms.
   d. Endotherms use more of their energy to maintain body temperature than ectotherms.

8. Which of these factors determines the amount of energy available at the highest trophic level in an ecosystem?
   a. only the gross primary productivity of the ecosystem at the highest trophic level
   b. only the net primary productivity of the ecosystem at the highest trophic level
   c. the net primary productivity and the ecological efficiencies of herbivores at the lowest trophic level
   d. the net primary productivity and the ecological efficiencies at all lower trophic levels

9. Which of the following materials has a sedimentary cycle?
   a. oxygen
   b. nitrogen
   c. phosphorus
   d. carbon

10. Which of these phenomena describes biological magnification?
    a. Certain materials become increasingly concentrated in the tissues of animals at higher trophic levels.
    b. Certain materials become most concentrated in the tissues of animals at the lowest trophic levels.
    c. Certain materials accumulate only in the tissues of tertiary consumers.
    d. Certain materials accumulate only in the tissues of detritivores.

Create/Evaluate

11. Suppose you want to create an experimental grazing food web. Which of the following would you need to include so that it closely resembles a real grazing food web?
    a. carnivores and decomposers
    b. producers, herbivores, and detritivores
    c. producers, herbivores, and carnivores
    d. detritivores and decomposers

12. Suppose that you analyze an ecosystem and you find that it has declining levels of carbon. Which of these statements may you conclude about this ecosystem?
    a. This will reflect mainly primary productivity.
    b. This will reflect mainly secondary productivity.
    c. This will reflect mainly tertiary productivity.
    d. This will reflect mainly quaternary productivity.

13. Relate pyramids of energy, biomass, and numbers to each other.

14. Compare processes of nitrogen fixation, ammonification, nitrification, and denitrification.

15. Using the figure below, provide an overview the phosphorus cycle.

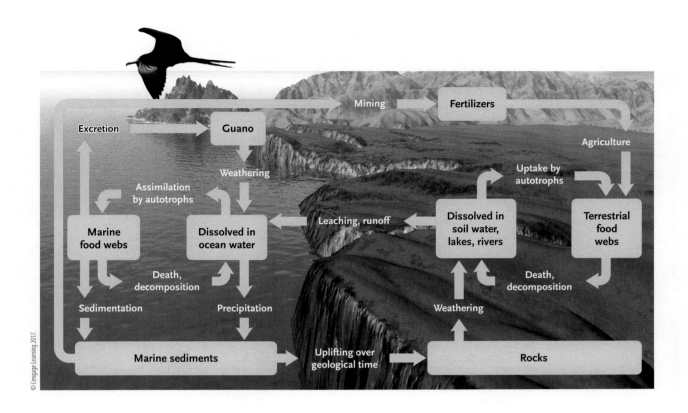

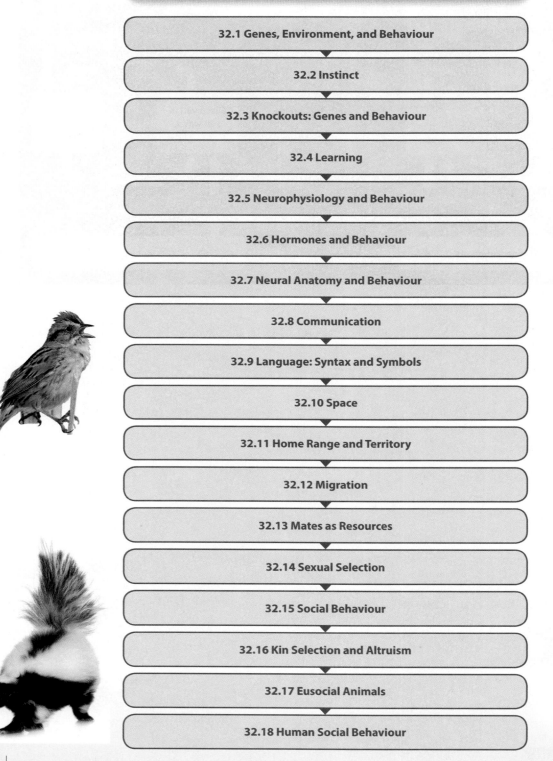

Animal Behaviour

Behaviours reflect a rich blend of genetic and environmental control as well as connections to form and function. They involve a combination of instinct and learning.

32.1 Genes, Environment, and Behaviour

32.2 Instinct

32.3 Knockouts: Genes and Behaviour

32.4 Learning

32.5 Neurophysiology and Behaviour

32.6 Hormones and Behaviour

32.7 Neural Anatomy and Behaviour

32.8 Communication

32.9 Language: Syntax and Symbols

32.10 Space

32.11 Home Range and Territory

32.12 Migration

32.13 Mates as Resources

32.14 Sexual Selection

32.15 Social Behaviour

32.16 Kin Selection and Altruism

32.17 Eusocial Animals

32.18 Human Social Behaviour

All Canada Photos/Alamy Stock Photo

Eric Isselee/Shutterstock.com

M.B. Fenton

A flying western sandpiper (*Calidris mauri*)

Animal Behaviour

32

Why it matters . . . Like many other birds, western sandpipers migrate considerable distances from their breeding grounds along the coast of western Alaska to their wintering grounds in the southern United States. Migration is a recurring theme among animals, and questions about how they navigate continue to intrigue biologists. Considerable experimental and observational evidence has indicated that animals orient using variations in Earth's magnetic field. Until recently, however, we have lacked information about how animals sense magnetic fields.

In 2015, biophysicist Xie Can and his colleagues used an electron microscope to observe assemblies of rod-shaped cryptochromes, proteins sensitive to magnetic fields. They named the proteins MagR and proposed them as the missing biocompass, a receptor that animals could use as a magnetic sensor. Experiments with fruit flies (*Drosophila melanogaster*) revealed that flies missing MagR lost their magnetic sense, supporting the hypothesis. Cryptochromes are blue-light absorbing flavoproteins and homologous proteins that also occur in other animals. Many animals from humans to bees, whales to birds, butterflies to pigeons appear to have the capacity to sense magnetic fields. Understanding how these animals sense magnetic fields was a fundamental discovery in animal behaviour.

Moving animals also use other mechanisms to find their way during migration. There are three categories of way-finding mechanisms: piloting, compass orientation, and navigation. Most species use some combination of these mechanisms to guide their movements. Arctic terns are seabirds that make annual round-trip migrations of 40 000 km **(Figure 32.1)**. Light-sensing geolocators allowed biologists to document the details of their movement paths. The exact mechanisms these birds use to navigate are still under investigation.

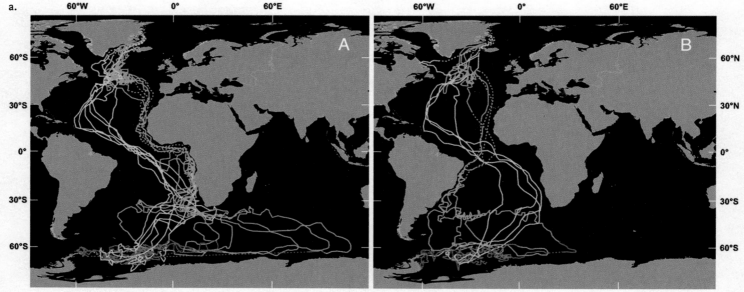

"Tracking of Arctic terns *Sterna paradisaea* reveals longest animal migration." Carsten Egevang, Iain J. Stenhouse, Richard A. Phillips, Aevar Petersen, James W. Fox, and Janet R. D. Silk. *PNAS* February 2, 2010 vol. 107 no. 5 2078–2081.

b.

c.

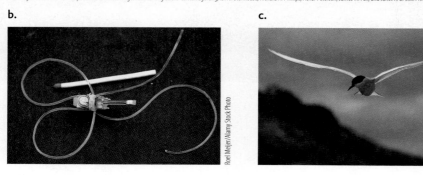

Roel Meijer/Alamy Stock Photo

Photos.com

FIGURE 32.1 **(a)** Geolocators provided details of the movements of 11 Arctic terns tagged at breeding colonies in Greenland (10 terns) and Iceland (1 tern). Two migration routes emerged, one along the coast of Africa (A) and the other along the coast of South America (B). **(b)** A small geolocator. **(c)** an Arctic tern

The purpose of this chapter is to introduce **animal behaviour**. Behaviours, such as migration, reflect a rich blend of genetic and environmental control as well as connections to form and function. They involve a combination of instinct and learning. Hormones exert a strong influence over an animal's behaviour. The nervous system and, by extension, the sensory system mediate behaviour. Some animals are territorial, defending all or part of their home range, usually in association with reproduction. Migration involves movements to and from different areas, usually between seasons, and implies the use of navigational cues. Animals show rich repertoires of behaviour around mating and reproduction. A few species live in large groups and others exhibit complex social behaviour. As we will see in what follows, animal behaviour covers this broad range of topics.

32.1 Genes, Environment, and Behaviour

Nature versus nurture is a long-standing topic of curiosity and discussion. How much of our behaviour is a function of what we inherited (nature) as opposed to the environment and setting in which we grow up and live (nurture)? And in this regard, how different are humans from other animals? Consider this in the

context of the following five examples of food-associated learning in other animals.

First, in Canada, moose (*Alces alces*) and deer (*Odocoileus virginiana*) respond to the sound of chainsaws to feed on the foliage of felled trees. The upper foliage is less chemically defended than the lower leaves.

Second, during the Vietnam War (1959–1975), tigers (*Panthera tigris*; **Figure 32.2**) learned to associate the sound of gunfire with an opportunity to eat. The tigers' behaviour meant that some wounded soldiers waiting for treatment received a different kind of attention than what they expected. During World War II, wolves (*Canis lupus*) showed the same behaviour in some areas of Poland. A food reward is a strong re-enforcer of behaviour.

In the 1970s, Kim McCleneghan and Jack Ames were studying sea otters (*Enhydra lutris*) in California coastal waters. These otters dive and collect food (sea urchins, *Pisaster brevispinus*, and clams, *Saxidomus nuttalli*) from the bottom and bring their catch to the surface to eat it. Some otters resurfaced with empty beverage cans. These otters would lie on their backs in the ocean swells, take a can and bite it open. In some cases they removed and ate something before discarding the can. Some cans appeared to be empty and were discarded after opening. The biologists collected their own beverage cans and

FIGURE 32.2 A tiger (*Panthera tigris*)

discovered that many harboured young octopods (*Octopus* species). Populations of these cephalopods are limited by the number of shelters available. Young octopods were exploiting new opportunities for shelter, and the sea otters, in turn, were exploiting the molluscs' behaviour.

Meanwhile, in savannah woodlands in Senegal (West Africa), Jill Pruetz and Paco Bertolani observed chimpanzees (*Pan troglodytes*) hunting Senegal galagos (*Galago senegalensis*; **Figure 32.3**). Chimps are not vegetarians. They had been reported using grass stalks to fish for termites and working in gangs to hunt and kill young baboons (*Papio ursinus*). The discovery that savannah chimps in Senegal used "spears" to impale Senegal galagos hidden in tree hollows further demonstrated chimps' repertoire of tool use. Pruetz and Bertolani watched chimps bite branches to sharpen them before using them against Senegal galagos. The chimps that Pruetz and Bertolani studied appeared to plan their hunts in advance.

Western scrub-jays (*Aphelocoma californica*) cache food in preparation for the next day's breakfast. Proving that animals consciously plan ahead means that the experimenters have to demonstrate that the animal executes a novel action or combination of actions anticipating an emotional state different from the one at the time of planning. These two conditions rule out such anticipatory behaviours that are genetically based, such as

those associated with migration and hibernation or those associated with meeting an immediate need for food.

These examples illustrate how some behaviour patterns are acquired rather than inherited. But are all behaviours acquired? Animal behaviourists have long debated whether animals are born with the ability to perform behaviours completely and whether experience is necessary to shape their actions. This was addressed in a classic study from a different perspective. White-crowned sparrows sing a song that no other species sings **(Figure 32.4)**. Is this behaviour innate (inborn)? If so, young sparrows should have the ability to produce their particular song from birth, an ability so reliable that young males should sing the "right" song the first time they try. According to this hypothesis, their distinctive song would be an **instinctive behaviour**, genetically or developmentally "programmed," that appears in complete and functional form the first time it is used. An alternative hypothesis is that they acquire the song through experiences such as hearing the songs of adult male white-crowned sparrows that live nearby. If so, this species' distinctive song might be a **learned behaviour** that depends on having a particular kind of experience during development.

How can one determine which of these two hypotheses is correct? If the white-crowned sparrow's song is instinctive, isolated male nestlings that have never heard other members of their species should sing their species' song when they mature. If the learning hypothesis is correct, young birds deprived of hearing other members of their species sing should not sing "properly" when they become adults.

Peter Marler tested these two hypotheses. He took newly hatched white-crowned sparrows from nests in the wild and reared them individually in soundproof cages in his laboratory. Some of the chicks heard recordings of a male white-crowned sparrow's song when they were 10–50 days of age. Others did not. Juvenile males in both groups first started to vocalize at about 150 days of age. For many days, these birds produced whistles and twitters that only vaguely resembled the songs of adults. Gradually, the young males that had listened to tapes of their species' song began to sing better and better approximations of that song. At about 200 days of age, these males were right on target, producing a song that was nearly indistinguishable from the one they had heard months before. Captive-raised males that had not heard recordings of white-crowned sparrow songs never sang anything close to the songs typical of wild males.

These results show that learning is essential for a young male white-crowned sparrow to acquire the full song of its species. Although birds isolated as nestlings sang instinctively, they needed the acoustical experience of listening to their species' song early in life if they were to reproduce it months later. These data allow us to reject the hypothesis that white-crowned sparrows hatch from their eggs with the ability to sing the "right" song. Their species-specific song, and perhaps the songs of many other songbirds, includes both instinctive and learned components.

FIGURE 32.3 A Senegal galago (Galago senegalensis)

White-crowned sparrow
(Zonotrichia leucophrys)

Song sparrow
(Melospiza melodia)

Swamp sparrow
(Melospiza georgiana)

Frequency (kHz)

Time

Time

Time

teekaygee/Shutterstock.com

Dr. Stephen Yezerinac

Stubblefield Photography/Shutterstock.com

Dr. Stephen Yezerinac

All Canada Photos/Alamy Stock Photo

Dr. Stephen Yezerinac

FIGURE 32.4 Songbirds and their songs. Sound spectrograms (visual representations of sound graphed as frequency versus time) illustrate differences in the songs of the white-crowned sparrow (*Zonotrichia leucophrys*), song sparrow (*Melospiza melodia*), and swamp sparrow (*Melospiza georgiana*).

In the past, researchers generally classified behaviours as either instinctive or learned; the current belief is that many behaviours include both instinctive and learned components. The emerging picture is that few behaviours are determined entirely by genetics or entirely by environmental factors. Rather, most behaviours develop through complex gene–environment interactions. Some behaviours have a stronger instinctive component than others, and these will be discussed next.

STUDY BREAK QUESTIONS

1. Is behaviour learned? How has the study of bird song advanced our understanding of the influence of learning versus genes on behaviour?
2. Give any example of your choice that demonstrates that behaviour in animals is learned.

32.2 Instinct

Instinctive behaviours can be performed without the benefit of previous experience. They can be grouped into functional categories such as feeding, defence, mating, and parental care. We assume that they have a strong genetic basis, and that natural selection has preserved them as adaptive behaviours.

These instinctive behaviours are highly stereotyped. When an animal is triggered by a specific cue, it performs the same response over and over in almost exactly the same way. These **fixed action patterns** are triggered by **sign stimuli**. Very young herring gull chicks use a begging response **(Figure 32.5a)**, a fixed action pattern, to secure food from their parents. Begging

chicks peck at the red spot on the parent's bill, and the tactile stimulus serves as a sign stimulus inducing the adult to regurgitate food from its crop. Baby gulls eat the chunks of fish, clams, or other food that have been regurgitated for them. We know that the spot on the parent's bill elicits the begging response of the young gull because the same response is triggered by an artificial bill that looks only vaguely like an adult bill, provided that it has a dark contrasting spot near the tip (Figure 32.5b). Simple cues can activate fixed action patterns. A nestling herring gull, is not reacting to every feature of a face but rather to simple cues that function as sign stimuli releasing a fixed behavioural response.

Natural selection has moulded the behaviour of some parasitic species to exploit the relationship between sign stimuli and fixed action patterns for their own benefit. In effect, they have broken another species' code. Birds that are brood parasites lay their eggs in the nests of other species of birds. When the brood parasite's egg hatches, the nestling mimics sign stimuli ordinarily exhibited by its host's own chicks. The parasitic chick begs for food by opening its mouth, bobbing its head, and calling more vigorously than the host's chicks. These exaggerated behaviours elicit feeding by the foster parents, and the young brood parasite often receives more food than the hosts' own young **(Figure 32.6)**.

The situation is more complicated when birds such as honeyguides (African family Indicatoridae) are the parasites. Female greater honeyguides (*Indicator indicator*) lay their eggs in the nests of several host species that nest in dark hollows. Greater honeyguides are not territorial, so more than one female may lay her eggs in the nest of a host. When laying her eggs, a female greater honeyguide minimizes future

FIGURE 32.5   **Experimental Research**

The Role of Sign Stimuli in Parent–Offspring Interactions

a.

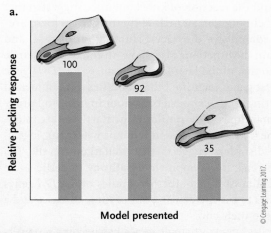

Relative pecking response

Model presented

© Cengage Learning 2017.

b. Herring gulls (Larus argentatus)

Johner Images/Alamy Stock Photo

Question: What feature of the parent's head triggers pecking behaviour in young herring gulls?

Experiment: Niko Tinbergen and A. C. Perdeck tested the responses of young herring gull *(Larus argentatus)* chicks to cardboard cutouts of an adult herring gull's head and bill. They waved these models in front of the chicks and recorded how often a particular model elicited a pecking response from the chicks. One cutout included an entire gull's head with a red spot near the tip of the bill, another cutout included just the bill with the red spot, and the third cutout included the entire head but lacked the red spot.

Result: Young herring gulls pecked at the model of the bill with a red spot almost as often as they pecked at the model of an entire head with a red spot, but they pecked much less frequently at the model of an entire head that lacked a red spot.

Conclusion: Begging behaviour by young herring gulls is triggered by a simple sign stimulus, the red spot on the parent's bill. Experimental tests revealed that herring gull chicks respond more to the presence of the contrasting spot than they do to the outline of an adult's head.

Stephen Dalton/Science Source

FIGURE 32.6 This European cuckoo (*Cuculus canorus*) is a brood parasite that stimulates food delivery by its foster parent, a hedge sparrow (*Prunella modularis*). The cuckoo elicits food delivery by displaying exaggerated versions of the sign stimuli used by the host offspring. The exaggerated stimuli are releasers, initiating the appropriate behaviour from a parent with food.

competition among nestlings by selectively piercing the eggs of other greater honeyguides (conspecifics) in the nest. After hatching, greater honeyguide chicks kill other nestlings, whether conspecifics or young of the hosts. Both egg piercing and killing nestlings increase the chances of the chick surviving and reproducing.

Although instinctive behaviours are often performed completely the first time an animal responds to a stimulus, they can be modified by an individual's experiences, as described in the previous section. The fixed action patterns of a young herring gull change over time. Although the youngster initially begs by pecking at almost anything remotely similar to an adult gull's bill, it eventually learns to recognize the distinctive visual and vocal features associated with its parents. The chick uses this information to become increasingly selective about which stimuli elicit its begging behaviour. During their early performances, instinctive behaviours can be modified in response to particular experiences.

Many other experiments have confirmed that genetic differences between individuals can translate into behavioural differences between them. Bear in mind, however, that single genes do not directly control complex behaviour patterns. Rather, the alleles determine the kinds of enzymes that cells can produce, influencing biochemical pathways involved in the development of an animal's nervous system. The resulting neurological differences translate into behavioural differences between individuals that have certain alleles and those that do not. In the following section we explore one way in which this has been demonstrated.

STUDY BREAK QUESTIONS

1. What are the differences between instinctive and learned behaviours?
2. What are fixed action patterns and sign stimuli?

32.3 Knockouts: Genes and Behaviour

Manipulating genes provides one way to assess the role of genetics in behaviour. The pathway called *wingless/Wnt* controls a series of development interactions shared by almost all eukaryotic organisms. Named after the original discovery in the fruit fly *Drosophila melanogaster*, mutant genes of the pathway cause alterations in the wings and other segmental structures. Three genes closely related to *wingless/Wnt* have been identified in mice but, as yet, we do not know which proteins are encoded in the mouse genes that are highly active in embryos and adults. Their function must be important, but what could it be?

Nardos Lijam and his co-workers developed a line of mice lacking *dishevelled* (*Dvl1* in genetic shorthand), one of the genes in the pathway. First, they constructed an artificial copy of the *Dvl1* gene with the central section scrambled so that no functional proteins could be made from its encoded directions. Next, they introduced the artificial gene into embryonic mouse cells. Cells that successfully incorporated the gene were injected into very early mouse embryos. Some mice grown from these embryos were heterozygotes, with one normal copy of the *Dvl1* gene and one dysfunctional copy. Interbreeding the heterozygotes produced some individuals that carried two copies of the altered *Dvl1* gene and no normal copies. Individuals lacking any copies of the normal gene are called *knockout* mice because the normal gene is completely missing.

Knockout mice grew to maturity with no apparent morphological defects in any tissue examined, including the brain. Their motor skills, sensitivity to pain, cognition, and memory all appeared normal. However, their social behaviour differed from that of control mice—mice with at least one copy of the normal gene. When placed in cages with control mice, knockout mice did not participate in activities common in mouse social groups, for example social grooming, tail pulling, mounting, and sniffing. While normal mice built nests and slept in huddled groups, knockout mice tended to sleep alone, and did not construct full nests. Mice heterozygous for the *Dvl1* gene (those with one normal and one altered copy of the gene) behaved normally in all these social activities.

Furthermore, knockout mice jumped around wildly in response to a startling sound. Normal mice did not. It appears that a neural circuit of the brain inhibits the startle response of normal mice, and the reaction of knockout mice suggested that this inhibitory circuit was altered. Humans with schizophrenia, obsessive-compulsive disorders, Huntington disease, and some other brain dysfunctions also show an intensified startle reflex similar to that of the *Dvl1* knockout mice. The *Dvl1* gene is one of the first genes identified that modifies developmental pathways affecting complex social behaviour in mice and probably in other mammals. The similarity in startle reflex intensity between the knockout mice and humans with neurological or psychiatric disorders suggests that mutations in the *Dvl* genes and the *wingless* developmental pathway underlie some human mental illnesses. If so, further studies of the *Dvl* genes may give us clues to the molecular basis of these diseases and a possible means to their cure.

The ability to knockout single genes has become a powerful tool that can be used to explore the genetic differences between individuals that translate into behavioural differences between them.

STUDY BREAK QUESTION

1. What are knockout experiments? What can they reveal?

32.4 Learning

Unlike instinctive behaviours, learned behaviours are not performed accurately or completely the first time an animal responds to a specific stimulus. Behavioural responses change in response to the environmental stimuli an individual experiences as it develops. Behavioural scientists generally define learning as a process in which experiences change an animal's behavioural responses. Different types of learning occur under different environmental circumstances.

Imprinting occurs when animals learn the identity of a caregiver or the key features of a suitable mate during a **critical period**, a stage of development early in life. Newly hatched geese imprint on their mother's appearance and identity, staying near her for months. When they reach sexual maturity, young geese try to mate with other geese exhibiting the visual and behavioural stimuli on which they had imprinted as youngsters. When Konrad Lorenz, a founder of **ethology** (the study of animal behaviour), tended a group of newly hatched greylag geese (*Anser anser*), they imprinted on him rather than on an adult of their own species. Male geese not only followed Lorenz, at sexual maturity they also courted humans.

Other forms of learning can occur throughout an animal's lifetime. Ivan Pavlov, a Russian physiologist, demonstrated

classical conditioning in experiments with dogs. Like many other animals, dogs can develop a mental association between two phenomena that are usually unrelated. Dogs typically salivate when they eat. Food is an unconditioned stimulus because the dogs instinctively salivate when presented with food. Pavlov rang a bell just before offering food to dogs. After about 30 trials in which dogs received food immediately after the bell rang, the dogs associated the bell with feeding time and drooled profusely whenever it rang, even when no food was forthcoming. The bell was a conditioned stimulus that elicited a particular learned response. In classical conditioning, an animal learns to respond to a conditioned stimulus (e.g., the bell) when it precedes an unconditioned stimulus (e.g., food) that normally triggers the response (e.g., salivation). If your pet cat becomes exceptionally friendly whenever it hears the sound of a can opener, its behaviour is the result of classical conditioning.

Operant conditioning, trial-and-error learning, is another form of associative learning. Here animals learn to link a voluntary activity, an **operant**, with its favourable consequences, a **reinforcement**. A laboratory rat will explore a new cage randomly. If the cage was equipped with a bar that released food when it was pressed by accident (the operant) and the rat immediately received a morsel of food (the reinforcement), after a few such experiences, a hungry rat learned to press the bar in its cage more frequently, provided that the bar-pressing behaviour was followed by access to food. Laboratory rats have also learned to press bars to turn off disturbing stimuli, such as bright lights.

Insight learning occurs when an animal abruptly learns to solve problems without apparent trial-and-error attempts at the solution. As an example, captive chimpanzees solved a novel problem: how to get bananas hung far out of reach. The chimps studied the situation and then stacked several boxes, stood on them, and used a stick to knock the fruit to the floor.

Habituation occurs when animals lose their responsiveness to frequent stimuli not immediately followed by the usual reinforcement. Habituation can save the animal the time and energy of responding to stimuli that are no longer important. Sea hares (*Aplysia* species) are shell-less molluscs that typically retract their gills when touched on the side. Gill retraction helps protect sea hares from approaching predators. But a sea hare stops retracting its gills when it is touched repeatedly over a short period of time with no harmful consequences.

32.4a Changing Behaviour

Animals often learn to exploit important resources. For example, salting of highways often is used to prevent dangerous buildups of ice on road surfaces. After snowplowing and runoff, the salt usually accumulates in roadside ditches. Moose (*Alces alces*) use these salty pools (salt licks) to supplement their mineral intake. Moose at roadsides often come dangerously close to high speed traffic, endangering themselves and the motoring public **(Figure 32.7).**

Roy Rea and his students at the University of Northern British Columbia work closely with the B.C. Ministry of Transportation and Infrastructure to decrease the attractiveness of roadside salt pools. For over five years, trail cameras installed

FIGURE 32.7 **Aftermath of a moose–car collision that occurred on 4 July 2014 in Maine**

at 15 pools (also known as *mineral licks*) and at multiple control sites have provided many pictures of roadside moose. One way to reduce the problem is to "decommission" the salt pools **(Figure 32.8)**. This can be accomplished by digging out and removing the salty soils, altering drainage patterns, and filling pool sites with materials such as rock and cedar mulch. In one case, human and dog hair were mixed and rototilled into the soils to make a lick unattractive to moose.

The salt licks attract moose, and individuals repeatedly visit the same licks and even bring their young to use the same sites. Furthermore, moose repeatedly visit decommissioned sites shortly after decommissioning, but spend less and less time there. Eventually, however, the absence of mineral soils and water drives moose from these roadside areas to seek natural salt licks outside the road corridor. This makes the highways safer for moose and for motorists.

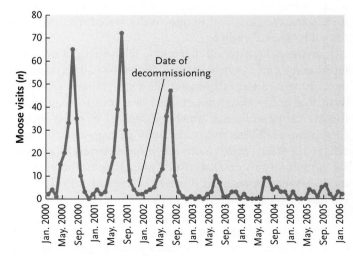

FIGURE 32.8 **Number of moose visits to a series of salt pools, showing the change in behaviour after the site was decommissioned.** Moose continued to visit the lick sites in the first summer after decommissioning. The number of moose visits then declined.

Source: Courtesy of Roy Rea

Until the practice of decommissioning roadside licks becomes more widespread, it will be up to road safety engineers to alter driver behaviours through education and increased warning signage in areas known to be visited regularly by moose. Interestingly, altering driver behaviour, may prove a much more difficult task than altering the behaviours of salt-hungry moose!

STUDY BREAK QUESTIONS

1. How do the examples of feeding behaviour (see also *Why It Matters*) inform us about learning?
2. Distinguish between instinctive and learned behaviours. Give examples of each.
3. How do collisions between moose and vehicles reflect behaviour?

FIGURE 32.9 Zebra finches (*Taeniopygia guttata*) are native to Indonesia. They have played an important role in studies of the physiological basis of song learning. The male has the striped throat.

32.5 Neurophysiology and Behaviour

All behavioural responses, whether mostly instinctive or mostly learned, depend on an elaborate physiological foundation. This is provided by the biochemistry and structure of nerve cells. This is where genetic information and environmental contributions intertwine. The anatomical and physiological basis for some behaviours is present at birth but when an individual's experiences alters the cells of its nervous system, these alterations produce changes in patterns of behaviour.

Marler's experiments described earlier (see Section 32.1) help explain the physiological underpinnings of singing behaviour in male white-crowned sparrows. Acoustical experience shaped singing, suggesting that a sparrow chick's brain must acquire and store information present in the songs of other males. Later, when the young male starts to sing, its nervous system matches its vocal output to the stored memory of the song it had heard earlier.

Marler demonstrated that young birds that did not hear a taped song during their critical period (10–50 days of age), never produced the full song of their species, and that young birds that heard recordings of other bird species' songs during the critical period never generated replicas of those songs as they matured. These and other findings suggested that nerve cells in the young male's brain are influenced only by appropriate stimuli, in this case, acoustical signals from individuals of its own species presented during the critical period. Neuroscientists have now identified nuclei—clusters of nerve cells—that make song learning and song production possible.

Every behavioural trait appears to have its own neural basis. In another songbird, a zebra finch (**Figure 32.9**), males discriminate between the songs of strangers and those of neighbours. These finches live in **territories** (see Section 32.10), spaces defended by individual males or breeding pairs. Defence of the territory ensures that the residents there have exclusive access to food and other necessary resources.

A nucleus in the forebrain allows zebra finches to discriminate between the songs of neighbours and those of strangers. Cells in this nucleus fire frequently the first time the zebra finch hears the song of a new conspecific. As the song is played again and again, the cells of this nucleus cease to respond, as the bird is habituated to a now familiar song. The same bird still reacts to the songs of strangers. Neurophysiological networks that make this selective learning possible enable male zebra finches to behave differently toward familiar neighbours, which they largely ignore, than they do to unfamiliar singers, which they attack and drive away. In 2016, Daniela Vallentin and her colleagues reported that adult and young zebra finches may show different responses. Here exposure of a young zebra finch to a tutor's song resulted in learning that occurs through stimulation of premotor neurons. But in adults, the same stimuli suppress learning. This finding indicates that, during development, suppression can be as important as stimulation and that adults and young may respond.

Researchers have used molecular and cellular techniques to identify the role of specific genes in this learning. When a zebra finch is exposed to songs of potential rivals of conspecifics, the gene called *ZENK* rapidly becomes active within neurons in the song-controlling nuclei of the bird's brain. This produces an enzyme that changes the structure and function of those neurons. The events that trigger additional changes in the bird's brain enhance its ability to detect and respond to new intruding conspecifics. These intruders can pose a real threat to the individual's continued control of its territory.

STUDY BREAK QUESTIONS

1. What role does the *ZENK* gene play?
2. How do nerve connections influence behaviour?
3. What makes zebra finches a good model organism for studying song learning?
4. What is a conspecific?

32.6 Hormones and Behaviour

Hormones are chemical signals that underlie the performance of specific behaviours. Hormones often work by regulating the development of neurons and neural networks, or by stimulating cells within endocrine organs to release chemical signals.

An example of how hormones alter the development of neurons and neural networks can be seen in the singing of courtship songs in male zebra finches. Normally, female zebra finches do not sing. Males do, and very early in life certain cells in their brains produce estrogen, which acts on target neurons in the higher vocal centre of the developing brain. Estrogen invokes a complex series of biochemical changes resulting in the production of more nerve cells in the parts of the brain regulating singing. Brains of developing females do not produce estrogen and females do not sing courtship songs. In the absence of estrogen, the number of neurons in the higher vocal centre of females declines over time (**Figure 32.10**). If young, female zebra finches are given estrogen, they produce more nerve cells in the higher vocal centre and they can sing. Specific stimuli, such as the songs of familiar or unfamiliar males, alter the genetic activity of the nerve cells controlling adult birds' behaviour.

Changes in the concentrations of hormones over time also affect behaviour. For example, as honeybees age, workers perform different tasks. Nurse bees—adults younger than 15 days—tend to care for larvae and maintain the hive; forager bees—adults older than 15 days—make foraging excursions from the hive to collect food (nectar and pollen) (**Figure 32.11**). This behavioural change is induced by rising concentrations of juvenile hormone (see Chapter 43) released by a gland near the bee's brain. Despite its name, circulating levels of juvenile hormone increase as a honeybee ages.

Juvenile hormone affects bee behaviour by stimulating genes in certain brain cells to produce proteins such as octopamine that affect the nervous system. Octopamine stimulates neural transmissions and reinforces memories. It is concentrated in the antennal lobes, the parts of the bee's brain that contribute to analysis of chemical scents in the external environment, and occurs at higher concentrations in older, foraging bees, those with higher levels of juvenile hormone. Experimentally delivered extra juvenile hormone causes bees to increase their production of octopamine. This, in turn, increases octopamine levels in the antennal lobes and helps the foraging bee recognize the odours of flowers where it can collect nectar and pollen.

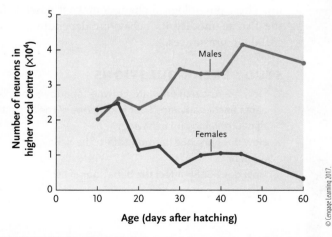

FIGURE 32.10 Hormonally induced changes in brain structure. The brains of young male zebra finches secrete estrogen, which stimulates production of additional neurons in the higher vocal centre. Lacking estrogen, young female zebra finches have fewer neurons in this region of the brain.

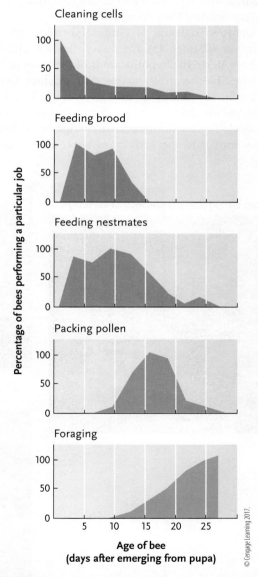

FIGURE 32.11 Age and task specialization in honeybee (*Apis mellifera*) workers. Newly emerged adult bees (nurses) typically clean cells and feed the brood, whereas older workers (foragers) leave the hive to forage for food.

The honeybee example illustrates how genes and hormones interact in the development of behaviour. Genes code for the production of hormones that become part of the intracellular environment of their target cells. Hormones then directly or indirectly change genetic activity and enzymatic biochemistry in these cells. When the target cells are neurons, changes in biochemistry translate into changes in the animal's behaviour.

An African cichlid fish illustrates how hormones regulate reproductive behaviour. Some adult male cichlids maintain nesting territories on the bottom of Lake Tanganyika in East Africa **(Figure 32.12)**. Territory holders are relatively brightly coloured and attract egg-laden females with elaborate behavioural displays. These males aggressively defend their territories against neighbouring territory holders and incursions by non-territorial males. Non-territorial males (drifters) are much less colourful and aggressive and do not control a patch of suitable nesting habitat. They do not court females.

Differences in levels of GnRH (gonadotropin-releasing hormone; see Chapter 43) are responsible for differences in male behaviour. In the hypothalamus of the brain of territorial males, large, biochemically active cells produce GnRH. The same cells in the brains of drifters are small and inactive. GnRH stimulates the testes to produce testosterone and sperm. When circulating sex hormones are carried to the brain of the fish, they modulate the activity of nerve cells that regulate sexual and aggressive behaviour. In the absence of GnRH, male fish do not court females or attack other males.

What causes the differences in the neuronal and hormonal physiology of the two types of male fish? Russell Fernald and his students manipulated the territorial status of males. Some territorial males were stripped of their territories and some non-territorial males were provided with territories. As a control, the territorial status of other males was unaltered. Four weeks after the changes, Fernald and his students compared experimental and control fishes. They considered coloration and behaviour, as well as the size of the GnRH-producing cells in the brains. Territorial males that had been changed to non-territorial males had lost their bright colours and stopped being combative. Moreover, their GnRH-producing cells were smaller than those of the territory-holding controls. Conversely, males that gained a territory had developed bright colours and displayed aggressive behaviours toward other males. GnRH-producing cells in their brains were larger than those of control fish.

This example shows that hormonal changes affect the fishes' success or failure at gaining and holding a territory. Fish can detect and store information about their aggressive interactions. Neurons that process this information transmit their input to the hypothalamus. There it affects the size of cells producing GnRH, in turn dictating the hormonal state of the male. A decrease in GnRH production turns a feisty territorial male into a subdued drifter. Drifters bide their time and build energy reserves for a future attempt at defeating a weaker male and taking over his territory. Males that regain territorial status develop higher levels GnRH, and show vigorous sexual and aggressive behaviour.

Note the general similarity of these processes to those described for song learning by white-crowned sparrows. The fish's brain has cells that secrete hormones that can change its biochemistry, structure, and function in response to well-defined social stimuli. These physiological changes make it possible for the fish to modify its behaviour depending on its social circumstances.

STUDY BREAK QUESTIONS

1. How has research on white-crowned sparrows and zebra finches advanced our knowledge of the impact of neurobiology on behaviour?
2. How does juvenile hormone affect the behaviour of adult bees?
3. How does GnRH affect the behaviour of fish?

a. **African cichlid fish (*Haplochromis burtoni*)**

Nonterritorial male

Territorial male

b.

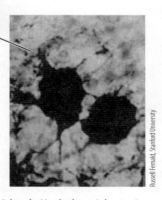

FIGURE 32.12 Photograph **(a)** compares a non-territorial male *Haplochromis burtoni* (top) with a territorial one. Photomicrographs **(b)** compare gonadotropin-releasing hormone (GnRH) cells in the corresponding non-territorial and territorial males.

32.7 Neural Anatomy and Behaviour

Sensory systems are often structured to acquire a disproportionately large amount of information about the stimuli that are most important to the survival and reproductive success of a species. In many cases, sensory information can be relayed directly to motor neurons with little central processing decreasing the time required to produce a response. For instance, insects such as crickets fly mainly at night and avoid most predatory birds. But nocturnal flight exposes them to hunting insectivorous bats. Most insectivorous bats hunt at night and rely on echolocation to detect, identify, and track flying prey (see Chapter 45). The echolocation calls of these bats are usually intense, about 130 dB at 10 cm distance, making the calls stronger than the sound of a smoke detector alarm. The echolocation calls of most bats, however, are beyond the range of human hearing (nominally 20 kHz). While bats use echolocation to obtain information about surroundings and potential prey, these calls can also warn crickets and other insects of an approaching bat.

Many orthopteran insects (grasshoppers and their relatives) have ears on their front legs **(Figure 32.13)** usually used to hear the advertising calls of males. Black field crickets also use these ears to listen to echolocating bats, and then initiate defensive behaviour. Sensory neurons connected to the ears fire in response to bats' echolocation calls, and the information is immediately translated into evasive action. When a bat attacks from the cricket's right side, the right ear receives stronger stimulation than the left ear. The cricket's nervous system relays incoming messages from the right ear to the motor neurons controlling the left hind leg. This stimulation induces firing of motor neurons that control the left hind leg, causing it to jerk up. This, in turn, blocks the movement of the left hindwing, reducing flight power generated on the cricket's left side. Now the cricket swerves sharply to the left and loses altitude, effectively diving down and away from the approaching bat **(Figure 32.14)**.

The structure and neural connections of sensory systems also allow some animals to distinguish potentially life-threatening from more mundane stimuli. Fiddler crabs live and feed on mud flats. They dig burrows providing safe refuge from predators such as gulls and shorebirds. Distinguishing between

A flying cricket usually holds its hind legs close to the body so that they don't get in the way of its wings.

Sound waves from a predatory bat

When a cricket hears the ultrasonic call of a bat coming from its left side, it automatically lifts its right hind leg.

The raised leg interrupts the right wing's movement, causing the insect to swerve down to the right and away from the approaching predator.

FIGURE 32.14 A neural mechanism for escape behaviour in the black field cricket (*Teleogryllus oceanicus*).

Source: May, M. 1991. Aerial defense tactics of flying insects. *American Scientist*, Volume 79, Issue 4, pp. 316–328

predators and other crabs allows a fiddler crab to use its burrow to best advantage. The crab does not dash for cover whenever anything moves in its field of vision, only when it sees a gull or shorebird.

Fiddler crabs have long-stalked eyes that they hold perpendicular to the ground **(Figure 32.15)**. John Layne wondered whether these crabs have a divided field of view to distinguish dangerous predators from fellow crabs. If so, an approaching large gull would stimulate receptors on the upper part of the eye. Movements of other crabs would stimulate receptors below the midpoint of the eyes. Receptors above and below the retinal equator would relay signals to different groups of neurons, effectively wiring the crab's nervous system for a split field of view. If this were correct, stimulation of receptors above the

FIGURE 32.13 A great grig (*Cyphoderris monstrosa*), an orthopteran with ears located on its forelegs (arrow shows grig's right ear)

FIGURE 32.15 A fiddler crab (*Uca pugilator*)

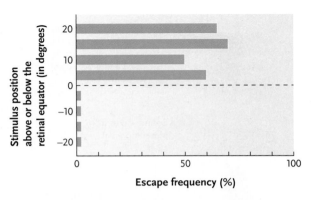

FIGURE 32.16 Stimuli that activated the upper part of the retinae of *Uca pugilator* elicited escape behaviour much more often than those activating the lower retinas.

midline of the eye would activate neurons controlling an escape response, triggering a dash for the burrow. A moving stimulus at or below eye level would not.

Layne placed crabs individually in a glass jar on an elevated platform. He presented a black square to each crab from two different heights. The stimulus circled the jar above or below the crab's eyes. Stimuli activating the upper part of the retina induced escape behaviour; those below the retinal equator were usually ignored (**Figure 32.16**). Specific nervous system connections between a fiddler crab's eyes and brain provide appropriate responses to different specific stimuli.

The match between the structure of an animal's nervous system and the real-world challenges it faces extends beyond the ability to avoid predators. Star-nosed moles live in wet tunnels in North American marshlands and spend almost all their lives in complete darkness. Like bats, its receptor–perceptual system enables it to find food in the dark. A star-nosed mole eats mainly earthworms it locates with its nose, but not by smell. As the mole proceeds down its tunnel, 22 fingerlike tentacles on its nose sweep the area directly ahead of it. Each tentacle is covered with thousands of Eimer's organs (touch receptors; **Figure 32.17**). Sensory nerve terminals in Eimer's organs generate complex and detailed patterns of signals about the objects they contact. These messages are relayed by neurons to the cortex of the mole's brain, much of which is devoted to the analysis of information received from the nose's touch receptors.

The structural basis of the mole's sensory analysis is reflected by the amount of brain tissue responding to signals from its nose. The mole's brain contains many more cells decoding input from Eimer's glands than the combined input received from all other parts of the animal's body (Figure 32.17b). Moreover, the brain does not treat inputs from all 22 of the mole's "nose fingers" equally. Instead, the brain devotes more cells to input from tentacles closest to the mouth. Fewer cells analyze messages from those farther away. The extra attention given to signals from tentacles closest to the mouth helps the star-nosed mole locate prey that are close to its mouth, in turn allowing it to feed more efficiently.

Animals' nervous systems do not offer neutral and complete pictures of the environment. Instead, the pictures are distorted, but the unbalanced perceptions of the world are advantageous because certain types of information are far more important than others for the animals' survival and reproductive success.

STUDY BREAK QUESTIONS

1. How do crickets hear the echolocation calls of bats?
2. How does what they see influence the behaviour of fiddler crabs?
3. What function is played by the star of a star-nosed mole?

32.8 Communication

In animal communication, one individual produces a signal that is received by another. This can change the behaviour of one or both individuals in a way that benefits the signaller and/or the signal receiver. The signaller is the individual transmitting information (the signal), and the signal receiver (**Figure 32.18**) is the one receiving the signal. Behaviour such as mimicry (see Section 30.4) and the success of nest parasites (see above) occurs when one species breaks the signal codes of another, exploiting them to advantage.

Animals use a variety of sensory modalities to transmit signals, including acoustical, chemical, electrical, vibrational, and visual. Some signals combine modalities. Sometimes the animal itself is a signal; in other situations, the animal's excretory or eliminated products are signals.

Bird songs are acoustical signals. The song of a male whippoorwill (*Caprimulgus vociferus*) or grey vireo, advertises his presence to females and may help him secure a mate. The same song is heard by other males, who recognize it as a territorial display. After the eggs have been laid, the same song is heard by the young developing in the eggs. This exposure influences the songs to which the animals respond when they mature. Other birds, such as male club-winged manakins (*Machaeropterus deliciosus*) and some hummingbirds, use courtship sounds produced by feather stridulations, rubbing one feather against another. Many other animals, from insects to rattlesnakes, use sounds as signals. Pacific herring (*Clupea pallasii*) communicate with conspecifics through the noise generated with little bursts of gas (known colloquially as "farts") passed from the anus.

A striped skunk's (*Mephitis mephitis*; **Figure 32.19a**) black and white stripes constitute a **visual signal**. Other examples of visual signals are humans' facial expressions and body language. These visual signals are available to anyone viewing them. Visual signals can be enhanced by morphological features, such as the erectile crest of a royal kingbird (*Onychorhynchus coronatus*; Figure 32.19b), or bioluminescent signals in animals living in darkness (e.g., Figure 39.4, Chapter 39). In many animals, visual signals are ritualized—exaggerated and stereotyped to enhance their function as signals, such as the swaggering gait of a striped skunk.

a. Sensory organs on the tentacle of a star-nosed mole

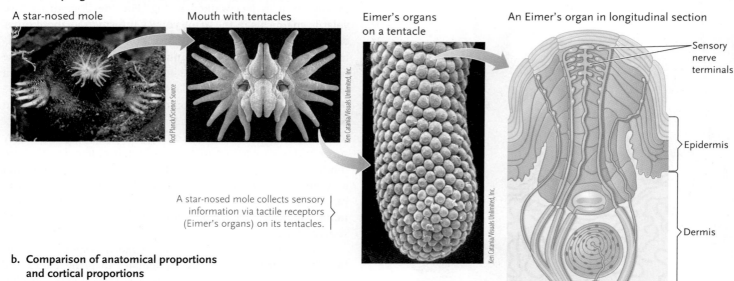

A star-nosed mole

Mouth with tentacles

Eimer's organs on a tentacle

An Eimer's organ in longitudinal section

Sensory nerve terminals

Epidermis

Dermis

A star-nosed mole collects sensory information via tactile receptors (Eimer's organs) on its tentacles.

b. Comparison of anatomical proportions and cortical proportions

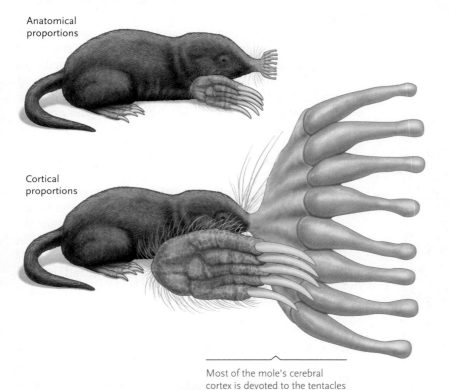

Anatomical proportions

Cortical proportions

Most of the mole's cerebral cortex is devoted to the tentacles and front, digging feet.

FIGURE 32.17 The collection and analysis of sensory information by the star-nosed mole (*Condylura cristata*). (a) The mole's nose has 22 fleshy tentacles covered with cylindrical tactile receptors called *Eimer's organs*. Each Eimer's organ contains sensory nerve terminals. **(b)** The mole's cerebral cortex devotes far more space and neurons to analysis of input from the tentacles than from elsewhere on the body. These drawings compare the relative amounts of sensory information coming from different parts of a mole's body.

FIGURE 32.18 Song birds, such as this grey vireo (*Vireo vicinior*), use songs to advertise their presence to unmated females and to other males

CHAPTER 32 ANIMAL BEHAVIOUR

a.

b.

FIGURE 32.19 **(a)** The distinctive black and white pattern of a striped skunk (*Mephitis mephitis*) warns predators about its chemical defence. **(b)** The distinctive crest of a female royal kingbird is a sexually dimorphic character: males have red crests; females have yellow crests.

Many species produce chemical signals, as is well known to anyone who has walked a dog. For the dog, distinctive volatile chemicals in the urine convey information about other dogs that have urinated there. Pheromones are distinctive volatile chemicals released in minute amounts to influence the behaviour of conspecifics. The body of a worker ant contains a battery of glands, each releasing a different pheromone **(Figure 32.20)**. One set of pheromones recruits fellow workers to battle colony invaders. Another stimulates workers to collect food discovered outside the colony. Pheromones are used by some animals to attract mates. For instance, female silkworm moths (*Bombyx mori*) produce the pheromone bombykol, and a single molecule of this pheromone stimulates specialized receptors on the antennae of any downwind, male silkworm moth. Males so stimulated fly upwind in search the female, the source of the stimulus.

Male silkworm moths (*Bombyx mori*) respond to bombykol produced and released by females to bring males and females together. Male *B. mori* detect bombykol using specialized receptors on their antennae (see Chapter 45).

Not surprisingly, some predators use pheromones to lure prey. Female bolas spiders (*Mastophora cornigera* and other species in the genus) use a sticky ball of web impregnated with a chemical that mimics the odour of sex pheromones secreted by female moths. Male moths respond to the lure of these odours, approach the pheromone-soaked web, and are captured by the spiders. Bolas spiders prey on more than one species of moth and produce different sex pheromone-like compounds to attract different species of moths. Another species of bolas spider, *Mastophora hutchinsoni*, adjusts the production of pheromone mimic to match the times of maximum activity by smoky tetanolita (*Tetanolita mynesalis*) and bristly cutworm (*Lacinipolia renigera*). The pheromone blend for the early-flying *L. renigera* does not attract late-flying *T. mynesalis*, so the spider adjusts the blend of pheromones on its lure. This spider lures the early-flying moth with one blend and the late-flying moth with another.

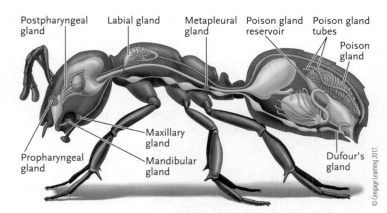

FIGURE 32.20 **Chemical signals.** An ant's body contains a host of pheromone-producing glands, each of which manufactures and releases its own volatile chemical or chemicals.

In many species, touch conveys important messages from a signaller to a receiver. **Tactile signals** can operate only over very short distances, but for social animals living in close company, they play a significant role in the development of friendly bonds between individuals (**Figure 32.21**).

Some freshwater fish species use weak **electric signals** to communicate. This is especially true of species living in murky tropical rivers where visual signals cannot be seen (see Figure 45.41, Chapter 45). These fish have electric organs that produce electric signals that vary in intensity, duration, and frequency. This gives the fish a considerable repertoire of signals. Among the New World knifefish (order Gymnotiformes), including the electric eel (Figure 45.41, Chapter 45), electrical discharges can signal threats, submission, or a readiness to breed.

Karl von Frisch demonstrated that the famous dance of the honeybee involves tactile, acoustical, and chemical signals (**Figure 32.22**). When a foraging honeybee discovers a source of pollen or nectar, it returns to its colony. There, in the darkness of the hive, it dances on the vertical surface of the honeycomb. The dancer moves in a circle, attracting a crowd of workers. Some workers follow and maintain physical contact with the dancer. The dance delivers information about the food source, its quality, and the distance and direction observers will need to fly to locate it.

The bee performs a round dance when the food source is less than 75 m from the hive (Figure 32.22a). Here the bee moves in tight circles, swinging its abdomen back and forth. Bees surrounding the dancer produce a brief acoustical signal that stimulates the dancer to regurgitate a sample of the food it discovered. The regurgitated sample serves as a chemical cue for other workers that search for the food. The bee uses a waggle dance when the food is farther away. This involves a half-circle in one direction,

then a straight line while waggling its abdomen, and finally a half-circle in the other direction (see Figure 32.22b). With each waggle, the dancer produces a brief buzzing sound. The angle of the waggle run relative to the vertical honeycomb indicates the direction of the food source relative to the position of the Sun (see Figure 32.22c). The duration of the waggles and buzzes carries information about distance to the food. The more time spent waggling and buzzing, the farther away the food is from the hive. Some people were loath to accept a "dance language" in bees, perhaps in the hopes that language was a feature unique to humans. Bees and many other insects use "simple eyes" (ocelli) to measure light intensity. By blackening the ocelli of dancing bees, James L. Gould manipulated their perception of the Sun. This affected the messages in the dances, effectively lying to other bees about the location of food. The bees observing the dance did not have blackened ocelli and went to find flowers in the location indicated by the dance. In reality, this was the wrong location because of differences in the dancing and observer bees' perceptions of the position of the Sun.

An echolocating animal stores the outgoing signal in its brain for comparison with returning echoes. The differences between what the animal "says" and what it hears are the data used in echolocation. However, when an echolocating bat or dolphin produces echolocation signals, the signals are audible

a. Round dance

b. Waggle dance

c. Coding direction in the waggle dance

When the bee moves straight down the comb, other bees fly to the source directly away from the Sun.

When the bee moves 45° to the right of vertical, other bees fly at a 45° angle to the right of the Sun.

When the bee moves straight up the comb, other bees fly straight toward the Sun.

© Cengage Learning 2017.

FIGURE 32.22 Dance communication by honeybees (*Apis mellifera*). Foraging honeybees transmit information about the location and quality of a food source by dancing on a vertical honeycomb. **(a)** If the food source is close to the hive, the forager performs a *round dance*. **(b)** When food is farther from the hive, the honeybee performs a *waggle dance*. **(c)** The dancing bee indicates the direction to the distant food source by the angle of the waggle run.

M. B. Fenton

FIGURE 32.21 Tactile signals. Grooming by hyacinth macaws (*Anodorhynchus hyacinthinus*) removes ectoparasites and dirt from feathers. The close physical contact promotes friendly relationships between groomer and groomee.

to some other animals as well. When the bat or dolphin is foraging, potential prey (certain insects for the bat; certain fish for the dolphin) hear the signals and move away from the sound source (= negative phonotaxis) in an effort to evade the approaching predator. When the bat is close (strong echolocation signals), moths with ears dive to the ground or use erratic flight to evade the bats. Moths with ears sensitive to bat echolocation calls evade bat attacks 40% of the time. Insects lacking bat detectors are caught at much higher rates, sometimes >90% of the time. Acoustic warfare between bats and insects and dolphins and fish intrigues biologists because of the measures and countermeasures used by both predator and prey.

The same echolocation calls that alert potential prey are available to any other animals within earshot, provided that their ears are sensitive to the frequencies in the signals. Little brown myotis **(Figure 32.23a)** eavesdrop on the calls of conspecifics to locate concentrations of prey. Spotted bats (*Euderma maculatum*; Figure 32.23b) either approach a calling conspecific, apparently to chase it away, or turn and leave the area. Resident killer whales (*Orcinus orca*) in the Pacific Ocean off the west coast of Canada typically use echolocation to detect, track, and locate the salmon they eat. Transient killer whales in the same area feed mainly on marine mammals. These killer whales rarely echolocate. Local marine mammals, such as seals, quickly leave the water when they hear the echolocation calls of approaching killer whales.

The study of echolocation is a rich source of information about signals, signal design, hearing systems, and behaviour. Signal receivers often respond to communications from signallers in predictable ways. A male white-crowned sparrow generally avoids entering a neighbouring territory when it hears the song of the resident male. Similarly, young male baboons and mandrills often retreat without a fight when they see an older male's visual threat display **(Figure 32.24)**, even when retreat means loss of a chance to mate with a female. Why do these individuals behave in ways that appear to benefit their rivals but not themselves?

Explaining behavioural interactions often means considering how an animal's actions affect its reproductive output. The retreating white-crowned sparrow avoids wasting time and energy on a battle it is likely to lose. By retreating, the would-be intruder minimizes the chances of being injured or killed by a resident male. Moreover, ousting the current resident might be more tiring and risky than finding a suitable unoccupied breeding site. Resident males usually win physical contests, and intruders typically succeed in gaining a territory from a resident only after a prolonged series of exhausting clashes. Observations of territorial species such as birds, lizards, frogs, fish, and insects generally support these predictions.

a.

b.

FIGURE 32.23 A little brown myotis (a) **and a spotted bat** (b)

FIGURE 32.24 The open-mouth threat display of a male chacma baboon (*Papio ursinus*) almost looks like a yawn but is much more menacing.

Applying a similar argument to competition among male baboons, smaller or younger males will concede females to threatening older rivals without fighting. Retreating means reducing the risk of losing a fight and being injured. Evolutionary analyses suggest that the signaller and signal receiver benefit from the exchange of signals. Here, both individuals avoid a physical altercation that might be damaging or fatal.

In winter, common ravens (*Corvus corax*) sometimes emit a "yell" call upon finding the carcass of a deer. The yell attracts a crowd of hungry ravens. The calling behaviour puzzled Bernd Heinrich, who noted that, when paired territory-holding adult ravens found a carcass, they fed quietly and did not yell. He noted young ravens without territories yelled when they happened upon a carcass in another bird's territory. The yells attracted other ravens, which collectively overwhelmed the residents' efforts to defend the carcass and their territory. Non-territorial ravens used yells to exploit the food supply, whereas residents just ate. Heinrich concluded that the reproductive benefit of resident ravens was enhanced by uninterrupted feeding. Non-territorial ravens succeeded in their trespassing only when they attracted others.

STUDY BREAK QUESTIONS

1. What sensory modalities do animals use in communication?
2. How do "yells" influence the behaviour of ravens? Explain.
3. What is echolocation? Which animals echolocate?

32.9 Language: Syntax and Symbols

Although language is communication, not all communication is language. Many people believe that language is the exclusive domain of humans, but the basis for the distinction between humans and other animals is not clear. The round and waggle dances of honeybees contain both syntax (the order in which information is presented) and symbols (a display that represents something else), and many consider them to meet the criteria for language.

Vervet monkeys also have a repertoire of signals to alert conspecifics to different predators. These monkeys use one signal for snakes, another for leopards, and still another for raptors. Furthermore, they show different predator-specific defensive behaviours. Chickadees (*Poecile atricapillus*) also use different alarm calls to alert others to approaching danger. Captive, trained chimpanzees and gorillas (*Gorilla gorilla*) have been reported to be able to learn and use American Sign Language (ASL).

When it comes to communication, humans are not as distinct from other animals as some people would like to believe. For example, like most other animals, humans used body language. To appreciate this, and redundancy in animal communication, observe the body language and facial expressions of someone talking on a telephone. The eloquence of these signals is not conveyed to the signal receiver at the other end of the phone!

As in the case of the songs of some birds, humans also show sex-specific transmission of language. In 2011, Peter Forster and Colin Renfrew reported that, in several parts of the world **(Figure 32.25)**, immigrant men are central to producing changes in local languages. Note that this has been documented in North America, Iceland, Africa, India, and the Malayo–Polynesian areas. The finding is based on the relationship between the incidence of Y-chromosome types (male lineages) on language change, while mtDNA types (female lineages) reflect the persistence of the more ancient language. The movement of animals—in this case people—influences the spread of behaviour, culture, and social norms.

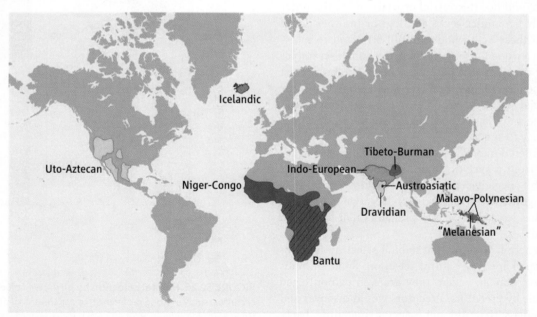

FIGURE 32.25 The relationship between Y-chromosome DNA types and language. This pattern does not emerge from mtDNA derived from the mother. Here, "Melanesian" indicates non–Malayo-Polynesian languages (New Guinea). The Niger–Congo language family includes Bantu (the hatched area).

Source: From Forster and Renfrew. 2011. "Mother Tongue and Y Chromosomes," *Science* Volume 333, page 1390. *Science* by American Association for the Advancement of Science

STUDY BREAK QUESTIONS

1. What is the meaning and importance of syntax and symbols in signalling?
2. What are the social implications of findings about the appearances of new languages in humans?
3. What other animals use language?

32.10 Space

The geographic range of many animal species includes a mosaic of habitat types. The breeding ranges of white-crowned sparrows can encompass forests, meadows, housing developments, and city dumps. Other animals have a limited geographic range; for example, a Kirtland's warbler (*Dendroica kirtlandii*) is found only in young jack pine forests. At the individual level, an animal's home range, its choice of habitat, is critically important because the habitat provides food, shelter, nesting sites, and the other organisms with which it interacts. If an animal chooses a habitat that does not provide appropriate resources, it will not survive and reproduce.

On a large spatial scale, animals almost certainly use multiple criteria to select the habitats they occupy, but we do not know the general principles about how animals make these choices. When a migrating bird arrives at its breeding range, it probably cues on large-scale geographic features, such as a pond or a patch of large trees. If the bird does not find the food or nesting resources it needs, or if other individuals already occupy the space, it may move to another habitat patch.

Thus, on a finer spatial scale, basic responses to physical factors enable animals to find suitable habitats. **Kinesis** (*kine* = movement; *es* = inward) is a change in the rate of movement or the frequency of turning movements in response to environmental stimuli. Wood lice (terrestrial crustaceans in the order Isopoda) typically live under rocks and logs or in other damp places. Although these arthropods are not attracted to moisture per se, when a wood louse encounters dry soil, it scrambles around, turning frequently. When it reaches a patch of moist soil, it moves much less. This kinesis results in wood lice accumulating in moist habitats. Wood lice exposed to dry soil quickly dehydrate and die, so those that move to moister habitats are more likely to survive.

A **taxis** (= ordered movement) is a response directed either toward or away from a specific stimulus. Cockroaches (order Blattodea) exhibit negative phototaxis, meaning that they actively avoid light and seek darkness. Negative phototaxis makes cockroaches less vulnerable to predators that use vision to find their food.

Biologists generally assume that habitat selection is adaptive and has been shaped by natural selection. Some animals instinctively select habitats where they are well camouflaged and less detectable by predators. Predators would discover and eliminate individuals that did not select a matching background, along with any alleles responsible for the mismatch.

Many insects have inherited preferences for the plants they eat as larvae (e.g., caterpillars). Adults often lay their eggs only on appropriate food plants, effectively selecting the habitats where their offspring will live and feed.

Vertebrates sometimes exhibit innate preferences, as demonstrated by two closely related species of European birds, blue tits (*Cyanistes caeruleus*) and coal tits (*Periparus ater*). Adult blue tits forage mainly in oak trees; coal tits in pine trees. When researchers reared the young of both species in cages without any vegetation and then offered them a choice between oak branches and pine branches, coal tits immediately gravitated toward pine branches and blue tits toward oak branches, suggesting an innate preference **(Figure 32.26)**. Each species feeds most efficiently in the tree species it prefers.

STUDY BREAK QUESTION

1. Define *kinesis* and *taxis*.

32.11 Home Range and Territory

Space is an important resource for animals. Although many animals are motile, moving about in space, others are sessile. Sessile species such as barnacles (see Chapter 27) anchor themselves to the substrate but are motile as larvae. Barnacles that live on whales or the hulls of ships are sessile but mobile because of the substrate they selected. Motile animals have a home range, the

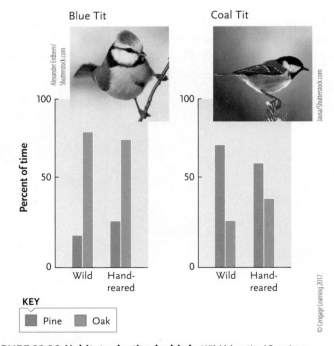

FIGURE 32.26 Habitat selection by birds. Wild blue tits (*Cyanistes caeruleus*) show a strong preference for oak trees; coal tits (*Periparus ater*) show a strong preference for pines. Hand-reared birds raised in a vegetation-free environment showed identical but slightly weaker responses.

space they regularly traverse during their lives. Home ranges or parts of home ranges become territories when they are defended. In species such as pronghorn antelopes **(Figure 32.27)**, some males hold territories. Female pronghorns are not usually territorial. There is a direct connection between territory quality and male reproductive success. Male pronghorn antelopes defending the "best" territories (those with the best food resources) attract the most females, offering the male the most opportunities to mate with the most females.

Territorial defence is always a costly activity. Patrolling territory borders, performing displays hundreds of times per day, and chasing intruders take time and energy. Moreover, territorial displays increase an animal's likelihood of being injured or detected and captured by a predator. But territorial behaviour has its benefits, such as access to females. Territorial surgeonfish (*Acanthurus lineatus*) living in coral reefs around American Samoa may engage in as many as 1900 chases per day, defending their small territories from incursions by other algae-eating fish. However, territorial surgeonfish eat five times as much food as non-territory-holders because they have more exclusive access to the food in their territories.

STUDY BREAK QUESTIONS

1. What is the difference between a home range and a territory?
2. How are home ranges and territories different from a species' range?

32.12 Migration

CONCEPT FIX Many people think that migrating animals travel in groups. But we now know that many animals migrate alone, including birds, bats, fur seals, and sea turtles. We know relatively little about the details of the migrations and migratory behaviour of most animals. ⬡

FIGURE 32.27 Pronghorn antelopes (*Antilocapra americana*)

Many animal species migrate. Seasonal migrations involve individuals travelling from the area where they were born or hatched to a distant and initially unfamiliar destination. The migration is complete when the same individuals later return to their natal site. Defining migration as seasonal movements of individuals to and from different areas readily applies to many birds and other animals. This definition does not, however, describe the migrations of other animals such as monarch butterflies (*Danaus plexippus*). Here, different individuals are involved in the migration. Seasonal changes in food supply underlie the migration of monarch butterflies, which eat milkweed leaves as caterpillars and milkweed nectar as adults **(Figure 32.28)**. In eastern North America, milkweed plants grow only during spring and summer. Many adult monarchs head south in late summer, when the plants begin to die. Some migrate as much as 4000 km from eastern and central North America to central Mexico, where they cluster in spectacular numbers (Figure 32.28b and c). They appear to use olfactory cues to find preferred resting places. Unlike migrant birds, these insects do not feed at their overwintering grounds. Instead, their metabolic rate decreases in the cool mountain air. The butterflies are inactive for months, conserving their energy reserves.

With the arrival of spring, the butterflies become active and begin the return migration to northern breeding habitats. The northward migration is slow, however, and many individuals stop along the way to feed and lay eggs. Their offspring, and their offspring's offspring, continue the northward migration through the summer. Some descendants of these migrants eventually reach Canada for a final round of breeding. The summer's last generation then returns south to the spot where their ancestors, two to five generations removed, spent the previous winter.

As we have seen there are many interesting facets to migration. What is the underlying physiology of the migrants? What determines the routes that migrants follow? What cues are used in orientation and navigation?

Fuel selection is an important aspect of migration physiology. For the most part, migrating birds appear to burn fat to fuel flight, and they are able to do this because they laid down fat stores in the period leading up to migration. In 2011, however, Alex Gerson and Chris Guglielmo reported their work on Swainson's thrushes (*Catharus ustulatus*). They flew birds in a wind tunnel continuously for up to five hours **(Figure 32.29)**. The birds flew in high or in low relative humidity. When flying in drier air, the birds increased their rates of loss of lean mass (i.e., turned to using protein stores for fuel). This increased production of endogenous water and increased the concentrations of uric acid in blood plasma (a method of conserving water). Humidity clearly influences the composition of fuel consumed by flying Swainson's thrushes. Understanding the physiology of migration is an intriguing area of research.

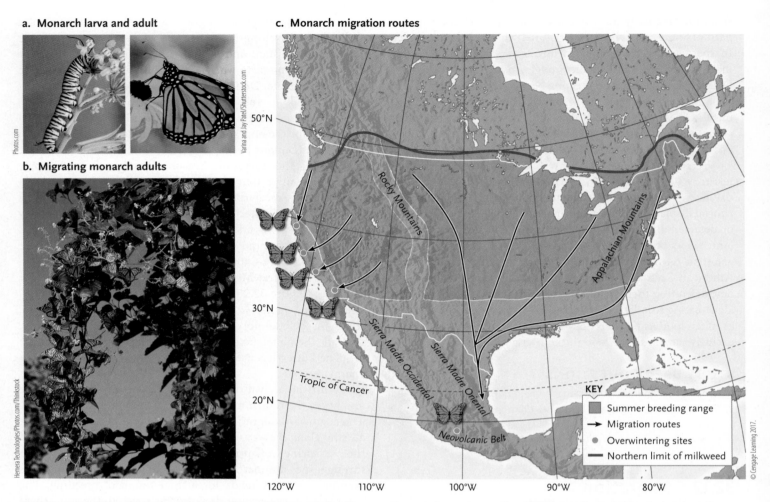

a. Monarch larva and adult

b. Migrating monarch adults

c. Monarch migration routes

50°N

Rocky Mountains

Appalachian Mountains

30°N

Sierra Madre Occidental

Sierra Madre Oriental

20°N

Tropic of Cancer

Neovolcanic Belt

KEY
- Summer breeding range
→ Migration routes
• Overwintering sites
— Northern limit of milkweed

120°W   110°W   100°W   90°W   80°W

© Cengage Learning 2017.

FIGURE 32.28 Migrating monarch butterflies. (a) Monarch butterflies eat milkweed plants as caterpillars. **(b)** When milkweed plants in their breeding range die back at the end of summer, monarchs migrate south. The following spring, after passing the winter in a semidormant state, they migrate north. **(c)** Monarchs that live and breed east of the Rocky Mountains migrate to Mexico. Those living west of the Rocky Mountains overwinter in coastal California.

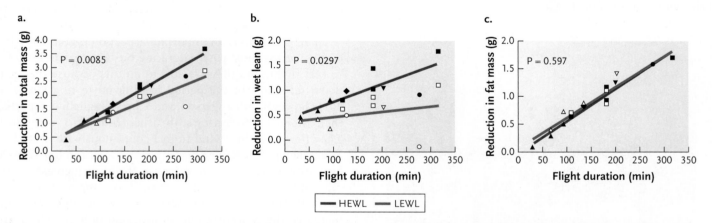

a.

P = 0.0085

b.

P = 0.0297

c.

P = 0.597

HEWL   LEWL

FIGURE 32.29 Loss of mass (a), **wet lean mass** (b), **and fat mass** (c) **by flying Swainson's thrushes differed significantly, depending upon humidity.** Closed symbols and red lines show data from high relative humidity (high evaporative water loss: HEWL); open symbols and blue lines are from low relative humidity (low evaporative water loss: LEWL).

Source: From Gerson, "Flight at Low Ambient Humidity Increases Protein Catabolism in Migratory Birds," *Science* 09 Sep 2011: Vol. 333, Issue 6048, pp. 1434-1436. *Science* by American Association for the Advancement of Science Reproduced with permission of AMERICAN ASSOCIATION FOR THE ADVANCEMENT OF SCIENCE in the format Republish in a book via Copyright Clearance Center.

How do young animals learn migration routes and destinations? In some cases, young migrate with adults, but this is not always the case. For most migrating animals, we do not know the details of what is involved. For instance, in North America, some bats appear to migrate between summer and winter ranges. For the most part, hoary bats (*Lasiurus cinereus*; **Figure 32.30a**) and silver-haired bats (*Lasionycteris noctivagans*; Figure 32.30b) are not found in the northern parts of their range in winter. Isotopic and other evidence suggests that these bats undertake seasonal north–south migrations but, to date, there are few records of the movements of tagged individuals.

Erin Baerwald and Robert Barclay (University of Calgary) assessed the possibility that young hoary and silver-haired bats migrated with their mothers. They analyzed microsatellite genotypes and stable isotopic values ($\delta^{13}C$, $\delta^{15}N$, and $\delta^{2}H$) in tissues obtained from bats killed (133 hoary bats and 87 silver-haired bats) at turbines on wind farms. They found no evidence that bats killed at the same time at the same turbines were close genetic relatives, or had spent the summer in the same geographic locations. These data indicate that at least hoary bats and silver-haired bats do not migrate with genetic relatives or with animals that might have been their summer neighbours.

What cues are used in orientation and navigation? Moving animals use three main categories of way-finding mechanisms: **piloting**, **compass orientation**, and **navigation**. Many species probably use some combination of these mechanisms to guide their movements.

32.12a Piloting

Piloting is the simplest way-finding mechanism; it involves the use of familiar landmarks to guide the journey. Grey whales migrate from Alaska to Baja California and back using visual cues provided by the Pacific coastline of North America. When it is time to breed and lay eggs, Pacific salmon use olfactory cues to pilot their way from the ocean back to the stream in which they hatched.

Often, animals that do not migrate use specific landmarks to identify their nest site or places where they have stored food. Female digger wasps (*Philanthus triangulum*) nest in soil. In 1938, Niko Tinbergen showed that, after foraging flights, these wasps used visual landmarks to find their nests **(Figure 32.31)**. While the female wasp was in the nest, Tinbergen arranged pinecones in a circle around it. As she left, the wasp flew around the area, apparently noting nearby landmarks. Tinbergen then moved the circle of pinecones a short distance away. Each time the female returned, she searched for her nest within the pinecone circle. She never once found her nest unless the pinecones were returned to their original position. Later, Tinbergen rearranged the pinecones into a triangle after females left their nests and added a ring of stones nearby. The returning females looked for their nest in the stone circle. Tinbergen concluded that digger wasps respond to the general outline or geometry of landmarks around their nests and not to the specific objects making up the landmarks.

a.

b.

FIGURE 32.30 A hoary bat (a) **and a silver-haired bat** (b)

Some birds that migrate at night determine their direction by using **celestial navigation**: the positions of stars. The indigo bunting flies about 3500 km from the northeastern United States to the Caribbean or Central America each fall and makes the return journey each spring. Stephen Emlen demonstrated that indigo buntings direct their migration using celestial cues

Wasp's flight pattern on leaving nest

Wasp's return, looking for nest

Nest

FIGURE 32.31 Female digger wasps find their nest. A ring of pinecones serves as a landmark for a female digger wasp (*Philanthus triangulum*). By moving landmarks, Niko Tinbergen demonstrated the role they serve in the wasp's orientation behaviour.

(Figure 32.32). Emlen confined individual buntings in cone-shaped test cages whose sides were lined with blotting paper. He placed inkpads on the cage bottoms and kept the cages in an outdoor enclosure so that the birds had a full view of the night sky. Whenever a bird made a directed movement, its inky footprints indicated the direction in which it was trying to move. On clear nights in fall, the footprints pointed to the south, but in spring, they pointed north. On cloudy nights, when the buntings could not see the stars, Emlen recorded that their footprints were evenly distributed in all directions. The data indicated that the compass of indigo buntings required a view of the stars.

32.12b Navigation

Navigation is the most complex way-finding mechanism. It occurs when an animal moves toward a specific destination, using both a compass and a mental map of where it is in relation to the destination. Hikers in unfamiliar surroundings routinely use navigation to find their way home. They use a map to determine their current position and the necessary direction of movement, as well as a compass to orient themselves in that direction.

To document navigation, biologists often use animals carrying radio transmitters, sometimes with GPS (Global Positioning System) capability. By releasing the animals from distant locations and following them, researchers obtain evidence of migration. This is true for homing pigeons (*Columba livia*), birds that can navigate to their home coops from any direction. Homing pigeons appear to use the Sun's position as their compass and olfactory cues as their map. In Israel, biologists demonstrated that Egyptian rousette bats (*Rousettus aegyptiacus*; **Figure 32.33**) have a mental map of their home

ranges. These bats locate preferred roosts and sources of food even when released 10s of kilometres outside their home range.

Genetic analyses of populations of dragonflies (the wandering glider; *Pantala flavescens*) from different parts of the world (North America, South America, and Asia) suggest one interbreeding (panmictic) population. This raises interesting questions about the physiology of these dragonflies on flights of several thousand kilometres, as well as others about navigational cues and performance.

32.12c Why Migrate?

Migrations by white-crowned sparrows and many other species are triggered by changes in day length. Shortening day length indicates approaching fall and winter; lengthening day length indicates spring. Day length changes the anterior pituitary of the bird's brain to generate a series of hormonal changes. In response, birds feed heavily and accumulate the fat reserves necessary to fuel their long journey. Sparrows also become increasingly restless at night until, one evening, they begin their nocturnal migration. Their ability to adopt and maintain a southerly orientation in autumn (and a northerly one in spring) rests in part on their capacity to use the positions of stars to provide directional information.

Not all animal species migrate and, in some species, individuals in some populations migrate, while others do not, for example, different populations of Brazilian free-tailed bats (*Tadarida brasiliensis*). Advantages to staying put can include effective exploitation of local resources, reflecting detailed local knowledge. This can be a combination of food, nest sites, mates, and local communities of predators and parasites.

Migratory behaviour entails obvious costs, such as the time and energy devoted to the journey and the risk of death

FIGURE 32.32 **Experimental Research**

Experimental Analysis of the Indigo Bunting's Star Compass

Indigo Bunting

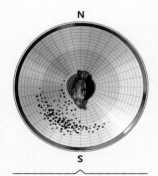

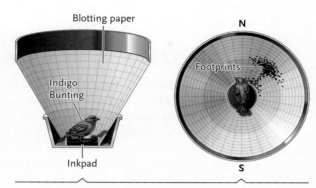

Side (left) and overhead (right) views of the test cage with blotting paper on the sides and an inkpad on the bottom.

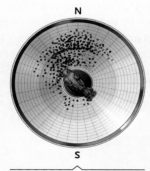 

In autumn, the bunting footprints indicated that they were trying to fly south.

In spring, the bunting footprints indicated that they were trying to fly north.

On cloudy nights, when buntings could not see the stars, their footprints indicated a random pattern of movement.

Question: Do indigo buntings (*Passerina cyanea*) use the positions of stars in the night sky to orient their migrations?

Experiment: Emlen placed individual buntings in cone-shaped test cages. He lined the sides of the cages with blotting paper, placed inkpads on the bottom, and kept the cages in an outdoor enclosure so that the birds had a full view of the sky. Whenever a bird made a directed movement, its inky footprints indicated the direction in which it was trying to fly. Emlen predicted that the footprints would show the buntings' inclination to migrate south in autumn and north in spring.

Results: On clear nights in autumn, the footprints pointed to the south; on clear nights in spring, they pointed north. On cloudy nights, when buntings could not see the stars, their footprints were evenly distributed in all directions.

Conclusion: Indigo buntings use the positions of the stars to direct their seasonal migrations. When they could see the stars above their test cages, they moved in the predicted direction; but when clouds obscured their view of the stars, they moved in random directions.

Source: © Cengage Learning 2017. Based on S. T. Emlen. 1967. "Migratory orientation of the indigo bunting, *Passerina cyanea*. Part I: Evidence for use of celestial cues." *The Auk* 84: 309–342.

FIGURE 32.33 A flying Egyptian rousette

from exhaustion or predation. Migratory behaviour is not universal: many animals never migrate, spending their lives in one location. Why do some species migrate? What ecological pressures give migrating individuals higher fitness than individuals that do not migrate? Remember that many species of terrestrial animals migrate, such as wildebeest and caribou.

For migratory birds, seasonal changes in food supply are the most widely accepted hypothesis to explain migratory behaviour. Insects can be abundant in higher-latitude (greater than 50 degrees north or south) habitats during the warm spring and summer, providing excellent resources for birds to raise offspring. As summer wanes and fall and winter approach, insects all but disappear. Bird species that remain in temperate habitats over winter eat mainly seeds and dormant insects.

When it is winter at higher latitudes, energy supplies are more predictably available in the tropical grounds used by overwintering migratory birds.

Two-way migratory journeys may provide other benefits. Avoiding the northern winter is probably adaptive because endotherms must increase their metabolic rates just to stay warm in cold climates (see Chapter 42). Moreover, summer days are longer at high latitudes than they are in the tropics (see *The Purple Pages*), giving adult birds more time to feed and rear a brood.

For other animals, migration to breeding grounds may provide the special conditions necessary for reproduction. Grey whales migrate south, where females give birth to their young in quiet, shallow lagoons where predators are rare and warm water temperatures are more conducive to the growth of their calves.

Global warming can have what may be unexpected negative effects on some migrating animals. Red knots (*Calidris canutus canutus*) summer in the Arctic and winter close to the equator (**Figure 32.34**). Young red knots raised in the far north and exposed to global warming are malnourished because of the warmer habitats. Malnourished red knots have shorter bills and smaller body size, and are vulnerable because those with shorter bills eat more seagrass rhizomes than molluscs. Global warming produces red knots with smaller bodies and shorter bills; they are less effective at obtaining molluscs buried in the mud and suffer higher overwinter mortality.

STUDY BREAK QUESTIONS

1. Define *migration*. Give examples of migratory animals, including some not mentioned in the text. Do any humans migrate?
2. How do migrating animals find their way? Distinguish between navigation and compass orientation.

32.13 Mates as Resources

Mating systems have evolved to maximize reproductive success, partly in response to the amount of parental care that offspring require and partly in response to other aspects of a species' ecology. **Monogamy** describes the situation in which a male and a female form a pair bond for a mating season or, in some cases, for the individuals' reproductive lives. **Polygamy** occurs when one male has active pair bonds with more than one female (**polygyny**), or one female has active pair bonds with more than one male (**polyandry**). **Promiscuity** occurs when males and females have no pair bonds beyond the time it takes to mate. In polygyny, males often contribute nothing but sperm to reproduction; in polyandry, females nothing but eggs. The details vary according to the physiology of reproduction. In viviparous animals, the animals that get pregnant (usually females) may bear the costs of housing and feeding developing young.

FIGURE 32.34 Red knots, their summer and winter ranges (a)**, and effects of ice melt on body size** (b)

Source: From van Gils, "Body shrinkage due to Arctic warming reduces red knot fitness in tropical wintering range," *Science* 13 May 2016: Vol. 352, Issue 6287, pp. 819-821. *Science* by American Association for the Advancement of Science Reproduced with permission of AMERICAN ASSOCIATION FOR THE ADVANCEMENT OF SCIENCE in the format Republish in a book via Copyright Clearance Center.

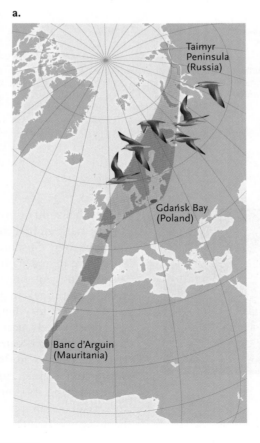

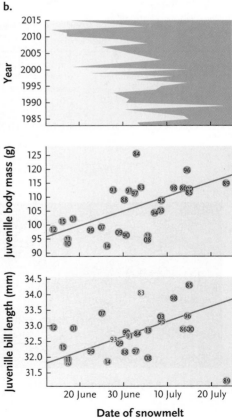

When young require a great deal of care that both parents can provide, monogamy often prevails. Songbirds, such as the white-crowned sparrow **(Figure 32.35)**, are altricial (naked and helpless) when they hatch. They beg for food, and both parents can bring it to them. Males and females achieve higher rates of reproduction when both parents are actively involved with raising young. In mammals, the situation is different because females provide the food (milk). Monogamy occurs in species in which males indirectly feed the young by bringing food to the mother.

If males have high-quality territories, the females living there may be able to raise young on their own. These males may be polygynous (mate with several females). The male's role is that of sperm donor and protector of the space rather than that of an active parent to all of his young. In birds such as red-winged blackbirds (*Agelaius phoeniceus*), some males hold large, resource-filled territories that support several females. These males will be attractive to females even if a female (or females) already lives on the territory. Polygyny is prevalent among mammals because, compared with males, females make a much larger investment in raising young (through egg development and care of the young).

Promiscuous mating systems occur when females are with males only long enough to receive sperm and there is no pair bond. These males make no contribution to raising young. Sage grouse **(Figure 32.36)** and hammer-headed bats (*Hypsignathus monstrosus*) are examples of this approach. Both species form **leks**, congregations of displaying males, where females come only to mate. There are more details about sage grouse below.

FIGURE 32.36 **Lekking behaviour.** Male sage grouse (*Centrocercus urophasianus*) use their ornamental feathers in visual courtship displays performed at a lek. There, each male has his own small territory. The smaller brown females observe the performing males before picking a mate.

STUDY BREAK QUESTION

1. What do the terms *monogamy*, *polygamy*, and *promiscuity* mean? How do they differ?

32.14 Sexual Selection

Given the drive to reproduce (see Chapter 44), competition for access to mates coupled with mate choice sets the stage for sexual selection. **Sexual dimorphism**, in which one gender is larger or more colourful than the other, can be an outcome of sexual selection. When males compete for females, males are often larger than females and may have ornaments and weapons, such as horns and antlers, for attracting females and for butting, stabbing, or intimidating rival males. Displays of adornments or weapons can simultaneously warn off other males and attract the attention of females. Peacocks strut in front of peahens while spreading a gigantic fan of tail feathers, which they shake, rattle, and roll.

Why should females choose males with exaggerated structures conspicuously displayed? A male's large size, bright feathers, or large horns might indicate that he is particularly healthy. His appearance could indicate that he can harvest resources efficiently or simply that he has managed to survive to an advanced age. The features are, in effect, signals of male quality, and if they reflect a male's genetic makeup, he is likely to fertilize a female's eggs with sperm containing successful alleles. Large showy males may hold large, rich territories. Females that choose these males can gain access to the resources their territories contain.

FIGURE 32.35 **Reproductive success.** Parental care is just one of the many behaviours required for successful reproduction in white-crowned sparrows and in many other animal species. The number of surviving nestlings will determine the reproductive success of their parents and the representation of their genes in the next generation.

The degree to which females actively choose genetically superior mates varies among species. In northern elephant seals, female choice is more or less passive. Large numbers of females gather on beaches to give birth to their pups before becoming sexually receptive again (see "Delaying Reproduction," Chapter 44). Males locate clusters of females and fight to keep other males away. Males that win have exceptional reproductive success because they mate with many females, but only after engaging in violent and relentless combat with rival males. In this mating system, the females struggle during a male's attempts to mate with them. A female's struggles attract other males, who try to interrupt the attempted mating. Only the largest and most powerful males are not interrupted in their copulations, and they inseminate the most females. These attributes may be associated with alleles that will increase their offspring's chances of living long enough to reproduce.

In other species, females exercise more active mate choice, mating only after inspecting several potential partners. Among birds, active female mate choice is most apparent at leks, display grounds where each male holds a small territory from which it courts attentive females. The male is the only resource on the territory. Male sage grouse in western North America gather in open areas among stands of sagebrush. Each male defends a few square metres, where it struts in circles while emitting booming calls and showing off its elegant tail feathers and big neck pouches (see Figure 32.36). Females wander among displaying males, presumably observing the males' visual and acoustical displays. Eventually, each female selects one mate from among the dozens of males that are present. Females repeatedly favour males that come to the lek daily, defend their small area vigorously, and display more frequently than the average lek participant. Males preferred by females sustain their territorial defence and high display rate over long periods, abilities that may correlate with other useful genetic traits. Ultimately, the male holding the "best" position in the lek mates with the most females.

The results of experiments with peafowl suggest that the top peacocks (*Pavo cristatus*) supply advantageous alleles to their offspring. In nature, peahens prefer males whose tails have many ornamental eyespots **(Figure 32.37)**. In an experiment on captive birds, some peahens were mated to peacocks with highly attractive tails, but others were paired with males with less impressive tails. The offspring of both groups were reared under uniform conditions for several months and then released into an English woodland. After three months on their own, the offspring of fathers with impressive tails survived better and weighed significantly more than did those whose fathers had less-attractive tails. The evidence demonstrates that a peahen's mate choice influences her offspring's chances of survival.

According to the handicap hypothesis, females select males that are successful: the ones with ornate structures. These structures may impede their locomotion, and their elaborate displays may attract the attention of predators. Females select ornate males because they have survived *despite* carrying such a handicap. Successful alleles responsible for the ornamental handicap are passed to the female's offspring.

FIGURE 32.37 Sexual selection for ornamentation. The attractiveness of a peacock to peahens depends in part on the number of eyespots in his extraordinary tail. The offspring of males with elaborate tails are more successful than the offspring of males with plainer tails.

In a study of ~6000 species of birds, James Dale and his colleagues examined the relationships between coloration of plumage of males and females and how this related to sexual selection and life history. In general, larger species of birds and tropical species are more ornamented. Females, but not males, are more colourful in species that breed cooperatively. This probably reflects female–female competition. Bird species in which males are more colourful than females typically show strong sexual selection and male–male competition. Here, females tend to be much less colourful than males. Dale and his colleagues conclude that there may be genetic constraints on the evolution of colourful plumage in birds.

STUDY BREAK QUESTIONS

1. What are the distinguishing features of a lek?
2. What is the handicap hypothesis?
3. Where are the most colourful birds found?

32.15 Social Behaviour

Social behaviour interactions among members of a species have profound effects on an individual's reproductive success. Some animals are solitary, getting together only briefly to mate (e.g., houseflies and leopards). Others spend most of their lives in small family groups (e.g., gorillas). Still others live in groups with thousands of relatives (e.g., termites and honeybees). Some species, such as caribou and humans, live in large social units composed primarily of nonrelatives. In many species, the level of social interactions varies seasonally, usually reflecting the timing of reproduction. This, in turn, is influenced by changes in day length. What follows are a few examples of social interactions.

32.15a African Lions and Infanticide

African lions (*Panthera leo*) usually live in prides, one adult male with several females and their young. Males typically sire the young born to the females in their pride and so achieve a high reproductive output. Females benefit from the support of the others in the group, which includes caring for young and cooperating in foraging. Female lions living in prides wean more young per litter than females living alone. The females in a pride are often genetically related, and their estrus cycles are usually synchronized. Male lions are bigger (~200 kg) than females (~150 kg), and males fight vigorously for the position of pride male. Males protect their females from incursions by other males.

When a new male takes over a pride, he kills all nursing young, bringing the females into estrus. At first, this infanticide seems counterproductive. However, it benefits the male because it increases the chances of his reproducing. Were he to wait until the females had weaned their young, his reproductive contributions could be delayed for some time, perhaps for a year or more. Furthermore, in the intervening period he could lose the opportunity to sire any young at all.

Females are not large enough to protect their young from the male. If a female takes her nursing young and leaves the pride, her efficiency as a hunter declines, and she is less able to protect and feed her young. Her reproductive success plummets. Females are more productive (measured by output of young) when they are part of a pride.

But why live in a group in the first place? By hunting together, lions are more efficient foragers than when they hunt alone. They raise more young. Perhaps more important is the threat posed by spotted hyenas (**Figure 32.38**), which live in large groups (clans). Although individually smaller (~60 kg), when spotted hyenas outnumber lions, they can chase lions from their kills. Furthermore, many of the lion's main prey also live in groups, and group defences affect lions' hunting success.

The situation in lions exemplifies some biological realities. Males and females do not have the same strategies when it comes to reproduction. Understanding behaviour means considering genetic relatedness and production of offspring, as well as the setting in which the animals live.

32.15b Costs and Benefits of Group Living

Ecological factors have a large impact on the reproductive benefits and costs of social living. Group living brings both costs and

FIGURE 32.38 These three spotted hyenas are part of a clan living in Kruger National Park

benefits. Groups of cooperating predators frequently capture prey more effectively than they would on their own. White pelicans (*Pelecanus erythrorhynchos*) often encircle a school of fish before attacking, so being part of a group provides a better yield to individuals than working alone. On the other hand, prey subject to intense predation may benefit from group defence. This can mean more pairs of watchful eyes or ears to detect an approaching danger. It may also translate into multiple lures so that, when a predator attacks, it is more difficult to focus on an individual. When you are part of a group that is attacked, it may be someone other than you that is captured, diluting the risk to any one group member.

When attacked by wolves, adult muskoxen form a circle around the young, so attackers are always confronted by horns and hooves (**Figure 32.39**). Insects such as Australian sawfly caterpillars also show cooperative defensive behaviour. When predators disturb the caterpillars, all group members rear up, writhe about, and regurgitate sticky, pungent oils. The caterpillars collect the oils from the eucalyptus leaves they eat. The oils do not harm the caterpillars but are toxic and repellent to birds.

Living in groups, however, can also be expensive. One cost can be increased competition for food. When thousands of royal penguins crowd together in huge colonies (**Figure 32.40**), the pressure on local food supplies is great, increasing the risk of starvation. Communal living may facilitate the spread of contagious diseases and parasites. Nestlings in large colonies of cliff swallows (*Petrochelidon pyrrhonota*) are often stunted in growth because the nests swarm with blood-feeding, bedbug-like parasites, *Oeciacus vicarius*. The parasites move readily from nest to nest in crowded conditions. Some social animals learn to recognize and avoid diseased group members. Caribbean spiny lobsters live in groups but avoid conspecifics infected by a lethal virus (PaV1). In 2016, Quinn Webber and his colleagues reported that big brown bats (*Eptesicus fuscus*) using buildings as summer roosts were more vulnerable to transmission of pathogens than individuals roosting in trees. The big difference between the two situations is that, on any given night, most of the bats in a building roost are more clustered than those spread among hollows in different trees.

Social animals usually live in groups characterized by some form of structure. Some individuals may dominate others (a **dominance hierarchy**), manifested in access to resources. Dominant (alpha, or α) individuals get priority access to food (or mates or sleeping sites). In some situations, only dominant individuals (a male and a female) reproduce. Dominance hierarchies may be absolute, such as when the same individual always has priority access to any resource. In relative dominance hierarchies, an individual's status depends on the circumstance. One individual may dominate at a food source, while another may dominate in access to mates.

Dominance brings its costs. In animals such as wild dogs (*Lycaon pictus*) and grey wolves, dominant animals must constantly defend their status. Dominants often have high levels of cortisol and other stress-related hormones in their blood (see Chapter 43) compared with subordinates. Elevated cortisol levels may induce high blood pressure, disruption of sugar metabolism, and other pathological conditions.

FIGURE 32.39 **Muskoxen**

FIGURE 32.40 Colonial living. Royal penguins (*Eudyptes schlegeli*) on Macquarie Island between New Zealand and Antarctica experience benefits and costs from living together in huge groups.

Subordination brings its benefits. Subordinate group members, like all members of the group, gain protection from predators. They may also gain experience by helping dominant individuals raise young. Over time, subordinate individuals can rise in a dominance hierarchy and avoid some of the side effects of dominance. Many social animals cannot survive on their own.

Not all animals that live in groups are social, a term implying some organization of the group. The 10 million Brazilian free-tailed bats emerging from a cave roost near San Antonio, Texas,

are no more a social group than the dozens of people leaving a high-rise apartment or university residence. Within the aggregation, there may be social units, but the aggregation itself is not necessarily a social unit.

STUDY BREAK QUESTIONS

1. What is infanticide? Why does it occur?
2. Give some examples of the advantages and disadvantages of group living.

32.16   Kin Selection and Altruism

Behavioural ecologist William D. Hamilton recognized that helping genetic relatives effectively propagates the helper's genes because family members share alleles inherited from their ancestors. By calculating the degree of relatedness, we can quantify the average percentage of alleles shared by relatives **(Figure 32.41)**. Individuals should be more likely to help close relatives because increasing a close relative's fitness means that the individual is helping to propagate some of its own alleles. This is **kin selection**.

32.16a   Degrees of Relatedness

The kin selection hypothesis suggests that the extent of altruistic behaviour exhibited by one individual to another is directly proportional to the percentage of alleles they share. The hypothesis predicts that individuals are more likely to help close relatives because, by increasing a close relative's fitness, the individual is helping to propagate some of its own alleles. To test this prediction, we must calculate the degrees of relatedness among individuals.

To do this between any two individuals, we first draw a family tree showing all the genetic links between them. The alleles of a parent are shuffled by recombination and independent assortment in the gametes they produce, so we can calculate only the average percentage of a parent's alleles that offspring are likely to share.

Half siblings share only one genetic parent. Each sibling receives half its alleles from its mother. Because a parent has only two alleles at each gene locus, the probability of sibling A getting a particular allele from its mother is 0.5, or 50%, as is the probability for sibling B. Statistically, the probability that two independent events—in this case, the transfer of an allele to sibling A and the transfer of the same allele to sibling

Half siblings

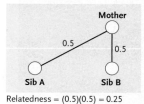

Relatedness = (0.5)(0.5) = 0.25

First cousins

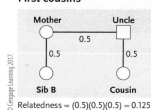

Relatedness = (0.5)(0.5)(0.5) = 0.125

© Cengage Learning 2017.

Full siblings

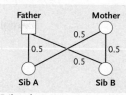

Relatedness
Through mother = (0.5)(0.5) = 0.25
Through father = (0.5)(0.5) = 0.25
Total relatedness = 0.25 + 0.25 = 0.5

FIGURE 32.41 Calculating degrees of relatedness

B—will both occur is the product of their separate probabilities. Thus, the likelihood that both siblings receive the same allele from their mother is $0.5 \times 0.5 = 0.25$. Two full siblings share 50% of their mother's and father's alleles. The degree of relatedness for full siblings is 0.50.

Each link drawn between a parent and an offspring or between full siblings indicates two individuals sharing, on average, 50% of their alleles. We can calculate the total relatedness (r) between any two individuals by multiplying out the probabilities across all of the links between them. The degree of relatedness between a nephew or niece and an aunt or an uncle is 0.25, and between first cousins it is 0.125.

A male grey wolf helps his parents rear four pups to adulthood, pups that would have died without the extra assistance he provided. The pups are his younger full siblings, sharing 0.5 of his genes, so, on average, the helper has created "by proxy" two ($0.50 \times 4 = 2$) copies of any allele they shared. However, the costs of his helping must be measured against this indirect reproductive success. If he had found a mate, sired offspring, and raised two of them, each would have carried half his alleles, preserving only one ($0.50 \times 2 = 1$) copy of a given allele. In this situation, reproducing on his own would have produced fewer copies of his alleles in the next generation than helping to raise his siblings. Sibling helpers have been documented in many species of birds and mammals. The phenomenon is especially common among animals in which inexperienced parents are not very successful at reproducing offspring on their own. By helping, they gain experience and realize some genetic benefit.

Among the many features of social animals, the evolution of cooperative behaviour can be one of the most challenging to understand. Why has cooperative behaviour arisen in populations of animals? How does it arise? And how is it maintained in populations? **Altruism** involves doing something that costs the actor while enhancing the situation of another individual (the receiver). Hamilton's kin selection theory demonstrates why parental behaviour (or helping parents raise siblings) is genetically selfish, not altruistic. Therefore, the behaviour of

the wolf mentioned above is not altruistic. Robert Trivers proposed that individuals will help nonrelatives if they are likely to return the favour in the future. Trivers called this **reciprocal altruism** because each member of the partnership can potentially benefit from the relationship. Trivers hypothesized that reciprocal altruism would be favoured by natural selection as long as cheaters—individuals that do not reciprocate—are denied future aid.

Many species of dolphins are long lived and social, living in groups. Dolphins and other cetaceans show many forms of aid-giving behaviour, from attending injured group members to assisting with difficult births. They also use group behaviour to protect themselves from attacks by sharks. Richard Connor and Kenneth Norris proposed that the persistent threat of attacks by sharks and the perils of living in the ocean combined to provide dolphins with many opportunities to help one another, or even members of other species. Connor and Norris did not have specific details of genetic relationships among group members, but they proposed that dolphins are reciprocal altruists.

John M. McNamara and three colleagues wrote about the coevolution of choosiness and cooperation. Using modelling and simulation experiments, these authors examined the consequences arising in situations in which one individual's cooperativeness influences the decisions about actions by other individuals toward group members. They postulated a situation of competitive altruism in which individuals actually compete with one another to be more cooperative.

The results of their analysis suggest that longer-lived species are more likely to develop cooperative behaviour than shorter-lived ones. This is important because the model does not require intermediate situations involving negotiation behaviour. The model helps us understand the appearance of cooperative behaviour in all animals, including in *Homo sapiens*.

The McNamara et al. model of competitive altruism helps explain the evolution of blood-sharing behaviour in vampire bats. Vampire bats are the only warm-blooded blood feeders and, like many other bats, they are long lived in the wild, recorded to at least 19 years of age). The three living species of vampire bats, the common vampire bat (*Desmodus rotundus*; **Figure 32.42**), the white-winged vampire bat (*Diaemus youngi*), and the hairy-legged vampire bat (*Diphylla ecaudata*), all practice food sharing. An individual unsuccessful in foraging can return to its roost and beg blood from a successful forager among its roost mates. The donor bat regurgitates some of its blood meal to the recipient. G. S. Wilkinson's work with common vampire bats demonstrated that individuals roost with both nonrelatives and genetic relatives. Familiarity, not relatedness, was the key to food sharing by these bats.

The selection process for the behaviour can be placed in context by evidence about a bat's success. Adult common vampire bats are typically unsuccessful in obtaining blood one night per month. An adult can survive two days (daytime periods) without feeding, but not three. This means that, on any night in any month in a colony of 30 adult vampire bats, one individual will benefit from the cooperativeness of a roost mate.

Even more important, young bats may be unsuccessful three or four times a week. Blood-feeding bats thus live on the edge of survival and likely depend on a network of cooperation by roost mates. The social network demonstrated for common vampire bats probably applies to white-winged and hairy-legged species as well. The network is based on cooperation and may be the key to being a successful warm-blooded blood-feeder.

STUDY BREAK QUESTIONS

1. What is the main argument in Hamilton's kin selection theory?
2. Imagine that four of your first cousins, two siblings, and two half-siblings are about to fall from a cliff and die. You have the option of taking their place. In terms of kin selection, which is more beneficial to you, your life or the life of your genetic relatives?
3. Which of the following behaviours is altruistic: parental care, mate selection, courtship feeding, self-defence, and/or helping nonrelatives? Explain your choices.
4. Why do common vampire bats regurgitate blood to others?

32.17 Eusocial Animals

Hamilton's insights led to the prediction that self-sacrificing behaviour should be directed to kin. Evidence from many species of animals, particularly bees, ants, termites, and wasps, overwhelmingly supports this prediction. In a colony of **eusocial** insects, thousands of genetically related individuals, most of them sterile workers, live and work together for the reproductive benefit of a single queen and her mate(s). The workers may even die in defence of their colonies.

How did this social behaviour evolve, and why does it persist over time? A colony of honeybees may contain 30–50 thousand related individuals, but only the queen bee is fertile. All the workers are her daughters **(Figure 32.43)**. Reproduction is the queen's role in the colony. The workers perform all the other tasks in maintaining the hive, from feeding the queen and her larvae to constructing new honeycomb and foraging for nectar and pollen. They also transfer food to one another (trophallaxis) and sometimes guard the entrance to the hive. Some pay the ultimate sacrifice when they sting intruders because stinging tears open the bee's abdomen, leaving the stinger and the poison sac behind in the intruder's skin and killing the bee.

In bees and other eusocial insects, sex is determined genetically through **haplodiploidy (Figure 32.44)**. Female bees are diploid because they receive a set of chromosomes from each parent. Male bees (drones), however, are haploid because they hatch from unfertilized eggs. All the sperm carried by a drone will be genetically identical because he has just one set of chromosomes. When a queen bee mates with just one male, all her worker offspring will inherit exactly the same set of alleles from their male parent, ensuring at least a 50% degree of relatedness among them. Like other diploid organisms, workers are related to each other by an average of 25% through their female parent. Adding these two components of relatedness, workers

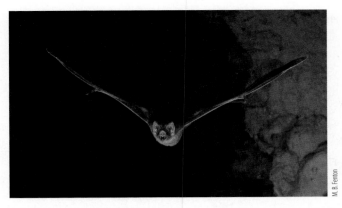

FIGURE 32.42 A common vampire bat leaving its roost in a tunnel in Belize

are related to each other by an average of 75%, a higher degree of relatedness than they would have to any offspring they would have produced had they been fertile.

The high degree of relatedness among workers in some colonies of eusocial insects may explain their exceptional level of cooperation. When Hamilton first worked out this explanation of eusocial behaviour, he suggested that workers devote their lives to caring for their siblings (the queen's other offspring) because a few of those siblings, those carrying 75% of the workers' alleles, may become future queens and produce enormous numbers of offspring themselves.

32.17a Naked Mole Rats

Naked mole rats are a mammalian example of eusocial animals with nonbreeding workers. In East Africa, these small, almost hairless animals live in underground colonies of 70–80 individuals. Like eusocial insects, naked mole rats share an exceptionally high proportion of alleles. Naked mole rats are sightless and

a. **Queen with sterile workers**

b. **Workers sharing food and passing pheromones**

FIGURE 32.43 (a) In a hive of honeybees, a court of sterile workers (daughters) surround their mother (the queen). **(b)** Worker bees routinely share food (trophallaxis) and transfer pheromones to one another.

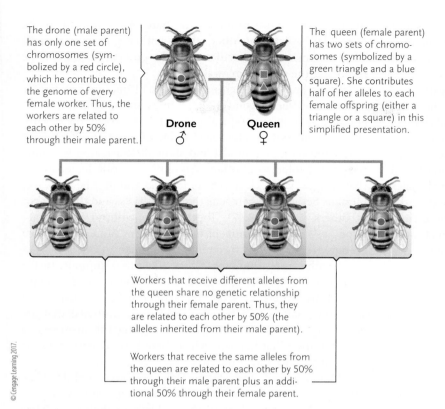

The drone (male parent) has only one set of chromosomes (symbolized by a red circle), which he contributes to the genome of every female worker. Thus, the workers are related to each other by 50% through their male parent.

Drone ♂

The queen (female parent) has two sets of chromosomes (symbolized by a green triangle and a blue square). She contributes half of her alleles to each female offspring (either a triangle or a square) in this simplified presentation.

Queen ♀

Workers that receive different alleles from the queen share no genetic relationship through their female parent. Thus, they are related to each other by 50% (the alleles inherited from their male parent).

Workers that receive the same alleles from the queen are related to each other by 50% through their male parent plus an additional 50% through their female parent.

© Cengage Learning 2017.

FIGURE 32.44 Haplodiploidy. The genetic system of eusocial insects produces full siblings with exceptionally high degrees of relatedness. Although this simplified model ignores recombination between the queen's two sets of chromosomes, it demonstrates how half the workers are related to each other by 50%, and half are related to each other by 100%. On average, the relatedness between workers is 75%.

essentially hairless burrowing mammals **(Figure 32.45)** that live in mazes of subterranean tunnels in parts of Ethiopia, Somalia, and Kenya. Colonies of naked mole rats may number from 25 to several hundred individuals. In each colony, a single "queen" and one to three males are the breeders. All the others, males and females, are nonbreeding workers that, like worker bees, ants, and termites in insect colonies, do all the labour, including digging and defending the tunnels and caring for the queen and her mates. H. Kern Reeve and his colleagues used molecular techniques resembling DNA fingerprint analysis (see Chapter 14) to determine if close kinship could explain the behaviour of worker naked mole rats. The technique depends on a group of repeated DNA sequences that vary to a greater or lesser extent among individuals (e.g., they are polymorphic). No two individuals (except identical twins) are likely to have exactly the same combination of sequences. Brothers and sisters with the same parents have the most closely related sequences, and differences increase as genetic relationships become more distant. Reeve and his colleagues captured mole rats living in four colonies in Kenya. Individuals from the same colony were placed together in a system of artificial tunnels. Samples of the entire DNA complement were extracted from individuals that died naturally in the artificial colonies. The extracted DNA was then "probed" with radioactively labelled DNA sequences that paired with and marked the

three distinct groups of polymorphic sequences in the mole rat DNA (see Chapter 14).

Naked mole rat sequences were then fragmented by treatment with a restriction endonuclease. This procedure produced a group of fragments that, reflecting the variations in polymorphic sequences, is unique for each individual. As a final experimental step, the fragments for each individual were separated into a pattern of bands by gel electrophoresis. The pattern of bands, different for each individual, is the DNA fingerprint.

Reeve and his colleagues compared the DNA fingerprint of each mole rat with those of other members of the same and other colonies. In the comparisons, bands that were the same in two individuals were scored as hits. The number of hits was then analyzed to assign relatedness by noting which individuals shared the greatest number of bands.

Individuals in the same mole rat colony were closely related. They shared an unusually high number of bands, higher than human siblings and approaching the kin similarity of identical twins. The number of bands shared between individuals of different colonies was significantly lower but still higher than that noted between unrelated individuals of other vertebrate species. Close relatedness of even separate colonies may be due to similar selection pressures or to recent common ancestry among colonies in the same geographic region.

In naked mole rats, close genetic relatedness among individuals in a colony could explain the altruistic behaviour of workers. The persistence of the social organization reflects its importance to the survival of individual naked mole rats, rather like the situation in lion prides.

The presence of non-reproductive workers is diagnostic of eusocial animals. Jason Olejarz and his colleagues demonstrated that non-reproductive individuals readily arise in situations where the "queen" has mated with several males

M. B. Fenton

FIGURE 32.45 Naked mole rat (*Heterocephalus glaber*), a colonial rodent whose colonies contain many workers that are effectively sterile.

(= polyandrous). The rate at which the colony reproduces and the fractions of non-reproductive workers in a colony emerged as key factors in their model. These observations may provide a clue about the evolution of eusociality among animals.

Animals living in groups, whether they are aggregations or social units, may be at greater risk of inbreeding than those living alone. Dispersal is a mechanism that can reduce the chances of incestuous matings and inbreeding. Although spotted hyenas live in clans, males tend to disperse from their natal units, minimizing the risk of inbreeding. O. P. Höner and colleagues used microsatellite profiling to show that a female preferred mates that had been born into or immigrated into the clan after she was born. As usual, it can be difficult to separate cause from effect. Are clans of spotted hyenas prone to this pattern of social organization, or is the pattern a result of their behaviour?

STUDY BREAK QUESTIONS

1. What is haplodiploidy? How does it relate to Hamilton's prediction about self-sacrificing behaviour?
2. Are naked mole rats eusocial?

32.18 Human Social Behaviour

Although humans and chimpanzees share 96% of their genomes, compared with humans, both chimpanzees and bonobos (*Pan paniscus*) live in relatively unstructured social groups. The difference has been attributed to brain size. The cultural intelligence hypothesis proposes that large brain size in humans reflects cognitive skill sets absent from great apes. Large brains allow humans to perform many cognitive tasks more rapidly and efficiently than other species with smaller brains. The tasks include those associated with memory, learning time, long-range planning, and complexity of inter-individual interactions.

To test this, Esther Herrmann and her colleagues administered a large battery of cognitive tests to chimpanzees, orangutans (*Pongo pygmaeus*), and two-and-a-half-year-old human children. The children in the experiment were preschool and preliterate. Although the children, chimpanzees, and orangutans had similar cognitive skills for dealing with the physical world, the children had more sophisticated cognitive skills for dealing with the social world **(Figure 32.46)**. The data support the hypothesis that cultural intelligence is an important way to distinguish humans from their closest living relatives.

The ultimatum game is an economic decision-making tool for assessing the responses of individuals to opportunities and the behaviour of others. Responses allow researchers to distinguish between players on the basis of sensitivity and sense of fairness. Keith Jensen and his colleagues used the ultimatum game to compare humans and chimpanzees. Two anonymous individuals can play a round of this game. One, the proposer, is offered a sum of money (or a food reward) and can decide whether to share it with the other, the responder. The responder can accept or reject the proposer's offer. If the responder accepts

the offer, then both receive their share of the reward. If the responder rejects the offer, then neither gets any reward. The economic model predicts that the proposer will offer the responder the minimum award.

When humans and chimps play the ultimatum game, their behaviour differs **(Figure 32.47)**. Chimps are rational maximizers because proposers typically offer 40% to 50% of the reward, and responders typically reject offers of less than 20%. They follow the economic model and show little sensitivity to fairness or the interests of others. More recent work demonstrates that chimps have a clear view of fairness and may be more like humans because of their sensitivity to fairness and the interests of others (Figure 32.47). Together, the cultural intelligence hypothesis and the results of the ultimatum game suggest that chimps are not so very different from humans.

In other ways, humans behave like other animals. In the area of reproduction and genetic selfishness, some humans show little difference from their mammalian cousins. Kin selection predicts that humans (and other animals) that are genetic relatives will benefit from assisting the members of their family. What happens when there is no close genetic tie between parents and children?

Margo Wilson and Martin Daly wondered if child abuse might be more common in families with step-parents who are not genetically related to all the children in their care. They examined data on criminal child abuse within families, made available by the police department of a Canadian city. They found that the chance that a young child would be subject to criminal abuse was 40 times as high when children lived with one step-parent and one genetic parent as with children living with both genetic parents **(Figure 32.48)**.

This example illustrates the insights that an evolutionary analysis of human behaviour can provide. Wilson and Daly made the point that humans may have some genetic characteristic that makes it more difficult to invest in children they know are not their own, particularly if they also care for their own genetic children. They did not excuse child abusers or claim that abusive step-parenting is acceptable. These results are not just academic. Most step-parents cope well with the difficulties of their role, but a few do not. Knowing the familial circumstances under which child abuse is more likely to occur may allow us to provide social assistance that could prevent some children from being abused in the future.

Violence and conflict are recurring themes in the behaviour of many animals, including humans. Killing of other members of the same species is widespread. Michael Wilson and his colleagues reported this in chimpanzees and bonobos. Their sample was of 152 killings, most of which involved intergroup interactions. Meanwhile, M. Mirazón Lahr and colleagues presented evidence of inter-group violence from humans living as hunter–gatherers perhaps 14 000–12 000 years ago in what is now Kenya. These data suggest that violence is not a new development in our species.

Intrinsic honesty and a sense of fairness may be fundamental aspects of human societies. Although deception is a common

a. Physical domain

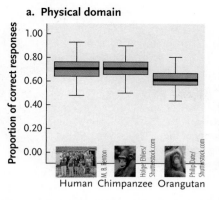

b. Social domain

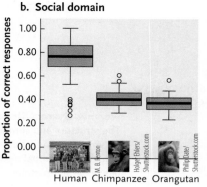

FIGURE 32.46 Humans, chimpanzees, and orangutans. Box plots showing the proportion of correct responses to survey questions in the physical and the social domains. In the social domain, outlying data points (circles) were at least 1.5 times the interquartile distances (shown by the error bars).

Source: From Esther Herrmann, Josep Call, Maria Victoria Hernandez-Lloreda, Brian Hare, Michael Tomasello, "Humans Have Evolved Specialized Skills of Social Cognition: The Cultural Intelligence Hypothesis," *Science*, vol. 317, Sep 7, 2007, pp. 1360 - 1366. *Science* by American Association for the Advancement of Science Reproduced with permission of AMERICAN ASSOCIATION FOR THE ADVANCEMENT OF SCIENCE in the format Republish in a book via Copyright Clearance Center.

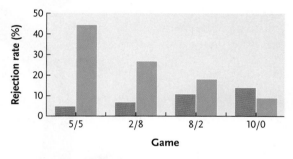

FIGURE 32.47 The ultimatum game. Data from chimpanzees (orange bars) and humans (green bars) show rejection rates (percentage of offers) indicating fundamental differences in the way that humans and chimps approach issues of fairness. The chimps are rational maximizers, whereas the humans are not.

Source: From Keith Jensen, Josep Call, Michael Tomasello, "Chimpanzees Are Rational Maximizers in an Ultimatum Game", *Science*, vol. 318, Oct 5, 2007, pp. 107-109. *Science* by American Association for the Advancement of Science Reproduced with permission of AMERICAN ASSOCIATION FOR THE ADVANCEMENT OF SCIENCE in the format Republish in a book via Copyright Clearance Center.

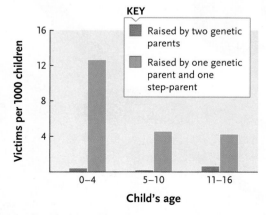

FIGURE 32.48 Children raised by one genetic parent and one step-parent were 40 times as likely to suffer criminal abuse at home as children living with two genetic parents.

behaviour among animals, stability in our societies involves some level of intrinsic honesty. Simon Gächter and Jonathan Schulz studied societies in 23 countries, and their sample involved 2568 "young" people. They focused on intrinsic honesty reflected by PRV, the prevalence of rule violations. They found that intrinsic honesty was more common in countries with a low incidence of PRV.

Among humans, there is considerable variation in the level of fairness in resource sharing. P. R. Blake and colleagues examined the development of fairness behaviour in seven human societies. They used a standardized resource decision task to test children from 4 to 15 years of age. They focused on two key aspects: first, where peer received more than self and, second, where self received more than peer. By middle childhood, the first aspect was common throughout the sample. The appearance of the second aspect was more variable, emerging only in later development in three of the societies. The level of fairness and perception of fairness does not appear to be under genetic control.

In recent years, the application of evolutionary thinking to human behaviour has produced research on many kinds of questions. Some questions are interesting or even profound: Why do some tightly knit ethnic groups discourage intermarriage with members of other groups? At other times, the issues may seem frivolous: Why do men often find women with certain physical characteristics attractive? Evolutionary hypotheses about the adaptive value of behaviour can be tested, and the results help us to understand why we behave as we do. Understanding why we get along or fail to get along with each other, and the ability to make moral judgments about our behaviour are uniquely human characteristics that set us apart from other animals.

Returning to behaviour related to food, Carey Morewedge and two colleagues reported how people thinking about eating a food reduced their consumption of that food. Their experiment included over 50 participants and involved different foods (cheese and m&m's). Individuals who thought about eating cheese consumed significantly less cheese when actually eating compared to those who imagined eating less cheese, or eating m&m's. These findings have implications for treating eating disorders, and illustrate how mental representations can lead to habituation. The findings also suggest similarities to other animals when it comes to food and feeding (see above).

STUDY BREAK QUESTIONS

1. What is the ultimatum game? How does it help us understand behaviour?
2. What genetic reason helps explain the domestic risks to foster children and stepchildren?
3. What is fairness? What is intrinsic honesty?
4. How does PRV vary across the community in which you live?

Summary Illustration

Animal behaviour is what animals do or how they behave. It is how they interact with conspecifics, other members of their community, and their environment. Animal behaviour is governed by genetic and environmental factors and involves instinct and learning. Nervous and sensory systems integrate internal and external cues and mediate behaviours such as communication, breeding, and foraging.

Nervous System Structure
The structure and complexity of the nervous system (including brain size) influence an animal's physiology and its behavioural repertoire.

Hormones and Neurotransmitters
Biochemical pathways within an animal's endocrine and nervous systems allow animals to respond to stimuli.

Anatomy/Physiology

Imprinting
Imprinting occurs when an animal learns the identity of a caregiver or features of a suitable mate during a critical period.

Instinctive Behaviours
Highly stereotyped behaviours performed without the benefit of previous experience.

Genes

Governors of Behaviour

Fixed Action Patterns
This denotes a response repeated over and over to a specific cue.

Classical Conditioning
This refers to the development of a mental association between two phenomena that are usually unrelated.

Environment

Operant Conditioning
Learning that occurs when animals link an action with a consequence. Example: rat pushing bar to receive food.

Insight Learning
Occurs when an animal learns to solve a problem without trial and error. Example: chimp getting bananas after stacking boxes to reach them

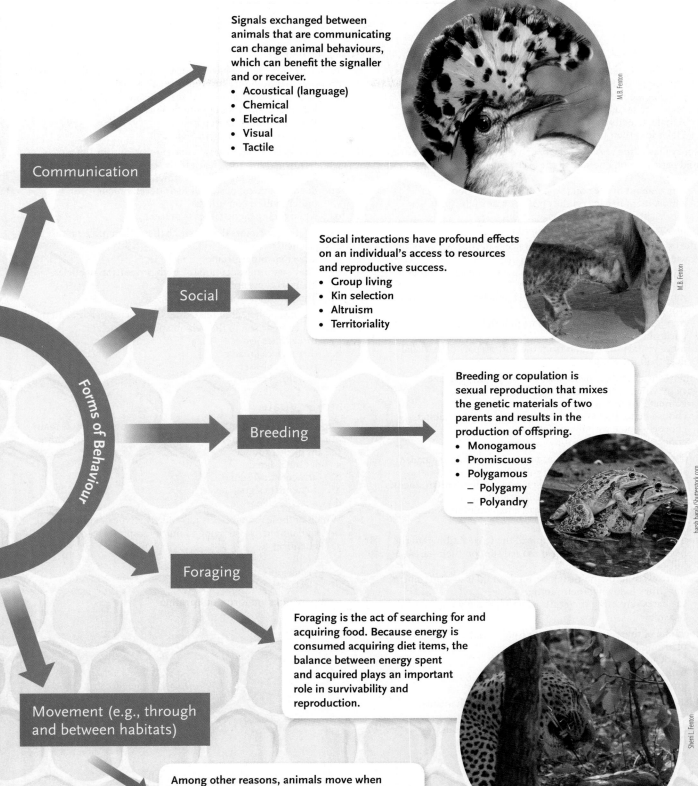

Communication

Signals exchanged between animals that are communicating can change animal behaviours, which can benefit the signaller and or receiver.
- Acoustical (language)
- Chemical
- Electrical
- Visual
- Tactile

M.B. Fenton

Social

Social interactions have profound effects on an individual's access to resources and reproductive success.
- Group living
- Kin selection
- Altruism
- Territoriality

M.B. Fenton

Forms of Behaviour

Breeding

Breeding or copulation is sexual reproduction that mixes the genetic materials of two parents and results in the production of offspring.
- Monogamous
- Promiscuous
- Polygamous
  - Polygamy
  - Polyandry

harsh.barala/Shutterstock.com

Foraging

Foraging is the act of searching for and acquiring food. Because energy is consumed acquiring diet items, the balance between energy spent and acquired plays an important role in survivability and reproduction.

Sherri L. Fenton

Movement (e.g., through and between habitats)

Among other reasons, animals move when dispersing to new habitats, when travelling between food patches or from summer to winter ranges, or when migrating from breeding to feeding grounds.
- Kinesis
- Migration
- Taxis

Alexander Erdbeer/Shutterstock.com

SELF-TEST QUESTIONS

Recall/Understand

1. Which of these behaviours occurs in cichlid fish with high levels of the hormone GnRH?
   a. Females are receptive to male attention.
   b. Males are sexually aggressive but not territorial.
   c. A male defends its territory.
   d. Males lose their bright colours.

2. Sensory bias in the nervous system of a cricket ensures that ultrasound perceived on one side of the body causes which of the following?
   a. a movement in a leg on the same side of the body
   b. a movement in a leg on the opposite side of the body
   c. the cricket's response by vocalization
   d. the cricket's flight toward the sound

3. In the brain of a star-nosed mole, more cells decode which of the following?
   a. more tactile information from its feet than from all other parts of its body
   b. more tactile information from the tentacles on its nose than from all other parts of its body
   c. more tactile information from its mouth than from all other parts of its body
   d. more visual information from the bottom part of its visual field than the top part

4. Compared with males, the females of many animal species engage in which of these behaviours?
   a. compete for mates
   b. choose mates that are well camouflaged in their habitats
   c. choose to mate with many partners
   d. choose their mates carefully

5. Which of these statements is an accurate description of altruism?
   a. It advances the welfare of the entire species.
   b. It decreases the number of offspring an individual produces.
   c. It can indirectly spread the altruist's alleles.
   d. It can evolve only in animals with a haplodiploid genetic system.

6. Which of the following is an example of the fixed action pattern?
   a. herring gull chicks pecking at the red spot on their parent's bill
   b. sparrows singing their song correctly at their first attempt
   c. ducklings following their mother
   d. sea hares retracting their gills when repeatedly touched on the side

7. Which one of these is an example of visual signals?
   a. pheromones released by a male
   b. black and white stripes on a skunk
   c. bats spreading their wings while flying
   d. grooming of another individual

8. Which are the three categories of way-finding mechanisms?
   a. sources of food, drinking water, and nesting sites
   b. pheromones, climate, and reproductive behaviours
   c. temperature, humidity, and winds
   d. piloting, compass orientation, and navigation

Apply/Analyze

9. Which of these people have made the greatest contribution to the proposal that dolphins are reciprocal altruists?
   a. John M. McNamara and three colleagues
   b. Richard Connor and Kenneth Norris
   c. Robert Trivers and Ken Reeve
   d. William D. Hamilton and Xie Can

10. As concluded by Peter Marler, under what circumstances can white-crowned sparrows learn their species' song?
    a. after receiving hormone treatments
    b. during a critical period of their development
    c. under natural conditions
    d. when their genetic father is present

11. Which of these factors demonstrate that naked mole rats are like eusocial bees?
    a. They live underground.
    b. They share an exceptionally high proportion of alleles.
    c. Their workers are only females.
    d. Their workers breed.

12. What is the coefficient of relatedness between a person and their sister in comparison to the person and their uncle?
    a. three times lesser
    b. three times greater
    c. two times lesser
    d. two times greater

Create/Evaluate

13. The squashing of an ant on a picnic blanket often attracts many other ants to its "funeral." What kind of signal does squashing of the ant likely produce?
    a. a visual signal
    b. an acoustical signal
    c. a chemical signal
    d. a tactile signal

14. Which of these modalities is most likely a type of communication signal used by fish living in murky tropical rivers?
    a. chemical
    b. tactile
    c. visual
    d. electrical

15. Compare different forms of learning.

Appendix A: Answers to Self-Test Questions

Chapter 16

1. c 2. c 3. d 4. b 5. c 6. c 7. d 8. d 9. b 10. a

11. Evolution is a change in the traits of a population over time. Natural selection is one of the mechanisms that can cause that change.
12. It is a non-random process because it selects individuals in a population with certain traits.
13. (1) Most organisms produce more than one or two offspring; (2) populations do not increase in size indefinitely; (3) food and other resources are limited for most populations.
14. (1) Individuals within populations exhibit variability in many characteristics; (2) many variations appear to be inherited by subsequent generations.
15. Monarch butterflies are able to ingest cardiac glycosides, and they benefit from this ability because they use these molecules to establish their own defence.

Chapter 17

1. c 2. d 3. d 4. b 5. a 6. c 7. b 8. c 9. c 10. c 11. b 12. b

13. It considers the number of surviving offspring that an individual produces in comparison to the number of offspring that other individuals produce in the same population.
14. In the case of reciprocal gene flow, the populations would probably become more phenotypically similar to each other after some time. In the case of non-reciprocal gene flow, one of the populations may become more different than it was before the gene flow, while the other may remain the same as it was at the beginning of the process.

Chapter 18

1. c 2. a 3. b 4. d 5. d 6. b 7. b 8. d 9. b 10. c 11. c 12. b

13. The concept cannot be applied to species known only from fossil records, to species that reproduce only asexually, or to species that do not overlap geographically or do not meet each other otherwise.
14. Individuals of the same species interbreed with no difficulty and their offspring look like their parents. Subspecies are local variants of a species. Individuals from different subspecies usually interbreed where their geographical distributions meet; their offspring often exhibit intermediate phenotypes.
15. Lions and tigers do not live in the same habitat, so they are naturally geographically isolated and do not come in contact unless captured. Since they are two species, their offspring would be a hybrid that is either sterile or has reduced fertility, hence exhibiting an example of the postzygotic reproductive barrier, which prevents it from being considered a separate species and present in the wilderness as such.

Chapter 19

1. a 2. b 3. b 4. b 5. d 6. c 7. c 8. a 9. b 10. d 11. d 12. c

13. A monophyletic taxon includes an ancestor and all its descendants. A polyphyletic taxon includes species from different evolutionary lineages. A paraphyletic taxon includes an ancestor and some, but not all its descendants.
14. You are surprised, because you understand that the class Reptilia, even though it includes turtles, lizards, snakes, and crocodilians, which are descendants of a common ancestor, it does not include all descendants of archosaurs, namely birds. As such, class Reptilia can only be considered a paraphyletic taxon.
15. Convergent evolution is used when referring to phylogenetically or distantly related organisms, and parallel evolution when referring to more closely related organisms.

Chapter 20

1. d 2. c 3. d 4. d 5. c 6. a 7. c 8. d 9. c 10. b 11. d 12. b

13. Improved predator detection; display of warning signs; more efficient walk over long distances; more efficient thermoregulation
14. This is an old notion, perhaps even a seductive idea, but it is dangerous to interpret the origin of a structure or function in terms of its current utility. It would be like saying that the human brain evolved in order to write symphonies, which is clearly nonsense.
15. The African emergence hypothesis suggests that all modern humans are descended from a fairly recent African ancestor, as early hominin descendants left Africa to establish populations elsewhere. The multiregional hypothesis suggests that populations of *H. erectus* and archaic humans spread through much of Europe and Asia, and that modern humans evolved from descendants of these earlier dispersals.

Chapter 21

1. c 2. b 3. a 4. a 5. d 6. d 7. b 8. c 9. d 10. b 11. b 12. d

13. To determine relative dates, scientists order fossils found in different strata in sequence from the lowest (oldest) to the highest (newest) strata. This sequencing reveals their relative ages. By using a technique called radiometric dating, scientists can estimate the age of a rock by noting how much of an unstable "parent" isotope has decayed to another form. By measuring the relative amounts of the parent radioisotope and its breakdown products, and comparing this ratio with the

isotope's half-life—the time it takes for half of a given amount of radio-isotope to decay—researchers can estimate the absolute age of the rock.

14. LUCA stands for Last Universal Common Ancestor, because the similarities across all domains of life present today indicate that only one of these primitive life forms has descendants that survive today.

15. Bacteria and archaea have circular chromosomes; eukaryotes have linear chromosomes. The location of DNA of prokaryotes is in the nucleoid region, and in eukaryotes it is in the nucleus. Chromosomes segregate by binary fission in prokaryotes, and by mitosis/meiosis in eukaryotes. Introns are rarely present in bacteria, but are common in archaea and eukaryotes.

Chapter 22

1. c 2. a 3. b 4. c 5. c 6. d 7. a 8. d 9. d 10. c 11. d 12. c

13. Treatment is difficult because viruses are incorporated into cells, since they use the cell's machinery to replicate. Therefore, it is difficult to target them specifically with drugs. They do not react to antibiotics, and usually take their own course before being eliminated by the cells of their host's immune system.

14. The phage attaches to the host cell and injects its DNA into the cell. Expression of phage genes produces an enzyme that breaks down bacterial chromosomes. The phage DNA then replicates inside the cell. Viral heads and tail units synthesize and assemble into "new" phage particles. The cell then ruptures, releasing the phage particles.

15. The lytic cycle begins with a phage binding to the host cell and releasing its DNA into the host cell's cytoplasm. The viral DNA is initially linear, but once inside the host cell, it forms a circle. Viral genes produce enzymes that break down the cell's chromosomes and proteins, along with linear copies of viral DNA. New viral particles assemble, with DNA packed

inside. Viral genes encode for the protein that breaks the cell open, releasing new viral particles out of the cell. In the lysogenic cycle, viral DNA integrates with the host cell's chromosome, allowing the viral DNA to be replicated along with the host cell's DNA. Following cell division, each daughter cell receives viral DNA incorporated in their own DNA.

Chapter 23

1. b 2. c 3. c 4. c 5. b 6. a 7. b 8. a 9. d 10. a 11. a 12. b

13. Obligate anaerobes are poisoned by oxygen. They perform either fermentation or anaerobic respiration. Facultative anaerobes use oxygen when present, and utilize fermentation or anaerobic respiration when oxygen is not present. Obligate aerobes cannot survive without oxygen.

14. Gram-positive bacteria appear purple under the microscope, due to a stain they retain in their cells; Gram-negatives appear pink. This is because Gram-positive bacteria contain a thick peptidoglycan layer in their cell walls, and Gram-negative bacteria have a very thin layer. Gram-negative bacteria have an outer layer external to the peptidoglycan layer, which inhibits entry of penicillin, thus making the Gram-negative bacteria less sensitive to penicillin than are Gram-positive bacteria.

15. Methanogens are archaea that live in low-oxygen environments. They are obligate anaerobes living in swamps, lakes, marshes, and sewage works, but also in guts of ruminants, termites, dogs, and humans. Methanogens convert some gases into methane. Halophiles are salt-loving extremophiles, living in highly saline environments. Most are aerobic chemoheterotrophs. Extreme thermophiles live in extremely hot environments, such as hot springs and hydrothermal vents at ocean bottoms, which makes them unique among living organisms.

Chapter 24

1. d 2. b 3. d 4. c 5. b 6. c 7. d 8. c 9. b 10. a

11. All animals are multicellular; protists are also unicellular. Animals have complex structures and internal organs. Protists do not have features that characterize animals, such as nerve cells, limbs, heart, tissues such as collagen.

12. Many protists can be photosynthetic and at the same time live as heterotrophs, which plants cannot do. Protists are not embryophytes like plants, and they do not have roots, stems, or leaves. Generally, photosynthetic protists live in aquatic environments, which is not true of land plants.

13. Most protists are aerobic, and are either heterotrophs or autotrophs. Many phototrophic protists may also live as heterotrophs. Some protists absorb small organic molecules from their environment.

14. Protists live in aqueous habitats, including aquatic or moist terrestrial environments such as oceans, lakes, ponds, streams, and moist soil, and within hosts. Their roles are different depending on the environment in which they live.

15. Reproduction in protists is asexual by mitosis and sexual by meiosis and gamete formation. Some protists reproduce utilizing both mitosis and meiosis, and their modes of cell division are often combined into a life cycle highly distinctive among the different protist groups.

Chapter 25

1. c 2. b 3. b 4. b 5. a 6. d 7. c 8. d 9. d 10. c 11. c

12. The human embryo is diploid. It grows by mitosis into a full organism, and when it becomes adult and mature, it starts producing haploid gametes by meiosis. Male and female gametes fertilize, forming a diploid zygote/embryo. Humans do not reproduce asexually. Fungi reproduce sexually but also asexually. In the asexual cycle, haploid spores are

produced by mitosis into mycelium, which produces spores again. In sexual reproduction, haploid spores grow into mycelium, which fuses with a compatible strain creating a binucleate mycelium (heterokaryotic stage). Karyogamy (fusion of nuclei) occurs later in the life cycle, creating diploid zygotes, which produce haploid spores by meiosis often within a fruiting body.

13. Similarities: Both penetrate root and increase surface area for absorption of nutrients. Differences: Arbuscular mycorrhizae have fungal hyphae that penetrate the cells of the root. In ectomycorrhizae, fungal hyphae form a sheath (called mantle) around a root and do not penetrate the cell walls of the root.

14. They break down organic matter, allowing nutrients to cycle in nature; some are edible; some damage our food; some are used in making alcoholic beverages; some help in baking processes; cause diseases of plants that humans are reliant on; cause diseases in humans, causing even death.

15. 15. You would need to find the evidence of absorptive nutrition, as this is the distinguishing characteristic of fungi.

Chapter 26

1. c 2. d 3. c 4. c 5. b 6. b 7. a 8. d 9. d 10. d 11. b 12. a 13. b 14. c

15. Two multicellular stages alternate throughout the lifetime of land plants: a diploid sporophyte and a haploid gametophyte. Sporophyte produces haploid spores by meiosis that grow directly into gametophytes. Gametophytes produce haploid gametes by mitosis. Gametes must fuse together (fertilize) to form a diploid zygote, which will grow by mitosis into a sporophyte, and the cycle will resume.

Chapter 27

1. b 2. c 3. d 4. c 5. a 6. b 7. d 8. c 9. c 10. a 11. d 12. d 13. a 14. a 15. b 16. b

17. This colonial, flagellated ancestor with unspecialized cells would have had a developmental reorganization that resulted in two cell layers. Certain cells became specialized for feeding and other functions. A developmental reorganization produced a two-layered animal with a sac-within-a-sac body plan. Such cell movements are similar to those that occur during the development of many animals. Associated with this, cells became specialized for different functions, such as the feeding cells giving rise to the digestive cavity.

18. Pizza cutting; crystal formations; graphical ornaments; spikes on a wheel, etc. Anything that shows body parts regularly arranged around a central axis.

19. *Hox* genes are homeotic genes that influence the three-dimensional shape of the animal and the locations of important structures such as eyes, wings, and legs, particularly along the head-to-tail axis of the body. *Hox* genes are arranged on chromosomes in a particular order, forming the *Hox* gene complex. Each gene in the complex governs the development of particular structures. Animal groups with the simplest structure, such as cnidarians, have two *Hox* genes. Those with more complex anatomy, such as insects, have 10. Chordates typically have up to 13 or 14. Lineages with many *Hox* genes generally have more complex anatomy than those with fewer *Hox* genes.

20. (1) Skin is waterproof: keratin and lipids in the cells make skin relatively impermeable to water. (2) Amniotic eggs can survive and develop on dry land because they have four specialized membranes and a hard or leathery shell perforated by microscopic pores. Amniotic eggs are resistant to desiccation. The membranes protect the developing embryo and facilitate gas exchange and excretion. The shell mediates the exchange of air and water between the egg and its envi-

ronment. Developing amniote embryos can excrete uric acid, which is stored in the allantois of the embryo, which will later become the bladder. Generous supplies of yolk in the egg are the developing embryo's main energy source; albumin supplies water and other materials. There is no larval stage, and hatchling amniotes are miniature versions of the adult. Amniotic eggs are the ancestral condition, but in some reptiles and most mammals, development takes place within the body of the mother. (3) Some amniotes produce urea and/or uric acid as a waste product of nitrogen metabolism. Although ammonia is less expensive (metabolically) to produce, it is toxic and must be flushed away with water. Urea is much less toxic than ammonia and therefore easier to store and to void. Uric acid is even less toxic and, because it is insoluble, it can be stored or voided without risk while conserving water. (4) A skeleton provides support and points of attachment for muscles, allowing locomotion and survival on land.

Chapter 28

1. c 2. c 3. d 4. c 5. b 6. b 7. b 8. b 9. c 10. c 11. a 12. a 13. c 14. b

15. An extirpated species no longer exists in one location in the wild, but occurs elsewhere in the wild. Endangered species face imminent extirpation or extinction.

Chapter 29

1. a 2. b 3. a 4. b 5. a 6. c 7. a 8. b 9. a 10. d 11. d 12. d 13. d 14. a

15. Type I curves reflect high survivorship until late in life. Type II curves reflect a relatively constant rate of mortality in all age classes, a pattern that produces steadily declining survivorship. Type III curves reflect high juvenile mortality, followed by a period of low mortality once offspring reach a critical age and size.

Chapter 30

1. c 2. b 3. a 4. b 5. d 6. a 7. b 8. c 9. b 10. b 11. c 12. d 13. d

14. Fundamental niche is the niche occupied in the absence of competition, and is wider. Realized niche is narrower, and is occupied in the presence of competition.

15. Gause grew cultures of two *Paramecium* species under constant laboratory conditions, regularly renewing food and removing wastes. Both species ate bacteria suspended in the culture medium. When grown alone, each species exhibited logistic growth. When grown together in the same dish, *Paramecium aurelia* persisted at high density, but *Paramecium caudatum* was almost eliminated. Gause explained such results by a competitive exclusion principle. Populations of two or more species cannot coexist indefinitely if they rely on the same limiting resources and exploit them in the same way. One species inevitably harvests resources more efficiently, produces more offspring than the other, and, by its actions, negatively affects the other species.

Chapter 31

1. d 2. c 3. c 4. a 5. c 6. d 7. d 8. d 9. d 10. a 11. c 12. a

13. Each trophic level uses energy for its own maintenance, and each subsequent trophic level has less energy available from primary productivity. The biomass at each trophic level is proportional to the amount of chemical energy temporarily stored there. The reduction of energy and biomass affects sizes of populations of organisms at the top of a food web. Top predators can be relatively large animals, so the limited biomass present in the highest trophic levels is concentrated in relatively few animals.

14. Nitrogen fixation is a conversion of gaseous nitrogen (N_2) to ammonia (NH_3), which dissolves to form ammonium (NH_4^+). Nitrogen fixation is performed by nitrogen-fixing bacteria. Ammonification is a process of conversion of residues to ammonia, which dissolves to form ammonium. Ammonification is performed by bacteria and fungi. Nitrification is a conversion of ammonium to nitrite (NO_2^-), and subsequent conversion of nitrite to nitrate (NO_3^-). Nitrification is performed by bacteria. Denitrification is conversion of nitrate to gaseous nitrogen by bacteria.

15. Phosphorus becomes available to biological systems when wind and rainfall dissolve phosphates in rocks and carry them into adjacent soil and freshwater ecosystems. Runoff carries dissolved phosphorus into marine ecosystems, where it precipitates out of solution and is incorporated into marine sediments.

Chapter 32

1. c 2. b 3. b 4. d 5. c 6. a 7. b 8. d 9. b 10. b 11. b 12. d 13. c 14. d

15. Imprinting occurs when animals learn the identity of a caregiver or the key features of a suitable mate during a critical period, a stage of development early in life. Classical conditioning happens when animals develop a mental association between two phenomena that are usually unrelated. Operant conditioning—trial-and-error learning—is another form of associative learning: animals learn to link a voluntary activity, an operant, with its favourable consequences, a reinforcement. Insight learning occurs when an animal abruptly learns to solve problems without apparent trial-and-error attempts at the solution. Habituation occurs when animals lose their responsiveness to frequent stimuli not immediately followed by the usual reinforcement.

Glossary

abductor muscle Muscles that abduct or move a body part away from the body (the opposite action to an adductor muscle that moves a body part toward the midline). p. 666

abiotic Nonbiological, often in reference to physical factors in the environment. p. 494

absorptive nutrition Mode of nutrition in which an organism secretes digestive enzymes into its environment and then absorbs the small molecules thus produced. p. 588

acetabulum Socket of hip joint, receives head of femur. p. 700

acoelomate A body plan of bilaterally symmetrical animals that lack a body cavity (coelom) between the gut and the body wall. p. 646

acorn worms Sedentary marine animals living in U-shaped tubes or burrows in coastal sand or mud. p. 684

active parental care Parents' investment of time and energy in caring for offspring after they are born or hatched. p. 754

adaptive zone A part of a habitat that may be occupied by a group of species exploiting the same resources in a similar manner. p. 704

aerobe An organism that requires oxygen for cellular respiration. p. 544

African emergence hypothesis A hypothesis proposing that modern humans first evolved in Africa and then dispersed to other continents. p. 405

age-specific fecundity The average number of offspring produced by surviving females of a particular age. p. 752

age-specific mortality The proportion of individuals alive at the start of an age interval that died during that age interval. p. 752

age-specific survivorship The proportion of individuals alive at the start of an age interval that survived until the start of the next age interval. p. 752

algin Alginic acid, found in the cell walls of brown algae. p. 572

allochthonous Sediment or rock that originated far from its present position. p. 836

allopatric speciation The evolution of reproductive isolating mechanisms between two populations that are geographically separated. p. 440

allopolyploidy The genetic condition of having two or more complete sets of chromosomes from different parent species. p. 445

alpine tundra A biome that occurs on high mountaintops throughout the world, in which dominant plants form cushions and mats. p. 619

alternation of generations The regular alternation of mode of reproduction in the life cycle of an organism, such as the alternation between diploid (sporophyte) and haploid (gametophyte) phases in plants. p. 612

altricial Newborns that are immobile and helpless for some considerable time after birth. p. 709

altruism A behavioural phenomenon in which individuals appear to sacrifice their own reproductive success to help other individuals. p. 873

ammocoetes Larval lamprey eel. p. 689

ammonification A metabolic process in which bacteria and fungi convert organic nitrogen compounds into ammonia and ammonium ions; part of the nitrogen cycle. p. 828

amniote (amniotic) egg A shelled egg that can survive and develop on land. p. 698

amoeboid Similar to an amoeba, particularly in type of movement. p. 651

anaerobic respiration The process by which molecules are oxidized to produce ATP via an electron transport chain and ATP synthase, but unlike aerobic respiration, oxygen is not the final electron acceptor. p. 544

anapsid (lineage Anapsida) A member of the group of amniote vertebrates with no temporal arches and no spaces on the sides of the skull (includes turtles). p. 699

ancestral character state A trait that was present in a distant common ancestor. p. 463

animal behaviour The responses of animals to specific internal and external stimuli. p. 846

antheridium (plural, **antheridia**) In plants, a structure in which sperm are produced. p. 619

Anthocerotophyta The phylum comprising hornworts. p. 622

Anthophyta The phylum comprising flowering plants. p. 633

antibiotic A natural or synthetic substance that kills or inhibits the growth of bacteria and other microorganisms. p. 546

apical growth Growth from the tip of a cell or tissue. p. 588

apical meristem A region of unspecialized dividing cells at the shoot tips and root tips of a plant. p. 615

apicomplexan A group of parasitic organisms with specific structures in their apical complex to penetrate and enter the cells they parasitize. p. 568

apomorphy A derived character state. p. 463

aposematic Refers to bright, contrasting patterns that advertise the unpalatability of poisonous or repellent species. p. 787

aquatic succession A process in which debris from rivers and runoff accumulates in a body of fresh water, causing it to fill in at the margins. p. 801

arbuscule Highly branched hypha produced inside root cells by arbuscular mycorrhizal fungi; nutrient exchange site between plant and fungus. p. 594

Archaea One of two domains of prokaryotes; archaeans have some unique molecular and biochemical traits, but they also share some traits with Bacteria and other traits with Eukarya. p. 538

archaeocytes A major group of the domain Archaea, members of which are found in different extreme environments. They include methanogens, extreme halophiles, and some extreme thermophiles. *See also* Euryarchaeota. p. 651

archegonium (plural, **archegonia**) The flask-shaped structure in which bryophyte eggs form. p. 619

archenteron The central endoderm-lined cavity of an embryo at the gastrula stage, which forms the primitive gut. p. 648

Archosauromorpha A diverse group of diapsids that comprises crocodilians, pterosaurs, and dinosaurs (including birds). p. 700

arctic tundra A treeless biome that stretches from the boreal forests to the polar ice cap in Europe, Asia, and North America. p. 619

artificial selection Selective breeding of animals or plants to ensure that certain desirable traits appear at higher frequency in successive generations. p. 399

ascocarp A reproductive body that bears or contains asci. p. 594

ascospore Spore formed by meiosis in the ascus, a saclike cell produced by ascomycete fungi. p. 596

assimilation efficiency The ratio of the energy absorbed from consumed food to the total energy content of the food. p. 819

atrial siphon A tube through which invertebrate chordates expel digestive and metabolic wastes. p. 685

atriopore The hole in the body wall of a cephalochordate through which water is expelled from the body. p. 685

atrium (plural, **atria**) A body cavity or chamber surrounding the perforated pharynx of invertebrate chordates; also one of the chambers that receive blood returning to the heart. p. 685

autopolyploidy The genetic condition of having more than two sets of chromosomes from the same parent species. p. 444

autotroph An organism that produces its own food using CO_2 and other simple inorganic compounds from its environment and energy from the Sun or from oxidation of inorganic substances. pp. 503, 543

axial skeleton The bones constituting the head and trunk of a vertebrate: the cranium, vertebral column, ribs, and sternum (breastbone). p. 687

axopods Slender, raylike strands of cytoplasm supported internally by long bundles of microtubules. p. 572

backbone (spine) Vertebral column of vertebrates. p. 685

Bacteria One of the two domains of prokaryotes; collectively, bacteria are the most metabolically diverse organisms. p. 538

bacteriophage A virus that infects bacteria. Also referred to as a *phage*. p. 523

balancing selection A type of natural selection in which more than one allele is actively maintained in a population. p. 425

basidiocarp A fruiting body of a basidiomycete; mushrooms are examples. p. 600

basidiospore A haploid sexual spore produced by basidiomycete fungi. p. 600

basidium (plural, **basidia**) A small, club-shaped structure in which sexual spores of basidiomycetes arise. p. 597

behavioural isolation A prezygotic reproductive isolating mechanism in which two species do not mate because of differences in courtship behaviour; also known as *ethological isolation*. p. 438

binomial Relating to or consisting of two names or terms. p. 454

binomial nomenclature The naming of species with a two-part scientific name, the first indicating the genus and the second indicating the species. p. 454

biofilm A microbial community consisting of a complex aggregation of microorganisms attached to a surface. p. 546

biogeochemical cycle Any of several global processes in which a nutrient circulates between the abiotic environment and living organisms. pp. 544, 823

biogeography The study of the geographic distributions of plants and animals. p. 396

biological magnification The increasing concentration of nondegradable poisons in the tissues of animals at higher trophic levels. p. 815

biological species concept The definition of species based on the ability of populations to interbreed and produce fertile offspring. p. 434

bioluminescent Refers to an organism that glows or releases a flash of light, particularly when disturbed. p. 568

biomass The dry weight of biological material per unit area or volume of habitat. pp. 538, 817

bioremediation Applications of chemical and biological knowledge to decontaminate polluted environments. p. 538

biotic Biological, often in reference to living components of the environment. p. 494

bipedalism The habit in animals of walking upright on two legs. p. 480

blastopore The opening at one end of the archenteron in the gastrula that gives rise to the mouth in protostomes and the anus in deuterostomes. p. 648

body plan Description of the way that animals are built; the "blueprint" of cellular organization that encompasses such things as symmetry, segmentation, and formation and position of limbs. p. 645

Bryophyta The phylum of nonvascular plants, including mosses and their relatives. p. 621

bryophyte A general term for plants (such as mosses) that lack internal transport vessels. p. 619

budding A mode of asexual reproduction in which a new individual grows and develops while attached to the parent. p. 588

capsid The protective layer of protein that surrounds the nucleic acid core of a virus. p. 522

capsule An external layer of sticky or slimy polysaccharides coating the cell wall in many prokaryotes. p. 542

captaculum (plural, **captacula**) In molluscs, a filamentous, tactile organ with an adhesive,

suckerlike end used to gather small particles of food in the sand and pass them to the mouth. p. 668

carapace A protective outer covering that extends backward behind the head on the dorsal side of an animal, such as the shell of a turtle or lobster. p. 675

carbon cycle The global circulation of carbon atoms, especially via the processes of photosynthesis and respiration. p. 824

carnivore An animal that primarily eats other animals. p. 710

carrageenan A chemical extracted from the red alga *Eucheuma* that is used to thicken and stabilize paints, dairy products such as pudding and ice cream, and many other creams and emulsions. p. 577

carrying capacity The maximum size of a population that an environment can support indefinitely. p. 758

celestial navigation Navigating by the positions of stars. p. 865

cell cycle The sequence of events during which a cell experiences a period of growth followed by nuclear division and cytokinesis. p. 506

cellular slime mould Any of a variety of primitive organisms of the phylum Acrasiomycota, especially of the genus *Dictyostelium;* the life cycle is characterized by a slimelike amoeboid stage and a multicellular reproductive stage. p. 575

cephalized An animal's sense organs are concentrated at the anterior end (i.e., the head). p. 645

character A heritable characteristic. p. 463

character displacement The phenomenon in which allopatric populations are morphologically similar and use similar resources, but sympatric populations are morphologically different and use different resources; may also apply to characters influencing mate choice. p. 791

character state One or more forms of a character used in a phylogenetic analysis. p. 463

charophyte A member of the group of green algae most similar to the algal ancestors of land plants. p. 579

chelicerae The first pair of fanglike appendages near the mouth of an arachnid, used for biting prey and often modified for grasping and piercing. p. 673

chelipeds The legs of arthropods that terminate in a claw or pincer. p. 675

chemical signal Any secretion from one cell type that can alter the behaviour of a different cell that bears a receptor for it; a means of cell communication. p. 575

chemoautotroph An organism that obtains energy by oxidizing inorganic substances such as hydrogen, iron, sulfur, ammonia, nitrites, and nitrates and uses carbon dioxide as a carbon source. p. 543

chemoheterotroph An organism that oxidizes organic molecules as an energy source and obtains carbon in organic form. p. 548

chemotroph An organism that obtains energy by oxidizing inorganic or organic substances. p. 543

choanocyte One of the inner layer of flagellated cells lining the body cavity of a sponge. p. 651

Choanoflagellata A group of minute, single-celled protists found in water; the flask-shaped body has a collar of closely packed microvilli that surrounds the single flagellum by which it moves and takes in food. p. 576

clade A monophyletic group of organisms that share homologous features derived from a common ancestor. p. 456

cladistics An approach to systematics that uses shared derived characters to infer the phylogenetic relationships and evolutionary history of groups of organisms. p. 462

claspers A pair of organs on the pelvic fins of male crustaceans and sharks, which help transfer sperm into the reproductive tract of the female. p. 692

classical conditioning A type of learning in which an animal develops a mental association between two phenomena that are usually unrelated. p. 850

classification An arrangement of organisms into hierarchical groups that reflect their relatedness. p. 455

cleavage Mitotic cell divisions of the zygote that produce a blastula from a fertilized ovum. p. 646

climax community A relatively stable, late successional stage in which the dominant vegetation replaces itself and persists until an environmental disturbance eliminates it, allowing other species to invade. p. 801

cline A pattern of smooth variation in a characteristic along a geographic gradient. p. 436

closed circulatory system A circulatory system in which the fluid, blood, is confined in blood vessels and is distinct from the interstitial fluid. p. 668

cnidocyte A prey-capturing and defensive cell in the epidermis of cnidarians. p. 653

coccoid Spherical prokaryotic cell. p. 538

cochlea A snail-shaped structure (in vertebrates) in the inner ear containing the organ of hearing. p. 538

coelom A fluid-filled body cavity in bilaterally symmetrical animals that is completely lined with derivatives of mesoderm. p. 646

coelomate A body plan of bilaterally symmetrical animals that have a coelom. p. 646

co-evolution The evolution of genetically based, reciprocal adaptations in two or more species that interact closely in the same ecological setting. p. 778

cohort A group of individuals of similar age. p. 752

colony Multiple individual organisms of the same species living in a group. p. 562

commensalism A symbiotic interaction in which one species benefits and the other is unaffected. p. 779

compass orientation A wayfinding mechanism that allows animals to move in a particular direction, often over a specific distance or for a prescribed length of time. p. 865

competitive exclusion principle The ecological principle stating that populations of two or more species cannot coexist indefinitely if they rely on the same limiting resources and exploit them in the same way. p. 790

complete metamorphosis The form of metamorphosis in which an insect passes through four separate stages of growth: egg, larva, pupa, and adult. p. 678

compound eye The eye of most insects and some crustaceans, composed of many-faceted, light-sensitive units called ommatidia fitted closely together, each with its own refractive system and each forming a portion of an image. p. 676

cone 1. In cone-bearing plants, a cluster of sporophylls. 2. In the vertebrate eye, a photoreceptor in the retina that is specialized for detection of different wavelengths (colours). p. 625

conidium (plural, **conidia**) An asexually produced fungal spore. p. 596

Coniferophyta The major phylum of cone-bearing gymnosperms, most of which are substantial trees; includes pines, firs, and other conifers. p. 630

conodont An abundant, bonelike fossil dating from the early Paleozoic era through the early Mesozoic era, now described as a

feeding structure of some of the earliest vertebrates. p. 689

consumer An organism that consumes other organisms in a community or ecosystem. p. 778

contractile vacuole A specialized cytoplasmic organelle that pumps fluid in a cyclical manner from within the cell to the outside by alternately filling and then contracting to release its contents at various points on the surface of the cell. p. 562

convergent evolution The evolution of similar adaptations in distantly related organisms that occupy similar environments. p. 459

cranial nerve A nerve that connects the brain directly to the head, neck, and body trunk. p. 687

cranium The part of the skull that encloses the brain. p. 687

Crenarchaeota A major group of the domain Archaea, separated from the other archaeans based mainly on rRNA sequences. p. 551

critical period A restricted stage of development early in life during which an animal has the capacity to respond to specific environmental stimuli. p. 850

ctenidium (plural, **ctenidia**) A comblike or featherlike structure. In mollusks they appear as gills, while in some insects they appear as rows of spines on their legs. p. 668

cuticle The outer layer of plants and some animals, which helps prevent desiccation by slowing water loss. p. 614

Cycadophyta A phylum of palmlike gymnosperms known as cycads; the pollen-bearing and seed-bearing cones (strobili) occur on separate plants. p. 630

cytoplasmic streaming Intracellular movement of cytoplasm. p. 589

decomposer A small organism, such as a bacterium or fungus, that feeds on the remains of dead organisms, breaking down complex biological molecules or structures into simpler raw materials. p. 778

demographic transition model A graphic depiction of the historical relationship between a country's economic development and its birth and death rates. p. 768

demography The statistical study of the processes that change a population's size and density through time. p. 752

denitrification A metabolic process in which certain bacteria convert nitrites or nitrates into nitrous oxide and then into molecular nitrogen, which enters the atmosphere. p. 828

density independent Description of environmental factors for which the strength of their effect on a population does not vary with the population's density. p. 762

derived character state A new version of a trait found in the most recent common ancestor of a group. p. 463

determinate cleavage A type of cleavage in protostomes in which each cell's developmental path is determined as the cell is produced. p. 647

detritus Dead organic matter. pp. 600, 778

deuterostome A division of the Bilateria in which blastopore forms the anus during development and the mouth appears later (includes Echinodermata and Chordata). p. 646

diapsid (lineage Diapsida) A member of a group within the amniote vertebrates with a skull with two temporal arches. Their living descendants include lizards and snakes, crocodilians, and birds. p. 700

diatom Photosynthetic single-celled organisms with a glassy silica shell; also called bacillariophytes. p. 570

dikaryotic hyphae Hyphae containing two separate nuclei in one cell. p. 596

diphyodont Having two generations of teeth, milk (baby) teeth and adult teeth. p. 708

diploblastic An animal body plan in which adult structures arise from only two cell layers, the ectoderm and the endoderm. p. 645

directional selection A type of selection in which individuals near one end of the phenotypic spectrum have the highest relative fitness. p. 421

disclimax community *See* disturbance climax (disclimax) community. p. 803

dispersion The spatial distribution of individuals within a population's geographic range. p. 749

disruptive selection A type of natural selection in which extreme phenotypes have higher relative fitness than intermediate phenotypes. p. 422

disturbance climax (disclimax) community An ecological community in which regular disturbance inhibits successional change. p. 803

dominance hierarchy A social system in which the behaviour of each individual is constrained by that individual's status in a highly structured social ranking. p. 871

echolocating animal An animal that makes squeaking or clicking noises, and then listens for the echoes that bounce back from objects in their environment. The animal stores the outgoing signal in its brain for comparison with returning echoes. p. 859

ecological efficiency The ratio of net productivity at one trophic level to net productivity at the trophic level below it. p. 819

ecological isolation A prezygotic reproductive isolating mechanism in which species that live in the same geographic region occupy different habitats. p. 437

ecological niche The resources a population uses and the environmental conditions it requires over its lifetime. p. 790

ecological pyramid A diagram illustrating the effects of energy transfer from one trophic level to the next. p. 821

ecosystem A group of biological communities interacting with their shared physical environment. p. 814

ecotone A wide transition zone between adjacent communities. p. 793

ectoderm The outermost of the three primary germ layers of an embryo, which develops into epidermis and nervous tissue. p. 645

ectognathous *Ecto* = outward; *gnathous* = having jaws. Insect mouthparts that project outward from the head and are not retracted within the head. p. 675

Elasmobranchii Cartilaginous fishes, including the skates and rays. p. 690

electric signal A means of animal communication in which a signaller emits an electric discharge that can be received by another individual. p. 859

electroreceptor A specialized sensory receptor that detects electrical fields. p. 691

emigration The movement of individuals out of a population. p. 752

endemic species A species that occurs in only one place on Earth. p. 734

endoderm The innermost of the three primary germ layers of an embryo, which develops into the gastrointestinal tract and, in some animals, the respiratory organs. p. 645

endoparasite A parasite that lives in the internal organs of its host organism. p. 781

endosporous Pattern of development in some plants (e.g., seed plants) in which the gametophyte develops inside the spore wall. p. 627

endosymbiosis A symbiotic association in which one symbiont or partner lives inside the other. p. 504

endothermic Refers to reactions that absorb energy. p. 708

endotoxin A lipopolysaccharide released from the outer membrane of the cell wall when a bacterium dies and lyses. p. 545

enterocoelom In deuterostomes, the body cavity pinched off by outpocketings of the archenteron. p. 648

entognathous The mouth parts can be withdrawn into a capsule in the head. p. 675

envelope Outer glycoprotein layer surrounding the capsid of some viruses, derived in part from host cell plasma membrane. p. 522

enveloped virus A virus that has a surface membrane derived from its host cell. p. 522

equilibrium theory of island biogeography A hypothesis suggesting that the number of species on an island is governed by a give and take between the immigration of new species to the island and the extinction of species already there. p. 805

esophagus A connecting passage of the digestive tube. p. 680

ethology A discipline that focuses on how animals behave. p. 850

eudicot A plant belonging to the Eudicotyledones, one of the two major classes of angiosperms; their embryos generally have two seed leaves (cotyledons), and their pollen grains have three grooves. p. 633

Eukarya The domain that includes all eukaryotes, organisms that contain a membrane-bound nucleus within each of their cells; all protists, plants, fungi, and animals. p. 538

Euryarchaeota A major group of the domain Archaea, members of which are found in different extreme environments. They include methanogens, extreme halophiles, and some extreme thermophiles. p. 551

eusocial A form of social organization, observed in some insect species, in which numerous related individuals—a large percentage of them sterile female workers—live and work together in a colony for the reproductive benefit of a single queen and her mate(s). p. 874

evolution The main unifying concept in biology, explaining how the diversity of life on Earth arose and how species change over time in response to changes in their abiotic and biotic environment. p. 414

exoskeleton A hard external covering of an animal's body that blocks the passage of water and provides support and protection. p. 673

exotoxin A toxic protein that leaks from or is secreted from a bacterium and interferes with the biochemical processes of body cells in various ways. p. 545

exploitative competition Form of competition in which two or more individuals or populations use the same limiting resources. p. 788

exponential model of population growth Model that describes unlimited population growth. p. 756

extracellular digestion Digestion that takes place outside body cells, in a pouch or tube enclosed within the body. p. 653

facilitation hypothesis A hypothesis that explains ecological succession, suggesting that species modify the local environment in ways that make it less suitable for themselves but more suitable for colonization by species typical of the next successional stage. p. 802

facultative anaerobe An organism that can live in the presence or absence of oxygen, using oxygen when it is present and living by fermentation under anaerobic conditions. p. 544

family planning program A program that educates people about ways to produce an optimal family size on an economically feasible schedule. p. 769

feather A sturdy, lightweight structure of birds, derived from scales in the skin of their ancestors. p. 706

fitness An individual's reproductive success. p. 400

fixed action pattern A highly stereotyped instinctive behaviour; when triggered by a specific cue, it is performed over and over in almost exactly the same way. p. 848

flagellum (plural, **flagella**) A long, threadlike, cellular appendage responsible for movement; found in both prokaryotes and eukaryotes, but with different structures and modes of locomotion. p. 542

flame cell The cell that forms the primary filtrate in the excretory system of many bilateria. The urine is propelled through ducts by the synchronous beating of cilia, resembling a flickering flame. p. 659

flower The reproductive structure of angiosperms, consisting of floral parts grouped on a stem; the structure in which seeds develop. p. 632

food web A set of interconnected food chains with multiple links. p. 619

founder effect An evolutionary phenomenon in which a population that was established by just a few colonizing individuals has only a fraction of the genetic diversity seen in the population from which it was derived. p. 419

frequency-dependent selection A form of natural selection in which rare phenotypes have a selective advantage simply because they are rare. p. 427

fruit A mature ovary, often with accessory parts, from a flower. p. 632

fruiting body In some fungi, a stalked, spore-producing structure such as a mushroom. p. 575

fundamental niche The range of conditions and resources that a population can possibly tolerate and use. p. 790

furculum Wishbone in birds. p. 704

gametangium (plural, **gametangia**) A cell or organ in which gametes are produced. pp. 592, 619

gamete A haploid cell; an egg or sperm. Haploid cells fuse during sexual reproduction to form a diploid zygote. p. 644

gametic isolation A prezygotic reproductive isolating mechanism caused by incompatibility between the sperm of one species and the eggs of another; may prevent fertilization. p. 439

gametophyte An individual of the haploid generation produced when a spore germinates and grows directly by mitotic divisions in organisms that undergo alternation of generations. pp. 572, 612

ganglion (plural, **ganglia**) A functional concentration of nervous system tissue composed principally of nerve cell bodies, usually lying outside the central nervous system. p. 659

gemma (plural, **gemmae**) Small cell mass that forms in cuplike growths on a thallus. p. 621

gemmules Clusters of cells with a resistant covering that allows them to survive unfavourable conditions. p. 652

gene flow The transfer of genes from one population to another through the movement of individuals or their gametes. p. 416

gene pool The sum of all alleles at all gene loci in all individuals in a population. p. 414

generalized compartment model A model used to describe nutrient cycling in which two criteria—organic versus inorganic nutrients and available versus unavailable nutrients—define four compartments where nutrients accumulate. p. 823

generation time The average time between the birth of an organism and the birth of its offspring. pp. 402, 751

genetic distance method An approach to phylogenetic analysis that calculates the overall proportion of nucleotide bases that differ among species. p. 466

genetic drift Random fluctuations in allele frequencies as a result of chance events; usually reduces genetic variation in a population. p. 419

genetic equilibrium The point at which neither the allele frequencies nor the genotype frequencies in a population change in succeeding generations. p. 416

genus A Linnaean taxonomic category ranking below a family and above a species. p. 454

geographic range The overall spatial boundaries within which a population lives. p. 749

germ layer The layers (up to three) of cells produced during the early development of the embryo of most animals. p. 645

gestation The period of mammalian development in which the embryo develops in the uterus of the mother. p. 708

gill arch One of the series of curved supporting structures between the slits in the pharynx of a chordate. p. 690

gill slit One of the openings in the pharynx of a chordate through which water passes out of the pharynx. p. 685

Ginkgophyta A plant phylum with a single living species, the ginkgo (or maidenhair) tree. p. 630

Gnathostomata The group of vertebrates with movable jaws. p. 688

Gram-negative Describing bacteria that do not retain the stain used in the Gram stain procedure. p. 541

Gram-positive Describing bacteria that appear purple when stained using the Gram stain technique. p. 541

Gram stain procedure A procedure of staining bacteria to distinguish between types of bacteria with different cell wall compositions. p. 541

greenhouse effect A phenomenon in which certain gases foster the accumulation of heat in the lower atmosphere, maintaining warm temperatures on Earth. p. 830

gross primary productivity The rate at which producers convert solar energy into chemical energy. p. 817

gymnosperm A seed plant that produces "naked" seeds not enclosed in an ovary. p. 628

habitat The specific environment in which a population lives, as characterized by its biotic and abiotic features. p. 749

habituation The learned loss of responsiveness to stimuli. p. 851

haplodiploidy A pattern of sex determination in insects in which females are diploid and males are haploid. p. 874

Hardy–Weinberg principle An evolutionary rule of thumb that specifies the conditions under which a population of diploid organisms achieves genetic equilibrium. p. 416

harvesting efficiency The ratio of the energy content of food consumed to with the energy content of food available. p. 819

head–foot In molluscs, the region of the body that provides the major means of locomotion and contains concentrations of nervous system tissues and sense organs. p. 665

helical virus A virus in which the protein subunits of the coat assemble in a rodlike spiral around the genome. p. 522

hemolymph The circulatory fluid of invertebrates with open circulatory systems, including molluscs and arthropods. p. 665

Hepatophyta The phylum that includes liverworts and their bryophyte relatives. p. 620

herbivore An animal that obtains energy and nutrients primarily by eating plants. p. 778

heterodont Having different teeth specialized for different jobs. p. 708

heterosporous Producing two types of spores, "male" microspores and "female" megaspores. p. 617

heterotroph An organism that acquires energy and nutrients by eating other organisms or their remains. pp. 502, 543, 644

heterozygote advantage An evolutionary circumstance in which individuals that are heterozygous at a particular locus have higher relative fitness than either homozygote. p. 425

Holocephali The chimeras, another group of cartilaginous fishes. p. 690

hominin A member of a monophyletic group of primates, characterized by an erect bipedal stance, that includes modern humans and their recent ancestors. p. 480

hominoid (Hominoidea) A member of the monophyletic group of primates that includes apes and humans. p. 480

homology A characteristic shared by a set of species because they inherited it from their common ancestor. pp. 396, 459

homoplasies Characteristics shared by a set of species, often because they live in similar environments, but not present in their common ancestor; often the product of convergent evolution. p. 459

homosporous Producing only one type of spore. p. 617

horizontal gene transfer Movement of genetic material between organisms other than by descent. p. 513

host A species that is fed upon by a parasite. p. 504

host race A population of insects that may be reproductively isolated from other populations of the same species as a consequence of their adaptation to feed on a specific host plant species. p. 442

hybrid An organism produced by a mating between parents of different species or subspecies. p. 437

hybrid breakdown A postzygotic reproductive isolating mechanism in which hybrids are capable of reproducing, but their offspring have either reduced fertility or reduced viability. p. 439

hybrid inviability A postzygotic reproductive isolating mechanism in which a hybrid individual has a low probability of survival to reproductive age. p. 439

hybrid sterility A postzygotic reproductive isolating mechanism in which hybrid offspring cannot form functional gametes. p. 439

hybrid zone A geographic area where the hybrid offspring of two divergent populations or species are common. p. 441

hydrogeological cycle The global cycling of water between the ocean, the atmosphere, land, freshwater ecosystems, and living organisms. p. 824

hydrostatic skeleton A structure consisting of muscles and fluid that, by themselves, provide support for the animal or part of the animal; no rigid support, such as a bone, is involved. p. 646

hyomandibular bones Bones that support the hyoid and throat. p. 690

hypha (plural, **hyphae**) Any of the threadlike filaments that form the mycelium of a fungus. pp. 570, 588

immigration Movement of organisms into a population. p. 752

imprinting The process of learning the identity of a caretaker and potential future mate during a critical period. p. 850

inbreeding A special form of nonrandom mating in which genetically related individuals mate with each other. p. 423

inbreeding depression A decline in the average fitness of inbred individuals in a population. p. 424

incomplete metamorphosis In certain insects, a life cycle characterized by the absence of a pupal stage between the immature and adult stages. p. 678

indeterminate cleavage A type of cleavage, observed in many deuterostomes, in which the developmental fates of the first few cells produced by mitosis are not determined as soon as cells are produced. p. 647

inhibition hypothesis A hypothesis suggesting that new species are prevented from occupying a community by whatever species are already present. p. 802

insight learning A phenomenon in which animals can solve problems without apparent trial-and-error attempts at the solution. p. 851

instar The stage between successive moults in insects and other arthropods. p. 677

instinctive behaviour A genetically "programmed" response that appears in complete and functional form the first time it is used. p. 847

interference competition Form of competition in which individuals fight over resources or otherwise harm each other directly. p. 788

intermediate disturbance hypothesis Hypothesis proposing that species richness is greatest in communities that experience fairly frequent disturbances of moderate intensity. p. 798

interspecific Between species. p. 788

intracellular digestion The process in which cells take in food particles by endocytosis. p. 653

intraspecific Among same species. p. 759

intraspecific competition The dependence of two or more individuals in a population on the same limiting resource. pp. 759, 788

intrinsic rate of increase The maximum possible per capita population growth rate in a population living under ideal conditions. p. 757

inversion Chromosomal alteration that occurs if a broken segment reattaches to the same chromosome from which it was lost, but in reversed orientation, so that the order of

genes in the segment is reversed with respect to the other genes of the chromosome. p. 420

karyogamy In plants, the fusion of two sexually compatible haploid nuclei after cell fusion (plasmogamy). p. 589

keeled sternum The ventrally extended breastbone of a bird to which the flight muscles attach. p. 704

keystone species A species that has a greater effect on community structure than its numbers might suggest. p. 791

kin selection Altruistic behaviour to close relatives, allowing them to produce proportionately more surviving copies of the altruist's genes than the altruist might otherwise have produced on its own. p. 872

kinesis A change in the rate of movement or the frequency of turning movements in response to environmental stimuli. p. 862

kingdom Animalia The taxonomic kingdom that includes all living and extinct animals. p. 644

kingdom Fungi The taxonomic kingdom that includes all living or extinct fungi. p. 590

kingdom Plantae The taxonomic kingdom encompassing all living or extinct plants. p. 613

Korarchaeota A group of Archaea recognized solely on the basis of rRNA coding sequences in DNA taken from environmental samples. p. 551

K-selected species Long-lived, slow-reproducing species that thrive in more stable environments. p. 763

latent phase The time during which a virus remains in the cell in an inactive form. p. 528

lateral bud A bud on the side of a plant stem from which a branch may grow. p. 528

lateral line system The complex of mechanoreceptors along the sides of some fishes and aquatic amphibians that detect vibrations in the water. p. 691

learned behaviour A response of an animal that depends on having a particular kind of experience during development. p. 847

left aortic arch In mammals, leads blood way from the heart to the aorta. p. 708

lek A display ground where males each possess a small territory from which they court attentive females. p. 869

Lepidosauromorpha A monophyletic lineage of diapsids that includes both marine and terrestrial animals, represented today by sphenodontids, lizards, and snakes. p. 700

life cycle The sequential stages through which individuals develop, grow, maintain themselves, and reproduce. p. 563

life table A chart that summarizes the demographic characteristics of a population. p. 752

limiting nutrient An element in short supply within an ecosystem, the shortage of which limits productivity. p. 817

lipopolysaccharide (LPS) A large molecule that consists of a lipid and a carbohydrate joined by a covalent bond. p. 541

locus The particular site on a chromosome at which a gene is located. p. 414

logistic model of population growth Model of population growth that assumes that a population's per capita growth rate decreases as the population gets larger. p. 758

Lokiarchaeota A candidate group of the domain Archaea, members of which contain more eukaryotic-like genes than any of the other known archaeal species. p. 551

lophophore The circular or U-shaped fold with one or two rows of hollow, ciliated tentacles that surrounds the mouth of brachiopods, bryozoans, and phoronids and is used to gather food. p. 659

Lycophyta The plant phylum that includes club mosses and their close relatives. p. 624

lysed Refers to a cell that has ruptured or undergone lysis. p. 526

lysogenic cycle Cycle in which the DNA of the bacteriophage is integrated into the DNA of the host bacterial cell and may remain for many generations. p. 526

lytic cycle The series of events from infection of one bacterial cell by a phage through the release of progeny phages from lysed cells. p. 526

macronucleus In ciliophorans, a single large nucleus that develops from a micronucleus but loses all genes except those required for basic "housekeeping" functions of the cell and for ribosomal RNAs. p. 567

Malpighian tubule The main organ of excretion and osmoregulation in insects, helping them maintain water and electrolyte balance. p. 676

mantle One or two folds of the body wall that lines the shell and secretes the substance that forms the shell in molluscs. p. 665

mantle cavity The protective chamber produced by the mantle in many molluscs. p. 665

mating systems The social systems describing how males and females pair up. p. 868

mating type A genetically defined strain of an organism (such as a fungus) that can only mate with an organism of the opposite mating type; mating types are often designated + and −. p. 592

maxilla (plural, **maxillae**) One of the paired head appendages posterior to the mouth used for feeding in arthropods. p. 691

maximum likelihood method A statistical technique that compares alternative phylogenetic trees with specific models of evolutionary change. p. 466

mechanical isolation A prezygotic reproductive isolating mechanism caused by differences in the structure of reproductive organs or other body parts. p. 438

medusa (plural, **medusae**) The tentacled, usually bell-shaped, free-swimming sexual stage in the life cycle of a coelenterate. p. 653

megaspore A plant spore that develops into a female gametophyte; usually larger than a microspore. p. 617

mesenteries Sheets of loose connective tissue, covered on both surfaces with epithelial cells, which suspend the abdominal organs in the coelom and provide lubricated, smooth surfaces that prevent chafing or abrasion between adjacent structures as the body moves. p. 646

mesoderm The middle layer of the three primary germ layers of an animal embryo, from which the muscular, skeletal, vascular, and connective tissues develop. p. 645

mesohyl The gelatinous middle layer of cells lining the body cavity of a sponge. p. 651

metagenomics The study of all DNA sequences, regardless of origin, isolated "in bulk" from ecosystems such as decaying animals, ocean water, termite gut, etc. p. 538

metamorphosis A reorganization of the form of certain animals during postembryonic development. p. 678

microclimate The abiotic conditions immediately surrounding an organism. p. 801

micronucleus In ciliophorans, one or more diploid nuclei that contain a complete complement of genes, functioning primarily in cellular reproduction. p. 567

microspore A plant spore from which a male gametophyte develops; usually smaller than a megaspore. pp. 617, 630

mixotroph An organisms that can act as an autotroph and a heterotroph. p. 564

molecular clock A technique for dating the time of divergence of two species or lineages, based on the number of molecular sequence differences between them. p. 469

monocot A plant belonging to the Monocotyledones, one of the two major classes of angiosperms; monocot embryos have a single seed leaf (cotyledon) and pollen grains with a single groove. p. 633

monoecious Having both "male" flowers (which possess only stamens) and "female" flowers (which possess only carpels). p. 651

monogamy A mating system in which one male and one female form a long-term association. p. 868

monomers Identical or nearly identical subunits that link together to form polymers during polymerization. p. 498

monophyletic taxon A group of organisms that includes a single ancestral species and all of its descendants. p. 458

monotreme A lineage of mammals that lay eggs instead of bearing live young. p. 708

morphological species concept The concept that all individuals of a species share measurable traits that distinguish them from individuals of other species. p. 434

motile Capable of self-propelled movement. p. 644

multiregional hypothesis A hypothesis proposing that after archaic humans migrated from Africa to many regions on Earth, their different populations evolved into modern humans simultaneously. p. 485

mutation A spontaneous and heritable change in DNA. pp. 401, 419

mutualism A symbiotic interaction between species in which both partners benefit. pp. 588, 780

mycelium A network of branching hyphae that constitutes the body of a multicellular fungus. pp. 570, 588

mycobiont The fungal component of a lichen. p. 601

mycorrhiza A mutualistic symbiosis in which fungal hyphae associate intimately with plant roots. p. 594

natural selection The evolutionary process by which alleles that increase the likelihood of survival and the reproductive output of the individuals that carry them become more common in subsequent generations. p. 399

navigation A wayfinding mechanism in which an animal moves toward a specific destination, using both a compass and a "mental map" of where it is in relation to the destination. p. 865

nematocyst A coiled thread, encapsulated in a cnidocyte, that cnidarians fire at prey or predators, sometimes releasing a toxin through its tip. p. 653

nerve net A simple nervous system that coordinates responses to stimuli but has no central control organ or brain. p. 654

net primary productivity The chemical energy remaining in an ecosystem after a producer's cellular respiration is deducted. p. 817

nitrification A metabolic process in which certain soil bacteria convert ammonia or ammonium ions into nitrites that are then converted by other bacteria to nitrates, a form usable by plants. pp. 544, 828

nitrogen cycle A biogeochemical cycle that moves nitrogen between the huge atmospheric pool of gaseous molecular nitrogen and several much smaller pools of nitrogen-containing compounds in soils, marine and freshwater ecosystems, and living organisms. p. 827

nitrogen fixation A metabolic process in which certain bacteria and cyanobacteria convert molecular nitrogen into ammonia and ammonium ions, forms usable by plants. pp. 544, 827

node The point on a stem where one or more leaves are attached. p. 456

nonvascular plant *See* bryophyte. p. 615

not at risk The category that identifies a species that is not at risk of extinction under current circumstances. p. 727

notochord A flexible rodlike structure constructed of fluid-filled cells surrounded by tough connective tissue, which supports a chordate embryo from head to tail. p. 685

nucleoid The central region of a prokaryotic cell with no boundary membrane separating it from the cytoplasm, where DNA replication and RNA transcription occur. p. 538

null hypothesis A prediction of what researchers would see if a particular factor had no effect. p. 415

obligate aerobe A microorganism that must use oxygen for cellular respiration and requires oxygen in its surroundings to support growth. p. 544

obligate anaerobe A microorganism that cannot use oxygen and can grow only in the absence of oxygen. p. 544

ocellus (plural, **ocelli**) The simplest eye, which detects light but does not form an image. p. 659

oocyte A developing gamete that becomes an ootid at the end of meiosis. p. 651

open circulatory system An arrangement of internal transport in some invertebrates in which the vascular fluid, hemolymph, is

released into sinuses, bathing organs directly, and is not always retained within vessels. p. 666

operant Involves the modification of a behaviour by the effects (positive or negative) of its own consequences. p. 851

operant conditioning A form of associative learning in which animals learn to link a voluntary activity, an operant, with its favourable consequences, the reinforcement. p. 851

operculum A lid or flap of the bone serving as the gill cover in some fishes. p. 693

opisthosoma The rear end of a chelicerate's body, derived from the abdomen in ancestral arthropods. p. 673

oral hood Soft fleshy structure at the anterior end of a cephalochordate that frames the opening of the mouth. p. 685

ostracoderm One of an assortment of extinct, jawless fishes that were covered with bony armour. p. 689

outer membrane In Gram-negative bacteria, an additional boundary membrane that covers the peptidoglycan layer of the cell wall. p. 541

outgroup comparison A technique used to identify ancestral and derived characters by comparing the group under study with more distantly related species that are not otherwise included in the analysis. p. 463

ovule In plants, the structure in a carpel in which a female gametophyte develops and fertilization takes place. p. 628

paraphyletic taxon A group of organisms that includes an ancestral species and some, but not all, of its descendants. p. 458

parasite An organism that feeds on the tissues of or otherwise exploits its host. p. 562

parasitism A symbiotic interaction in which one species, the parasite, uses another, the host, in a way that is harmful to the host. pp. 588, 780

passive parental care The amount of energy invested in offspring—in the form of the energy stored in eggs or seeds or energy transferred to developing young through a placenta—before they are born. p. 754

pectoral girdle A bony or cartilaginous structure in vertebrates that supports and is attached to the forelimbs. p. 687

pedicellaria (plural, **pedicellariae**) Small pincer at the base of short spines in starfishes and sea urchins. p. 682

pellicle A layer of supportive protein fibres located inside the cell, just under the plasma membrane, providing strength and flexibility instead of a cell wall. p. 562

pelvic girdle A bony or cartilaginous structure in vertebrates that supports and is attached to the hindlimbs. p. 687

peptidoglycan A polymeric substance formed from a polysaccharide backbone tied together by short polypeptides, which is the primary structural molecule of bacterial cell walls. p. 540

per capita growth rate The difference between the per capita birth rate and the per capita death rate of a population. p. 757

peritoneum The thin tissue derived from mesoderm that lines the abdominal wall and covers most of the organs in the abdomen. p. 646

phage *See* bacteriophage. p. 523

phenotypic variation Differences in appearance or function between individual organisms. p. 412

phloem The food-conducting tissue of a vascular plant. p. 615

phosphorus cycle A biogeochemical cycle in which weathering and erosion carry phosphate ions from rocks to soil and into streams and rivers, which eventually transport them to the ocean, where they are slowly incorporated into rocks. p. 829

photobiont The photosynthetic component of a lichen. p. 601

photoheterotroph An organism that uses light as the ultimate energy source but obtains carbon in organic form rather than as carbon dioxide. p. 543

phototroph An organism that obtains energy from light. p. 543

PhyloCode A formal set of rules governing phylogenetic nomenclature. p. 464

phylogenetic species concept A concept that seeks to delineate species as the smallest aggregate population that can be united by shared derived characters. p. 435

phylogenetic tree A branching diagram depicting the evolutionary relationships of groups of organisms. p. 456

phylogeny The evolutionary history of a group of organisms. p. 456

phytoplankton Microscopic, free-flowing aquatic plants and protists. p. 562

piloting A wayfinding mechanism in which animals use familiar landmarks to guide their journey. p. 865

pilus (plural, **pili**) A hair or hairlike appendage on the surface of a prokaryote. p. 542

pinacoderm In sponges, an unstratified outer layer of cells. p. 651

placenta A specialized temporary organ that connects the embryo and fetus with the uterus in mammals, mediating the delivery of oxygen and nutrients. Analagous structures occur in other animals. p. 709

planula a ciliated larval stage that settles and undergoes metamorphosis into the polyp form. p. 654

plasmid A DNA molecule in the cytoplasm of certain prokaryotes, which often contains genes with functions that supplement those in the nucleoid and can replicate independently of the nucleoid DNA and be passed along during cell division. p. 540

plasmodial slime mould A slime mould of the class Myxomycetes. p. 575

plasmodium The composite mass of plasmodial slime moulds consisting of individual nuclei suspended in a common cytoplasm surrounded by a single plasma membrane. p. 575

plasmogamy The sexual stage of fungi during which the cytoplasm of two genetically different partners fuse. p. 589

plastron The ventral part of the shell of a turtle. p. 702

poikilohydric Having little control over internal water content. p. 614

pollen grain The male gametophyte of a seed plant. p. 628

pollen tube A tube that grows from a germinating pollen grain through the tissues of a carpel and carries the sperm cells to the ovary. p. 628

polyandry A polygamous mating system in which one female mates with multiple males. p. 868

polygamy A mating system in which either males or females may have many mating partners. p. 868

polygyny A polygamous mating system in which one male mates with many females. p. 868

polyhedral virus A virus in which the coat proteins form triangular units that fit together like the parts of a geodesic sphere. p. 522

polyp The tentacled, usually sessile stage in the life cycle of a coelenterate. p. 653

polyphyletic taxon A group of organisms that belong to different evolutionary lineages

and do not share a recent common ancestor. p. 458

polyploidy The condition of having one or more extra copies of the entire haploid complement of chromosomes. p. 443

population All individuals of a single species that live together in the same place and time. p. 399

population density The number of individuals per unit area or per unit volume of habitat. p. 749

population genetics The branch of science that studies the prevalence and variation in genes among populations of individuals. p. 414

population size The number of individuals in a population at a specified time. p. 749

porocyte A cylindrical cell that allows water to pass. p. 651

postzygotic isolating mechanism A reproductive isolating mechanism that acts after zygote formation. p. 437

precocial Newborns that can stand immediately after birth and are soon able to run. p. 709

predator Any organism that preys upon another. p. 778

premaxillae bone in vertebrates that bears the upper incisor teeth. p. 691

prezygotic isolating mechanism A reproductive isolating mechanism that acts prior to the production of a zygote, or fertilized egg. p. 437

primary consumer A herbivore, a member of the second trophic level. p. 778

primary endosymbiosis In the model for the origin of plastids in eukaryotes, the first event in which a eukaryotic cell engulfed a photosynthetic cyanobacterium. p. 580

primary producer An autotroph, usually a photosynthetic organism, a member of the first trophic level. p. 778

principle of parsimony A principle of systematic biology that states that a particular trait is unlikely to evolve independently in separate evolutionary lineages. p. 464

prion An infectious agent that contains only protein and does not include a nucleic acid molecule. p. 530

production efficiency The ratio of the energy content of new tissue produced to the energy assimilated from food. p. 819

proglottid One of the segmentlike repeating units that constitute the body of a tapeworm. p. 662

promiscuity A mating system in which individuals do not form close pair bonds, and both males and females mate with multiple partners. p. 868

prophage A viral genome inserted in the host cell DNA. p. 526

proportion of reproducing individuals percent of reproducing individuals in a poplation. p. 751

prosoma The fused head and thorax of chelicerates. p. 673

protist Organism currently classified in the kingdom Protista. p. 560

protobiont The term given to a group of abiotically produced organic molecules that are surrounded by a membrane or membranelike structure. p. 499

protonema The structure that arises when a liverwort or moss spore germinates and eventually gives rise to a mature gametophyte. p. 621

protostome A division of the Bilateria in which the blastopore forms the mouth during development of the embryo and the anus appears later. p. 646

pseudocoelom A fluid- or organ-filled body cavity between the gut (a derivative of endoderm) and the muscles of the body wall (a derivative of mesoderm). p. 646

pseudopod (plural, **pseudopodia**) A temporary cytoplasmic extension of a cell. p. 562

psychrophile An archaean or bacterium that grows optimally at temperatures in the range of –10 to –20°C. p. 553

Pterophyta The plant phylum of ferns and their close relatives. p. 624

pupa The nonfeeding stage between the larva and adult in the complete metamorphosis of some insects, during which the larval tissues are completely reorganized within a protective cocoon or hardened case. p. 678

purine A type of nitrogenous base with two carbon–nitrogen rings. p. 497

pyramid of biomass A diagram that illustrates differences in standing crop biomass in a series of trophic levels. p. 821

pyramid of energy A diagram that illustrates the amount of energy that flows through a series of trophic levels. p. 820

pyramid of numbers A diagram that illustrates the number of individual organisms present in a series of trophic levels. p. 821

pyrimidine A type of nitrogenous base with one carbon–nitrogen ring. p. 497

qualitative variation Variation that exists in two or more discrete states, with intermediate forms often being absent. p. 412

quantitative variation Variation that is measured on a continuum (such as height in human beings) rather than in discrete units or categories. p. 412

quorum sensing The use of signalling molecules by prokaryotes to communicate and to coordinate their behaviour. p. 547

radial cleavage A cleavage pattern in deuterostomes in which newly formed cells lie directly above and below other cells of the embryo. p. 646

radial symmetry A body plan of organisms in which structures are arranged regularly around a central axis, like spokes radiating out from the centre of a wheel. p. 646

radiometric dating A dating method that uses measurements of certain radioactive isotopes to calculate the absolute ages in years of rocks and minerals. p. 509

radula The tooth-lined "tongue" of molluscs that scrapes food into small particles or drills through the shells of prey. p. 665

random dispersion A pattern of distribution in which the individuals in a population are distributed unpredictably in their habitat. p. 751

realized niche The range of conditions and resources that a population actually uses in nature. p. 790

reciprocal altruism Form of altruistic behaviour in which individuals help nonrelatives if they are likely to return the favour in the future. p. 873

recognition protein Protein in the plasma membrane that identifies a cell as part of the same individual or as foreign. p. 525

red tide A growth in dinoflagellate populations that causes red, orange, or brown discoloration of coastal ocean waters. p. 567

reinforcement 1. The enhancement of reproductive isolation that had begun to develop while populations were geographically separated. 2. Encouraging or establishing a pattern of behaviour using a positive or negative stimulus. pp. 441, 851

reproductive isolating mechanism A biological characteristic that prevents the gene pools of two species from mixing. p. 437

resource partitioning The use of different resources or the use of resources in different ways by species living in the same place. p. 791

rhizoid A modified hypha that anchors a fungus to its substrate and absorbs moisture. p. 619

rhizome A horizontal, modified stem that can penetrate a substrate and anchor the plant. p. 623

rhynchocoel A coelomic cavity that contains the proboscis of nemerteans. p. 662

ribozyme An RNA-based catalyst that is part of the biochemical machinery of all cells. p. 500

ring species A species with a geographic distribution that forms a ring around uninhabitable terrain. p. 436

rod In the vertebrate eye, a type of photoreceptor in the retina that is specialized for detection of light at low intensities. p. 538

root An anchoring structure in land plants that also absorbs water and nutrients and (in some plant species) stores food. p. 456

root system An underground (or submerged) network of roots with a large surface area that favours the rapid uptake of soil water and dissolved mineral ions. p. 615

***r*-selected species** A short-lived species adapted to function well in a rapidly changing environment. p. 763

saprotroph An organism nourished by dead or decaying organic matter. p. 588

savannah A biome comprising grasslands with few trees, which grows in areas adjacent to tropical deciduous forests. p. 782

schizocoelom In protostomes, the body cavity that develops as inner and outer layers of mesoderm separate. p. 648

schizocoelous Having a coelom formed by a split in the mesoderm in segmented coelomates. p. 649

sclerocyte Specialized cells that secrete the mineralized structures in the body wall of some invertebrates. p. 651

scolex The anterior (head) of a tapeworm, adapted for fastening the worm to the intestinal epithelium of its host. p. 662

secondary consumer A carnivore that feeds on herbivores, a member of the third trophic level. p. 778

secondary contact Contact after a period of geographical isolation. p. 441

secondary endosymbiosis In the model for the origin of plastids in eukaryotes, the second event, in which a non-photosynthetic eukaryote engulfed a photosynthetic eukaryote. p. 580

secondary metabolite Organic compound not required for the growth or survival of an organism; tends to be biologically active. p. 589

secondary productivity Energy stored in new consumer biomass as energy is transferred from producers to consumers. p. 818

secondary succession Predictable changes in species composition in an ecological community that develops after existing vegetation is destroyed or disrupted by an environmental disturbance. p. 801

seed The structure that forms when an ovule matures after a pollen grain reaches it and a sperm fertilizes the egg. p. 628

segment A body structure that repeats along an anterior–posterior axis and itself has an anterior–posterior polarity. p. 648

selectively permeable Membranes that selectively allow, impede, or block the passage of atoms and molecules. p. 499

septum (plural, **septa**) A thin partition or cross wall that separates body segments. pp. 589, 662

sexual dimorphism Differences in the size or appearance of males and females. p. 869

sexual selection A form of natural selection established by male competition for access to females and by the females' choice of mates. p. 424

shoot system The stems and leaves of a plant. p. 616

sign stimulus A simple cue that triggers a fixed action pattern. p. 848

simulation modelling An analytical method in which researchers gather detailed information about a system and then create a series of mathematical equations that predict how the components of the system interact and respond to change. p. 832

sister clades Two evolutionary lineages (i.e., clades) that emerge from the same node in a phylogenetic tree. p. 456

sister species Two species that are descended from the same recent ancestral species. p. 456

social behaviour The interactions that animals have with other members of their species. p. 480

soredium (plural, **soredia**) A specialized cell cluster produced by lichens, consisting of a mass of algal cells surrounded by fungal hyphae; soredia function like reproductive spores and can give rise to a new lichen. p. 601

sorus (plural, **sori**) A cluster of sporangia on the underside of a fern frond; reproductive spores arise by meiosis inside each sporangium. p. 625

specialized transduction Transfer of bacterial genes between bacteria using

temperate phages that have incorporated fragments of the bacterial genome as they make the transition from the lysogenic cycle to the lytic cycle. p. 527

speciation The process of species formation. p. 434

species cluster A group of closely related species recently descended from a common ancestor. p. 441

species composition The particular combination of species that occupy a site. p. 797

species diversity A community characteristic defined by species richness and the relative abundance of species. p. 795

species fusion Merger of two populations into one after the establishment of secondary contact. p. 441

species richness The number of species that live within an ecological community. p. 794

specific epithet The species name in a binomial. p. 454

spine *See* backbone. p. 685

spiral cleavage The cleavage pattern in many protostomes in which newly produced cells lie in the space between the two cells immediately below them. p. 646

spiral valve A corkscrew-shaped fold of mucous membrane in the digestive system of elasmobranchs, which slows the passage of material and increases the surface area available for digestion and absorption. p. 691

spongocoel The central cavity in a sponge. p. 651

sporangium (plural, **sporangia**) A single-celled or multicellular structure in fungi and plants in which spores are produced. p. 592

sporophyll A specialized leaf that bears sporangia (spore-producing structures). p. 625

sporophyte An individual of the diploid generation produced through fertilization in organisms that undergo alternation of generations; it produces haploid spores. pp. 572, 612

squalene A liver oil found in sharks that is lighter than water, which increases their buoyancy. p. 691

stability The ability of a community to maintain its species composition and relative abundances when environmental disturbances eliminate some species from the community. p. 793

stabilizing selection A type of natural selection in which individuals expressing intermediate phenotypes have the highest relative fitness. p. 422

standing crop biomass The total dry weight of plants present in an ecosystem at a given time. p. 817

stapes The smallest of three sound-conducting bones in the middle ear of tetrapod vertebrates. p. 696

stoma (plural, **stomata**) The opening between a pair of guard cells in the epidermis of a plant leaf or stem, through which gases and water vapour pass. p. 614

strobilus *See* cone (of a plant). p. 625

stromatolite Fossilized remains of ancient cyanobacterial mats that carried out photosynthesis by the water-splitting reaction. p. 509

subspecies A taxonomic subdivision of a species. p. 435

succession The change from one community type to another. p. 799

survivorship curve Graphic display of the rate of survival of individuals over a species' life span. p. 753

suspension feeder An animal that ingests small food items suspended in water. p. 651

swim bladder A gas-filled internal organ that helps fish maintain buoyancy. p. 694

swimmeret small paddle-like fin used in swimming. p. 675

symbiont An organism living in symbiosis with another organism; the symbionts are not usually closely related. p. 588

symbiosis An interspecific interaction in which the ecological relations of two or more species are intimately tied together. p. 504

sympatric speciation Speciation that occurs without the geographic isolation of populations. p. 442

synapomorphy A derived character state found in two or more species. p. 463

Synapsida A group of amniotes with one temporal arch on each side of the head, which includes living mammals. p. 700

systematics The branch of biology that studies the diversity of life and its evolutionary relationships. p. 454

tactile signal A means of animal communication in which the signaller uses touch to convey a message to the signal receiver. p. 859

taiga *See* boreal forest. p. 818

taxis A behavioural response that is directed either toward or away from a specific stimulus. p. 862

taxon (plural, **taxa**) A name designating a group of organisms included within a category in the Linnaean taxonomic hierarchy. p. 455

taxonomic hierarchy A system of classification based on arranging organisms into ever more inclusive categories. p. 455

taxonomy The science of the classification of organisms into an ordered system that indicates natural relationships. p. 454

temperate bacteriophage Bacteriophage that may enter an inactive phase (lysogenic cycle) in which the host cell replicates and passes on the bacteriophage DNA for generations before the phage becomes active and kills the host (lytic cycle). p. 525

temperate deciduous forest A forested biome found at low to middle altitudes at temperate latitudes, with warm summers, cold winters, and annual precipitation between 75 and 250 cm. p. 795

temperate grassland A nonforested biome that stretches across the interiors of most continents, where winters are cold and snowy and summers are warm and fairly dry. p. 818

temperate rainforest A coniferous forest biome supported by heavy rain and fog, which grows where winters are mild and wet and the summers are cool. p. 572

temporal isolation A prezygotic reproductive isolating mechanism in which species live in the same habitat but breed at different times of day or different times of year. p. 438

tertiary consumer A carnivore that feeds on other carnivores, a member of the fourth trophic level. p. 797

Tetrapoda A monophyletic lineage of vertebrates that includes animals with four feet, legs, or leglike appendages. p. 688

T-even bacteriophage Virulent bacteriophages, T2, T4, and T6, that have been valuable for genetic studies of bacteriophage structure and function. p. 525

thallus (plural, **thalli**) A plant body not differentiated into stems, roots, or leaves. pp. 601, 620

time lag The delayed response of organisms to changes in environmental conditions. p. 759

tolerance hypothesis Hypothesis asserting that ecological succession proceeds because competitively superior species replace competitively inferior ones. p. 803

tracheal system A branching network of tubes that carries air from small openings in the exoskeleton of an insect to tissues throughout its body. p. 676

traditional systematics An approach to systematics that uses phenotypic similarities and differences to infer evolutionary relationships, grouping together species that share both ancestral and derived characters. p. 461

transfer RNA (tRNA) The RNA that brings amino acids to the ribosome for addition to the polypeptide chain. p. 512

trichocyst A dartlike protein thread that can be discharged from a surface organelle for defence or to capture prey. p. 567

triploblastic An animal body plan in which adult structures arise from three primary germ layers: endoderm, mesoderm, and ectoderm. p. 645

trochophore The small, free-swimming, ciliated aquatic larva of various invertebrates, including certain molluscs and annelids. p. 659

trophic cascade The effects of predator–prey interactions that reverberate through other population interactions at two or more trophic levels in an ecosystem. p. 822

trophic level A position in a food chain or web that defines the feeding habits of organisms. p. 797

trophozoite Motile, feeding stage of *Giardia* and other single-celled protists. p. 559

tropical forest Any forest that grows between the Tropics of Capricorn and Cancer, a region characterized by high temperature and rainfall and thin, nutrient-poor topsoil. p. 630

turnover rate The rate at which one generation of producers in an ecosystem is replaced by the next. p. 821

tympanum A thin membrane in the auditory canal that vibrates back and forth when struck by sound waves. p. 696

uncinate process Forward-protrusion from rib in birds. p. 704

undulating membrane In parabasalid protists, a finlike structure formed by a flagellum buried in a fold of the cytoplasm that facilitates movement through thick and viscous fluids. An expansion of the plasma membrane in some flagellates that is usually associated with a flagellum. p. 565

uniform dispersion A pattern of distribution in which the individuals in a population are evenly spaced in their habitat. p. 750

unreduced gamete A gamete that contains the same number of chromosomes as a somatic cell. p. 444

vascular plant A plant with xylem, phloem, and usually well-developed roots, stems, and leaves. p. 615

vascular tissue In plants, tissue that transports water and nutrients or the products of photosynthesis through the plant body. p. 615

vertical gene transfer Inheritance from one generation to the next. p. 513

vestigial structure An anatomical feature of living organisms that no longer retains its function. p. 396

virion A complete virus particle. p. 524

viroid A plant pathogen that consists of strands or circles of RNA, smaller than any viral DNA or RNA molecule, that have no protein coat. p. 530

virulent bacteriophage Bacteriophage that kills its host bacterial cells during each cycle of infection. p. 525

visceral mass In molluscs, the region of the body containing the internal organs. p. 665

visual signal A means of communication in which animals use facial expressions or body language to send messages to other individuals. p. 856

viviparous Referring to animals that retain the embryo within the mother's body and nourish it during at least early embryo development. p. 709

water vascular system A locomotor system, including internal canals and tube feet, unique to Echinodermata. p. 680

wetland A highly productive ecotone often at the border between a freshwater biome and a terrestrial biome. p. 632

zero population growth A circumstance in which the birth rate of a population equals the death rate. p. 757

zooplankton Small, usually microscopic, animals that float in aquatic habitats. p. 562

zygosporangium A thick-walled sporangium in which spores are produced, characteristic of Zygomycetes. p. 592

zygospore A multinucleate, thick-walled sexual spore in some fungi that is formed from the union of two gametes. p. 592

zygote A fertilized egg. p. 644

Index

The letter i denotes an illustration; t *denotes a table;* b *denotes a box;* **bold** *denotes a defined or introduced term.*

Animal cells
   viruses affecting, 524t, 527–528
Animal pollinators, 636–637, 637i
Animalia, 458, 512, **644**
Animals, 643–644. *See also specific animals*
   Agnathans, 689–690
   amniote origin and Mesozoic radiations, 698–701
   basal, phyla, 650–658
   birds, 704–708
   body cavities, 646, 647i
   defining, 644–645
   deuterostomes, 680–687
   developmental patterns, 646–648
   early tetrapods and modern amphibians, 696–698
   Ecdysozoa protosteomes, 670–680
   evolution of, 644–648
   jawed fishes, 690–693
   lineage, 645
   living diapsids: sphenodontids, squamates, and crocodilians, 702–704
   Lophotrochozoa protostomes, 659–670
   mammalia: monotremes, marsupials, and placentals, 708–713
   morphology, 650
   origin and diversification, 645i
   phylogeny and classification, 649i, 649–650
   vs. protists, 561–562
   protostomes, 658–659
   relationships of higher phyla, 659i
   segmentation, 648
   structure and behaviour, 644
   symmetry, 645–646
   tissue and tissue layers, 645
   transport in. *See* Circulatory system
   turtles and tortoises, 702
   vertebrate origin and diversification, 687–689
   viruses, 527–528
Annelida, phylum, 662, 664i
Annelids, 648, 660i, 662, 664i
Annual bluegrass (*Poa annua*), 752t
Annual dune grass (*Vulpia fasciculata*), 760i
Annulus, 626i
Anopheles maculipennis, 453, 454, 454i, 747
Ant (*Crematogaster mimosae*), 782
Antagonistic interactions, 793
Antelopes, 778–779
Antheridia, 620i, **620**, 622, 625
Antheridium, 620, 621i, 625, 626i
Anthocerophyta, 618i, 623t
Anthoceros, 622i
Anthocerotophyta, **622**, 623t
Anthophyta, 618i, 623t, **633**
Anthophytes, 623t
Anthozoa, class, 654, 656i
Anthrax, 549
Anthropocene, 720–721
Anthropoidea, 457i
Antibiotic resistance, 540, 546, 546i
Antibiotics, 393, **546**, 587, 597, 604–605
Antimicrobial Resistance and Use in Canada: A Federal Framework for Action, 393–394
Antithamnion plumula, 577i
Ants, 710–711, 780, 780i, 858, 858i
Anura, 697–698
Anus, 647i
Apatosaurus, 701
Aphthovirus, 524t
Apical complex, 568
Apical growth, **589**
Apical meristems, **615**
Apicomplexans, **568**–569
Apomorphy, **463**
Aposematic, 787i, **787**
Apple maggot, 442i, 442–443
Apple snails (*Pomacea paludosa*), 783
Aquatic succession, **801**

Arabian Sea humpback whales (ASHW), 411
Arachnida, class, 674i
Arbuscular mycorrhizal fungus, 595i
Arbuscules, **594**, 595i
Archaea domain, 506, 512, 513i, 513t, **538**
   biogeochemical cycle, 544
   characteristics of, 551t
   diversity of, 538
   evolutionary branches, 551–553
   habitats, 550i
   phylogenetic tree, 548i
   unique characteristics, 551
Archaeal ribosomes, 540
Archaeocytes, **651**
Archegonia (singular, archegonium), **619**–620, 621, 621i, 622, 625, 626i, 629i, 631i
Archelosauromorpha, 462, 464
Archenteron, **648**
Archosauria, 469
Archosauromorpha, 464, **700**
Archosaurs, 699i
Arctic char (*Salvelinus alpinus*), 822–823
Arctic terns, 845, 846i
Arctic tundra, **619**
Ardipithecus, 478b, 478i, 482
Aristotle, 394, 394i
Arm, 482–483
Armadillo, 395, 396i
Armillaria ostoyae, 588i, 600
Armour, 785–786, 786i
Arrow worms, 658
Arrowhead frog (*Dendrobates tinctorius*), 787i
Artemisinin-based combination therapy (ACT), 748
Arthropoda, phylum, 646, 673i, 673–680
Arthropods, 673–680, 806, 806i
Artificial selection, 398i, 398–**399**
Asci, **594**, 595i
Ascocarp, **594**, 595i
Ascomycetes, 590t, 594–597, 595i, 596i, 598, 600
Ascomycota, 590t, 591, 591i, 594–597
Ascospores, **596**
Asexual reproduction, 544–545
   ascomycetes, 596, 597i
   cellular slime moulds, 576i
   in diatoms, 571
   green algae, 579i
   structures of, 620i
   zygomycetes, 593i, 593–594
Aspergillus, 596, 597
Assault rifles, 723, 723i
Assimilation efficiency, **819**
Asteriod impact, 721
Asteroidea, class, 682, 683i
Athlete's foot, 596
Atlantic flounder, 694i
ATP (adenosine triphosphate). *See* Adenosine-triphosphate (ATP)
Atrial siphon, **685**
Atriopore, **685**
Atrium, **685**
Aurelia, 655i
Australian emu, 396i
Australian lungfish, 695i
Australian sawfly caterpillars, 871
Australopithecus, 478b, 478i, 480
Australopithecus afarensis, **478b**, 478i, 481–482, 482i
Australopithecus africanus, **478b**, 478i, 480
Australopithecus anamensis, **479b**
Australopithecus sediba, **479b**, 482
Autopolyploidy, 444i, **444**–445
Autotrophs, **503**, **543**
Aves, class, 704–708
   diversity, 705i
   flight adaptation, 704i
   Hesperornis, 707
Avian influenza, 739–740

Axe, stone, 483
Axial skeleton, **687**
Axopods, **572**

Baboons, 847, 860i, 860–861
Bacillus anthracis, 549
Bacillus bacteria, 539i
Backbone (spine), **685**
Bacteria, 537–538
    antibiotic resistance, 546
    biochemical flexibility, 506
    biogeochemical cycle, 544
    characteristics of, 551t
    diversity of, 538
    exotoxins, 545
    genetic recombination in, 541b
    population growth, 756, 756i
    structure of, 540i
Bacteria domain, 512, 513i, 513t, **538**, 548i, 548–550
Bacterial cells, viruses affecting, 525–527
Bacteriophages, 495i, **523**, 525i, 525–527
Baerwald, Erin, 865
Bahaman land snails, 412i
Balancing selection, **425**–427
Bald eagles (*Haliaeetus leucocephalus*), 815, 838, 838i
Ballast water, 732–733
Baltimore oriole, 441, 442i
Banded iron, 503, 503i
Banding patterns, 446
Barberry, 605
Barbie pagoda fungus (*Podoserpula miranda*), 453i
Barclay, Robert, 865
Barcode of Life project, 779, 779i
Barley, 605
Barnacles, 675, 676i, 788–789, 789b, 789i, 862
Barndoor skates (*Dipterus laevis*), 736
Barton, Nick H., 446
Basal, phyla, 651i
    Cnidaria, phylum, 653–658
    Ctenophora, phylum, 650–651
    Placozoa, phylum, 652–653
    Porifera, phylum, 651–652
Baseline thematic mapping, 722i
Basidia, **598**, 600
Basidiocarps, **600**
Basidiomycete mycelia, 600
Basidiomycetes, 590t, 597, 597–600, 598i, 599i, 601, 605
Basidiomycota, 590t, 591, 591i, 597–600
Basidiospores, **600**, 605
Bassler, Bonnie, 537
Bates, Henry W., 787
Batesian mimicry, 787, 788i
Bathynomus, 675
Batrachochytrium dendrobatidis, 592i
Bats, 396, 397i, 460, 460i, 637i, 724–725, 725i, 729–730, 736–737, 779i, 781i, 782, 836, 837i, 860i, 865, 865i, 866, 867i, 869, 871, 872, 873–874, 874i
Bay scallops (*Argopecten irradians*), 734, 734i, 735i
Bears, 454–455, 455i, 783
Bedbugs (*Cimex lectularius*), 815
Bees, 637
Behavioural characters, 460–461, 461i
Behavioural isolation, 437t, 438i, **438**
Bertolani, Paco, 847
Betacoronavirus, 524t
Bettencourt, Luís, 838
Big brown bats (*Eptesicus fuscus*), 711i, 736, 871
Bilateral symmetry, 645i, 646, 647i
Binary fission, 544, 545i, 588, 756
Binomial, **454**
Binomial nomenclature, **454**–455, 455i
Biodiversity, conservation of, 719–720
    agriculture, 729–730
    Anthropocene, 720–721
    climate change, 725–726
    economic value, 736–737

    effecting conservation, 737–738
    eligibility for protection, 727–729
    extinction, vulnerability to, 721–725
    human populations as problem for conservation, 739
    motivation, 736–737
    natural systems, contamination of, 730–736
    protecting species, 726–727
    stress, signs of, 739–740
    taking action, 740–741
Biofilm, **546**–547, 547i, 814
Biogeochemical cycles, **544**, **823**
Biogeography, **396**, 397
Biological energy sources, 501–502
Biological evolution, 400–403
Biological hot spots, 797
Biological magnification, 815i, **815**
Biological species concept, **434**
Bioluminescent, **568**
Bioluminescent dinoflagellates, 568i
Biomass, **538**, **817**, 819i, 821–823
Bioremediation, **538**, 598
Biotic, **494**
Bipedal locomotion, 478b
Bipedalism, **480**, 481–484
Bird flu, 739–740
Birds, 704i, 704–708. *See also* Aves, class
    bills, 705i, 705–706, 706i
    eggs, 706i
    evolution of, 462, 707i
    finches, Darwin's, 400
    flightless, 396i
    homologous characters, 460, 460i
    signs of stress, 739–740
    skeletons, 704i, 705i
    using phylogenetic trees to test hypotheses, 469
Birds of paradise, 433, 433i
Birth, 483–484
Birth control pills, 770i, 770–771
Birth weight, 422, 422b, 422i
Biston moths, 401
Bivalve molluscs, 734
Bivalves, 666i, 666–667
Bivalvia, class, 666–667
Black rhino, 721–723, 723i
Blake, P. R., 877
Blastopore, **648**
Blood vessels
    in annelids, 664i
Blood-feeding insects, 780–781, 781i
Blue jay, 418, 418i
Blue tits (*Cyanistes caeruleus*), 862, 862i
Bluegill sunfishes, 783, 783i
Blue-headed wrasse, 440i
Blue-stain fungi, 596, 596i
Bobolink (*Dolichonyx oryzivorus*), 720, 720i
Bodmer, Walter, 422b
Body cavity, 646, 647i
Body language, 484, 484i, 861
Body plans, 645i, **645**, 647i, 648i, 652i, 653i, 665i, 667i, 677i
Body size, 751i
Body symmetry, 645i, 645–646
Bolas spiders, 858
Bombykol, 858
Bonobos (*Pan paniscus*), 876
Bony fishes, 693–695
Boreal forest, 818t, 819i
Borrelia burgdorferi, 540
Bosch, Carl, 828
Botulin, 545, 545i
Bouchard, Lucien, 545
Bovine spongiform encephalopathy (BSE), 530–531, 531i
Box jellyfish, 656
Brachiopoda, phylum, 650, 669i, 669–670
Brain,
    hormonally induced changes in structure of, 853, 853i

monocots and eudicots, 633–634
  origin of, 633
Flowers, 439, **632**, 633i
Fly agaric mushroom, 598i
Flying fringe-lipped bat (*Trachops cirrhosus*), 779i
Fontaine, Colin, 793
Food, competition for, 871
Food chain, 797–798
Food web, **619**, 796i, 816, 816i, 822
Food-associated learning, 846
Foot, 481–482
Foot-and-mouth disease, 524t
Footprints, 481i
Foraminifera, 573
Forams, 573, 574i
Forcipules, 675i
Forster, Peter, 861
Fossil record, 395–396, 480, 481i, 485
Fossilized dung, 484
Fossils, 509i, 633i
  earliest, 508i, 508–509, 509i
  evidence of evolution, 395–396
  feet, legs, and pelvis, 481–482
  formation of, 507
  hands, 483
  hominin fossil record, 480
  hominins, 478b–480b, 480
  pelvis and birth, 483–484
  radiometric dating, 509, 511b
  record, 507–509
  shoulders and arms, 482–483
  value of, 507
Founder effect, **419**
FOXP2 gene, 485
Frequency, of traits, 413
Frequency-dependent selection, 427
Freshwater ecosystems, 818t, 821
Frisch, Karl von, 859
Frogs, 696–698, 697i, 760i
Fruit, **632**
Fruit fly (*Drosophila* spp.), 438, 439, 440, 443, 678i, 845, 850
Fruiting bodies, 548–549, 549i, **575**, 589i
Fucus gardneri, 560i
Fuel selection, 863
Full siblings, 873i
Fundamental niche, **790–791**, 791i
Fungal phyla, 590t
Fungi, 512, 587–588, 588i
  characteristics of, 588–589
  evolution and diversity of, 590–600
  lifestyles of, 600–605
  lineages of, 590–600
  little brown myotis and, 724–725
  phylogeny of, 590t, 591i
  structure of, 588i
  symbiotic associations with, 614
Fungi Imperfecti, 596
Furculum, **704**

Gächter, Simon, 877
Galápagos Islands, 399–400
Galápagos mockingbirds, 400i
Gallery forest, 751
Gametangium (plural, gametangia), **592**, **619**, 620i
Gametes, 612, **644**
Gametic isolation, 437t, **439**
Gametophytes, **572**, **612**, 617–619, 620i, 621i, 625, 626i, 627i, 630, 636i
Ganglia (singular, ganglion), **659**
Gar, 693, 693i
Gas bladders, 571i
Gastrodermis, 653–654
Gastroenteritis, 524t
Gastropoda, class, 667i, 667–668

Gastrotricha, phylum, 662
Gastrovascular cavity, 653
Gause, G. F., 790b, 790i
Geese, snow, 413i
Gemmae, **621**
Gemmules, **652**
Gene duplication, 420i
Gene flow, **416**, 418, 418i, 423t, 427i, 435–436
Gene pool, 414i, **414**
Gene sequences, 512
Genera, 626
Generalized compartment model, **823–824**
Generation time, **402**, 403i, 751i, **751**, 758i
Genes
  animal behaviour and, 846–848
  FOXP2 gene, 485
Genetic cohesiveness, 434
Genetic distance method, **466**, 468b
Genetic distinctness, 434
Genetic divergence, 443–444
Genetic drift, **419**, 423t
Genetic equilibrium, **416**
Genetic information, supporting theory of endosymbiosis, 505
Genetic recombination
  in bacteria, 541b
Genetic structure of populations, 415
Genetic variation
  maintenance, 425–427
  in populations, 414–415, 415i
  sources, 416–423
Genetic-based change. *See* Heritable changes
Genital warts, 524t, 528
Genome duplication, 420i
Genome sequence analysis, 514
Genotype
  frequencies, 415, 416t, 417i, 417b–418b, 427t
Genus, **454**
Geographic distribution of species, 396
Geographic range, **749**
Geographical variation, 435–437, 440–443
Geology, 395–396
Germ layer, 645i, **645**
Gerson, Alex, 863
Gestation period, **708–709**
Giant clams, 643, 666i
Giant hogweed (*Heracleum mantegazzianum*), 733
Giant kelp, 571i, 572
Giant pandas, 726, 726i
Giardia lamblia, 559–560, 565
Gill arch, **690**
Gill slits, **685**
Gills, 666
Ginkgo trees, 632i, 720
Ginkgoes, 618i, 630–631
Ginkgophyta, 623t, **630–631**
Giraffe (*Giraffa camelopardalis*), 777i
Glaciers, 800i
Glenoid fossa, 482i, 483
Global Fund to Fight AIDS, Tuberculosis, and Malaria, 748i
Global Malaria Eradication Programme (GMEP), 748i
Global Positioning Satellite (GPS), 779
Global warming. *See* Climate change
Glomeromycetes, 590t, 594, 595i
Glomeromycota, 590t, 591, 591i, 594
Glomus versiforme, 595i
Glyptodont, 395, 396i
Gnathifera, 658–659
Gnathostomata, **688**
Gnathostomulids, 659
Gnetophyta, 623t, 631–632
Gnetophytes, 623t, 631–632, 632i
Gnetum, 631–632
Goblin shark, 692i
Golden algae, 571i, 571–572
Golden eagles (*Aquila chrysaetos*), 737, 766

brain size, 478b
dispersal, 485
hand, 482i
language, 485
scapula, 482i
skeleton, 481i
Homologous characters, 459i, 459–460
Homologous traits, 396i
Homology, **397**, **459**, 460i
Homoplasy, **459**, 464
Homosporous, 617, 627
Höner, O. P., 876
Honesty, 876–877
Honey badgers, (*Mellivora cape)*, 780
Honeybees, 679i, 736, 853i, 853–854, 859, 859i, 874, 874i, 875i
Honeyguide birds (*Indicator indicator*), 780, 848–849
Hooded warblers, 730, 730i
Hookworms (*Ancylostoma duodenale* and *Necator americanus*), 770
Horizontal gene transfer (HGT), 513–514, **513–514**, 514i, 515i, 540, 546, 604
Hormones
    animal behaviour and, 853i, 853–854
Hornworts, 622, 622i
Horsehair worms, 672
Horses, 439, 439i
Horseshoe crabs, 674, 720, 786
Horseshoe worms, 669
Horsetails, 626–627, 627i
Host, **504**, 527i
Host race, **442**
House cats, 731–732
House dust mites, 674i
House sparrow, 437i
Houseflies, 678i
Hox genes, 645, 646i, 687, 688i
Hudson's Bay Company, 764, 765i
Human. *See Homo sapiens*
Human genome
    dispersal, 485
Human herpesvirus, 524t
Human immunodeficiency virus (HIV), 470–471, 471i, 524t, 527i, 527–528
Humans
    as harvesters, 734–736
    as invasive species, 734, 734i
    location variation in population growth rates, 767i
    population growth, 739, 766i, 766–770
    as root problem for conservation, 739
    social behaviour, 876–877, 877i
Humans and evolution, 477–487
    dispersal, 486i
    evolutionary impacts, 393–394
    features that do not fossilize, 484–485
    fossil hominins, 478b–480b
    hominin fossil record, 480, 481i
    hominins and the species concept, 485–487
    impacts, 393–394
    morphology and bipedalism, 481–484
    skeletons, 481i
    social networks, 484
    species concepts, 485, 487
Hummingbirds, 637i, 706i, 856
Humpback whale, 411, 411i
Hutton, James, 395
Huxley, Thomas, 403
Hyacinth macaws, 859i
Hybrid, **437**
Hybrid breakdown, 437t, 439, **440**
Hybrid inviability, 437t, 439, **439**
Hybrid sterility, 437t, 439, **439**, 443
Hybrid vigour, 425
Hybrid zones, **441**, 442i
Hydrangea, 413, 413i
Hydras, 654i, 656, 657i
Hydrogeological cycle, **824**, 825i

Hydroids, 653–658
Hydrostatic skeletons, **646**, 673
Hydrothermal vent, 544i
Hydrozoa, class, 656
Hygrophorus (scarlet hood), 598i
Hyomandibular bones, **690**
Hyphae, **570**, 588i, **588–589**, 594, 602
Hypothesis, 469

Ichthyostega, 696
Ideonella sakiaiensis, 731
Immigration, **752**, 805i, 805–806, 807
Immune system, 485
Imperfect fungi, 596
Imprinting, **850**
Inbreeding, **423**–424, 424i
Inbreeding depression, 424i, **424**
Incisors, **479b**
Incomplete metamorphosis, **678**
Incurrent siphon, 667
Indeterminate cleavage, **648**
Indian mallow (*Abutilon theophrasti*), 791i
Indian pipe, 611, 611i
Indices, 795–796
Indigo bunting, 865–866, 867b, 867i
Indirect flight muscles, 679i
Individualistic hypothesis, 794i
Industrialization, 768–769
Infanticide, 870–871
Infectious biological particles, 521–522
    evolution of viruses, 530
    prions, 530–531
    treating and preventing viral infections, 528–530
    viroids, 530–531
    viruses, 521–530
Infectious diseases, 470–471, 471i
Inference, in phylogeny, 469
Influenza, 521, 524t, 528–529
Ingroup, 463
Inhibition hypothesis, **802**
Ink sac, 669
Innate preferences, 862
Inorganic materials, 823i, 824
Insectivorous plants, 598–599
Insects, 678i
    body plan, 677i
    development, 678i
    diversity, 677i
    juvenile hormone, 678i
    mouthparts, 678i
    physiology, 678i
Insertion, 420i, **420**
Insight learning, **851**
Instar, **677**
Instinct, animal behaviour and, 848–850
Instinctive behaviour, **847**–848, 849
Insulin, 784
Interactive hypothesis, 794i
Interference competition, **788**
Intermediate disturbance hypothesis, **798**, 799i
International Union for Conservation of Nature (IUCN), 412, 726
International Wheat Genome Sequencing Consortium, 445
Intersexual selection, 425, 426b, 426i
Interspecific competition, **788**, 790b, 790i, 798
Interspecific hybrids, 439i
Intertidal zones, 613
Intracellular digestion, **654**
Intrasexual selection, 425, 426b, 426i
Intraspecific competition, **759**, **788**
Intrinsic control, 764
Intrinsic rate of increase, **757**, 758i
Invasive species, 731–733, 733i
    humans as, 734, 734i
Inversion, 420i, **420**
Irish potato famine, 569–570

Isistius plutodus, 691
Island biogeography, equilibrium theory of, 805–807
Island foxes (*Urocyon littoralis*), 766
Isthmus of Panama, 440, 440i

Jack pine, 614i
Jackrabbits, 783
Jacky dragons, 725i, 725–726
Jambiyas, 723
Jawed fish, 690–693, 691i
Jawless fish, 689–690
Jaws, 691i
Jellies, 653–658
Jellyfish, 656
Jensen, Keith, 876
Jet propulsion, 669
Joint-legged animals, 673–680
Jordano, P., 802
Juvenile hormone (JH), 678i, 678–679, 853
Juvenile mortality, 753

Kalashnikov assault rifles, 723, 723i
Kangaroo rat, 803, 803i
Kangaroos, 710i
Karenia brevis, 567i
Karyogamy, **589**
Keast, Allen, 791
Keeled sternum, **704**
Keeling, Patrick, 564, 580
Kelp, 572
    beds and reefs, 818t
Keystone species, **791**
Kidd, Karen A., 771
Kidneyshell mussels, 732i
Killer whales (*Orcinus orca*), 727, 727i, 860
Killifish (*Rivulus hartii*), 755, 755i
Kin selection, 872–874, 873i, 876
Kinesis, **862**
Kinetoplast, 565
Kinetoplastids, 564–565
Kingdom Animalia, 644
Kingdom Fungi, **590**
Kingdom Plantae, **613**, 614i
Kingdome of Animalia, **644**
Kinorhyncha, phylum, 648, 670, 670i
Kirtland's warblers (*Dendroica kirtlandii*), 782, 862
Kissing bugs (*Rhodnius prolixus*), 781i
Klironomos, J. N., 795
Knockout mouse, 850
Koalas, 710i, 783
Korarchaeota, **551**, 553
Krakatoa explosion, 739, 805
Krebs, Charles, 765
k-selected species, 763i, **763**–764, 764i, 798, 801–802
Kuru, 530

Labium, 678i
x*Lactobacillus*, 550
Lahr, M. Mirazón, 876
Lake and stream, 818t, 819i, 822
Lake Erie, 829
Lamarck, Jean Baptiste de, 394
Lambda, 526i, 526–527
Lambeosaurus, 701i
Lamp shells, 669–670
Lampreys, 689, 689i
Lancelet bodies, 685, 687i
Land plants
    defining characteristics of, 612
    phylogenetic relationships between major groups of, 618i
Land use mapping, 722i
Landfills, 838, 838i
Language, 485, 861i, 861–862

Larva (larval form), 645
Last eukaryote common ancestor (LECA), 561
Latent phase, **528**
Lateral line system, **691**
Latex sap, 784i
Latitudinal effects, 804, 804i
Layered forests, 794i
Layne, John, 855–856
Leaf endophytes, 604
Leakey, Louis, 479b
Leakey, Mary, 481i
Leander, Brian, 580
Learned behaviour, **847**–848
Learning, 850–852
Leavened, **587**
Leaves, 616, 616i
Leclerc, George-Louis, 396
Lederberg, Joshua, 541b
Leeches, 664i
Left aortic arch, **708**
Leg, 481–482
Legumes, 828
Lekking behaviour, 869i, 870
Leks, 870
"Leopard" alarm, 485
Leopard tortoise (*Stigmochelys pardalis*), 786i
Leopards (*Panthera pardus*), 728i, 728–729, 785–786
Lepidodendron, 624, 624i
Lepidoptera, 389i
Lepidosauromorpha, 462, 464, **700**
Lepidosaurs, 699i, 701
Lichens, 595, 601–603, 602b, 602i, 799, 801
Life, 493–494
    characteristics of life-forms, 494
    chemical origins of, 494–499
    earliest forms of, 502–504
    eukaryotes and multicellularity, 504–507
    eukaryotic cells, 504–507
    fossil record, 507–509
    geological time scale, 510t
    macromolecules and, 494, 499–502
    major evolutionary events, 510t
    multicellularity, 504–507
    Tree of Life, 509–514
Life cycles, **563**
    alternation of generations, 612, 612i
    ascomycetes, 597i
    basidiomycetes, 599i
    bread mould, 593i
    brown algae, 572, 573i
    cellular slime moulds, 576i
    chain fern, 626i
    flowering plants, 636i
    green algae, 578, 579i
    of moss *Polytrichum*, 621i
    of pines, 630, 631i
    of plants, 616–617
Life history, 753–755, 755, 755i
Life table, 752t, **752**
Lignin, 598, 598i, 615
Lijam, Nardos, 850
Limiting nutrient, **818**
Limnognathia, 659
Limpet, common, 667i
Limulus polyphemus, 674i
Lineages. *See* Monophyletic taxa
Lineus longissimus, 662
Lingulodinium polyedrum, 568i
Linnaeus, Carolus, 394, 454–456, 458
Linné, Carl von. *See* Linnaeus, Carolus
Lipid spheres, 499–500
Lipopolysaccharides (LPSs), **542**
Liposomes, 499, 499i
Lithotrophs, 544
Little brown myotis (*Myotis lucifugus*), 724–725, 725i, 736, 764, 860, 860i

Liver fluke, 661i
Liverworts, 620i, 620–621
Lizards, 702–703, 703i, 725i, 725–726, 753, 761, 762b, 762i
Lobster, 648, 669, 676i
Locus, 414i, **414**
Logistic model of population growth, 758i, 758t, **758**–760, 759i
Lokiarchaeota, **551**, 553
Longlining, 736i
Lophophorate, 670
Lophophore, **659**, 669i
Lophotrochozoa, 650
Lophotrochozoa protostomes, 659–670, 660i
Lorenz, Konrad, 850
Loricifera, phylum, 671
Lotka, Alfred J., 790
Lower Fraser Valley, 722i
Lubchenco, Jane, 792, 792b
LUCA (Last Universal Common Ancestor), 512–513, 513i
Lucernaria quadricornis, 657i
"Lucy," 478b, 478i
Luna moths, 677i
Lungfish, 695, 695i
Lycophyta, 618i, 623t, **624**
Lycophyte tree, 624i
Lycophytes (club mosses), 616i, 617i, 625, 625i
Lycopodium, 617i, 625, 625i
Lyell, Charles, 395
Lyme disease, 540
Lynx, 764–765, 765i
Lysed, **526**
Lysogenic cycle, 526i, **526–527**
Lysozymes, 525–526
Lytic cycle, 526i, 526–527, **526**

MacArthur, Robert, 797, 805
MacArthur–Wilson model, 805–806
Macrocystis pyrifera, 571i
Macroevolution, 433–434
    genetic mechanisms of speciation, 443–446
    geography of spciation, 440–443
    reproductive isolation, 437–440
    species, 434–437
Macromolecules, 494, 496, 499–502
Macronucleus, **567**
"Mad cow disease," 530
MagR proteins, 845
Mahaleb cherry (*Prunus mahaleb*), 802, 802i
Maherali, H., 795
Maintenance of high species richness, 804
Malaria (*Plasmodium falciparum*), 453–454, 454i, 568, 569i, 747–749, 748i
Malaria Initiative, 748i
Malarial parasite, 426, 427i
Malnourishment, 762
Malpighian tubules, **676**
Malthus, Thomas, 398
Mammalia, class
    diversity, 710–712
    evolutionary convergence and mammalian diversity, 710–712
    phylogeny, 709i
    radiation of, 708–710
    teeth, 709i, 711–712, 712i, 713i
    variations, 708–710
Mammals
    forelimbs and locomotion, 397i
    phylogenies, 709i
    teeth, 709i, 711–712, 712i, 713i
Mammoths, 508i
Mana Pools National Park, 723
Mandible, 675
Mann, Nicholas, 523
Manta ray, 692i
Mantle, **666**

Mantle cavity, **666**
Maple leaf mussel, 732i
Marchantia, 620i, 621
Marine diplonemids, 565b
Marine ecosystems, 818t, 821, 821i
Marine food web, 796i
Marine nudibranch, 667i
Marine phytoplankton, 567–568
Marler, Peter, 847, 852
Marsh marigold, 637i
Marsupials, 708–709, 710i, 708–713
Mass extinctions, 720
Mastax, 659
Mates, as resources, 868–869
Mathews, Sarah J., 635b
Mating calls, 460, 461i
Mating system, **868**
Mating types, **592**
Mauritian Calvaria trees, 724
Maxillae, 675, **691i**
Maximum likelihood method, **466**
Mayan temple, 826i
Mayr, Ernst, 433, 434
McCleneghan, Kim, 846–847
McNamara, John M., 873
Mean, 412
Meara stichopi, 658i
Measles, 524t
Mechanical isolation, 437t, **438**–439, 439i
Medusae, **653**, 655i, 657i
Meerkats (*Suricata suricatta*), 785i
Megaphylls, 616, 616i
Megasporangium, 628, 629i
Megaspores, 617i, **618**, 627, 628, 629i, 630, 636i
Megestrol, 770, 770i
Megnetic fields, 845
Menarche, 769–770
Mendel, Gregor, 400, 412, 413, 458–459
Mercury contamination, 815
Meristem tissue, 615
Mesenteries, **646**
Mesoderm, **645**, 647i,
Mesoglea, 654
Mesohyl, **651**, 652
Mesozoic era, 628, 630, 633
Messenger RNA (mRNA), 500i, 512
Metacarpal, 483
Metamerism, 648
Metamorphosis, 678, 678i
Metanephridia (singular, metanephridium), 669
Metaspriggina, 688i
Metatarsal bone, 482i
Metazoa, 644, 644i, 645, 649i, 650, 652
Meteorites, 493
Methane, 831i
Methanogens, 551
Methanosarcina, 552i
Methyl bromide, 806
Mexican cavefish (*Astyanax mexicanus*), 814, 814i, 836, 836i
Michael Smith Labor, 528
Michel, Andrew P., 443
Micrasterias, 560i
Microclimate, **801**
Microevolution, 411–**412**
    agents of, 416–423
    evolutionary agents, 416–423
    maintenance of variation, 425–427
    population genetics, 414–416
    variation in natural populations, 412–413
Micronucleus, **567**
Microphylls, 616, 616i
Microplana termitophaga, 660, 660i
Microspores, 617i, **618**, 627, **630**, 631i
Microsporocytes, 631i
Midges (*Metriocnemus knabi*), 835, 835i

Nitrification, **544**, 828t, **828**
Nitrogen, 544, 827–828
Nitrogen cycle, **826**–828, 827i, 828t, 829i
Nitrogen fixation, **544**, **826**–828, 828t
Nitrous oxide (NO), 831i
Node, **456**, 457i
Nomenclature, 454–456
Non-random mating, 423–425, 423t
Nonvascular plants, **615**, 617i, 619–622. *See also* Bryophyte
Norell, Mark A., 469
Norris, Kenneth, 873
Northern elephant seals, 419, 870
Northern spotted owls (*Strix occidentalis caurina*), 752
Norway lemming (*Lemmus lemmus*), 764
Norway lobster, 669
Norway with brown trout (*Salmo trutta*), 822
Not at risk species, **727**
Notochord, **685**
Nourishment levels, 796–797
Novocrania anomala, 650
Nuclear envelope, 505, 506i
Nucleoid, **540**
Null hypothesis, **416**
Null models, 416
Nurse bees, 853, 853i
Nutrient cycling, 823i, 823–830
    carbon, 824–826
    nitrogen, 826–828
    phosphorus, 829–830
    water, 824
Nutrition
    modes of, 543t

Oak tree (Quercus spp.), 418, 418i
Oats, 605
Obelia, 655i, 656i
Obligate aerobes, **544**
Obligate anaerobes, **544**
Ocelloid, 581i
Ocellus (plural, ocelli), **659**
Octopamine, 853
Octopods, 847
Octopus, 643i, 668i, 668–669
Old Order Amish, 419
Olejarz, Jason, 875
Oligochaeta, class, 662, 664i
Omnivores, 797
On the Origin of Species by Means of Natural Selection (Darwin), 12, 397
Ontogenetic-transitional wing (OTW) hypothesis, 706
Onychophora, phylum, 649, 672, 672i
Oocytes, **651**
Oomycetes, 569–570, 570i
Oparin, Aleksander, 497
Oparin-Haldane hypothesis, 497
Open circulatory systems, **666**
Open ocean, 818t, 819i
Open-ocean killer whales, 727
Operant, **851**
Operant conditioning, **851**
Operculum (plural, opercula), 690, **694**
Ophiuroidea, class, 682, 683i
Opisthokonta, 576
Opisthosoma, **673**
Opossum, 710i
Optimal foraging theory, **783**
Optimal phylogenic trees, 464–466
Oque macaques (*Macaca sinica*), 750i
Oral hood, **685**
Orange bread mould, 594
Orange palm dart butterfly, 463i
Orangutans, 876, 877i. *See also Pongo labelii*
Orchids, 614i, 637, 637i
Organic material, 823i, 824
Origin of high species richness, 804
Ornamentation, 870, 870i

Ornithischian, 700i
Ornithischian dinosaurs, 700i, 701i
Ornithurines, 707
Orrorin tugenensis, 478b, 478i, **478**
Orthomyxovirus, 524t
Osculum, 651, 652i
Osprey (*Pandion haliaetus*), 815i
Ossicles, 684i
Osteolepiformes, 696
Ostracoderms, **689**
Ostriches, 706i
Outbreeding, 424, 424i
Outer membrane, **542**
Outgroup comparison, 463i, **463**
Ovules, 628, 629i, 630, 631i, 636i
Oxidation, 502
Oxidation-reduction reactions, 502
Oxidizing atmosphere, 497
Oxygenic photosynthesis, role in rise in oxygen in atmosphere, 503–504
Oyster mushrooms, 598
Oysters, 666–667

Pacific herring (*Clupea pallasii*), 856
Pacific tailed frog, 698
Pacific water shrew, 721, 721i, 722i, 738
Pacific yew tree, 604
Paddlefish, 692
Paine, Robert, 791
Painted Desert, Arizona, 508i
Paleozoic era, 622–623, 625
Palp, 667
Pan troglodytes, 482i
Panarthropoda, 670
Pandanus spp., 485
Papillomavirus, 524t
Papovavirus, 524t
Papua New Guinea, 433
Parabasal bodies, 565
Parabasalids, 565, **565**, 566i
Paracatenula, 659
Paramecium, 563i, 567, 790, 790b, 790i
Paramyxovirus, 524t
Paranthropus, 478i, 479b, 480
Paraphyletic groups, 461–462
Paraphyletic taxon, 458i, **458**
Parasites, **562**
Parasitism, **588**, 601, 778t, **780**–782
Parasitoids, 782
Parental care, 754, 869, 869i
Parsimony, principle of, **464**, 467i
Passenger pigeons (*Ectopistes migratorius*), 719i, 719–720, 721
Passive parental care, 754
Pavlov, Ivan, 850–851
Peacocks (*Pavo cristatus*), 870, 870i
Peafowl, 870
Pearl fish, 684
Peat moss, 619
Pectoral girdle, **687**
Pedicellariae, **682**
Pellicle, **562**, 563i
Pelvic girdle, **687**
Pelvis, 481–482, 483–484
Penicillin, 393
Penicillium, 589, 596–597, 597i
Penis worms, 671
Peppered moth (*Biston betularia*), 401i, 401–402
Peptidoglycan, **540**–541
Per capita growth rate, **757**, 758t
Perdeck, A. C., 849b
Peregrine falcons (*Falco peregrinus*), 815
Perennial desert shrub (*Cleome droserifolia*), 753, 753i
Peritoneum, **646**
Periwinkle snails (*Littorina littorea*), 792b, 792i
Permian extinction, 720
Permian period, 628

Radioisotope, 511b
Radiolaria, 572, 574i
Radiometric dating, **509**, 511b
Radula, **666**
Rainbow mussel, 732i
Ramaria (coral fungus), 598i
Random dispersion, **751**
Random mutation, 400–401
Raphanobrassica, 446
Rat snake, 435i
Ratfish, 692i
Rattlesnakes, 783–784
Ravens (*Corvus corax*), 861
Rays, 690–693, 692i, 735i
Rea, Roy, 851
Realized niche, **790**, 791i
Recessive alleles, 425, 427t
Reciprocal altruism, **873**
Recognition proteins, **525**
Recruitment rates, 798
Red algae, 577i, 577–578
Red knots (*Calidris canutus canutus*), 868, 868i
Red oak (*Quercus rubra*), 795
Red tides, 567i, **567–568**
Red-billed oxpeckers (*Buphagus erythrorhynchus*), 777i
Red-eyed tree frog, 494i
Reducing atmosphere, 497–498
Red-winged blackbirds (*Agelaius phoeniceus*), 869
Redwood trees, 726
Reeve, H. Kern, 875
Regulation, population, 760–765
Reinforcement, **442**, **851**
Relatedness, 457i, 872–874, 873i
Relative ages, 509
Renfrew, Colin, 861
Reproduction. *See also* Speciation
   age at first reproduction, 754–755, 769
   apicomlexans, 569
   biological species concept, 434
   .as characteristic of life, 495i
   controlling reproductive output, 769–770
   courtship displays, 438
   geographical speciation, 440–443
   gymnosperms, 628–630
   inbreeding, 423–424
   isolating mechanisms, 437–440
   nonrandom mating, 423–425, 423t
   polyploidy speciation, 444i
   proportion, 751
   protists, 563
   supporting theory of endosymbiosis, 504–505
Reproductive isolating mechanism, 437t, **437–440**
Reproductive isolation, 434
Reproductive output, controlling, 769–770
Reptiles, 700i
   skulls of, 700i
   teeth, 701i
Reptilia, 462, 464
Resident killer whales, 727, 860
Resiliency, 730–731, 793i
Resource partitioning, 791i, **791**
Resource use efficiency (RUE), 733, 733i
Retrovirus, 524t
Reznick, David, 755
Rhabdovirus, 524t
Rhamphorynchus meunsteri, 700i
Rhino horn, 721, 723, 723i
Rhinovirus, 524t
Rhizaria, 561i, 572–574
Rhizobium, 542i, 544
Rhizoids, **619**, 620, 621i, 622, 625, 626
Rhizomes, 624i, **624**, 626, 626i
Rhizomnium, 620i
Rhizomorphs, 588i
Rhizopus nigricans, 594i

Rhizopus stolonifer, 594, 594i
Rhodophyta, 577–578
Rhynchocoel, **665**
Rhynia, 623–624, 624i
Rhynia gwynne-vaughnii, 624i
Ribbon worm, 662–665, 665i
Ribosomal RNA (rRNA), 548
Ribosomes, 512, 540
Ribozyme, 500i, **500**
Riftia pachyptila, 643–644, 644i
Ring canal, 680
Ring species, 436i, **436**
Ringworm, 596
Ritualized, 856
RNA
   flow of information from DNA to, 500, 500i
   replaced by DNA, 501, 501i
RNA replication, 528
Rods, **538**
Roosting bats (*Kerivoula hardwickii*), 782
Root systems, **616**
Roots, **456**, 615–616
Rotifera, phylum, 659, 659i
Rotifers (*Habrotrocha rosa*), 835, 835i
Round dance, 859, 859i, 861
Round pigtoe mussel, 732i
Roundworms (*Ascaris lumbricoides*), 770, 671i, 671–672
Royal kingbird (*Onychorhynchus coronatus*), 856, 858i
Royal penguins, 871, 872i
r-selected species, 763i, **763–764**, 764i, 798, 801–802
Ruffed grouse (*Bonasa umbellus*), 764
Rust, 605
Rust fungus, 605i
Rye, 605

Sac fungi, 595i
Saccharomyces cerevisiae, 587
Safari hunts, 728–729
Sage grouse, 869, 869i, 870
Salamander, 436, 436i, 696–698, 697i
Salem witch trials, possible connection of to lysergic acid, 596
Salmon, 833–834, 834i, 865
Salmonella, 539i, 546
Salt licks, 851–852
Sand dollar, 682
Sap, 784, 784i
Saprolegnia parasitica, 570i
Saprotrophic fungi, 600–601
Saprotrophs, **588**, 592
Sarcopterygians, 695i
Sarcopterygii, class, 695, 695i
Sarracenia purpurea, 836i
SARS (Severe Acute Respiratory Syndrome), 524t, 528
Saurischian dinosaurs, 700i, 701i
Savannah, **782**, 818t, 819i
Sawfish, 692i
Scala Naturae (Scale of Nature), 394
Scale of interactions, 833–834
Scale of nature, 394, 394i
Scalidophora, 670
Scallops, 666–667, 735
Scaphopoda, class, 668
Scapula, 482, 482i
Scarlet cup fungus, 595i
Scarlet monkey-flower, 439i
Scherer, Stephen, 477
Schizocoelom, **648**
Schizocoelous, **649**
Schoener, Amy, 806
Schoener, Tom (Thomas W.), 761, 762b, 762i, 788
Schulz, Jonathan, 877
Schwarzenegger, Arnold, 394, 395i
Sclerocytes, **651**
Scolex, **662**, 663i
Scorpion, 674i